W9-ARY-806

COLLEGE ALGEBRA

INSTRUCTOR'S ANNOTATED EDITION

FIFTH EDITION

COLLEGE ALGEBRA
INSTRUCTOR'S ANNOTATED EDITION

Richard N. Aufmann

Vernon C. Barker

Richard D. Nation

Palomar College

Houghton Mifflin Company

Boston   New York

Publisher: Jack Shira
Senior Sponsoring Editor: Lynn Cox
Senior Development Editor: Dawn Nuttall
Associate Editor: Jennifer King
Assistant Editor: Melissa Parkin
Senior Project Editor: Tamela Ambush
Editorial Assistant: Lisa Sullivan
Senior Production/Design Coordinator: Carol Merrigan
Manufacturing Manager: Florence Cadran
Marketing Manager: Danielle Potvin
Marketing Associate: Nicole Mollica

Cover photograph: © A & L Sinibaldi / Getty Images

PHOTO CREDITS

Chapter P: *p. 1* NASA, N. Benitez, T. Broadhurst (The Hebrew University), H. Ford (JHU), M. Clampin (STScI), G. Hartig (STScI), G. Illingworth (UCO/Link Observatory), the ACS Science Team and ESA; *p. 2* AP/Wide World Photos; *p. 64* NASA, ESA, and the Hubble Heritage Team (STScI/AURA). **Chapter 1:** *p. 81* Bettmann /CORBIS; *p. 81* Spencer Grant / PhotoEdit, Inc.; *p. 93* Mona Lisa by Leonardo da Vinci. © Gianni Dagli Orti/CORBIS; *p. 98* © The British Museum / Topham - HIP / The Image Works; *p. 108* The Granger Collection; *p. 112* Jeff Greenberg / PhotoEdit, Inc.; *p. 139* AP/Wide Wolrd Photos; *p. 148* Danielle Austen / Syracuse Newspapers / The Image Works. **Chapter 2:** *p. 161* Charles O'rear / CORBIS; *p. 224* CORBIS. **Chapter 3:** *p. 277* Sonda Dawes / The Image Works; *p. 278* David Young-Wolff / PhotoEdit, Inc.; *p. 288* Syndicated Features Limited / The Image Works; *p. 309* The Granger Collection; *p. 319* Bettmann/CORBIS; *p. 321* Bettmann / CORBIS; *p. 342* Richard T. Nowitz / CORBIS. **Chapter 4:** *p. 353* Chris McLaughlin / CORBIS; *p. 373* Bettmann / CORBIS; *p. 379* Charles O'rear / CORBIS; *p. 379* David James / Getty Images; *p. 383* Bettmann / CORBIS; *p. 428* Tom Brakefield / CORBIS; *p. 435* Bettmann / CORBIS; *p. 440* AP / Wide World Photos. **Chapter 5:** *p. 459* John Gay, US Navy /Getty Images; *p. 468* 1998 International Conference on Quality Control by Artificial Vision-QCAV'98. Kagawa Convention Center, Takamatsu, Kagawa, Japan, November 10-12, 1998, pp. 521-528; *p. 469* Reprinted with permission of Ian Morison, Jodrell Bank Conservatory; *p. 485* Hugh Rooney / Eye Ubiquitous / CORBIS; *p. 493* The Granger Collectoin. **Chapter 6:** n/a. **Chapter 7:** *p. 567* Boyd Norton / The Image Works; *p. 599* Comstock images. **Chapter 8:** *p. 637* Stephen Johnson / Getty Images; *p. 637* Stephen Johnson / Getty Images.

Copyright © 2005 Houghton Mifflin Company. All rights reserved.

No part of this work may be reproduced or transmitted in any form or by any means, electronic or mechanical, including photographing and recording, or by any information storage or retrieval system without the prior written permission of Houghton Mifflin Company unless such copying is expressly permitted by federal copyright law. Address inquiries to College Permissions, Houghton Mifflin Company, 222 Berkeley Street, Boston, MA 02116-3764.

Printed in the U.S.A.

Library of Congress Control Number: 2003110129

ISBNs:
Student's Edition: 0-618-38670-X
Instructor's Annotated Edition: 0-618-38671-8

123456789-DOW-08 07 06 05 04

CONTENTS

5   TOPICS IN ANALYTIC GEOMETRY   *459*

6   SYSTEMS OF EQUATIONS   *503*

PREFACE

With each successive edition of *College Algebra* we strive to enhance and refine our instructional materials. In this edition we have continued our emphasis on *doing* mathematics rather than duplicating mathematics through extensive drill. Students are urged to investigate concepts, apply those concepts, and then present their findings. We are ever cognizant of the motivating influence that contemporary, relevant applications have on students. As a result, we have added many new application exercises and deleted those that are of little student interest.

Technology is introduced naturally to illustrate or enhance the current topic. We integrate technology into a discussion when it can be used to foster and promote a better understanding of a concept. The optional *Integrating Technology* boxes and graphing calculator exercises are designed to instill in students an appreciation of both the power and the limitations of technology.

In this edition, we have retained our basic philosophy, which is to deliver a comprehensive and mathematically sound treatment of the topics considered essential for a college algebra course. To help students master these concepts, we have tried to maintain a balance among theory, application, modeling, and drill. Carefully developed mathematics is complemented by abundant, creative applications that are both contemporary and representative of a wide range of disciplines. Many application exercises are accompanied by a diagram that helps the student visualize the mathematics of the application.

Changes for the Fifth Edition

Many new student support features have been added to this edition:

A *Focus on Problem Solving* feature has been added at the beginning of each chapter. This feature reviews and demonstrates the strategies used by successful problem-solvers.

Review Notes, identified by ⇆ , direct students to the page where a previously discussed concept can be reviewed. Students needing to review this concept can do so before proceeding with new material.

Prepare for Next Section Exercises, found in each section's exercise set (except the last section of a chapter), allow students to practice prerequisite skills and concepts needed to be successful in the next section. Each exercise references the section of the text that contains the concepts related to the question for students to easily review. All answers are provided in the student answer section.

Cumulative Review Exercises have been added to every chapter, after Chapter P. These 20 Cumulative Review Exercises allow students to review material from previous chapters. The answers for all of these exercises are included in the student answer section. Next to each answer is a section reference that directs the student to the section of the text from which the exercise was taken.

Answers to All Chapter Review Exercises are now included in the student answer section. Next to each answer is a section reference that directs the student to the section of the text from which the exercise was taken.

Some specific chapter changes are indicated below.

Chapter P, *Preliminary Concepts*, has been reorganized and now includes a review of the basic operations on complex numbers. This chapter is a review of many topics that are a prerequisite to success in college algebra. Students who have successfully completed an intermediate algebra course may not need to cover this chapter.

Chapter 1, *Equations and Inequalities*, now includes several new Examples that illustrate contemporary applications of mathematics. Also, each exercise set includes some new application exercises. For instance, in Section 1.2 formulas are provided for assessing the reading grade level of written material and for assessing the passing performance of quarterbacks.

Chapter 2, *Functions and Graphs*, includes a completely new discussion on composition of functions that is motivated through an application problem. Concise reviews of vertical and horizontal translations have been added. Many new application exercises were added.

Chapter 3, *Polynomial and Rational Functions*, starts with a more detailed discussion of polynomial division. Several new worked examples and contemporary application exercises have been included in this chapter.

Chapter 4, *Exponential and Logarithmic Functions*, now includes additional contemporary application exercises. For instance, some exercises illustrate an exponential relationship between various water temperatures and the time required for a scuba diver to reach hypothermia.

In Chapter 5, *Topics in Analytic Geometry*, we have included several new applications of a more contemporary nature. We have continued the use of graphing utilities to illustrate important concepts.

Chapter 7, *Matrices*, now includes some application exercises involving heat transfer that can be solved using matrices.

CHAPTER OPENER FEATURES

CHAPTER OPENER

Each chapter begins with a **Chapter Opener** that illustrates a specific application of a concept from the chapter. There is a reference to a particular exercise within the chapter that asks the student to solve a problem related to the chapter opener topic.

The icons VIDEO & DVD SSG WWW at the bottom of the page let students know of additional resources available on CD, video/DVD, in the *Student Study Guide*, and online at math.college.hmco.com/students.

Page 353

CHAPTER 4

EXPONENTIAL AND LOGARITHMIC FUNCTIONS

4.1 Inverse Functions
4.2 Exponential Functions and Their Applications
4.3 Logarithmic Functions and Their Applications
4.4 Logarithms and Logarithmic Scales
4.5 Exponential and Logarithmic Equations
4.6 Exponential Growth and Decay
4.7 Modeling Data with Exponential and Logarithmic Functions

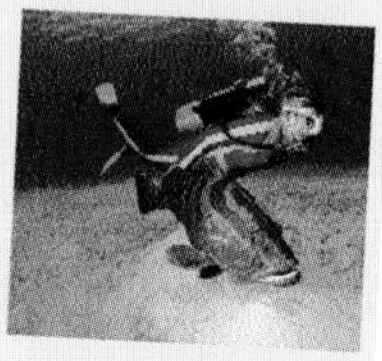

Modeling Data with an Exponential Function

The following table shows the time, in hours, before the body of a scuba diver, wearing a 5-millimeter-thick wet suit, reaches hypothermia (95°F) for various water temperatures.

Water Temperature, °F	Time, hours
36	1.5
41	1.8
46	2.6
50	3.1
55	4.9

Source: Data extracted from the *American Journal of Physics*, vol. 71, no. 4 (April 2003), Fig. 3, p. 336.

The following function, which is an example of an exponential function, closely models the data in the table:

$$T(F) = 0.1509(1.0639)^F$$

In this function F represents the Fahrenheit temperature of the water, and T represents the time in hours. A diver can use the function to determine the time it takes to reach hypothermia for water temperatures that are not included in the table. See Exercise 21, page 445. The function $T(F)$ was determined by using exponential regression, which is one of the topics in Section 4.7.

21. HYPOTHERMIA The following table shows the time T, in hours, before a scuba diver wearing a 3-millimeter-thick wet suit reaches hypothermia (95°F) for various water temperatures F, in degrees Fahrenheit.

Water temperature, °F	Time T, hours
41	1.1
46	1.4
50	1.8
59	3.7

a. Find an exponential regression model for the data. Round the constants a and b to the nearest hundred thousandth.

b. Use the model from part **a.** to estimate the time it takes for the diver to reach hypothermia in water that has a temperature of 65°F. Round to the nearest tenth of an hour.

Page 445

Page 354

FOCUS ON PROBLEM SOLVING

Use Two Methods to Solve and Compare Results

Sometimes it is possible to solve a problem in two or more ways. In such situations it is recommended that you use at least two methods to solve the problem, and compare your results. Here is an example of an application that can be solved in more than one way.

Example

In a league of eight basketball teams, each team plays every other team in the league exactly once. How many league games will take place?

Solution

Method 1: *Use an analytic approach.* Each of the eight teams must play the other seven teams. Using this information, you might be tempted to conclude that there will be $8 \cdot 7 = 56$ games, but this result is too large because it counts each game between two individual teams as two different games. Thus the number of league games will be

$$\frac{8 \cdot 7}{2} = \frac{56}{2} = 28$$

Method 2: *Make an organized list.* Use the letters A, B, C, D, E, F, G, and H to represent the eight teams. Use the notation AB to represent the game between team A and team B. Do not include BA in your list because it represents the same game between team A and team B.

AB	AC	AD	AE	AF	AG	AH
	BC	BD	BE	BF	BG	BH
		CD	CE	CF	CG	CH
			DE	DF	DG	DH
				EF	EG	EH
					FG	FH
						GH

The list shows that there will be 28 league games.

The procedure of using two different solution methods and comparing results is employed often in this chapter. For instance, see Example 2, page 409. In this example, a solution is found by applying algebraic procedures and also by graphing. Notice that both methods produce the same result.

NEW! ***FOCUS ON PROBLEM SOLVING***

A **Focus on Problem Solving** follows the Chapter Opener. This feature highlights and demonstrates a problem-solving strategy that may be used to successfully solve some of the problems presented in the chapter.

AUFMANN INTERACTIVE METHOD (AIM)

Page 360

INTERACTIVE PRESENTATION

College Algebra is written in a style that encourages the student to interact with the textbook.

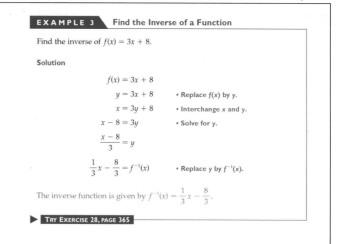

EXAMPLE 3   Find the Inverse of a Function

Find the inverse of $f(x) = 3x + 8$.

Solution

$$f(x) = 3x + 8$$
$$y = 3x + 8 \qquad \text{• Replace } f(x) \text{ by } y.$$
$$x = 3y + 8 \qquad \text{• Interchange } x \text{ and } y.$$
$$x - 8 = 3y \qquad \text{• Solve for } y.$$
$$\frac{x - 8}{3} = y$$
$$\frac{1}{3}x - \frac{8}{3} = f^{-1}(x) \qquad \text{• Replace } y \text{ by } f^{-1}(x).$$

The inverse function is given by $f^{-1}(x) = \frac{1}{3}x - \frac{8}{3}$.

▶ **TRY EXERCISE 28, PAGE 365**

EXAMPLES

Each section contains a variety of worked examples. Examples are **titled** so that the student can see at a glance the type of problem being illustrated, often accompanied by **annotations** that assist the student in moving from step to step; and offers the **final answer in color** so that it is readily identifiable.

TRY EXERCISES

Following every example is a suggested **Try Exercise** from that section's exercise set for the student to work. The exercises are color coded by number in the exercise set and the *complete solution* of that exercise can be found in an appendix to the text.

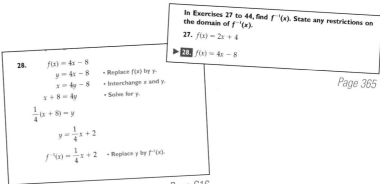

In Exercises 27 to 44, find $f^{-1}(x)$. State any restrictions on the domain of $f^{-1}(x)$.

27. $f(x) = 2x + 4$

▶ **28.** $f(x) = 4x - 8$

Page 365

28.
$$f(x) = 4x - 8$$
$$y = 4x - 8 \qquad \text{• Replace } f(x) \text{ by } y.$$
$$x = 4y - 8 \qquad \text{• Interchange } x \text{ and } y.$$
$$x + 8 = 4y \qquad \text{• Solve for } y.$$
$$\frac{1}{4}(x + 8) = y$$
$$y = \frac{1}{4}x + 2$$
$$f^{-1}(x) = \frac{1}{4}x + 2 \qquad \text{• Replace } y \text{ by } f^{-1}(x).$$

Page S16

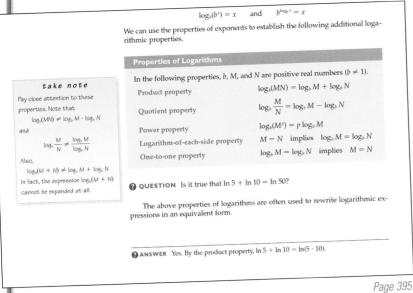

$$\log_b(b^x) = x \qquad \text{and} \qquad b^{\log_b x} = x$$

We can use the properties of exponents to establish the following additional logarithmic properties.

Properties of Logarithms

In the following properties, b, M, and N are positive real numbers ($b \neq 1$).

Product property	$\log_b(MN) = \log_b M + \log_b N$
Quotient property	$\log_b \dfrac{M}{N} = \log_b M - \log_b N$
Power property	$\log_b(M^p) = p \log_b M$
Logarithm-of-each-side property	$M = N \text{ implies } \log_b M = \log_b N$
One-to-one property	$\log_b M = \log_b N \text{ implies } M = N$

take note

Pay close attention to these properties. Note that
$$\log_b(MN) \neq \log_b M \cdot \log_b N$$
and
$$\log_b \frac{M}{N} \neq \frac{\log_b M}{\log_b N}$$
Also,
$$\log_b(M + N) \neq \log_b M + \log_b N$$
In fact, the expression $\log_b(M + N)$ cannot be expanded at all.

❓ **QUESTION** Is it true that $\ln 5 + \ln 10 = \ln 50$?

The above properties of logarithms are often used to rewrite logarithmic expressions in an equivalent form.

❓ **ANSWER** Yes. By the product property, $\ln 5 + \ln 10 = \ln(5 \cdot 10)$.

QUESTION/ANSWER

In every section, we pose at least one **Question** to the student about the material being read. This question encourages the reader to pause and think about the current discussion and to answer the question. To make sure the student does not miss important information, the **Answer** to the question is provided as a footnote on the same page.

Page 395

REAL DATA AND APPLICATIONS

APPLICATIONS

One way to motivate an interest in mathematics is through applications. Applications require the student to use problem-solving strategies, along with the skills covered in a section, to solve practical problems. This careful integration of applications generates student awareness of the value of algebra as a real-life tool.

Applications are taken from many disciplines including agriculture, business, chemistry, construction, Earth science, education, economics, manufacturing, nutrition, real estate, and sociology.

Page 428

428 Chapter 4 Exponential and Logarithmic Functions

In the following example we determine a logistic growth model for a coyote population.

EXAMPLE 8 Find and Use a Logistic Model

At the beginning of 2002, the coyote population in a wilderness area was estimated at 200. By the beginning of 2004, the coyote population had increased to 250. A park ranger estimates that the carrying capacity of the wilderness area is 500 coyotes.

a. Use the given data to determine the growth rate constant for the logistic model of this coyote population.

b. Use the logistic model determined in part **a.** to predict the year in which the coyote population will first reach 400.

Solution

a. If we represent the beginning of the year 2002 by $t = 0$, then the beginning of the year 2004 will be represented by $t = 2$. In the logistic model, make the following substitutions: $P(2) = 250$, $c = 500$, and

$$a = \frac{c - P_0}{P_0} = \frac{500 - 200}{200} = 1.5.$$

$$P(t) = \frac{c}{1 + ae^{-bt}}$$

$$P(2) = \frac{500}{1 + 1.5e^{-b \cdot 2}} \quad \bullet \text{ Substitute the given values.}$$

$$250 = \frac{500}{1 + 1.5e^{-b \cdot 2}}$$

$$250(1 + 1.5e^{-b \cdot 2}) = 500 \quad \bullet \text{ Solve for the growth rate constant } b.$$

$$1 + 1.5e^{-b \cdot 2} = \frac{500}{250}$$

$$1.5e^{-b \cdot 2} = 2 - 1$$

$$e^{-b \cdot 2} = \frac{1}{1.5}$$

$$-2b = \ln\left(\frac{1}{1.5}\right)$$

$$b = -\frac{1}{2}\ln\left(\frac{1}{1.5}\right)$$

$$b \approx 0.20273255$$

Page 448

448 Chapter 4 Exponential and Logarithmic Functions

Time t (minutes)	0	5	10	15	20	25
Coffee temp. T (°F)	165°	140°	121°	107°	97°	89°
T − 70°	95°	70°	51°	37°	27°	19°

a. Use a graphing utility to find an exponential model for the difference $T - 70°$ as a function of t.

b. Use the model to predict how long it will take (to the nearest minute) for the coffee to cool to 80°F.

35. OLYMPIC DISTANCES The following table shows the winning Olympic distances for the men's shot put for the years 1948 to 2000.

Men's Olympic Shot Put, 1948 to 2000

Year	Distance	Year	Distance
1948	56 ft 2 in.	1976	69 ft $\frac{3}{4}$ in.
1952	57 ft 1$\frac{1}{2}$ in.	1980	70 ft $\frac{1}{2}$ in.
1956	60 ft 11 in.	1984	69 ft 9 in.
1960	64 ft 6$\frac{3}{4}$ in.	1988	73 ft 8$\frac{3}{4}$ in.
1964	66 ft 8$\frac{1}{4}$ in.	1992	71 ft 2$\frac{1}{2}$ in.
1968	67 ft 4$\frac{3}{4}$ in.	1996	70 ft 11$\frac{1}{4}$ in.
1972	69 ft 6 in.	2000	69 ft 10$\frac{1}{4}$ in.

Source: Time Almanac 2002

Represent the year 1948 by $t = 48$.

a. Use the regression features of a graphing utility to determine a logistic growth model and a logarithmic model for the data.

b. Use graphs of the models in part **a.** to determine which model provides the better fit for the data.

c. Use the model you selected in part **b.** to predict the men's shot put distance for the year 2008. Round to the nearest hundredth of a foot.

36. WORLD POPULATION The following table lists the years in which the world's population first reached 3, 4, 5, and 6 billion.

World Population Milestones

Year	Population
1960	3 billion
1974	4 billion
1987	5 billion
1999	6 billion

Source: Time Almanac 2002, p. 708.

a. Find a logistic growth model, $P(t)$, for the data in the table. Let t represent the number of years after 1960 ($t = 0$ represents the year 1960).

b. According to the logistic growth model, what will the world's population approach as $t \to \infty$? Round to the nearest billion.

37. DESALINATION The following table shows the amount of fresh water w (in cubic yards) produced from saltwater after t hours of a desalination process.

t	1	2.5	3.5	4.0	5.1	6.5
w	18.2	46.6	57.4	61.5	68.7	76.2

a. Use a graphing utility to find a linear model and a logarithmic model for the data.

b. Examine the correlation coefficients of the two regression models to determine which model provides the better fit for the data. State the correlation coefficient r for each model.

c. Use the model you selected in part **b.** to predict the amount of fresh water that will be produced after 10 hours of the desalination process. Round to the nearest tenth of a cubic yard.

38. A CORRELATION COEFFICIENT OF 1 A scientist uses a graphing utility to model the data set {(2, 5), (4, 6)} with a logarithmic function. The following display shows the results.

What is the significance of the fact that the correlation coefficient for the regression equation is $r = 1$?

```
LnReg
y=a+blnx
a=4
b=1.442695041
r²=1
r=1
```

REAL DATA

Real data examples and exercises, identified by 🌐, ask students to analyze and create mathematical models from actual situations. Students are often required to work with tables, graphs, and charts drawn from a variety of disciplines.

TECHNOLOGY

INTEGRATING TECHNOLOGY

The **Integrating Technology** feature contains optional discussions that can be used to further explore a concept using technology. Some introduce technology as an alternative way to solve certain problems and others provide suggestions for using a calculator to solve certain problems and applications. Additionally, optional graphing calculator examples and exercises (identified by) are presented throughout the text.

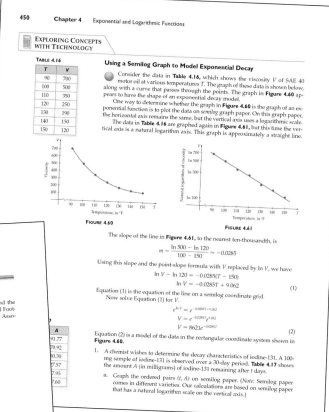

INTEGRATING TECHNOLOGY

The graph of $y^2 = -8x$ is shown in **Figure 5.5**. Note that the graph is not the graph of a function. To graph $y^2 = -8x$ with a graphing utility, we first solve for y to produce $y = \pm\sqrt{-8x}$. From this equation we can see that for any $x < 0$, there are two values of y. For example, when $x = -2$,

$$y = \pm\sqrt{(-8)(-2)} = \pm\sqrt{16} = \pm 4$$

The graph of $y^2 = -8x$ in **Figure 5.5** was drawn by graphing both $y_1 = \sqrt{-8x}$ and $y_2 = -\sqrt{-8x}$ in the same window.

FIGURE 5.5

Page 463

EXPLORING CONCEPTS WITH TECHNOLOGY

A special end-of-chapter feature, **Exploring Concepts with Technology**, extends ideas introduced in the text by using technology (graphing calculator, CAS, etc.) to investigate extended applications or mathematical topics. These explorations can serve as group projects, class discussions, or extra-credit assignments.

Page 256

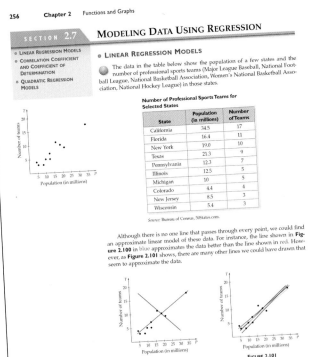

450   Chapter 4   Exponential and Logarithmic Functions

EXPLORING CONCEPTS WITH TECHNOLOGY

TABLE 4.16

T	V
90	700
100	500
110	350
120	250
130	190
140	150
150	120

Using a Semilog Graph to Model Exponential Decay

Consider the data in **Table 4.16**, which shows the viscosity V of SAE 40 motor oil at various temperatures T. The graph of these data is shown below, along with a curve that passes through the points. The graph in **Figure 4.60** appears to have the shape of an exponential decay model.

One way to determine whether the graph in **Figure 4.60** is the graph of an exponential function is to plot the data on *semilog* graph paper. On this graph paper, the horizontal axis remains the same, but the vertical axis uses a logarithmic scale.

The data in **Table 4.16** are graphed again in **Figure 4.61**, but this time the vertical axis is a natural logarithm axis. This graph is approximately a straight line.

FIGURE 4.60   **FIGURE 4.61**

The slope of the line in **Figure 4.61**, to the nearest ten-thousandth, is

$$m = \frac{\ln 500 - \ln 120}{100 - 150} \approx -0.0285$$

Using this slope and the point-slope formula with V replaced by $\ln V$, we have

$$\ln V - \ln 120 = -0.0285(T - 150)$$
$$\ln V \approx -0.0285T + 9.062 \qquad (1)$$

Equation (1) is the equation of the line on a semilog coordinate grid.
Now solve Equation (1) for V.

$$e^{\ln V} = e^{-0.0285T + 9.062}$$
$$V = e^{-0.0285T} e^{9.062}$$
$$V \approx 8621 e^{-0.0285T} \qquad (2)$$

Equation (2) is a model of the data in the rectangular coordinate system shown in **Figure 4.60**.

1. A chemist wishes to determine the decay characteristics of iodine-131. A 100-mg sample of iodine-131 is observed over a 30-day period. **Table 4.17** shows the amount A (in milligrams) of iodine-131 remaining after t days.

   a. Graph the ordered pairs (t, A) on semilog paper. (*Note:* Semilog paper comes in different varieties. Our calculations are based on semilog paper that has a natural logarithm scale on the vertical axis.)

Page 450

MODELING

Special modeling sections, which rely heavily on the use of a graphing calculator, are incorporated throughout the text. These optional sections introduce the idea of a mathematical model using various real-world data sets that further motivate students and help them see the relevance of mathematics.

STUDENT PEDAGOGY

TOPIC LIST

At the beginning of each section is a list of the major topics covered in the section.

KEY TERMS AND CONCEPTS

Key terms, in bold, emphasize important terms. Key concepts are presented in blue boxes in order to highlight these important concepts and to provide for easy reference.

MATH MATTERS

These margin notes contain interesting sidelights about mathematics, its history, or its application.

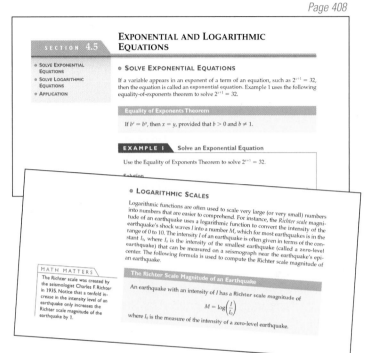

Page 408

SECTION 4.5

- SOLVE EXPONENTIAL EQUATIONS
- SOLVE LOGARITHMIC EQUATIONS
- APPLICATION

EXPONENTIAL AND LOGARITHMIC EQUATIONS

• SOLVE EXPONENTIAL EQUATIONS

If a variable appears in an exponent of a term of an equation, such as $2^{x+1} = 32$, then the equation is called an exponential equation. Example 1 uses the following equality-of-exponents theorem to solve $2^{x+1} = 32$.

Equality of Exponents Theorem

If $b^x = b^y$, then $x = y$, provided that $b > 0$ and $b \neq 1$.

EXAMPLE 1   Solve an Exponential Equation

Use the Equality of Exponents Theorem to solve $2^{x+1} = 32$.

Solution

• LOGARITHMIC SCALES

Logarithmic functions are often used to scale very large (or very small) numbers into numbers that are easier to comprehend. For instance, the *Richter scale* magnitude of an earthquake uses a logarithmic function to convert the intensity of the earthquake's shock waves I into a number M, which for most earthquakes is in the range of 0 to 10. The intensity I of an earthquake is often given in terms of the constant I_0, where I_0 is the intensity of the smallest earthquake (called a zero-level earthquake) that can be measured on a seismograph near the earthquake's epicenter. The following formula is used to compute the Richter scale magnitude of an earthquake.

MATH MATTERS

The Richter scale was created by the seismologist Charles F. Richter in 1935. Notice that a tenfold increase in the intensity level of an earthquake only increases the Richter scale magnitude of the earthquake by 1.

The Richter Scale Magnitude of an Earthquake

An earthquake with an intensity of I has a Richter scale magnitude of

$$M = \log\left(\frac{I}{I_0}\right)$$

where I_0 is the measure of the intensity of a zero-level earthquake.

Page 398

Page 462

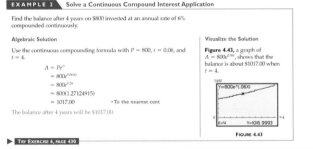

$$(\sqrt{(x-0)^2 + (y-p)^2})^2 = (y + p)^2$$
$$x^2 + y^2 - 2py + p^2 = y^2 + 2py + p^2$$
$$x^2 = 4py$$

This is an equation of a parabola with vertex at the origin and the y-axis as its axis of symmetry. The equation of a parabola with vertex at the origin and the x-axis as its axis of symmetry is derived in a similar manner.

To review **AXIS OF SYMMETRY**, *see p. 214.*

Standard Forms of the Equation of a Parabola with Vertex at the Origin

Axis of Symmetry Is the y-Axis

The standard form of the equation of a parabola with vertex $(0, 0)$ and the y-axis as its axis of symmetry is $x^2 = 4py$. The focus is $(0, p)$, and the equation of the directrix is $y = -p$.

Axis of Symmetry Is the x-Axis

The standard form of the equation of a parabola with vertex $(0, 0)$ and the x-axis as its axis of symmetry is $y^2 = 4px$. The focus is $(p, 0)$ and the equation of the directrix is $x = -p$.

take note

The tests for y-axis and x-axis symmetry can be used to verify these statements and provide connections to earlier topics on symmetry.

In the equation $x^2 = 4py$, $x^2 \geq 0$. Therefore, $4py \geq 0$. Thus if $p > 0$, then $y \geq 0$, and the parabola opens up. If $p < 0$, then $y \leq 0$, and the parabola opens down. A similar analysis shows that for $y^2 = 4px$, the parabola opens to the right when

EXAMPLE 2   Solve a Continuous Compound Interest Application

Find the balance after 4 years on $800 invested at an annual rate of 6% compounded continuously.

Algebraic Solution

Use the continuous compounding formula with $P = 800$, $r = 0.06$, and $t = 4$.

$$A = Pe^{rt}$$
$$= 800e^{0.06(4)}$$
$$= 800e^{0.24}$$
$$\approx 800(1.27124915)$$
$$\approx 1017.00 \qquad \bullet \text{To the nearest cent}$$

The balance after 4 years will be $1017.00.

Visualize the Solution

Figure 4.43, a graph of $A = 800e^{0.06t}$, shows that the balance is about $1017.00 when $t = 4$.

Y=800e^(.06X)

X=4   Y=1016.9993

FIGURE 4.43

▶ **TRY EXERCISE 6, PAGE 430**

Page 422

NEW! REVIEW NOTES

A ⬄ directs the student to the place in the text where the student can review a concept that was previously discussed.

TAKE NOTE

These margin notes alert students to a point requiring special attention or are used to amplify the concept under discussion.

VISUALIZE THE SOLUTION

For appropriate examples within the text, we have provided both an algebraic solution and a graphical representation of the solution. This approach creates a link between the algebraic and visual components of a solution.

EXERCISES

TOPICS FOR DISCUSSION

These special exercises provide questions related to key concepts in the section. Instructors can use these to initiate class discussions or to ask students to write about concepts presented.

EXERCISES

The exercise sets in *College Algebra* were carefully developed to provide a wide variety of exercises. The exercises range from drill and practice to interesting challenges. They were chosen to illustrate the many facets of topics discussed in the text. Each exercise set emphasizes skill building, skill maintenance, and, as appropriate, applications. **Icons** identify appropriate writing , group , data analysis , web ,

and graphing calculator exercises.

Page 429

TOPICS FOR DISCUSSION

1. Explain the difference between compound interest and simple interest.
2. What is an exponential growth model? Give an example of an application for which the exponential growth model might be appropriate.
3. What is an exponential decay model? Give an example of an application for which the exponential decay model might be appropriate.
4. Consider the exponential model $P(t) = P_0 e^{kt}$ and the logistic model $P(t) = \dfrac{c}{1 + ae^{-bt}}$. Explain the similarities and differences between the two models.

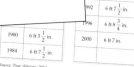

b. Use the model you chose in part a. to find the q-value associated with a pH of 8.2. Round to the nearest tenth.

30. WORLD POPULATION The following table lists the years in which the world's population first reached 3, 4, 5, and 6 billion.

World Population Milestones

Year	Population
1960	3 billion
1974	4 billion
1987	5 billion
1999	6 billion

Source: Time Almanac 2002, p. 708.

a. Find an exponential model for the data in the table. Let $x = 0$ represent the year 1960.

b. Use the model to predict the year in which the world's population will first reach 7 billion.

31. PANDA POPULATION One estimate gives the world panda population as 3200 in 1980 and 590 in 2000.

a. Find an exponential model for the data and use the model to predict the year in which the panda population p will be reduced to 200. (Let $t = 0$ represent the year 1980.)

b. Because the exponential model in part a. fits the data perfectly, does this mean that the model will accurately predict future panda populations? Explain.

32. OLYMPIC RECORDS The following table shows the Olympic gold medal distances for the women's high jump from 1968 to 2000.

mp, 1968 to 2000

Year	Distance
1988	6 ft 8 in.
1992	6 ft $7\frac{1}{2}$ in.
1996	6 ft 8 $\frac{3}{4}$ in.
2000	6 ft 7 in.
1980	6 ft 5 $\frac{1}{2}$ in.
1984	6 ft 7 $\frac{1}{2}$ in.

Source: Time Almanac 2002.

Represent the year 1968 by 68.

a. Use a graphing utility to determine a linear model and a logarithmic model for the data, with the distance measured in inches. State the correlation coefficient r for each model.

b. Use the correlation coefficient for each of the models in part a. to determine which model provides the better fit for the data.

c. Use the model you selected in part b. to predict the women's Olympic gold medal high jump distance in 2012. Round to the nearest tenth of an inch.

33. NUMBER OF AUTOMOBILES In 1900, the number of automobiles in the United States was around 8000. By 2000, the number of automobiles in the United States had reached 200 million.

a. Find an exponential model for the data and use the model to predict the number of automobiles, to the nearest 100,000, in the United States in 2010. Use $t = 0$ to represent the year 1900.

b. According to the model, in what year will the number of automobiles in the United States first reach 300 million?

34. TEMPERATURE OF COFFEE A cup of coffee is placed in a room that maintains a constant temperature of 70°F. The following table shows both the coffee temperature T after t minutes and the difference between the coffee temperature and the room temperature after t minutes.

Page 447

Included in each exercise set are **Connecting Concepts** exercises. These exercises extend some of the concepts discussed in the section and require students to connect ideas studied earlier with new concepts.

NEW! EXERCISES TO PREPARE FOR THE NEXT SECTION

Every section's exercise set (except for the last section of a chapter) contains exercises that allow students to practice the previously-learned skills they will need to be successful in the next section. Next to each question, in brackets, is a reference to the section of the text that contains the concepts related to the question for students to easily review. All answers are provided in the Answer Appendix.

PROJECTS

Projects are provided at the end of each exercise set. They are designed to encourage students to do research and write about what they have learned. These Projects generally emphasize critical thinking skills and can be used as collaborative learning exercises or as extra-credit assignments.

Page 381

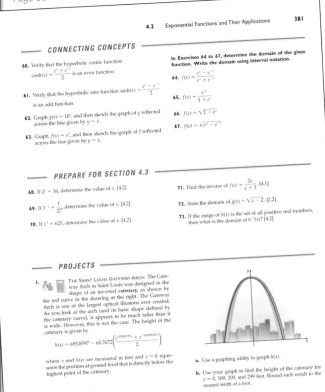

4.2 Exponential Functions and Their Applications   **381**

CONNECTING CONCEPTS

60. Verify that the hyperbolic cosine function $\cosh(x) = \dfrac{e^x + e^{-x}}{2}$ is an even function.

61. Verify that the hyperbolic sine function $\sinh(x) = \dfrac{e^x - e^{-x}}{2}$ is an odd function.

62. Graph $g(x) = 10^x$, and then sketch the graph of g reflected across the line given by $y = x$.

63. Graph $f(x) = e^x$, and then sketch the graph of f reflected across the line given by $y = x$.

In Exercises 64 to 67, determine the domain of the given function. Write the domain using interval notation.

64. $f(x) = \dfrac{e^x - e^{-x}}{e^x + e^{-x}}$

65. $f(x) = \dfrac{e^x}{1 + e^x}$

66. $f(x) = \sqrt{1 - e^x}$

67. $f(x) = \sqrt{e^x - e^{-x}}$

PREPARE FOR SECTION 4.3

68. If $2^x = 16$, determine the value of x. [4.2]

69. If $3^{-x} = \dfrac{1}{27}$, determine the value of x. [4.2]

70. If $x^4 = 625$, determine the value of x. [4.2]

71. Find the inverse of $f(x) = \dfrac{2x}{x + 3}$. [4.1]

72. State the domain of $g(x) = \sqrt{x - 2}$. [2.2]

73. If the range of $h(x)$ is the set of all positive real numbers, then what is the domain of $h^{-1}(x)$? [4.2]

PROJECTS

1. THE SAINT LOUIS GATEWAY ARCH The Gateway Arch in Saint Louis was designed in the shape of an inverted **catenary**, as shown by the red curve in the drawing at the right. The Gateway Arch is one of the largest optical illusions ever created. As you look at the arch (and its basic shape defined by the catenary curve), it appears to be much taller than it is wide. However, this is not the case. The height of the catenary is given by

$$h(x) = 693.8597 - 68.7672\left(\frac{e^{0.0100333x} + e^{-0.0100333x}}{2}\right)$$

where x and $h(x)$ are measured in feet and $x = 0$ represents the position at ground level that is directly below the highest point of the catenary.

a. Use a graphing utility to graph $h(x)$.

b. Use your graph to find the height of the catenary for $x = 0, 100, 200,$ and 299 feet. Round each result to the nearest tenth of a foot.

END OF CHAPTER

CHAPTER SUMMARY

At the end of each chapter there is a Chapter Summary that provides a concise section-by-section review of the chapter topics.

Page 451

CHAPTER 4 SUMMARY

4.1 Inverse Functions

- If f is a one-to-one function with domain X and range Y, and g is a function with domain Y and range X, then g is the inverse function of f if and only if $(f \circ g)(x) = x$ for all x in the domain of g and $(g \circ f)(x) = x$ for all x in the domain of f.

- A function f has an inverse function if and only if it is a one-to-one function. The graph of a function f and the graph of the inverse function f^{-1} are symmetric with respect to the line given by $y = x$.

4.2 Exponential Functions and Their Applications

- For all positive real numbers b, $b \neq 1$, the exponential function defined by $f(x) = b^x$ has the following properties:
  1. f has the set of real numbers as its domain.
  2. f has the set of positive real numbers as its range.
  3. f has a graph with a y-intercept of $(0, 1)$.
  4. f has a graph asymptotic to the x-axis.
  5. f is a one-to-one function.

TRUE/FALSE EXERCISES

Following each chapter summary are true/false exercises. These exercises are intended to help students understand concepts and can be used to initiate class discussions.

CHAPTER 4 TRUE/FALSE EXERCISES

In Exercises 1 to 16, answer true or false. If the statement is false, give an example or state a reason to demonstrate that the statement is false.

1. Every function has an inverse function.
2. If $(f \circ g)(a) = a$ and $(g \circ f)(a) = a$ for some constant a, then f and g are inverse functions.
3. If $7^x = 40$, then $\log_7 40 = x$.
4. If $\log_4 x = 3.1$, then $4^{3.1} = x$.
5. If $f(x) = \log x$ and $g(x) = 10^x$, then $f[g(x)] = x$ for all real numbers x.
6. If $f(x) = \log x$ and $g(x) = 10^x$, then $g[f(x)] = x$ for all real numbers x.
7. The exponential function $h(x) = b^x$ is an increasing function.
8. The logarithmic function $j(x) = \log_b x$ is an increasing function.
9. The exponential function $h(x) = b^x$ is a one-to-one function.
10. The logarithmic function $j(x) = \log_b x$ is a one-to-one function.
11. The graph of $f(x) = \dfrac{2^x + 2^{-x}}{2}$ is symmetric with respect to the y-axis.
12. The graph of $f(x) = \dfrac{2^x - 2^{-x}}{2}$ is symmetric with respect to the origin.
13. If $x > 0$ and $y > 0$, then $\log(x + y) = \log x + \log y$.
14. If $x > 0$, then $\log x^2 = 2 \log x$.
15. If M and N are positive real numbers, then $\ln \dfrac{M}{N} = \ln M - \ln N$.
16. For all $p > 0$, $e^{\ln p} = p$.

Page 453

Page 454

CHAPTER 4 REVIEW EXERCISES

In Exercises 1 to 4, determine whether the given functions are inverses.

1. $F(x) = 2x - 5$ $G(x) = \dfrac{x + 5}{2}$
2. $h(x) = \sqrt{x}$ $k(x) = x^2$, $x \geq 0$
3. $l(x) = \dfrac{x + 3}{x}$ $m(x) = \dfrac{3}{x - 1}$
4. $p(x) = \dfrac{x - 5}{2x}$ $q(x) = \dfrac{2x}{x - 5}$

In Exercises 5 to 8, find the inverse of the function. Sketch the graph of the function and its inverse on the same set of coordinate axes.

5. $f(x) = 3x - 4$
6. $g(x) = -2x + 3$
7. $h(x) = -\dfrac{1}{2}x - 2$
8. $k(x) = \dfrac{1}{x}$

In Exercises 31 and 32, use a graphing utility each function.

31. $f(x) = \dfrac{4^x + 4^{-x}}{2}$
32. $f(x) = \dfrac{3^x - 3^{-x}}{2}$

In Exercises 33 to 36, change each logarithmic equation to its exponential form.

33. $\log_4 64 = 3$
34. $\log_{1/2} 8 = -3$
35. $\log_{\sqrt{5}} 4 = 4$
36. $\ln 1 = 0$

In Exercises 37 to 40, change each exponential equation to its logarithmic form.

37. $5^3 = 125$
38. $2^{10} = 1024$
39. $10^0 = 1$
40. $8^{1/2} = 2\sqrt{2}$

In Exercises 41 to 44, write the given logarithm in terms of logarithms of x, y, and z.

CHAPTER REVIEW EXERCISES

Review exercises are found at the end of each chapter. These exercises are selected to help the student integrate all of the topics presented in the chapter.

CHAPTER TEST

The Chapter Test exercises are designed to simulate a possible test of the material in the chapter.

NEW! CUMULATIVE REVIEW EXERCISES

Cumulative Review Exercises, which appear at the end of each chapter (except Chapter P), help students maintain skills learned in previous chapters.

NEW! The answers to all **Chapter Review Exercises,** all **Chapter Test Exercises,** and all **Cumulative Review Exercises** are given in the Answer Section. Along with the answer, there is a reference to the section that pertains to each exercise.

CHAPTER 4 TEST

1. Find the inverse of $f(x) = 2x - 3$. Graph f and f^{-1} on the same coordinate axes.
2. Find the inverse of $f(x) = \dfrac{x}{4x - 8}$. State the domain and the range of f^{-1}.
3. a. Write $\log_5(3x - 3) = c$ in exponential form.
   b. Write $3^{5/2} = y$ in logarithmic form.
4. Write $\log_b \dfrac{z^2}{y^3\sqrt{x}}$ in terms of logarithms of x, y, and z.
5. Write $\log(2x + 3) - 3\log(x - 2)$ as a single logarithm with a coefficient of 1.
6. Use the change-of-base formula and a calculator to approximate $\log_4 12$. Round your result to the nearest ten thousandth.
7. Graph: $f(x) = 3^{-x/2}$
8. Graph: $f(x) = -\ln(x + 1)$
9. Solve: $5^x = 22$. Round your solution to the nearest ten thousandth.
10. Find the exact solution of $4^{5-x} = 7^x$.
11. Solve: $\log(x + 99) - \log(3x - 2) = 2$
12. Solve: $\ln(2 - x) + \ln(5 - x) = \ln(37 - x)$

Page 456

CUMULATIVE REVIEW EXERCISES

1. Solve $|x - 4| \leq 2$. Write the solution set using interval notation.
2. Solve $\dfrac{x}{2x - 6} \geq 1$. Write the solution set using set-builder notation.
3. Find, to the nearest tenth, the distance between the points $(5, 2)$ and $(11, 7)$.
4. The height, in feet, of a ball released with an initial upward velocity of 44 feet per second and at an initial height of 8 feet is given by $h(t) = -16t^2 + 44t + 8$, where t is the time in seconds after the ball is released. Find the maximum height the ball will reach.
5. Given $f(x) = 2x + 1$ and $g(x) = x^2 - 5$, find $(g \circ f)$.
6. Find the inverse of $f(x) = 3x - 5$.
7. The load that a horizontal beam can safely support varies jointly as the width and the square of the depth of the beam. It has been determined that a beam with a width of 4 inches and a depth of 8 inches can safely support a load of 1500 pounds. How many pounds can a beam of the same material and the same length safely support if it has

Page 457

INSTRUCTOR'S ANNOTATED EDITION

The **Instructor's Annotated Edition** includes:

MARGIN NOTES

NEW! There is an **Alternative Example** for every numbered Example that can be used as another in-class example or as an in-class exercise for students to try.

Instructor Notes give suggestions for teaching concepts, warnings about common student errors, or historical notes.

DIGITAL ART AND TABLES

Next to many of the graphs and tables in the text, there is a 🅿 that indicates that a Microsoft PowerPoint® slide of that figure is available. These slides (along with PowerPoint Viewer) are available on the **Class Prep CD** and also can be downloaded from our website at math.college.hmco.com/instructors. These slides also can be printed as transparency masters.

Page 139

Alternative to Example 9
A basketball player has made 27 out of 60 field goals. Her present field goal average is 45%. If she has a shooting streak in which she makes every field goal attempt, how many more shots must she take to get her field goal average above 52%?
● **9 or more shots**

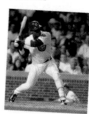

EXAMPLE 9   Solve an Application Involving Batting Averages

During a recent season, Sammy Sosa had 53 hits out of 163 at-bats. At that time his batting average was approximately 0.325. If Sosa goes into a batting slump in which he gets no hits, how many more at-bats will it take for his batting average to fall below 0.300?

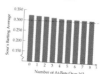

Solution

A baseball player's batting average is determined by dividing the player's number of hits by the number of times the player has been at bat. Let x be the number of additional at-bats that Sosa takes over 163. During this period, his batting average will be $\dfrac{53}{163 + x}$, and we wish to solve

$$\frac{53}{163 + x} < 0.300$$

This rational inequality can be solved by using the critical value method, but there is an easier method. In this application we know that $163 + x$ is positive. Thus, if we multiply each side of the preceding inequality by $163 + x$, we will obtain the linear inequality $53 < 48.9 + 0.300x$, with the condition that x is a positive integer. Solving this inequality produces

$$53 < 48.9 + 0.300x$$
$$4.1 < 0.300x$$
$$x > 13.6$$

Because x must be a positive integer, Sosa's average will fall below 0.300 if he goes hitless for 14 or more at-bats.

▶ **TRY EXERCISE 66, PAGE 142**

🔍 ✎ **TOPICS FOR DISCUSSION**

Vertical asymptotes of the graph of a rational function can be found by using the following theorem.

INSTRUCTOR NOTE
Stress that the Theorem on Vertical Asymptotes is valid only for rational functions whose numerator and denominator have no common factor.

🅿 **Theorem on Vertical Asymptotes**

If the real number a is a zero of the denominator $Q(x)$, then the graph of $F(x) = P(x)/Q(x)$, where $P(x)$ and $Q(x)$ have no common factors, has the vertical asymptote $x = a$.

Page 332

Page 98

EXERCISE SET 1.2   —*Suggested Assignment: Exercises 1–15, odd; 17–51, every other odd; 61–68, all.*

In Exercises 1 to 10, solve the formula for the specified variable.

1. $V = \frac{1}{3}\pi r^2 h$; h (geometry) $h = \dfrac{3V}{\pi r^2}$

2. $P = S - Sdt$; t (business) $t = \dfrac{S - P}{Sd}$

3. $I = Prt$; t (business) $t = \dfrac{I}{Pr}$

▶ 4. $A = P + Prt$; P (business) $\dfrac{A}{1 + rt} = P$

5. $F = \dfrac{Gm_1 m_2}{d^2}$; m_1 (physics) $m_1 = \dfrac{Fd^2}{Gm_2}$

6. $A = \frac{1}{2}h(b_1 + b_2)$; b_1 (geometry) $\dfrac{2A - hb_2}{h} = b_1$

7. $a_n = a_1 + (n - 1)d$; d (mathematics) $d = \dfrac{a_n - a_1}{n - 1}$

8. $y - y_1 = m(x - x_1)$; x (mathematics) $\dfrac{y - y_1 + mx_1}{m} = x$

9. $S = \dfrac{a_1}{1 - r}$; r (mathematics) $r = \dfrac{S - a_1}{S}$

10. $\dfrac{P_1 V_1}{T_1} = \dfrac{P_2 V_2}{T_2}$; V_2 (chemistry) $\dfrac{P_1 V_1 T_2}{P_2 T_1} = V_2$

11. 📊 QUARTERBACK RATING During the 2002 season, Peyton Manning, the quarterback of the Indianapolis Colts, completed 66.33% of his passes. He averaged 7.11 yards per pass attempt, 4.57% of his passes were for touchdowns, and 3.21% of his passes were intercepted. Determine Manning's quarterback rating for the 2002 season. Round to the nearest tenth. (*Hint:* See Example 2, page 92.) 88.8

12. 📊 QUARTERBACK RATING During the 2002 season, Drew Bledsoe, the quarterback of the Buffalo Bills, completed 61.48% of his passes. He averaged 7.15 yards per pass attempt, 3.93% of his passes were for touchdowns, and 2.46% of his passes were intercepted. Determine Bledsoe's quarterback rating for the 2002

season. Round to the nearest tenth. (*Hint:* See Example 2, page 92.) 86.0

The **SMOG** (Simplified Measure of Gobbledygook) readability formula is often used to estimate the reading grade level required for a person if he or she is to *fully understand* the written material being assessed. The formula is given by

$$\text{SMOG reading grade level} = \sqrt{w} + 3$$

where w is the number of words that have three or more syllables in a sample of 30 sentences.

13. ASSESSING A READING LEVEL A sample of 30 sentences from *Alice's Adventures in Wonderland*, by Lewis Carroll, shows a total of 42 words that have three or more syllables. Use the SMOG reading grade level formula to estimate the reading grade level required to fully understand this novel. Round the reading grade level to the nearest tenth. 9.5

▶ 14. ASSESSING A READING LEVEL A sample of 30 sentences from *A Tale of Two Cities*, by Charles Dickens, shows a total of 105 words that have three or more syllables. Use the SMOG reading grade level formula to estimate the reading grade level required to fully understand this novel. Round the reading grade level to the nearest tenth. 13.2

Another popular readability formula is the **Gunning Fog Index**. Here is the formula:

$$\text{Gunning Fog Index} = 0.4(A + W)$$

where A is the average number of words per sentence and W is the percentage of words that have four or more syllables. The Gunning Fog Index is defined as the minimum grade level at which the writing is easily read.

15. ASSESSING A READING LEVEL In a sample of sentences from the novel *Bridget Jones's Diary*, by Helen Fielding, the average number of words per sentence is 23.0, and

A **Suggested Assignment** is provided for each section.

NEW! Answers for all exercises are provided.

Instructor Resources

College Algebra has a complete set of support materials for the instructor.

Instructor's Annotated Edition   This edition contains a replica of the student text with additional resources for the instructor. These include: *Instructor Notes, Alternative Example* notes, *PowerPoint* icons, *Suggested Assignments,* and answers to all exercises.

Instructor's Solutions Manual   The *Instructor's Solutions Manual* contains worked-out solutions for all exercises in the text.

Instructor's Resource Manual with Testing   This resource includes six ready-to-use printed *Chapter Tests* per chapter, and a *Printed Test Bank* providing a print-out of one example of each of the algorithmic items on the *HM Testing* CD-ROM program.

HM ClassPrep w/ HM Testing CD-ROM   *HM ClassPrep* contains a multitude of text-specific resources for instructors to use to enhance the classroom experience. These resources can be easily accessed by chapter or resource type and also can link you to the text's website. *HM Testing* is our computerized test generator and contains a database of algorithmic test items, as well as providing **online testing** and **gradebook** functions.

Instructor Text-specific Website   The resources available on the *ClassPrep CD* are also available on the instructor website at math.college.hmco.com/instructors. Appropriate items are password protected. Instructors also have access to the student part of the text's website.

Student Resources

Student Study Guide   The *Student Study Guide* contains complete solutions to all odd-numbered exercises in the text, as well as study tips and a practice test for each chapter.

Math Study Skills Workbook *by Paul D. Nolting*   This workbook is designed to reinforce skills and minimize frustration for students in any math class, lab, or study skills course. It offers a wealth of study tips and sound advice on note taking, time management, and reducing math anxiety. In addition, numerous opportunities for self assessment enable students to track their own progress.

HM Eduspace® Online Learning Environment   *Eduspace* is a text-specific, web-based learning environment that combines an algorithmic tutorial program with homework capabilities. Specific content is available 24 hours a day to help you further understand your textbook.

HM mathSpace® Tutorial CD-ROM   This tutorial CD-ROM allows students to practice skills and review concepts as many times as necessary by providing algorithmically-generated exercises and step-by-step solutions for practice.

SMARTHINKING™ Live, Online Tutoring   Houghton Mifflin has partnered with SMARTHINKING to provide an easy-to-use and effective online tutorial service.

Whiteboard Simulations and **Practice Area** promote real-time visual interaction. Three levels of service are offered.

- **Text-specific Tutoring** provides real-time, one-on-one instruction with a specially qualified 'e-structor.'
- **Questions Any Time** allows students to submit questions to the tutor outside the scheduled hours and receive a reply within 24 hours.
- **Independent Study Resources** connect students with around-the-clock access to additional educational services, including interactive websites, diagnostic tests, and Frequently Asked Questions posed to SMARTHINKING e-structors.

Houghton Mifflin Instructional Videos and DVDs   Text-specific videos and DVDs, hosted by Dana Mosely, cover all sections of the text and provide a valuable resource for further instruction and review.

Student Text-specific Website   Online student resources can be found at this text's website at math.college.hmco.com/students.

Acknowledgments

The authors would like to thank the people who have reviewed this manuscript and provided many valuable suggestions.

Ioannis K. Argyros, *Cameron University, OK*
Peter Arvanites, *Rockland Community College, NY*
Linda Berg, *University of Great Falls, MT*
Paul Bialek, *Trinity College, IL*
Zhixiong Cai, *Barton College, NC*
Cheryl F. Cavaliero, *Butler County Community College, PA*
Jennie Cox, *Central Georgia Technical College, GA*
Marilyn Danchanko, *Cambria County Area Community College, PA*
Laura Davis, *Garland County Community College, AR*
Sylvia Dorminey, *Savannah Technical College, GA*
Gay Grubbs, *Griffin Technical College, GA*
Kathryn Hodge, *Midland College, TX*
Clement S. Lam, *Mission College, CA*
Dr. Helen Medley
Carla Monticelli, *Camden County College, NJ*
J. Reid Mowrer, *University of New Mexico–Valencia Campus, NM*
Sue Neal, *Wichita State University, KS*
Georgie O'Leary, *Warner Southern College, FL*
Suzanne Pauly, *Delaware Technical and Community College, DE*
Lauri Semarne
Mike Shirazi, *Germanna Community College, VA*
Anthony Tongen, *Trinity International University, IL*
Hanson Umoh, *Delaware State University, DE*
Rebecca Wells, *Henderson Community College, KY*

Special thanks to Christi Verity for her diligent preparation of the solutions manuals and to Sandy Doerfel for her contribution to this project.

PRELIMINARY CONCEPTS

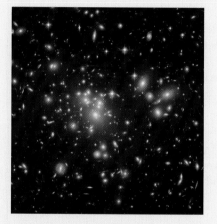

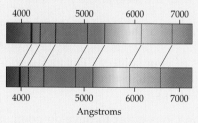

4000   5000   6000   7000
Angstroms

Source: Original art at
http://www.astro.ucla.edu/~wright/
doppler.htm.

The Red Shift

You may have noticed that the sound of an approaching siren has a higher pitch (frequency) than that of a receding siren. Like sound, when a light source moves toward or away from us, the frequency of the light changes. Astronomers use this fact to measure the distance of a galaxy from us.

The photograph at the left was taken by the Hubble Space Telescope. Many of the bright objects in this photograph are galaxies. When a galaxy is moving away from us, the characteristic frequencies of certain light waves, the black lines in the spectrum below the photo, are shifted to the red side of the spectrum. The amount of this *red shift*, as astronomers call it, can be used to determine the speed at which the galaxy is receding from Earth. The formula used to compute the speed involves a rational expression, which is one of the topics of this chapter. **Exercise 67 on page 64** is an example of this formula.

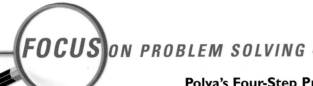

Polya's Four-Step Process

Your success in mathematics and your success in the workplace are heavily dependent on your ability to solve problems. George Polya (1887–1985) was one of the foremost mathematicians to study problem solving. The basic structure that Polya advocated for problem solving has four steps, as outlined below.

1. Understand the problem.
   - Can you restate the problem in your own words?
   - Can you determine what is known about this type of problem?
   - Is there missing information that you need in order to solve the problem?
   - Is there information given that is not needed?
   - What is the goal?

2. Devise a plan.
   - Make a list of the known information.
   - Make a list of information that is needed to solve the problem.
   - Make a table or draw a diagram.
   - Work backwards.
   - Try to solve a similar but simpler problem.
   - Research the problem to determine whether there are known techniques for solving problems of its kind.
   - Try to determine whether some pattern exists.
   - Write an equation.

3. Carry out the plan.
   - Work carefully.
   - Keep an accurate and neat record of all your attempts.
   - Realize that some of your initial plans will not work and that you may have to return to step 2 and devise another plan or modify your existing plan.

4. Review your solution.
   - Make sure that the solution is consistent with the facts of the problem.
   - Interpret the solution in the context of the problem.
   - Ask yourself whether there are generalizations of the solution that could apply to other problems.
   - Determine the strengths and weaknesses of your solution. For instance, is your solution only an approximation to the actual solution?
   - Consider the possibility of alternative solutions.

As you go through this course, make a conscious effort to develop good problem-solving skills. One way to do this is to create problems and then solve them. Do not focus only on math problems. Think about your major or strategy games and create problems in those areas and then solve them. Here is one to get you started.

> Three containers A, B, and C can hold, respectively, 8, 5, and 3 gallons of water. Initially container A is filled completely, and the other two containers are empty. Without using any measuring devices other than these containers, divide the water into two equal parts by pouring from one container to another.

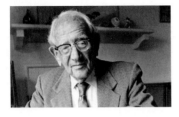

MATH MATTERS

George Polya was born in Hungary and moved to the United States in 1940. In 1942, he moved to California and began teaching at Stanford University, and remained there until his retirement. While at Stanford, he published 10 books and a number of articles for mathematics journals. Of the books Polya published, *How to Solve It* (1945) is one of his best known. In this book Polya outlines a strategy for solving problems. This strategy is frequently applied to problems in mathematics, but it can be used to solve problems from virtually any discipline.

THE REAL NUMBER SYSTEM

• SETS

Human beings share the desire to organize and classify. Ancient astronomers classified stars into groups called *constellations*. Modern astronomers continue to classify stars by such characteristics as color, mass, size, temperature, and distance from Earth. In mathematics it is useful to place numbers with similar characteristics into **sets**. The following sets of numbers are used extensively in the study of algebra:

Integers	$\{\ldots, -3, -2, -1, 0, 1, 2, 3, \ldots\}$
Rational numbers	{all terminating or repeating decimals}
Irrational numbers	{all nonterminating, nonrepeating decimals}
Real numbers	{all rational or irrational numbers}

If a number in decimal form terminates or repeats a block of digits, then the number is a rational number. Here are two examples of rational numbers.

0.75 is a terminating decimal.

$0.2\overline{45}$ is a repeating decimal. The bar over the 45 means that the digits 45 repeat without end. That is, $0.2\overline{45} = 0.24545454\ldots$.

Rational numbers also can be written in the form $\dfrac{p}{q}$, where p and q are integers and $q \neq 0$. Examples of rational numbers written in this form are

$$\frac{3}{4} \qquad \frac{27}{110} \qquad -\frac{5}{2} \qquad \frac{7}{1} \qquad \frac{-4}{3}$$

Note that $\dfrac{7}{1} = 7$, and in general, $\dfrac{n}{1} = n$ for any integer n. Therefore, all integers are rational numbers.

When a rational number is written in the form $\dfrac{p}{q}$, the decimal form of the rational number can be found by dividing the numerator by the denominator.

$$\frac{3}{4} = 0.75 \qquad \frac{27}{110} = 0.2\overline{45}$$

In its decimal form, an irrational number neither terminates nor repeats. For example, $0.272272227\ldots$ is a nonterminating, nonrepeating decimal and thus is an irrational number. One of the best-known irrational numbers is pi, denoted by the Greek symbol π. The number π is defined as the ratio of the circumference of a circle to its diameter. Often in applications the rational number 3.14 or the rational number $\dfrac{22}{7}$ is used as an approximation of the irrational number π.

Every real number is either a rational number or an irrational number. If a real number is written in decimal form, it is a terminating decimal, a repeating decimal, or a nonterminating and nonrepeating decimal.

MATH MATTERS

Archimedes (c. 287–212 B.C.) was the first to calculate π with any degree of precision. He was able to show that

$$3\frac{10}{71} < \pi < 3\frac{1}{7}$$

from which we get the approximation

$$3\frac{1}{7} = \frac{22}{7} \approx \pi.$$

The use of the symbol π for this quantity was introduced by Leonhard Euler (1707–1783) in 1739, approximately 2000 years after Archimedes.

MATH MATTERS

Sophie Germain (1776–1831) was born in Paris, France. Because enrollment in the university she wanted to attend was available only to men, Germain attended under the name of Antoine-August Le Blanc. Eventually her ruse was discovered but not before she came to the attention of Pierre Lagrange, one of the best mathematicians of the time. He encouraged her work and became a mentor to her. A certain type of prime number is named after her called a *Germain prime number*. It is one such that p and $2p + 1$ are both prime. For instance, 11 is a Germain prime because $2(11) + 1$ and 23 and 11 are prime numbers. Germain primes are used in public key cryptography, a method used to send secure communications over the Internet.

The relationship between the various sets of numbers is shown in **Figure P.1**.

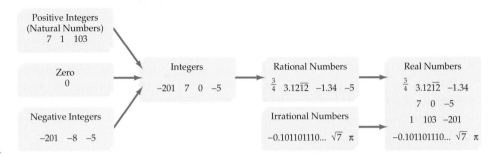

FIGURE P.1

Prime numbers and *composite numbers* play an important role in almost every branch of mathematics. A **prime number** is a positive integer other than 1 that has no positive-integer factors[1] other than itself and 1. The 10 smallest prime numbers are 2, 3, 5, 7, 11, 13, 17, 19, 23, and 29. Each of these numbers has only itself and 1 as factors.

A **composite number** is a positive integer greater than 1 that is not a prime number. For example, 10 is a composite number because 10 has both 2 and 5 as factors. The 10 smallest composite numbers are 4, 6, 8, 9, 10, 12, 14, 15, 16, and 18.

Alternative to Example 1

For each number, check all that apply.

N = Natural
I = Integer
Q = Rational
R = Real

	N	I	Q	R
-57		✔	✔	✔
3.3719			✔	✔
$7.42\overline{917}$			✔	✔
0		✔	✔	✔
$1.191191119\ldots$				✔
101	✔	✔	✔	✔

EXAMPLE 1   **Classify Real Numbers**

Determine which of the following numbers are

a. integers   b. rational numbers   c. irrational numbers
d. real numbers   e. prime numbers   f. composite numbers

$$-0.2, \quad 0, \quad 0.\overline{3}, \quad \pi, \quad 6, \quad 7, \quad 41, \quad 51, \quad 0.71771777177771\ldots$$

Solution

a. Integers: $0, 6, 7, 41, 51$

b. Rational numbers: $-0.2, 0, 0.\overline{3}, 6, 7, 41, 51$

c. Irrational numbers: $0.71771777177771\ldots, \pi$

d. Real numbers: $-0.2, 0, 0.\overline{3}, \pi, 6, 7, 41, 51, 0.71771777177771\ldots$

e. Prime numbers: $7, 41$

f. Composite numbers: $6, 51$

▶ **TRY EXERCISE 2, PAGE 15**

[1] Recall that a factor of a number divides the number evenly. For instance, 3 and 7 are factors of 21; 5 is not a factor of 21.

Each member of a set is called an **element** of the set. For instance, if $C = \{2, 3, 5\}$, then the elements of C are 2, 3, and 5. The notation $2 \in C$ is read "2 is an element of C." Set A is a **subset** of set B if every element of A is also an element of B, and we write $A \subseteq B$. For instance, the set of **negative integers** $\{-1, -2, -3, -4, \ldots\}$ is a subset of the set of integers. The set of **positive integers** $\{1, 2, 3, 4, \ldots\}$ (also known as the set of **natural numbers**) is also a subset of the set of integers.

❓ QUESTION   Are the integers a subset of the rational numbers?

The **empty set,** or **null set,** is the set that contains no elements. The symbol $\varnothing$ is used to represent the empty set. The set of people who have run a two-minute mile is the empty set.

The set of natural numbers less than 6 is $\{1, 2, 3, 4, 5\}$. This is an example of a **finite set;** all the elements of the set can be listed. The set of all natural numbers is an example of an **infinite set.** There is no largest natural number, so all the elements of the set of natural numbers cannot be listed.

Sets are often written using **set-builder notation.** Set-builder notation can be used to describe almost any set, but it is especially useful when writing infinite sets. For instance, the set

$$\{2n \mid n \in \text{natural numbers}\}$$

is read as "the set of elements $2n$ such that n is a natural number." By replacing n by each of the natural numbers, this is the set of positive even integers: $\{2, 4, 6, 8, \ldots\}$.

The set of real numbers greater than 2 is written:

$$\{x \mid x > 2, x \in \text{real numbers}\}$$

and is read "the set of x such that x is greater than 2 and x is an element of the real numbers."

Much of the work we do in this text uses the real numbers. With this in mind, we will frequently write, for instance, $\{x \mid x > 2, x \in \text{real numbers}\}$ in a shortened form as $\{x \mid x > 2\}$, where we assume that x is a real number.

take note

The order of the elements of a set is not important. For instance, the set of natural numbers less than 6 given at the right could have been written $\{3, 5, 2, 1, 4\}$. It is customary, however, to list elements of a set in numerical order.

MATH MATTERS

A **fuzzy set** is one in which each element is given a "degree" of membership. The concepts behind fuzzy sets are used in a wide variety of applications such as traffic lights, washing machines, and computer speech recognition programs.

Alternative to Example 2
List the four smallest elements in $\{n^2 \mid n \in \text{integers}\}$.
● **0, 1, 4, 9**

EXAMPLE 2   **Use Set-Builder Notation**

List the four smallest elements in $\{n^3 \mid n \in \text{natural numbers}\}$.

Solution
Because we want the four *smallest* elements, we choose the four smallest natural numbers. Thus $n = 1, 2, 3,$ and 4. Therefore, the four smallest elements of $\{n^3 \mid n \in \text{natural numbers}\}$ are $1, 8, 27,$ and 64.

▶ **TRY EXERCISE 6, PAGE 15**

❓ ANSWER   Yes.

• UNION AND INTERSECTION OF SETS

Just as operations such as addition and multiplication are performed on real numbers, operations are performed on sets. Two operations performed on sets are union and intersection. The union of two sets A and B is the set of elements that belong to A or to B or to both A and B.

Union of Two Sets

The **union** of two sets, written $A \cup B$, is the set of all elements that belong to either A or B. In set-builder notation, this is written

$$A \cup B = \{x \mid x \in A \text{ or } x \in B\}$$

For instance, given $A = \{2, 3, 4\}$ and $B = \{0, 1, 2, 3\}$, then $A \cup B = \{0, 1, 2, 3, 4\}$. Note that an element that belongs to both sets is listed only once.

The intersection of the two sets A and B is the set of elements that belong to both A and B.

Intersection of Two Sets

The **intersection** of two sets, written $A \cap B$, is the set of all elements that are common to both A and B. In set-builder notation, this is written

$$A \cap B = \{x \mid x \in A \text{ and } x \in B\}$$

For instance, given $A = \{2, 3, 4\}$ and $B = \{0, 1, 2, 3\}$, $A \cap B = \{2, 3\}$.

If the intersection of two sets is the empty set, the two sets are said to be **disjoint**. For example, if $A = \{2, 3, 4\}$ and $B = \{7, 8\}$, then $A \cap B = \varnothing$ and A and B are disjoint sets.

Alternative to Example 3
Given $A = \{-3, 0, 3, 6, 9\}$,
$B = \{-3, -2, -1, 0, 1, 2, 3\}$, and
$C = \{5, 6, 7\}$, find
a. $A \cup B$
b. $B \cap (A \cup C)$
c. $B \cap C$
○ **a.** $\{-3, -2, -1, 0, 1, 2, 3, 6, 9\}$
○ **b.** $\{-3, 0, 3\}$
○ **c.** $\varnothing$

EXAMPLE 3   Find the Union and Intersection of Sets

Find each intersection or union given $A = \{0, 2, 4, 6, 10, 12\}$,
$B = \{0, 3, 6, 12, 15\}$, and $C = \{1, 2, 3, 4, 5, 6, 7\}$.

a. $A \cup C$ **b.** $B \cap C$
c. $A \cap (B \cup C)$ **d.** $B \cup (A \cap C)$

Solution

a. $A \cup C = \{0, 1, 2, 3, 4, 5, 6, 7, 10, 12\}$ • The elements that belong to A or C

b. $B \cap C = \{3, 6\}$ • The elements that belong to B and C

c. First determine $B \cup C = \{0, 1, 2, 3, 4, 5, 6, 7, 12, 15\}$. Then

$$A \cap (B \cup C) = \{0, 2, 4, 6, 12\}$$

• **The elements that belong to A and ($B \cup C$)**

d. First determine $A \cap C = \{2, 4, 6\}$. Then

$$B \cup (A \cap C) = \{0, 2, 3, 4, 6, 12, 15\}$$

• **The elements that belong to B or ($A \cap C$)**

▶ **TRY EXERCISE 16, PAGE 15**

● ABSOLUTE VALUE AND DISTANCE

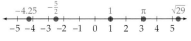

FIGURE P.2

The real numbers can be represented geometrically by a **coordinate axis** called a **real number line**. **Figure P.2** shows a portion of a real number line. The number associated with a point on a real number line is called the **coordinate** of the point. The point corresponding to zero is called the **origin**. Every real number corresponds to a point on the number line, and every point on the number line corresponds to a real number.

The *absolute value* of a real number a, denoted $|a|$, is the distance between a and 0 on the number line. For instance, $|3| = 3$ and $|-3| = 3$ because both 3 and -3 are 3 units from zero. See **Figure P.3**.

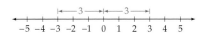

FIGURE P.3

In general, if $a \geq 0$, then $|a| = a$; however, if $a < 0$, then $|a| = -a$ because $-a$ is positive when $a < 0$. This leads to the following definition.

take note

The second part of the definition of absolute value states that if $a < 0$, then $|a| = -a$. For instance, if $a = -4$, then

$$|a| = |-4| = -(-4) = 4$$

Definition of Absolute Value

The **absolute value** of the real number a is defined by

$$|a| = \begin{cases} a & \text{if } a \geq 0 \\ -a & \text{if } a < 0 \end{cases}$$

The definition of *distance* between two points on a real number line makes use of absolute value.

Distance Between Points on a Real Number Line

If a and b are the coordinates of two points on a number line, the **distance** between the graph of a and the graph of b, denoted by $d(a, b)$, is given by $d(a, b) = |a - b|$.

As an example of this definition, the distance between the point whose coordinate is -2 and the point whose coordinate is 5 is given by

$$d(-2, 5) = |-2 - 5| = |-7| = 7$$

Note from **Figure P.4** that there are 7 units between -2 and 5 on the number line. Also note that the order of the coordinates does not matter.

$$d(5, -2) = |5 - (-2)| = |7| = 7$$

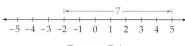

FIGURE P.4

Alternative to Example 4
Express "the distance between x and 4 is less than 5" using absolute value notation.
● $|x - 4| < 5$

EXAMPLE 4   **Use Absolute Value to Express the Distance Between Two Points**

Express the distance between a and -3 on the number line using absolute value.

Solution

$$d(a, -3) = |a - (-3)| = |a + 3|$$

▶ **TRY EXERCISE 48, PAGE 16**

● **INTERVAL NOTATION**

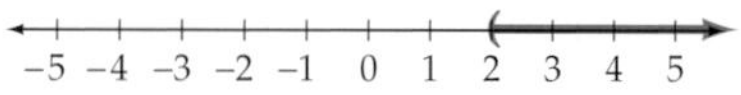

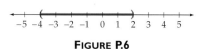

FIGURE P.5

The graph of $\{x \mid x > 2\}$ is shown in **Figure P.5**. The set is the real numbers greater than 2. The parenthesis at 2 indicates that 2 is not included in the set. Rather than write this set of real numbers using set-builder notation, we frequently write the set in **interval notation** as $(2, \infty)$.

In general, the interval notation

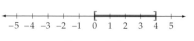

FIGURE P.6

(a, b) represents all real numbers between a and b, not including a and b. This is an **open interval**. In set-builder notation, we write $\{x \mid a < x < b\}$. For instance, the graph of $(-4, 2)$ is shown in **Figure P.6**.

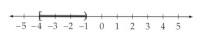

FIGURE P.7

$[a, b]$ represents all real numbers between a and b, including a and b. This is a **closed interval**. In set-builder notation, we write $\{x \mid a \leq x \leq b\}$. For instance, the graph of $[0, 4]$ is shown in **Figure P.7**. The brackets at 0 and 4 indicate that those numbers are included in the graph.

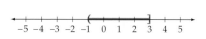

FIGURE P.8

$(a, b]$ represents all real numbers between a and b, not including a but including b. This is a **half-open interval**. In set-builder notation, we write $\{x \mid a < x \leq b\}$. For instance, the graph of $(-1, 3]$ is shown in **Figure P.8**.

FIGURE P.9

$[a, b)$ represents all real numbers between a and b, including a but not including b. This is a **half-open interval**. In set-builder notation, we write $\{x \mid a \leq x < b\}$. For instance, the graph of $[-4, -1)$ is shown in **Figure P.9**.

Subsets of the real numbers whose graphs extend forever in one or both directions can be represented by interval notation using the **infinity symbol** ∞ or the **negative infinity symbol** $-\infty$.

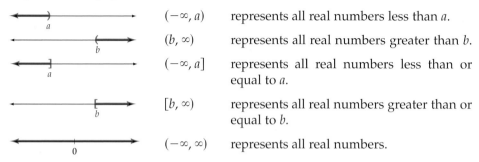

$(-\infty, a)$ represents all real numbers less than a.

(b, ∞) represents all real numbers greater than b.

$(-\infty, a]$ represents all real numbers less than or equal to a.

$[b, \infty)$ represents all real numbers greater than or equal to b.

$(-\infty, \infty)$ represents all real numbers.

Alternative to Example 5

Graph the interval $(-4, 3)$. Write the interval in set-builder notation.

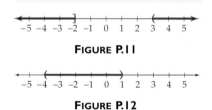

$\{x \,|\, -4 < x < 3\}$

---

t a k e   n o t e

It is *never* correct to use a bracket when using the infinity symbol. For instance, $[-\infty, 3]$ is not correct. Nor is $[2, \infty]$ correct. Neither negative infinity nor positive infinity is a real number and therefore cannot be contained in an interval.

FIGURE P.11

FIGURE P.12

Alternative to Example 6

Graph the following. Write **a.** using interval notation and write **b.** using set-builder notation.

a. $\{x \,|\, x \geq -1\} \cup \{x \,|\, x \geq 3\}$
b. $(-\infty, 1) \cap [-1, 3]$

a.

$[-1, \infty)$

b.

$\{x \,|\, -1 \leq x < 1\}$

EXAMPLE 5   **Graph a Set in Interval Notation**

Graph $(-\infty, 3]$. Write the interval in set-builder notation.

Solution

The set is the real numbers less than or equal to 3. In set-builder notation, this is the set $\{x \,|\, x \leq 3\}$. Draw a right bracket at 3, and darken the number line to the left of 3, as shown in **Figure P.10.**

FIGURE P.10

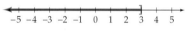

▶ **TRY EXERCISE 54, PAGE 16**

The set $\{x \,|\, x \leq -2\} \cup \{x \,|\, x > 3\}$ is the set of real numbers that are either less than or equal to -2 or greater than 3. We also could write this in interval notation as $(-\infty, -2] \cup (3, \infty)$. The graph of the set is shown in **Figure P.11.**

The set $\{x \,|\, x > -4\} \cap \{x \,|\, x < 1\}$ is the set of real numbers that are greater than -4 *and* less than 1. Note from **Figure P.12** that this set is the interval $(-4, 1)$, which can be written in set-builder notation as $\{x \,|\, -4 < x < 1\}$.

EXAMPLE 6   **Graph Intervals**

Graph the following. Write **a.** and **b.** using interval notation. Write **c.** and **d.** using set-builder notation.

a. $\{x \,|\, x \leq -1\} \cup \{x \,|\, x \geq 2\}$ **b.** $\{x \,|\, x \geq -1\} \cap \{x \,|\, x < 5\}$
c. $(-\infty, 0) \cup [1, 3]$ **d.** $[-1, 3] \cap (1, 5)$

Solution

a. $(-\infty, -1] \cup [2, \infty)$

b. $[-1, 5)$

Continued ▶

c.   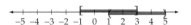 $\{x \mid x < 0\} \cup \{x \mid 1 \leq x \leq 3\}$

d. The graphs of $[-1, 3]$, in red, and $(1, 5)$, in blue, are shown below.

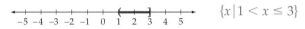

Note that the intersection of the sets occurs where the graphs intersect. Although $1 \in [-1, 3]$, $1 \notin (1, 5)$. Therefore, 1 does not belong to the intersection of the sets. On the other hand, $3 \in [-1, 3]$ and $3 \in (1, 5)$. Therefore, 3 belongs to the intersection of the sets. Thus we have the following.

$\{x \mid 1 < x \leq 3\}$

▶ **TRY EXERCISE 64, PAGE 16**

• ORDER OF OPERATIONS AGREEMENT

The approximate pressure p, in pounds per square inch, on a scuba diver x feet below the water's surface is given by

$$p = 15 + 0.5x$$

The pressure on the diver at various depths is given below.

10 feet	$15 + 0.5(10) = 15 + 5 = 20$ pounds
20 feet	$15 + 0.5(20) = 15 + 10 = 25$ pounds
40 feet	$15 + 0.5(40) = 15 + 20 = 35$ pounds
70 feet	$15 + 0.5(70) = 15 + 35 = 50$ pounds

Note that the expression $15 + 0.5(70)$ has two operations, addition and multiplication. When an expression contains more than one operation, the operations must be performed in a specified order, as listed below in the Order of Operations Agreement.

The Order of Operations Agreement

If grouping symbols are present, evaluate by performing the operations within the grouping symbols, innermost grouping symbols first, while observing the order given in steps 1 to 3.

Step 1   Evaluate exponential expressions.
Step 2   Do multiplication and division as they occur from left to right.
Step 3   Do addition and subtraction as they occur from left to right.

Therefore, the expression $15 + 0.5(70)$ is simplified by first performing the multiplication and then performing the addition, as we did above.

take note

Recall that subtraction can be rewritten as addition of the opposite. Therefore,

$3x^2 - 4xy + 5x - y - 7$
$= 3x^2 + (-4)xy + 5x + (-y) + (-7)$

In this form, we can see that the terms (addends) are $3x^2$, $-4xy$, $5x$, $-y$, and -7.

One of the ways the Order of Operations Agreement is used is to evaluate variable expressions. The addends of a variable expression are called **terms.** The terms for the expression at the right are $3x^2$, $-4xy$, $5x$, $-y$, and -7. Observe that the sign of a term is the sign that immediately precedes it.

$$3x^2 - 4xy + 5x - y - 7$$

The terms $3x^2$, $-4xy$, $5x$, and $-y$ are **variable terms.** The term -7 is a **constant term.** Each variable term has a **numerical coefficient** and a **variable part.** The numerical coefficient for the term $3x^2$ is 3; the numerical coefficient for the term $-4xy$ is -4; the numerical coefficient for the term $5x$ is 5; and the numerical coefficient for the term $-y$ is -1. When the numerical coefficient is 1 or -1 (as in x and $-x$), the 1 is usually not written.

To **evaluate** a variable expression, replace the variables by their given values and then use the Order of Operations Agreement to simplify the result.

Alternative to Example 7

Evaluate $3ab - 4(2a - 3b)$ when $a = 4$ and $b = -3$.

● **-104**

EXAMPLE 7   Evaluate a Variable Expression

a. Evaluate $\dfrac{x^3 - y^3}{x^2 + xy + y^2}$ when $x = 2$ and $y = -3$.

b. Evaluate $(x + 2y)^2 - 4z$ when $x = 3$, $y = -2$, and $z = -4$.

Solution

a. $\dfrac{x^3 - y^3}{x^2 + xy + y^2}$

$\dfrac{2^3 - (-3)^3}{2^2 + 2(-3) + (-3)^2} = \dfrac{8 - (-27)}{4 - 6 + 9} = \dfrac{35}{7} = 5$

b. $(x + 2y)^2 - 4z$

$(3 + 2(-2))^2 - 4(-4) = (3 + (-4))^2 - 4(-4)$
$= (-1)^2 - 4(-4) = 1 - 4(-4)$
$= 1 + 16 = 17$

▶ **TRY EXERCISE 74, PAGE 16**

● **SIMPLIFYING VARIABLE EXPRESSIONS**

Addition, multiplication, subtraction, and *division* are the operations of arithmetic. **Addition** of the two real numbers a and b is designated by $a + b$. If $a + b = c$, then c is the **sum** and the real numbers a and b are called **terms.**

Multiplication of the real numbers a and b is designated by ab or $a \cdot b$. If $ab = c$, then c is the **product** and the real numbers a and b are called **factors** of c.

The number $-b$ is referred to as the **additive inverse** of b. **Subtraction** of the real numbers a and b is designated by $a - b$ and is defined as the sum of a and the additive inverse of b. That is,

$$a - b = a + (-b)$$

If $a - b = c$, then c is called the **difference** of a and b.

The **multiplicative inverse** or **reciprocal** of the nonzero number b is $1/b$. The **division** of a and b, designated by $a \div b$ with $b \neq 0$, is defined as the product of a and the reciprocal of b. That is,

$$a \div b = a\left(\frac{1}{b}\right) \qquad \text{provided that } b \neq 0$$

If $a \div b = c$, then c is called the **quotient** of a and b.

The notation $a \div b$ is often represented by the fractional notation a/b or $\frac{a}{b}$.

The real number a is the **numerator,** and the nonzero real number b is the **denominator** of the fraction.

Properties of Real Numbers

Let a, b, and c be real numbers.

	Addition Properties	Multiplication Properties
Closure	$a + b$ is a unique real number.	ab is a unique real number.
Commutative	$a + b = b + a$	$ab = ba$
Associative	$(a + b) + c = a + (b + c)$	$(ab)c = a(bc)$
Identity	There exists a unique real number 0 such that $a + 0 = 0 + a = a$.	There exists a unique real number 1 such that $a \cdot 1 = 1 \cdot a = a$.
Inverse	For each real number a, there is a unique real number $-a$ such that $a + (-a) = (-a) + a = 0$.	For each *nonzero* real number a, there is a unique real number $1/a$ such that $a \cdot \frac{1}{a} = \frac{1}{a} \cdot a = 1$.
Distributive	$a(b + c) = ab + ac$	

Alternative to Example 8
Identify the property.
a. $a(bc) = a(cb)$
⊙ **Commutative property of multiplication**
b. $a + (-a) = 0$
⊙ **Inverse property of addition**
c. $c + 0 = c$
⊙ **Identity property of addition**
d. $3(x + y) = 3(y + x)$
⊙ **Commutative property of addition**

EXAMPLE 8 **Identify Properties of Real Numbers**

Identify the property of real numbers illustrated in each statement.

a. $(2a)b = 2(ab)$ **b.** $\left(\frac{1}{5}\right)11$ is a real number.

c. $4(x + 3) = 4x + 12$ **d.** $(a + 5b) + 7c = (5b + a) + 7c$

e. $\left(\frac{1}{2} \cdot 2\right)a = 1 \cdot a$ **f.** $1 \cdot a = a$

Solution

a. Associative property of multiplication

b. Closure property of multiplication of real numbers

c. Distributive property

d. Commutative property of addition

e. Inverse property of multiplication

f. Identity property of multiplication

▶ TRY EXERCISE 86, PAGE 16

We can identify which property of real numbers has been used to rewrite expressions by closely comparing the expressions and noting any changes. For instance, to simplify $(6x)2$, both the commutative property and associative property of multiplication are used.

$$(6x)2 = 2(6x)$$ • **Commutative property of multiplication**
$$= (2 \cdot 6)x$$ • **Associative property of multiplication**
$$= 12x$$

To simplify $3(4p + 5)$, use the distributive property.

$$3(4p + 5) = 3(4p) + 3(5)$$ • **Distributive property**
$$= 12p + 15$$

Terms that have the same variable part are called **like terms**. The distributive property is also used to simplify an expression with like terms such as $3x^2 + 9x^2$.

$$3x^2 + 9x^2 = (3 + 9)x^2$$ • **Distributive property**
$$= 12x^2$$

Note from this example that like terms are combined by adding the coefficients of the like terms.

❓ QUESTION Are the terms $2x^2$ and $3x$ like terms?

---

take note

Normally, we will not show, as we did at the right, all the steps in the simplification of a variable expression. For instance, we will just write $(6x)2 = 12x$, $3(4p + 5) = 12p + 15$, and $3x^2 + 9x^2 = 12x^2$. It is important to know, however, that every step in the simplification depends on one of the properties of real numbers.

Alternative to Example 9
Simplify the following.
a. $6 - 3(5a - 4)$
b. $-3(2a - 5b + 1) + 5(3a - b + 2)$
○ a. $-15a + 18$
○ b. $9a + 10b + 7$

EXAMPLE 9   **Simplify Variable Expressions**

a. Simplify $5 + 3(2x - 6)$.

b. Simplify $4x - 2[7 - 5(2x - 3)]$.

Continued ▶

❓ ANSWER No. The variable parts are not the same. The variable part of $2x^2$ is $x \cdot x$. The variable part of $3x$ is x.

Solution

a. $5 + 3(2x - 6) = 5 + 6x - 18$ • **Use the distributive property.**

$\qquad\qquad\qquad = 6x - 13$ • **Add the constant terms.**

b. $4x - 2[7 - 5(2x - 3)]$

$\qquad = 4x - 2[7 - 10x + 15]$ • **Use the distributive property to remove the inner parentheses.**

$\qquad = 4x - 2[-10x + 22]$ • **Simplify.**

$\qquad = 4x + 20x - 44$ • **Use the distributive property to remove the brackets.**

$\qquad = 24x - 44$ • **Simplify.**

▶ **TRY EXERCISE 106, PAGE 17**

An **equation** is a statement of equality between two numbers or two expressions. There are four basic properties of equality that relate to equations.

Properties of Equality

Let a, b, and c be real numbers.

Reflexive	$a = a$
Symmetric	If $a = b$, then $b = a$.
Transitive	If $a = b$ and $b = c$, then $a = c$.
Substitution	If $a = b$, then a may be replaced by b in any expression that involves a.

Alternative to Example 10
Identify the property of equality illustrated in the following statement:
If $2x + 3y = 7$ and $x^2 + y^2 = 7$, then $2x + 3y = x^2 + y^2$.
● **Substitution**

EXAMPLE 10   Identify Properties of Equality

Identify the property of equality illustrated in each statement.

a. If $3a + b = c$, then $c = 3a + b$.

b. $5(x + y) = 5(x + y)$

c. If $4a - 1 = 7b$ and $7b = 5c + 2$, then $4a - 1 = 5c + 2$.

d. If $a = 5$ and $b(a + c) = 72$, then $b(5 + c) = 72$.

Solution

a. Symmetric   **b.** Reflexive   **c.** Transitive   **d.** Substitution

▶ **TRY EXERCISE 90, PAGE 16**

TOPICS FOR DISCUSSION

1. Archimedes determined that $\dfrac{223}{71} < \pi < \dfrac{22}{7}$. Is it possible to find an exact representation for π of the form $\dfrac{a}{b}$, where a and b are integers?

2. If $I = \{\text{irrational numbers}\}$ and $Q = \{\text{rational numbers}\}$, name the sets $I \cup Q$ and $I \cap Q$.

3. If the proposed simplification shown at the right is correct, so state. If it is incorrect, show a correct simplification. $2 \cdot 3^2 = 6^2 = 36$

4. Are there any even prime numbers? If so, name them.

5. Does every real number have an additive inverse? Does every real number have a multiplicative inverse?

6. What is the difference between an open interval and a closed interval?

EXERCISE SET P.1

—*Suggested Assignment: Exercises 1–105, every other odd; 107–123, odd; 127, 129, 133–138, all.*
—*Answers for Exercises 1, 2, 19–30 and 51–66 are on page AA1.*

In Exercises 1 and 2, determine whether each number is an integer, a rational number, an irrational number, a prime number, or a real number.

1. $-\dfrac{1}{5}, 0, -44, \pi, 3.14, 5.05005000500005\ldots, \sqrt{81}, 53$

▶ **2.** $\dfrac{5}{\sqrt{7}}, \dfrac{5}{7}, 31, -2\dfrac{1}{2}, 4.235653907493, 51, 0.888\ldots$

In Exercises 3 to 8, list the four smallest elements of each set.

3. $\{2x \,|\, x \in \text{positive integers}\}$ 2, 4, 6, 8

4. $\{|x| \,|\, x \in \text{integers}\}$ 0, 1, 2, 3

5. $\{y \,|\, y = 2x + 1, x \in \text{natural numbers}\}$ 3, 5, 7, 9

▶ **6.** $\{y \,|\, y = x^2 - 1, x \in \text{integers}\}$ −1, 0, 3, 8

7. $\{z \,|\, z = |x|, x \in \text{integers}\}$ 0, 1, 2, 3

8. $\{z \,|\, z = |x| - x, x \in \text{negative integers}\}$ 2, 4, 6, 8

In Exercises 9 to 18, perform the operations given
$A = \{-3, -2, -1, 0, 1, 2, 3\}$, $B = \{-2, 0, 2, 4, 6\}$,
$C = \{0, 1, 2, 3, 4, 5, 6\}$, and $D = \{-3, -1, 1, 3\}$.

9. $A \cup B$
   $\{-3, -2, -1, 0, 1, 2, 3, 4, 6\}$

10. $C \cup D$
    $\{-3, -1, 0, 1, 2, 3, 4, 5, 6\}$

11. $A \cap C$ $\{0, 1, 2, 3\}$

12. $C \cap D$ $\{1, 3\}$

13. $B \cap D$ $\varnothing$

14. $B \cup (A \cap C)$
    $\{-2, 0, 1, 2, 3, 4, 6\}$

15. $D \cap (B \cup C)$ $\{1, 3\}$

▶ **16.** $(A \cap B) \cup (A \cap C)$
    $\{-2, 0, 1, 2, 3\}$

17. $(B \cup C) \cap (B \cup D)$
    $\{-2, 0, 1, 2, 3, 4, 6\}$

18. $(A \cap C) \cup (B \cap D)$
    $\{0, 1, 2, 3\}$

In Exercises 19 to 30, graph each set. Write sets given in interval notation in set-builder notation and write sets given in set-builder notation in interval notation.

19. $(-2, 3)$ $\{x \,|\, -2 < x < 3\}$

20. $[1, 5]$ $\{x \,|\, 1 \le x \le 5\}$

21. $[-5, -1]$ $\{x \,|\, -5 \le x \le -1\}$

22. $(-3, 3)$ $\{x \,|\, -3 < x < 3\}$

23. $[2, \infty)$ $\{x \,|\, x \ge 2\}$

24. $(-\infty, 4)$ $\{x \,|\, x < 4\}$

25. $\{x \,|\, 3 < x < 5\}$ $(3, 5)$

26. $\{x \,|\, x < -1\}$ $(-\infty, -1)$

27. $\{x \mid x \geq -2\}$ $[-2, \infty)$

28. $\{x \mid -1 \leq x < 5\}$ $[-1, 5)$

29. $\{x \mid 0 \leq x \leq 1\}$ $[0, 1]$

30. $\{x \mid -4 < x \leq 5\}$ $(-4, 5]$

In Exercises 31 to 40, write each expression without absolute value symbols.

31. $-|-5|$ -5

32. $-|-4|^2$ -16

33. $|3| \cdot |-4|$ 12

34. $|3| - |-7|$ -4

35. $|\pi^2 + 10|$ $\pi^2 + 10$

36. $|\pi^2 - 10|$ $10 - \pi^2$

37. $|x - 4| + |x + 5|$, given $0 < x < 1$ 9

38. $|x + 6| + |x - 2|$, given $2 < x < 3$ $2x + 4$

39. $|2x| - |x - 1|$, given $0 < x < 1$ $3x - 1$

40. $|x + 1| + |x - 3|$, given $x > 3$ $2x - 2$

In Exercises 41 to 50, use absolute value notation to describe the given situation.

41. Distance between x and 3 $|x - 3|$

42. Distance between a and -2 $|a + 2|$

43. The distance between x and -2 is 4. $|x + 2| = 4$

44. The distance between z and 5 is 1. $|z - 5| = 1$

45. $d(m, n)$ $|m - n|$

46. $d(p, 8)$ $|p - 8|$

47. The distance between a and 4 is less than 5. $|a - 4| < 5$

▶ **48.** The distance between z and 5 is greater than 7. $|z - 5| > 7$

49. The distance between x and -2 is greater than 4.
$|x + 2| > 4$

50. The distance between y and -3 is greater than 6.
$|y + 3| > 6$

In Exercises 51 to 66, graph each set.

51. $(-\infty, 0) \cup [2, 4]$

52. $(-3, 1) \cup (3, 5)$

53. $(-4, 0) \cap [-2, 5]$

▶ **54.** $(-\infty, 3] \cap (2, 6)$

55. $(1, \infty) \cup (-2, \infty)$

56. $(-4, \infty) \cup (0, \infty)$

57. $(1, \infty) \cap (-2, \infty)$

58. $(-4, \infty) \cap (0, \infty)$

59. $[-2, 4] \cap [4, 5]$

60. $(-\infty, 1] \cap [1, \infty)$

61. $(-2, 4) \cap (4, 5)$

62. $(-\infty, 1) \cap (1, \infty)$

63. $\{x \mid x < -3\} \cup \{x \mid 1 < x < 2\}$

▶ **64.** $\{x \mid -3 \leq x < 0\} \cup \{x \mid x \geq 2\}$

65. $\{x \mid x < -3\} \cup \{x \mid x < 2\}$

66. $\{x \mid x < -3\} \cap \{x \mid x < 2\}$

In Exercises 67 to 78, evaluate the variable expression for $x = 3$, $y = -2$, and $z = -1$.

67. $-y^3$ 8

68. $-y^2$ -4

69. $2xyz$ 12

70. $-3xz$ 9

71. $-2x^2y^2$ -72

72. $2y^3z^2$ -16

73. $xy - z(x - y)^2$ 19

▶ **74.** $(z - 2y)^2 - 3z^3$ 12

75. $\dfrac{x^2 + y^2}{x + y}$ 13

76. $\dfrac{2xy^2z^4}{(y - z)^4}$ 24

77. $\dfrac{3y}{x} - \dfrac{2z}{y}$ -3

78. $(x - z)^2(x + z)^2$ 64

In Exercises 79 to 92, state the property of real numbers or the property of equality that is used.

79. $(ab^2)c = a(b^2c)$ Associative property of multiplication

80. $2x - 3y = -3y + 2x$ Commutative property of addition

81. $4(2a - b) = 8a - 4b$ Distributive property

82. $6 + (7 + a) = 6 + (a + 7)$ Commutative property of addition

83. $(3x)y = y(3x)$ Commutative property of multiplication

84. $4ab + 0 = 4ab$ Identity property of addition

85. $1 \cdot (4x) = 4x$ Identity property of multiplication

▶ **86.** $7(a + b) = 7(b + a)$ Commutative property of addition

87. $x^2 + 1 = x^2 + 1$ Reflexive property of equality

88. If $a + b = 2$, then $2 = a + b$. Symmetric property of equality

89. If $2x + 1 = y$ and $3x - 2 = y$, then $2x + 1 = 3x - 2$.
Transitive property of equality

▶ **90.** If $4x + 2y = 7$ and $x = 3$, then $4(3) + 2y = 7$.
Substitution property of equality

91. $4 \cdot \dfrac{1}{4} = 1$ Inverse property of multiplication

92. $ab + (-ab) = 0$ Inverse property of addition

In Exercises 93 to 106, simplify the variable expression.

93. $3(2x)$ $6x$

94. $-2(4y)$ $-8y$

95. $3(2 + x)$ $3x + 6$

96. $-2(4 + y)$ $-2y - 8$

97. $\dfrac{2}{3}a + \dfrac{5}{6}a$ $\dfrac{3}{2}a$

98. $\dfrac{3}{4}x - \dfrac{1}{2}x$ $\dfrac{1}{4}x$

99. $2 + 3(2x - 5)$ $6x - 13$

100. $4 + 2(2a - 3)$ $4a - 2$

101. $5 - 3(4x - 2y)$
$-12x + 6y + 5$

102. $7 - 2(5n - 8m)$
$16m - 10n + 7$

103. $3(2a - 4b) - 4(a - 3b)$ $2a$

104. $5(4r - 7t) - 2(10r + 3t)$ $-41t$

105. $5a - 2[3 - 2(4a + 3)]$ $21a + 6$

▶ **106.** $6 + 3[2x - 4(3x - 2)]$ $-30x + 30$

107. **AREA OF A TRIANGLE** The area of a triangle is given by
area $= \dfrac{1}{2}bh$, where b is the base of the triangle and h
is its height. Find the area of a triangle whose base is
3 inches and whose height is 4 inches. 6 in.^{2}

108. **VOLUME OF A BOX** The volume of a
rectangular box is given by

volume $= lwh$

where l is the length, w is the width,
and h is the height of the box. Find the
volume of a classroom that is 40 feet long, 30 feet wide,
and 12 feet high. 1440 ft^3

109. **PROFIT FROM SALES** The profit, in dollars, a company
earns from the sale of x bicycles is given by

profit $= -0.5x^2 + 120x - 2000$

Find the profit the company earns from selling 110 bicycles.
$5150

110. **MAGAZINE CIRCULATION** The circulation, in thousands
of subscriptions, of a new magazine n months after its
introduction can be approximated by

circulation $= \sqrt{n^2 - n + 1}$

Find, to the nearest hundred, the circulation of the magazine after 12 months. 11,500 subscriptions

111. **HEART RATE** The heart rate, in beats per minute, of a certain runner during a cool-down period can be approximated by

$$\text{Heart rate} = 65 + \frac{53}{4t + 1}$$

where t is the number of minutes after the start of cool-
down. Find the runner's heart rate in 10 minutes. Round
to the nearest whole number. 66 beats per minute

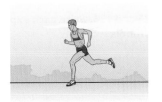

112. **BODY MASS INDEX** According to the National Institutes of Health, body mass index (BMI) is measure of body fat based on height and weight that applies
to both adult men and women, with values between 18.5
and 24.9 considered healthy. BMI is calculated as
BMI $= \dfrac{705w}{h^2}$, where w is the weight of the person in
pounds and h is the person's height in inches. Find the
BMI for a person who weighs 160 pounds and is 5 feet
10 inches tall. Round to the nearest whole number. 23

113. **PHYSICS** The height, in feet, of a ball t seconds after it is
thrown upward is given by height $= -16t^2 + 80t + 4$.
Find the height of the ball 2 seconds after it has been
released. 100 ft

114. **CHEMISTRY** Salt is being added to water in such a way
that the concentration, in grams per liter, is given by
concentration $= \dfrac{50t}{t + 1}$, where t is the time in minutes
after the introduction of the salt. Find the concentration
of salt after 24 minutes. 48 grams per liter

CONNECTING CONCEPTS

**In Exercises 115 to 118, perform the given operation given
A is any set.**

115. $A \cup A$ A

116. $A \cap A$ A

117. $A \cap \varnothing$ $\varnothing$

118. $A \cup \varnothing$ A

119. If A and B are two sets and $A \cup B = A$, what can be said
about B? B is a subset of A.

120. If A and B are two sets and $A \cap B = B$, what can be said
about B? B is a subset of A.

121. Is division of real numbers an associative operation? Give a reason for your answer.
No. $(8 \div 4) \div 2 = 2 \div 2 = 1, 8 \div (4 \div 2) = 8 \div 2 = 4$

122. Is subtraction of real numbers a commutative operation? Give a reason for your answer.
No. $5 - 3 = 2, 3 - 5 = -2$

123. Which of the properties of real numbers are satisfied by the integers? All but the multiplicative inverse property

124. Which of the properties of real numbers are satisfied by the rational numbers? All

In Exercises 125 and 126, write each expression without absolute value symbols.

125. $\left| \dfrac{x + 7}{|x| + |x - 1|} \right|$, given $0 < x < 1$. $x + 7$

126. $\left| \dfrac{x + 3}{\left| x - \dfrac{1}{2} \right| + \left| x + \dfrac{1}{2} \right|} \right|$, given $0 < x < 0.2$. $x + 3$

In Exercises 127 to 132, use absolute value notation to describe the given statement.

127. x is closer to 2 than it is to 6. $|x - 2| < |x - 6|$

128. x is closer to a than it is to b. $|x - a| < |x - b|$

129. x is farther from 3 than it is from -7. $|x - 3| > |x + 7|$

130. x is farther from 0 than it is from 5. $|x| > |x - 5|$

131. x is more than 2 units from 4 but less than 7 units from 4.
$2 < |x - 4| < 7$

132. x is more than b units from a but less than c units from a.
$b < |x - a| < c$

PREPARE FOR SECTION P.2

133. Simplify: $2^2 \cdot 2^3$ [P.1]
32

134. Simplify: $\dfrac{4^3}{4^5}$ [P.1]
$\dfrac{1}{16}$

135. Simplify: $(2^3)^2$ [P.1]
64

136. Simplify: $3.14(10^5)$ [P.1]
314,000

137. True or false: $3^4 \cdot 3^2 = 9^6$ [P.1]
False

138. True or false: $(3 + 4)^2 = 3^2 + 4^2$ [P.1]
False

PROJECTS

1. NUMBER PUZZLE A number n has the following properties:

When n is divided by 6, the remainder is 5.

When n is divided by 5, the remainder is 4.

When n is divided by 4, the remainder is 3.

When n is divided by 3, the remainder is 2.

When n is divided by 2, the remainder is 1.

What is the smallest value of n?

2. OPERATIONS ON INTERVALS Besides finding unions and intersections of intervals, it is possible to apply other operations to intervals. For instance, $(-1, 2)^2$ is the interval that results from squaring every number in the interval $(-1, 2)$. This gives $[0, 4)$. Thus $(-1, 2)^2 = [0, 4)$.

a. Find $(-4, 2)^2$.

b. Find $ABS(-4, 5)$, the absolute value of every number in $(-4, 5)$.

c. Find $\sqrt{(0, 9)}$, the square root of every number in $(0, 9)$.

d. Find $\dfrac{1}{(0, 1)}$, the reciprocal of every number in $(0, 1)$.

3. FACTORS OF A NUMBER Explain why the square of a natural number always has an odd number of natural number factors.

INTEGER AND RATIONAL NUMBER EXPONENTS

- PROPERTIES OF EXPONENTS
- SCIENTIFIC NOTATION
- RATIONAL EXPONENTS AND RADICALS
- SIMPLIFY RADICAL EXPRESSIONS

● PROPERTIES OF EXPONENTS

A compact method of writing $5 \cdot 5 \cdot 5 \cdot 5$ is 5^4. The expression 5^4 is written in **exponential notation**. Similarly, we can write

$$\frac{2x}{3} \cdot \frac{2x}{3} \cdot \frac{2x}{3} \quad \text{as} \quad \left(\frac{2x}{3}\right)^3$$

Exponential notation can be used to express the product of any expression that is used repeatedly as a factor.

Definition of Natural Number Exponents

If b is any real number and n is a natural number, then

$$b^n = \overbrace{b \cdot b \cdot b \cdot \,\cdots\, \cdot b}^{b \text{ is a factor } n \text{ times}}$$

where b is the **base** and n is the **exponent.**

For instance,

$$5^4 = 5 \cdot 5 \cdot 5 \cdot 5 = 625$$
$$-5^4 = -(5 \cdot 5 \cdot 5 \cdot 5) = -625$$
$$(-5)^4 = (-5)(-5)(-5)(-5) = 625$$

Pay close attention to the difference between -5^4 (the base is 5) and $(-5)^4$ (the base is -5).

❓ QUESTION What is the value of **a.** -2^5 and **b.** $(-2)^5$?

We can extend the definition of an exponent to all the integers. We first deal with the case of zero as an exponent.

Definition of b^0

For any nonzero real number b, $b^0 = 1$.

Some examples of this definition are

$$3^0 = 1 \qquad \left(\frac{3}{4}\right)^0 = 1 \qquad (-7)^0 = 1 \qquad (a^2 + 1)^0 = 1$$

MATH MATTERS

The expression 10^{100} is called a *googol*. The term was coined by the 9-year-old nephew of the American mathematician Edward Kasner. Many calculators do not provide for numbers of this magnitude, but it is no serious loss. To appreciate the magnitude of a googol, consider that if all the atoms in the known universe were counted, the number would not even be close to a googol. But if a googol is too small for you, try 10^{googol}, which is called a *googolplex*. As a final note, the name of the Internet site Google.com is a takeoff on the word *googol*.

❓ ANSWER **a.** $-2^5 = -(2 \cdot 2 \cdot 2 \cdot 2 \cdot 2) = -32$
b. $(-2)^5 = (-2)(-2)(-2)(-2)(-2) = -32$

<table>
<tr><td>

take note

Using the definition of b^{-n},

$$\frac{5^{-2}}{7^{-1}} = \frac{\frac{1}{5^2}}{\frac{1}{7}}$$

Using the rules for dividing fractions, we have

$$\frac{\frac{1}{5^2}}{\frac{1}{7}} = \frac{1}{5^2} \div \frac{1}{7} = \frac{1}{5^2} \cdot \frac{7}{1} = \frac{7}{5^2}$$

</td></tr>
</table>

Now we extend the definition to include negative integers.

Definition of b^{-n}

If $b \neq 0$ and n is a natural number, then $b^{-n} = \dfrac{1}{b^n}$ and $\dfrac{1}{b^{-n}} = b^n$.

Here are some examples.

$$3^{-2} = \frac{1}{3^2} = \frac{1}{9} \qquad \frac{1}{4^{-3}} = 4^3 = 64 \qquad \frac{5^{-2}}{7^{-1}} = \frac{7}{5^2} = \frac{7}{25}$$

Alternative to Example 1
Evaluate.
a. $6^{-3}(-3)^4$
b. -6^0

○ **a.** $\dfrac{3}{8}$
○ **b.** -1

EXAMPLE 1   Evaluate an Exponential Expression

a. $(-2^4)(-3)^2$ **b.** $\dfrac{(-4)^{-3}}{(-2)^{-5}}$ **c.** $-\pi^0$

Solution

a. $(-2^4)(-3)^2 = -(2 \cdot 2 \cdot 2 \cdot 2)(-3)(-3) = -(16)(9) = -144$

b. $\dfrac{(-4)^{-3}}{(-2)^{-5}} = \dfrac{(-2)(-2)(-2)(-2)(-2)}{(-4)(-4)(-4)} = \dfrac{-32}{-64} = \dfrac{1}{2}$

c. $-\pi^0 = -(\pi^0) = -1$

▶ **TRY EXERCISE 10, PAGE 31**

<table>
<tr><td>

take note

Part **c.** is similar to $-5^4 = -625$, which was discussed earlier.

</td></tr>
</table>

When working with exponential expressions containing variables, we must ensure that a value of the variable does not result in an undefined expression. For instance, $x^{-2} = \dfrac{1}{x^2}$. Because division by zero is not allowed, for the expression x^{-2}, we must assume that $x \neq 0$. Therefore, to avoid problems with undefined expressions, we will use the following restriction agreement.

Restriction Agreement

The expressions 0^0, 0^n (where n is a negative integer), and $\dfrac{a}{0}$ are all undefined expressions. Therefore, all values of variables in this text are restricted to avoid any one of these expressions.

For instance, in the expression

$$\frac{x^0 y^{-3}}{z - 4}, \, x \neq 0, y \neq 0, \text{ and } z \neq 4.$$

For the expression

$$\frac{(a - 1)^0}{b + 2}, a \neq 1 \text{ and } b \neq -2.$$

Exponential expressions containing variables are simplified by using the following properties of exponents.

Properties of Exponents

If m, n, and p are integers and a and b are real numbers, then

Product $b^m \cdot b^n = b^{m+n}$

Quotient $\dfrac{b^m}{b^n} = b^{m-n}, \qquad b \neq 0$

Power $(b^m)^n = b^{mn} \qquad (a^m b^n)^p = a^{mp} b^{np}$

$\left(\dfrac{a^m}{b^n}\right)^p = \dfrac{a^{mp}}{b^{np}}, \qquad b \neq 0$

Here are some examples of these properties.

$a^4 \cdot a \cdot a^3 = a^{4+1+3} = a^8$ • Recall that $a = a^1$.

$(x^4 y^3)(x y^5 z^2) = x^{4+1} y^{3+5} z^2 = x^5 y^8 z^2$ • Add the exponents on the like bases.

$\dfrac{a^7 b}{a^2 b^5} = a^{7-2} b^{1-5} = a^5 b^{-4} = \dfrac{a^5}{b^4}$ • Subtract the exponents on the like bases.

$(u v^3)^5 = u^{1 \cdot 5} v^{3 \cdot 5} = u^5 v^{15}$ • Multiply the exponents.

❓ QUESTION Can the exponential expression $x^5 y^3$ be simplified using the properties of exponents?

INTEGRATING TECHNOLOGY

Exponential expressions such as a^{b^c} can be confusing. The generally accepted meaning of a^{b^c} is $a^{(b^c)}$. However, some graphing calculators do not evaluate exponential expressions in this way. Enter 2^3^4 in a graphing calculator. If the result is approximately 2.42×10^{24}, then the calculator evaluated $2^{(3^4)}$. If the result is 4096, then the calculator evaluated $(2^3)^4$. To ensure that you calculate the value you intend, we strongly urge you to use parentheses. For instance, entering 2^(3^4) will produce 2.42×10^{24} and entering (2^3)^4 will produce 4096.

❓ ANSWER No. The bases are not the same.

To simplify an expression involving exponents, write the expression in a form in which *each base appears at most once* and *no powers of powers or negative exponents appear.*

Alternative to Example 2
Simplify.
a. $(-3ab^4)(-6a^2b^{-4})$
b. $-2ab^2(-3a^2b)^3$
c. $\left(\dfrac{5x^{-2}y^3}{15x^2y}\right)^{-1}$

○ a. $18a^3$
○ b. $54a^7b^5$
○ c. $\dfrac{3x^4}{y^2}$

EXAMPLE 2 **Simplify Exponential Expressions**

Simplify.   a. $(5x^2y)(-4x^3y^5)$ b. $(3x^2yz^{-4})^3$ c. $\left(\dfrac{4p^2q}{6pq^4}\right)^{-2}$

Solution

a. $(5x^2y)(-4x^3y^5) = [5(-4)]x^{2+3}y^{1+5}$ • **Multiply the coefficients. Multiply the variables by adding the exponents on the like bases.**

$$= -20x^5y^6$$

b. $(3x^2yz^{-4})^3 = 3^{1\cdot3}x^{2\cdot3}y^{1\cdot3}z^{-4\cdot3}$ • **Use the power property of exponents.**

$$= 3^3x^6y^3z^{-12} = \frac{27x^6y^3}{z^{12}}$$

c. $\left(\dfrac{4p^2q}{6pq^4}\right)^{-2} = \left(\dfrac{2p^{2-1}q^{1-4}}{3}\right)^{-2} = \left(\dfrac{2pq^{-3}}{3}\right)^{-2}$ • **Use the quotient property of exponents.**

$$= \frac{2^{1(-2)}p^{1(-2)}q^{-3(-2)}}{3^{1(-2)}} = \frac{2^{-2}p^{-2}q^6}{3^{-2}}$$ • **Use the power property of exponents.**

$$= \frac{9q^6}{4p^2}$$ • **Write the answer in simplest form.**

▶ **TRY EXERCISE 30, PAGE 32**

● SCIENTIFIC NOTATION

MATH MATTERS

● Approximately 3.1×10^6 orchid seeds weigh 1 ounce.

● Computer scientists measure an operation in nanoseconds.

1 nanosecond $= 1 \times 10^{-9}$ second

● If a spaceship traveled 25,000 mph, it would require approximately 2.7×10^9 years to travel from one end of the universe to the other.

The exponent theorems provide a compact method of writing very large or very small numbers. The method is called *scientific notation*. A number written in **scientific notation** has the form $a \cdot 10^n$, where n is an integer and $1 \le a < 10$. The following procedure is used to change a number from its decimal form to scientific notation.

For numbers greater than 10, move the decimal point to the position to the right of the first digit. The exponent n will equal the number of places the decimal point has been moved. For example,

$$7{,}430{,}000 = 7.43 \times 10^6$$

6 places

For numbers less than 1, move the decimal point to the right of the first nonzero digit. The exponent n will be negative, and its absolute value will equal the number of places the decimal point has been moved. For example,

$$0.00000078 = 7.8 \times 10^{-7}$$

7 places

To change a number from scientific notation to its decimal form, reverse the procedure. That is, if the exponent is positive, move the decimal point to the right the same number of places as the exponent. For example,

$$3.5 \times 10^5 = 350,000$$

5 places

If the exponent is negative, move the decimal point to the left the same number of places as the absolute value of the exponent. For example,

$$2.51 \times 10^{-8} = 0.0000000251$$

8 places

Most scientific calculators display very large and very small numbers in scientific notation. The number $450,000^2$ is displayed as $\boxed{2.025 \quad E \ 11}$. This means $450,000^2 = 2.025 \times 10^{11}$.

Alternative to Example 3
The approximate diameter of the Milky Way galaxy is 9.5×10^4 light-years. If one light-year is 5.7×10^{12} miles, what is the approximate diameter, in miles, of the Milky Way galaxy?

◉ **5.4×10^{17} miles**

EXAMPLE 3   Simplify an Expression Using Scientific Notation

The Andromeda galaxy is approximately 1.4×10^{19} miles from Earth. If a spacecraft could travel 2.8×10^{12} miles in 1 year (about one-half the speed of light), how many years would it take to reach the Andromeda galaxy?

Solution

To find the time, divide the distance by the speed.

$$t = \frac{1.4 \times 10^{19}}{2.8 \times 10^{12}} = \frac{1.4}{2.8} \times 10^{19-12} = 0.5 \times 10^7 = 5.0 \times 10^6$$

It would take 5.0×10^6 (or 5,000,000) years to reach the Andromeda galaxy.

▶ **TRY EXERCISE 46, PAGE 32**

◉ RATIONAL EXPONENTS AND RADICALS

To this point, the expression b^n has been defined for real numbers b and integers n. Now we wish to extend the definition of exponents to include rational numbers so that expressions such as $2^{1/2}$ will be meaningful. Not just any definition will do. We want a definition of rational exponents for which the properties of integer exponents are true. The following example shows the direction we can take to accomplish our goal.

If the product property for exponential expressions is to hold for rational exponents, then for rational numbers p and q, $b^p b^q = b^{p+q}$. For example,

$$9^{1/2} \cdot 9^{1/2} \quad \text{must equal} \quad 9^{1/2+1/2} = 9^1 = 9$$

Thus $9^{1/2}$ must be a square root of 9. That is, $9^{1/2} = 3$.

The example suggests that $b^{1/n}$ can be defined in terms of roots according to the following definition.

Definition of $b^{1/n}$

If n is an even positive integer and $b \geq 0$, then $b^{1/n}$ is the nonnegative real number such that $(b^{1/n})^n = b$.

If n is an odd positive integer, then $b^{1/n}$ is the real number such that $(b^{1/n})^n = b$.

As examples,

- $25^{1/2} = 5$ because $5^2 = 25$.
- $(-64)^{1/3} = -4$ because $(-4)^3 = -64$.
- $16^{1/2} = 4$ because $4^2 = 16$.
- $-16^{1/2} = -(16^{1/2}) = -4$.
- $(-16)^{1/2}$ is not a real number.
- $(-32)^{1/5} = -2$ because $(-2)^5 = -32$.

If n is an even positive integer and $b < 0$, then $b^{1/n}$ is a *complex number*. Complex numbers are discussed in Section P.6.

To define expressions such as $8^{2/3}$, we will extend our definition of exponents even further. Because we want the power property $(b^p)^q = b^{pq}$ to be true for rational exponents also, we must have $(b^{1/n})^m = b^{m/n}$. With this in mind, we make the following definition.

Definition of $b^{m/n}$

For all positive integers m and n such that m/n is in simplest form, and for all real numbers b for which $b^{1/n}$ is a real number,

$$b^{m/n} = (b^{1/n})^m = (b^m)^{1/n}$$

Because $b^{m/n}$ is defined as $(b^{1/n})^m$ and also as $(b^m)^{1/n}$, we can evaluate expressions such as $8^{4/3}$ in more than one way. For example, because $8^{1/3}$ is a real number, $8^{4/3}$ can be evaluated in either of the following ways:

$$8^{4/3} = (8^{1/3})^4 = 2^4 = 16$$
$$8^{4/3} = (8^4)^{1/3} = 4096^{1/3} = 16$$

Of the two methods, the $b^{m/n} = (b^{1/n})^m$ method is usually easier to apply, provided you can evaluate $b^{1/n}$.

Here are some additional examples.

$$64^{2/3} = (64^{1/3})^2 = 4^2 = 16$$

$$32^{-6/5} = \frac{1}{32^{6/5}} = \frac{1}{(32^{1/5})^6} = \frac{1}{2^6} = \frac{1}{64}$$

$$81^{0.75} = 81^{3/4} = (81^{1/4})^3 = 3^3 = 27$$

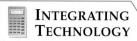

INTEGRATING
TECHNOLOGY

For the examples on page 24, the base of the exponential expression was an integer power of the denominator of the exponent.

$$64 = 4^3 \qquad 32 = 2^5 \qquad 81 = 3^4$$

If the base of the exponential expression is not a power of the denominator of the exponent, a calculator is used to evaluate the expression. Here are some examples.

```
16^(3/8)
              2.828427125
25^(-1/5)
               .5253055609
42^(.14)
               1.687543205
```

In each of these examples, the value of the exponential expression is an irrational number. The decimal display is only an approximation of the actual result.

The following exponent properties were stated earlier, but they are restated here to remind you that they have now been extended to apply to rational exponents.

Properties of Rational Exponents

If p, q, and r represent rational numbers and a and b are positive real numbers, then

Product $b^p \cdot b^q = b^{p+q}$

Quotient $\dfrac{b^p}{b^q} = b^{p-q}$

Power $(b^p)^q = b^{pq} \qquad (a^p b^q)^r = a^{pr} b^{qr}$

$\left(\dfrac{a^p}{b^q}\right)^r = \dfrac{a^{pr}}{b^{qr}} \qquad b^{-p} = \dfrac{1}{b^p}$

Recall that an exponential expression is in simplest form when no powers of powers or negative exponents appear and each base occurs at most once.

Alternative to Example 4

1. Simplify: $\left(-\dfrac{2x^2y}{3xy^3}\right)^{-2}$

● $\dfrac{9y^4}{4x^2}$

2. Simplify: $(x^n)^2$

● x^{2n}

EXAMPLE 4   **Simplify Exponential Expressions**

Simplify: $\left(\dfrac{x^2y^3}{x^{-3}y^5}\right)^{1/2}$ (Assume $x > 0$, $y > 0$.)

Solution

$$\left(\frac{x^2y^3}{x^{-3}y^5}\right)^{1/2} = (x^{2-(-3)}y^{3-5})^{1/2} = (x^5y^{-2})^{1/2} = x^{5/2}y^{-1} = \frac{x^{5/2}}{y}$$

▶ **TRY EXERCISE 62, PAGE 32**

● SIMPLIFY RADICAL EXPRESSIONS

Radicals, expressed by the notation $\sqrt[n]{b}$, are also used to denote roots. The number b is the **radicand,** and the positive integer n is the **index** of the radical.

Definition of $\sqrt[n]{b}$

If n is a positive integer and b is a real number such that $b^{1/n}$ is a real number, then $\sqrt[n]{b} = b^{1/n}$.

If the index n equals 2, then the radical $\sqrt[2]{b}$ is written as simply $\sqrt{b}$, and it is referred to as the **principal square root of b** or simply the **square root of b.**

The symbol $\sqrt{b}$ is reserved to represent the nonnegative square root of b. To represent the negative square root of b, write $-\sqrt{b}$. For example, $\sqrt{25} = 5$, whereas $-\sqrt{25} = -5$.

Definition of $(\sqrt[n]{b})^m$

For all positive integers n, all integers m, and all real numbers b such that $\sqrt[n]{b}$ is a real number, $(\sqrt[n]{b})^m = \sqrt[n]{b^m} = b^{m/n}$.

When $\sqrt[n]{b}$ is a real number, the equations

$$b^{m/n} = \sqrt[n]{b^m} \qquad \text{and} \qquad b^{m/n} = (\sqrt[n]{b})^m$$

can be used to write exponential expressions such as $b^{m/n}$ in radical form. Use the denominator n as the index of the radical and the numerator m as the power of the radicand or as the power of the radical. For example,

$$(5xy)^{2/3} = (\sqrt[3]{5xy})^2 = \sqrt[3]{25x^2y^2}$$

     • **Use the denominator 3 as the index of the radical and the numerator 2 as the power of the radical.**

The equations

$$b^{m/n} = \sqrt[n]{b^m} \qquad \text{and} \qquad b^{m/n} = (\sqrt[n]{b})^m$$

MATH MATTERS

The formula for kinetic energy (energy of motion) that is used in Einstein's Theory of Relativity involves a radical.

$$\text{K.E}_r = mc^2\left(\frac{1}{\sqrt{1 - \dfrac{v^2}{c^2}}} - 1\right)$$

where m is the mass of the object at rest, v is the speed of the object, and c is the speed of light.

also can be used to write radical expressions in exponential form. For example,

$$\sqrt{(2ab)^3} = (2ab)^{3/2}$$

    • **Use the index 2 as the denominator of the power and the exponent 3 as the numerator of the power.**

The definition of $\left(\sqrt[n]{b}\right)^m$ often can be used to evaluate radical expressions. For instance,

$$(\sqrt[3]{8})^4 = 8^{4/3} = (8^{1/3})^4 = 2^4 = 16$$

Care must be exercised when simplifying even roots (square roots, fourth roots, sixth roots,…) of variable expressions. Consider $\sqrt{x^2}$ when $x = 5$ and when $x = -5$.

Case I   If $x = 5$, then $\sqrt{x^2} = \sqrt{5^2} = \sqrt{25} = 5 = x$.

Case 2   If $x = -5$, then $\sqrt{x^2} = \sqrt{(-5)^2} = \sqrt{25} = 5 = -x$.

These two cases suggest that

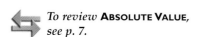
To review **ABSOLUTE VALUE**, *see p. 7.*

$$\sqrt{x^2} = \begin{cases} x, & \text{if } x \geq 0 \\ -x, & \text{if } x < 0 \end{cases}$$

Recalling the definition of absolute value, we can write this more compactly as $\sqrt{x^2} = |x|$.

Simplifying odd roots of a variable expression does not require using the absolute value symbol. Consider $\sqrt[3]{x^3}$ when $x = 5$ and when $x = -5$.

Case I   If $x = 5$, then $\sqrt[3]{x^3} = \sqrt[3]{5^3} = \sqrt[3]{125} = 5 = x$.

Case 2   If $x = -5$, then $\sqrt[3]{x^3} = \sqrt[3]{(-5)^3} = \sqrt[3]{-125} = -5 = x$.

Thus $\sqrt[3]{x^3} = x$.

Although we have illustrated this principle only for square roots and cube roots, the same reasoning can be applied to other cases. The general result is given below.

Definition of $\sqrt[n]{b^n}$

If n is an even natural number and b is a real number, then

$$\sqrt[n]{b^n} = |b|$$

If n is an odd natural number and b is a real number, then

$$\sqrt[n]{b^n} = b$$

Here are some examples of these properties.

$$\sqrt[4]{16z^4} = 2|z| \qquad \sqrt[5]{32a^5} = 2a$$

Because radicals are defined in terms of rational powers, the properties of radicals are similar to those of exponential expressions.

Properties of Radicals

If m and n are natural numbers and a and b are nonnegative real numbers, then

Product $\sqrt[n]{a} \cdot \sqrt[n]{b} = \sqrt[n]{ab}$

Quotient $\dfrac{\sqrt[n]{a}}{\sqrt[n]{b}} = \sqrt[n]{\dfrac{a}{b}}$

Index $\sqrt[m]{\sqrt[n]{a}} = \sqrt[mn]{a}$

A radical is in **simplest form** if it meets all of the following criteria.

1. The radicand contains only powers less than the index. ($\sqrt{x^5}$ does not satisfy this requirement because 5, the exponent, is greater than 2, the index.)

2. The index of the radical is as small as possible. ($\sqrt[9]{x^3}$ does not satisfy this requirement because $\sqrt[9]{x^3} = x^{3/9} = x^{1/3} = \sqrt[3]{x}$.)

3. The denominator has been rationalized. That is, no radicals appear in the denominator. ($1/\sqrt{2}$ does not satisfy this requirement.)

4. No fractions appear under the radical sign. ($\sqrt[4]{2/x^3}$ does not satisfy this requirement.)

Radical expressions are simplified by using the properties of radicals. Here are some examples.

Alternative to Example 5
1. Simplify: $\sqrt{18x^4y^3}$
• $3x^2|y|\sqrt{2y}$
2. Simplify: $\sqrt[3]{-16x^4y^6}$
• $-2xy^2\sqrt[3]{2x}$

EXAMPLE 5   **Simplify Radical Expressions**

Simplify.

a. $\sqrt[4]{32x^3y^4}$ b. $\sqrt[3]{162x^4y^6}$

Solution

a. $\sqrt[4]{32x^3y^4} = \sqrt[4]{2^5x^3y^4} = \sqrt[4]{(2^4y^4) \cdot (2x^3)}$ • Factor and group factors that can be written as a power of the index.

$= \sqrt[4]{2^4y^4} \cdot \sqrt[4]{2x^3}$ • Use the product property of radicals.

$= 2|y|\sqrt[4]{2x^3}$ • Recall that for n even, $\sqrt[n]{b^n} = |b|$.

b. $\sqrt[3]{162x^4y^6} = \sqrt[3]{(2 \cdot 3^4)x^4y^6}$ • Factor and group factors that can be written as a power of the index.

$= \sqrt[3]{(3xy^2)^3 \cdot (2 \cdot 3x)}$

$= \sqrt[3]{(3xy^2)^3} \cdot \sqrt[3]{6x}$ • Use the product property of radicals.

$= 3xy^2\sqrt[3]{6x}$ • Recall that for n odd, $\sqrt[n]{b^n} = b$.

▶ **TRY EXERCISE 78, PAGE 32**

Like radicals have the same radicand and the same index. For instance,

$$3\sqrt[3]{5xy^2} \qquad \text{and} \qquad -4\sqrt[3]{5xy^2}$$

are like radicals. Addition and subtraction of like radicals are accomplished by using the distributive property. For example,

$$4\sqrt{3x} - 9\sqrt{3x} = (4-9)\sqrt{3x} = -5\sqrt{3x}$$
$$2\sqrt[3]{y^2} + 4\sqrt[3]{y^2} - \sqrt[3]{y^2} = (2+4-1)\sqrt[3]{y^2} = 5\sqrt[3]{y^2}$$

The sum $2\sqrt{3} + 6\sqrt{5}$ cannot be simplified further because the radicands are not the same. The sum $3\sqrt[3]{x} + 5\sqrt[4]{x}$ cannot be simplified because the indices are not the same.

Sometimes it is possible to simplify radical expressions that do not appear to be like radicals by simplifying each radical expression.

Alternative to Example 6

1. Simplify: $2\sqrt{2x^3} + 4x\sqrt{8x}$. Assume $x \geq 0$.
   ● $10x\sqrt{2x}$
2. Simplify: $2b\sqrt[3]{16b^2} + \sqrt[3]{128b^5}$
   ● $8b\sqrt[3]{2b^2}$

EXAMPLE 6   **Combine Radical Expressions**

Simplify: $5x\sqrt[3]{16x^4} - \sqrt[3]{128x^7}$

Solution

$5x\sqrt[3]{16x^4} - \sqrt[3]{128x^7}$

$\quad = 5x\sqrt[3]{2^4 x^4} - \sqrt[3]{2^7 x^7}$ • Factor.

$\quad = 5x\sqrt[3]{2^3 x^3} \cdot \sqrt[3]{2x} - \sqrt[3]{2^6 x^6} \cdot \sqrt[3]{2x}$ • Group factors that can be written as a power of the index.

$\quad = 5x(2x\sqrt[3]{2x}) - 2^2 x^2 \cdot \sqrt[3]{2x}$ • Use the product property of radicals.

$\quad = 10x^2\sqrt[3]{2x} - 4x^2\sqrt[3]{2x}$ • Simplify.

$\quad = 6x^2\sqrt[3]{2x}$

▶ **TRY EXERCISE 86, PAGE 32**

Multiplication of radical expressions is accomplished by using the distributive property. For instance,

$$\sqrt{5}(\sqrt{20} - 3\sqrt{15}) = \sqrt{5}(\sqrt{20}) - \sqrt{5}(3\sqrt{15}) \qquad \text{• Use the distributive property.}$$

$$= \sqrt{100} - 3\sqrt{75} \qquad \text{• Multiply the radicals.}$$

$$= 10 - 3 \cdot 5\sqrt{3} \qquad \text{• Simplify.}$$

$$= 10 - 15\sqrt{3}$$

The product of more complicated radical expressions may require repeated use of the distributive property.

Alternative to Example 7
1. Simplify: $(2\sqrt{x} - 3)^2$
   ● $4x - 12\sqrt{x} + 9$
2. Simplify: $(3\sqrt{x} + 4)(3\sqrt{x} - 4)$
   ● $9x - 16$

EXAMPLE 7   Multiply Radical Expressions

Perform the indicated operation:

$$(\sqrt{3} + 5)(\sqrt{3} - 2)$$

Solution

$$
\begin{aligned}
(\sqrt{3} + 5)&(\sqrt{3} - 2) \\
&= (\sqrt{3} + 5)\sqrt{3} - (\sqrt{3} + 5)2 && \text{• Use the distributive property.} \\
&= (\sqrt{3}\sqrt{3} + 5\sqrt{3}) - (2\sqrt{3} + 2 \cdot 5) && \text{• Use the distributive property.} \\
&= 3 + 5\sqrt{3} - 2\sqrt{3} - 10 \\
&= -7 + 3\sqrt{3}
\end{aligned}
$$

▶ **TRY EXERCISE 96, PAGE 33**

To **rationalize the denominator** of a fraction means to write it in an equivalent form that does not involve any radicals in its denominator.

Alternative to Example 8

1. Simplify: $\sqrt{\dfrac{5x}{10y}}$
   ● $\dfrac{\sqrt{2xy}}{2y}$
2. Simplify: $\dfrac{6}{\sqrt[3]{9}}$
   ● $2\sqrt[3]{3}$
3. Simplify: $\dfrac{a^2}{\sqrt[3]{a}}$
   ● $a\sqrt[3]{a^2}$

EXAMPLE 8   Rationalize the Denominator

Rationalize the denominator.   **a.** $\dfrac{5}{\sqrt[3]{a}}$ **b.** $\sqrt{\dfrac{3}{32y}}$

Solution

a. $\dfrac{5}{\sqrt[3]{a}} = \dfrac{5}{\sqrt[3]{a}} \cdot \dfrac{\sqrt[3]{a^2}}{\sqrt[3]{a^2}} = \dfrac{5\sqrt[3]{a^2}}{\sqrt[3]{a^3}} = \dfrac{5\sqrt[3]{a^2}}{a}$ • Use $\sqrt[3]{a} \cdot \sqrt[3]{a^2} = \sqrt[3]{a^3} = a$.

b. $\sqrt{\dfrac{3}{32y}} = \dfrac{\sqrt{3}}{\sqrt{32y}} = \dfrac{\sqrt{3}}{4\sqrt{2y}} = \dfrac{\sqrt{3}}{4\sqrt{2y}} \cdot \dfrac{\sqrt{2y}}{\sqrt{2y}} = \dfrac{\sqrt{6y}}{8y}$

▶ **TRY EXERCISE 106, PAGE 33**

To rationalize the denominator of a fractional expression such as

$$\frac{1}{\sqrt{m} + \sqrt{n}}$$

we make use of the conjugate of $\sqrt{m} + \sqrt{n}$, which is $\sqrt{m} - \sqrt{n}$. The product of these conjugate pairs does not involve a radical.

$$(\sqrt{m} + \sqrt{n})(\sqrt{m} - \sqrt{n}) = m - n$$

In Example 9 we use the conjugate of the denominator to rationalize the denominator.

Alternative to Example 9

1. Simplify: $\dfrac{3}{2 - \sqrt{7}}$

• $-(2 + \sqrt{7})$

2. Simplify: $\dfrac{\sqrt{x}}{\sqrt{x} + 2}$

• $\dfrac{x - 2\sqrt{x}}{x - 4}$

EXAMPLE 9   **Rationalize the Denominator**

Rationalize the denominator.

a. $\dfrac{2}{\sqrt{3} + \sqrt{2}}$ **b.** $\dfrac{a + \sqrt{5}}{a - \sqrt{5}}$

Solution

a. $\dfrac{2}{\sqrt{3} + \sqrt{2}} = \dfrac{2}{\sqrt{3} + \sqrt{2}} \cdot \dfrac{\sqrt{3} - \sqrt{2}}{\sqrt{3} - \sqrt{2}} = \dfrac{2\sqrt{3} - 2\sqrt{2}}{3 - 2} = 2\sqrt{3} - 2\sqrt{2}$

b. $\dfrac{a + \sqrt{5}}{a - \sqrt{5}} = \dfrac{a + \sqrt{5}}{a - \sqrt{5}} \cdot \dfrac{a + \sqrt{5}}{a + \sqrt{5}} = \dfrac{a^2 + 2a\sqrt{5} + 5}{a^2 - 5}$

▶ **TRY EXERCISE 110, PAGE 33**

 TOPICS FOR DISCUSSION

1. Given that a is a real number, discuss when the expression $a^{p/q}$ represents a real number.

2. The expressions $-a^n$ and $(-a)^n$ do not always represent the same number. Discuss the situations in which the two expressions are equal and those in which they are not equal.

3. The following calculator screen shows the value of the quotient of two radical expressions. Is the answer correct? Explain what happened.

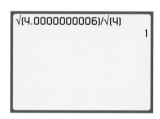

√(4.0000000006)/√(4)
                    1

4. If you enter the expression for $\sqrt{5}$ on your calculator, the calculator will respond with 2.236067977 or some number close to that. Is this the exact value of $\sqrt{5}$? Is it possible to find the exact decimal value of $\sqrt{5}$ with a calculator? with a computer?

EXERCISE SET P.2

—Suggested Assignment: Exercises 1–109, every other odd; 113–125, odd; 138–143, all.

In Exercises 1 to 12, evaluate each expression.

1. -5^3 -125

2. $(-5)^3$ -125

3. $\left(\dfrac{2}{3}\right)^0$ 1

4. -6^0 -1

5. 4^{-2} $\dfrac{1}{16}$

6. 3^{-4} $\dfrac{1}{81}$

7. $\dfrac{1}{2^{-5}}$ 32

8. $\dfrac{1}{3^{-3}}$ 27

9. $\dfrac{2^{-3}}{6^{-3}}$ 27

▶ **10.** $\dfrac{4^{-2}}{2^{-3}}$ $\dfrac{1}{2}$

11. $-2x^0$ -2

12. $\dfrac{x^0}{4}$ $\dfrac{1}{4}$

In Exercises 13 to 32, write the exponential expression in simplest form.

13. $2x^{-4}$ $\dfrac{2}{x^4}$

14. $3y^{-2}$ $\dfrac{3}{y^2}$

15. $(-2ab^4)(-3a^2b^4)$ $6a^3b^8$

16. $(9xy^2)(-2x^2y^2)$ $-18x^3y^4$

17. $\dfrac{6a^4}{8a^8}$ $\dfrac{3}{4a^4}$

18. $\dfrac{12x^3}{16x^4}$ $\dfrac{3}{4x}$

19. $\dfrac{12x^3y^4}{18x^5y^2}$ $\dfrac{2y^2}{3x^2}$

20. $\dfrac{5v^4w^{-3}}{10v^8}$ $\dfrac{1}{2v^4w^3}$

21. $\dfrac{36a^{-2}b^3}{3ab^4}$ $\dfrac{12}{a^3b}$

22. $\dfrac{-48ab^{10}}{-32a^4b^3}$ $\dfrac{3b^7}{2a^3}$

23. $(-2m^3n^2)(-3mn^2)^2$ $-18m^5n^6$

24. $(2a^3b^2)^3(-4a^4b^2)$ $-32a^{13}b^8$

25. $(x^{-2}y)^2(xy)^{-2}$ $\dfrac{1}{x^6}$

26. $(x^{-1}y^2)^{-3}(x^2y^{-4})^{-3}$ $\dfrac{y^6}{x^3}$

27. $\left(\dfrac{3a^2b^3}{6a^4b^4}\right)^2$ $\dfrac{1}{4a^4b^2}$

28. $\left(\dfrac{2ab^2c^3}{5ab^2}\right)^3$ $\dfrac{8c^9}{125}$

29. $\dfrac{(-4x^2y^3)^2}{(2xy^2)^3}$ $2x$

▶ **30.** $\dfrac{(-3a^2b^3)^2}{(-2ab^4)^3}$ $-\dfrac{9a}{8b^6}$

31. $\left(\dfrac{a^{-2}b}{a^3b^{-4}}\right)^2$ $\dfrac{b^{10}}{a^{10}}$

32. $\left(\dfrac{x^{-3}y^{-4}}{x^{-2}y}\right)^{-2}$ x^2y^{10}

In Exercises 33 to 36, write the number in scientific notation.

33. $2,011,000,000,000$ 2.011×10^{12} **34.** $49,100,000,000$ 4.91×10^{10}

35. 0.000000000562 5.62×10^{-10} **36.** 0.000000402 4.02×10^{-7}

In Exercises 37 to 40, change the number from scientific notation to decimal notation.

37. 3.14×10^7 $31,400,000$

38. 4.03×10^9 $4,030,000,000$

39. -2.3×10^{-6} -0.0000023

40. 6.14×10^{-8} 0.0000000614

In Exercises 41 to 48, perform the indicated operation and write the answer in scientific notation.

41. $(3 \times 10^{12})(9 \times 10^{-5})$ 2.7×10^8

42. $(8.9 \times 10^{-5})(3.4 \times 10^{-6})$ 3.026×10^{-10}

43. $\dfrac{9 \times 10^{-3}}{6 \times 10^8}$ 1.5×10^{-11}

44. $\dfrac{2.5 \times 10^8}{5 \times 10^{10}}$ 5×10^{-3}

45. $\dfrac{(3.2 \times 10^{-11})(2.7 \times 10^{18})}{1.2 \times 10^{-5}}$ 7.2×10^{12}

▶ **46.** $\dfrac{(6.9 \times 10^{27})(8.2 \times 10^{-13})}{4.1 \times 10^{15}}$ 1.38×10^0

47. $\dfrac{(4.0 \times 10^{-9})(8.4 \times 10^5)}{(3.0 \times 10^{-6})(1.4 \times 10^{18})}$ 8×10^{-16}

48. $\dfrac{(7.2 \times 10^8)(3.9 \times 10^{-7})}{(2.6 \times 10^{-10})(1.8 \times 10^{-8})}$ 6×10^{19}

In Exercises 49 to 70, simplify each exponential expression.

49. $4^{3/2}$ 8

50. $-16^{3/2}$ -64

51. $-64^{2/3}$ -16

52. $125^{4/3}$ 625

53. $9^{-3/2}$ $\dfrac{1}{27}$

54. $32^{-3/5}$ $\dfrac{1}{8}$

55. $\left(\dfrac{4}{9}\right)^{1/2}$ $\dfrac{2}{3}$

56. $\left(\dfrac{16}{25}\right)^{3/2}$ $\dfrac{64}{125}$

57. $\left(\dfrac{1}{8}\right)^{-4/3}$ 16

58. $\left(\dfrac{8}{27}\right)^{-2/3}$ $\dfrac{9}{4}$

59. $(4a^{2/3}b^{1/2})(2a^{1/3}b^{3/2})$ $8ab^2$

60. $(6a^{3/5}b^{1/4})(-3a^{1/5}b^{3/4})$ $-18a^{4/5}b$

61. $(-3x^{2/3})(4x^{1/4})$ $-12x^{11/12}$

▶ **62.** $(-5x^{1/3})(-4x^{1/2})$ $20x^{5/6}$

63. $(81x^8y^{12})^{1/4}$ $3x^2y^3$

64. $(27x^3y^6)^{2/3}$ $9x^2y^4$

65. $\dfrac{16z^{3/5}}{12z^{1/5}}$ $\dfrac{4z^{2/5}}{3}$

66. $\dfrac{6a^{2/3}}{9a^{1/3}}$ $\dfrac{2a^{1/3}}{3}$

67. $(2x^{2/3}y^{1/2})(3x^{1/6}y^{1/3})$ $6x^{5/6}y^{5/6}$

68. $\dfrac{x^{1/3}y^{5/6}}{x^{2/3}y^{1/6}}$ $\dfrac{y^{2/3}}{x^{1/3}}$

69. $\dfrac{9a^{3/4}b}{3a^{2/3}b^2}$ $\dfrac{3a^{1/12}}{b}$

70. $\dfrac{12x^{1/6}y^{1/4}}{16x^{3/4}y^{1/2}}$ $\dfrac{3}{4x^{7/12}y^{1/4}}$

In Exercises 71 to 80, simplify each radical expression.

71. $\sqrt{45}$ $3\sqrt{5}$

72. $\sqrt{75}$ $5\sqrt{3}$

73. $\sqrt[3]{24}$ $2\sqrt[3]{3}$

74. $\sqrt[3]{135}$ $3\sqrt[3]{5}$

75. $\sqrt[3]{-135}$ $-3\sqrt[3]{5}$

76. $\sqrt[3]{-250}$ $-5\sqrt[3]{2}$

77. $\sqrt{24x^2y^3}$ $2|x|y\sqrt{6y}$

▶ **78.** $\sqrt{18x^2y^5}$ $-5\sqrt[3]{2}$ $3|x|y^2\sqrt{2y}$

79. $\sqrt[3]{16a^3y^7}$ $2ay^2\sqrt[3]{2y}$

80. $\sqrt[3]{54m^2n^7}$ $3n^2\sqrt[3]{2m^2n}$

In Exercises 81 to 88, simplify each radical and then combine like radicals.

81. $2\sqrt{32} - 3\sqrt{98}$ $-13\sqrt{2}$

82. $5\sqrt[3]{32} + 2\sqrt[3]{108}$ $16\sqrt[3]{4}$

83. $-8\sqrt[4]{48} + 2\sqrt[4]{243}$ $-10\sqrt[4]{3}$

84. $2\sqrt[3]{40} - 3\sqrt[3]{135}$ $-5\sqrt[3]{5}$

85. $4\sqrt[3]{32y^4} + 3y\sqrt[3]{108y}$ $17y\sqrt[3]{4y}$

▶ **86.** $-3x\sqrt[3]{54x^4} + 2\sqrt[3]{16x^7}$ $-5x^2\sqrt[3]{2x}$

87. $x\sqrt[3]{8x^3y^4} - 4y\sqrt[3]{64x^6y}$ $-14x^2y\sqrt[3]{y}$

88. $4\sqrt{a^5b} - a^2\sqrt{ab}$ $3a^2\sqrt{ab}$

In Exercises 89 to 98, find the indicated products and express each result in simplest form.

89. $(\sqrt{5} + 3)(\sqrt{5} + 4)$
$17 + 7\sqrt{5}$

90. $(\sqrt{7} + 2)(\sqrt{7} - 5)$
$-3 - 3\sqrt{7}$

91. $(\sqrt{2} - 3)(\sqrt{2} + 3)$ -7

92. $(2\sqrt{7} + 3)(2\sqrt{7} - 3)$ 19

93. $(3\sqrt{z} - 2)(4\sqrt{z} + 3)$ $12z + \sqrt{z} - 6$

94. $(4\sqrt{a} - \sqrt{b})(3\sqrt{a} + 2\sqrt{b})$ $12a + 5\sqrt{ab} - 2b$

95. $(\sqrt{x} + 2)^2$ $x + 4\sqrt{x} + 4$ ▶ **96.** $(3\sqrt{5y} - 4)^2$ $45y - 24\sqrt{5y} + 16$

97. $(\sqrt{x - 3} + 2)^2$
$x + 4\sqrt{x - 3} + 1$

98. $(\sqrt{2x + 1} - 3)^2$
$2x - 6\sqrt{2x + 1} + 10$

In Exercises 99 to 112, simplify each expression by rationalizing the denominator. Write the result in simplest form.

99. $\dfrac{2}{\sqrt{2}}$ $\sqrt{2}$

100. $\dfrac{3x}{\sqrt{3}}$ $x\sqrt{3}$

101. $\sqrt{\dfrac{5}{18}}$ $\dfrac{\sqrt{10}}{6}$

102. $\sqrt{\dfrac{7}{40}}$ $\dfrac{\sqrt{70}}{20}$

103. $\dfrac{3}{\sqrt[3]{2}}$ $\dfrac{3\sqrt[3]{4}}{2}$

104. $\dfrac{2}{\sqrt[3]{4}}$ $\sqrt[3]{2}$

105. $\dfrac{4}{\sqrt[3]{8x^2}}$ $\dfrac{2\sqrt[3]{x}}{x}$

▶ **106.** $\dfrac{2}{\sqrt[4]{4y}}$ $\dfrac{\sqrt[4]{4y^3}}{y}$

107. $\dfrac{3}{\sqrt{3} + 4}$ $-\dfrac{3\sqrt{3} - 12}{13}$

108. $\dfrac{2}{\sqrt{5} - 2}$ $2\sqrt{5} + 4$

109. $\dfrac{6}{2\sqrt{5} + 2}$ $\dfrac{3\sqrt{5} - 3}{4}$

▶ **110.** $\dfrac{-7}{3\sqrt{2} - 5}$ $3\sqrt{2} + 5$

111. $\dfrac{3}{\sqrt{5} + \sqrt{x}}$ $\dfrac{3\sqrt{5} - 3\sqrt{x}}{5 - x}$

112. $\dfrac{5}{\sqrt{y} - \sqrt{3}}$ $\dfrac{5\sqrt{y} + 5\sqrt{3}}{y - 3}$

113. NATIONAL DEBT In February of 2003, the U.S. national debt was approximately 6.4×10^{12} dollars. At that time, the population of the U.S. was 2.89×10^8 people. In February of 2003, what was the U.S. debt per person? $\approx 2.21 \times 10^4$ dollars

114. COLOR MONITORS A color monitor for a computer can display 2^{32} colors. A physiologist estimates that the human eye can detect approximately 36,000 different colors. How many colors, to the nearest thousand, would go undetected by a human eye using this monitor?
4,294,931,000 colors

115. WEIGHT OF AN ORCHID SEED An orchid seed weighs approximately 3.2×10^{-8} ounce. If a package of seeds contains 1 ounce of orchid seeds, how many seeds are in the package? $\approx 3.13 \times 10^7$

116. LASER WAVELENGTH The wavelength of a certain helium-neon laser is 800 nanometers. (1 nanometer is 1×10^{-9} meter.) The frequency, in cycles per second, of this wave is $\dfrac{1}{\text{wavelength}}$. What is the frequency of this laser?
1.25×10^6 cycles per second

117. DOPPLER EFFECT Astronomers can approximate the distance to a galaxy by measuring its *red shift*, which is a shift in the wavelength of light due to the velocity of the galaxy. This is similar to the way the sound of a siren coming toward you seems to have a higher pitch than when the siren is moving away from you. A formula for red shift is red shift $= \dfrac{\lambda_r - \lambda_s}{\lambda_s}$, where λ_r and λ_s are wavelengths of a certain frequency of light. Calculate the red shift for a galaxy for which $\lambda_r = 5.13 \times 10^{-7}$ meter and $\lambda_s = 5.06 \times 10^{-7}$ meter. $\approx 1.38 \times 10^{-2}$

118. ASTRONOMICAL UNIT Earth's mean distance from the sun is 9.3×10^7 miles. This distance is called the *astronomical unit* (AU). Jupiter is 5.2 AU from the sun. Find the distance in miles from Jupiter to the sun.
$\approx 4.84 \times 10^8$ mi

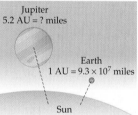

Jupiter
5.2 AU = ? miles

Earth
1 AU = 9.3×10^7 miles

Sun

119. ASTRONOMY The sun is approximately 1.44×10^{11} meters from Earth. If light travels 3×10^8 meters per second, how many minutes does it take light from the sun to reach Earth? 8 min

120. MASS OF AN ATOM One gram of hydrogen contains 6.023×10^{23} atoms. Find the mass of one hydrogen atom. $\approx 1.66 \times 10^{-24}$ g

121. CELLULAR PHONE PRODUCTION An electronics firm estimates that the revenue R it will receive from the sale of x cell phones (in thousands) can be approximated by $R = 1250x(2^{-0.007x})$. What is the estimated revenue when the company sells 20,000 cell phones? Round to the nearest dollar. $22,688

122. DRUG POTENCY The amount A (in milligrams) of digoxin, a drug taken by cardiac patients, remaining in the blood t hours after a patient takes a 2-milligram dose is given by $A = 2(10^{-0.0078t})$.

   a. How much digoxin remains in the blood of a patient 4 hours after taking a 2-milligram dose? ≈ 1.86 mg

b. Suppose that a patient takes a 2-milligram dose of digoxin at 1:00 P.M. and another 2-milligram dose at 5:00 P.M. How much digoxin remains in the patient's blood at 6:00 P.M.? ≈3.79 mg

123. WORLD POPULATION An estimate of the world's future population P is given by $P = 5.9(2^{0.0119n})$, where n is the number of years after 2000 and P is in billions. Using this estimate, what will the world's population be in 2050? ≈8.91 billion

124. LEARNING THEORY In a psychology experiment, students were given a nine-digit number to memorize. The percent P of students who remembered the number t minutes after it was read to them can be given by $P = 90 - 3t^{2/3}$. What percent of the students remembered the number after 1 hour? ≈44.02%

125. OCEANOGRAPHY The percent P of light that will pass to a depth d, in meters, at a certain place in the ocean is given by $P = 10^{2-(d/40)}$. Find, to the nearest percent, the amount of light that will pass to a depth of **a.** 10 meters and **b.** 25 meters below the surface of the ocean.
a. 56%   b. 24%

CONNECTING CONCEPTS

126. If $2^x = y$, then find 2^{x-4} in terms of y. $\dfrac{y}{2^4}$

127. If a and b are nonzero numbers and $a < b$, is the statement $a^{-1} < b^{-1}$ a true statement? Give a reason for your answer. No. $2 < 3$, but $\dfrac{1}{2} > \dfrac{1}{3}$.

128. How many digits are in the product $4^{50} \cdot 5^{100}$? 101 digits

In Exercises 129 to 132, find the value of p for which the statement is true.

129. $a^{2/5}a^p = a^2$ $\dfrac{8}{5}$

130. $b^{-3/4}b^{2p} = b^3$ $\dfrac{15}{8}$

131. $\dfrac{x^{-3/4}}{x^{3p}} = x^4$ $-\dfrac{19}{12}$

132. $(x^4 x^{2p})^{1/2} = x$ -1

In Exercises 133 to 136, rationalize the numerator.

133. $\dfrac{\sqrt{4+h}-2}{h}$ $\dfrac{1}{\sqrt{4+h}+2}$

134. $\dfrac{\sqrt{9+h}-3}{h}$ $\dfrac{1}{\sqrt{9+h}+3}$

135. $\sqrt{n^2+1}-n$ $\left(Hint: \sqrt{n^2+1}-n = \dfrac{\sqrt{n^2+1}-n}{1}\right)$ $\dfrac{1}{\sqrt{n^2+1}+n}$

136. $\sqrt{n^2+n}-n$ $\left(Hint: \sqrt{n^2+n}-n = \dfrac{\sqrt{n^2+n}-n}{1}\right)$ $\dfrac{n}{\sqrt{n^2+n}+n}$

137. Evaluate: $\left(\sqrt{2}^{\sqrt{2}}\right)^{\sqrt{2}}$ 2

PREPARE FOR SECTION P.3

138. Simplify: $-3(2a - 4b)$ [P.1] $-6a + 12b$

139. Simplify: $5 - 2(2x - 7)$ [P.1] $-4x + 19$

140. Simplify: $2x^2 + 3x - 5 + x^2 - 6x - 1$ [P.1] $3x^2 - 3x - 6$

141. Simplify: $4x^2 - 6x - 1 - 5x^2 + x$ [P.1] $-x^2 - 5x - 1$

142. True or false: $4 - 3x - 2x^2 = 2x^2 - 3x + 4$ [P.1] False

143. True or false: $\dfrac{12 + 15}{4} = \dfrac{\overset{3}{\cancel{12}} + 15}{\cancel{4}} = 18$ [P.1] False

PROJECTS

1. RELATIVITY THEORY A moving object has energy, called *kinetic energy*, by virtue of its motion. As mentioned earlier in this chapter, the theory of relativity uses the formula at the right for kinetic energy.

$$K.E._r = mc^2\left(\dfrac{1}{\sqrt{1 - \dfrac{v^2}{c^2}}} - 1\right)$$

When the speed of an object is much less than the speed of light (3.0×10^8 meters per second) the formula

$$\text{K.E.}_n = \frac{1}{2}mv^2$$

is used. In each formula, v is the velocity of the object in meters per second, m is its rest mass in kilograms, and c is the speed of light given above. Calculate the percent error (in **a.** through **e.**) for each of the given velocities. The formula for percent error is

$$\% \text{ error} = \frac{|\text{K.E.}_r - \text{K.E.}_n|}{\text{K.E.}_r} \times 100$$

a. $v = 30$ meters per second (speeding car on an expressway)

b. $v = 240$ meters per second (speed of a commercial jet)

c. $v = 3.0 \times 10^7$ meters per second (10% of the speed of light)

d. $v = 1.5 \times 10^8$ meters per second (50% of the speed of light)

e. $v = 2.7 \times 10^8$ meters per second (90% of the speed of light)

f. Use your answers from **a.** through **e.** to give a reason why the formula for kinetic energy given by K.E._n is adequate for most of our common experiences involving motion (walking, running, bicycle, car, plane).

g. According to Relativity Theory, the mass, m, of an object changes as its velocity according to

$$m = \frac{m_0}{\sqrt{1 - \dfrac{v^2}{c_2}}}$$

where m_0 is the rest mass of the object. The approximate rest mass of an electron is 9.11×10^{-31} kilogram. What is the percent change, from its rest mass, in the mass of an electron that is traveling at $0.99c$ (99% of the speed of light)?

h. According to the Theory of Relativity, a particle (such as an electron or a spacecraft) cannot exceed the speed of light. Explain why the equation for K.E._r suggests such a conclusion.

POLYNOMIALS

- OPERATIONS ON POLYNOMIALS
- APPLICATIONS OF POLYNOMIALS

OPERATIONS ON POLYNOMIALS

A **monomial** is a constant, a variable, or a product of a constant and one or more variables, with the variables having only nonnegative integer exponents. The constant is called the **numerical coefficient** or simply the **coefficient** of the monomial. The **degree of a monomial** is the sum of the exponents of the variables. For example, $-5xy^2$ is a monomial with coefficient -5 and degree 3.

The algebraic expression $3x^{-2}$ is not a monomial because it cannot be written as a product of a constant and a variable with a *nonnegative* integer exponent.

A sum of a finite number of monomials is called a **polynomial.** Each monomial is called a **term** of the polynomial. The **degree of a polynomial** is the largest degree of the terms in the polynomial.

Terms that have exactly the same variables raised to the same powers are called **like terms.** For example, $14x^2$ and $-31x^2$ are like terms; however, $2x^3y$ and $7xy$ are not like terms because x^3y and xy are not identical.

A polynomial is said to be simplified if all its like terms have been combined. For example, the simplified form of $4x^2 + 3x + 5x$ is $4x^2 + 8x$. A simplified polynomial that has two terms is a **binomial,** and a simplified polynomial that has three terms is a **trinomial.** For example, $4x + 7$ is a binomial, and $2x^3 - 7x^2 + 11$ is a trinomial.

A nonzero constant, such as 5, is called a **constant polynomial.** It has degree zero because $5 = 5x^0$. The number 0 is defined to be a polynomial with no degree.

Standard Form of a Polynomial

The **standard form of a polynomial** of degree n in the variable x is

$$a_n x^n + a_{n-1} x^{n-1} + \cdots + a_2 x^2 + a_1 x + a_0$$

where $a_n \neq 0$ and n is a nonnegative integer. The coefficient a_n is the **leading coefficient**, and a_0 is the **constant term.**

If a polynomial in the variable x is written with decreasing powers of x, then it is in **standard form.** For example, the polynomial

$$3x^2 - 4x^3 + 7x^4 - 1$$

is written in standard form as

$$7x^4 - 4x^3 + 3x^2 - 1$$

The following table shows the leading coefficient, degree, terms, and coefficients of the given polynomials.

Polynomial	Leading Coefficient	Degree	Terms	Coefficients
$9x^2 - x + 5$	9	2	$9x^2, -x, 5$	$9, -1, 5$
$11 - 2x$	-2	1	$-2x, 11$	$-2, 11$
$x^3 + 5x - 3$	1	3	$x^3, 5x, -3$	$1, 5, -3$

Alternative to Example 1
Write the polynomial
$5x^3 - x^4 + 2x^2 - 7x - 8$ in standard form. Identify the degree, terms, constant term, leading coefficient, and coefficients of the polynomial.
● $-x^4 + 5x^3 + 2x^2 - 7x - 8$; 4; $-x^4$, $5x^3, 2x^2, -7x, -8$; -8; -1; $-1, 5, 2,$ $-7, -8$

EXAMPLE 1   Identify Terms Related to a Polynomial

Write the polynomial $6x^3 - x + 5 - 2x^4$ in standard form. Identify the degree, terms, constant term, leading coefficient, and coefficients of the polynomial.

Solution

A polynomial is in standard form when the terms are written in decreasing powers of the variable. The standard form of the polynomial is $-2x^4 + 6x^3 - x + 5$. In this form, the degree is 4; the terms are $-2x^4, 6x^3,$ $-x$, and 5; the constant term is 5. The leading coefficient is -2; the coefficients are $-2, 6, -1$, and 5.

▶ **TRY EXERCISE 12, PAGE 41**

To add polynomials, add the coefficients of the like terms.

Alternative to Example 2
Add:
$(2x^2 - 6x + 7) + (4x^3 - 2x^2 + 8x - 3)$
● $4x^3 + 2x + 4$

EXAMPLE 2   **Add Polynomials**

Add: $(3x^3 - 2x^2 - 6) + (4x^2 - 6x - 7)$

Solution

$(3x^3 - 2x^2 - 6) + (4x^2 - 6x - 7)$
$= 3x^3 + (-2x^2 + 4x^2) + (-6x) + [(-6) + (-7)]$
$= 3x^3 + 2x^2 - 6x - 13$

▶ **TRY EXERCISE 24, PAGE 41**

The **additive inverse of the polynomial** $3x - 7$ is

$$-(3x - 7) = -3x + 7$$

❓ QUESTION   What is the additive inverse of $3x^2 - 8x + 7$?

To subtract a polynomial, we add its additive inverse. For example,

$$(2x - 5) - (3x - 7) = (2x - 5) + (-3x + 7)$$
$$= [2x + (-3x)] + [(-5) + 7]$$
$$= -x + 2$$

The distributive property is used to find the product of polynomials. For instance, to find the product of $(3x - 4)$ and $(2x^2 + 5x + 1)$, we treat $3x - 4$ as a *single* quantity and *distribute it* over the trinomial $2x^2 + 5x + 1$, as shown in Example 3.

Alternative to Example 3
1. Multiply: $(x^2 - 5x - 6)(2x - 5)$
● $2x^3 - 15x^2 + 13x + 30$
2. Multiply: $(2x^3 + 3x - 4)(x + 5)$
● $2x^4 + 10x^3 + 3x^2 + 11x - 20$

EXAMPLE 3   **Multiply Polynomials**

Simplify: $(3x - 4)(2x^2 + 5x + 1)$

Solution

$(3x - 4)(2x^2 + 5x + 1)$
$= (3x - 4)(2x^2) + (3x - 4)(5x) + (3x - 4)(1)$
$= (3x)(2x^2) - 4(2x^2) + (3x)(5x) - 4(5x) + (3x)(1) - 4(1)$
$= 6x^3 - 8x^2 + 15x^2 - 20x + 3x - 4$
$= 6x^3 + 7x^2 - 17x - 4$

▶ **TRY EXERCISE 32, PAGE 41**

In the following calculation, a vertical format has been used to find the product of $(x^2 + 6x - 7)$ and $(5x - 2)$. Note that like terms are arranged in the same vertical column.

❓ ANSWER   The additive inverse is $-3x^2 + 8x - 7$.

$$\begin{array}{r} x^2 + 6x - 7 \\ 5x - 2 \\ \hline \end{array}$$

$$\begin{array}{ll} -2x^2 - 12x + 14 & = -2(x^2 + 6x - 7) \\ 5x^3 + 30x^2 - 35x & = 5x(x^2 + 6x - 7) \\ \hline 5x^3 + 28x^2 - 47x + 14 \end{array}$$

If the terms of the binomials $(a + b)$ and $(c + d)$ are labeled as shown below, then the product of the two binomials can be computed mentally by the **FOIL** method.

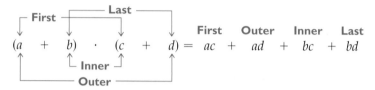

In the following illustration, we find the product of $(7x - 2)$ and $(5x + 4)$ by the FOIL method.

$$\begin{array}{lcccc} & \text{First} & \text{Outer} & \text{Inner} & \text{Last} \\ (7x - 2)(5x + 4) = & (7x)(5x) & + (7x)(4) & + (-2)(5x) & + (-2)(4) \\ = & 35x^2 & + 28x & - 10x & - 8 \\ = & 35x^2 + 18x - 8 \end{array}$$

Certain products occur so frequently in algebra that they deserve special attention.

Special Product Formulas

Special Form	Formula(s)
(Sum)(Difference)	$(x + y)(x - y) = x^2 - y^2$
(Binomial)^2	$(x + y)^2 = x^2 + 2xy + y^2$ $(x - y)^2 = x^2 - 2xy + y^2$

The variables x and y in these special product formulas can be replaced by other algebraic expressions, as shown in Example 4.

Alternative to Example 4
1. Multiply: $(2x^2 - 3)(2x^2 + 3)$
⊙ $4x^4 - 9$
2. Multiply: $(3x + 4y)^2$
⊙ $9x^2 + 24xy + 16y^2$

EXAMPLE 4   Use the Special Product Formulas

Find each special product.   a. $(7x + 10)(7x - 10)$ b. $(2y^2 + 11z)^2$

Solution

a. $(7x + 10)(7x - 10) = (7x)^2 - (10)^2 = 49x^2 - 100$

b. $(2y^2 + 11z)^2 = (2y^2)^2 + 2[(2y^2)(11z)] + (11z)^2 = 4y^4 + 44y^2z + 121z^2$

▶ TRY EXERCISE 56, PAGE 41

Many application problems require you to *evaluate polynomials*. To **evaluate a polynomial,** substitute the given value(s) for the variable(s) and then perform the indicated operations using the Order of Operations Agreement.

Alternative to Example 5
1. Evaluate $3x^3 + 4x^2 - 6x - 7$ when $x = -2$.
● **−3**

2. Evaluate $x^2 - x + 1$ when $x = \dfrac{1}{2}$.

● $\dfrac{3}{4}$

EXAMPLE 5   Evaluate a Polynomial

Evaluate the polynomial $2x^3 - 6x^2 + 7$ for $x = -4$.

Solution

$2x^3 - 6x^2 + 7$

$2(-4)^3 - 6(-4)^2 + 7 = 2(-64) - 6(16) + 7$ • Substitute -4 for x. Evaluate the powers.

$\qquad\qquad\qquad\qquad = -128 - 96 + 7$ • Perform the multiplications.

$\qquad\qquad\qquad\qquad = -217$ • Perform the additions and subtractions.

▶ **TRY EXERCISE 66, PAGE 41**

● APPLICATIONS OF POLYNOMIALS

Alternative to Example 6
Exercise 72, page 42.

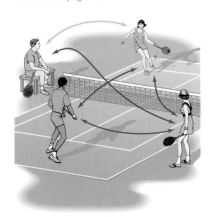

FIGURE P.13
4 tennis players can play a total of 6 singles matches.

Alternative to Example 7
Exercise 74, page 42.

EXAMPLE 6   Solve an Application

The number of singles tennis matches that can be played among n tennis players is given by the polynomial $\dfrac{1}{2}n^2 - \dfrac{1}{2}n$. Find the number of singles tennis matches that can be played among 4 tennis players.

Solution

$\dfrac{1}{2}n^2 - \dfrac{1}{2}n$

$\dfrac{1}{2}(4)^2 - \dfrac{1}{2}(4) = \dfrac{1}{2}(16) - \dfrac{1}{2}(4) = 8 - 2 = 6$ • Substitute 4 for n. Then simplify.

Therefore, 4 tennis players can play a total of 6 singles matches. See **Figure P.13.**

▶ **TRY EXERCISE 76, PAGE 42**

EXAMPLE 7   Solve an Application

A scientist determines that the average time in seconds that it takes a particular computer to determine whether an n-digit natural number is prime or composite is given by

$$0.002n^2 + 0.002n + 0.009, \quad 20 \le n \le 40$$

The average time in seconds that it takes the computer to factor an n-digit number is given by

$$0.00032(1.7)^n, \quad 20 \le n \le 40$$

Continued ▶

MATH MATTERS

The procedure used by the computer to determine whether a number is prime or composite is a
polynomial time algorithm, because
the time required can be estimated
via a polynomial. The procedure
used to factor a number is an *exponential time algorithm*. In the field
of *computational complexity*, it is
important to distinguish between
polynomial time algorithms and
exponential time algorithms. Example 7 illustrates that the polynomial
time algorithm can be run in about
2 seconds, whereas the exponential
time algorithm requires about
44 minutes!

Estimate the average time it takes the computer to

a.   determine whether a 30-digit number is prime or composite

b.   factor a 30-digit number

Solution

a. $0.002n^2 + 0.002n + 0.009$

$0.002(30)^2 + 0.002(30) + 0.009 = 1.8 + 0.06 + 0.009 = 1.869 \approx 2$ seconds

b. $0.00032(1.7)^n$

$0.00032(1.7)^{30} \approx 0.00032(8,193,465.726)$

≈ 2600 seconds

▶ **TRY EXERCISE 78, PAGE 42**

TOPICS FOR DISCUSSION

1.   Discuss the definition of the term *polynomial*. Give some examples of expressions that are polynomials and some examples of expressions that are not
polynomials.

2.   Suppose that P and Q are both polynomials of degree n. Discuss the degrees
of $P + Q$, $P - Q$, PQ, $P + P$, and $P - P$.

3.   Suppose that you evaluate a polynomial P of degree n for larger and larger
values of x (for instance, when $x = 1, 2, 3, 4, \ldots$). Discuss whether the value of
the polynomial would eventually (for very large values of x) continually increase, decrease, or fluctuate between increasing and decreasing.

4.   Discuss the similarities and differences among monomials, binomials, trinomials, and polynomials.

EXERCISE SET P.3   —*Suggested Assignment: Exercises 1–69, every other odd; 71–83, odd; 90–95, all.*

**In Exercises I to 10, match the descriptions, labeled A, B,
C,...., J, with the appropriate examples.**

A. $x^3y + xy$ **B.** $7x^2 + 5x - 11$

C. $\frac{1}{2}x^2 + xy + y^2$ **D.** $4xy$

E. $8x^3 - 1$ **F.** $3 - 4x^2$

G. 8 **H.** $3x^5 - 4x^2 + 7x - 11$

I. $8x^4 - \sqrt{5}x^3 + 7$ **J.** 0

 1. A monomial of degree 2. D

 2. A binomial of degree 3. E

 3. A polynomial of degree 5. H

4. A binomial with leading coefficient of -4. F

5. A zero-degree polynomial. G

6. A fourth-degree polynomial that has a third-degree term.
I

7. A trinomial with integer coefficients. B

8. A trinomial in x and y. C

9. A polynomial with no degree. J

10. A fourth-degree binomial. A

In Exercises 11 to 16, for each polynomial determine its *a*. standard form, *b*. degree, *c*. coefficients, *d*. leading coefficient, *e*. terms.

11. $2x + x^2 - 7$ a. $x^2 + 2x - 7$ b. 2   c. 1, 2, −7   d. 1   e. $x^2, 2x, -7$

▶ 12. $-3x^2 - 11 - 12x^4$ a. $-12x^4 - 3x^2 - 11$ b. 4   c. −12, −3, −11
d. −12   e. $-12x^4, -3x^2, -11$

13. $x^3 - 1$ a. $x^3 - 1$ b. 3   c. 1, −1   d. 1   e. $x^3, -1$

14. $4x^2 - 2x + 7$ a. $4x^2 - 2x + 7$ b. 2   c. 4, −2, 7   d. 4   e. $4x^2, -2x, 7$

15. $2x^4 + 3x^3 + 5 + 4x^2$
a. $2x^4 + 3x^3 + 4x^2 + 5$ b. 4
c. 2, 3, 4, 5   d. 2   e. $2x^4, 3x^3, 4x^2, 5$

16. $3x^2 - 5x^3 + 7x - 1$
a. $-5x^3 + 3x^2 + 7x - 1$ b. 3
c. −5, 3, 7, −1   d. −5
e. $-5x^3, 3x^2, 7x, -1$

In Exercises 17 to 22, determine the degree of the given polynomial.

17. $3xy^2 - 2xy + 7x$ 3

18. $x^3 + 3x^2y + 3xy^2 + y^3$ 3

19. $4x^2y^2 - 5x^3y^2 + 17xy^3$ 5

20. $-9x^5y + 10xy^4 - 11x^2y^2$ 6

21. xy 2

22. $5x^2y - y^4 + 6xy$ 4

In Exercises 23 to 34, perform the indicated operations and simplify if possible by combining like terms. Write the result in standard form.

23. $(3x^2 + 4x + 5) + (2x^2 + 7x - 2)$ $5x^2 + 11x + 3$

▶ 24. $(5y^2 - 7y + 3) + (2y^2 + 8y + 1)$ $7y^2 + y + 4$

25. $(4w^3 - 2w + 7) + (5w^3 + 8w^2 - 1)$ $9w^3 + 8w^2 - 2w + 6$

26. $(5x^4 - 3x^2 + 9) + (3x^3 - 2x^2 - 7x + 3)$
$5x^4 + 3x^3 - 5x^2 - 7x + 12$

27. $(r^2 - 2r - 5) - (3r^2 - 5r + 7)$ $-2r^2 + 3r - 12$

28. $(7s^2 - 4s + 11) - (-2s^2 + 11s - 9)$ $9s^2 - 15s + 20$

29. $(u^3 - 3u^2 - 4u + 8) - (u^3 - 2u + 4)$ $-3u^2 - 2u + 4$

30. $(5v^4 - 3v^2 + 9) - (6v^4 + 11v^2 - 10)$ $-v^4 - 14v^2 + 19$

31. $(4x - 5)(2x^2 + 7x - 8)$ $8x^3 + 18x^2 - 67x + 40$

▶ 32. $(5x - 7)(3x^2 - 8x - 5)$ $15x^3 - 61x^2 + 31x + 35$

33. $(3x^2 - 2x + 5)(2x^2 - 5x + 2)$ $6x^4 - 19x^3 + 26x^2 - 29x + 10$

34. $(2y^3 - 3y + 4)(2y^2 - 5y + 7)$
$4y^5 - 10y^4 + 8y^3 + 23y^2 - 41y + 28$

In Exercises 35 to 48, use the **FOIL** method to find the indicated product.

35. $(2x + 4)(5x + 1)$
$10x^2 + 22x + 4$

36. $(5x - 3)(2x + 7)$
$10x^2 + 29x - 21$

37. $(y + 2)(y + 1)$
$y^2 + 3y + 2$

38. $(y + 5)(y + 3)$
$y^2 + 8y + 15$

39. $(4z - 3)(z - 4)$
$4z^2 - 19z + 12$

40. $(5z - 6)(z - 1)$
$5z^2 - 11z + 6$

41. $(a + 6)(a - 3)$
$a^2 + 3a - 18$

42. $(a - 10)(a + 4)$
$a^2 - 6a - 40$

43. $(5x - 11y)(2x - 7y)$
$10x^2 - 57xy + 77y^2$

44. $(3a - 5b)(4a - 7b)$
$12a^2 - 41ab + 35b^2$

45. $(9x + 5y)(2x + 5y)$
$18x^2 + 55xy + 25y^2$

46. $(3x - 7z)(5x - 7z)$
$15x^2 - 56xz + 49z^2$

47. $(3p + 5q)(2p - 7q)$
$6p^2 - 11pq - 35q^2$

48. $(2r - 11s)(5r + 8s)$
$10r^2 - 39rs - 88s^2$

In Exercises 49 to 54, perform the indicated operations and simplify.

49. $(4d - 1)^2 - (2d - 3)^2$
$12d^2 + 4d - 8$

50. $(5c - 8)^2 - (2c - 5)^2$
$21c^2 - 60c + 39$

51. $(r + s)(r^2 - rs + s^2)$
$r^3 + s^3$

52. $(r - s)(r^2 + rs + s^2)$
$r^3 - s^3$

53. $(3c - 2)(4c + 1)(5c - 2)$ $60c^3 - 49c^2 + 4$

54. $(4d - 5)(2d - 1)(3d - 4)$ $24d^3 - 74d^2 + 71d - 20$

In Exercises 55 to 62, use the special product formulas to perform the indicated operation.

55. $(3x + 5)(3x - 5)$
$9x^2 - 25$

▶ 56. $(4x^2 - 3y)(4x^2 + 3y)$
$16x^4 - 9y^2$

57. $(3x^2 - y)^2$
$9x^4 - 6x^2y + y^2$

58. $(6x + 7y)^2$
$36x^2 + 84xy + 49y^2$

59. $(4w + z)^2$
$16w^2 + 8wz + z^2$

60. $(3x - 5y^2)^2$
$9x^2 - 30xy^2 + 25y^4$

61. $[(x + 5) + y][(x + 5) - y]$ $x^2 + 10x + 25 - y^2$

62. $[(x - 2y) + 7][(x - 2y) - 7]$ $x^2 - 4xy + 4y^2 - 49$

In Exercises 63 to 70, evaluate the given polynomial for the indicated value of the variable.

63. $x^2 + 7x - 1$, for $x = 3$ 29

64. $x^2 - 8x + 2$, for $x = 4$ −14

65. $-x^2 + 5x - 3$, for $x = -2$ −17

▶ 66. $-x^2 - 5x + 4$, for $x = -5$ 4

67. $3x^3 - 2x^2 - x + 3$, for $x = -1$ −1

68. $5x^3 - x^2 + 5x - 3$, for $x = -1$ −14

69. $1 - x^5$, for $x = -2$ 33

70. $1 - x^3 - x^5$, for $x = 2$ −39

71. RECREATION The air resistance (in pounds) on a cyclist riding a bicycle in an upright position can be given by $0.016v^2$, where v is the speed of the cyclist in miles per hour. Find the air resistance on a cyclist when

a. $v = 10$ mph 1.6 lb
b. $v = 15$ mph 3.6 lb

72. HIGHWAY ENGINEERING On an expressway, the recommended *safe distance* between cars in feet is given by $0.015v^2 + v + 10$, where v is the speed of the car in miles per hour. Find the safe distance when

a. $v = 30$ mph 53.5 ft
b. $v = 55$ mph 110.375 ft

73. GEOMETRY The volume of a right circular cylinder (as shown below) is given by $\pi r^2 h$, where r is the radius of the base and h is the height of the cylinder. Find the volume when

a. $r = 3$ inches, $h = 8$ inches
72π in^3

b. $r = 5$ cm, $h = 12$ cm
300π cm^3

74. AUTOMOTIVE ENGINEERING The fuel efficiency (in miles per gallon of gas) of a car is given by the expression $-0.02v^2 + 1.5v + 2$, where v is the speed of the car in miles per hour. Find the fuel efficiency when

a. $v = 45$ mph
29 mi/gal
b. $v = 60$ mph
20 mi/gal

75. PSYCHOLOGY Based on data from one experiment, the reaction time, in hundredths of a second, of a person to visual stimulus varies according to age and is given by $0.005x^2 - 0.32x + 12$, where x is the age of the person. Find the reaction time to the stimulus for a person when

a. $x = 20$ years old
0.076 s
b. $x = 50$ years old
0.085 s

▶ **76. COMMITTEE MEMBERSHIP** The number of committees consisting of exactly 3 people that can be formed from a group of n people is given by the polynomial

$$\frac{1}{6}n^3 - \frac{1}{2}n^2 + \frac{1}{3}n$$

Find the number of committees consisting of exactly 3 people that can be formed from a group of 21 people.
1330 committees

77. CHESS MATCHES Find the number of chess matches that can be played between the members of a group of 150 people. Use the formula from Example 6. 11,175 matches

▶ **78. COMPUTER SCIENCE** A computer scientist determines that the time in seconds it takes a particular computer to calculate n digits of π is given by the polynomial

$$4.3 \times 10^{-6}n^2 - 2.1 \times 10^{-4}n$$

where $1000 \le n \le 10,000$. Estimate the time it takes the computer to calculate π to

a. 1000 digits
4.09 s
b. 5000 digits
106.45 s
c. 10,000 digits
427.9 s

79. COMPUTER SCIENCE If n is a positive integer, then $n!$, which is read "n factorial," is given by

$$n(n - 1)(n - 2) \cdots 2 \cdot 1$$

For example, $4! = 4 \cdot 3 \cdot 2 \cdot 1 = 24$. A computer scientist determines that each time a program is run on a particular computer, the time in seconds required to compute $n!$ is given by the polynomial

$$1.9 \times 10^{-6}n^2 - 3.9 \times 10^{-3}n$$

where $1000 \le n \le 10,000$. Using this polynomial, estimate the time it takes this computer to calculate 4000! and 8000!.
14.8 s; 90.4 s

80. AIR VELOCITY OF A COUGH The velocity, in meters per second, of the air that is expelled during a cough is given by velocity $= 6r^2 - 10r^3$, where r is the radius of the trachea in centimeters.

a. Find the velocity as a polynomial in standard form.
$-10r^3 + 6r^2$ m/s

b. Find the velocity of the air in a cough when the radius of the trachea is 0.35 cm. Round to the nearest hundredth. 0.31 m/s

81. SPORTS The height, in feet, of a baseball released by a pitcher t seconds after it is released is given by (ignoring air resistance)

$$\text{Height} = -16t^2 + 4.7881t + 6$$

For the pitch to be a strike, it must be at least 2 feet high when it crosses home plate and must be no higher than 5 feet high. If it takes 0.5 second for the ball to reach home plate, will the ball be high enough to be a strike?
Yes. The ball is approximately 4.4 ft high when it crosses home plate.

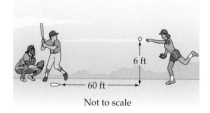

Not to scale

82. MEDICINE The temperature, in degrees Fahrenheit, of a patient after receiving a medication is given by

$$\text{Temperature} = 0.0002t^3 - 0.0114t^2 + 0.0158t + 104$$

where t is the number of minutes after receiving the medication.

a. What was the patient's temperature just before the medication was taken? 104°F

b. What was the patient's temperature 25 minutes after taking the medication? ≈100.4°F

83. PRIME FACTORIZATION Find n given

$$n! = 2^{11} \cdot 3^6 \cdot 5^3 \cdot 7^2 \cdot 11 \cdot 13 \quad 15$$

CONNECTING CONCEPTS

The following special product formulas can be used to find the cube of a binomial.

$$(x + y)^3 = x^3 + 3x^2y + 3xy^2 + y^3$$
$$(x - y)^3 = x^3 - 3x^2y + 3xy^2 - y^3$$

In Exercises 84 to 89, make use of the given special product formulas to find the indicated products.

84. $(a + b)^3$ **85.** $(a - b)^3$ **86.** $(x - 1)^3$
$a^3 + 3a^2b + 3ab^2 + b^3$ $a^3 - 3a^2b + 3ab^2 - b^3$ $x^3 - 3x^2 + 3x - 1$

87. $(y + 2)^3$ **88.** $(2x - 3y)^3$ **89.** $(3x + 5y)^3$
$y^3 + 6y^2 + 12y + 8$ $8x^3 - 36x^2y + 54xy^2 - 27y^3$ $27x^3 + 135x^2y + 225xy^2 + 125y^3$

PREPARE FOR SECTION P.4

90. Simplify: $\dfrac{6x^3}{2x}$ [P.2] $3x^2$

91. Simplify: $(-12x^4)3x^2$ [P.2] $-36x^6$

92. Express x^6 as a power of **a.** x^2 and **b.** x^3. [P.2]
    a. $(x^2)^3$ b. $(x^3)^2$

In Exercises 93 to 95, replace the question mark to make a true statement.

93. $6a^3b^4 \cdot ? = 18a^3b^7$ [P.2] $3b^3$

94. $-3(5a - ?) = -15a + 21$ [P.1] 7

95. $2x(3x - ?) = 6x^2 - 2x$ [P.1] 1

PROJECTS

1.   **ODD NUMBERS** Every odd number can be written in the form $2n - 1$, and every even number can be expressed as $2n$, where n is a natural number. Explain, by writing a few paragraphs and giving the supporting mathematics, why the product of two odd numbers is an odd number, the product of two even numbers is an even number, and the product of an even number and an odd number is an even number.

2.   **PRIME NUMBERS** Fermat's Little Theorem states, "If n is a prime number and a is *any* natural number, then $a^n - a$ is divisible by n." For instance, for $n = 11$ and $a = 14$, $\dfrac{14^{11} - 14}{11} = 368{,}142{,}288{,}150$. The important aspect of this theorem is that no matter what natural number is chosen for a, $a^{11} - a$ is evenly divisible by 11.

Knowing whether a number is prime plays a central role in the security of computer systems. A restatement (called the *contrapositive*) of Fermat's Little Theorem is "If n is a number and a is some number for which $a^n - a$ is *not*

divisible by n, then n is *not* a prime number" is used to determine when a number is *not* prime. For example, if $n = 14$, then $\dfrac{2^{14} - 2}{14} = \dfrac{8191}{7}$, and thus there is some number ($a = 2$) for which $2^{14} - 2$ is not evenly divisible by 14. Therefore, 14 is not prime.

a. Explain the meaning of the *contrapositive* (used above) of a theorem. Use your explanation to write the contrapositive of "If two triangles are congruent, then they are similar."

b. $7^{14} - 7$ is divisible by 14. Explain why this does not contradict the fact that 14 is not a prime.

c. Explain the meaning of the *converse* of a theorem. State the converse of Fermat's Little Theorem.

d. The number 561 has the property that $a^{561} - a$ is divisible by 561 for all natural numbers a. Can you use

Fermat's Little Theorem to conclude that 561 is a prime number? Explain.

e. Suppose that $a^n - a$ is divisible by n for all values of a. Can you conclude that n is a prime number? Explain your answer.

f. Find a definition of a Carmichael number. What do Carmichael numbers have to do with the information in part **e.**?

FACTORING

Writing a polynomial as a product of polynomials of lower degree is called **factoring**. Factoring is an important procedure that is often used to simplify fractional expressions and to solve equations.

In this section we consider only the factorization of polynomials that have integer coefficients. Also, we are concerned only with **factoring over the integers**. That is, we search only for polynomial factors that have integer coefficients.

• GREATEST COMMON FACTOR

The first step in any factorization of a polynomial is to use the distributive property to factor out the **greatest common factor (GCF)** of the terms of the polynomial. Given two or more exponential expressions with the same prime number base or the same variable base, the GCF is the exponential expression with the smallest exponent. For example,

2^3 is the GCF of 2^3, 2^5, and 2^8 and a is the GCF of a^4 and a

The GCF of two or more monomials is the product of the GCFs of all the *common* bases. For example, to find the GCF of $27a^3b^4$ and $18b^3c$, factor the coefficients into prime factors and then write each common base with its smallest exponent.

$$27a^3b^4 = 3^3 \cdot a^3 \cdot b^4 \qquad 18b^3c = 2 \cdot 3^2 \cdot b^3 \cdot c$$

The only common bases are 3 and b. The product of these common bases with their smallest exponents is 3^2b^3. The GCF of $27a^3b^4$ and $18b^3c$ is $9b^3$.

The expressions $3x(2x + 5)$ and $4(2x + 5)$ have a common *binomial* factor that is $2x + 5$. Thus the GCF of $3x(2x + 5)$ and $4(2x + 5)$ is $2x + 5$.

Alternative to Example 1
Factor out the GCF.
1. $-6x^2y^2 + 3xy^2$
  ◦ $-3xy^2(2x - 1)$
2. $2x(3x + 1) - (3x + 1)$
  ◦ $(3x + 1)(2x - 1)$

EXAMPLE 1   **Factor Out the Greatest Common Factor**

Factor out the GCF.

a. $10x^3 + 6x$ **b.** $15x^{2n} + 9x^{n+1} - 3x^n$ (where n is a positive integer)

c. $(m + 5)(x + 3) + (m + 5)(x - 10)$

Solution

a. $10x^3 + 6x = (2x)(5x^2) + (2x)(3)$ • **The GCF is 2x.**

$\qquad\qquad = 2x(5x^2 + 3)$ • **Factor out the GCF.**

b. $15x^{2n} + 9x^{n+1} - 3x^n$

$\qquad = (3x^n)(5x^n) + (3x^n)(3x) - (3x^n)(1)$ • **The GCF is 3x^n.**

$\qquad = 3x^n(5x^n + 3x - 1)$ • **Factor out the GCF.**

c. $(m + 5)(x + 3) + (m + 5)(x - 10)$ • **Use the distributive property to factor out (m + 5).**

$\qquad = (m + 5)[(x + 3) + (x - 10)]$

$\qquad = (m + 5)(2x - 7)$ • **Simplify.**

▶ **TRY EXERCISE 6, PAGE 53**

● FACTORING TRINOMIALS

Some trinomials of the form $x^2 + bx + c$ can be factored by a trial procedure. This method makes use of the FOIL method in reverse. For example, consider the following products:

$(x + 3)(x + 5) = x^2 + 5x + 3x + (3)(5) \quad = x^2 + 8x + 15$

$(x - 2)(x - 7) = x^2 - 7x - 2x + (-2)(-7) = x^2 - 9x + 14$

$(x + 4)(x - 9) = x^2 - 9x + 4x + (4)(-9) \quad = x^2 - 5x - 36$

The coefficient of *x* is the sum of the constant terms of the binomials.

The constant term of the trinomial is the product of the constant terms of the binomials.

❷ QUESTION   Is $(x - 2)(x + 7)$ the correct factorization of $x^2 - 5x - 14$?

Points to Remember to Factor $x^2 + bx + c$

1.   The constant term c of the trinomial is the product of the constant terms of the binomials.

2.   The coefficient b in the trinomial is the sum of the constant terms of the binomials.

3.   If the constant term c of the trinomial is positive, the constant terms of the binomials have the same sign as the coefficient b of the trinomial.

4.   If the constant term c of the trinomial is negative, the constant terms of the binomials have opposite signs.

❷ ANSWER   No. $(x - 2)(x + 7) = x^2 + 5x - 14$.

Alternative to Example 2
1. Factor: $x^2 - 5x - 6$
 • $(x - 6)(x + 1)$
2. Factor: $x^2 + 6x - 27$
 • $(x + 9)(x - 3)$

EXAMPLE 2   Factor a Trinomial of the Form $x^2 + bx + c$

Factor: $x^2 + 7x - 18$

Solution

We must find two binomials whose first terms have a product of x^2 and whose last terms have a product of -18; also, the sum of the product of the outer terms and the product of the inner terms must be $7x$. Begin by listing the possible integer factorizations of -18 and the sum of those factors.

Factors of −18	Sum of the Factors
$1 \cdot (-18)$	$1 + (-18) = -17$
$(-1) \cdot 18$	$(-1) + 18 = 17$
$2 \cdot (-9)$	$2 + (-9) = -7$
$(-2) \cdot 9$	$(-2) + 9 = 7$

• Stop. This is the desired sum.

Thus -2 and 9 are the numbers whose sum is 7 and whose product is -18. Therefore,

$$x^2 + 7x - 18 = (x - 2)(x + 9)$$

The FOIL method can be used to verify that the factorization is correct.

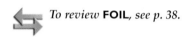
To review **FOIL**, *see p. 38.*

▶ **TRY EXERCISE 12, PAGE 53**

The trial method sometimes can be used to factor trinomials of the form $ax^2 + bx + c$, which do not have a leading coefficient of 1. We use the factors of a and c to form trial binomial factors. Factoring trinomials of this type may require testing many factors. To reduce the number of trial factors, make use of the following points.

Points to Remember to Factor $ax^2 + bx + c, a > 0$

1. If the constant term of the trinomial is positive, the constant terms of the binomials have the same sign as the coefficient b in the trinomial.

2. If the constant term of the trinomial is negative, the constant terms of the binomials have opposite signs.

3. If the terms of the trinomial do not have a common factor, then neither binomial will have a common factor.

Alternative to Example 3
1. Factor: $6x^2 + 17x - 10$
 • $(2x - 1)(3x + 10)$
2. Factor: $4x^2 - 17x - 21$
 • $(4x - 21)(x + 1)$

EXAMPLE 3   Factor a Trinomial of the Form $ax^2 + bx + c$

Factor: $6x^2 - 11x + 4$

Solution

Because the constant term of the trinomial is positive and the coefficient of the x term is negative, the constant terms of the binomials will both be negative. This time we find factors of the first term as well as factors of the constant term.

Factors of $6x^2$	Factors of 4 (both negative)
$x, 6x$	$-1, -4$
$2x, 3x$	$-2, -2$

Use these factors to write trial factors. Use the FOIL method to see whether any of the trial factors produce the correct middle term. If the terms of a trinomial do not have a common factor, then a binomial factor cannot have a common factor (point 3). Such trial factors need not be checked.

Trial Factors	Middle Term	
$(x - 1)(6x - 4)$	Common factor	• $6x$ and 4 have a common factor.
$(x - 4)(6x - 1)$	$-1x - 24x = -25x$	
$(x - 2)(6x - 2)$	Common factor	• $6x$ and 2 have a common factor.
$(2x - 1)(3x - 4)$	$-8x - 3x = -11x$	• This is the correct middle term.

Thus $6x^2 - 11x + 4 = (2x - 1)(3x - 4)$.

▶ **TRY EXERCISE 16, PAGE 53**

Sometimes it is impossible to factor a polynomial into the product of two polynomials having integer coefficients. Such polynomials are said to be **nonfactorable over the integers.** For example, $x^2 + 3x + 7$ is nonfactorable over the integers because there are no integers whose product is 7 and whose sum or difference is 3.

If you have difficulty factoring a trinomial, you may wish to use the following theorem. It will indicate whether the trinomial is factorable over the integers.

Factorization Theorem

The trinomial $ax^2 + bx + c$, with integer coefficients a, b, and c, can be factored as the product of two binomials with integer coefficients if and only if $b^2 - 4ac$ is a perfect square.

Alternative to Example 4
1. Determine whether $2x^2 + x - 3$ is factorable over the integers.
● **Yes**
2. Determine whether $4x^2 + 2x + 9$ is factorable over the integers.
● **No**

EXAMPLE 4   **Apply the Factorization Theorem**

Determine whether each trinomial is factorable over the integers.

a. $4x^2 + 8x - 7$ **b.** $6x^2 - 5x - 4$

Continued ▶

Solution

a. The coefficients of $4x^2 + 8x - 7$ are $a = 4$, $b = 8$, and $c = -7$. Applying the factorization theorem yields

$$b^2 - 4ac = 8^2 - 4(4)(-7) = 176$$

Because 176 is not a perfect square, the trinomial is nonfactorable over the integers.

b. The coefficients of $6x^2 - 5x - 4$ are $a = 6$, $b = -5$, and $c = -4$. Thus

$$b^2 - 4ac = (-5)^2 - 4(6)(-4) = 121$$

Because 121 is a perfect square, the trinomial is factorable over the integers. Using the methods we have developed, we find

$$6x^2 - 5x - 4 = (3x - 4)(2x + 1)$$

▶ **TRY EXERCISE 24, PAGE 53**

Certain trinomials can be expressed as quadratic trinomials by making suitable variable substitutions. A trinomial is **quadratic in form** if it can be written as

$$au^2 + bu + c$$

If we let $x^2 = u$, the trinomial $x^4 + 5x^2 + 6$ can be written as shown at the right.

$$\begin{aligned} x^4 + 5x^2 + 6 \\ = (x^2)^2 + 5(x^2) + 6 \end{aligned}$$

The trinomial is quadratic in form.

$$= u^2 + 5u + 6$$

If we let $xy = u$, the trinomial $2x^2y^2 + 3xy - 9$ can be written as shown at the right.

$$\begin{aligned} 2x^2y^2 + 3xy - 9 \\ = 2(xy)^2 + 3(xy) - 9 \end{aligned}$$

The trinomial is quadratic in form.

$$= 2u^2 + 3u - 9$$

When a trinomial that is quadratic in form is factored, the variable part of the first term in each binomial factor will be u. For example, because $x^4 + 5x^2 + 6$ is quadratic in form when $x^2 = u$, the first term in each binomial factor will be x^2.

$$\begin{aligned} x^4 + 5x^2 + 6 &= (x^2)^2 + 5(x^2) + 6 \\ &= (x^2 + 2)(x^2 + 3) \end{aligned}$$

The trinomial $x^2y^2 - 2xy - 15$ is quadratic in form when $xy = u$. The first term in each binomial factor will be xy.

$$\begin{aligned} x^2y^2 - 2xy - 15 &= (xy)^2 - 2(xy) - 15 \\ &= (xy + 3)(xy - 5) \end{aligned}$$

Alternative to Example 5
Factor: $3x^4 + 4x^2 - 4$
● $(3x^2 - 2)(x^2 + 2)$

EXAMPLE 5

Factor: a. $6x^2y^2 - xy - 12$ b. $2x^4 + 5x^2 - 12$

Solution

a. $6x^2y^2 - xy - 12$

$$= (3xy + 4)(2xy - 3)$$

• The trinomial is quadratic in form when $xy = u$.

b. $2x^4 + 5x^2 - 12$
    $= (x^2 + 4)(2x^2 - 3)$

• The trinomial is quadratic in form when $x^2 = u$.

▶ **TRY EXERCISE 36, PAGE 53**

● SPECIAL FACTORING

The product of a term and itself is called a **perfect square.** The exponents on variables of perfect squares are always even numbers. The **square root of a perfect square** is one of the two equal factors of the perfect square. To find the square root of a perfect square variable term, divide the exponent by 2. For the examples below, assume the variables represent positive numbers.

Term		Perfect Square	Square Root
7	$7 \cdot 7 =$	49	$\sqrt{49} = 7$
y	$y \cdot y =$	y^2	$\sqrt{y^2} = y$
$2x^3$	$2x^3 \cdot 2x^3 =$	$4x^6$	$\sqrt{4x^6} = 2x^3$
x^n	$x^n \cdot x^n =$	x^{2n}	$\sqrt{x^{2n}} = x^n$

take note

The **sum** of two squares does not factor over the integers. For instance, $49x^2 + 144$ does not factor over the integers.

The factors of the difference of two perfect squares are the sum and difference of the square roots of the perfect squares.

Factors of the Difference of Two Perfect Squares

$$a^2 - b^2 = (a + b)(a - b)$$

Alternative to Example 6
1. Factor: $2x^2 - 18$
   ● $2(x - 3)(x + 3)$
2. Factor: $x^2y^2 - 81$
   ● $(xy - 9)(xy + 9)$

EXAMPLE 6   Factor the Difference of Squares

Factor: $49x^2 - 144$

Solution

$49x^2 - 144 = (7x)^2 - (12)^2$

• Recognize the difference-of-squares form.

$= (7x + 12)(7x - 12)$

• The binomial factors are the sum and the difference of the square roots of the squares.

▶ **TRY EXERCISE 40, PAGE 53**

A **perfect-square trinomial** is a trinomial that is the square of a binomial. For example, $x^2 + 6x + 9$ is a perfect-square trinomial because

$$(x + 3)^2 = x^2 + 6x + 9$$

Every perfect-square trinomial can be factored by the trial method, but it generally is faster to factor perfect-square trinomials by using the following factoring formulas.

Factors of a Perfect-Square Trinomial

$$a^2 + 2ab + b^2 = (a + b)^2$$
$$a^2 - 2ab + b^2 = (a - b)^2$$

Alternative to Example 7
Factor: $12x^2 + 36x + 27$
● $3(2x + 3)^2$

---

take note

It is important to check the proposed factorization. For instance, consider $x^2 + 13x + 36$. Because x^2 is the square of x and 36 is the square of 6, it is tempting to factor, using the perfect-square trinomial formulas, as $x^2 + 13x + 36 \overset{?}{=} (x + 6)^2$. Note, however, that $(x + 6)^2 = x^2 + 12x + 36$, which is not the original trinomial. The correct factorization is
$x^2 + 13x + 36 = (x + 4)(x + 9)$

EXAMPLE 7   **Factor a Perfect-Square Trinomial**

Factor: $16m^2 - 40mn + 25n^2$

Solution

Because $16m^2 = (4m)^2$ and $25n^2 = (5n)^2$, try factoring $16m^2 - 40mn + 25n^2$ as the square of a binomial.

$$16m^2 - 40mn + 25n^2 \overset{?}{=} (4m - 5n)^2$$

Check:

$$(4m - 5n)^2 = (4m - 5n)(4m - 5n)$$
$$= 16m^2 - 20mn - 20mn + 25n^2$$
$$= 16m^2 - 40mn + 25n^2$$

The factorization checks. Therefore, $16m^2 - 40mn + 25n^2 = (4m - 5n)^2$.

▶ **TRY EXERCISE 50, PAGE 54**

The product of the same three terms is called a **perfect cube**. The exponents on variables of perfect cubes are always divisible by 3. The **cube root of a perfect cube** is one of the three equal factors of the perfect cube. To find the cube root of a perfect cube variable term, divide the exponent by 3.

Term		Perfect Cube	Cube Root
5	$5 \cdot 5 \cdot 5 =$	125	$\sqrt[3]{125} = 5$
z	$z \cdot z \cdot z =$	z^3	$\sqrt[3]{z^3} = z$
$3x^2$	$3x^2 \cdot 3x^2 \cdot 3x^2 =$	$27x^6$	$\sqrt[3]{27x^6} = 3x^2$
x^n	$x^n \cdot x^n \cdot x^n =$	x^{3n}	$\sqrt[3]{x^{3n}} = x^n$

The following factoring formulas are used to factor the sum or difference of two perfect cubes.

---

take note

Note the pattern of the signs when factoring the sum or difference of two perfect cubes.

Same
sign
$a^3 + b^3 = (a + b)(a^2 - ab + b^2)$
Opposite signs

Same
sign
$a^3 - b^3 = (a - b)(a^2 + ab + b^2)$
Opposite signs

Factors of the Sum or Difference of Two Perfect Cubes

$$a^3 + b^3 = (a + b)(a^2 - ab + b^2)$$
$$a^3 - b^3 = (a - b)(a^2 + ab + b^2)$$

Alternative to Example 8
1. Factor: $27 - y^3$
● $(3 - y)(9 + 3y + y^2)$
2. Factor: $x^4 + 8x$
● $x(x + 2)(x^2 - 2x + 4)$

EXAMPLE 8   **Factor the Sum or Difference of Cubes**

Factor: **a.** $8a^3 + b^3$ **b.** $a^3 - 64$

Solution

a. $8a^3 + b^3 = (2a)^3 + b^3$ • Recognize the sum-of-cubes form.

    $= (2a + b)(4a^2 - 2ab + b^2)$ • Factor.

b. $a^3 - 64 = a^3 - 4^3$ • Recognize the difference-of-cubes form.

    $= (a - 4)(a^2 + 4a + 16)$ • Factor.

▶ **TRY EXERCISE 56, PAGE 54**

● FACTOR BY GROUPING

take note

$-a + b = -(a - b)$. Thus, $-4y + 14 = -(4y - 14)$.

Some polynomials can be **factored by grouping**. Pairs of terms that have a common factor are first grouped together. The process makes repeated use of the distributive property, as shown in the following factorization of $6y^3 - 21y^2 - 4y + 14$.

$$6y^3 - 21y^2 - 4y + 14$$
$$= (6y^3 - 21y^2) - (4y - 14)$$ • Group the first two terms and the last two terms.
$$= 3y^2(2y - 7) - 2(2y - 7)$$ • Factor out the GCF from each of the groups.
$$= (2y - 7)(3y^2 - 2)$$ • Factor out the common binomial factor.

When you factor by grouping, some experimentation may be necessary to find a grouping that is of the form of one of the special factoring formulas.

Alternative to Example 9

1. Factor: $2ax + 4bx - 3ay - 6by$

● $(a + 2b)(2x - 3y)$

2. Factor: $xy - 3x - 4y + 12$

● $(x - 4)(y - 3)$

EXAMPLE 9   Factor by Grouping

Factor by grouping.   a. $a^2 + 10ab + 25b^2 - c^2$ b. $p^2 + p - q - q^2$

Solution

a. $a^2 + 10ab + 25b^2 - c^2$
$$= (a^2 + 10ab + 25b^2) - c^2$$ • Group the terms of the perfect-square trinomial.
$$= (a + 5b)^2 - c^2$$ • Factor the trinomial.
$$= [(a + 5b) + c][(a + 5b) - c]$$ • Factor the difference of squares.
$$= (a + 5b + c)(a + 5b - c)$$ • Simplify.

b. $p^2 + p - q - q^2$
$$= p^2 - q^2 + p - q$$ • Rearrange the terms.
$$= (p^2 - q^2) + (p - q)$$ • Regroup.
$$= (p + q)(p - q) + (p - q)$$ • Factor the difference of squares.
$$= (p - q)(p + q + 1)$$ • Factor out the common factor $(p - q)$.

▶ **TRY EXERCISE 66, PAGE 54**

● GENERAL FACTORING

Here is a general factoring strategy for polynomials:

General Factoring Strategy

1. Factor out the GCF of all terms.

2. Try to factor a binomial as

   a. the difference of two squares

   b. the sum or difference of two cubes

3. Try to factor a trinomial

   a. as a perfect-square trinomial

   b. using the trial method

4. Try to factor a polynomial with more than three terms by grouping.

5. After each factorization, examine the new factors to see whether they can be factored.

Alternative to Example 10
1. Factor: $x^3 - 2x^2 - x + 2$
● $(x - 2)(x + 1)(x - 1)$
2. Factor: $4x^2 + 4x + 1 - y^2$
● $(2x + 1 - y)(2x + 1 + y)$

EXAMPLE 10   Factor Using the General Factoring Strategy

Completely factor: $x^6 + 7x^3 - 8$

Solution
Factor $x^6 + 7x^3 - 8$ as the product of two binomials.

$$x^6 + 7x^3 - 8 = (x^3 + 8)(x^3 - 1)$$

Now factor $x^3 + 8$, which is the sum of two cubes, and factor $x^3 - 1$, which is the difference of two cubes.

$$x^6 + 7x^3 - 8 = (x + 2)(x^2 - 2x + 4)(x - 1)(x^2 + x + 1)$$

▶ **TRY EXERCISE 72, PAGE 54**

 TOPICS FOR DISCUSSION

1. Discuss the meaning of the phrase *nonfactorable over the integers*.

2. You know that if $ab = 0$, then $a = 0$ or $b = 0$. Suppose a polynomial is written in factored form and then set equal to zero. For instance, suppose

$$x^2 - 2x - 15 = (x - 5)(x + 3) = 0$$

Discuss what implications this has for the values of x. Do not answer this question only for the polynomial above, but also for any polynomial written as a product of linear factors and then set equal to zero.

3. Let P be a polynomial of degree n. Discuss the number of possible distinct linear polynomials that can be a factor of P.

4. A method of evaluating polynomials, sometimes called Horner's method, involves factoring a polynomial in a certain manner. For instance,

$$4x^3 - 2x^2 + 5x - 3 = [(4x - 2)x + 5]x - 3$$
$$5x^4 - 2x^3 + 4x^2 + x - 6 = \{[(5x - 2)x + 4]x + 1\}x - 6$$

To evaluate the polynomial, the factored form is evaluated. Discuss the advantages and disadvantages of using this method to evaluate a polynomial.

5. If n is a natural number, $n! = n(n - 1)(n - 2) \cdots 3 \cdot 2 \cdot 1$. Explain why none of the following consecutive integers is a prime number.

$$5! + 2 \qquad 5! + 3 \qquad 5! + 4 \qquad 5! + 5$$

How many numbers are in the following list of consecutive integers? How many of those numbers are prime numbers?

$$k! + 2, \quad k! + 3, \quad k! + 4, \quad k! + 5, \quad \ldots, \quad k! + k$$

Explain why this result means that there are arbitrarily long sequences of consecutive natural numbers that do not contain a prime number.

EXERCISE SET P.4   —*Suggested Assignment: Exercises 1–91, every other odd; 99–105, all.*

In Exercises 1 to 8, factor out the GCF from each polynomial.

1. $5x + 20$
   $5(x + 4)$

2. $8x^2 + 12x - 40$
   $4(2x^2 + 3x - 10)$

3. $-15x^2 - 12x$
   $-3x(5x + 4)$

4. $-6y^2 - 54y$
   $-6y(y + 9)$

5. $10x^2y + 6xy - 14xy^2$
   $2xy(5x + 3 - 7y)$

▶ 6. $6a^3b^2 - 12a^2b + 72ab^3$
   $6ab(a^2b - 2a + 12b^2)$

7. $(x - 3)(a + b) + (x - 3)(a + 2b)$
   $(x - 3)(2a + 3b)$

8. $(x - 4)(2a - b) + (x + 4)(2a - b)$
   $(2a - b)(2x)$

In Exercises 9 to 22, factor each trinomial over the integers.

9. $x^2 + 7x + 12$
   $(x + 3)(x + 4)$

10. $x^2 + 9x + 20$
    $(x + 4)(x + 5)$

11. $a^2 - 10a - 24$
    $(a - 12)(a + 2)$

▶ 12. $b^2 + 12b - 28$
    $(b + 14)(b - 2)$

13. $6x^2 + 25x + 4$
    $(6x + 1)(x + 4)$

14. $8a^2 - 26a + 15$
    $(4a - 3)(2a - 5)$

15. $51x^2 - 5x - 4$
    $(17x + 4)(3x - 1)$

▶ 16. $57y^2 + y - 6$
    $(19y - 6)(3y + 1)$

17. $6x^2 + xy - 40y^2$
    $(3x + 8y)(2x - 5y)$

18. $8x^2 + 10xy - 25y^2$
    $(4x - 5y)(2x + 5y)$

19. $x^4 + 6x^2 + 5$
    $(x^2 + 5)(x^2 + 1)$

20. $x^4 + 11x^2 + 18$
    $(x^2 + 9)(x^2 + 2)$

21. $6x^4 + 23x^2 + 15$
    $(6x^2 + 5)(x^2 + 3)$

22. $9x^4 + 10x^2 + 1$
    $(9x^2 + 1)(x^2 + 1)$

In Exercises 23 to 28, use the factorization theorem to determine whether each trinomial is factorable over the integers.

23. $8x^2 + 26x + 15$
    factorable over the integers

▶ 24. $16x^2 + 8x - 35$
    factorable over the integers

25. $4x^2 - 5x + 6$
    not factorable over the integers

26. $6x^2 + 8x - 3$
    not factorable over the integers

27. $6x^2 - 14x + 5$
    not factorable over the integers

28. $10x^2 - 4x - 5$
    not factorable over the integers

In Exercises 29 to 36, factor over the integers.

29. $x^4 - x^2 - 6$
    $(x^2 - 3)(x^2 + 2)$

30. $x^4 + 3x^2 + 2$
    $(x^2 + 1)(x^2 + 2)$

31. $x^2y^2 - 2xy - 8$
    $(xy - 4)(xy + 2)$

32. $2x^2y^2 + xy - 1$
    $(2xy - 1)(xy + 1)$

33. $3x^4 + 11x^2 - 4$
    $(3x^2 - 1)(x^2 + 4)$

34. $2x^4 + 3x^2 - 9$
    $(2x^2 - 3)(x^2 + 3)$

35. $3x^6 + 2x^3 - 8$
    $(3x^3 - 4)(x^3 + 2)$

▶ 36. $8x^6 - 10x^3 - 3$
    $(4x^3 + 1)(2x^3 - 3)$

In Exercises 37 to 46, factor each difference of squares over the integers.

37. $x^2 - 9$
    $(x - 3)(x + 3)$

38. $x^2 - 64$
    $(x - 8)(x + 8)$

39. $4a^2 - 49$
    $(2a - 7)(2a + 7)$

▶ 40. $81b^2 - 16c^2$
    $(9b - 4c)(9b + 4c)$

41. $1 - 100x^2$
    $(1 - 10x)(1 + 10x)$

42. $1 - 121y^2$
    $(1 - 11y)(1 + 11y)$

43. $x^4 - 9$
    $(x^2 - 3)(x^2 + 3)$

44. $y^4 - 196$
    $(y^2 - 14)(y^2 + 14)$

45. $(x + 5)^2 - 4$
    $(x + 3)(x + 7)$

46. $(x - 3)^2 - 16$
    $(x - 7)(x + 1)$

In Exercises 47 to 54, factor each perfect-square trinomial.

47. $x^2 + 10x + 25$
$(x + 5)^2$

48. $y^2 + 6y + 9$
$(y + 3)^2$

49. $a^2 - 14a + 49$
$(a - 7)^2$

▶ **50.** $b^2 - 24b + 144$
$(b - 12)^2$

51. $4x^2 + 12x + 9$
$(2x + 3)^2$

52. $25y^2 + 40y + 16$
$(5y + 4)^2$

53. $z^4 + 4z^2w^2 + 4w^4$
$(z^2 + 2w^2)^2$

54. $9x^4 - 30x^2y^2 + 25y^4$
$(3x^2 - 5y^2)^2$

In Exercises 55 to 62, factor each sum or difference of cubes over the integers.

55. $x^3 - 8$
$(x - 2)(x^2 + 2x + 4)$

▶ **56.** $b^3 + 64$
$(b + 4)(b^2 - 4b + 16)$

57. $8x^3 - 27y^3$
$(2x - 3y)(4x^2 + 6xy + 9y^2)$

58. $64u^3 - 27v^3$
$(4u - 3v)(16u^2 + 12uv + 9v^2)$

59. $8 - x^6$
$(2 - x^2)(4 + 2x^2 + x^4)$

60. $1 + y^{12}$
$(1 + y^4)(1 - y^4 + y^8)$

61. $(x - 2)^3 - 1$
$(x - 3)(x^2 - 3x + 3)$

62. $(y + 3)^3 + 8$
$(y + 5)(y^2 + 4y + 7)$

In Exercises 63 to 68, factor (over the integers) by grouping in pairs.

63. $3x^3 + x^2 + 6x + 2$
$(3x + 1)(x^2 + 2)$

64. $18w^3 + 15w^2 + 12w + 10$
$(6w + 5)(3w^2 + 2)$

65. $ax^2 - ax + bx - b$
$(x - 1)(ax + b)$

▶ **66.** $a^2y^2 - ay^3 + ac - cy$
$(a - y)(ay^2 + c)$

67. $6w^3 + 4w^2 - 15w - 10$
$(3w + 2)(2w^2 - 5)$

68. $10z^3 - 15z^2 - 4z + 6$
$(2z - 3)(5z^2 - 2)$

In Exercises 69 to 88, use the general factoring strategy to completely factor each polynomial. If the polynomial does not factor, then state that it is nonfactorable over the integers.

69. $18x^2 - 2$
$2(3x - 1)(3x + 1)$

70. $4bx^3 + 32b$
$4b(x + 2)(x^2 - 2x + 4)$

71. $16x^4 - 1$
$(2x - 1)(2x + 1)(4x^2 + 1)$

▶ **72.** $81y^4 - 16$
$(3y - 2)(3y + 2)(9y^2 + 4)$

73. $12ax^2 - 23axy + 10ay^2$
$a(3x - 2y)(4x - 5y)$

74. $6ax^2 - 19axy - 20ay^2$
$a(6x + 5y)(x - 4y)$

75. $3bx^3 + 4bx^2 - 3bx - 4b$
$b(3x + 4)(x - 1)(x + 1)$

76. $2x^6 - 2$ $2(x - 1) \times$
$(x^2 + x + 1)(x + 1)(x^2 - x + 1)$

77. $72bx^2 + 24bxy + 2by^2$
$2b(6x + y)^2$

78. $64y^3 - 16y^2z + yz^2$
$y(8y - z)^2$

79. $(w - 5)^3 + 8$
$(w - 3)(w^2 - 12w + 39)$

80. $5xy + 20y - 15x - 60$
$5(x + 4)(y - 3)$

81. $x^2 + 6xy + 9y^2 - 1$
$(x + 3y - 1)(x + 3y + 1)$

82. $4y^2 - 4yz + z^2 - 9$
$(2y - z - 3)(2y - z + 3)$

83. $8x^2 + 3x - 4$
not factorable over the integers

84. $16x^2 + 81$
not factorable over the integers

85. $5x(2x - 5)^2 - (2x - 5)^3$
$(2x - 5)^2(3x + 5)$

86. $6x(3x + 1)^3 - (3x + 1)^4$
$(3x + 1)^3(3x - 1)$

87. $4x^2 + 2x - y - y^2$
$(2x - y)(2x + y + 1)$

88. $a^2 + a + b - b^2$
$(a + b)(a - b + 1)$

CONNECTING CONCEPTS

In Exercises 89 and 90, find all positive values of k such that the trinomial is a perfect-square trinomial.

89. $x^2 + kx + 16$
8

90. $36x^2 + kxy + 100y^2$
120

In Exercises 91 and 92, find k such that the trinomial is a perfect-square trinomial.

91. $x^2 + 16x + k$
64

92. $x^2 - 14xy + ky^2$
49

In Exercises 93 and 94, use the general strategy to factor each polynomial. In each exercise n represents a positive integer.

93. $x^{4n} - 1$
$(x^n - 1)(x^n + 1)(x^{2n} + 1)$

94. $x^{4n} - 2x^{2n} + 1$
$(x^n - 1)^2(x^n + 1)^2$

In Exercises 95 to 98, write, in its factored form, the area of the shaded portion of each geometric figure.

95.

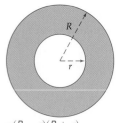

$\pi(R - r)(R + r)$

96.

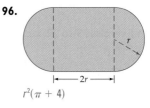

$r^2(\pi + 4)$

97.

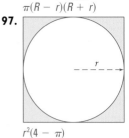

$r^2(4 - \pi)$

98.

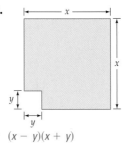

$(x - y)(x + y)$

PREPARE FOR SECTION P.5

---

99. Simplify: $1 + \dfrac{1}{2 - \dfrac{1}{3}}$ [P.1] $\dfrac{8}{5}$

100. Simplify: $\left(\dfrac{w}{x}\right)^{-1}\left(\dfrac{y}{z}\right)^{-1}$ [P.2] $\dfrac{xz}{wy}$

101. What is the common binomial factor of $x^2 + 2x - 3$ and $x^2 + 7x + 12$? [P.4] $x + 3$

In Exercises 102 to 104, factor completely over the integers.

102. $(2x - 3)(3x + 2) - (2x - 3)(x + 2)$ [P.4] $2x(2x - 3)$

103. $x^2 - 5x - 6$ [P.4] $(x - 6)(x + 1)$

104. $x^3 - 64$ [P.4] $(x - 4)(x^2 + 4x + 16)$

PROJECTS

---

1. GEOMETRY The ancient Greeks used geometric figures and the concept of area to illustrate many algebraic concepts. The factoring formula $x^2 - y^2 = (x + y)(x - y)$ can be illustrated by the figure below.

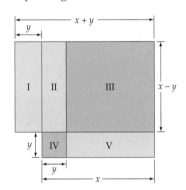

a. Which regions are represented by $(x + y)(x - y)$?

b. Which regions are represented by $x^2 - y^2$?

c. Explain why the area of the regions listed in **a.** must equal the area of the regions listed in **b.**

2. GEOMETRY What algebraic formula does the geometric figure below illustrate?

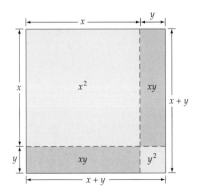

3. GEOMETRY Show how the figure below can be used to illustrate the factoring formula for the difference of two cubes.

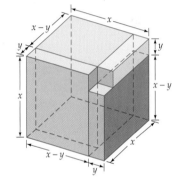

RATIONAL EXPRESSIONS

A **rational expression** is a fraction in which the numerator and denominator are polynomials. For example,

$$\frac{3}{x+1} \quad \text{and} \quad \frac{x^2 - 4x - 21}{x^2 - 9}$$

are rational expressions.

The **domain of a rational expression** is the set of all real numbers that can be used as replacements for the variable. Any value of the variable that causes division by zero is excluded from the domain of the rational expression. For example, the domain of

$$\frac{x+3}{x^2 - 5x}, \quad x \neq 0, x \neq 5$$

is the set of all real numbers except 0 and 5. Both 0 and 5 are excluded values because the denominator $x^2 - 5x$ equals zero when $x = 0$ and also when $x = 5$. Sometimes the excluded values are specified to the right of a rational expression, as shown here. However, a rational expression is meaningful only for those real numbers that are not excluded values, regardless of whether the excluded values are specifically stated.

MATH MATTERS

Evidence from work left by early Egyptians more than 3600 years ago shows that they used, with one exception, unit fractions—that is, fractions whose numerators are 1. The one exception was 2/3. A unit fraction was represented by placing an oval over the symbol for the number in the denominator. For instance, 1/4 = ⬭.
                    ‖‖

? QUESTION What values of x must be excluded from the domain of $\frac{3x}{x^2 - x - 2}$?

Rational expressions have properties similar to the properties of rational numbers.

Properties of Rational Expressions

For all rational expressions $\frac{P}{Q}$ and $\frac{R}{S}$ where $Q \neq 0$ and $S \neq 0$,

Equality $\qquad\qquad \frac{P}{Q} = \frac{R}{S}$ if and only if $PS = QR$

Equivalent expressions $\qquad \frac{P}{Q} = \frac{PR}{QR}, \quad R \neq 0$

Sign $\qquad\qquad -\frac{P}{Q} = \frac{-P}{Q} = \frac{P}{-Q}$

? ANSWER When $x = -1$ and $x = 2$, $x^2 - x - 2 = 0$. Therefore, -1 and 2 must be excluded from the domain.

● SIMPLIFY A RATIONAL EXPRESSION

To **simplify a rational expression,** factor the numerator and the denominator. Then use the equivalent expressions property to eliminate factors common to both the numerator and the denominator. A rational expression is *simplified* when 1 is the only common factor of both the numerator and the denominator.

Alternative to Example 1

1. Simplify: $\dfrac{6x^3 - 15x^2}{12x^2 - 30x}$

● $\dfrac{x}{2}$

2. Simplify: $\dfrac{3x^2 + 10x - 8}{8 - 14x + 3x^2}$

● $\dfrac{x + 4}{x - 4}$

EXAMPLE 1   **Simplify a Rational Expression**

Simplify: $\dfrac{7 + 20x - 3x^2}{2x^2 - 11x - 21}$

Solution

$$\frac{7 + 20x - 3x^2}{2x^2 - 11x - 21} = \frac{(7 - x)(1 + 3x)}{(x - 7)(2x + 3)} \qquad \text{• Factor.}$$

$$= \frac{-(x - 7)(1 + 3x)}{(x - 7)(2x + 3)} \qquad \text{• Use } (7 - x) = -(x - 7).$$

$$= \frac{-\cancel{(x - 7)}(1 + 3x)}{\cancel{(x - 7)}(2x + 3)}$$

$$= \frac{-(1 + 3x)}{2x + 3} = -\frac{3x + 1}{2x + 3}, \quad x \neq 7, x \neq -\frac{3}{2}$$

▶ **TRY EXERCISE 2, PAGE 62**

---

take note

A rational expression like $(x + 3)/3$ does not simplify to $x + 1$ because

$$\frac{x + 3}{3} = \frac{x}{3} + \frac{3}{3} = \frac{x}{3} + 1$$

Rational expressions can be simplified by dividing nonzero factors common to the numerator and the denominator, but not terms.

● OPERATIONS ON RATIONAL EXPRESSIONS

Arithmetic operations are defined on rational expressions just as they are on rational numbers.

Arithmetic Operations Defined on Rational Expressions

For all rational expressions $\dfrac{P}{Q}, \dfrac{R}{Q}$, and $\dfrac{R}{S}$ where $Q \neq 0$ and $S \neq 0$,

Addition	$\dfrac{P}{Q} + \dfrac{R}{Q} = \dfrac{P + R}{Q}$
Subtraction	$\dfrac{P}{Q} - \dfrac{R}{Q} = \dfrac{P - R}{Q}$
Multiplication	$\dfrac{P}{Q} \cdot \dfrac{R}{S} = \dfrac{PR}{QS}$
Division	$\dfrac{P}{Q} \div \dfrac{R}{S} = \dfrac{P}{Q} \cdot \dfrac{S}{R} = \dfrac{PS}{QR}, \quad R \neq 0$

Factoring and the equivalent expressions property of rational expressions are used in the multiplication and division of rational expressions.

Alternative to Example 2

1. Simplify:

$$\frac{12 + x - 6x^2}{6x^2 + 29x + 28} \cdot \frac{2x^2 + x - 21}{4x^2 - 9}$$

○ $-\dfrac{x - 3}{2x + 3}$

2. Simplify: $\dfrac{2x - 6}{6x^2 - 15x} \div \dfrac{4x^2 - 12x}{18x^3 - 45x^2}$

○ $\dfrac{3}{2}$

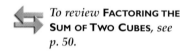

To review **FACTORING THE SUM OF TWO CUBES,** *see* p. 50.

EXAMPLE 2   Divide a Rational Expression

Simplify: $\dfrac{x^2 + 6x + 9}{x^3 + 27} \div \dfrac{x^2 + 7x + 12}{x^3 - 3x^2 + 9x}$

Solution

$\dfrac{x^2 + 6x + 9}{x^3 + 27} \div \dfrac{x^2 + 7x + 12}{x^3 - 3x^2 + 9x}$

$= \dfrac{(x + 3)^2}{(x + 3)(x^2 - 3x + 9)} \div \dfrac{(x + 4)(x + 3)}{x(x^2 - 3x + 9)}$ • Factor.

$= \dfrac{(x + 3)^2}{(x + 3)(x^2 - 3x + 9)} \cdot \dfrac{x(x^2 - 3x + 9)}{(x + 4)(x + 3)}$ • Multiply by the reciprocal.

$= \dfrac{\cancel{(x + 3)^2}\,x\cancel{(x^2 - 3x + 9)}}{\cancel{(x + 3)}\cancel{(x^2 - 3x + 9)}(x + 4)\cancel{(x + 3)}}$ • Simplify.

$= \dfrac{x}{x + 4}$

▶ **TRY EXERCISE 16, PAGE 63**

Addition of rational expressions with a **common denominator** is accomplished by writing the sum of the numerators over the common denominator. For example,

$$\frac{5x}{18} + \frac{x}{18} = \frac{5x + x}{18} = \frac{6x}{18} = \frac{x}{3}$$

If the rational expressions do not have a common denominator, then they can be written as equivalent rational expressions that have a common denominator by multiplying the numerator and denominator of each of the rational expressions by the required polynomials. The following procedure can be used to determine the least common denominator (LCD) of rational expressions. It is similar to the process used to find the LCD of rational numbers.

● DETERMINING THE **LCD** OF **RATIONAL EXPRESSIONS**

1. Factor each denominator completely and express repeated factors using exponential notation.

2. Identify the largest power of each factor in any single factorization. The LCD is the product of each factor raised to its largest power.

For example,

$$\frac{1}{x + 3} \qquad \text{and} \qquad \frac{5}{2x - 1}$$

have an LCD of $(x + 3)(2x - 1)$. The rational expressions

$$\frac{5x}{(x + 5)(x - 7)^3} \quad \text{and} \quad \frac{7}{x(x + 5)^2(x - 7)}$$

have an LCD of $x(x + 5)^2(x - 7)^3$.

Alternative to Example 3

1. Simplify: $\dfrac{2x}{x - 3} - \dfrac{3x}{x - 5}$

● $\dfrac{-x^2 - x}{(x - 3)(x - 5)}$

2. Simplify: $\dfrac{3x - 4}{4x + 1} + \dfrac{3x + 6}{4x^2 + 9x + 2}$

● $\dfrac{3x - 1}{4x + 1}$

EXAMPLE 3   Add and Subtract Rational Expressions

Perform the indicated operation and then simplify if possible.

a. $\dfrac{5x}{48} + \dfrac{x}{15}$ **b.** $\dfrac{x}{x^2 - 4} - \dfrac{2x - 1}{x^2 - 3x - 10}$

Solution

a. Determine the prime factorization of the denominators.

$$48 = 2^4 \cdot 3 \quad \text{and} \quad 15 = 3 \cdot 5$$

The desired common denominator is the product of each of the prime factors raised to its largest power. Thus the common denominator is $2^4 \cdot 3 \cdot 5 = 240$. Write each rational expression as an equivalent rational expression with a denominator of 240.

$$\frac{5x}{48} + \frac{x}{15} = \frac{5x \cdot 5}{48 \cdot 5} + \frac{x \cdot 16}{15 \cdot 16} = \frac{25x}{240} + \frac{16x}{240} = \frac{41x}{240}$$

b. Factor each denominator to determine the LCD of the rational expressions.

$$x^2 - 4 = (x + 2)(x - 2)$$
$$x^2 - 3x - 10 = (x + 2)(x - 5)$$

The LCD is $(x + 2)(x - 2)(x - 5)$. Forming equivalent rational expressions that have the LCD, we have

$$\frac{x}{x^2 - 4} - \frac{2x - 1}{x^2 - 3x - 10}$$

$$= \frac{x(x - 5)}{(x + 2)(x - 2)(x - 5)} - \frac{(2x - 1)(x - 2)}{(x + 2)(x - 5)(x - 2)}$$

$$= \frac{x^2 - 5x - (2x^2 - 5x + 2)}{(x + 2)(x - 2)(x - 5)} = \frac{x^2 - 5x - 2x^2 + 5x - 2}{(x + 2)(x - 2)(x - 5)}$$

$$= \frac{-x^2 - 2}{(x + 2)(x - 2)(x - 5)} = -\frac{x^2 + 2}{(x + 2)(x - 2)(x - 5)}$$

▶ **TRY EXERCISE 30, PAGE 63**

● **COMPLEX FRACTIONS**

A **complex fraction** is a fraction whose numerator or denominator contains one or more fractions. Complex fractions can be simplified by using one of the following two methods.

Methods for Simplifying Complex Fractions

Method 1: Multiply by 1 in the form $\dfrac{LCD}{LCD}$.

1. Determine the LCD of all the fractions in the complex fraction.

2. Multiply both the numerator and the denominator of the complex fraction by the LCD.

3. If possible, simplify the resulting rational expression.

Method 2: Multiply the numerator by the reciprocal of the denominator.

1. Simplify the numerator to a single fraction and the denominator to a single fraction.

2. Using the definition for dividing fractions, multiply the numerator by the reciprocal of the denominator.

3. If possible, simplify the resulting rational expression.

Alternative to Example 4

1. Simplify: $\dfrac{\dfrac{x}{3x-2}}{\dfrac{x}{9x^2-4}}$

⊚ $3x + 2$

2. Simplify: $\dfrac{x - 1 + \dfrac{2}{x-4}}{x + 3 + \dfrac{6}{x-4}}$

⊚ $\dfrac{x-2}{x+2}$

EXAMPLE 4 Simplify Complex Fractions

Simplify: $\dfrac{\dfrac{2}{x-2}+\dfrac{1}{x}}{\dfrac{3x}{x-5}-\dfrac{2}{x-5}}$

Solution

First simplify the numerator to a single fraction and then simplify the denominator to a single fraction.

$$\dfrac{\dfrac{2}{x-2}+\dfrac{1}{x}}{\dfrac{3x}{x-5}-\dfrac{2}{x-5}} = \dfrac{\dfrac{2\cdot x}{(x-2)\cdot x}+\dfrac{1\cdot(x-2)}{x\cdot(x-2)}}{\dfrac{3x-2}{x-5}}$$

• Simplify numerator and denominator.

$$= \dfrac{\dfrac{2x+(x-2)}{x(x-2)}}{\dfrac{3x-2}{x-5}} = \dfrac{\dfrac{3x-2}{x(x-2)}}{\dfrac{3x-2}{x-5}}$$

$$= \dfrac{\cancel{3x-2}}{x(x-2)}\cdot\dfrac{x-5}{\cancel{3x-2}}$$

• Multiply the numerator by the reciprocal of the denominator.

$$= \dfrac{x-5}{x(x-2)}$$

▶ **TRY EXERCISE 42, PAGE 63**

Alternative to Example 5

1. Simplify: $\dfrac{x^{-1}}{y^{-1}} + \dfrac{y^{-1}}{x^{-1}}$

$\bullet \dfrac{x^2 + y^2}{xy}$

2. Simplify: $\dfrac{x^{-1} + y^{-1}}{x^{-1} - y^{-1}}$

$\bullet \dfrac{y + x}{y - x}$

---

take note

It is a mistake to write

$$\dfrac{c^{-1}}{a^{-1} + b^{-1}} \quad \text{as} \quad \dfrac{a + b}{c}$$

because a^{-1} and b^{-1} are terms and cannot be treated as factors.

EXAMPLE 5   Simplify a Fraction

Simplify the fraction $\dfrac{c^{-1}}{a^{-1} + b^{-1}}$.

Solution

The fraction written without negative exponents becomes

$$\dfrac{c^{-1}}{a^{-1} + b^{-1}} = \dfrac{\dfrac{1}{c}}{\dfrac{1}{a} + \dfrac{1}{b}}$$

• Using $x^{-n} = \dfrac{1}{x^n}$

$$= \dfrac{\dfrac{1}{c} \cdot abc}{\left(\dfrac{1}{a} + \dfrac{1}{b}\right)abc}$$

• Multiply the numerator and the denominator by abc, which is the LCD of the fraction in the numerator and the fraction in the denominator.

$$= \dfrac{ab}{bc + ac}$$

▶ **TRY EXERCISE 60, PAGE 64**

● **APPLICATION OF RATIONAL EXPRESSIONS**

EXAMPLE 6   Solve an Application

The *average speed* for a round trip is given by the complex fraction

$$\dfrac{2}{\dfrac{1}{v_1} + \dfrac{1}{v_2}}$$

where v_1 is the average speed on the way to your destination and v_2 is the average speed on your return trip. Find the average speed for a round trip if $v_1 = 50$ mph and $v_2 = 40$ mph.

Solution

Evaluate the complex fraction with $v_1 = 50$ and $v_2 = 40$.

$$\dfrac{2}{\dfrac{1}{v_1} + \dfrac{1}{v_2}} = \dfrac{2}{\dfrac{1}{50} + \dfrac{1}{40}} = \dfrac{2}{\dfrac{1 \cdot 4}{50 \cdot 4} + \dfrac{1 \cdot 5}{40 \cdot 5}}$$

• Substitute and simplify the denominator.

$$= \dfrac{2}{\dfrac{4}{200} + \dfrac{5}{200}} = \dfrac{2}{\dfrac{9}{200}}$$

$$= 2 \cdot \dfrac{200}{9} = \dfrac{400}{9} = 44\dfrac{4}{9}$$

The average speed for the round trip is $44\dfrac{4}{9}$ mph.

▶ **TRY EXERCISE 64, PAGE 64**

Alternative to Example 6

The total resistance R in an electric circuit consisting of three resistors in parallel is given by

$$R = \dfrac{1}{\dfrac{1}{R_1} + \dfrac{1}{R_2} + \dfrac{1}{R_3}}$$

Find the total resistance when $R_1 = 2$ ohms, $R_2 = 4$ ohms, and $R_3 = 8$ ohms.

$\bullet \dfrac{8}{7}$ ohms

❓ QUESTION In Example 6, why is the speed for the round trip *not* the average of v_1 and v_2?

👥✎ TOPICS FOR DISCUSSION

1. Discuss the meaning of the phrase *rational expression*. Is a rational expression the same as a fraction? If not, give some examples of fractions that are not rational expressions.

2. What is the domain of a rational expression?

3. Explain why the following is *not* correct.

$$\frac{2x^2 + 5}{x^2} = 2 + 5 = 7$$

4. Consider the rational expression $\dfrac{x^2 - 3x - 10}{x^2 + x - 30}$. By simplifying this expression, we have

$$\frac{x^2 - 3x - 10}{x^2 + x - 30} = \frac{(x - 5)(x + 2)}{(x - 5)(x + 6)} = \frac{x + 2}{x + 6}$$

Does this really mean that $\dfrac{x^2 - 3x - 10}{x^2 + x - 30} = \dfrac{x + 2}{x + 6}$ for every value of x? If not, for what values of x are the two expressions equal?

❓ ANSWER Because you were traveling slower on the return trip, the return trip took longer than the time spent going to your destination. More time was spent traveling at the slower speed. Thus the average speed is less than the average of v_1 and v_2.

EXERCISE SET P.5   —*Suggested Assignment: Exercises 1–69, odd; 71–84, all.*

In Exercises 1 to 10, simplify each rational expression.

1. $\dfrac{x^2 - x - 20}{3x - 15} \cdot \dfrac{x + 4}{3}$

▶ 2. $\dfrac{2x^2 - 5x - 12}{2x^2 + 5x + 3} \cdot \dfrac{x - 4}{x + 1}$

3. $\dfrac{x^3 - 9x}{x^3 + x^2 - 6x} \cdot \dfrac{x - 3}{x - 2}$

4. $\dfrac{x^3 + 125}{2x^3 - 50x} \cdot \dfrac{x^2 - 5x + 25}{2x(x - 5)}$

5. $\dfrac{a^3 + 8}{a^2 - 4} \cdot \dfrac{a^2 - 2a + 4}{a - 2}$

6. $\dfrac{y^3 - 27}{-y^2 + 11y - 24} \cdot \dfrac{y^2 + 3y + 9}{y - 8}$

7. $\dfrac{x^2 + 3x - 40}{-x^2 + 3x + 10} \cdot \dfrac{x + 8}{x + 2}$

8. $\dfrac{2x^3 - 6x^2 + 5x - 15}{9 - x^2} \cdot \dfrac{2x^2 + 5}{x + 3}$

9. $\dfrac{4y^3 - 8y^2 + 7y - 14}{\dfrac{-y^2 - 5y + 14}{4y^2 + 7}}$ $\dfrac{}{y + 7}$

10. $\dfrac{x^3 - x^2 + x}{x^3 + 1} \cdot \dfrac{x}{x + 1}$

In Exercises 11 to 40, simplify each expression.

11. $\left(-\dfrac{4a}{3b^2}\right)\left(\dfrac{6b}{a^4}\right) \cdot \dfrac{8}{a^3 b}$

12. $\left(\dfrac{12x^2 y}{5z^4}\right)\left(-\dfrac{25x^2 z^3}{15y^2}\right) \cdot \dfrac{4x^4}{yz}$

13. $\left(\dfrac{6p^2}{5q^2}\right)^{-1}\left(\dfrac{2p}{3q^2}\right)^2 \cdot \dfrac{10}{27q^2}$

14. $\left(\dfrac{4r^2 s}{3t^3}\right)^{-1}\left(\dfrac{6rs^3}{5t^2}\right) \cdot \dfrac{9ts^2}{10r}$

15. $\dfrac{x^2 + x}{2x + 3} \cdot \dfrac{3x^2 + 19x + 28}{x^2 + 5x + 4} \cdot \dfrac{x(3x + 7)}{2x + 3}$

▶ **16.** $\dfrac{x^2-16}{x^2+7x+12} \cdot \dfrac{x^2-4x-21}{x^2-4x}$ $\dfrac{x-7}{x}$

17. $\dfrac{3x-15}{2x^2-50} \cdot \dfrac{2x^2+16x+30}{6x+9}$ $\dfrac{x+3}{2x+3}$

18. $\dfrac{y^3-8}{y^2+y-6} \cdot \dfrac{y^2+3y}{y^3+2y^2+4y}$ 1

19. $\dfrac{12y^2+28y+15}{6y^2+35y+25} \div \dfrac{2y^2-y-3}{3y^2+11y-20}$ $\dfrac{(2y+3)(3y-4)}{(2y-3)(y+1)}$

20. $\dfrac{z^2-81}{z^2-16} \div \dfrac{z^2-z-20}{z^2+5z-36}$ $\dfrac{(z-9)(z+9)(z+9)}{(z+4)(z-5)(z+4)}$

21. $\dfrac{a^2+9}{a^2-64} \div \dfrac{a^3-3a^2+9a-27}{a^2+5a-24}$ $\dfrac{1}{a-8}$

22. $\dfrac{6x^2+13xy+6y^2}{4x^2-9y^2} \div \dfrac{3x^2-xy-2y^2}{2x^2+xy-3y^2}$ $\dfrac{2x+3y}{2x-3y}$

23. $\dfrac{p+5}{r} + \dfrac{2p-7}{r}$ $\dfrac{3p-2}{r}$ **24.** $\dfrac{2s+5t}{4t} + \dfrac{-2s+3t}{4t}$ 2

25. $\dfrac{x}{x-5} + \dfrac{7x}{x+3}$ $\dfrac{8x(x-4)}{(x-5)(x+3)}$ **26.** $\dfrac{2x}{3x+1} + \dfrac{5x}{x-7}$ $\dfrac{x(17x-9)}{(3x+1)(x-7)}$

27. $\dfrac{5y-7}{y+4} - \dfrac{2y-3}{y+4}$ $\dfrac{3y-4}{y+4}$ **28.** $\dfrac{6x-5}{x-3} - \dfrac{3x-8}{x-3}$ $\dfrac{3(x+1)}{x-3}$

29. $\dfrac{4z}{2z-3} + \dfrac{5z}{z-5}$ $\dfrac{7z(2z-5)}{(2z-3)(z-5)}$ ▶ **30.** $\dfrac{3y-1}{3y+1} - \dfrac{2y-5}{y-3}$ $\dfrac{-3y^2+3y+8}{(3y+1)(y-3)}$

31. $\dfrac{x}{x^2-9} - \dfrac{3x-1}{x^2+7x+12}$ $\dfrac{-2x^2+14x-3}{(x-3)(x+3)(x+4)}$

32. $\dfrac{m-n}{m^2-mn-6n^2} + \dfrac{3m-5n}{m^2+mn-2n^2}$ $\dfrac{4(m-2n)^2}{(m+2n)(m-3n)(m-n)}$

33. $\dfrac{1}{x} + \dfrac{2}{3x-1} \cdot \dfrac{3x^2+11x-4}{x-5}$ $\dfrac{(2x-1)(x+5)}{x(x-5)}$

34. $\dfrac{2}{y} - \dfrac{3}{y+1} \cdot \dfrac{y^2-1}{y+4}$ $\dfrac{-3y^2+5y+8}{y(y+4)}$

35. $\dfrac{q+1}{q-3} - \dfrac{2q}{q-3} \div \dfrac{q+5}{q-3}$ $\dfrac{-q^2+12q+5}{(q-3)(q+5)}$

36. $\dfrac{p}{p+5} + \dfrac{p}{p-4} \div \dfrac{p+2}{p^2-p-12}$ $\dfrac{p(p^2+9p+17)}{(p+5)(p+2)}$

37. $\dfrac{1}{x^2+7x+12} + \dfrac{1}{x^2-9} + \dfrac{1}{x^2-16}$ $\dfrac{3x^2-7x-13}{(x+3)(x+4)(x-3)(x-4)}$

38. $\dfrac{2}{a^2-3a+2} + \dfrac{3}{a^2-1} - \dfrac{5}{a^2+3a-10}$ $\dfrac{3(7a-5)}{(a-1)(a-2)(a+1)(a+5)}$

39. $\left(1+\dfrac{2}{x}\right)\left(3-\dfrac{1}{x}\right)$ $\dfrac{(x+2)(3x-1)}{x^2}$ **40.** $\left(4-\dfrac{1}{z}\right)\left(4+\dfrac{2}{z}\right)$ $\dfrac{2(4z-1)(2z+1)}{z^2}$

In Exercises 41 to 58, simplify each complex fraction.

41. $\dfrac{4+\dfrac{1}{x}}{1-\dfrac{1}{x}}$ $\dfrac{4x+1}{x-1}$ ▶ **42.** $\dfrac{3-\dfrac{2}{a}}{5+\dfrac{3}{a}}$ $\dfrac{3a-2}{5a+3}$ **43.** $\dfrac{\dfrac{x}{y}-2}{y-x}$ $\dfrac{x-2y}{y(y-x)}$

44. $\dfrac{3+\dfrac{2}{x-3}}{4+\dfrac{1}{2+\dfrac{1}{x}}}$ $\dfrac{(3x-7)(2x+1)}{(x-3)(9x+4)}$ **45.** $\dfrac{5-\dfrac{1}{x+2}}{1+\dfrac{3}{1+\dfrac{3}{x}}}$ $\dfrac{(5x+9)(x+3)}{(x+2)(4x+3)}$ **46.** $\dfrac{\dfrac{1}{(x+h)^2}-1}{h}$ $\dfrac{1-x^2-2xh-h^2}{h(x+h)^2}$

47. $\dfrac{1+\dfrac{1}{b-2}}{1-\dfrac{1}{b+3}}$ $\dfrac{(b+3)(b-1)}{(b-2)(b+2)}$ **48.** $r - \dfrac{r}{r+\dfrac{1}{3}}$ $\dfrac{r(3r-2)}{3r+1}$

49. $\dfrac{1-\dfrac{1}{x^2}}{1+\dfrac{1}{x}}$ $\dfrac{x-1}{x}$ **50.** $\dfrac{1}{\dfrac{1}{a}+\dfrac{1}{b}}$ $\dfrac{ab}{b+a}$

51. $2 - \dfrac{m}{1-\dfrac{1-m}{-m}}$ $2-m^2$ **52.** $\dfrac{\dfrac{x+h+1}{x+h}-\dfrac{x}{x+1}}{h}$ $\dfrac{2x+h+1}{h(x+h)(x+1)}$

53. $\dfrac{\dfrac{1}{x}-\dfrac{x-4}{x+1}}{\dfrac{x}{x+1}}$ $\dfrac{-x^2+5x+1}{x^2}$ **54.** $\dfrac{\dfrac{2}{y}-\dfrac{3y-2}{y-1}}{\dfrac{y}{y-1}}$ $\dfrac{-3y^2+4y-2}{y^2}$

55. $\dfrac{\dfrac{1}{x+3}-\dfrac{2}{x-1}}{\dfrac{x}{x-1}+\dfrac{3}{x+3}}$ $\dfrac{-x-7}{x^2+6x-3}$ **56.** $\dfrac{\dfrac{x+2}{x^2-1}+\dfrac{1}{x+1}}{\dfrac{x}{2x^2-x-1}+\dfrac{1}{x-1}}$ $\dfrac{(2x+1)^2}{(3x+1)(x+1)}$

57. $\dfrac{\dfrac{x^2+3x-10}{x^2+x-6}}{\dfrac{x^2-x-30}{2x^2-15x+18}}$ $\dfrac{2x-3}{x+3}$ **58.** $\dfrac{\dfrac{2y^2+11y+15}{y^2-4y-21}}{\dfrac{6y^2+11y-10}{3y^2-23y+14}}$ 1

In Exercises 59 to 62, simplify each algebraic fraction. Write all answers with positive exponents.

59. $\dfrac{a^{-1} + b^{-1}}{a - b} \cdot \dfrac{a + b}{ab(a - b)}$

▶ **60.** $\dfrac{e^{-2} - f^{-1}}{ef} \cdot \dfrac{f - e^2}{e^3 f^2}$

61. $\dfrac{a^{-1}b - ab^{-1}}{a^2 + b^2} \cdot \dfrac{(b - a)(b + a)}{ab(a^2 + b^2)}$

62. $(a + b^{-2})^{-1} \cdot \dfrac{b^2}{ab^2 + 1}$

63. AVERAGE SPEED According to Example 6, the average speed for a round trip in which the average speed on the way to your destination is v_1 and your average speed on your return is v_2 is given by the complex fraction

$$\dfrac{2}{\dfrac{1}{v_1} + \dfrac{1}{v_2}}$$

a. Find the average speed for a round trip by helicopter with $v_1 = 180$ mph and $v_2 = 110$ mph. ≈136.55 mph

b. Simplify the complex fraction. $\dfrac{2v_1 v_2}{v_1 + v_2}$

▶ **64. RELATIVITY THEORY** Using Einstein's Theory of Relativity, the "sum" of the two speeds v_1 and v_2 is given by the complex fraction

$$\dfrac{v_1 + v_2}{1 + \dfrac{v_1 v_2}{c^2}}$$

where c is the speed of light.

a. Evaluate this expression with $v_1 = 1.2 \times 10^8$ mph, $v_2 = 2.4 \times 10^8$ mph, and $c = 6.7 \times 10^8$ mph. ≈ 3.4 × 10⁸

b. Simplify the complex fraction. $\dfrac{c^2(v_1 + v_2)}{c^2 + v_1 v_2}$

65. 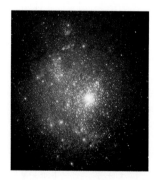 **DOPPLER SHIFT** The photograph at the right shows the central region of a galaxy named NGC 1705, which is approximately 17 million light-years from Earth. The distance to this galaxy can be determined by measuring its red shift. (See the Chapter Opener on page 1.) The amount of this red shift z is given by

$$z = \dfrac{\lambda_O - \lambda_S}{\lambda_S}$$

where λ_O is the wavelength of light from the receding galaxy and λ_S is the wavelength of the same light on Earth. Find the red shift of a galaxy for a wavelength that normally measures 375.4×10^{-9} meters on Earth but measures 390.5×10^{-9} meters coming from the receding galaxy. Round to the nearest thousandth. 0.040

66. DOPPLER SHIFT Calculate the red shift (see Exercise 65) for a wavelength that normally measures 401.5×10^{-9} meters on Earth but measures 412.3×10^{-9} meters coming from the receding galaxy. Round to the nearest thousandth. 0.027

67. SPEED OF A GALAXY The relative speed v, in kilometers per second, at which a galaxy is receding from Earth can be determined from

$$v = c\left[\dfrac{(z + 1)^2 - 1}{(z + 1)^2 + 1}\right]$$

where c is the speed of light (3×10^5 kilometers per second) and z is the red shift (see Exercise 65) of the galaxy. Find the relative speed of a receding galaxy whose red shift is 0.032. Round to the nearest kilometer per second. 9446 km/s

68. SPEED OF A GALAXY Find the relative speed (see Exercise 67) of a receding galaxy whose red shift is 0.041. Round to the nearest kilometer per second. 12,048 km/s

69. Find the rational expression in simplest form that represents the sum of the reciprocals of the consecutive integers x and $x + 1$. $\dfrac{2x + 1}{x(x + 1)}$

70. Find the rational expression in simplest form that represents the positive difference between the reciprocals of the consecutive even integers x and $x + 2$. $\dfrac{2}{x(x + 2)}$

71. Find the rational expression in simplest form that represents the sum of the reciprocals of the consecutive even integers $x - 2$, x, and $x + 2$. $\dfrac{3x^2 - 4}{x(x - 2)(x + 2)}$

72. Find the rational expression in simplest form that represents the sum of the reciprocals of the squares of the consecutive even integers $x - 2$, x, and $x + 2$. $\dfrac{3x^4 + 16}{x^2(x - 2)^2(x + 2)^2}$

CONNECTING CONCEPTS

In Exercises 73 to 76, simplify each algebraic fraction.

73. $\dfrac{(x + 5) - x(x + 5)^{-1}}{x + 5} \quad \dfrac{x^2 + 9x + 25}{(x + 5)^2}$

74. $\dfrac{(y + 2) + y^2(y + 2)^{-1}}{y + 2} \quad \dfrac{2(y^2 + 2y + 2)}{(y + 2)^2}$

75. $\dfrac{x^{-1} - 4y}{(x^{-1} - 2y)(x^{-1} + 2y)} \quad \dfrac{x(1 - 4xy)}{(1 - 2xy)(1 + 2xy)}$

76. $\dfrac{x + y}{x - y} \cdot \dfrac{x^{-1} - y^{-1}}{x^{-1} + y^{-1}} \quad -1$

77. FINANCE The **present value** of an ordinary annuity is given by

$$R\left[\dfrac{1-\dfrac{1}{(1+i)^n}}{i}\right]$$

where n is the number of payments of R dollars invested at an interest rate of i per conversion period. Simplify the complex fraction. $R\left[\dfrac{(1+i)^n-1}{i(1+i)^n}\right]$

78. ELECTRICITY The total resistance of the three resistances R_1, R_2, and R_3 in parallel is given by

$$\dfrac{1}{\dfrac{1}{R_1}+\dfrac{1}{R_2}+\dfrac{1}{R_3}}$$

Simplify the complex fraction.
$\dfrac{R_1R_2R_3}{R_2R_3+R_1R_3+R_1R_2}$

PREPARE FOR SECTION P.6

In Exercises 79 to 84, simplify the expression.

79. $(2-3x)(4-5x)$ [P.3]
$15x^2-22x+8$

80. $(2-5x)^2$ [P.3]
$25x^2-20x+4$

81. $\sqrt{96}$ [P.2]
$4\sqrt{6}$

82. $\left(2+3\sqrt{5}\right)\left(3-4\sqrt{5}\right)$
[P.2] $-54+\sqrt{5}$

83. $\dfrac{5+\sqrt{2}}{3-\sqrt{2}}$ [P.2] $\dfrac{17+8\sqrt{2}}{7}$

84. Which of the following polynomials, if any, does not factor over the integers? [P.4] b

a. $81-x^2$ b. $9+z^2$

PROJECTS

1. CONTINUED FRACTIONS The complex fraction shown at the right is called a **continued fraction.** The three dots in $\dfrac{1}{1+\cdots}$ indicate that the pattern continues in the same manner. A **convergent** of a complex fraction is an approximation of the continued fraction that is found by stopping the process at some point.

$$\cfrac{1}{1+\cfrac{1}{1+\cfrac{1}{1+\cfrac{1}{1+\cdots}}}}$$

a. Calculate the convergent $C_2=\cfrac{1}{1+\cfrac{1}{1+1}}$.

b. Calculate the convergent $C_3=\cfrac{1}{1+\cfrac{1}{1+\cfrac{1}{1+1}}}$.

c. Calculate the convergent $C_5=\cfrac{1}{1+\cfrac{1}{1+\cfrac{1}{1+\cfrac{1}{1+\cfrac{1}{1+1}}}}}$.

d. Show that $C_5\approx\dfrac{-1+\sqrt{5}}{2}$. Using some techniques from more advanced math courses, it can be shown that as n increases, C_n becomes closer and closer to $\dfrac{-1+\sqrt{5}}{2}$.

2. REPRESENTATION OF π There are a few continued-fraction representations for π. Find two of these representations. Compute the value of π accurate to four decimal places using a convergent from each of the continued fractions you found.

COMPLEX NUMBERS

● **INTRODUCTION TO COMPLEX NUMBERS**

Recall that $\sqrt{9} = 3$ because $3^2 = 9$. Now consider the expression $\sqrt{-9}$. To find $\sqrt{-9}$, we need to find a number c such that $c^2 = -9$. However, the square of any real number c (except zero) is a *positive* number. Consequently, we must expand our concept of number to include numbers whose squares are negative numbers.

Around the 17th century, a new number, called an *imaginary number*, was defined so that a negative number would have a square root. The letter i was chosen to represent the number whose square is -1.

MATH MATTERS

It may seem strange to just invent new numbers, but that is how mathematics evolves. For instance, negative numbers were not an accepted part of mathematics until well into the 13th century. In fact, these numbers often were referred to as "fictitious numbers."

In the 17th century, Rene Descartes called square roots of negative numbers "imaginary numbers," an unfortunate choice of words, and started using the letter i to denote these numbers. These numbers were subjected to the same skepticism as negative numbers.

It is important to understand that these numbers are not *imaginary* in the dictionary sense of the word. It is similar to the situation of negative numbers being called fictitious.

If you think of a number line, then the numbers to the right of zero are positive numbers and the numbers to the left of zero are negative numbers. One way to think of an imaginary number is to visualize it as *up* or *down* from zero. See the Project on page 73 for more information on this topic.

Definition of i
The number i, called the **imaginary unit,** is the number such that $i^2 = -1$.

The principal square root of a negative number is defined in terms of i.

Principal Square Root of a Negative Number
If a is a positive real number, then $\sqrt{-a} = i\sqrt{a}$. The number $i\sqrt{a}$ is called an **imaginary number.**

Here are some examples of imaginary numbers.

$$\sqrt{-36} = i\sqrt{36} = 6i \qquad \sqrt{-18} = i\sqrt{18} = 3i\sqrt{2}$$
$$\sqrt{-23} = i\sqrt{23} \qquad \sqrt{-1} = i\sqrt{1} = i$$

It is customary to write i in front of a radical sign, as we did for $i\sqrt{23}$, to avoid confusing $\sqrt{a}\,i$ with $\sqrt{ai}$.

Complex Numbers
A **complex number** is a number of the form $a + bi$, where a and b are real numbers and $i = \sqrt{-1}$. The number a is the **real part** of $a + bi$, and b is the **imaginary part.**

Here are some examples of complex numbers.

$-3 + 5i$	• Real part: -3; imaginary part: 5
$2 - 6i$	• Real part: 2; imaginary part: -6
5	• Real part: 5; imaginary part: 0
$7i$	• Real part: 0; imaginary part: 7

Note from these examples that a real number is a complex number whose imaginary part is zero and that an imaginary number is a complex number whose real part is zero.

MATH MATTERS

The imaginary unit *i* is important in the field of electrical engineering. However, because the letter *i* is used by engineers as the symbol for electric current, these engineers use *j* for the complex unit.

❓ QUESTION   What is the real part and the imaginary part of $3 - 5i$?

Note from the following diagram that the real numbers are a subset of the complex numbers, and imaginary numbers are a subset of the complex numbers. The real numbers and imaginary numbers are disjoint sets.

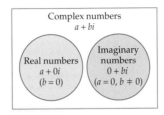

Example 1 illustrates writing a complex number in the standard form $a + bi$.

Alternative to Example 1
Write $4 - \sqrt{-72}$ in the form $a + bi$.
● $4 - 6i\sqrt{2}$

EXAMPLE 1   Write a Complex Number in Standard Form

Write $7 + \sqrt{-45}$ in the form $a + bi$.

Solution

$$7 + \sqrt{-45} = 7 + i\sqrt{45}$$
$$= 7 + i\sqrt{9} \cdot \sqrt{5}$$
$$= 7 + 3i\sqrt{5}$$

▶ **TRY EXERCISE 8, PAGE 71**

● **ADDITION AND SUBTRACTION OF COMPLEX NUMBERS**

All the standard arithmetic operations that are applied to real numbers can be applied to complex numbers.

Definition of Addition and Subtraction of Complex Numbers
If $a + bi$ and $c + di$ are complex numbers, then
Addition $(a + bi) + (c + di) = (a + c) + (b + d)i$
Subtraction $(a + bi) - (c + di) = (a - c) + (b - d)i$

Basically, these rules say that to add two complex numbers, add the real parts and add the imaginary parts. To subtract two complex numbers, subtract the real parts and subtract the imaginary parts.

❓ ANSWER   Real part: 3; imaginary part: -5

Alternative to Example 2
Simplify.
a. $(-3 + 5i) + (-7 - 5i)$
b. $(6 - 3i) - (6 - 4i)$
● **a.** -10
● **b.** i

EXAMPLE 2   **Add or Subtract Complex Numbers**

Simplify.

a. $(7 - 2i) + (-2 + 4i)$ **b.** $(-9 + 4i) - (2 - 6i)$

Solution

a. $(7 - 2i) + (-2 + 4i) = (7 + (-2)) + (-2 + 4)i = 5 + 2i$

b. $(-9 + 4i) - (2 - 6i) = (-9 - 2) + (4 - (-6))i = -11 + 10i$

▶ **TRY EXERCISE 18, PAGE 72**

● **MULTIPLICATION OF COMPLEX NUMBERS**

When multiplying complex numbers, the term i^2 is frequently a part of the product. Recall that $i^2 = -1$. Therefore,

$$3i(5i) = 15i^2 = 15(-1) = -15$$
$$-2i(6i) = -12i^2 = -12(-1) = 12$$
$$4i(3 - 2i) = 12i - 8i^2 = 12i - 8(-1) = 8 + 12i$$

When multiplying square roots of negative numbers, first rewrite the radical expressions using i. For instance,

$$\sqrt{-6} \cdot \sqrt{-24} = i\sqrt{6} \cdot i\sqrt{24}$$
$$= i^2\sqrt{144} = -1 \cdot 12$$
$$= -12$$

● $\sqrt{-6} = i\sqrt{6}, \sqrt{-24} = i\sqrt{24}$

take note

Recall that the definition of the product of radical expressions required that the radicand be a positive number. Therefore, when multiplying expressions containing negative radicands, we must first rewrite the expression using i and a positive radicand.

Note from this example that it would have been incorrect to multiply the radicands of the two radical expressions. To illustrate:

$$\sqrt{-6} \cdot \sqrt{-24} \neq \sqrt{(-6)(-24)}$$

❓ **QUESTION** What is the product of $\sqrt{-2}$ and $\sqrt{-8}$?

To multiply two complex numbers, we use the following definition.

Definition of Multiplication of Complex Numbers

If $a + bi$ and $c + di$ are complex numbers, then

$$(a + bi)(c + di) = (ac - bd) + (ad + bc)i$$

Because every complex number can be written as a sum of two terms, it is natural to perform multiplication on complex numbers in a manner consistent

---

❓ **ANSWER** $\sqrt{-2} \cdot \sqrt{-8} = i\sqrt{2} \cdot i\sqrt{8} = i^2\sqrt{16} = -1 \cdot 4 = -4$

with the operation defined on binomials and the definition $i^2 = -1$. By using this analogy, you can multiply complex numbers without memorizing the definition.

Alternative to Example 3
Simplify.
a. $(5 + 2i)(2 - 3i)$
b. $(1 + 4\sqrt{-5})(2 - 3\sqrt{-5})$
● **a.** $16 - 11i$
● **b.** $62 + 5i\sqrt{5}$

EXAMPLE 3	**Multiply Complex Numbers**

Simplify.   **a.** $(3 - 4i)(2 + 5i)$ **b.** $\left(2 + \sqrt{-3}\right)\left(4 - 5\sqrt{-3}\right)$

Solution

a.
$$(3 - 4i)(2 + 5i) = 6 + 15i - 8i - 20i^2$$
$$= 6 + 15i - 8i - 20(-1)   \quad • \textbf{ Replace } i^2 \textbf{ by } -1.$$
$$= 6 + 15i - 8i + 20   \quad • \textbf{ Simplify.}$$
$$= 26 + 7i$$

b.
$$\left(2 + \sqrt{-3}\right)\left(4 - 5\sqrt{-3}\right) = \left(2 + i\sqrt{3}\right)\left(4 - 5i\sqrt{3}\right)$$
$$= 8 - 10i\sqrt{3} + 4i\sqrt{3} - 5i^2\sqrt{9}$$
$$= 8 - 10i\sqrt{3} + 4i\sqrt{3} - 5(-1)(3)$$
$$= 8 - 10i\sqrt{3} + 4i\sqrt{3} + 15 = 23 - 6i\sqrt{3}$$

▶ **TRY EXERCISE 34, PAGE 72**

▦ **INTEGRATING TECHNOLOGY**

Some graphing calculators can be used to perform operations on complex numbers. Here are some typical screens for a TI-83 Plus.

Press MODE. Use the down arrow key to highlight $a + bi$.

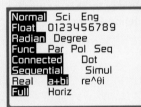

Press ENTER 2nd [QUIT].

Here are two examples of computations on complex numbers. To enter an i, use 2nd [i], which is above the decimal point key.

(3-4i)(2+5i)
                        26+7i
(16-11i)/(5+2i)
                        2-3i

● **DIVISION OF COMPLEX NUMBERS**

Recall that the number $\dfrac{3}{\sqrt{2}}$ is not in simplest form because there is a radical expression in the denominator. Similarly, $\dfrac{3}{i}$ is not in simplest form because $i = \sqrt{-1}$. To write this expression in simplest form, multiply the numerator and denominator by i.

$$\frac{3}{i} \cdot \frac{i}{i} = \frac{3i}{i^2} = \frac{3i}{-1} = -3i$$

Here is another example.

$$\frac{3 - 6i}{2i} = \frac{3 - 6i}{2i} \cdot \frac{i}{i} = \frac{3i - 6i^2}{2i^2} = \frac{3i - 6(-1)}{2(-1)}$$
$$= \frac{3i + 6}{-2} = -3 - \frac{3}{2}i$$

Recall that to simplify the quotient $\dfrac{2 + \sqrt{3}}{5 + 2\sqrt{3}}$, we multiply the numerator and denominator by the conjugate of $5 + 2\sqrt{3}$, which is $5 - 2\sqrt{3}$. In a similar manner, to find the quotient of two complex numbers, we multiply the numerator and denominator by the conjugate of the denominator.

The complex numbers $a + bi$ and $a - bi$ are called **complex conjugates** or **conjugates** of each other. The conjugate of the complex number z is denoted by $\bar{z}$. For instance,

$$\overline{2 + 5i} = 2 - 5i \quad \text{and} \quad \overline{3 - 4i} = 3 + 4i$$

Consider the product of a complex number and its conjugate. For instance,

$$(2 + 5i)(2 - 5i) = 4 - 10i + 10i - 25i^2$$
$$= 4 - 25(-1) = 4 + 25$$
$$= 29$$

Note that the product is a *real* number. This is always true.

INSTRUCTOR NOTE

Some students do not see that multiplying the numerator and denominator by the conjugate of the denominator is really division. It may help for these students to see that $\dfrac{8}{2} = 4$ and $2 \cdot 4 = 8$.

Similarly, $\dfrac{16 - 11i}{5 + 2i} = 2 - 3i$ and

$(5 + 2i)(2 - 3i) = 16 - 11i$.

> ### Product of Complex Conjugates
>
> The product of a complex number and its conjugate is a real number. That is, $(a + bi)(a - bi) = a^2 + b^2$.

For instance, $(5 + 3i)(5 - 3i) = 5^2 + 3^2 = 25 + 9 = 34$.

The next example shows how the quotient of two complex numbers is determined by using conjugates.

Alternative to Example 4

Simplify: $\dfrac{3 + 2i}{5 - i}$

• $\dfrac{1}{2} + \dfrac{1}{2}i$

EXAMPLE 4   **Divide Complex Numbers**

Simplify: $\dfrac{16 - 11i}{5 + 2i}$

Solution

$$\frac{16 - 11i}{5 + 2i} = \frac{16 - 11i}{5 + 2i} \cdot \frac{5 - 2i}{5 - 2i}$$

    • **Multiply numerator and denominator by the conjugates of the denominator.**

$$= \frac{80 - 32i - 55i + 22i^2}{5^2 + 2^2}$$

$$= \frac{80 - 32i - 55i + 22(-1)}{25 + 4}$$

$$= \frac{80 - 87i - 22}{29}$$

$$= \frac{58 - 87i}{29}$$

$$= \frac{29(2 - 3i)}{29} = 2 - 3i$$

▶ **TRY EXERCISE 48, PAGE 72**

• POWERS OF *i*

The following powers of *i* illustrate a pattern:

$$i^1 = i \qquad\qquad\qquad i^5 = i^4 \cdot i = 1 \cdot i = i$$
$$i^2 = -1 \qquad\qquad\quad i^6 = i^4 \cdot i^2 = 1(-1) = -1$$
$$i^3 = i^2 \cdot i = (-1)i = -i \qquad i^7 = i^4 \cdot i^3 = 1(-i) = -i$$
$$i^4 = i^2 \cdot i^2 = (-1)(-1) = 1 \qquad i^8 = (i^4)^2 = 1^2 = 1$$

Because $i^4 = 1$, $(i^4)^n = 1^n = 1$ for any integer n. Thus it is possible to evaluate powers of i by factoring out powers of i^4, as shown in the following:

$$i^{27} = (i^4)^6 \cdot i^3 = 1^6 \cdot i^3 = 1 \cdot (-i) = -i$$

The following theorem can be used to evaluate powers of i.

Powers of i

If n is a positive integer, then $i^n = i^r$, where r is the remainder of the division of n by 4.

Alternative to Example 5
Evaluate: i^{214}
● -1

EXAMPLE 5   **Evaluate a Power of i**

Evaluate: i^{153}

Solution

Use the powers of i theorem.

$$i^{153} = i^1 = i \qquad \text{• Remainder of 153 ÷ 4 is 1.}$$

▶ **TRY EXERCISE 60, PAGE 72**

 TOPICS FOR DISCUSSION

1. What is an imaginary number? What is a complex number?

2. How are the real numbers related to the complex numbers?

3. Is zero a complex number?

4. What is the conjugate of a complex number?

5. If a and b are real numbers and $ab = 0$, then $a = 0$ or $b = 0$. Is the same true for complex numbers? That is, if u and v are complex numbers and $uv = 0$, must one of the numbers be zero?

EXERCISE SET P.6   —*Suggested Assignment: Exercises 1–67, odd; 71, 75, 78.*

In Exercises 1 to 10, write the complex number in standard form.

1. $\sqrt{-81}$ $9i$

2. $\sqrt{-64}$ $8i$

3. $\sqrt{-98}$ $7i\sqrt{2}$

4. $\sqrt{-27}$ $3i\sqrt{3}$

5. $\sqrt{16} + \sqrt{-81}$ $4 + 9i$

6. $\sqrt{25} + \sqrt{-9}$ $5 + 3i$

7. $5 + \sqrt{-49}$ $5 + 7i$

▶ **8.** $6 - \sqrt{-1}$ $6 - i$

9. $8 - \sqrt{-18}$ $8 - 3i\sqrt{2}$

10. $11 + \sqrt{-48}$ $11 + 4i\sqrt{3}$

In Exercises 11 to 36, simplify and write the complex number in standard form.

11. $(5 + 2i) + (6 - 7i)$
$11 - 5i$

12. $(4 - 8i) + (5 + 3i)$
$9 - 5i$

13. $(-2 - 4i) - (5 - 8i)$
$-7 + 4i$

14. $(3 - 5i) - (8 - 2i)$
$-5 - 3i$

15. $(1 - 3i) + (7 - 2i)$
$8 - 5i$

16. $(2 - 6i) + (4 - 7i)$
$6 - 13i$

17. $(-3 - 5i) - (7 - 5i)$
-10

▶ **18.** $(5 - 3i) - (2 + 9i)$
$3 - 12i$

19. $8i - (2 - 8i)$
$-2 + 16i$

20. $3 - (4 - 5i)$
$-1 + 5i$

21. $5i \cdot 8i$
-40

22. $(-3i)(2i)$
6

23. $\sqrt{-50} \cdot \sqrt{-2}$
-10

24. $\sqrt{-12} \cdot \sqrt{-27}$
-18

25. $3(2 + 5i) - 2(3 - 2i)$
$19i$

26. $3i(2 + 5i) + 2i(3 - 4i)$
$-7 + 12i$

27. $(4 + 2i)(3 - 4i)$
$20 - 10i$

28. $(6 + 5i)(2 - 5i)$
$37 - 20i$

29. $(-3 - 4i)(2 + 7i)$
$22 - 29i$

30. $(-5 - i)(2 + 3i)$
$-7 - 17i$

31. $(4 - 5i)(4 + 5i)$
41

32. $(3 + 7i)(3 - 7i)$
58

33. $(3 + \sqrt{-4})(2 - \sqrt{-9})$
$12 - 5i$

▶ **34.** $(5 + 2\sqrt{-16})(1 - \sqrt{-25})$
$45 - 17i$

35. $(3 + 2\sqrt{-18})(2 + 2\sqrt{-50})$
$-114 + 42i\sqrt{2}$

36. $(5 - 3\sqrt{-48})(2 - 4\sqrt{-27})$
$-422 - 84i\sqrt{3}$

In Exercises 37 to 54, write each expression as a complex number in standard form.

37. $\dfrac{6}{i}$ $-6i$

38. $\dfrac{-8}{2i}$ $4i$

39. $\dfrac{6 + 3i}{i}$ $3 - 6i$

40. $\dfrac{4 - 8i}{4i}$ $-2 - i$

41. $\dfrac{1}{7 + 2i}$ $\dfrac{7}{53} - \dfrac{2}{53}i$

42. $\dfrac{5}{3 + 4i}$ $\dfrac{3}{5} - \dfrac{4}{5}i$

43. $\dfrac{2i}{1 + i}$ $1 + i$

44. $\dfrac{5i}{2 - 3i}$ $-\dfrac{15}{13} + \dfrac{10}{13}i$

45. $\dfrac{5 - i}{4 + 5i}$ $\dfrac{15}{41} - \dfrac{29}{41}i$

46. $\dfrac{4 + i}{3 + 5i}$ $\dfrac{1}{2} - \dfrac{1}{2}i$

47. $\dfrac{3 + 2i}{3 - 2i}$ $\dfrac{5}{13} + \dfrac{12}{13}i$

▶ **48.** $\dfrac{8 - i}{2 + 3i}$ $1 - 2i$

49. $\dfrac{-7 + 26i}{4 + 3i}$ $2 + 5i$

50. $\dfrac{-4 - 39i}{5 - 2i}$ $2 - 7i$

51. $(3 - 5i)^2$ $-16 - 30i$

52. $(2 + 4i)^2$ $-12 + 16i$

53. $(1 + 2i)^3$ $-11 - 2i$

54. $(2 - i)^3$ $2 - 11i$

In Exercises 55 to 62, evaluate the power of i.

55. i^{15} $-i$

56. i^{66} -1

57. $-i^{40}$ -1

58. $-i^{51}$ i

59. $\dfrac{1}{i^{25}}$ $-i$

▶ **60.** $\dfrac{1}{i^{83}}$ i

61. i^{-34} -1

62. i^{-52} 1

In Exercises 63 to 68, evaluate $\dfrac{-b + \sqrt{b^2 - 4ac}}{2a}$ **for the given values of** $a, b,$ **and** $c.$ **Write your answer as a complex number in standard form.**

63. $a = 3, b = -3, c = 3$ $\dfrac{1}{2} + \dfrac{\sqrt{3}}{2}i$

64. $a = 2, b = 4, c = 4$ $-1 + i$

65. $a = 2, b = 6, c = 6$ $-\dfrac{3}{2} + \dfrac{\sqrt{3}}{2}i$

66. $a = 2, b = 1, c = 3$ $-\dfrac{1}{4} + \dfrac{\sqrt{23}}{4}i$

67. $a = 4, b = -4, c = 2$ $\dfrac{1}{2} + \dfrac{1}{2}i$

68. $a = 3, b = -2, c = 4$ $\dfrac{1}{3} + \dfrac{\sqrt{11}}{3}i$

CONNECTING CONCEPTS

The property that the product of conjugates of the form $(a + bi)(a - bi)$ is equal to $a^2 + b^2$ can be used to factor the sum of two perfect squares over the set of complex numbers. For example, $x^2 + y^2 = (x + yi)(x - yi)$. In Exercises 69 to 74, factor the binomial over the set of complex numbers.

69. $x^2 + 16$ $(x + 4i)(x - 4i)$

70. $x^2 + 9$ $(x + 3i)(x - 3i)$

71. $z^2 + 25$ $(z + 5i)(z - 5i)$

72. $z^2 + 64$ $(z + 8i)(z - 8i)$

73. $4x^2 + 81$ $(2x + 9i)(2x - 9i)$

74. $9x^2 + 1$ $(3x + i)(3x - i)$

75. Show that if $x = 1 + 2i$, then $x^2 - 2x + 5 = 0$.

76. Show that if $x = 1 - 2i$, then $x^2 - 2x + 5 = 0$.

77. When we think of the cube root of 8, $\sqrt[3]{8}$, we normally mean the *real* cube root of 8 and write $\sqrt[3]{8} = 2$. However, there are two other cube roots of 8 that are complex numbers. Verify that $-1 + i\sqrt{3}$ and $-1 - i\sqrt{3}$ are cube roots of 8 by showing that $(-1 + i\sqrt{3})^3 = 8$ and $(-1 - i\sqrt{3})^3 = 8$.

78. It is possible to find the square root of a complex number.

Verify that $\sqrt{i} = \dfrac{\sqrt{2}}{2}(1 + i)$ by showing that

$$\left[\frac{\sqrt{2}}{2}(1 + i)\right]^2 = i.$$

79. Simplify $i + i^2 + i^3 + i^4 + \cdots + i^{28}$. 0

80. Simplify $i + i^2 + i^3 + i^4 + \cdots + i^{100}$. 0

———— *PROJECTS* ———— —*Answer graph to Exercises 1–8 is on page AA1.*

ARGAND DIAGRAM Just as we can graph a real number on a real number line, we can graph a complex number. This is accomplished by using one number line for the real part of the complex number and one number line for the imaginary part of the complex number. These two number lines are drawn perpendicular to each other and pass through their respective origins, as shown below.

The result is called the *complex plane* or an *Argand diagram* after Jean-Robert Argand (1768–1822), an accountant and amateur mathematician. Although he is given credit for this representation of complex numbers, Caspar Wessel (1745–1818) actually conceived the idea before Argand.

To graph the complex number $3 + 4i$, start at 3 on the real axis. Now move 4 units up (for positive numbers move up, for negative numbers move down) and place a dot at that point, as shown in the diagram. Graphs of several other complex numbers are also shown.

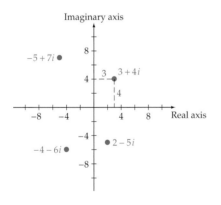

In Exercises 1 to 8, graph the complex number.

1. $2 + 5i$ **2.** $4 - 3i$ **3.** $-2 + 6i$ **4.** $-3 - 5i$

5. 4   **6.** $-2i$ **7.** $3i$ **8.** -5

The absolute value of a complex number is given by $|a + bi| = \sqrt{a^2 + b^2}$. In Exercises 9 to 12, find the absolute value of the complex number.

9. $2 + 5i$ **10.** $4 - 3i$ **11.** $-2 + 6i$ **12.** $-3 - 5i$

13. The additive inverse of $a + bi$ is $-a - bi$. Show that the absolute value of a complex number and the absolute value of its additive inverse are equal.

14. A *real* number and its additive inverse are the same distance from zero but on opposite sides of zero on a real number line. Describe the relationship between the graphs of a complex number and its additive inverse.

EXPLORING CONCEPTS WITH TECHNOLOGY

Can You Trust Your Calculator?

You may think that your calculator always produces correct results in a *predictable* manner. However, the following experiment may change your opinion.

First note that the algebraic expression

$$p + 3p(1 - p)$$

is equal to the expression

$$4p - 3p^2$$

Use a graphing calculator to evaluate both expressions with $p = 0.05$. You should find that both expressions equal 0.1925. So far we do not observe any unexpected results. Now replace p in each expression with the current value of that expression (0.1925 in this case). This is called *feedback* because we are feeding our outputs back into each expression as inputs. Each new evaluation is referred to as an *iteration*. This time each expression takes on the value 0.65883125. Still no surprises. Continue the feedback process. That is, replace p in each expression *with the current value* of that expression. Now each expression takes on the value 1.33314915207, as shown in the following table. The iterations were performed on a *TI-85* calculator.

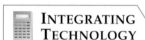

INTEGRATING TECHNOLOGY

To perform these iterations with a *TI* graphing calculator, first store 0.05 in p and then store $p + 3p(1 - p)$ in p as shown below.

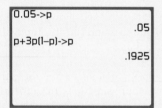

Each time you press ENTER , the expression $p + 3p(1 - p)$ will be evaluated with p equal to the previous result.

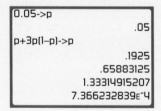

Iteration	$p + 3p(1 - p)$	$4p - 3p^2$
1	0.1925	0.1925
2	0.65883125	0.65883125
3	1.33314915207	1.33314915207

The following table shows that if we continue this feedback process on a calculator, the expressions $p + 3p(1 - p)$ and $4p - 3p^2$ will start to take on different values starting with the fourth iteration. By the 37th iteration, the values do not even agree to two decimal places.

Iteration	$p + 3p(1 - p)$	$4p - 3p^2$
4	7.366232839E-4	7.366232838E-4
5	0.002944865294	0.002944865294
6	0.011753444481	0.0117534448
7	0.046599347553	0.046599347547
20	1.12135618652	1.12135608405
30	0.947163304835	0.947033128433
37	0.285727963839	0.300943417861

1. Use a calculator to find the first 20 iterations of $p + 3p(1 - p)$ and $4p - 3p^2$, with the initial value of $p = 0.5$.

2. Write a report on chaos and fractals. Include information on the "butterfly effect." An excellent source is *Chaos and Fractals, New Frontiers of Science* by Heinz-Otto Peitgen, Hartmut Jurgens, and Dietmar Saupe (New York: Springer-Verlag, 1992).

3. Equations of the form $p_{n+1} = p_n + rp_n(1 - p_n)$ are called Verhulst population models. Write a report on Verhulst population models.

CHAPTER P SUMMARY

P.1 The Real Number System

- The following sets of numbers are used extensively in algebra:

  Integers $\{\ldots, -3, -2, -1, 0, 1, 2, 3, \ldots\}$

  Rational numbers {all terminating or repeating decimals}

  Irrational numbers {all nonterminating, nonrepeating decimals}

  Real numbers {all rational and irrational numbers}

- Set-builder notation is a method of writing sets and has the form {variable | condition on the variable}.

- Union and intersection are two operations on sets.

- The absolute value of a real number a is given by

$$|a| = \begin{cases} a, & a \geq 0 \\ -a, & a < 0 \end{cases}$$

- For any two real numbers a and b, the distance between the graph of a and the graph of b is given by $d(a, b) = |a - b|$.

- The Order of Operations Agreement is used to simplify expressions.

P.2 Integer and Rational Number Exponents

- If b is any real number and n is any natural number, then

$$b^n = \underbrace{b \cdot b \cdot b \cdot \cdots \cdot b}_{n \text{ factors of } b}$$

- For any nonzero real number b, $b^0 = 1$.

- If $b \neq 0$ and n is any natural number, then $b^{-n} = \dfrac{1}{b^n}$ and $\dfrac{1}{b^{-n}} = b^n$.

- **Properties of Rational Exponents**
  If p, q, and r represent rational numbers, and a and b are positive real numbers, then

  Product $b^p \cdot b^q = b^{p+q}$

  Quotient $\dfrac{b^p}{b^q} = b^{p-q}$

  Power $(b^p)^q = b^{pq}$ $(a^p b^q)^r = a^{pr} b^{qr}$

  $\left(\dfrac{a^p}{b^q}\right)^r = \dfrac{a^{pr}}{b^{qr}}$ $b^{-p} = \dfrac{1}{b^p}$

- **Properties of Radicals**
  If m and n are natural numbers, and a and b are positive real numbers, then

  Product $\sqrt[n]{a} \cdot \sqrt[n]{b} = \sqrt[n]{ab}$

  Quotient $\dfrac{\sqrt[n]{a}}{\sqrt[n]{b}} = \sqrt[n]{\dfrac{a}{b}}$

  Index $\sqrt[m]{\sqrt[n]{b}} = \sqrt[mn]{b}$

P.3 Polynomials

- A polynomial is an expression of the form

$$a_n x^n + a_{n-1} x^{n-1} + \cdots + a_2 x^2 + a_1 x + a_0$$

- Special product formulas are as follows:

Special Form	Formula(s)
(Sum)(Difference)	$(x + y)(x - y) = x^2 - y^2$
(Binomial)^2	$(x + y)^2 = x^2 + 2xy + y^2$ $(x - y)^2 = x^2 - 2xy + y^2$

P.4 Factoring

- Factoring formulas are as follows:

Special Form	Formula(s)
Difference of two squares	$x^2 - y^2 = (x + y)(x - y)$
Perfect-square trinomials	$x^2 + 2xy + y^2 = (x + y)^2$ $x^2 - 2xy + y^2 = (x - y)^2$
Sum of cubes	$x^3 + y^3 = (x + y)(x^2 - xy + y^2)$
Difference of cubes	$x^3 - y^3 = (x - y)(x^2 + xy + y^2)$

- To factor a polynomial, use the general factoring strategy.

P.5 Rational Expressions

- A rational expression is a fraction in which the numerator and denominator are polynomials. The properties of rational expressions are used to simplify a rational expression and to find the sum, difference, product, and quotient of two rational expressions.

- Complex fractions can be simplified in either of the following ways:

  Method 1: Multiply both the numerator and the denominator by the LCD of all the fractions in the complex fraction.

  Method 2: Simplify the numerator to a single fraction and the denominator to a single fraction. Multiply the numerator by the reciprocal of the denominator.

P.6 Complex Numbers

- The number i, called the *imaginary unit,* is the number such that $i^2 = -1$.

- If a is a positive real number, then $\sqrt{-a} = i\sqrt{a}$. The number $i\sqrt{a}$ is called an *imaginary number.*

- A *complex number* is a number of the form $a + bi$, where a and b are real numbers and $i = \sqrt{-1}$. The number a is the *real part* of $a + bi$, and b is the *imaginary part.*

- The complex numbers $a + bi$ and $a - bi$ are called *complex conjugates* or *conjugates* of each other.

- **Operations on Complex Numbers**

  $(a + bi) + (c + di) = (a + c) + (b + d)i$

  $(a + bi) - (c + di) = (a - c) + (b - d)i$

  $(a + bi)(c + di) = (ac - bd) + (ad + bc)i$

  $\dfrac{a + bi}{c + di} = \dfrac{a + bi}{c + di} \cdot \dfrac{c - di}{c - di}$ • **Multiply numerator and denominator by the conjugate of the denominator.**

CHAPTER P TRUE/FALSE EXERCISES

In Exercises 1 to 10, answer true or false. If the statement is false, give an example or a reason to show that the statement is false.

1. If a and b are real numbers, then $|a - b| = |b - a|$.
   True

2. If a is a real number, then $a^2 \geq a$.
   False; if $a = \dfrac{1}{2}$, then $\left(\dfrac{1}{2}\right)^2 = \dfrac{1}{4} < \dfrac{1}{2}$.

3. The set of rational numbers is closed under the operation of addition. True

4. The set of irrational numbers is closed under the operation of addition.
   False; $\sqrt{2} + \left(-\sqrt{2}\right) = 0$, which is a rational number.

5. Let $x \oplus y$ denote the average of the two real numbers x and y. That is,

   $$x \oplus y = \frac{x + y}{2}$$

   The operation $\oplus$ is an associative operation because $(x \oplus y) \oplus z = x \oplus (y \oplus z)$ for all real numbers x, y, and z.
   False; $(2 \oplus 4) \oplus 6 \neq 2 \oplus (4 \oplus 6)$.

6. Using interval notation, we write the inequality $x > a$ as $[a, \infty)$. False; $x > a$ is written as (a, ∞).

7. If n is a real number, then $\sqrt{n^2} = n$.
   False; $\sqrt{(-2)^2} \neq -2$.

8. $(a + b)^2 = a^2 + b^2$
   False; let $a = 2$ and $b = 3$.

9. $\sqrt[3]{a^3 + b^3} = a + b$
   False; let $a = 1$ and $b = 2$.

10. $\sqrt{-2}\sqrt{-8} = 4$
    False; $\sqrt{-2}\sqrt{-8} = i\sqrt{2} \cdot i\sqrt{8} = i^2\sqrt{16} = -4$.

CHAPTER P REVIEW EXERCISES

—Answer graphs to Exercises 15–18 are on pages AA1–AA2.

In Exercises 1 to 4, classify each number as one or more of the following: integer, rational number, irrational number, real number, prime number, composite number.

1. 3
integer, rational number, real number, prime number [P.1]

2. $\sqrt{7}$
irrational number, real number [P.1]

3. $-\dfrac{1}{2}$
rational number, real number [P.1]

4. $0.\overline{5}$
rational number, real number [P.1]

In Exercises 5 and 6, use $A = \{1, 5, 7\}$ and $B = \{2, 3, 5, 11\}$ to find the indicated intersection or union.

5. $A \cup B$ $\{1, 2, 3, 5, 7, 11\}$ [P.1]

6. $A \cap B$ $\{5\}$ [P.1]

In Exercises 7 to 14, identify the real number property or the property of equality that is illustrated.

7. $5(x + 3) = 5x + 15$ Distributive property [P.1]

8. $a(3 + b) = a(b + 3)$ Commutative property of addition [P.1]

9. $(6c)d = 6(cd)$ Associative property of multiplication [P.1]

10. $\sqrt{2} + 3$ is a real number. Closure property of addition [P.1]

11. $7 + 0 = 7$ Identity property of addition [P.1]

12. $1x = x$ Identity property of multiplication [P.1]

13. If $7 = x$, then $x = 7$. Symmetric property of equality [P.1]

14. If $3x + 4 = y$, and $y = 5z$, then $3x + 4 = 5z$.
Transitive property of equality [P.1]

In Exercises 15 and 16, graph each inequality and write the inequality using interval notation.

15. $-4 < x \le 2$ $(-4, 2]$ [P.1]

16. $x \le -1$ or $x > 3$
$(-\infty, -1] \cup (3, \infty)$ [P.1]

In Exercises 17 and 18, graph each interval and write each interval as an inequality.

17. $[-3, 2)$ $-3 \le x < 2$ [P.1]

18. $(-1, \infty)$ $x > -1$ [P.1]

In Exercises 19 to 22, write each real number without absolute value symbols.

19. $|7|$ 7 [P.1]

20. $|2 - \pi|$ $\pi - 2$ [P.1]

21. $|4 - \pi|$ $4 - \pi$ [P.1]

22. $|-11|$ 11 [P.1]

In Exercises 23 and 24, find the distance on the real number line between the points whose coordinates are given.

23. $-3, 14$ 17 [P.1]

24. $\sqrt{5}, -\sqrt{2}$
$\sqrt{5} + \sqrt{2}$ [P.1]

In Exercises 25 and 26, evaluate each expression.

25. $-5^2 + (-11)$ -36 [P.1]

26. $\dfrac{(2^2 \cdot 3^{-2})^2}{3^{-1} \cdot 2^3}$ $\dfrac{2}{27}$ [P.1]

In Exercises 27 and 28, simplify each expression.

27. $(3x^2y)(2x^3y)^2$ $12x^8y^3$ [P.2]

28. $\left(\dfrac{2a^2b^3c^{-2}}{3ab^{-1}}\right)^2$ $\dfrac{4a^2b^8}{9c^4}$ [P.2]

In Exercises 29 and 30, evaluate each exponential expression.

29. $25^{1/2}$ 5 [P.2]

30. $-27^{2/3}$ -9 [P.2]

In Exercises 31 to 34, simplify each expression.

31. $x^{2/3} \cdot x^{3/4}$ $x^{17/12}$ [P.2]

32. $\left(\dfrac{8x^{5/4}}{x^{1/2}}\right)^{2/3}$ $4x^{1/2}$ [P.2]

33. $\left(\dfrac{x^2y}{x^{1/2}y^{-3}}\right)^{1/2}$ $x^{3/4}y^2$ [P.2]

34. $(x^{1/2} - y^{1/2})(x^{1/2} + y^{1/2})$
$x - y$ [P.2]

In Exercises 35 to 44, simplify each radical expression. Assume the variables are positive real numbers.

35. $\sqrt{48a^2b^7}$ $4ab^3\sqrt{3b}$ [P.2]

36. $\sqrt{12a^3b}$ $2a\sqrt{3ab}$ [P.2]

37. $\sqrt{72x^2y}$ $6x\sqrt{2y}$ [P.2]

38. $\sqrt{18x^3y^5}$ $3xy^2\sqrt{2xy}$ [P.2]

39. $\sqrt{\dfrac{54xy^3}{10x}}$ $\dfrac{3y\sqrt{15y}}{5}$ [P.2]

40. $-\sqrt{\dfrac{24xyz^3}{15z^6}}$ $-\dfrac{2\sqrt{10xyz}}{5z^2}$ [P.2]

41. $\dfrac{7x}{\sqrt[3]{2x^2}}$ $\dfrac{7\sqrt[3]{4x}}{2}$ [P.2]

42. $\dfrac{5y}{\sqrt[3]{9y}}$ $\dfrac{5\sqrt[3]{3y^2}}{3}$ [P.2]

43. $\sqrt[3]{-135x^2y^7}$
$-3y^2\sqrt[3]{5x^2y}$ [P.2]

44. $\sqrt[3]{-250xy^6}$
$-5y^2\sqrt[3]{2x}$ [P.2]

In Exercises 45 and 46, write each number in scientific notation.

45. 620,000 6.2×10^5 [P.2]

46. 0.0000017 1.7×10^{-6} [P.2]

In Exercises 47 and 48, change each number from scientific notation to decimal form.

47. 3.5×10^4 35,000 [P.2]

48. 4.31×10^{-7}
0.000000431 [P.2]

In Exercises 49 to 52, perform the indicated operation and express each result as a polynomial in standard form.

49. $(2a^2 + 3a - 7) + (-3a^2 - 5a + 6)$ $-a^2 - 2a - 1$ [P.3]

50. $(5b^2 - 11) - (3b^2 - 8b - 3)$ $2b^2 + 8b - 8$ [P.3]

51. $(2x^2 + 3x - 5)(3x^2 - 2x + 4)$
$6x^4 + 5x^3 - 13x^2 + 22x - 20$ [P.3]

52. $(3y - 5)^3$ $27y^3 - 135y^2 + 225y - 125$ [P.3]

In Exercises 53 to 56, completely factor each polynomial over the integers.

53. $3x^2 + 30x + 75$
$3(x + 5)^2$ [P.4]

54. $25x^2 - 30xy + 9y^2$
$(5x - 3y)^2$ [P.4]

55. $20a^2 - 4b^2$
$4(5a^2 - b^2)$ [P.4]

56. $16a^3 + 250$
$2(2a + 5)(4a^2 - 10a + 25)$ [P.4]

In Exercises 57 and 58, simplify each rational expression.

57. $\dfrac{6x^2 - 19x + 10}{2x^2 + 3x - 20}$
$\dfrac{3x - 2}{x + 4}$ [P.5]

58. $\dfrac{4x^3 - 25x}{8x^4 + 125x}$
$\dfrac{2x - 5}{4x^2 - 10x + 25}$ [P.5]

In Exercises 59 to 62, perform the indicated operation and simplify if possible.

59. $\dfrac{10x^2 + 13x - 3}{6x^2 - 13x - 5} \cdot \dfrac{6x^2 + 5x + 1}{10x^2 + 3x - 1}$ $\dfrac{2x + 3}{2x - 5}$ [P.5]

60. $\dfrac{15x^2 + 11x - 12}{25x^2 - 9} \div \dfrac{3x^2 + 13x + 12}{10x^2 + 11x + 3}$ $\dfrac{2x + 1}{x + 3}$ [P.5]

61. $\dfrac{x}{x^2 - 9} + \dfrac{2x}{x^2 + x - 12}$ $\dfrac{x(3x + 10)}{(x + 3)(x - 3)(x + 4)}$ [P.5]

62. $\dfrac{3x}{x^2 + 7x + 12} - \dfrac{x}{2x^2 + 5x - 3}$ $\dfrac{x(5x - 7)}{(x + 3)(x + 4)(2x - 1)}$ [P.5]

In Exercises 63 and 64, simplify each complex fraction.

63. $\dfrac{2 + \dfrac{1}{x - 5}}{3 - \dfrac{2}{x - 5}}$ $\dfrac{2x - 9}{3x - 17}$ [P.5]

64. $\dfrac{1}{2 + \dfrac{3}{1 + \dfrac{4}{x}}}$ $\dfrac{x + 4}{5x + 8}$ [P.5]

In Exercises 65 and 66, write the complex number in standard form.

65. $5 + \sqrt{-64}$ $5 + 8i$ [P.6]

66. $2 - \sqrt{-18}$ $2 - 3i\sqrt{2}$ [P.6]

In Exercises 67 to 74, perform the indicated operation and write the answer in simplest form.

67. $(2 - 3i) + 4 + 2i$ $6 - i$ [P.6]

68. $(4 + 7i) - (6 - 3i)$ $-2 + 10i$ [P.6]

69. $2i(3 - 4i)$ $8 + 6i$ [P.6]

70. $(4 - 3i)(2 + 7i)$ $29 + 22i$ [P.6]

71. $(3 + i)^2$ $8 + 6i$ [P.6]

72. i^{345} i [P.6]

73. $\dfrac{4 - 6i}{2i}$ $-3 - 2i$ [P.6]

74. $\dfrac{2 - 5i}{3 + 4i}$ $-\dfrac{14}{25} - \dfrac{23}{25}i$ [P.6]

CHAPTER P TEST

1. For real numbers a, b, and c, identify the property that is illustrated by $(a + b)c = ac + bc$. Distributive property [P.1]

2. Given $A = \{0, 2, 4, 6, 8\}$ and $B = \{1, 3, 5, 7, 9\}$, find $A \cup B$. $\{0, 1, 2, 3, 4, 5, 6, 7, 8, 9\}$ [P.1]

3. Find the distance between the points -12 and -5 on the number line. 7 [P.1]

4. Simplify: $(-2x^0y^{-2})^2(-3x^2y^{-1})^{-2}$ $\dfrac{4}{9x^4y^2}$ [P.2]

5. Simplify: $\dfrac{(2a^{-1}bc^{-2})^2}{(3^{-1}b)(2^{-1}ac^{-2})^3}$ $\dfrac{96bc^2}{a^5}$ [P.2]

6. Write 0.00137 in scientific notation. 1.37×10^{-3} [P.2]

7. Simplify: $\dfrac{x^{1/3}y^{-3/4}}{x^{-1/2}y^{3/2}}$ $\dfrac{x^{5/6}}{y^{9/4}}$ [P.2]

8. Simplify: $3x\sqrt[3]{81xy^4} - 2y\sqrt[3]{3x^4y}$ $7xy\sqrt[3]{3xy}$ [P.2]

9. Simplify: $\dfrac{x}{\sqrt[4]{2x^3}}$ $\dfrac{\sqrt[4]{8x}}{2}$ [P.2]

10. Simplify: $\dfrac{3}{\sqrt{x} + 2}$ $\dfrac{3\sqrt{x} - 6}{x - 4}$ [P2]

11. Simplify: $(x - 2y)(x^2 - 2x + y)$ $x^3 - 2x^2 + 5xy - 2x^2y - 2y^2$ [P.3]

12. Evaluate the polynomial $3y^3 - 2y^2 - y + 2$ for $y = -3$. -94 [P.4]

13. Factor: $7x^2 + 34x - 5$ $(7x - 1)(x + 5)$ [P.4]

14. Factor: $3ax - 12bx - 2a + 8b$ $(a - 4b)(3x - 2)$ [P.4]

15. Factor: $16x^4 - 2xy^3$ $2x(2x - y)(4x^2 + 2xy + y^2)$ [P.4]

16. Simplify: $\dfrac{x^2 - 2x - 15}{25 - x^2}$ $-\dfrac{x + 3}{x + 5}$ [P.5]

17. Simplify: $\dfrac{x}{x^2 + x - 6} - \dfrac{2}{x^2 - 5x + 6}$ $\dfrac{(x - 6)(x + 1)}{(x + 3)(x - 2)(x - 3)}$ [P.5]

18. Simplify: $\dfrac{2x^2 + 3x - 2}{x^2 - 3x} \div \dfrac{2x^2 - 7x + 3}{x^3 - 3x^2}$ $\dfrac{x(x + 2)}{x - 3}$ [P.5]

19. Simplify: $\dfrac{3}{a + b} \cdot \dfrac{a^2 - b^2}{2a - b} - \dfrac{5}{a} \cdot \dfrac{3a^2 - 3ab - 10a + 5b}{a(2a - b)}$ [P.5]

20. Simplify: $x - \dfrac{x}{x + \dfrac{1}{2}}$ $\dfrac{x(2x - 1)}{2x + 1}$ [P.5]

21. Write $7 + \sqrt{-20}$ in standard form. $7 + 2i\sqrt{5}$ [P.6]

In Exercises 22 to 25, write the complex number in simplest form.

22. $(4 - 3i) - (2 - 5i)$
$2 + 2i$ [P.6]

23. $(2 + 5i)(1 - 4i)$
$22 - 3i$ [P.6]

24. $\dfrac{3 + 4i}{5 - i}$ $\dfrac{11}{26} + \dfrac{23}{26}i$ [P.6]

25. i^{97} i [P.6]

EQUATIONS AND INEQUALITIES

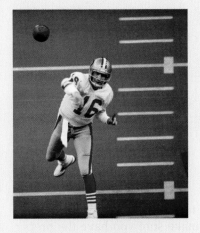

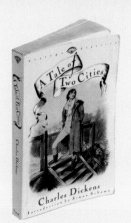

Quarterback Ratings and the Reading Level of Written Material

This chapter concerns equations and inequalities. Equations that express a relationship between two or more variables are called *formulas*. Formulas are used in a wide variety of applications. For instance, the National Football League (NFL) uses a formula to rate quarterbacks based on their performance in the passing aspect of the game. According to this formula, the top five all-time leading passers in the NFL are as follows:

Player	Rating
1. Steve Young	96.8
2. Joe Montana	92.3
3. Brett Favre	86.8
4. Dan Marino	86.4
5. Peyton Manning	85.1

Source: Time Almanac 2003, p. 936.

The NFL quarterback rating formula is given in **Example 2 on page 92.** In **Exercises 11 and 12, page 98,** you will use the quarterback rating formula to rate quarterbacks.

Formulas are also used to estimate the reading level of written material. In **Exercises 13 and 14, page 98,** you will use the SMOG (Simplified Measure of Gobbledygook) readability formula to estimate the reading level of two novels.

VIDEO & DVD

SSG

WWW

Verifying Results

One important aspect of problem solving involves the process of checking to see if your results satisfy the conditions of the original problem. This process will be especially important in this chapter when you solve an equation or an inequality.

Here is an example that illustrates the importance of checking your results. The problem seems easy, but many students fail to get the correct answer on their first attempt.

Two volumes of the series *Mathematics: Its Content, Methods, and Meaning* are on a shelf, with no space between the volumes. Each volume is 1 inch thick without its covers. Each cover is $\frac{1}{8}$ inch thick. A bookworm bores horizontally from the first page of Volume I to the last page of Volume II. How far does the bookworm travel?

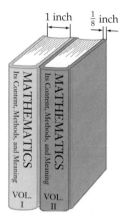

Once you have obtained your solution, try to check it by closely examining two books placed as shown above. Check to make sure you have the proper starting and ending positions. The correct answer is $\frac{1}{4}$ inch.

LINEAR AND ABSOLUTE VALUE EQUATIONS

• LINEAR EQUATIONS

An **equation** is a statement about the equality of two expressions. If either of the expressions contains a variable, the equation may be a true statement for some values of the variable and a false statement for other values. For example, the equation $2x + 1 = 7$ is a true statement for $x = 3$, but it is false for any number except 3. The number 3 is said to **satisfy** the equation $2x + 1 = 7$ because substituting 3 for x produces $2(3) + 1 = 7$, which is a true statement.

To **solve** an equation means to find all values of the variable that satisfy the equation. The values that satisfy an equation are called **solutions** or **roots** of the equation. For instance, 2 is a solution of $x + 3 = 5$.

Equivalent equations are equations that have exactly the same solution(s). The process of solving an equation involving the variable x is often accomplished by producing a sequence of equivalent equations until we produce an equation or equations of the form

$$x = \text{a constant}$$

To produce these equivalent equations that lead us to the solution(s), we often perform one or more of the following procedures.

P **Procedures That Produce Equivalent Equations**

1. Simplification of an expression on either side of the equation by such procedures as (i) combining like terms and (ii) applying the properties explained in Chapter P, such as the commutative, associative, and distributive properties.

    $2x + 3 + 5x = -11$ and $7x + 3 = -11$ are equivalent equations.

2. Addition or subtraction of the same quantity on both sides of an equation.

    $3x - 7 = 2$ and $3x = 9$ are equivalent equations.

3. Multiplication or division by the same nonzero quantity on both sides of an equation.

    $\dfrac{5}{6}x = 10$ and $x = 12$ are equivalent equations.

Many applications can be modeled by *linear equations.*

P **Definition of a Linear Equation**

A **linear equation** in the single variable x is an equation that can be written in the form

$$ax + b = 0$$

where a and b are real numbers, with $a \neq 0$.

Linear equations generally are solved by applying the procedures that produce equivalent equations.

Alternative to Example 1

Solve: $\dfrac{5}{6}x + 2 = -8$

● $x = -12$

EXAMPLE 1   Solve a Linear Equation

Solve: $\dfrac{3}{4}x - 6 = 0$

Solution

$\dfrac{3}{4}x - 6 = 0$ • Use the procedures on page 83 to rewrite the equation in the form x = a constant.

$\dfrac{3}{4}x - 6 + 6 = 0 + 6$ • Add **6** to each side.

$\dfrac{3}{4}x = 6$ • Simplify.

$\left(\dfrac{4}{3}\right)\left(\dfrac{3}{4}x\right) = \left(\dfrac{4}{3}\right)(6)$ • Multiply each side by $\dfrac{4}{3}$.

$x = 8$

Because 8 satisfies the original equation (see the *Take Note*), 8 is the solution.

▶ **TRY EXERCISE 2, PAGE 88**

---

take note

Check the proposed solution by substituting 8 for x in the original equation.

$\dfrac{3}{4}x - 6 = 0$

$\dfrac{3}{4}(8) - 6 \overset{?}{=} 0$

$0 = 0$ True

If an equation involves fractions, it is helpful to multiply each side of the equation by the LCD (least common denominator) of all the denominators to produce an equivalent equation that does not contain fractions.

Alternative to Example 2

Solve: $\dfrac{x}{4} - 2 + \dfrac{4}{5}x = 19$

● $x = 20$

EXAMPLE 2   Solve by Clearing Fractions

Solve: $\dfrac{2}{3}x + 10 - \dfrac{x}{5} = \dfrac{36}{5}$

Solution

$\dfrac{2}{3}x + 10 - \dfrac{x}{5} = \dfrac{36}{5}$

$15\left(\dfrac{2}{3}x + 10 - \dfrac{x}{5}\right) = 15\left(\dfrac{36}{5}\right)$ • Multiply each side of the equation by 15, the LCD of the denominators.

$10x + 150 - 3x = 108$ • Simplify.

$7x + 150 = 108$

$7x + 150 - 150 = 108 - 150$ • Subtract 150 from each side.

$7x = -42$

$\dfrac{7x}{7} = \dfrac{-42}{7}$ • Divide each side by 7.

$x = -6$ • Check as before.

▶ **TRY EXERCISE 12, PAGE 88**

Alternative to Example 3
Solve: $(x - 2)(2x + 3) = 2x(x - 1)$
- $x = 6$

EXAMPLE 3   **Solve an Equation by Applying Properties**

Solve: $(x + 2)(5x + 1) = 5x(x + 1)$

Solution

$$(x + 2)(5x + 1) = 5x(x + 1)$$
$$5x^2 + 11x + 2 = 5x^2 + 5x \qquad \text{• Simplify each product.}$$
$$11x + 2 = 5x \qquad \text{• Subtract } 5x^2 \text{ from each side.}$$
$$6x + 2 = 0 \qquad \text{• Subtract } 5x \text{ from each side.}$$
$$6x = -2 \qquad \text{• Subtract 2 from each side.}$$
$$x = -\frac{1}{3} \qquad \text{• Divide each side of the equation by 6.}$$

▶ **TRY EXERCISE 18, PAGE 88**

CONTRADICTIONS, CONDITIONAL EQUATIONS, AND IDENTITIES

An equation that has no solutions is called a **contradiction.** The equation $x = x + 1$ is a contradiction. No number is equal to itself increased by 1.

An equation that is true for some values of the variable but not true for other values of the variable is called a **conditional equation.** For example, $x + 2 = 8$ is a conditional equation because it is true for $x = 6$ and false for any number not equal to 6.

An **identity** is an equation that is true for all values of the variable for which all terms of the equation are defined. Examples of identities include the equations $x + x = 2x$ and $4(x + 3) - 1 = 4x + 11$.

Alternative to Example 4
Exercise 30, page 88.

EXAMPLE 4   **Classify Equations**

Classify each equation as a contradiction, a conditional equation, or an identity.

a. $x + 1 = x + 4$ b. $4x + 3 = x - 9$

c. $5(3x - 2) - 7(x - 4) = 8x + 18$

Solution

a.   Subtract x from both sides of $x + 1 = x + 4$ to produce the equivalent equation $1 = 4$. Because $1 = 4$ is a false statement, the original equation $x + 1 = x + 4$ has no solutions. It is a contradiction.

b.   Solve using the procedures that produce equivalent equations.

$$4x + 3 = x - 9$$
$$3x + 3 = -9 \qquad \text{• Subtract } x \text{ from each side.}$$
$$3x = -12 \qquad \text{• Subtract 3 from each side.}$$
$$x = -4 \qquad \text{• Divide each side by 3.}$$

Continued ▶

Check to confirm that -4 is a solution. The equation $4x + 3 = x - 9$ is true for $x = -4$, but it is not true for any other values of x. Thus $4x + 3 = x - 9$ is a conditional equation.

c. Simplify the left side of the equation to show that it is *identical* to the right side.

$$5(3x - 2) - 7(x - 4) = 8x + 18$$
$$15x - 10 - 7x + 28 = 8x + 18$$
$$8x + 18 = 8x + 18$$

The original equation $5(3x - 2) - 7(x - 4) = 8x + 18$ is true for all real numbers x. The equation is an identity.

▶ **TRY EXERCISE 24, PAGE 88**

❓ QUESTION Dividing each side of $x = 4x$ by x produces $1 = 4$. Are the equations $x = 4x$ and $1 = 4$ equivalent equations?

● ABSOLUTE VALUE EQUATIONS

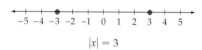

$|x| = 3$

FIGURE 1.1

The absolute value of a real number x is the distance between the number x and 0 on the real number line. Thus the solutions of $|x| = 3$ are all real numbers that are 3 units from 0. Therefore, the solutions of $|x| = 3$ are $x = 3$ or $x = -3$. See **Figure 1.1.**

The following property is used to solve absolute value equations.

Alternative to Example 5
Solve each of the equations.
a. $|2x - 3| = 5$
◉ **−1 and 4**
b. $|3x + 2| = 4$
◉ **−2 and $\dfrac{2}{3}$**
c. $|4x - 1| = 0$
◉ $\dfrac{1}{4}$
d. $|3x + 5| = -2$
◉ **no solution**

Ⓟ **A Property of Absolute Value Equations**

For any variable expression E and any nonnegative real number k,

$$|E| = k \quad \text{if and only if} \quad E = k \quad \text{or} \quad E = -k$$

EXAMPLE 5   **Solve an Absolute Value Equation**

Solve: $|2x - 5| = 21$

Solution

$|2x - 5| = 21$ implies $2x - 5 = 21$ or $2x - 5 = -21$. Solving each of these linear equations produces

$$2x - 5 = 21 \qquad \text{or} \qquad 2x - 5 = -21$$
$$2x = 26 \qquad\qquad\qquad 2x = -16$$
$$x = 13 \qquad\qquad\qquad x = -8$$

The solutions of $|2x - 5| = 21$ are -8 and 13.

▶ **TRY EXERCISE 38, PAGE 88**

take note

Some absolute value equations have no solutions. For example, $|x + 2| = -5$ is false for all values of x. Because an absolute value is always nonnegative, the equation is never true.

❓ ANSWER   No. The real number 0 is a solution of $x = 4x$, but 0 is not a solution of $1 = 4$.

• APPLICATIONS

Linear equations often can be used to model real-world data.

Alternative to Example 6
Exercise 54, page 89.

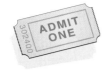

TABLE 1.1   Average U.S. Movie Theater Ticket Price

Year	Price (in dollars)
1998	4.69
1999	5.06
2000	5.39
2001	5.65
2002	5.80

Source: National Association of Theatre Owners, http://www.na-toonline.org/statisticstickets.htm.

EXAMPLE 6   Movie Theater Ticket Prices

Movie theater ticket prices have been increasing steadily in recent years (see **Table 1.1**). An equation that models the average U.S. movie theater ticket price p, in dollars, is given by

$$p = 0.281t + 4.756$$

where t is the number of years after 1998. (This means that $t = 0$ corresponds to the year 1998.) Use this equation to predict in what year the average U.S. movie theater ticket price will reach \$7.50.

Solution

$$p = 0.281t + 4.756$$
$$7.50 = 0.281t + 4.756 \qquad \bullet \text{ Substitute 7.50 for } p.$$
$$2.744 = 0.281t \qquad\qquad \bullet \text{ Solve for } t.$$
$$t \approx 9.8$$

Our equation predicts that the average U.S. movie theater ticket price will reach \$7.50 about 9.8 years after 1998, which is the year 2007.

▶ **TRY EXERCISE 50, PAGE 89**

Alternative to Example 7
Exercise 56, page 89.

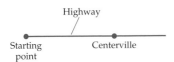

FIGURE 1.2

EXAMPLE 7   Driving Time

Alicia is driving along a highway that passes through Centerville (see **Figure 1.2**). Her distance d, in miles, from Centerville is given by the equation

$$d = |135 - 60t|$$

where t is the time in hours since the start of her trip and $0 \leq t \leq 5$. Determine when Alicia will be exactly 15 miles from Centerville.

Solution

Substitute 15 for d.

$$d = |135 - 60t|$$
$$15 = |135 - 60t|$$

$$15 = 135 - 60t \qquad \text{or} \qquad -15 = 135 - 60t \qquad \bullet \text{ Solve for } t.$$
$$-120 = -60t \qquad\qquad\qquad -150 = -60t$$
$$2 = t \qquad\qquad\qquad\qquad \frac{5}{2} = t$$

Alicia will be exactly 15 miles from Centerville after she has driven for 2 hours and also after she has driven for $2\frac{1}{2}$ hours.

▶ **TRY EXERCISE 52, PAGE 89**

TOPICS FOR DISCUSSION

1. A student multiplies each side of the equation $\frac{1}{2}x + 3 = 4$ by 2 to produce the equation $x + 3 = 8$. Has the student produced an equivalent equation? Explain.

2. If $P = Q$, is it also true that $Q = P$?

3. Consider the equation $|x + y| = |x| + |y|$. Is this equation true for all values of x and y, true for some values of x and y, or never true?

EXERCISE SET 1.1   —*Suggested Assignment: Exercises 1–57, odd; 67–72, all.*

In Exercises 1 to 28, solve each equation and check your solution.

1. $2x + 10 = 40$
15

▶ **2.** $-3y + 20 = 2$
6

3. $5x + 2 = 2x - 10$
−4

4. $4x - 11 = 7x + 20$
$-\frac{31}{3}$

5. $2(x - 3) - 5 = 4(x - 5)$ $\frac{9}{2}$

6. $5(x - 4) - 7 = -2(x - 3)$ $\frac{33}{7}$

7. $4(2r - 17) + 5(3r - 8) = 0$ $\frac{108}{23}$

8. $6(5s - 11) - 12(2s + 5) = 0$ 21

9. $\frac{3}{4}x + \frac{1}{2} = \frac{2}{3}$ $\frac{2}{9}$

10. $\frac{x}{4} - 5 = \frac{1}{2}$ 22

11. $\frac{2}{3}x - 5 = \frac{1}{2}x - 3$ 12

▶ **12.** $\frac{1}{2}x + 7 - \frac{1}{4}x = \frac{19}{2}$ 10

13. $0.2x + 0.4 = 3.6$ 16

14. $0.04x - 0.2 = 0.07$ 6.75

15. $x + 0.08(60) = 0.20(60 + x)$ 9

16. $6(t + 1.5) = 12t$ $\frac{3}{2}$

17. $3(x + 5)(x - 1) = (3x + 4)(x - 2)$ $\frac{1}{2}$

▶ **18.** $5(x + 4)(x - 4) = (x - 3)(5x + 4)$ $\frac{68}{11}$

19. $5[x - (4x - 5)] = 3 - 2x$ $\frac{22}{13}$

20. $6[3y - 2(y - 1)] - 2 + 7y = 0$ $-\frac{10}{13}$

21. $\frac{40 - 3x}{5} = \frac{6x + 7}{8}$ $\frac{95}{18}$

22. $\frac{12 + x}{-4} = \frac{5x - 7}{3} + 2$ $-\frac{32}{23}$

In Exercises 23 to 32, classify each equation as a contradiction, a conditional equation, or an identity.

23. $-3(x - 5) = -3x + 15$
identity

▶ **24.** $2x + \frac{1}{3} = \frac{6x + 1}{3}$
identity

25. $2x + 7 = 3(x - 1)$
conditional equation

26. $4[2x - 5(x - 3)] = 6$
conditional equation

27. $\frac{4x + 8}{4} = x + 8$
contradiction

28. $3[x - (4x - 1)] = -3(2x - 5)$
conditional equation

29. $3[x - 2(x - 5)] - 1 = -3x + 29$
identity

30. $4[3(x - 5) + 7] = 12x - 32$
identity

31. $2x - 8 = -x + 9$
conditional equation

32. $|3(x - 4) + 7| = |3x - 5|$
identity

In Exercises 33 to 48, solve each absolute value equation for x.

33. $|x| = 4$
−4, 4

34. $|x| = 7$
7, −7

35. $|x - 5| = 2$
7, 3

36. $|x - 8| = 3$
11, 5

37. $|2x - 5| = 11$
8, −3

▶ **38.** $|2x - 3| = 21$
12, −9

39. $|2x + 6| = 10$
2, −8

40. $|2x + 14| = 60$
23, −37

41. $\left|\frac{x - 4}{2}\right| = 8$
20, −12

42. $\left|\frac{x + 3}{4}\right| = 6$
21, −27

43. $|2x + 5| = -8$
no solution

44. $|4x - 1| = -17$
no solution

45. $2|x + 3| + 4 = 34$
12, −18

46. $3|x - 5| - 16 = 2$
11, −1

47. $|2x - a| = b$ $(b > 0)$
$(a + b)/2, (a - b)/2$

48. $3|x - d| = c$ $(c > 0)$
$d + \dfrac{c}{3}, d - \dfrac{c}{3}$

49. **RECREATION** The revenues of all the amusement and theme parks in the United States have been increasing since 1990. An equation that approximates the total revenues of all parks is given by

$$\text{Revenues (in billions of dollars)} = 0.35x + 5.7$$

where x is the number of years after 1990. Use this equation to predict the year in which the revenues for all amusement and theme parks in the U.S. will first reach \$12 billion. (*Source: Amusement Business* magazine as reported in the San Diego *Union-Tribune*, March 19, 2000)
2008

▶ 50. **PATENTS** Data from the U.S. Patent and Trademark Office suggest that the number of patents P, in thousands, that have been issued each year in the U.S. since 1993 can be approximated by the equation

$$P = 5.4x + 110$$

where x is the number of years after 1993. Use this equation to predict in what year the number of patents will first exceed 175,000 patents. 2005

51. **TRAVEL** Ruben is driving along a highway that passes through Barstow. His distance d, in miles, from Barstow is given by the equation $d = |210 - 50t|$, where t is the time, in hours, since the start of his trip and $0 \le t \le 6$. When will Ruben be exactly 60 miles from Barstow?
after 3 h and after 5 h 24 min

▶ 52. **AUTOMOBILE GAS MILEAGE** The gas mileage m, in miles per gallon, obtained during a long trip is given by

$$m = -\frac{1}{2}|s - 55| + 25$$

where s is the speed of Kate's automobile in miles per hour and $40 \le s \le 70$. At what constant speed can Kate drive to obtain a gas mileage of exactly 22 miles per gallon?
49 mph or 61 mph

53. **OFFICE CARPETING** The cost to install new carpet in an office is determined by a \$550 fixed fee plus a fee of \$45 per square yard of floor space to be covered. How many square yards of floor space can be carpeted at a cost of \$3800? Round to the nearest square yard. 72 sq yd

54. **WHOLESALE PRICE** A retailer determines the retail price of a coat by first computing 175% of the wholesale price of the coat and then adding an additional markup of \$8.00. What is the wholesale price of a coat that has a retail price of \$156.75? \$85.00

55. **COMPUTER SCIENCE** The percent of a file that remains to be downloaded using a dialup Internet connection for a certain modem is given by the equation

$$\text{Percent remaining} = 100 - \frac{42{,}000}{N}t$$

where N is the size of the file in bytes and t is the number of seconds since the download began. In how many minutes will 25% of a 500,000-byte file remain to be downloaded? Round to the nearest minute. 15 min

56. **AVIATION** The number of miles that remain to be flown by a commercial jet traveling from Boston to Los Angeles can be approximated by the equation

$$\text{Miles remaining} = 2650 - 475t$$

where t is the number of hours since leaving Boston. In how many hours will the plane be 1000 miles from Los Angeles? Round to the nearest tenth of an hour. 3.5 h

To benefit from an aerobic exercise program, many experts recommend that you exercise three to five times a week for 20 minutes to an hour. It is also important that your heart rate be in the *training* **zone, which is defined by the following linear equations, where** *a* **is your age in years and the heart rate is in beats per minute.**[1]

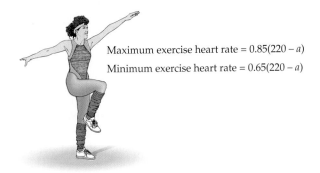

$$\text{Maximum exercise heart rate} = 0.85(220 - a)$$
$$\text{Minimum exercise heart rate} = 0.65(220 - a)$$

57. **MAXIMUM EXERCISE HEART RATE** Find the maximum exercise heart rate and the minimum exercise heart rate for a person who is 25 years of age. (Round to the nearest beat per minute.)
maximum 166 beats per minute, minimum 127 beats per minute

58. **MAXIMUM EXERCISE HEART RATE** How old is a person who has a maximum exercise heart rate of 153 beats per minute? 40 years

---

[1] "The Heart of the Matter," *American Health*, September 1995.

CONNECTING CONCEPTS

59. Let a, b, and c be real constants. Show that an equation of the form $ax + b = c$ has $x = \dfrac{c - b}{a}$ $(a \neq 0)$ as its solution.

60. Let a, b, c, and d be real constants. Show that an equation of the form $ax + b = cx + d$ has $x = \dfrac{d - b}{a - c}$ $(a - c \neq 0)$ as its solution.

In Exercises 61 to 66, solve each equation.

61. $|x + 4| = x + 4$
$\{x \mid x \geq -4\}$

62. $|x - 1| = x - 1$
$\{x \mid x \geq 1\}$

63. $|x + 7| = -(x + 7)$
$\{x \mid x \leq -7\}$

64. $|x - 3| = -(x - 3)$
$\{x \mid x \leq 3\}$

65. $|2x + 7| = 2x + 7$
$\left\{ x \mid x \geq -\dfrac{7}{2} \right\}$

66. $|3x - 11| = -3x + 11$
$\left\{ x \mid x \leq \dfrac{11}{3} \right\}$

PREPARE FOR SECTION 1.2

67. The sum of two numbers is 32. If one of the numbers is represented by x, then the expression $32 - x$ represents the other number. Evaluate $32 - x$ for $x = 8\dfrac{1}{2}$. [P.1] $23\dfrac{1}{2}$

68. Evaluate $\dfrac{1}{2} bh$ for $b = \dfrac{2}{3}$ and $h = \dfrac{4}{5}$. [P.1] $\dfrac{4}{15}$

69. What property has been applied to rewrite $2l + 2w$ as $2(l + w)$? [P.1] Distributive property

70. What property has been applied to rewrite $\left(\dfrac{1}{2} b \right) h$ as $\dfrac{1}{2} (bh)$? [P.1] Associative property of multiplication

71. Add: $\dfrac{2}{5} x + \dfrac{1}{3} x$ [P.1] $\dfrac{11}{15} x$

72. Simplify: $\dfrac{1}{\dfrac{1}{a} + \dfrac{1}{b}}$ [P.5] $\dfrac{ab}{a + b}$

PROJECTS

1. **PERFECT GAMES** In baseball, a **perfect game** is a game in which one of the teams gives up no hits, no walks, and no errors. Statistics show that a batter will get on base roughly 30% of the time. Thus the probability that a pitcher will retire the batter is 70%, or 0.7 as a decimal. The probability that a pitcher will retire two batters in a row is $0.7^2 = 0.49$. The probability is 0.7^{27} that a pitcher will retire 27 batters in succession and thus pitch a perfect game.[2]

a. Explain why the linear equation
$$p = 2(0.7^{27})x$$
provides a good estimate of the number of perfect games p we can expect after x games are completed.

b. Check a major league baseball almanac to determine how many perfect games have been played in the last 40 years and how many games have been played in the last 40 years.

c. Use the linear equation in **a.** to estimate how many perfect games we should expect to have been pitched over the last 40 years of major league baseball. How does this result compare with the actual result found in **b.**?

[2] *A Mathematician Reads the Newspaper*, by John Allen Paulos (New York: BasicBooks, A Division of HarperCollins Publishers, Inc., 1995).

FORMULAS AND APPLICATIONS

- ● FORMULAS
- ● APPLICATIONS

● FORMULAS

A **formula** is an equation that expresses known relationships between two or more variables. **Table 1.2** lists several formulas from geometry that are used in this text. The variable P represents perimeter, C represents circumference of a circle, A represents area, S represents surface area of an enclosed solid, and V represents volume.

TABLE 1.2   Formulas from Geometry

Rectangle	Square	Triangle	Circle	Parallelogram
$P = 2l + 2w$	$P = 4s$	$P = a + b + c$	$C = \pi d = 2\pi r$	$P = 2b + 2s$
$A = lw$	$A = s^2$	$A = \dfrac{1}{2}bh$	$A = \pi r^2$	$A = bh$

Rectangular Solid	Right Circular Cone	Sphere	Right Circular Cylinder	Frustum of a Cone
$S = 2(wh + lw + hl)$	$S = \pi r\sqrt{r^2 + h^2}$ $+ \pi r^2$	$S = 4\pi r^2$	$S = 2\pi rh + 2\pi r^2$	$S = \pi(R + r)\sqrt{h^2 + (R - r)^2}$ $+ \pi r^2 + \pi R^2$
$V = lwh$	$V = \dfrac{1}{3}\pi r^2 h$	$V = \dfrac{4}{3}\pi r^3$	$V = \pi r^2 h$	$V = \dfrac{1}{3}\pi h(r^2 + rR + R^2)$

It is often necessary to solve a formula for a specified variable. Begin the process by isolating all terms that contain the specified variable on one side of the equation and all terms that do not contain the specified variable on the other side.

Alternative to Example 1

1. Solve $V = \dfrac{1}{3}\pi r^2 h$ for h.

- ● $h = \dfrac{3V}{\pi r^2}$

2. Solve $S = 2(wh + lw + hl)$ for w.

- ● $w = \dfrac{S - 2hl}{2(h + l)}$ or $w = \dfrac{S - 2hl}{2h + 2l}$

EXAMPLE 1   Solve a Formula for a Specified Variable

a. Solve $2l + 2w = P$ for l.   **b.** Solve $S = 2(wh + lw + hl)$ for h.

Solution

a. $2l + 2w = P$

$2l = P - 2w$ • **Subtract 2w from each side to isolate the 2l term.**

$l = \dfrac{P - 2w}{2}$ • **Divide each side by 2.**

Continued ▶

MATH MATTERS

In Example 1a, the solution $l = \dfrac{P - 2w}{2}$ also can be written as $l = \dfrac{P}{2} - w.$

b.

$$S = 2(wh + lw + hl)$$

$$S = 2wh + 2lw + 2hl$$

$$S - 2lw = 2wh + 2hl$$ • Isolate the terms that involve the variable *h* on the right side.

$$S - 2lw = 2h(w + l)$$ • Factor **2h** from the right side.

$$\dfrac{S - 2lw}{2(w + l)} = h$$ • Divide each side by **2(w + l)**.

▶ **TRY EXERCISE 4, PAGE 98**

Formulas are often used to compare the performances of athletes. Here is an example of a formula that is used in professional football.

Alternative to Example 2
Exercise 12, page 98.

EXAMPLE 2   **Calculate a Quarterback Rating**

  The National Football League uses the following formula to rate quarterbacks:

$$\text{qb rating} = \dfrac{100}{6}[0.05(C - 30) + 0.25(Y - 3) + 0.2T + (2.375 - 0.25I)]$$

In this formula, *C* is the percentage of pass completions, *Y* is the average number of yards gained per pass attempt, *T* is the percentage of touchdown passes, and *I* is the percentage of interceptions.

During the 2002 season, Brad Johnson, the quarterback of the Tampa Bay Buccaneers, completed 62.31% of his passes. He averaged 6.76 yards per pass attempt, 4.88% of his passes were for touchdowns, and 1.33% of his passes were intercepted. Determine Brad Johnson's quarterback rating for the 2002 season.

Solution

Because *C* is defined as a percentage, $C = 62.31$. We are also given $Y = 6.76$, $T = 4.88$, and $I = 1.33$.

Substitute 62.31 for *C*, 6.76 for *Y*, 4.88 for *T*, and 1.33 for *I* in the rating formula.

qb rating

$$= \dfrac{100}{6}[0.05(62.31 - 30) + 0.25(6.76 - 3) + 0.2(4.88) + (2.375 - 0.25(1.33))]$$

$$= 92.9$$

Brad Johnson's quarterback rating for the 2002 season was 92.9.

▶ **TRY EXERCISE 14, PAGE 98**

? QUESTION If $ax + b = c$, does $x = \dfrac{c}{a} - b$?

• APPLICATIONS

Linear equations emerge in a variety of application problems. In solving such problems, it generally helps to apply specific techniques in a series of small steps. The following general strategies should prove to be helpful in the remaining portion of this section.

INSTRUCTOR NOTE

Encourage your students to use these strategies even on "simple" application problems. For instance, have your students solve the following problem.

    A shirt and a tie together cost $41.00. If the shirt costs $40.00 more than the tie, what is the cost of the shirt and what is the cost of the tie?

Some students may respond that the shirt costs $40.00 and the tie costs $1.00; however, those students whose use the problem solving guidelines will find the correct solution: the shirt costs $40.50 and the tie costs $.50.

Alternative to Example 3
The length of a room is 9 feet less than twice the width of the room. The perimeter of the room is 48 feet. Find the width and the length of the room.
● **width is 11 ft; length is 13 ft**

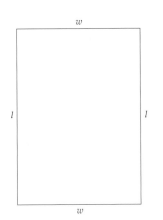

FIGURE 1.3

Strategies for Solving Application Problems

1. Read the problem carefully. If necessary, reread the problem several times.

2. When appropriate, draw a sketch and label parts of the drawing with the specific information given in the problem.

3. Determine the unknown quantities, and label them with variables. Write down any equation that relates the variables.

4. Use the information from step 3, along with a known formula or some additional information given in the problem, to write an equation.

5. Solve the equation obtained in step 4, and check to see whether these results satisfy all the conditions of the original problem.

EXAMPLE 3   Dimensions of a Painting

One of the best known paintings is *Mona Lisa* by Leonardo da Vinci. It is on display at the Musee du Louvre, in Paris. The length (or height) of this rectangular-shaped painting is 24 centimeters more than its width. The perimeter of the painting is 260 centimeters. Find the width and the length of the painting.

Solution

1. Read the problem carefully.

2. Draw a rectangle. See **Figure 1.3**.

3. Label the rectangle. We have used w for its width and l for its length. The problem states that the length is 24 centimeters more than the width. Thus l and w are related by the equation

$$l = w + 24$$

Continued ▶

? ANSWER   No. $x = \dfrac{c - b}{a}$, provided $a \neq 0$.

4. The perimeter of a rectangle is given by the formula $P = 2l + 2w$. To produce an equation that involves only constants and a single variable (say, w), substitute 260 for P and $w + 24$ for l.

$$P = 2l + 2w$$
$$260 = 2(w + 24) + 2w$$

5. Solve for w.

$$260 = 2w + 48 + 2w$$
$$260 = 4w + 48$$
$$212 = 4w$$
$$w = 53$$

The length is 24 centimeters more than the width. Thus $l = 53 + 24 = 77$.

A check verifies that 77 is 24 more than 53 and that twice the length (77) plus twice the width (53) gives the perimeter (260). The width of the painting is 53 centimeters and its length is 77 centimeters.

▶ **TRY EXERCISE 20, PAGE 99**

Many *uniform motion* problems can be solved by using the formula $d = rt$, where d is the distance traveled, r is the rate of speed, and t is the time.

Alternative to Example 4
a. A bicyclist traveling at 20 mph overtakes an in-line skater who is traveling at 10 mph and had a 0.5-hour head start. How far from the starting point did the bicyclist overtake the in-line skater?
● **10 mi**
b. Two planes are 2280 miles apart and are traveling toward each other. One plane is traveling 60 mph faster than the other plane. The planes meet in 2 hours. Find the speed of the faster plane.
● **600 mph**

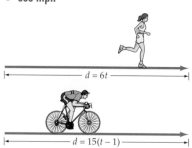

FIGURE 1.4

INSTRUCTOR NOTE
Encourage your students to make a sketch for all uniform motion applications. Without a sketch, some students will not be able to write the equation that relates the given information and the unknown.

EXAMPLE 4   **A Uniform Motion Problem**

A runner runs a course at a constant speed of 6 mph. One hour after the runner begins, a cyclist starts on the same course at a constant speed of 15 mph. How long after the runner starts does the cyclist overtake the runner?

Solution

If we represent the time the runner has spent on the course by t, then the time the cyclist takes to overtake the runner is $t - 1$. The following table organizes the information and helps us determine how to write the distances each person travels.

	rate r	·	time t	=	distance d
Runner	6	·	t	=	$6t$
Cyclist	15	·	$t - 1$	=	$15(t - 1)$

Figure 1.4 indicates that the runner and the cyclist cover the same distance. Thus

$$6t = 15(t - 1)$$
$$6t = 15t - 15$$
$$-9t = -15$$
$$t = 1\frac{2}{3}$$

The cyclist overtakes the runner $1\frac{2}{3}$ hours after the runner starts.

▶ **TRY EXERCISE 24, PAGE 99**

Many business applications can be solved by using the equation

$$\text{Profit} = \text{revenue} - \text{cost}$$

Alternative to Example 5
A lamp manufacturer spends $12.45 to produce a lamp that sells for $39.95. How many lamps must the manufacturer sell to make a profit of $11,000?
● **400 lamps**

EXAMPLE 5   **A Business Application**

It costs a tennis shoe manufacturer $26.55 to produce a pair of tennis shoes that sells for $49.95. How many pairs of tennis shoes must the manufacturer sell to make a profit of $14,274.00?

Solution

The *profit* is equal to the *revenue* minus the *cost*. If x equals the number of pairs of tennis shoes to be sold, then the revenue will be $49.95x$ and the cost will be $26.55x$. Therefore,

$$\text{Profit} = \text{revenue} - \text{cost}$$
$$14{,}274.00 = 49.95x - 26.55x$$
$$14{,}274.00 = 23.40x$$
$$610 = x$$

The manufacturer must sell 610 pairs of tennis shoes to make the desired profit.

▶ **TRY EXERCISE 32, PAGE 100**

Simple interest problems can be solved by using the formula $I = Prt$, where I is the interest, P is the principal, r is the simple interest rate per period, and t is the number of periods.

Alternative to Example 6
A technician invests part of $5000 in a 4% simple interest account and the remainder of the money at 6% simple interest. Together the investments earn $270 per year. Find the amount invested at each rate.
● **$1500 at 4%, $3500 at 6%**

EXAMPLE 6   **An Investment Problem**

An accountant invests part of a $6000 bonus in a 5% simple interest account and the remainder of the money is invested at 8.5% simple interest. Together the investments earn $370 per year. Find the amount invested at each rate.

Solution

Let x be the amount invested at 5%. The remainder of the money is $6000 - x$, which will be the amount invested at 8.5%. Using the simple interest formula, $I = Prt$, with $t = 1$ year, yields

$$\text{Interest at 5\%} = x \cdot 0.05 = 0.05x$$
$$\text{Interest at 8.5\%} = (6000 - x) \cdot (0.085) = 510 - 0.085x$$

The interest earned on the two accounts equals $370.

$$0.05x + (510 - 0.085x) = 370$$
$$-0.035x + 510 = 370$$
$$-0.035x = -140$$
$$x = 4000$$

The accountant invested $4000 at 5% and the remaining $2000 at 8.5%. Check as before.

▶ **TRY EXERCISE 36, PAGE 100**

Percent mixture problems involve combining solutions or alloys that have different concentrations of a common substance. Percent mixture problems can be solved by using the formula $pA = Q$, where p is the percent of concentration, A is the amount of the solution or alloy, and Q is the quantity of a substance in the solution or alloy. For example, in 4 liters of a 25% acid solution, p is the percent of acid (25%), A is the amount of solution (4 liters), and Q is the amount of acid in the solution, which equals $(0.25) \cdot (4)$ liters = 1 liter.

Alternative to Example 7
A jeweler mixed 10 grams of a 50% gold alloy with 40 grams of a 15% gold alloy. What is the percent concentration of the resulting alloy?

● **22%**

EXAMPLE 7   A Percent Mixture Problem

A chemist mixes an 11% hydrochloric acid solution with a 6% hydrochloric acid solution. How many milliliters (ml) of each solution should the chemist use to make a 600-milliliter solution that is 8% hydrochloric acid?

Solution

Let x be the number of milliliters of the 11% solution. Because the final solution will have a total of 600 milliliters of fluid, $600 - x$ is the number of milliliters of the 6% solution. See **Figure 1.5.**

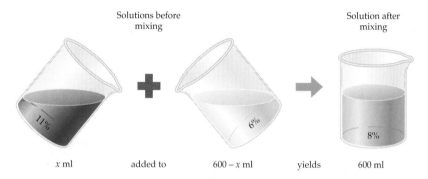

Solutions before mixing   Solution after mixing

x ml   added to $600 - x$ ml   yields   600 ml

FIGURE 1.5

Because all the hydrochloric acid in the final solution comes from either the 11% solution or the 6% solution, the number of milliliters of hydrochloric acid in the 11% solution added to the number of milliliters of hydrochloric acid in the 6% solution must equal the number of milliliters of hydrochloric acid in the 8% solution.

INSTRUCTOR NOTE
Encourage students to ask, "Does the answer seem reasonable?" For example, in Example 7, if 300 milliliters of the 11% solution are mixed with 300 milliliters of the 6% solution, the result is 600 milliliters of $8\frac{1}{2}$% solution (the average of 11% and 6%). To get a weaker 8% solution requires slightly more of the 6% solution and less of the 11% solution.

$$\begin{pmatrix} \text{ml of acid in} \\ \text{11\% solution} \end{pmatrix} + \begin{pmatrix} \text{ml of acid in} \\ \text{6\% solution} \end{pmatrix} = \begin{pmatrix} \text{ml of acid in} \\ \text{8\% solution} \end{pmatrix}$$

$$0.11x \qquad + \quad 0.06(600 - x) \quad = \qquad 0.08(600)$$
$$0.11x + 36 - 0.06x = 48$$
$$0.05x + 36 = 48$$
$$0.05x = 12$$
$$x = 240$$

The chemist should use 240 milliliters of the 11% solution and 360 milliliters of the 6% solution to make a 600-milliliter solution that is 8% hydrochloric acid.

▶ **TRY EXERCISE 40, PAGE 100**

take note

In all work problems in this chapter, we assume the rate of work for any worker remains constant throughout the entire time period.

Alternative to Example 8
One member of a gardening team can landscape a new lawn in 45 hours. The other member of the team can do the job in 30 hours. How long would it take to landscape a lawn if both gardeners worked together?
● **18 hours**

INSTRUCTOR NOTE
Encourage your students to write down what their variables represent. It will be difficult for them to establish an equation if they do not know precisely what the variable represents.

To solve a *work problem*, use the equation

Rate of work $\times$ time worked = part of task completed

For example, if a painter can paint a wall in 15 minutes, then the painter can paint 1/15 of the wall in 1 minute. The painter's *rate of work* is 1/15 of the wall each minute. In general, if a task can be completed in x minutes, then the rate of work is $1/x$ of the task each minute.

EXAMPLE 8   A Work Problem

Pump A can fill a pool in 6 hours, and pump B can fill the same pool in 3 hours. How long will it take to fill the pool if both pumps are used?

Solution

Because pump A fills the pool in 6 hours, $\dfrac{1}{6}$ represents the part of the pool filled by pump A in 1 hour. Because pump B fills the pool in 3 hours, $\dfrac{1}{3}$ represents the part of the pool filled by pump B in 1 hour.

Let t = the number of hours to fill the pool together. Then

$$t \cdot \frac{1}{6} = \frac{t}{6}$$ • **Part of the pool filled by pump A**

$$t \cdot \frac{1}{3} = \frac{t}{3}$$ • **Part of the pool filled by pump B**

$$\left(\begin{array}{c}\text{Part filled}\\\text{by pump A}\end{array}\right) + \left(\begin{array}{c}\text{Part filled}\\\text{by pump B}\end{array}\right) = \left(\begin{array}{c}\text{1 filled}\\\text{pool}\end{array}\right)$$

$$\frac{t}{6} \quad + \quad \frac{t}{3} \quad = \quad 1$$

Multiplying each side of the equation by 6 produces

$$t + 2t = 6$$
$$3t = 6$$
$$t = 2$$

Check: Pump A fills $\dfrac{2}{6}$, or $\dfrac{1}{3}$, of the pool in 2 hours and pump B fills $\dfrac{2}{3}$ of the pool in 2 hours, so 2 hours is the time required to fill the pool if both pumps are used.

▶ **TRY EXERCISE 50, PAGE 100**

 TOPICS FOR DISCUSSION

1. A student solves the formula $A = P + Prt$ for the variable P. The student's answer is $P = A - Prt$. Is this a correct response? Explain.

2. A student takes reciprocals of each term to write the formula

    $$\frac{1}{f} = \frac{1}{d_0} + \frac{1}{d_i}$$

    as $f = d_0 + d_i$. Did this technique produce a valid formula? Explain.

3. In the formula $S = \dfrac{a_1}{(1-r)}$, what restrictions are placed on the variable r?

4. The formula $A = \dfrac{1}{2}bh$ can also be expressed as $A = \dfrac{bh}{2}$. Do you agree?

EXERCISE SET 1.2   —*Suggested Assignment: Exercises 1–15, odd; 17–51, every other odd; 61–66, all.*

In Exercises I to 10, solve the formula for the specified variable.

1. $V = \dfrac{1}{3}\pi r^2 h;\quad h$ (geometry) $h = \dfrac{3V}{\pi r^2}$

2. $P = S - Sdt;\quad t$ (business) $t = \dfrac{S-P}{Sd}$

3. $I = Prt;\quad t$ (business) $t = \dfrac{I}{Pr}$

▶ **4.** $A = P + Prt;\quad P$ (business) $\dfrac{A}{1+rt} = P$

5. $F = \dfrac{Gm_1m_2}{d^2};\quad m_1$ (physics) $m_1 = \dfrac{Fd^2}{Gm_2}$

6. $A = \dfrac{1}{2}h(b_1 + b_2);\quad b_1$ (geometry) $\dfrac{2A - hb_2}{h} = b_1$

7. $a_n = a_1 + (n-1)d;\quad d$ (mathematics) $d = \dfrac{a_n - a_1}{n-1}$

8. $y - y_1 = m(x - x_1);\quad x$ (mathematics) $\dfrac{y - y_1 + mx_1}{m} = x$

9. $S = \dfrac{a_1}{1-r};\quad r$ (mathematics) $r = \dfrac{S - a_1}{S}$

10. $\dfrac{P_1V_1}{T_1} = \dfrac{P_2V_2}{T_2};\quad V_2$ (chemistry) $\dfrac{P_1V_1T_2}{P_2T_1} = V_2$

11. **QUARTERBACK RATING** During the 2002 season, Peyton Manning, the quarterback of the Indianapolis Colts, completed 66.33% of his passes. He averaged 7.11 yards per pass attempt, 4.57% of his passes were for touchdowns, and 3.21% of his passes were intercepted. Determine Manning's quarterback rating for the 2002 season. Round to the nearest tenth. (*Hint:* See Example 2, page 92.) 88.8

12. **QUARTERBACK RATING** During the 2002 season, Drew Bledsoe, the quarterback of the Buffalo Bills, completed 61.48% of his passes. He averaged 7.15 yards per pass attempt, 3.93% of his passes were for touchdowns, and 2.46% of his passes were intercepted. Determine Bledsoe's quarterback rating for

the 2002 season. Round to the nearest tenth. (*Hint:* See Example 2, page 92.) 86.0

The SMOG (Simplified Measure of Gobbledygook) readability formula is often used to estimate the reading grade level required by a person if he or she is to *fully* understand the written material being assessed. The formula is given by

SMOG reading grade level = $\sqrt{w}$ + 3

where *w* is the number of words that have three or more syllables in a sample of 30 sentences.

13. **ASSESSING A READING LEVEL** A sample of 30 sentences from *Alice's Adventures in Wonderland*, by Lewis Carroll, shows a total of 42 words that have three or more syllables. Use the SMOG reading grade level formula to estimate the reading grade level required to fully understand this novel. Round the reading grade level to the nearest tenth. 9.5

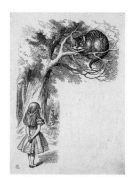

▶ **14.** **ASSESSING A READING LEVEL** A sample of 30 sentences from *A Tale of Two Cities*, by Charles Dickens, shows a total of 105 words that have three or more syllables. Use the SMOG reading grade level formula to estimate the reading grade level required to fully understand this novel. Round the reading grade level to the nearest tenth. 13.2

Another popular readability formula is the Gunning Fog Index. Here is the formula:

Gunning Fog Index = 0.4(A + W)

where *A* is the average number of words per sentence and *W* is the percentage of words that have four or more syllables. The Gunning Fog Index is defined as the minimum grade level at which the writing is *easily* read.

15. **ASSESSING A READING LEVEL** In a sample of sentences from the novel *Bridget Jones's Diary*, by Helen Fielding, the average number of words per sentence is

23.0, and five words have four or more syllables. Use the Gunning Fog Index to estimate the reading grade level required to easily read this material. 11.2

16. ● **Assessing a Reading Level** In a sample of sentences from the book *Winnie-the-Pooh Meets Tigger*, by A. A. Milne, the average number of words per sentence is 11.47, and only one word has four or more syllables. Use the Gunning Fog Index to estimate the reading grade level required to easily read this material. Round the reading grade level to the nearest tenth. 5.0

In Exercises 17 to 52, solve by using the Strategies for Solving Application Problems (see page 93).

17. One-fifth of a number plus one-fourth of the number is 5 less than one-half the number. What is the number? 100

18. The numerator of a fraction is 4 less than the denominator. If the numerator is increased by 14 and the denominator is decreased by 10, the resulting number is 5. What is the original fraction? $\frac{11}{15}$

19. **Geometry** The length of a rectangle is 3 feet less than twice the width of the rectangle. If the perimeter of the rectangle is 174 feet, find the width and the length. 30 ft by 57 ft

▶ **20.** **Geometry** The width of a rectangle is 1 meter more than half the length of the rectangle. If the perimeter of the rectangle is 110 meters, find the width and the length. length, 36 m; width, 19 m

21. **Geometry** A triangle has a perimeter of 84 centimeters. Each of the two longer sides of the triangle is three times as long as the shortest side. Find the length of each side of the triangle. 12 cm, 36 cm, 36 cm

22. **Geometry** A triangle has a perimeter of 161 miles. Each of the two smaller sides of the triangle is two-thirds the length of the longest side. Find the length of each side of the triangle. The longest side is 69 mi. The two shorter sides are each 46 mi.

23. **Uniform Motion** Running at an average rate of 6 meters per second, a sprinter ran to the end of a track and then jogged back to the starting point at an average rate of 2 meters per second. The total time for the sprint and the jog back was 2 minutes 40 seconds. Find the length of the track. 240 m

▶ **24.** **Uniform Motion** A motorboat left a harbor and traveled to an island at an average rate of 15 knots. The average speed on the return trip was 10 knots. If the total trip took 7.5 hours, how far is the harbor from the island? 45 nautical miles

25. **Uniform Motion** A plane leaves an airport traveling at an average speed of 240 kilometers per hour. How long will it take a second plane traveling the same route at an average speed of 600 kilometers per hour to catch up with the first plane if it leaves 3 hours later? 2 h

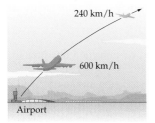

26. **Uniform Motion** A plane leaves Chicago headed for Los Angeles at 540 mph. One hour later, a second plane leaves Los Angeles headed for Chicago at 660 mph. If the air route from Chicago to Los Angeles is 1800 miles, how long will it take for the first plane to pass the second plane? How far from Chicago will they be at that time? 2.05 h, 1107 mi

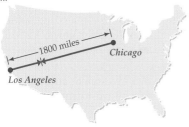

27. **Uniform Motion** Marlene rides her bicycle to her friend Jon's house and returns home by the same route. Marlene rides her bike at constant speeds of 6 mph on level ground, 4 mph when going uphill, and 12 mph when going downhill. If her total time riding was 1 hour, how far is it to Jon's house? 3 mi

28. **Uniform Motion** A car traveling at 80 kilometers per hour is passed by a second car going in the same direction at a constant speed. After 30 seconds, the two cars are 500 meters apart. Find the speed of the second car. 140 km/h

29. **Finding an Average** A student has test scores of 80, 82, 94, and 71. What score does the student need on the next test to produce an average score of 85? 98

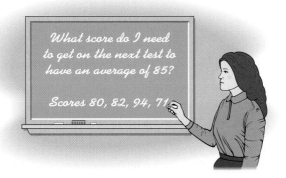

30. **FINDING AN AVERAGE** A student has test scores of 90, 74, 82, and 90. The next examination is the final examination, which will count as two tests. What score does the student need on the final examination to produce an average score of 85?
87

31. **BUSINESS** It costs a manufacturer of sunglasses $8.95 to produce sunglasses that sell for $29.99. How many sunglasses must the manufacturer sell to make a profit of $17,884?
850

▶ **32.** **BUSINESS** It costs a restaurant owner 18 cents per glass for orange juice, which is sold for 75 cents per glass. How many glasses of orange juice must the restaurant owner sell to make a profit of $2337?
4100

33. **BUSINESS** The price of a computer fell 20% this year. If the computer now costs $750, how much did it cost last year?
$937.50

34. **BUSINESS** The price of a magazine subscription rose 4% this year. If the subscription now costs $26, how much did it cost last year?
$25

35. **INVESTMENT** An investment adviser invested $14,000 in two accounts. One investment earned 8% annual simple interest, and the other investment earned 6.5% annual simple interest. The amount of interest earned for 1 year was $1024. How much was invested in each account?
$7600 invested at 8%, $6400 invested at 6.5%

▶ **36.** **INVESTMENT** A total of $7500 is deposited into two simple interest accounts. On one account the annual simple interest rate is 5%, and on the second account the annual simple interest rate is 7%. The amount of interest earned for 1 year was $405. How much was invested in each account?
$6000 invested at 5%, $1500 invested at 7%

37. **INVESTMENT** An investment of $2500 is made at an annual simple interest rate of 5.5%. How much additional money must be invested at an annual simple interest rate of 8% so that the total interest earned is 7% of the total investment?
$3750

38. **INVESTMENT** An investment of $4600 is made at an annual simple interest rate of 6.8%. How much additional money must be invested at an annual simple interest rate of 9% so that the total interest earned is 8% of the total investment?
$5520

39. **METALLURGY** How many grams of pure silver must a silversmith mix with a 45% silver alloy to produce 200 grams of a 50% alloy?
$18\frac{2}{11}$ g

▶ **40.** **CHEMISTRY** How many liters of a 40% sulfuric acid solution should be mixed with 4 liters of a 24% sulfuric acid solution to produce a 30% solution?
2.4 l

41. **CHEMISTRY** How many liters of water should be evaporated from 160 liters of a 12% saline solution so that the solution that remains is a 20% saline solution?
64 l

42. **AUTOMOTIVE** A radiator contains 6 liters of a 25% antifreeze solution. How much should be drained and replaced with pure antifreeze to produce a 33% antifreeze solution?
0.64 l

43. **COMMERCE** A ballet performance brought in $61,800 on the sale of 3000 tickets. If the tickets sold for $14 and $25, how many of each were sold?
1200 at $14 and 1800 at $25

44. **COMMERCE** A vending machine contains $41.25. The machine contains 255 coins, which consist only of nickels, dimes, and quarters. If the machine contains twice as many dimes as nickels, how many of each type of coin does the machine contain?
45 nickels, 90 dimes, 120 quarters

45. **COMMERCE** A coffee shop decides to blend a coffee that sells for $12 per pound with a coffee that sells for $9 per pound to produce a blend that will sell for $10 per pound. How much of each should be used to yield 20 pounds of the new blend?
$6\frac{2}{3}$ lb of the $12 coffee and $13\frac{1}{3}$ lb of the $9 coffee

46. **DETERMINE NUMBER OF COINS** A bag contains 42 coins, with a total weight of 246 grams. If the bag contains only gold coins that weigh 8 grams each and silver coins that weigh 5 grams each, how many gold and how many silver coins are in the bag?
12 gold coins; 30 silver coins

47. **METALLURGY** How much pure gold should be melted with 15 grams of 14-karat gold to produce 18-karat gold? (*Hint:* A karat is a measure of the purity of gold in an alloy. Pure gold measures 24 karats. An alloy that measures x karats is $\dfrac{x}{24}$ gold. For example, 18-karat gold is $\dfrac{18}{24} = \dfrac{3}{4}$ gold.)
10 g

48. **METALLURGY** How much 14-karat gold should be melted with 4 ounces of pure gold to produce 18-karat gold? (*Hint:* See Exercise 47.)
6 oz

49. **INSTALL ELECTRICAL WIRES** An electrician can install the electric wires in a house in 14 hours. A second electrician requires 18 hours. How long would it take both electricians, working together, to install the wires?
7.875 h

▶ **50.** **PRINT A REPORT** Printer A can print a report in 3 hours. Printer B can print the same report in 4 hours. How long would it take both printers, working together, to print the report?
$\dfrac{12}{7}$ h

51. **DETERMINE INDIVIDUAL PRICES** A book and a bookmark together sell for $10.10. If the price of the book is $10.00 more than the price of the bookmark, find the price of the book and the price of the bookmark.
$10.05 for book, $0.05 for bookmark

52. SHARE AN EXPENSE Three people decide to share the cost of a yacht. By bringing in an additional partner, they can reduce the cost for each person by $4000. What is the total cost of the yacht?
$48,000

CONNECTING CONCEPTS

The *Archimedean law of the lever* **states that for a lever to be in a state of balance with respect to a point called the** *fulcrum,* **the sum of the downward forces times their respective distances from the fulcrum on one side of the fulcrum must equal the sum of the downward forces times their respective distances from the fulcrum on the other side of the fulcrum. The accompanying figure shows this relationship.**

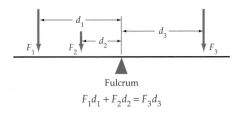

Fulcrum

$$F_1 d_1 + F_2 d_2 = F_3 d_3$$

53. LOCATE THE FULCRUM A 100-pound person 8 feet to the left of the fulcrum and a 40-pound person 5 feet to the left of the fulcrum balance with a 160-pound person on a teeter-totter. How far from the fulcrum is the 160-pound person?
6.25 ft

54. LOCATE THE FULCRUM A lever 21 feet long has a force of 117 pounds applied to one end of the lever and a force of 156 pounds applied to the other end. Where should the fulcrum be located to produce a state of balance?
12 ft from the 117-lb force

55. DETERMINE A FORCE How much force applied 5 feet from the fulcrum is needed to lift a 400-pound weight that is located on the other side, 0.5 foot from the fulcrum?
40 lb

56. DETERMINE A FORCE Two workers need to lift a 1440-pound rock. They use a 6-foot steel bar with the fulcrum 1 foot from the rock, as the accompanying figure shows. One worker applies 180 pounds of force to the other end of the lever. How much force will the second worker need to apply 1 foot from that end to lift the rock?
135 lb

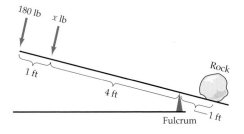

57. SPEED OF SOUND IN AIR Two seconds after firing a rifle at a target, the shooter hears the impact of the bullet. Sound travels at 1100 feet per second and the bullet at 1865 feet per second. Determine the distance to the target (to the nearest foot).
1384 ft

58. SPEED OF SOUND IN WATER Sound travels through sea water 4.62 times faster than through air. The sound of an exploding mine on the surface of the water and partially submerged reaches a ship through the water 4 seconds before it reaches the ship through the air. How far is the ship from the explosion (to the nearest foot)? Use 1100 feet per second as the speed of sound through the air.
5615 ft

59. AGE OF DIOPHANTUS The work of the ancient Greek mathematician Diophantus had great influence on later European number theorists. Nothing is known about his personal life except for the information given in the following epigram. "Diophantus passed $\frac{1}{6}$ of his life in childhood, $\frac{1}{12}$ in youth, and $\frac{1}{7}$ more as a bachelor. Five years after his marriage was born a son who died four years before his father, at $\frac{1}{2}$ his father's (final) age." How old was Diophantus when he died?
84 years old

60. EQUIVALENT TEMPERATURES The relationship between the Fahrenheit temperature (F) and the Celsius temperature (C) is given by the formula

$$F = \frac{9}{5}C + 32$$

At what temperature will a Fahrenheit thermometer and a Celsius thermometer read the same?
$-40°$

PREPARE FOR SECTION 1.3
---

61. Factor: $x^2 - x - 42$ [P.4] $(x + 6)(x - 7)$

62. Factor: $6x^2 - x - 15$ [P.4] $(2x + 3)(3x - 5)$

63. Write $3 + \sqrt{-16}$ in $a + bi$ form. [P.6] $3 + 4i$

64. If $a = -3$, $b = -2$, and $c = 5$, evaluate
$$\frac{-b - \sqrt{b^2 - 4ac}}{2a} \text{ [P.1/P.2] } 1$$

65. If $a = 2$, $b = -3$, and $c = 1$, evaluate
$$\frac{-b + \sqrt{b^2 - 4ac}}{2a} \text{ [P.1/P.2] } 1$$

66. If $x = 3 - i$, evaluate $x^2 - 6x + 10$. [P.6] 0

PROJECTS
---

1. A WORK PROBLEM AND ITS EXTENSIONS If a pump can fill a pool in A hours, and a second pump can fill the same pool in B hours, then the total time T, in hours, needed to fill the pool with both pumps working together is given by

$$T = \frac{AB}{A + B}$$

a. Verify this formula.

b. Consider the case where a pool is to be filled by three pumps. One can fill the pool in A hours, a second in B hours, and a third in C hours. Derive a formula in terms of A, B, and C for the total time T needed to fill the pool.

c. Consider the case where a pool is to be filled by n pumps. One pump can fill the pool in A_1 hours, a second in A_2 hours, a third in A_3 hours,..., and the nth pump can fill the pool in A_n hours. Write a formula in terms of $A_1, A_2, A_3, \ldots, A_n$ for the total time T needed to fill the pool.

The following chart is called an *alignment chart* or a *nomogram*. If you know any two of the values A, B, and T, then you can use the alignment chart to determine the unknown value. For example, the straight line segment that connects 3 on the A-axis with 6 on the B-axis crosses the T-axis at 2. Thus the total time required for a pump that takes 3 hours to fill the pool and a pump that takes 6 hours to fill the pool is 2 hours when they work together.

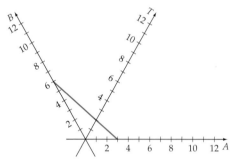

Alignment Chart for $T = \dfrac{AB}{A + B}$

d. Consider the case where a pool is to be filled by three pumps. One can fill the pool in $A = 6$ hours, a second in $B = 8$ hours, and a third in $C = 12$ hours. Write a few sentences explaining how you could make use of the alignment chart above to show that it takes about 2.7 hours for the three pumps to fill the pool when they work together.

2. RESISTANCE OF PARALLEL CIRCUITS The alignment chart shown in Project 1 can be used to solve some problems in electronics that concern the total resistance of a *parallel* circuit. Read an electronics text, and write a paragraph or two that explain this problem and how it is related to the problem of filling a pool with two pumps.

QUADRATIC EQUATIONS

- SOLVE QUADRATIC EQUATIONS BY FACTORING
- SOLVE QUADRATIC EQUATIONS BY TAKING SQUARE ROOTS
- SOLVE QUADRATIC EQUATIONS BY COMPLETING THE SQUARE
- SOLVE QUADRATIC EQUATIONS BY USING THE QUADRATIC FORMULA
- THE DISCRIMINANT OF A QUADRATIC EQUATION
- APPLICATIONS OF QUADRATIC EQUATIONS

• SOLVE QUADRATIC EQUATIONS BY FACTORING

In Section 1.1 you solved linear equations. In this section you will learn to solve a type of equation that is referred to as a *quadratic equation*.

Definition of a Quadratic Equation

A **quadratic equation** in x is an equation that can be written in the standard quadratic form

$$ax^2 + bx + c = 0$$

where a, b, and c are real numbers and $a \neq 0$.

Several methods can be used to solve a quadratic equation. For instance, if you can factor $ax^2 + bx + c$ into linear factors, then $ax^2 + bx + c = 0$ can be solved by applying the following property.

The Zero Product Principle

If A and B are algebraic expressions such that $AB = 0$, then $A = 0$ or $B = 0$.

The zero product principle states that if the product of two factors is zero, then at least one of the factors must be zero. In Example 1, the zero product principle is used to solve a quadratic equation.

MATH MATTERS

The term *quadratic* is derived from the Latin word *quadrare*, which means "to make square." Because the area of a square that measures x units on each side is x^2, we refer to equations that can be written in the form $ax^2 + bx + c = 0$ as equations that are quadratic in x.

Alternative to Example 1
Solve each quadratic equation.
1. $4x^2 - 2 = 7x$

● $-\dfrac{1}{4}, 2$

2. $36x^2 - 12x + 1 = 0$

● $x = \dfrac{1}{6}$

EXAMPLE I   Solve by Factoring

Solve each quadratic equation by factoring.

a. $x^2 + 2x - 15 = 0$ **b.** $2x^2 - 5x = 12$

Solution

a. $x^2 + 2x - 15 = 0$

$(x - 3)(x + 5) = 0$ • Factor.

$x - 3 = 0 \quad x + 5 = 0$ • Set each factor equal to zero.

$x = 3 \qquad x = -5$ • Solve each linear equation.

A check shows that 3 and -5 are both solutions of $x^2 + 2x - 15 = 0$.

Continued ▶

INSTRUCTOR NOTE
Encourage students to check possible solutions in the original equation rather than checking by using an equation they produced from the original equation.

b.
$$2x^2 - 5x = 12$$
$$2x^2 - 5x - 12 = 0 \qquad \text{• Write in standard quadratic form.}$$
$$(x - 4)(2x + 3) = 0 \qquad \text{• Factor.}$$
$$x - 4 = 0 \qquad 2x + 3 = 0 \qquad \text{• Set each factor equal to zero.}$$
$$x = 4 \qquad 2x = -3 \qquad \text{• Solve each linear equation.}$$
$$x = -\frac{3}{2}$$

A check shows that 4 and $-\dfrac{3}{2}$ are both solutions of $2x^2 - 5x = 12$.

▶ **TRY EXERCISE 6, PAGE 113**

Some quadratic equations have a solution that is called a *double root*. For instance, consider $x^2 - 8x + 16 = 0$. Solving this equation by factoring, we have

$$x^2 - 8x + 16 = 0$$
$$(x - 4)(x - 4) = 0 \qquad \text{• Factor.}$$
$$x - 4 = 0 \qquad x - 4 = 0 \qquad \text{• Set each factor equal to zero.}$$
$$x = 4 \qquad x = 4 \qquad \text{• Solve each linear equation.}$$

The only solution of $x^2 - 8x + 16 = 0$ is 4. In this situation, the single solution 4 is called a **double solution** or **double root** because it was produced by solving the two identical equations $x - 4 = 0$, both of which have 4 as a solution.

● SOLVE QUADRATIC EQUATIONS BY TAKING SQUARE ROOTS

In the following example we solve $x^2 = 25$ by factoring.

$$x^2 = 25$$
$$x^2 - 25 = 0$$
$$(x - 5)(x + 5) = 0 \qquad \text{• Factor.}$$
$$x - 5 = 0 \qquad x + 5 = 0 \qquad \text{• Set each factor equal to zero.}$$
$$x = 5 \qquad x = -5 \qquad \text{• Solve each linear equation.}$$

The solutions of $x^2 = 25$ also can be found by taking the square root of each side of the equation. In the following work a plus or minus sign is placed in front of the square root of 25 to produce both solutions. The notation $x = \pm 5$ means $x = 5$ or $x = -5$.

$$x^2 = 25$$
$$x = \pm\sqrt{25} \qquad \text{• Take the square root of each side of the equation.}$$
$$\qquad\qquad\qquad\quad \text{Insert a plus or minus sign in front of the radical}$$
$$\qquad\qquad\qquad\quad \text{on the right.}$$
$$x = \pm 5$$
$$x = 5 \quad \text{or} \quad x = -5$$

We will refer to the preceding method of solving a quadratic equation as the *square root procedure*.

P **The Square Root Procedure**

If $x^2 = c$, then $x = \sqrt{c}$ or $x = -\sqrt{c}$, which can also be written as $x = \pm\sqrt{c}$.

Alternative to Example 2
Use the square root procedure to solve:
a. $(x + 8)^2 = 81$
● **−17, 1**
b. $(x − 4)^2 = 25$
● **−1, 9**

EXAMPLE 2   **Solve by Using the Square Root Procedure**

Use the square root procedure to solve each equation.

a. $3x^2 + 12 = 0$ **b.** $(x + 1)^2 = 49$

Solution

a. $3x^2 + 12 = 0$

$$3x^2 = -12$$ • Solve for x^2.

$$x^2 = -4$$

$$x = \pm\sqrt{-4}$$ • Take the square root of each side of the equation and insert a plus or minus sign in front of the radical.

$$x = \pm 2i$$

b. $(x + 1)^2 = 49$

$$x + 1 = \pm\sqrt{49}$$ • Take the square root of each side of the equation and insert a plus or minus sign in front of the radical.

$$x = -1 \pm 7$$ • Simplify.

$$x = 6 \quad \text{or} \quad -8$$

▶ **TRY EXERCISE 20, PAGE 113**

● **SOLVE QUADRATIC EQUATIONS BY COMPLETING THE SQUARE**

Consider the following binomial squares and their perfect-square trinomial products.

Square of a Binomial	=	Perfect-Square Trinomial
$(x + 5)^2$	=	$x^2 + 10x + 25$
$(x - 3)^2$	=	$x^2 - 6x + 9$

In each of the preceding perfect-square trinomials, the coefficient of x^2 is 1, and the constant term is the square of half the coefficient of the x term.

$$x^2 + 10x + 25, \qquad \left(\frac{1}{2} \cdot 10\right)^2 = 25$$

$$x^2 - 6x + 9, \qquad \left(\frac{1}{2} \cdot (-6)\right)^2 = 9$$

MATH MATTERS

Mathematicians have studied quadratic equations for centuries. Many of the initial quadratic equations they studied were a result of trying to solve geometry problems. One of the most famous, which dates from around 500 B.C., concerns "squaring a circle." The question was, "Is it possible to construct a square whose area is the same as the area of a given circle?" For these early mathematicians, to construct meant to draw with only a straightedge and a compass. It was approximately 2300 years later that mathematicians were able to prove that such a construction is impossible.

Adding to a binomial of the form $x^2 + bx$ the constant term that makes the binomial a perfect-square trinomial is called **completing the square**. For example, to complete the square of $x^2 + 8x$, add

$$\left(\frac{1}{2} \cdot 8\right)^2 = 16$$

to produce the perfect-square trinomial $x^2 + 8x + 16$.

Completing the square is a powerful procedure because it can be used to solve *any* quadratic equation. For instance, to solve $x^2 - 6x + 13 = 0$, begin by writing the variable terms on one side of the equation and the constant term on the other side.

$$x^2 - 6x = -13$$ • Subtract 13 from each side of the equation.

$$x^2 - 6x + 9 = -13 + 9$$ • Complete the square by adding $\left[\frac{1}{2}(-6)\right]^2 = 9$ to each side of the equation.

$$(x - 3)^2 = -4$$ • Factor and solve by the square root procedure.

$$x - 3 = \pm\sqrt{-4}$$
$$x - 3 = \pm 2i$$
$$x = 3 \pm 2i$$

The solutions of $x^2 - 6x + 13 = 0$ are $3 - 2i$ and $3 + 2i$. You can check these solutions by substituting each solution into the original equation. For instance, the following check shows that $3 - 2i$ does satisfy the original equation.

$$x^2 - 6x + 13 = 0$$
$$(3 - 2i)^2 - 6(3 - 2i) + 13 = 0$$ • Substitute $3 - 2i$ for x.
$$9 - 12i + 4i^2 - 18 + 12i + 13 = 0$$ • Simplify.
$$4 + 4(-1) = 0$$
$$0 = 0$$ • The left side equals the right side, so $3 - 2i$ checks.

Alternative to Example 3
Solve: $x^2 + 2 = x$
● $\frac{1}{2} + \frac{i\sqrt{7}}{2}, \frac{1}{2} - \frac{i\sqrt{7}}{2}$

EXAMPLE 3 **Solve by Completing the Square**

Solve $x^2 = 2x + 6$ by completing the square.

Solution

$$x^2 = 2x + 6$$
$$x^2 - 2x = 6$$ • Isolate the constant term.
$$x^2 - 2x + 1 = 6 + 1$$ • Complete the square.
$$(x - 1)^2 = 7$$ • Factor and simplify.
$$x - 1 = \pm\sqrt{7}$$ • Apply the square root procedure.
$$x = 1 \pm \sqrt{7}$$ • Solve for x.

The exact solutions of $x^2 = 2x + 6$ are $x = 1 - \sqrt{7}$ and $x = 1 + \sqrt{7}$. A calculator can be used to show that $1 - \sqrt{7} \approx -1.646$ and $1 + \sqrt{7} \approx 3.646$. The decimals -1.646 and 3.646 are approximate solutions of $x^2 = 2x + 6$.

▶ **TRY EXERCISE 26, PAGE 113**

Completing the square by adding the square of half the coefficient of the x term requires that the coefficient of the x^2 term be 1. If the coefficient of the x^2 term is not 1, then first multiply each term on each side of the equation by the reciprocal of the coefficient of x^2 to produce a coefficient of 1 for the x^2 term.

Alternative to Example 4

Solve: $3x^2 + 18x - 4 = 0$

● $\dfrac{-9 + \sqrt{93}}{3}, \dfrac{-9 - \sqrt{93}}{3}$

MATH MATTERS

Ancient mathematicians thought of "completing the square" in a geometric manner. For instance, to complete the square of $x^2 + 8x$, draw a square that measures x units on each side, and add four rectangles that measure 1 unit by x units to the right side and the bottom of the square.

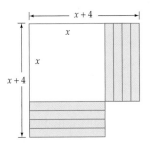

Each of the rectangles has an area of x square units, so the total area of the figure is $x^2 + 8x$. To make this figure a complete square, we must add 16 squares that measure 1 unit by 1 unit, as shown below.

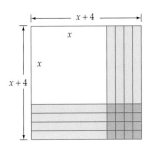

This figure is a *complete square* Ⓟ whose area is

$$(x + 4)^2 = x^2 + 8x + 16$$

EXAMPLE 4   Solve by Completing the Square

Solve $2x^2 + 8x - 1 = 0$ by completing the square.

Solution

$$2x^2 + 8x - 1 = 0$$

$$2x^2 + 8x = 1 \qquad \text{• Isolate the constant term.}$$

$$\frac{1}{2}(2x^2 + 8x) = \frac{1}{2}(1) \qquad \text{• Multiply both sides of the equation by the reciprocal of the coefficient of } x^2.$$

$$x^2 + 4x = \frac{1}{2}$$

$$x^2 + 4x + 4 = \frac{1}{2} + 4 \qquad \text{• Complete the square.}$$

$$(x + 2)^2 = \frac{9}{2} \qquad \text{• Factor and simplify.}$$

$$x + 2 = \pm\sqrt{\frac{9}{2}} \qquad \text{• Apply the square root procedure.}$$

$$x = -2 \pm 3\sqrt{\frac{1}{2}} \qquad \text{• Solve for } x.$$

$$x = -2 \pm 3\frac{\sqrt{2}}{2} \qquad \text{• Simplify.}$$

$$x = \frac{-4 \pm 3\sqrt{2}}{2}$$

The solutions of $2x^2 + 8x - 1 = 0$ are $x = \dfrac{-4 + 3\sqrt{2}}{2}$ and $x = \dfrac{-4 - 3\sqrt{2}}{2}$.

▶ **TRY EXERCISE 30, PAGE 113**

● **SOLVE QUADRATIC EQUATIONS BY USING THE QUADRATIC FORMULA**

Completing the square on $ax^2 + bx + c = 0$ $(a \neq 0)$ produces a formula for x in terms of the coefficients a, b, and c. The formula is known as the *quadratic formula*, and it can be used to solve *any* quadratic equation.

Ⓟ **The Quadratic Formula**

If $ax^2 + bx + c = 0$, $a \neq 0$, then

$$x = \frac{-b \pm \sqrt{b^2 - 4ac}}{2a}$$

MATH MATTERS

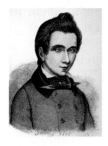

Evariste Galois (1811–1832)

The quadratic formula provides the solutions to the general quadratic equation

$$ax^2 + bx + c = 0$$

and formulas have been developed to solve the general cubic

$$ax^3 + bx^2 + cx + d = 0$$

and the general quartic

$$ax^4 + bx^3 + cx^2 + dx + e = 0$$

However, the French mathematician Evariste Galois, shown above, was able to prove that there are no formulas that can be used to solve "by radicals" general equations of degree 5 or larger.

Shortly after completion of his remarkable proof, Galois was shot in a duel. It has been reported that as Galois lay dying, he asked his brother, Alfred, to "Take care of my work. Make it known. Important." When Alfred broke into tears, Evariste said, "Don't cry Alfred. I need all my courage to die at twenty." (*Source: Whom the Gods Love*, by Leopold Infeld, The National Council of Teachers of Mathematics, 1978, p. 299.)

Alternative to Example 5
Solve:
1. $4x^2 - 24x + 5 = 0$
• $\dfrac{6 + \sqrt{31}}{2}, \dfrac{6 - \sqrt{31}}{2}$
2. $x^2 + 7 = 5x$
• $\dfrac{5}{2} + \dfrac{i\sqrt{3}}{2}, \dfrac{5}{2} - \dfrac{i\sqrt{3}}{2}$

Proof   We assume a is a positive real number. If a were a negative real number, then we could multiply each side of the equation by -1 to make it positive.

$$ax^2 + bx + c = 0 \quad (a \neq 0)$$ • Given.

$$ax^2 + bx = -c$$ • Isolate the constant term.

$$x^2 + \frac{b}{a}x = -\frac{c}{a}$$ • Multiply each term on each side of the equation by $\dfrac{1}{a}$.

$$x^2 + \frac{b}{a}x + \left(\frac{b}{2a}\right)^2 = \left(\frac{b}{2a}\right)^2 - \frac{c}{a}$$ • Complete the square.

$$\left(x + \frac{b}{2a}\right)^2 = \frac{b^2}{4a^2} - \frac{c}{a}$$ • Factor the left side. Simplify the powers on the right side.

$$\left(x + \frac{b}{2a}\right)^2 = \frac{b^2}{4a^2} - \frac{4a}{4a} \cdot \frac{c}{a}$$ • Use a common denominator to simplify the right side.

$$x + \frac{b}{2a} = \pm \sqrt{\frac{b^2 - 4ac}{4a^2}}$$ • Apply the square root procedure.

$$x + \frac{b}{2a} = \pm \frac{\sqrt{b^2 - 4ac}}{2a}$$ • Because $a > 0$, $\sqrt{4a^2} = 2a$.

$$x = -\frac{b}{2a} \pm \frac{\sqrt{b^2 - 4ac}}{2a}$$ • Add $-\dfrac{b}{2a}$ to each side.

$$x = \frac{-b \pm \sqrt{b^2 - 4ac}}{2a}$$ ◆

As a general rule, you should first try to solve quadratic equations by factoring. If the factoring process proves difficult, then solve by using the quadratic formula.

EXAMPLE 5   **Solve by Using the Quadratic Formula**

Use the quadratic formula to solve each of the following.

a. $4x^2 - 4x - 3 = 0$ **b.** $x^2 = 3x + 5$

Solution

a. For the equation $4x^2 - 4x - 3 = 0$, we have $a = 4$, $b = -4$, and $c = -3$. Substituting in the quadratic formula produces

$$x = \frac{-b \pm \sqrt{b^2 - 4ac}}{2a}$$

$$= \frac{-(-4) \pm \sqrt{(-4)^2 - 4(4)(-3)}}{2(4)}$$

$$= \frac{4 \pm \sqrt{64}}{8} = \frac{4 \pm 8}{8} = \frac{1 \pm 2}{2} = \frac{3}{2} \text{ or } -\frac{1}{2}$$

The solutions of $4x^2 - 4x - 3 = 0$ are $x = \dfrac{3}{2}$ and $x = -\dfrac{1}{2}$.

take note

Although the equation in Example
5a can be solved by factoring, we
have solved it by using the
quadratic formula to illustrate the
procedures involved in applying the
quadratic formula.

b. The standard form of $x^2 = 3x + 5$ is $x^2 - 3x - 5 = 0$. Substituting $a = 1$, $b = -3$, and $c = -5$ in the quadratic formula produces

$$x = \frac{-(-3) \pm \sqrt{(-3)^2 - 4(1)(-5)}}{2(1)}$$

$$= \frac{3 \pm \sqrt{29}}{2}$$

The solutions of $x^2 = 3x + 5$ are $x = \dfrac{3 + \sqrt{29}}{2}$ and $x = \dfrac{3 - \sqrt{29}}{2}$.

▶ **TRY EXERCISE 38, PAGE 113**

❓ QUESTION Can the quadratic formula be used to solve any quadratic equation $ax^2 + bx + c = 0$ with real coefficients and $a \neq 0$?

● THE DISCRIMINANT OF A QUADRATIC EQUATION

The solutions of $ax^2 + bx + c = 0$, $a \neq 0$, are given by

$$x = \frac{-b \pm \sqrt{b^2 - 4ac}}{2a}$$

The expression under the radical, $b^2 - 4ac$, is called the **discriminant** of the equation $ax^2 + bx + c = 0$. If $b^2 - 4ac \geq 0$, then $\sqrt{b^2 - 4ac}$ is a real number. If $b^2 - 4ac < 0$, then $\sqrt{b^2 - 4ac}$ is not a real number. Thus the sign of the discriminant can be used to determine whether the solutions of a quadratic equation are real numbers.

To review **COMPLEX
CONJUGATES**, *see p. 69.*

The Discriminant and the Solutions of a Quadratic Equation

The equation $ax^2 + bx + c = 0$, with real coefficients and $a \neq 0$, has as its discriminant $b^2 - 4ac$.

● If $b^2 - 4ac > 0$, then $ax^2 + bx + c = 0$ has *two distinct real solutions.*

● If $b^2 - 4ac = 0$, then $ax^2 + bx + c = 0$ has *one real solution.* The solution is a double solution.

● If $b^2 - 4ac < 0$, then $ax^2 + bx + c = 0$ has *two distinct nonreal complex solutions.* The solutions are conjugates of each other.

Alternative to Example 6
Determine the discriminant of
$4x^2 - 4x + 1 = 0$, and state the number
of real solutions for the equation.
● **discriminant 0; one real solution**

EXAMPLE 6 Use the Discriminant to Determine the Number of Real Solutions

For each equation, determine the discriminant and state the number of real solutions.

a. $2x^2 - 5x + 1 = 0$ **b.** $3x^2 + 6x + 7 = 0$ **c.** $x^2 + 6x + 9 = 0$

Continued ▶

❓ ANSWER Yes. However, it is sometimes easier to find the solutions by factoring, by the square root procedure, or by completing the square.

Solution

a. The discriminant of $2x^2 - 5x + 1 = 0$ is $b^2 - 4ac = (-5)^2 - 4(2)(1) = 17$. Because the discriminant is positive, $2x^2 - 5x + 1 = 0$ has two distinct real solutions.

b. The discriminant of $3x^2 + 6x + 7 = 0$ is $b^2 - 4ac = 6^2 - 4(3)(7) = -48$. Because the discriminant is negative, $3x^2 + 6x + 7 = 0$ has no real solutions.

c. The discriminant of $x^2 + 6x + 9 = 0$ is $b^2 - 4ac = 6^2 - 4(1)(9) = 0$. Because the discriminant is 0, $x^2 + 6x + 9 = 0$ has one real solution.

▶ **TRY EXERCISE 48, PAGE 113**

• APPLICATIONS OF QUADRATIC EQUATIONS

A **right triangle** contains one 90° angle. The side opposite the 90° angle is called the **hypotenuse.** The other two sides are called **legs.** The lengths of the sides of a right triangle are related by a theorem known as the Pythagorean Theorem.

P **The Pythagorean Theorem**

If a and b denote the lengths of the legs of a right triangle and c the length of the hypotenuse, then $c^2 = a^2 + b^2$.

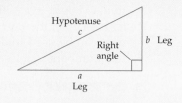

The Pythagorean Theorem states that the square of the length of the hypotenuse of a right triangle is equal to the sum of the squares of the lengths of the legs. This theorem is often used to solve applications that involve right triangles.

Alternative to Example 7
A 12-foot ladder is leaning against a building. How high on the building will the ladder reach when the bottom of the ladder is 4 feet from the building? Round to the nearest tenth of a foot.
● **11.3 ft**

take note

Many movies are designed to be shown on a screen that has a 16 to 9 aspect ratio.

EXAMPLE 7   Determine the Dimensions of a Television Screen

A television screen measures 60 inches diagonally, and its *aspect ratio* is 16 to 9. This means that the ratio of the width of the screen to the height of the screen is 16 to 9. Find the width and height of the screen.

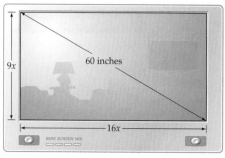

A 60-inch television screen with a 16:9 aspect ratio.

Solution

Let $16x$ represent the width of the screen and let $9x$ represent the height of the screen. Applying the Pythagorean Theorem gives us

$$(16x)^2 + (9x)^2 = 60^2$$
$$256x^2 + 81x^2 = 3600 \qquad \text{• Solve for } x.$$
$$337x^2 = 3600$$
$$x^2 = \frac{3600}{337} \qquad \text{• Apply the square root procedure.}$$
$$x = \sqrt{\frac{3600}{337}} \approx 3.268 \text{ inches} \qquad \text{• The plus or minus sign is not used in this application because we know } x \text{ is positive.}$$

The height of the screen is about $9(3.268) \approx 29.4$ inches and the width of the screen is about $16(3.268) \approx 52.3$ inches.

▶ **TRY EXERCISE 58, PAGE 114**

Alternative to Example 8
Exercise 66, page 114.

EXAMPLE 8   **Determine the Dimensions of a Candy Bar**

At the present time, a company makes rectangular solid candy bars that measure 5 inches by 2 inches by 0.5 inch. Due to difficult financial times, the company has decided to keep the price of the candy bar fixed and reduce the volume of the bar by 20%. What should be the dimensions of the new candy bar if it is decided to keep the height at 0.5 inch and to keep the length of the candy bar 3 inches longer than the width?

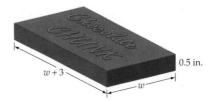

Solution

The volume of a rectangular solid is given by $V = lwh$. The original candy bar had a volume of $5 \cdot 2 \cdot 0.5 = 5$ cubic inches. The new candy bar will have a volume of $80\%(5) = 0.80(5) = 4$ cubic inches.

Let w represent the width and $w + 3$ represent the length of the new candy bar. For the new candy bar we have:

$$lwh = V$$
$$(w + 3)(w)(0.5) = 4 \qquad \text{• Substitute in the volume formula.}$$
$$(w + 3)(w) = 8 \qquad \text{• Multiply each side by 2.}$$
$$w^2 + 3w = 8$$
$$w^2 + 3w - 8 = 0 \qquad \text{• Write in } ax^2 + bx + c = 0 \text{ form.}$$

Continued ▶

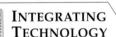
INTEGRATING TECHNOLOGY

In many application problems it is helpful to use a calculator to estimate the solutions of a quadratic equation by applying the quadratic formula. For instance, the following figure shows the use of a graphing calculator to estimate the solutions of $w^2 + 3w - 8 = 0$.

```
(-3+√(3²–4*1*(-8)))/2
                1.701562119
(-3-√(3²–4*1*(-8)))/2
               -4.701562119
```

INSTRUCTOR NOTE
Inform your students that many calculators have a "recall procedure" that allows a user to quickly recall and edit a previous entry. For instance, in the TI-83 calculator display on page 111, the second entry was produced by recalling the first entry and changing the plus sign in front of the radical to a subtraction sign. On a TI-83 calculator, this recall procedure is accomplished by pressing 2nd ENTRY.

$$w = \frac{-(3) \pm \sqrt{(3)^2 - 4(1)(-8)}}{2(1)}$$ • Use the quadratic formula.

$$= \frac{-3 \pm \sqrt{41}}{2}$$

$$\approx 1.7 \quad \text{or} \quad -4.7$$

We can disregard the negative value because the width must be positive. The width of the new candy bar should be 1.7 inches, to the nearest tenth of an inch. The length should be 3 inches longer, which is 4.7 inches.

▶ **TRY EXERCISE 70, PAGE 115**

Quadratic equations are often used to determine the height (position) of an object that has been dropped or projected. For instance, the *position equation* $s = -16t^2 + v_0t + s_0$ can be used to estimate the height of a projected object near the surface of the earth at a given time t, in seconds. In this equation, v_0 is the initial velocity of the object in feet per second, and s_0 is the initial height of the object in feet.

Alternative to Example 9
Exercise 78, page 116.

EXAMPLE 9   **Determine the Time of Descent**

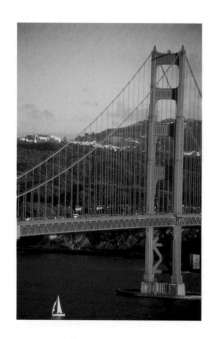

A ball is thrown downward with an initial velocity of 5 feet per second from the Golden Gate Bridge, which is 220 feet above the water. How long will it take for the ball to hit the water? Round your answer to the nearest hundreth of a second.

Solution

The distance s, in feet, of the ball above the water after t seconds is given by $s = -16t^2 - 5t + 220$. We have replaced v_0 with -5 because the ball is thrown downward. (If the ball had been thrown upward, we would use $v_0 = 5$). To determine the time it takes the ball to hit the water, substitute 0 for s in the equation $s = -16t^2 - 5t + 220$ and solve for t. In the following work, we have solved by using the quadratic formula.

$$0 = -16t^2 - 5t + 220$$

$$t = \frac{-(-5) \pm \sqrt{(-5)^2 - 4(-16)(220)}}{2(-16)}$$ • Use the quadratic formula.

$$= \frac{5 \pm \sqrt{14{,}105}}{-32}$$ • Use a calculator to estimate t.

$$\approx -3.87 \quad \text{or} \quad 3.56$$

Because the time must be positive, we disregard the negative value. The ball will hit the water in about 3.56 seconds.

▶ **TRY EXERCISE 72, PAGE 115**

 TOPICS FOR DISCUSSION

1. Name the four methods of solving a quadratic equation that have been discussed in this section. What are the advantages and disadvantages of each?

2. If x and y are real numbers and $xy = 0$, then $x = 0$ or $y = 0$. Do you agree with this statement? Explain.

3. If x and y are real numbers and $xy = 1$, then $x = 1$ or $y = 1$. Do you agree with this statement? Explain.

4. Explain how to complete the square on $x^2 + bx$.

5. If the discriminant of $ax^2 + bx + c = 0$ with real coefficients and $a \neq 0$ is negative, then what can be said concerning the solutions of the equation?

EXERCISE SET 1.3   —Suggested Assignment: Exercises 1–77, every other odd; 87–92, all.

In Exercises 1 to 10, solve each quadratic equation by factoring and applying the zero product principle.

1. $x^2 - 2x - 15 = 0$
   $-3, 5$

2. $x^2 + 3x - 10 = 0$
   $-5, 2$

3. $2x^2 - x = 1$ $-\dfrac{1}{2}, 1$

4. $2x^2 + 5x = 3$ $-3, \dfrac{1}{2}$

5. $8x^2 + 189x - 72 = 0$ $-24, \dfrac{3}{8}$

▶ 6. $12x^2 - 41x + 24 = 0$ $\dfrac{8}{3}, \dfrac{3}{4}$

7. $3x^2 - 7x = 0$ $0, \dfrac{7}{3}$

8. $5x^2 = -8x$ $0, -\dfrac{8}{5}$

9. $(x - 5)^2 - 9 = 0$
   $2, 8$

10. $(3x + 4)^2 - 16 = 0$
    $-\dfrac{8}{3}, 0$

In Exercises 11 to 20, use the square root procedure to solve each quadratic equation.

11. $x^2 = 81$
    ± 9

12. $x^2 = 225$
    ± 15

13. $2x^2 = 48$
    $\pm 2\sqrt{6}$

14. $3x^2 = 144$
    $\pm 4\sqrt{3}$

15. $3x^2 + 12 = 0$
    $\pm 2i$

16. $4x^2 + 20 = 0$
    $\pm i\sqrt{5}$

17. $(x - 5)^2 = 36$
    $-1, 11$

18. $(x + 4)^2 = 121$
    $-15, 7$

19. $(x - 3)^2 + 16 = 0$
    $3 \pm 4i$

▶ 20. $(x + 2)^2 + 28 = 0$
    $-2 \pm 2i\sqrt{7}$

In Exercises 21 to 32, solve each quadratic equation by completing the square.

21. $x^2 + 6x + 1 = 0$
    $-3 \pm 2\sqrt{2}$

22. $x^2 + 8x - 10 = 0$
    $-4 \pm \sqrt{26}$

23. $x^2 - 2x - 15 = 0$
    $-3, 5$

24. $x^2 + 2x - 8 = 0$
    $-4, 2$

25. $x^2 + 4x + 5 = 0$
    $-2 \pm i$

▶ 26. $x^2 - 6x + 10 = 0$
    $3 \pm i$

27. $x^2 + 3x - 1 = 0$ $\dfrac{-3 \pm \sqrt{13}}{2}$

28. $x^2 + 7x - 2 = 0$ $\dfrac{-7 \pm \sqrt{57}}{2}$

29. $2x^2 + 4x - 1 = 0$ $\dfrac{-2 \pm \sqrt{6}}{2}$

▶ 30. $2x^2 + 10x - 3 = 0$ $\dfrac{-5 \pm \sqrt{31}}{2}$

31. $3x^2 - 8x = -1$ $\dfrac{4 \pm \sqrt{13}}{3}$

32. $4x^2 - 4x = -15$ $\dfrac{1}{2} \pm \dfrac{\sqrt{14}}{2}i$

In Exercises 33 to 46, solve each quadratic equation by using the quadratic formula.

33. $x^2 - 2x = 15$
    $-3, 5$

34. $x^2 - 5x = 24$
    $-3, 8$

35. $x^2 = -x + 1$ $\dfrac{-1 \pm \sqrt{5}}{2}$

36. $x^2 = -x - 1$ $-\dfrac{1}{2} \pm \dfrac{\sqrt{3}}{2}i$

37. $2x^2 + 4x = -1$ $\dfrac{-2 \pm \sqrt{2}}{2}$

▶ 38. $2x^2 + 4x = 1$ $\dfrac{-2 \pm \sqrt{6}}{2}$

39. $3x^2 - 5x + 3 = 0$ $\dfrac{5}{6} \pm \dfrac{\sqrt{11}}{6}i$

40. $3x^2 - 5x + 4 = 0$ $\dfrac{5}{6} \pm \dfrac{\sqrt{23}}{6}i$

41. $\dfrac{1}{2}x^2 + \dfrac{3}{4}x - 1 = 0$ $\dfrac{-3 \pm \sqrt{41}}{4}$

42. $\dfrac{2}{3}x^2 - 5x + \dfrac{1}{2} = 0$ $\dfrac{15 \pm \sqrt{213}}{4}$

43. $24x^2 = 22x + 35$ $-\dfrac{5}{6}, \dfrac{7}{4}$

44. $72x^2 + 13x = 15$ $-\dfrac{5}{9}, \dfrac{3}{8}$

45. $0.5x^2 + 0.6x = 0.8$ $-2, \dfrac{4}{5}$

46. $1.2x^2 + 0.4x - 0.5 = 0$ $-\dfrac{5}{6}, \dfrac{1}{2}$

In Exercises 47 to 56, determine the discriminant of the quadratic equation, and then state the number of real solutions of the equation. Do not solve the equation.

47. $2x^2 - 5x - 7 = 0$
    81; two real solutions

▶ 48. $x^2 + 3x - 11 = 0$
    53; two real solutions

49. $3x^2 - 2x + 10 = 0$
    -116; no real solutions

50. $x^2 + 3x + 3 = 0$
    -3; no real solutions

51. $x^2 - 20x + 100 = 0$
    0; one real solution

52. $4x^2 + 12x + 9 = 0$
    0; one real solution

53. $24x^2 = -10x + 21$
    2116; two real solutions

54. $32x^2 - 44x = -15$
    16; two real solutions

55. $12x^2 + 15x = -7$
    -111; no real solutions

56. $8x^2 = 5x - 3$
    -71; no real solutions

57. **GEOMETRY** The length of each side of an equilateral triangle is 31 centimeters. Find the altitude of the triangle. Round to the nearest tenth of a centimeter. 26.8 cm

▶ **58.** DIMENSIONS OF A BASEBALL DIAMOND How far, to the nearest tenth of a foot, is it from home plate to second base on a baseball diamond? (*Hint:* The bases in a baseball diamond form a square that measures 90 feet on each side.) 127.3 ft

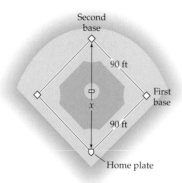

Second base

90 ft

First base

90 ft

x

Home plate

59. DIMENSIONS OF A TELEVISION SCREEN A television screen measures 54 inches diagonally, and its aspect ratio is 4 to 3. Find the width and the height of the screen.
width 43.2 in.; height 32.4 in.

60. PUBLISHING COSTS The cost, in dollars, of publishing x books is $C(x) = 40,000 + 20x + 0.0001x^2$. How many books can be published for $250,000? 10,000 books

61. COST OF A WEDDING The average cost of a wedding, in dollars, is modeled by

$$C(t) = 38t^2 + 291t + 15,208$$

where $t = 0$ represents the year 1990 and $0 \leq t \leq 14$. Use the model to determine the year during which the average cost of a wedding first reached $19,000. 1996

62. REVENUE The demand for a certain product is given by $p = 26 - 0.01x$, where x is the number of units sold per month and p is the price, in dollars, at which each item is sold. The monthly revenue is given by $R = xp$. What number of items sold produces a monthly revenue of $16,500?
1100 or 1500 items

63. PROFIT A company has determined that the profit, in dollars, it can expect from the manufacture and sale of x tennis racquets is given by

$$P = -0.01x^2 + 168x - 120,000$$

How many racquets should the company manufacture and sell to earn a profit of $518,000?
5800 or 11,000 racquets

64. QUADRATIC GROWTH A plant's ability to create food through the process of photosynthesis depends on the surface area of its leaves. A biologist has determined that the surface area A of a maple leaf can be closely approximated by the formula $A = 0.72(1.28)h^2$, where h is the height of the leaf in inches.

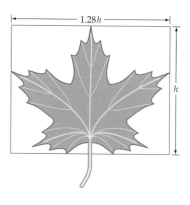

1.28h

h

a. Find the surface area of a maple leaf with a height of 7 inches. Round to the nearest tenth of a square inch.
45.2 in²

b. Find the height of a maple leaf with an area of 92 square inches. Round to the nearest tenth of an inch.
10.0 in.

65. DIMENSIONS OF AN ANIMAL ENCLOSURE A veterinarian wishes to use 132 feet of chain-link fencing to enclose a rectangular region and subdivide the region into two smaller rectangular regions, as shown in the following figure. If the total enclosed area is 576 square feet, find the dimensions of the enclosed region.
12 ft by 48 ft or 32 ft by 18 ft

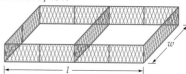

w

l

66. CONSTRUCTION OF A BOX A square piece of cardboard is formed into a box by cutting out 3-inch squares from each of the corners and folding up the sides, as shown in the following figure. If the volume of the box needs to be 126.75 cubic inches, what size square piece of cardboard is needed?
12.5 in. by 12.5 in.

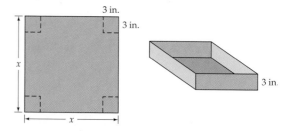

3 in.

3 in.

x

x

3 in.

67. POPULATION DENSITY OF A CITY The population density D (in people per square mile) of a city is related to the horizontal distance x, in miles, from the center of the city by $D = -45x^2 + 190x + 200$, $0 < x < 5$. At what distances from the center of the city does the population density equal 250 people per square mile? Round each result to the nearest tenth of a mile.
0.3 mi and 3.9 mi

68. TRAFFIC CONTROL Traffic engineers install "flow lights" at the entrances of freeways to control the number of cars entering the freeway during times of heavy traffic. For a particular freeway entrance, the number of cars N waiting to enter the freeway during the morning hours can be approximated by $N = -5t^2 + 80t - 280$, where t is the time of the day and $6 \le t \le 10.5$. According to this model, when will there be 35 cars waiting to enter the freeway?
7 A.M. and 9 A.M.

69. DAREDEVIL MOTORCYCLE JUMP In March of 2000, Doug Danger made a successful motorcycle jump over an L-1011 jumbo jet. The horizontal distance of his jump was 160 feet, and his height, in feet, during the jump was approximated by $h = -16t^2 + 25.3t + 20$, $t \ge 0$. He left the takeoff ramp at a height of 20 feet, and he landed on the landing ramp at a height of about 17 feet. How long, to the nearest tenth of a second, was he in the air?
1.7 s

▶70. DIMENSIONS OF A CANDY BAR At the present time a company makes rectangular solid candy bars that measure 5 inches by 2 inches by 0.5 inch. Due to difficult financial times, the company has decided to keep the price of the candy bar fixed and reduce the volume of the bar by 20%. What should be the dimensions, to the nearest tenth of an inch, of the new candy bar if it is decided to keep the height at 0.5 inch and to make the length of the new candy bar 2.5 times longer than its width?
width 1.8 in., length 4.5 in., height 0.5 in.

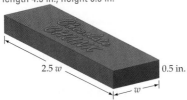
2.5 w   0.5 in.
w

71. HEIGHT OF A ROCKET A model rocket is launched upward with an initial velocity of 220 feet per second. The height, in feet, of the rocket t seconds after the launch is given by $h = -16t^2 + 220t$. How many seconds after the launch will the rocket be 350 feet above the ground? Round to the nearest tenth of a second.
1.8 s and 11.9 s

▶72. BASEBALL The height h, in feet, of a baseball above the ground t seconds after it is hit is given by $h = -16t^2 + 52t + 4.5$. Use this equation to determine the number of seconds, to the nearest tenth of a second, from the time the ball is hit until the ball hits the ground.
3.3 s

73. BASEBALL Two equations can be used to track the position of a baseball t seconds after it is hit. For instance, suppose $h = -16t^2 + 50t + 4.5$ gives the height, in feet, of a baseball t seconds after it is hit, and $s = 103.9t$ gives the horizontal distance, in feet, the ball is from home plate t seconds after it is hit. See the figure at the top of the next column. Use these equations to determine whether this particular baseball will clear a 10-foot fence positioned 360 feet from home plate.
No

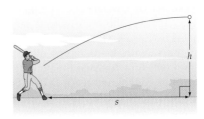

74. BASKETBALL Michael Jordan was known for his "hang time," which is the amount of time a player is in the air when making a jump toward the basket. An equation that approximates the height s, in inches, of one of Jordan's jumps is given by $s = -16t^2 + 26.6t$, where t is time in seconds. Use this equation to determine Michael Jordan's hang time, to the nearest tenth of a second, for this jump.
1.7 s

75. NUMBER OF HANDSHAKES If everyone in a group of n people shakes hands with everyone other than themselves, then the total number of handshakes h is given by

$$h = \frac{1}{2}n(n - 1)$$

The total number of handshakes that are exchanged by a group of people is 36. How many people are in the group?
9 people

76. MEDIAN AGE AT FIRST MARRIAGE During the first 60 years of the 20th century, couples tended to marry at younger and younger ages. During the last 40 years, that trend was reversed. The median age A, in years, at first marriage for women can be modeled by

$$A = 0.0013x^2 - 0.1048x + 22.5256$$

where $x = 0$ represents the year 1900 and $x = 100$ represents the year 2000. Use the model to predict in what year in the future the median age at first marriage for women will first reach 26 years. (*Source:* U.S. Census Bureau, www.Census.gov.)
2005

Median Age at First Marriage, for Women

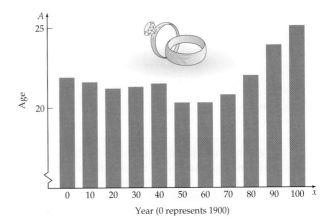

Year (0 represents 1900)

77. 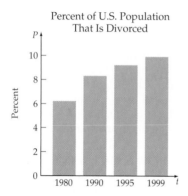 **PERCENT OF DIVORCED CITIZENS** The percent P of U.S. citizens who are divorced can be closely approximated by $P = -0.0016t^2 + 0.225t + 6.201$, where t is time in years, with $t = 0$ representing 1980. Use this model to predict in what year the percent of U.S. citizens who are divorced will first reach 11.0%. (*Source:* U.S. Census Bureau, www.Census.gov.)
2006

Percent of U.S. Population
That Is Divorced

78. AUTOMOTIVE ENGINEERING The number of feet N that a car needs to stop on a certain road surface is given by

$N = -0.015v^2 + 3v$, $0 \le v \le 90$, where v is the speed of the car in miles per hour when the driver applies the brakes. What is the maximum speed, to the nearest mile per hour, that a motorist can be traveling and stop the car within 100 feet?
42 mph

79. 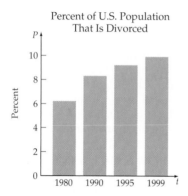 **ORBITAL DEBRIS** The amount of space debris orbiting Earth has been increasing at an alarming rate. In 1995, there were about 14 million pounds of debris orbiting Earth, and by the year 2000, the amount of debris had increased to over 25 million pounds. (*Source:* http://orbitaldebris.jsc.nasa.gov/.)

The equation $A = 0.05t^2 + 2.25t + 14$ closely models the amount of debris orbiting Earth, where A is the amount of debris in millions of pounds and t is the time in years, with $t = 0$ representing the year 1995. Use the equation to

a. estimate the amount of orbital debris we can expect in the year 2006
44.8 million pounds

b. estimate in what year the amount of orbital debris will first reach 50 million pounds
2007

CONNECTING CONCEPTS

80. a. Show that the equation $x^2 + bx - 4 = 0$ always has two distinct real number solutions, regardless of the value of b.
The discriminant is $b^2 + 16$, which is positive for any value of b.

b. For what values of k does $x^2 - 6x + k = 0$ have two distinct real number solutions?
$k < 9$

81. GOLDEN RECTANGLES A rectangle is called a *golden rectangle* provided its length l and its width w satisfy the equation

$$\frac{l}{w} = \frac{l + w}{l}$$

a. Solve this formula for l. (*Hint:* Multiply both sides of the equation by wl, and then use the quadratic formula to solve for l in terms of w. Because l must be positive, state only the positive solution.)
$l = \left(\dfrac{1 + \sqrt{5}}{2}\right)w$

b. If the width of a golden rectangle measures 101 feet, what is the length of the rectangle? Round to the nearest tenth of a foot.
163.4 ft

c. Measure the width and the length of a credit card. Would you say that the credit card closely approximates a golden rectangle?
Answers will vary.

The following theorem is known as the *sum and product of the roots theorem.*

Let $ax^2 + bx + c = 0$, $a \neq 0$, be a quadratic equation. Then r_1 and r_2 are roots of the equation if and only if

$$r_1 + r_2 = -\frac{b}{a} \quad \text{and} \quad r_1 r_2 = \frac{c}{a}$$

In Exercises 82 to 86, use the sum and product of the roots theorem to determine whether the given numbers are roots of the quadratic equation.

82. $x^2 + 4x - 21 = 0$; $-7, 3$
Yes

83. $2x^2 - 7x - 30 = 0$; $-\dfrac{5}{2}, 6$
Yes

84. $9x^2 - 12x - 1 = 0$; $\dfrac{2 + \sqrt{5}}{3}, \dfrac{2 - \sqrt{5}}{3}$
Yes

85. $x^2 - 2x + 2 = 0$; $1 + i, 1 - i$
Yes

86. $x^2 - 4x + 12 = 0$; $2 + 3i, 2 - 3i$
No

PREPARE FOR SECTION 1.4

87. Factor: $x^3 - 16x$ [P.4]
$x(x + 4)(x - 4)$

88. Factor: $x^4 - 36x^2$ [P.4]
$x^2(x + 6)(x - 6)$

89. Evaluate: $8^{2/3}$ [P.2]
4

90. Evaluate: $16^{3/2}$ [P.2]
64

91. Find $\left(1 + \sqrt{x - 5}\right)^2$, $x > 5$ [P.2/P.3]
$x + 2\sqrt{x - 5} - 4$

92. Find $\left(2 - \sqrt{x + 3}\right)^2$, $x > -3$ [P.2/P.3]
$x - 4\sqrt{x + 3} + 7$

PROJECTS

1. THE SUM AND PRODUCT OF THE ROOTS THEOREM Use the quadratic formula to prove the sum and product of the roots theorem stated just before Exercise 82.

2. VISUAL INSIGHT

President James A. Garfield is credited with the following proof of the Pythagorean Theorem. Write the supporting reasons for each of the steps in this proof.

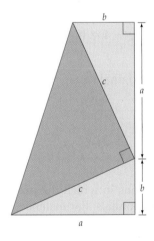

$$\text{Area} = \frac{1}{2}c^2 + 2\left(\frac{1}{2}ab\right) = \frac{1}{2}(\text{height})(\text{sum of bases})$$

$$\frac{1}{2}c^2 + ab = \frac{1}{2}(a + b)(a + b)$$

$$\frac{1}{2}c^2 = \frac{1}{2}a^2 + \frac{1}{2}b^2$$

$$c^2 = a^2 + b^2$$

SECTION 1.4

OTHER TYPES OF EQUATIONS

- POLYNOMIAL EQUATIONS
- RATIONAL EQUATIONS
- RADICAL EQUATIONS
- EQUATIONS THAT ARE QUADRATIC IN FORM

● POLYNOMIAL EQUATIONS

Some polynomial equations that are neither linear nor quadratic can be solved by the various techniques presented in this section. For instance, the **third-degree equation**, or **cubic equation**, in Example 1 can be solved by factoring the polynomial and using the zero product property.

Alternatives to Example 1
1. Solve: $x^3 - 36x = 0$
 ● $-6, 0, 6$
2. Solve: $x^4 - 81 = 0$
 ● $-3, 3, -3i, 3i$
3. Solve: $x^4 + 3x^3 - 8x - 24 = 0$
 ● $-3, 2, -1 - i\sqrt{3}, -1 + i\sqrt{3}$

EXAMPLE 1 Solve a Polynomial Equation by Factoring

Solve: $x^3 - 16x = 0$

Solution

$$x^3 - 16x = 0$$
$$x(x^2 - 16) = 0 \qquad \text{• Factor out the GCF, } x.$$
$$x(x + 4)(x - 4) = 0 \qquad \text{• Factor the difference of squares.}$$

Set each factor equal to zero.

$$x = 0 \quad \text{or} \quad x + 4 = 0 \quad \text{or} \quad x - 4 = 0$$
$$x = 0 \quad \text{or} \quad x = -4 \quad \text{or} \quad x = 4$$

A check will show that -4, 0, and 4 are roots of the original equation.

▶ **TRY EXERCISE 6, PAGE 125**

take note

If you attempt to solve Example 1 by dividing each side by x, you will produce the equation $x^2 - 16 = 0$, which has roots of only -4 and 4. In this case the division of each side of the equation by the variable x does not produce an equivalent equation. To avoid this common mistake, factor out any variable factors that are common to each term instead of dividing each side of the equation by the factor.

● RATIONAL EQUATIONS

A **rational equation** is an equation that involves fractions in which the numerators and/or the denominators of the fractions are polynomials. For instance,

$$\frac{x}{x - 3} = \frac{9}{x - 3} - 5$$

is a rational equation.

Many rational equations can be solved by multiplying each side of the equation by a variable expression to produce a polynomial equation. When we multiply each side of an equation by a variable expression, we restrict the variable so that the expression is not equal to zero. Example 2b illustrates the fact that you may produce incorrect results if you fail to restrict the variable.

Alternative to Example 2
Solve each equation.
1. $\dfrac{4x}{x + 3} = 3 - \dfrac{4}{x + 3}$
 ● $x = 5$
2. $\dfrac{x}{x - 5} = 1 - \dfrac{5}{x - 5}$
 ● no solution

EXAMPLE 2 Solve Rational Equations

Solve each equation.

a. $\dfrac{x}{x - 3} = \dfrac{9}{x - 3} - 5$ b. $1 + \dfrac{x}{x - 5} = \dfrac{5}{x - 5}$

take note

When we multiply both sides of an equation by $x - a$, we assume that $x \neq a$.

MATH MATTERS

Determine the incorrect step in the following "proof" that $2 = 1$.

$a = b$	Given.
$a^2 = ab$	Multiply by a.
$a^2 - b^2 = ab - b^2$	Subtract b^2.
$(a + b)(a - b) = b(a - b)$	Factor.
$\dfrac{(a + b)(a - b)}{(a - b)} = \dfrac{b(a - b)}{(a - b)}$	Divide by $a - b$.
$a + b = b$	Simplify.
$b + b = b$	Substitute b for a.
$2b = b$	Simplify.
$2 = 1$	Divide by b.

Solution

a. First, note that the denominator $x - 3$ would equal zero if x were 3. To produce a simpler equivalent equation, multiply each side by $x - 3$, with the restriction that $x \neq 3$.

$$(x - 3)\left(\frac{x}{x - 3}\right) = (x - 3)\left(\frac{9}{x - 3} - 5\right) \qquad \bullet\ x \neq 3.$$

$$x = (x - 3)\left(\frac{9}{x - 3}\right) - (x - 3)5$$

$$x = 9 - 5x + 15$$

$$6x = 24$$

$$x = 4$$

Substituting 4 for x in the original equation establishes that 4 is the solution.

b. To produce a simpler equivalent equation, multiply each side of the equation by $x - 5$, with the restriction that $x \neq 5$.

$$(x - 5)\left(1 + \frac{x}{x - 5}\right) = (x - 5)\left(\frac{5}{x - 5}\right) \qquad \bullet\ x \neq 5.$$

$$(x - 5)1 + (x - 5)\left(\frac{x}{x - 5}\right) = 5$$

$$x - 5 + x = 5$$

$$2x = 10$$

$$x = 5$$

Although we have obtained 5 as a proposed solution, 5 is *not* a solution of the original equation because it contradicts our restriction $x \neq 5$. Substitution of 5 for x in the original equation results in denominators of 0. In this case the original equation has no solution.

▶ **TRY EXERCISE 14, PAGE 125**

Alternative to Example 3
Exercise 58, page 126.

EXAMPLE 3   **A Medical Application**

Young's rule is often used by physicians to determine what portion of the recommended adult dosage of a medication should be administered to a child. In equation form, Young's rule is given by

$$\text{Portion of an adult dosage} = \frac{x}{x + 12}$$

where x represents the age, in years, of the child. Using Young's rule, a physician has determined that Elizabeth should receive only $\frac{1}{7}$ the recommended adult dosage of a medication. Determine Elizabeth's age.

Continued ▶

Solution

Elizabeth is to receive $\dfrac{1}{7}$ of an adult dosage of a particular medication. Thus we need to solve the following rational equation for x.

$$\frac{1}{7} = \frac{x}{x + 12}$$

$$7(x + 12)\frac{1}{7} = 7(x + 12)\left(\frac{x}{x + 12}\right) \qquad \bullet \text{ Multiply each side by } 7(x + 12).$$

$$x + 12 = 7x \qquad\qquad\qquad \bullet \text{ Simplify.}$$

$$12 = 6x \qquad\qquad\qquad\quad \bullet \text{ Solve for } x.$$

$$x = 2$$

Elizabeth is 2 years old.

▶ TRY EXERCISE 60, PAGE 126

● RADICAL EQUATIONS

Some equations that involve radical expressions can be solved by using the following result.

The Power Principle

If P and Q are algebraic expressions and n is a positive integer, then every solution of $P = Q$ is a solution of $P^n = Q^n$.

Alternative to Example 4
Solve: $\sqrt{2x - 3} = 7$
● 26

EXAMPLE 4 **Solve a Radical Equation**

Use the power principle to solve $\sqrt{x + 4} = 3$.

Solution

$$\sqrt{x + 4} = 3$$

$$\left(\sqrt{x + 4}\right)^2 = 3^2 \qquad \bullet \text{ Square each side of the equation. (Apply the power principle with } n = 2.)$$

$$x + 4 = 9$$

$$x = 5$$

$$\textit{Check: } \sqrt{x + 4} = 3$$

$$\sqrt{5 + 4} \stackrel{?}{=} 3 \qquad \bullet \text{ Substitute 5 for } x.$$

$$\sqrt{9} \stackrel{?}{=} 3$$

$$3 = 3 \qquad \bullet \text{ 5 checks.}$$

The only solution is 5.

▶ TRY EXERCISE 28, PAGE 126

? QUESTION Does squaring both sides of $x + b = c$ produce the equation $x^2 + b^2 = c^2$?

Alternative to Example 5
Exercise 66, pages 126–127.

EXAMPLE 5   An Application Concerning Reading Levels

The SMOG (Simplified Measure of Gobbledygook) readability formula estimates the reading grade level required by a person if he or she is to fully understand the written material being assessed. The SMOG formula is

$$\text{SMOG reading grade level} = \sqrt{w} + 3$$

where w is the number of words that have three or more syllables in a sample of 30 sentences.

An author of books for adolescents has decided to write a book that can be fully understood by adolescents at the ninth grade reading level. According to the SMOG reading level formula, what is the maximum number of words with three or more syllables that should appear in a sample of 30 sentences of this book?

Solution

$9 = \sqrt{w} + 3$ • Substitute 9 for the SMOG reading grade level.

$6 = \sqrt{w}$ • Subtract 3 from each side of the equation.

$36 = w$ • Square both sides to solve for *w*.

To produce a ninth grade reading level, the author should strive to use a maximum of 36 words with three or more syllables in any sample of 30 sentences.

▶ **TRY EXERCISE 62, PAGE 126**

Some care must be taken when using the power principle because the equation $P^n = Q^n$ may have more solutions than the original equation $P = Q$. As an example, consider $x = 3$. The only solution is the real number 3. Square each side of the equation to produce $x^2 = 9$, which has both 3 and -3 as solutions. The -3 is called an *extraneous solution* because it is not a solution of the original equation $x = 3$.

Extraneous Solutions

Any solution of $P^n = Q^n$ that is not a solution of $P = Q$ is called an **extraneous solution.** Extraneous solutions *may* be introduced whenever we raise each side of an equation to an *even* power.

? ANSWER No. Squaring both sides of the equation produces $x^2 + 2bx + b^2 = c^2$.

Alternative to Example 6
1. Solve: $x + 2\sqrt{x - 1} = 9$
   ○ 5
2. Solve: $x - 2\sqrt{x - 2} = x + 8$
   ○ no solution

EXAMPLE 6   Solve a Radical Equation

Solve $x = 2 + \sqrt{2 - x}$. Check all proposed solutions.

Solution

$$x = 2 + \sqrt{2 - x}$$
$$x - 2 = \sqrt{2 - x} \qquad \text{• Isolate the radical.}$$
$$(x - 2)^2 = \left(\sqrt{2 - x}\right)^2 \qquad \text{• Square each side of the equation.}$$
$$x^2 - 4x + 4 = 2 - x$$
$$x^2 - 3x + 2 = 0 \qquad \text{• Collect and combine like terms.}$$
$$(x - 2)(x - 1) = 0 \qquad \text{• Factor.}$$
$$x - 2 = 0 \quad \text{or} \quad x - 1 = 0$$
$$x = 2 \quad \text{or} \qquad x = 1 \qquad \text{• Proposed solutions}$$

Check for $x = 2$: $x = 2 + \sqrt{2 - x}$
$$2 \overset{?}{=} 2 + \sqrt{2 - (2)} \qquad \text{• Substitute 2 for } x.$$
$$2 \overset{?}{=} 2 + \sqrt{0}$$
$$2 = 2 \qquad \text{• 2 is a solution.}$$

Check for $x = 1$: $x = 2 + \sqrt{2 - x}$
$$1 \overset{?}{=} 2 + \sqrt{2 - (1)} \qquad \text{• Substitute 1 for } x.$$
$$1 \overset{?}{=} 2 + \sqrt{1}$$
$$1 \neq 3 \qquad \text{• 1 is not a solution.}$$

The preceding check shows that 1 is not a solution. It is an extraneous solution that was created by squaring each side of the equation. The only solution is 2.

▶ **TRY EXERCISE 30, PAGE 126**

In Example 7 it will be necessary to square $\left(1 + \sqrt{2x - 5}\right)$. Recall the special product formula $(x + y)^2 = x^2 + 2xy + y^2$. Using this special product formula to square $\left(1 + \sqrt{2x - 5}\right)$ produces

$$\left(1 + \sqrt{2x - 5}\right)^2 = 1 + 2\sqrt{2x - 5} + (2x - 5)$$

Alternative to Example 7
1. Solve: $\sqrt{x - 2} = \sqrt{x} - 2$
   ○ no solution
2. Solve: $\sqrt{4x + 1} - \sqrt{2x + 4} = 1$
   ○ 6
3. Solve: $\sqrt{5x - 1} - \sqrt{3x - 2} = 1$
   ○ 1, 2

EXAMPLE 7   Solve a Radical Equation

Solve $\sqrt{x + 1} - \sqrt{2x - 5} = 1$. Check all proposed solutions.

Solution

First write an equivalent equation in which one radical is isolated on one side of the equation.

$$\sqrt{x + 1} - \sqrt{2x - 5} = 1$$
$$\sqrt{x + 1} = 1 + \sqrt{2x - 5}$$

The next step is to square each side. Using the result from the discussion preceding this example, we have

$$\left(\sqrt{x+1}\right)^2 = \left(1 + \sqrt{2x-5}\right)^2$$
$$x + 1 = 1 + 2\sqrt{2x-5} + (2x-5)$$
$$-x + 5 = 2\sqrt{2x-5}$$

• **Isolate the remaining radical.**

The right side still contains a radical, so we square each side again.

$$(-x+5)^2 = \left(2\sqrt{2x+5}\right)^2$$
$$x^2 - 10x + 25 = 4(2x-5)$$
$$x^2 - 10x + 25 = 8x - 20$$
$$x^2 - 18x + 45 = 0$$
$$(x-3)(x-15) = 0$$
$$x = 3 \quad \text{or} \quad x = 15$$

• **Proposed solutions**

3 checks as a solution, but 15 does not. Therefore, 3 is the only solution.

▶ **TRY EXERCISE 34, PAGE 126**

● EQUATIONS THAT ARE QUADRATIC IN FORM

The equation $4x^4 - 25x^2 + 36 = 0$ is said to be **quadratic in form,** which means it can be written in the form

$$au^2 + bu + c = 0 \qquad a \neq 0$$

where u is an algebraic expression involving x. For example, if we make the substitution $u = x^2$ (which implies $u^2 = x^4$), then our original equation can be written as

$$4u^2 - 25u + 36 = 0$$

This quadratic equation can be solved for u, and then, using the relationship $u = x^2$, we can find the solutions of the original equation.

Alternative to Example 8
Solve: $x^8 - 17x^4 + 16 = 0$
● $-2, -1, 1, 2, -2i, -i, i, 2i$

EXAMPLE 8 Solve an Equation That Is Quadratic in Form

Solve: $4x^4 - 25x^2 + 36 = 0$

Solution

Make the substitutions $u = x^2$ and $u^2 = x^4$ to produce the quadratic equation $4u^2 - 25u + 36 = 0$. Factor the quadratic polynomial on the left side of the equation.

$$(4u-9)(u-4) = 0$$
$$4u - 9 = 0 \quad \text{or} \quad u - 4 = 0$$
$$u = \frac{9}{4} \quad \text{or} \quad u = 4$$

Continued ▶

Substitute x^2 for u to produce

$$x^2 = \frac{9}{4} \qquad \text{or} \qquad x^2 = 4$$

$$x = \pm\sqrt{\frac{9}{4}} \qquad \text{or} \qquad x = \pm\sqrt{4}$$

$$x = \pm\frac{3}{2} \qquad \text{or} \qquad x = \pm 2 \qquad \text{• Check as before.}$$

The solutions are $-2, -\frac{3}{2}, \frac{3}{2}$, and 2.

▶ **TRY EXERCISE 42, PAGE 126**

Following is a table of equations that are quadratic in form. Each equation is accompanied by an appropriate substitution that will enable it to be written in the form $au^2 + bu + c = 0$.

Equations That Are Quadratic in Form

Original Equation	Substitution	$au^2 + bu + c = 0$ Form
$x^4 - 8x^2 + 15 = 0$	$u = x^2$	$u^2 - 8u + 15 = 0$
$x^6 + x^3 - 12 = 0$	$u = x^3$	$u^2 + u - 12 = 0$
$x^{1/2} - 9x^{1/4} + 20 = 0$	$u = x^{1/4}$	$u^2 - 9u + 20 = 0$
$2x^{2/3} + 7x^{1/3} - 4 = 0$	$u = x^{1/3}$	$2u^2 + 7u - 4 = 0$
$15x^{-2} + 7x^{-1} - 2 = 0$	$u = x^{-1}$	$15u^2 + 7u - 2 = 0$

Alternative to Example 9
Solve: $4x^{2/3} - 4x^{1/3} - 3 = 0$
● $-\frac{1}{8}, \frac{27}{8}$

EXAMPLE 9   Solve an Equation That Is Quadratic in Form

Solve: $3x^{2/3} - 5x^{1/3} - 2 = 0$

Solution

Substituting u for $x^{1/3}$ gives us

$$3u^2 - 5u - 2 = 0$$
$$(3u + 1)(u - 2) = 0 \qquad \text{• Factor.}$$
$$3u + 1 = 0 \qquad \text{or} \qquad u - 2 = 0$$
$$u = -\frac{1}{3} \qquad \text{or} \qquad u = 2$$
$$x^{1/3} = -\frac{1}{3} \qquad \text{or} \qquad x^{1/3} = 2 \qquad \text{• Replace } u \text{ with } x^{1/3}.$$
$$x = -\frac{1}{27} \qquad \text{or} \qquad x = 8 \qquad \text{• Cube each side.}$$

A check will verify that both $-\frac{1}{27}$ and 8 are solutions.

▶ **TRY EXERCISE 50, PAGE 126**

It is possible to solve equations that are quadratic in form without making a formal substitution. For example, to solve $x^4 + 5x^2 - 36 = 0$, factor the equation and apply the zero product property.

$$x^4 + 5x^2 - 36 = 0$$
$$(x^2 + 9)(x^2 - 4) = 0$$

$x^2 + 9 = 0$	or	$x^2 - 4 = 0$
$x^2 = -9$	or	$x^2 = 4$
$x = \pm 3i$	or	$x = \pm 2$

TOPICS FOR DISCUSSION

1. If P and Q are algebraic expressions and n is a positive integer, then the equation $P^n = Q^n$ is equivalent to the equation $P = Q$. Do you agree? Explain.

2. Consider the equation $(x^2 - 1)(x - 2) = 3(x - 2)$. Dividing each side of the equation by $x - 2$ yields $x^2 - 1 = 3$. Is this second equation equivalent to the first equation?

3. A tutor claims that cubing each side of $(4x - 1)^{1/3} = -2$ will not introduce any extraneous solutions. Do you agree?

4. What would be an appropriate substitution that would enable you to write $x^{-2} - \dfrac{2}{x} = 15$ as a quadratic equation?

5. A classmate solves the equation $x^2 + y^2 = 25$ for y and produces the equation $y = \sqrt{25 - x^2}$. Do you agree with this result?

EXERCISE SET 1.4   *—Suggested Assignment: Exercises 1–65, every other odd; 73–78, all.*

In Exercises 1 to 12, solve each polynomial equation by factoring and using the zero product principle.

1. $x^3 - 25x = 0$
$0, \pm 5$

2. $x^3 - x = 0$
$0, \pm 1$

3. $x^3 - 2x^2 - x + 2 = 0$
$2, \pm 1$

4. $x^3 - 4x^2 - 2x + 8 = 0$
$4, \pm \sqrt{2}$

5. $2x^5 - 18x^3 = 0$
$0, \pm 3$

▶ **6.** $x^4 - 36x^2 = 0$
$0, \pm 6$

7. $x^4 - 3x^3 - 40x^2 = 0$
$0, -5, 8$

8. $x^4 + 3x^3 - 8x - 24 = 0$
$-3, 2, -1 \pm i\sqrt{3}$

9. $x^4 - 16x^2 = 0$
$0, \pm 4$

10. $x^4 - 16 = 0$
$\pm 2, \pm 2i$

11. $x^3 - 8 = 0$
$2, -1 \pm i\sqrt{3}$

12. $x^3 + 8 = 0$
$-2, 1 \pm i\sqrt{3}$

In Exercises 13 to 26, solve each rational equation and check your solution(s).

13. $\dfrac{3}{x + 2} = \dfrac{5}{2x - 7}$
31

▶ **14.** $\dfrac{4}{y + 2} = \dfrac{7}{y - 4}$
-10

15. $\dfrac{30}{10 + x} = \dfrac{20}{10 - x}$
2

16. $\dfrac{6}{8 + x} = \dfrac{4}{8 - x}$
$\dfrac{8}{5}$

17. $\dfrac{3x}{x + 4} = 2 - \dfrac{12}{x + 4}$
no solution

18. $\dfrac{8}{2m + 1} - \dfrac{1}{m - 2} = \dfrac{5}{2m + 1}$
7

19. $2 + \dfrac{9}{r-3} = \dfrac{3r}{r-3}$
no solution

20. $\dfrac{t}{t-4} + 3 = \dfrac{4}{t-4}$
no solution

21. $\dfrac{5}{x-3} - \dfrac{3}{x-2} = \dfrac{4}{x-3}$ $\dfrac{7}{2}$

22. $\dfrac{4}{x-1} + \dfrac{7}{x+7} = \dfrac{5}{x-1}$ $\dfrac{7}{3}$

23. $\dfrac{x}{x-3} = \dfrac{x+4}{x+2}$
-12

24. $\dfrac{x}{x-5} = \dfrac{x+7}{x+1}$
35

25. $\dfrac{x+3}{x+5} = \dfrac{x-3}{x-4}$
1

26. $\dfrac{x-6}{x+4} = \dfrac{x-1}{x+2}$
$-\dfrac{8}{7}$

In Exercises 27 to 40, use the power principle to solve each radical equation. Check all proposed solutions.

27. $\sqrt{x-4} - 6 = 0$
40

▶ **28.** $\sqrt{10-x} = 4$
-6

29. $x = 3 + \sqrt{3-x}$
3

▶ **30.** $x = \sqrt{5-x} + 5$
5

31. $\sqrt{3x-5} - \sqrt{x+2} = 1$
7

32. $\sqrt{6-x} + \sqrt{5x+6} = 6$
$6, 2$

33. $\sqrt{2x+11} - \sqrt{2x-5} = 2$
7

▶ **34.** $\sqrt{x+7} - 2 = \sqrt{x-9}$
18

35. $\sqrt{x+7} + \sqrt{x-5} = 6$
9

36. $x = \sqrt{12x-35}$
$5, 7$

37. $2x = \sqrt{4x+15}$ $\dfrac{5}{2}$

38. $\sqrt[3]{7x-3} = \sqrt[3]{2x+7}$
2

39. $\sqrt[3]{2x^2+5x-3} = \sqrt[3]{x^2+3}$
$1, -6$

40. $\sqrt[4]{x^2+20} = \sqrt[4]{9x}$
$4, 5$

In Exercises 41 to 56, find all the real solutions of each equation by first rewriting each equation as a quadratic equation.

41. $x^4 - 9x^2 + 14 = 0$
$\pm\sqrt{7}, \pm\sqrt{2}$

▶ **42.** $x^4 - 10x^2 + 9 = 0$
$\pm 3, \pm 1$

43. $2x^4 - 11x^2 + 12 = 0$ $\pm 2, \pm\dfrac{\sqrt{6}}{2}$

44. $6x^4 - 7x^2 + 2 = 0$ $\pm\dfrac{\sqrt{2}}{2}, \pm\dfrac{\sqrt{6}}{3}$

45. $x^6 + x^3 - 6 = 0$
$\sqrt[3]{2}, -\sqrt[3]{3}$

46. $6x^6 + x^3 - 15 = 0$ $\dfrac{\sqrt[3]{12}}{2}$ and $-\dfrac{\sqrt[3]{45}}{3}$

47. $x^{1/2} - 3x^{1/4} + 2 = 0$
$1, 16$

48. $2x^{1/2} - 5x^{1/4} - 3 = 0$
81

49. $3x^{2/3} - 11x^{1/3} - 4 = 0$ $-\dfrac{1}{27}, 64$

▶ **50.** $6x^{2/3} - 7x^{1/3} - 20 = 0$ $-\dfrac{64}{27}$ and $\dfrac{125}{8}$

51. $9x^4 = 30x^2 - 25$ $\pm\dfrac{\sqrt{15}}{3}$

52. $4x^4 - 28x^2 = -49$ $\dfrac{\sqrt{14}}{2}$ and $-\dfrac{\sqrt{14}}{2}$

53. $x^{2/5} - 1 = 0$
± 1

54. $2x^{2/5} - x^{1/5} = 6$ $-\dfrac{243}{32}$ and 32

55. $9x - 52\sqrt{x} + 64 = 0$ $\dfrac{256}{81}, 16$

56. $8x - 38\sqrt{x} + 9 = 0$ $\dfrac{1}{16}, \dfrac{81}{4}$

57. FENCE CONSTRUCTION A worker can build a fence in 8 hours. With the help of an assistant, the fence can be built in 5 hours. How long should it take the assistant, working alone, to build the fence? $13\dfrac{1}{3}$ h

58. ROOF REPAIR A roofer and an assistant can repair a roof together in 6 hours. Working alone the assistant can complete the repair in 14 hours. If both the roofer and the assistant work together for 2 hours and then the assistant is left alone to finish the job, how much longer should the assistant need to finish the repairs? $9\dfrac{1}{3}$ h

59. AVERAGE GOLF SCORE Renee has played four rounds of golf this season. Her average score is 92. If she can score 86 on each round she plays in the future, how many more rounds will she need to play to bring her average down to 88? (*Hint:* A player's average golf score is equal to the total number of strokes divided by the total number of rounds played.)
8 rounds

▶ **60. MEDICAL DOSAGE FOR A CHILD** A physician has used Young's rule (see Example 3) to determine that Sandy should receive $\dfrac{1}{2}$ of an adult dose of a medication. How old is Sandy?
12 years old

61. WRITING FOR A PARTICULAR READING LEVEL A writer of books for adolescents has decided to write a book that can be fully understood by adolescents at the sixth grade level. According to the SMOG reading grade level formula, what is the maximum number of words with three or more syllables that should appear in any sample of 30 sentences of the book? (*Hint:* See Example 5.)
9 words with three or more syllables

▶ **62. WRITING FOR A PARTICULAR READING LEVEL** A writer of books for children has decided to write a book that can be fully understood by children at the fourth grade level. According to the SMOG reading grade level formula, what is the maximum number of words with three or more syllables that should appear in any sample of 30 sentences of the book? (*Hint:* See Example 5.)
1 word with three or more syllables

63. RADIUS OF A CONE A conical funnel has a height h of 4 inches and a lateral surface area L of 15π square inches. Find the radius r of the cone. (*Hint:* Use the formula $L = \pi r\sqrt{r^2 + h^2}$.)
3 in.

64. DIAMETER OF A CONE As flour is poured onto a table, it forms a right circular cone whose height is one-third the diameter of the base. What is the diameter of the base when the cone has a volume of 192 cubic inches? Round to the nearest tenth of an inch.
13.0 in.

65. PRECIOUS METALS A solid silver sphere has a diameter of 8 millimeters, and a second silver sphere has a diameter of 12 millimeters. The spheres are melted down and recast to form a single cube. What is the length s of each edge of the cube? Round your answer to the nearest tenth of a millimeter.
10.5 mm

66. PENDULUM The period T of a pendulum is the time it takes the pendulum to complete one swing from left to right and back. For a pendulum near the surface of the earth,

$$T = 2\pi\sqrt{\frac{L}{32}}$$

where T is measured in seconds and L is the length of the pendulum in feet. Find the length of a pendulum that has a period of 4 seconds. Round to the nearest tenth of a foot.
13.0 ft

67. **DISTANCE TO THE HORIZON** On a ship, the distance d that you can see to the horizon is given by $d = 1.5\sqrt{h}$, where h is the height of your eye measured in feet above sea level and d is measured in miles. How high is the eye level of a navigator who can see 14 miles to the horizon? Round to the nearest foot.
87 ft

CONNECTING CONCEPTS

68. **RADIUS OF A CIRCLE** The radius r of a circle inscribed in a triangle with sides of lengths a, b, and c is given by

$$r = \sqrt{\frac{(s-a)(s-b)(s-c)}{s}}$$

where $s = \dfrac{1}{2}(a + b + c)$.

a. Find the length of the radius of a circle inscribed in a triangle with sides of 5 inches, 6 inches, and 7 inches. Round to the nearest hundredth of an inch.
1.63 in.

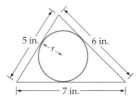

b. The radius of a circle inscribed in an equilateral triangle measures 2 inches. What is the exact length of each side of the equilateral triangle?
$4\sqrt{3}$ in.

69. **RADIUS OF A CIRCLE** The radius r of a circle that is circumscribed about a triangle with sides of lengths a, b, and c is given by

$$r = \frac{abc}{4\sqrt{s(s-a)(s-b)(s-c)}}$$

where $s = \dfrac{1}{2}(a + b + c)$.

a. Find the radius of a circle that is circumscribed about a triangle with sides of 7 inches, 10 inches, and 15 inches. Round to the nearest hundredth of an inch.
8.93 in.

b. A circle with radius 5 inches is circumscribed about an equilateral triangle (see the following figure). What is the exact length of each side of the equilateral triangle?
$5\sqrt{3}$ in.

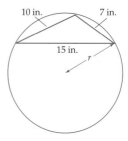

FIGURE FOR EXERCISE 69(b)

In Exercises 70 and 71, the depth s from the opening of a well to the water can be determined by measuring the total time between the instant you drop a stone and the moment you hear it hit the water. The time (in seconds) it takes the stone to hit the water is given by $\sqrt{s}/4$, where s is measured in feet. The time (also in seconds) required for the sound of the impact to travel up to your ears is given by $s/1100$. Thus the total time T (in seconds) between the instant you drop the stone and the moment you hear its impact is

$$T = \frac{\sqrt{s}}{4} + \frac{s}{1100}$$

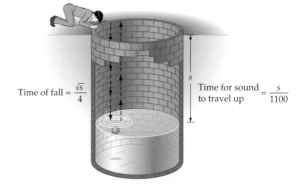

70. **TIME OF FALL** One of the world's deepest water wells is 7320 feet deep. Find the time between the instant you

drop a stone and the time you hear it hit the water if the surface of the water is 7100 feet below the opening of the well. Round your answer to the nearest tenth of a second.
27.5 s

71. Solve $T = \dfrac{\sqrt{s}}{4} + \dfrac{s}{1100}$ for s. $s = \left(\dfrac{-275 + 5\sqrt{3025 + 176T}}{2} \right)^2$

72. **DEPTH OF A WELL** Use the result of Exercise 71 to determine the depth from the opening of a well to the water level if the time between the instant you drop a stone and the moment you hear its impact is 3 seconds. Round your answer to the nearest foot.
133 ft

PREPARE FOR SECTION 1.5

73. Find: $\{x \mid x > 2\} \cap \{x \mid x > 5\}$ [P.1]
$\{x \mid x > 5\}$

74. Evaluate $3x^2 - 2x + 5$ for $x = -3$. [P.1]
38

75. Evaluate $\dfrac{x + 3}{x - 2}$ for $x = 7$. [P.1/P.5]
2

76. Factor: $10x^2 + 9x - 9$ [P.4]
$(2x + 3)(5x - 3)$

77. For what value of x is $\dfrac{x - 3}{2x - 7}$ undefined? [P.1/P.5]
$\dfrac{7}{2}$

78. Solve: $2x^2 - 11x + 15 = 0$ [1.3]
$\dfrac{5}{2}, 3$

PROJECTS

1. **THE REDUCED CUBIC** The mathematician Francois Vieta knew a method of solving the "reduced cubic" $x^3 + mx + n = 0$ by using the substitution
$$x = \frac{m}{3z} - z.$$

a. Show that this substitution results in the equation
$$z^6 - nz^3 - \frac{m^3}{27} = 0.$$

b. Show that the equation in **a.** is quadratic in form.

c. Solve the equation in **a.** for z.

d. Use your solution from **c.** to find the real solution of the equation $x^3 + 3x = 14$.

2. **FERMAT'S LAST THEOREM** One of the most famous theorems is known as *Fermat's Last Theorem*. Write an essay on Fermat's Last Theorem. Include information about

- the history of Fermat's Last Theorem.

- the relationship between Fermat's Last Theorem and the Pythagorean Theorem.

- Dr. Andrew Wiles's proof of Fermat's Last Theorem.

The following list includes a few of the sources you may wish to consult.

- *Fermat's Enigma,* by Simon Singh. Walker and Company, New York, 1997.

- *The Last Problem,* by Eric Temple Bell. The Mathematical Association of America, 1990.

- "Andrew Wiles: A Math Whiz Battles 350-Year-Old Puzzle," by Gina Kolata, *Math Horizons,* Winter 1993, pp. 8–11. The Mathematical Association of America.

- "Introduction to Fermat's Last Theorem," by David A. Cox, *The American Mathematical Monthly,* vol. 101, no. 1 (January 1994), pp. 3–14.

SECTION 1.5

INEQUALITIES

- **PROPERTIES OF INEQUALITIES**
- **COMPOUND INEQUALITIES**
- **ABSOLUTE VALUE INEQUALITIES**
- **THE CRITICAL VALUE METHOD**
- **RATIONAL INEQUALITIES**
- **APPLICATIONS**

• PROPERTIES OF INEQUALITIES

In Section P.1 we used inequalities to describe the order of real numbers and to represent subsets of real numbers. In this section we consider inequalities that involve a variable. In particular, we consider how to determine which real numbers make an inequality a true statement.

The **solution set** of an inequality is the set of all real numbers for which the inequality is a true statement. For instance, the solution set of $x + 1 > 4$ is the set of all real numbers greater than 3. Two inequalities are **equivalent inequalities** if they have the same solution set. We can solve many inequalities by producing *simpler* but equivalent inequalities until the solutions are readily apparent. To produce these simpler but equivalent inequalities, we often apply the following properties.

MATH MATTERS

Another property of inequalities, called the *transitive property*, states that for real numbers a, b, and c, if $a > b$ and $b > c$, then $a > c$. We say that the relationship "is greater than" is a transitive relationship.

Not all relationships are transitive relationships. For instance, consider the game of scissors, paper, rock. In this game, scissors wins over paper, paper wins over rock, but scissors does not win over rock!

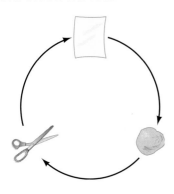

Properties of Inequalities

Let a, b, and c be real numbers.

1. *Addition-Subtraction Property*   If the same real number is added to or subtracted from each side of an inequality, the resulting inequality is equivalent to the original inequality.

$a < b$ and $a + c < b + c$ are equivalent inequalities.

2. *Multiplication-Division Property*

a. Multiplying or dividing each side of an inequality by the same *positive* real number produces an equivalent inequality.

If $c > 0$, then $a < b$ and $ac < bc$ are equivalent inequalities.

b. Multiplying or dividing each side of an inequality by the same *negative* real number produces an equivalent inequality provided the direction of the inequality symbol is *reversed*.

If $c < 0$, then $a < b$ and $ac > bc$ are equivalent inequalities.

Note the difference between Property 2a and Property 2b. Property 2a states that an equivalent inequality is produced when each side of a given inequality is multiplied (divided) by the same *positive* real number and the inequality symbol is not changed. By contrast, Property 2b states that when each side of a given inequality is multiplied (divided) by a *negative* real number, we must *reverse* the direction of the inequality symbol to produce an equivalent inequality. For instance, multiplying both sides of $-b < 4$ by -1 produces the equivalent inequality $b > -4$. (We multiplied both sides of the first inequality by -1, and we changed the less than symbol to a greater than symbol.)

Alternative to Example 1
Solve each of the following inequalities.
a. $3x - 5 < 7$
 ⦿ **$x < 4$**
b. $-2x + 8 \geq 14$
 ⦿ **$x \leq -3$**

> **take note**
>
> Solutions of inequalities are often stated using set-builder notation or interval notation. For instance, the solutions of $2x + 1 < 7$ can be written in set-builder notation as $\{x \mid x < 3\}$ or in interval notation as $(-\infty, 3)$.

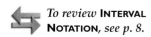

To review **INTERVAL NOTATION**, *see p. 8.*

EXAMPLE 1   **Solve Linear Inequalities**

Solve each of the following inequalities.

a. $2x + 1 < 7$ **b.** $-3x - 2 \leq 10$

Solution

a. $2x + 1 < 7$

$\qquad 2x < 6$ • Add -1 to each side and keep the inequality symbol as is.

$\qquad x < 3$ • Divide each side by 2 and keep the inequality symbol as is.

The inequality $2x + 1 < 7$ is true for all real numbers less than 3. In set-builder notation the solution set is given by $\{x \mid x < 3\}$. In interval notation the solution set is $(-\infty, 3)$. See the following figure.

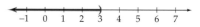

b. $-3x - 2 \leq 10$

$\qquad -3x \leq 12$ • Add 2 to each side and keep the inequality symbol as is.

$\qquad x \geq -4$ • Divide each side by -3 and reverse the direction of the inequality symbol.

The inequality $-3x - 2 \leq 10$ is true for all real numbers greater than or equal to -4. In set-builder notation the solution set is given by $\{x \mid x \geq -4\}$. In interval notation the solution set is $[-4, \infty)$. See the following figure.

▶ **TRY EXERCISE 6, PAGE 140**

⦿ **COMPOUND INEQUALITIES**

A **compound inequality** is formed by joining two inequalities with the connective word *and* or *or*. The inequalities shown below are compound inequalities.

$$x + 1 > 3 \quad \text{and} \quad 2x - 11 < 7$$
$$x + 3 > 5 \quad \text{or} \quad x - 1 < 9$$

The solution set of a compound inequality with the connective word *or* is the *union* of the solution sets of the two inequalities. The solution set of a compound inequality with the connective word *and* is the *intersection* of the solution sets of the two inequalities.

Alternative to Example 2
Solve each compound inequality. Write each solution in set-builder notation.
a. $4x < -8$ and $1 - 2x > -5$
 ⦿ **$\{x \mid x < -2\}$**
b. $x + 3 < 7$ or $2x > 12$
 ⦿ **$\{x \mid x < 4 \text{ or } x > 6\}$**

EXAMPLE 2   **Solve Compound Inequalities**

Solve each compound inequality. Write each solution in set-builder notation.

a. $2x < 10$ or $x + 1 > 9$ **b.** $x + 3 > 4$ and $2x + 1 > 15$

Solution

a. $2x < 10$ or $x + 1 > 9$
     $x < 5$ $x > 8$ • Solve each inequality.
     $\{x \mid x < 5\}$ $\{x \mid x > 8\}$ • Write each solution as a set.

   $\{x \mid x < 5\} \cup \{x \mid x > 8\} = \{x \mid x < 5 \text{ or } x > 8\}$ • Write the union of the solution sets.

b. $x + 3 > 4$ and $2x + 1 > 15$
          $x > 1$ $2x > 14$ • Solve each inequality.
                                    $x > 7$
     $\{x \mid x > 1\}$ $\{x \mid x > 7\}$ • Write each solution as a set.
     $\{x \mid x > 1\} \cap \{x \mid x > 7\} = \{x \mid x > 7\}$ • Write the intersection of the solution sets.

▶ **TRY EXERCISE 10, PAGE 140**

❓ QUESTION What is the solution set of the compound inequality $x > 1$ or $x < 3$?

take note

We reserve the notation $a < b < c$ to mean $a < b$ and $b < c$. Thus the solution set of $2 > x > 5$ is the empty set, because there are no numbers less than 2 and greater than 5.

The inequality given by
$$12 < x + 5 < 19$$
is equivalent to the compound inequality $12 < x + 5$ *and* $x + 5 < 19$. You can solve $12 < x + 5 < 19$ by either of the following methods.

Method 1   Find the intersection of the solution sets of the inequalities $12 < x + 5$ and $x + 5 < 19$.

$$12 < x + 5 \quad \text{and} \quad x + 5 < 19$$
$$7 < x \quad \text{and} \quad x < 14$$

The solution set is $\{x \mid x > 7\} \cap \{x \mid x < 14\} = \{x \mid 7 < x < 14\}$.

take note

The compound inequality $a < b$ and $b < c$ can be written in the compact form $a < b < c$. However, the compound inequality $a < b$ or $b > c$ cannot be expressed in a compact form.

Method 2   Subtract 5 from each of the three parts of the inequality.

$$12 < \quad x + 5 \quad < 19$$
$$12 - 5 < x + 5 - 5 < 19 - 5$$
$$7 < \quad x \quad < 14$$

The solution set is $\{x \mid 7 < x < 14\}$.

● **ABSOLUTE VALUE INEQUALITIES**

The solution set of the absolute value inequality $|x - 1| < 3$ is the set of all real numbers whose distance from 1 is *less than* 3. Therefore, the solution set consists of all numbers between -2 and 4. See **Figure 1.6.** In interval notation, the solution set is $(-2, 4)$.

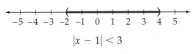

$|x - 1| < 3$

FIGURE 1.6

❓ ANSWER The set of all real numbers. Using interval notation, the solution set is written as $(-\infty, \infty)$.

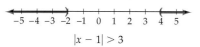

$$|x - 1| > 3$$

Figure 1.7

The solution set of the absolute value inequality $|x - 1| > 3$ is the set of all real numbers whose distance from 1 is *greater than* 3. Therefore, the solution set consists of all real numbers less than -2 *or* greater than 4. See **Figure 1.7**. In interval notation, the solution set is $(-\infty, -2) \cup (4, \infty)$.

The following properties are used to solve absolute value inequalities.

P | **Properties of Absolute Value Inequalities**

For any variable expression E and any nonnegative real number k,

$$|E| \leq k \quad \text{if and only if} \quad -k \leq E \leq k$$
$$|E| \geq k \quad \text{if and only if} \quad E \leq -k \quad \text{or} \quad E \geq k$$

These properties also hold true when the $<$ symbol is substituted for the $\leq$ symbol and when the $>$ symbol is substituted for the $\geq$ symbol.

> **take note**
>
> Some inequalities have a solution set that consists of all real numbers. For example, $|x + 9| \geq 0$ is true for all values of x. Because an absolute value is always nonnegative, the equation is always true.

In Example 3 we make use of the above properties to solve absolute value inequalities.

Alternative to Example 3
Solve. Write the answer using interval notation.

a. $|3x - 2| \leq 4$
○ $\left[-\dfrac{2}{3}, 2\right]$

b. $|5 - 2x| < 7$
○ $(-1, 6)$

c. $|2x + 5| > 3$
○ $(-\infty, -4) \cup (-1, \infty)$

d. $|8 - 2x| \geq 6$
○ $(-\infty, 1] \cup [7, \infty)$

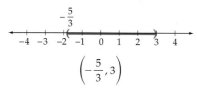

$$\left(-\dfrac{5}{3}, 3\right)$$

Figure 1.8

EXAMPLE 3 | **Solve Absolute Value Inequalities**

Solve each of the following inequalities.

a. $|2 - 3x| < 7$ **b.** $|4x - 3| \geq 5$

Solution

a. $|2 - 3x| < 7$ if and only if $-7 < 2 - 3x < 7$. Solve this compound inequality.

$$-7 < 2 - 3x < 7$$
$$-9 < -3x < 5 \qquad \text{• Subtract 2 from each of the three parts of the inequality.}$$
$$3 > x > -\frac{5}{3} \qquad \text{• Multiply each part of the inequality by } -\frac{1}{3} \text{ and reverse the inequality symbols.}$$

In interval notation, the solution set is given by $\left(-\dfrac{5}{3}, 3\right)$. See **Figure 1.8**.

b. $|4x - 3| \geq 5$ implies $4x - 3 \leq -5$ or $4x - 3 \geq 5$. Solving each of these inequalities produces

$$
\begin{array}{ccc}
4x - 3 \leq -5 & \text{or} & 4x - 3 \geq 5 \\
4x \leq -2 & & 4x \geq 8 \\
x \leq -\dfrac{1}{2} & & x \geq 2
\end{array}
$$

The solution set is $\left(-\infty, -\dfrac{1}{2}\right] \cup [2, \infty)$. See **Figure 1.9**.

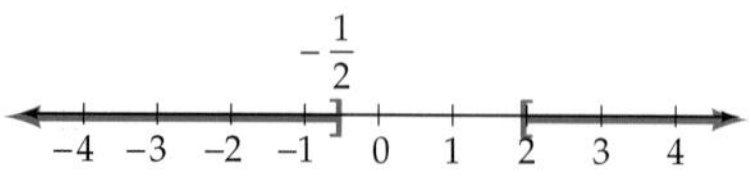

$$\left(-\infty, -\dfrac{1}{2}\right] \cup [2, \infty)$$

Figure 1.9

▶ **TRY EXERCISE 18, PAGE 140**

● THE CRITICAL VALUE METHOD

Any value of x that causes a polynomial in x to equal zero is called a **zero of the polynomial**. For example, -4 and 1 are both zeros of the polynomial $x^2 + 3x - 4$, because $(-4)^2 + 3(-4) - 4 = 0$ and $1^2 + 3 \cdot 1 - 4 = 0$.

A Sign Property of Polynomials

Polynomials in x have the property that for all values of x between two consecutive real zeros, all values of the polynomial are positive or all values of the polynomial are negative.

In our work with inequalities that involve polynomials, the real zeros of the polynomial are also referred to as **critical values of the inequality**. On a number line the critical values of an inequality separate the real numbers that make the inequality true from those that make it false. In Example 4, we use critical values and the sign property of polynomials to solve an inequality.

Alternative to Example 4
1. Solve: $x^2 - 2x - 15 < 0$
● $(-3, 5)$
2. Solve: $x^2 - 2x - 15 > 0$
● $(-\infty, -3) \cup (5, \infty)$

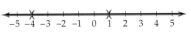

FIGURE 1.10

E X A M P L E 4   **Solve a Quadratic Inequality**

Solve: $x^2 + 3x - 4 < 0$

Solution

Factoring the polynomial $x^2 + 3x - 4$ produces the equivalent inequality

$$(x + 4)(x - 1) < 0$$

The zeros of the polynomial $x^2 + 3x - 4$ are -4 and 1. They are the critical values of the inequality $x^2 + 3x - 4 < 0$. They separate the real number line into the three intervals shown in **Figure 1.10.**

To determine the intervals on which $x^2 + 3x - 4 < 0$, pick a number called a **test value** from each of the three intervals and then determine whether $x^2 + 3x - 4 < 0$ for each of these test values. For example, in the interval $(-\infty, -4)$, pick a test value of, say, -5. Then

$$x^2 + 3x - 4 = (-5)^2 + 3(-5) - 4 = 6$$

Because 6 is not less than 0, by the sign property of polynomials, no number in the interval $(-\infty, -4)$ makes $x^2 + 3x - 4 < 0$.

Now pick a test value from the interval $(-4, 1)$, say, 0. When $x = 0$,

$$x^2 + 3x - 4 = 0^2 + 3(0) - 4 = -4$$

Because -4 is less than 0, by the sign property of polynomials, all numbers in the interval $(-4, 1)$ make $x^2 + 3x - 4 < 0$.

If we pick a test value of 2 from the interval $(1, \infty)$, then

$$x^2 + 3x - 4 = (2)^2 + 3(2) - 4 = 6$$

Because 6 is not less than 0, by the sign property of polynomials, no number in the interval $(1, \infty)$ makes $x^2 + 3x - 4 < 0$.

Continued ▶

The following table is a summary of our work.

Interval	Test Value x	$x^2 + 3x - 4 \overset{?}{<} 0$
$(-\infty, -4)$	-5	$(-5)^2 + 3(-5) - 4 < 0$ $6 < 0$ False
$(-4, 1)$	0	$(0)^2 + 3(0) - 4 < 0$ $-4 < 0$ True
$(1, \infty)$	2	$(2)^2 + 3(2) - 4 < 0$ $6 < 0$ False

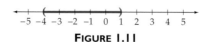

FIGURE 1.11

In interval notation, the solution set of $x^2 + 3x - 4 < 0$ is $(-4, 1)$. The solution set is graphed in **Figure 1.11.** Note that in this case the critical values -4 and 1 are not included in the solution set because they do not make $x^2 + 3x - 4$ less than 0.

▶ **TRY EXERCISE 34, PAGE 140**

To avoid the arithmetic in Example 4, we often use a *sign diagram*. For example, note that the factor $(x + 4)$ is negative for all $x < -4$ and positive for all $x > -4$. The factor $(x - 1)$ is negative for all $x < 1$ and positive for all $x > 1$. These results are shown in **Figure 1.12.**

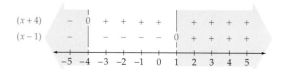

A sign diagram for $(x + 4)$ and $(x - 1)$.

FIGURE 1.12

To determine on which intervals the product $(x + 4)(x - 1)$ is negative, we examine the sign diagram to see where the factors have opposite signs. This occurs only on the interval $(-4, 1)$, where $(x + 4)$ is positive and $(x - 1)$ is negative, so the original equality is true only on the interval $(-4, 1)$.

Following is a summary of the steps used to solve polynomial inequalities by the critical value method.

Ⓟ **Solving a Polynomial Inequality by the Critical Value Method**

1. Write the inequality so that one side of the inequality is a nonzero polynomial and the other side is 0.

2. Find the real zeros of the polynomial.[3] They are the critical values of the original inequality.

3. Use test values to determine which of the consecutive intervals formed by the critical values are to be included in the solution set.

---

[3]In Chapter 3, additional ways to find the zeros of a polynomial are developed. For the present, however, we will find the zeros by factoring or by using the quadratic formula.

● RATIONAL INEQUALITIES

A rational expression is the quotient of two polynomials. **Rational inequalities** involve rational expressions, and they can be solved by an extension of the critical value method.

Critical Values of a Rational Expression

The **critical values of a rational expression** are the numbers that cause the numerator of the rational expression to equal zero or the denominator of the rational expression to equal zero.

Rational expressions also have the property that they remain either positive for all values of the variable between consecutive critical values or negative for all values of the variable between consecutive critical values.

Following is a summary of the steps used to solve rational inequalities by the critical value method.

Solving a Rational Inequality by the Critical Value Method

1. Write the inequality so that one side of the inequality is a rational expression and the other side is 0.

2. Find the real zeros of the numerator of the rational expression and the real zeros of its denominator. They are the critical values of the inequality.

3. Use test values to determine which of the consecutive intervals formed by the critical values are to be included in the solution set.

Alternative to Example 5

Solve: $\dfrac{5x - 9}{x - 5} \le 3$

● $[-3, 5)$

Solve: $\dfrac{(x - 3)(x - 5)}{x + 2} \ge 0$

● $(-2, 3] \cup [5, \infty)$

EXAMPLE 5   Solve a Rational Inequality

Solve: $\dfrac{3x + 4}{x + 1} \le 2$

Solution

Write the inequality so that 0 appears on the right side of the inequality.

$$\frac{3x + 4}{x + 1} \le 2$$

$$\frac{3x + 4}{x + 1} - 2 \le 0$$

Continued ▶

Write the left side as a rational expression.

$$\frac{3x + 4}{x + 1} - \frac{2(x + 1)}{x + 1} \le 0 \qquad \bullet \text{ The LCD is } x + 1.$$

$$\frac{3x + 4 - 2x - 2}{x + 1} \le 0 \qquad \bullet \text{ Simplify.}$$

$$\frac{x + 2}{x + 1} \le 0$$

The critical values of this inequality are -2 and -1 because the numerator $x + 2$ is equal to zero when $x = -2$, and the denominator $x + 1$ is equal to zero when $x = -1$. The critical values -2 and -1 separate the real number line into the three intervals $(-\infty, -2)$, $(-2, -1)$, and $(-1, \infty)$.

All values of x on the interval $(-2, -1)$ make $\dfrac{x + 2}{x + 1}$ negative, as desired. On the other intervals, the quotient $\dfrac{x + 2}{x + 1}$ is positive. See the sign diagram in **Figure 1.13.**

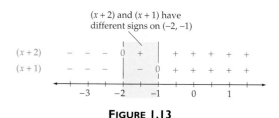

FIGURE 1.13

The solution set is $[-2, -1)$. The graph of the solution set is shown in **Figure 1.14.** Note that -2 is included in the solution set because $\dfrac{x + 2}{x + 1} = 0$ when $x = -2$. However, -1 is not included in the solution set because the denominator $(x + 1)$ is zero when $x = -1$.

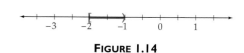

FIGURE 1.14

▶ **TRY EXERCISE 46, PAGE 140**

● APPLICATIONS

Many applied problems can be solved by using inequalities.

Alternative to Example 6
Exercise 56, page 141.

EXAMPLE 6   **Solve an Application Concerning Leases**

A real estate company needs a new copy machine. The company has decided to lease either the model ABC machine for $75 a month plus 5 cents per copy or the model XYZ machine for $210 a month and 2 cents per copy. Under what conditions is it less expensive to lease the XYZ machine?

Solution

Let x represent the number of copies the company produces per month. The dollar costs per month are $75 + 0.05x$ for model ABC and $210 + 0.02x$ for model XYZ. It will be less expensive to lease model XYZ provided

$$210 + 0.02x < 75 + 0.05x$$
$$210 - 0.03x < 75 \qquad \text{• Subtract 0.05x from each side.}$$
$$-0.03x < -135 \qquad \text{• Subtract 210 from each side.}$$
$$x > 4500 \qquad \text{• Divide each side by } -0.03. \text{ Reverse the inequality symbol.}$$

The company will find it less expensive to lease model XYZ if it produces over 4500 copies per month.

▶ **TRY EXERCISE 52, PAGE 141**

Alternative to Example 7
Exercise 60, page 141.

EXAMPLE 7   Solve an Application Concerning Test Scores

Tyra has test scores of 70 and 81 in her biology class. To receive a C grade, she must obtain an average greater than or equal to 72 but less than 82. What range of test scores on the one remaining test will enable Tyra to get a C for the course?

Solution

The average of three test scores is the sum of the scores divided by 3. Let x represent Tyra's next test score. The requirements for a C grade produce the following inequality:

$$72 \leq \frac{70 + 81 + x}{3} < 82$$
$$216 \leq 70 + 81 + x < 246 \qquad \text{• Multiply each part of the inequality by 3.}$$
$$216 \leq \quad 151 + x \quad < 246 \qquad \text{• Simplify.}$$
$$65 \leq \qquad x \qquad < 95 \qquad \text{• Solve for x by subtracting 151 from each part of the inequality.}$$

To get a C in the course, Tyra's remaining test score must be in the interval $[65, 95)$.

▶ **TRY EXERCISE 58, PAGE 141**

In many business applications a company is interested in the cost C of manufacturing x items, the revenue R generated by selling all the items, and the profit P made by selling the items.

In the next example the cost of manufacturing x tennis racquets is given by $C = 32x + 120{,}000$ dollars. The 120,000 represents the fixed cost because it remains constant regardless of how many racquets are manufactured. The $32x$ represents the variable cost because this term varies depending on how many racquets are manufactured. Each additional racquet costs the company an additional \$32.

The revenue received from the sale of x tennis racquets is given by $R = x(200 - 0.01x)$ dollars. The quantity $(200 - 0.01x)$ is the price the company charges for each tennis racquet. The price varies depending on the number of racquets that are manufactured. For instance, if the number of racquets x that the company manufactures is small, the company will be able to demand almost $200 for each racquet. As the number of racquets that the company manufactures increases (approaches 20,000), the company will only be able to sell *all* the racquets if it decreases the price of each racquet.

The following profit formula shows the relationship between profit P, revenue R, and cost C:

$$P = R - C$$

Alternative to Example 8
Exercise 64, page 142.

EXAMPLE 8   **Solve a Business Application**

A company determines that the cost C, in dollars, of producing x tennis racquets is $C = 32x + 120,000$. The revenue R, in dollars, from selling all of the tennis racquets is $R = x(200 - 0.01x)$.

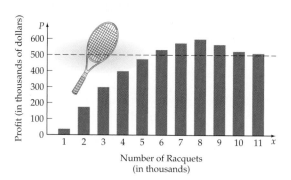

How many racquets should the company manufacture and sell if the company wishes to earn a profit of at least $500,000?

Solution

The profit is given by

$$\begin{aligned} P &= R - C \\ &= x(200 - 0.01x) - (32x + 120,000) \\ &= 200x - 0.01x^2 - 32x - 120,000 \\ &= -0.01x^2 + 168x - 120,000 \end{aligned}$$

The profit will be at least $500,000 provided

$$-0.01x^2 + 168x - 120,000 \geq 500,000$$
$$-0.01x^2 + 168x - 620,000 \geq 0$$

Using the quadratic formula, we find that the approximate critical values of this last inequality are 5474.3 and 11,325.7. Test values show that the inequality is positive only on the interval (5474.3, 11,325.7). The company should manufacture at least 5475 tennis racquets but not more than 11,325 tennis racquets to produce the desired profit.

▶ **TRY EXERCISE 54, PAGE 141**

Alternative to Example 9
A basketball player has made 27 out of 60 field goals. Her present field goal average is 45%. If she has a shooting streak in which she makes every field goal attempt, how many more shots must she take to get her field goal average above 52%?
● **9 or more shots**

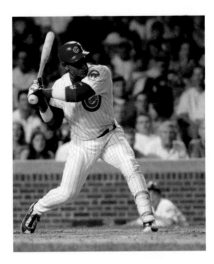

EXAMPLE 9   **Solve an Application Involving Batting Averages**

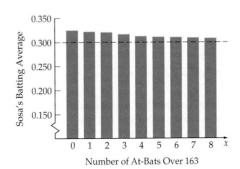

During a recent season, Sammy Sosa had 53 hits out of 163 at-bats. At that time his batting average was approximately 0.325. If Sosa goes into a batting slump in which he gets no hits, how many more at-bats will it take for his batting average to fall below 0.300?

Solution

A baseball player's batting average is determined by dividing the player's number of hits by the number of times the player has been at bat. Let x be the number of additional at-bats that Sosa takes over 163. During this period, his batting average will be $\dfrac{53}{163 + x}$, and we wish to solve

$$\frac{53}{163 + x} < 0.300$$

This rational inequality can be solved by using the critical value method, but there is an easier method. In this application we know that $163 + x$ is positive. Thus, if we multiply each side of the preceding inequality by $163 + x$, we will obtain the linear inequality $53 < 48.9 + 0.300x$, with the condition that x is a positive integer. Solving this inequality produces

$$53 < 48.9 + 0.300x$$
$$4.1 < 0.300x$$
$$x > 13.\overline{6}$$

Because x must be a positive integer, Sosa's average will fall below 0.300 if he goes hitless for 14 or more at-bats.

▶ **TRY EXERCISE 66, PAGE 142**

 TOPICS FOR DISCUSSION

1. If $x < y$, then $y > x$. Do you agree?

2. Can the solution set of the compound inequality

    $$x < -3 \text{ or } x > 5$$

    be expressed as $-3 > x > 5$? Explain.

3. If $-a < b$, then it must be true that $a > -b$. Do you agree? Explain.

4. Do the inequalities $x < 4$ and $x^2 < 4^2$ both have the same solution set? Explain.

5. True or False: If $k < 0$, then $|k| = -k$.

EXERCISE SET 1.5

—Suggested Assignment: Exercises 1–65, every other odd; 81–86, all.
—Answer graphs to Exercises 1–16 are on page AA2.

In Exercises 1 to 8, use the properties of inequalities to solve each inequality. Write the solution set using set-builder notation, and graph the solution set.

5. $\left\{x \mid x \geq -\dfrac{13}{8}\right\}$

1. $2x + 3 < 11$
   $\{x \mid x < 4\}$

2. $3x - 5 > 16$
   $\{x \mid x > 7\}$

3. $x + 4 > 3x + 16$
   $\{x \mid x < -6\}$

4. $5x + 6 < 2x + 1$
   $\left\{x \mid x < -\dfrac{5}{3}\right\}$

5. $-3(x + 2) \leq 5x + 7$

▶ 6. $-4(x - 5) \geq 2x + 15$
   $\left\{x \mid x \leq \dfrac{5}{6}\right\}$

7. $-4(3x - 5) > 2(x - 4)$
   $\{x \mid x < 2\}$

8. $3(x + 7) \leq 5(2x - 8)$
   $\left\{x \mid x \geq \dfrac{61}{7}\right\}$

In Exercises 9 to 16, solve each compound inequality. Write the solution set using set-builder notation, and graph the solution set.

9. $4x + 1 > -2$ and $4x + 1 \leq 17$ $\left\{x \mid -\dfrac{3}{4} < x \leq 4\right\}$

▶ 10. $2x + 5 > -16$ and $2x + 5 < 9$ $\left\{x \mid -\dfrac{21}{2} < x < 2\right\}$

11. $10 \geq 3x - 1 \geq 0$ $\left\{x \mid \dfrac{1}{3} \leq x \leq \dfrac{11}{3}\right\}$

12. $0 \leq 2x + 6 \leq 54$
    $\{x \mid -3 \leq x \leq 24\}$

13. $x + 2 < -1$ or $x + 3 \geq 2$
    $\{x \mid x < -3 \text{ or } x \geq -1\}$

14. $x + 1 > 4$ or $x + 2 \leq 3$
    $\{x \mid x \leq 1 \text{ or } x > 3\}$

15. $-4x + 5 > 9$ or $4x + 1 < 5$
    $\{x \mid x < 1\}$

16. $2x - 7 \leq 15$ or $3x - 1 \leq 5$
    $\{x \mid x \leq 11\}$

In Exercises 17 to 28, use interval notation to express the solution set of each inequality.

17. $|2x - 1| > 4$ $\left(-\infty, -\dfrac{3}{2}\right) \cup \left(\dfrac{5}{2}, \infty\right)$

▶ 18. $|2x - 9| < 7$
    $(1, 8)$

19. $|x + 3| \geq 5$
    $(-\infty, -8] \cup [2, \infty)$

20. $|x - 10| \geq 2$
    $(-\infty, 8] \cup [12, \infty)$

21. $|3x - 10| \leq 14$ $\left[-\dfrac{4}{3}, 8\right]$

22. $|2x - 5| \geq 1$
    $(-\infty, 2] \cup [3, \infty)$

23. $|4 - 5x| \geq 24$ $\left(-\infty, -4\right] \cup \left[\dfrac{28}{5}, \infty\right)$

24. $|3 - 2x| \leq 5$
    $[-1, 4]$

25. $|x - 5| \geq 0$
    $(-\infty, \infty)$

26. $|x - 7| \geq 0$
    $(-\infty, \infty)$

27. $|x - 4| \leq 0$
    $\{4\}$

28. $|2x + 7| \leq 0$ $\left\{-\dfrac{7}{2}\right\}$

In Exercises 29 to 36, use the critical value method to solve each polynomial inequality. Use interval notation to write each solution set.

29. $x^2 + 7x > 0$
    $(-\infty, -7) \cup (0, \infty)$

30. $x^2 - 5x \leq 0$
    $[0, 5]$

31. $x^2 - 16 \leq 0$
    $[-4, 4]$

32. $x^2 - 49 > 0$
    $(-\infty, -7) \cup (7, \infty)$

33. $x^2 + 7x + 10 < 0$
    $(-5, -2)$

▶ 34. $x^2 + 5x + 6 < 0$
    $(-3, -2)$

35. $x^2 - 3x \geq 28$
    $(-\infty, -4] \cup [7, \infty)$

36. $x^2 < -x + 30$
    $(-6, 5)$

In Exercises 37 to 50, use the critical value method to solve each rational inequality. Write each solution set in interval notation.

37. $\dfrac{x + 4}{x - 1} < 0$
    $(-4, 1)$

38. $\dfrac{x - 2}{x + 3} > 0$
    $(-\infty, -3) \cup (2, \infty)$

39. $\dfrac{x - 5}{x + 8} \geq 3$ $\left[-\dfrac{29}{2}, -8\right)$

40. $\dfrac{x - 4}{x + 6} \leq 1$
    $(-6, \infty)$

41. $\dfrac{x}{2x + 7} \geq 4$ $\left[-4, -\dfrac{7}{2}\right)$

42. $\dfrac{x}{3x - 5} \leq -5$ $\left[\dfrac{25}{16}, \dfrac{5}{3}\right)$

43. $\dfrac{(x + 1)(x - 4)}{x - 2} < 0$
    $(-\infty, -1) \cup (2, 4)$

44. $\dfrac{x(x - 4)}{x + 5} > 0$
    $(-5, 0) \cup (4, \infty)$

45. $\dfrac{x + 2}{x - 5} \leq 2$
    $(-\infty, 5) \cup [12, \infty)$

▶ 46. $\dfrac{3x + 1}{x - 2} \geq 4$
    $(2, 9]$

47. $\dfrac{6x^2 - 11x - 10}{x} > 0$ $\left(-\dfrac{2}{3}, 0\right) \cup \left(\dfrac{5}{2}, \infty\right)$

48. $\dfrac{3x^2 - 2x - 8}{x - 1} \geq 0$ $\left[-\dfrac{4}{3}, 1\right) \cup [2, \infty)$

49. $\dfrac{x^2 - 6x + 9}{x - 5} \leq 0$
    $(-\infty, 5)$

50. $\dfrac{x^2 + 10x + 25}{x + 1} \geq 0$
    $\{-5\} \cup (-1, \infty)$

51. PERSONAL FINANCE A bank offers two checking account plans. The monthly fee and charge per check for each plan are shown below. Under what conditions is it less expensive to use the LowCharge plan?

if you write more than 57 checks a month

Account Plan	Monthly Fee	Charge per Check
LowCharge	$5.00	$.01
FeeSaver	$1.00	$.08

▶ **52. PERSONAL FINANCE** You can rent a car for the day from Company A for $29.00 plus $0.12 a mile. Company B charges $22.00 plus $0.21 a mile. Find the number of miles m (to the nearest mile) per day for which it is cheaper to rent from Company A.

at least 78 mi

53. SHIPPING REQUIREMENTS United Parcel Service (UPS) will only ship packages for which the length is less than or equal to 108 inches and the length plus the girth is less than or equal to 130 inches. The length of a package is defined as the length of the longest side. The girth is defined as twice the width plus twice the height of the package. If a box has a length of 34 inches and a width of 22 inches, determine the possible range of heights h for this package if you wish to ship it by UPS. (*Source:* http://www.iship.com.)

$0 < h \le 26$ in.

▶ **54. MOVIE TICKET PRICES** The average U.S. movie ticket price P, in dollars, can be modeled by

$$P = 0.218t + 4.02, \quad t \ge 0$$

where $t = 0$ represents the year 1994. According to this model, in what year will the average price of a movie ticket first exceed $6.50? (*Source:* National Association of Theatre Owners, http://www.natoonline.org/satistics-tickets.htm.)

2005

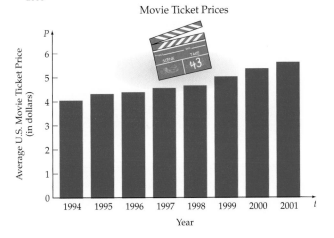

Movie Ticket Prices

55. PERSONAL FINANCE A sales clerk has a choice between two payment plans. Plan A pays $100.00 a week plus $8.00 a sale. Plan B pays $250.00 a week plus $3.50 a sale. How many sales per week must be made for plan A to yield the greater paycheck?

at least 34 sales

56. PERSONAL FINANCE A video store offers two rental plans. The yearly membership fee and the daily charge per video for each plan are shown below. How many one-night rentals can be made per year if the No-fee plan is to be the less expensive of the plans?

30 rentals or less

THE VIDEO STORE

Rental Plan	Yearly Fee	Daily Charge per Video
Low-rate	$15.00	$1.49
No-fee	None	$1.99

57. AVERAGE TEMPERATURES The average daily minimum-to-maximum temperature range for the city of Palm Springs during the month of September is 68 to 104 degrees Fahrenheit. What is the corresponding temperature range measured on the Celsius temperature scale? (*Hint:* Let F be the average daily temperature. Then $68 \le F \le 104$. Now substitute $\frac{9}{5}C + 32$ for F and solve the resulting inequality for C.)

$20° \le C \le 40°$

▶ **58. AVERAGE TEMPERATURES** The average daily minimum-to-maximum temperature range for the city of Palm Springs during the month of January is 41 to 68 degrees Fahrenheit. What is the corresponding temperature range measured on the Celsius temperature scale? (*Hint:* See Exercise 57.)

$5° \le C \le 20°$

59. CONSECUTIVE EVEN INTEGERS The sum of three consecutive even integers is between 36 and 54. Find all possible sets of integers that satisfy these conditions.

{12, 14, 16}, {14, 16, 18}

60. CONSECUTIVE ODD INTEGERS The sum of three consecutive odd integers is between 63 and 81. Find all possible sets of integers that satisfy these conditions.

{21, 23, 25}, {23, 25, 27}

61. FORENSIC SCIENCE Forensic specialists can estimate the height of a deceased person from the lengths of the person's bones. These lengths are substituted into mathematical inequalities. For instance, an inequality that relates the height h, in centimeters, of an adult female and the length f, in centimeters, of her femur is

$$|h - (2.47f + 54.10)| \le 3.72$$

Use this inequality to estimate the possible range of heights, rounded to the nearest 0.1 centimeter, for an adult female whose femur measures 32.24 centimeters.

130.0 to 137.5 cm

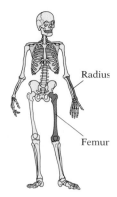

Radius

Femur

62. 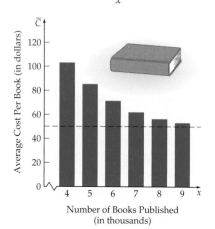 **FORENSIC SCIENCE** An inequality that is used to calculate the height h of an adult male from the length r of his radius is

$$|h - (3.32r + 85.43)| \le 4.57$$

where h and r are both in centimeters. Use this inequality to estimate the possible range of heights for an adult male whose radius measures 26.36 centimeters.

168.4 to 177.5 cm

63. REVENUE The monthly revenue R for a product is given by $R = 420x - 2x^2$, where x is the price in dollars of each unit produced. Find the interval, in terms of x, for which the monthly revenue is greater than zero.

(0, 210)

64. REVENUE A shoe manufacturer finds that the monthly revenue R from a particular style of aerobics shoe is given by $R = 312x - 3x^2$, where x is the price in dollars of each pair of shoes sold. Find the interval, in terms of x, for which the monthly revenue is greater than or equal to $5925.

[25, 79]

65. PUBLISHING A publisher has determined that if x books are published, the average cost per book is given by

$$\overline{C} = \frac{14.25x + 350,000}{x}$$

How many books should be published if the company wants to bring the average cost per book below $50?

at least 9791 books

66. MANUFACTURING A company manufactures running shoes. The company has determined that if it manufactures x pairs of shoes, the average cost, in dollars, per pair is

$$\overline{C} = \frac{0.00014x^2 + 12x + 400,000}{x}$$

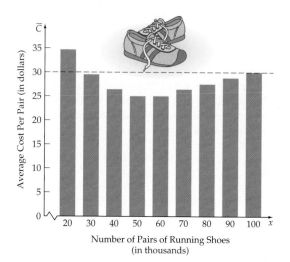

How many pairs of running shoes should the company manufacture if it wishes to bring the average cost below $30 per pair?

from 28,572 to 99,999 pairs of shoes

━━━ CONNECTING CONCEPTS ━━━

67. **TOLERANCE** A machinist is producing a circular cylinder on a lathe. The circumference of the cylinder must be 28 inches, with a tolerance of 0.15 inch. What maximum and minimum radii (to the nearest 0.001 inch) must the machinist stay between to produce an acceptable cylinder?
maximum radius: 4.480 in.; minimum radius: 4.432 in.

68. **TOLERANCE** A tall, narrow beaker has an inner radius of 2 centimeters. How high h (to the nearest 0.1 centimeter) should we fill the beaker if we need to measure $\dfrac{3}{4}$ liter (750 cubic centimeters) of a solution with an error of 15 cubic centimeters or less?
58.5 to 60.9 cm

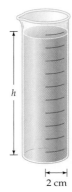

h

2 cm

In Exercises 69 to 72, use the critical value method to solve each inequality. Use interval notation to write each solution set.

69. $\dfrac{(x-3)^2}{(x-6)^2} > 0$
$(-\infty, 3) \cup (3, 6) \cup (6, \infty)$

70. $\dfrac{(x-1)^2}{(x-4)^4} \geq 0$
$(-\infty, 4) \cup (4, \infty)$

71. $\dfrac{(x-4)^2}{(x+3)^3} \geq 0$
$(-3, \infty)$

72. $\dfrac{(2x-7)}{(x-1)^2(x+2)^2} \geq 0$
$\left[\dfrac{7}{2}, \infty\right)$

In Exercises 73 to 78, use interval notation to express the solution set of each inequality.

73. $1 < |x| < 5$
$(-5, -1) \cup (1, 5)$

74. $2 < |x| < 3$
$(-3, -2) \cup (2, 3)$

75. $3 \leq |x| < 7$
$(-7, -3] \cup [3, 7)$

76. $0 < |x| \leq 3$
$[-3, 0) \cup (0, 3]$

77. $0 < |x - a| < \delta \quad (\delta > 0)$
$(a - \delta, a) \cup (a, a + \delta)$

78. $0 < |x - 5| < 2$
$(3, 5) \cup (5, 7)$

79. **HEIGHT OF A PROJECTILE** The equation

$$s = -16t^2 + v_0 t + s_0$$

gives the height s, in feet above ground level, at the time t seconds, of an object thrown directly upward from a height s_0 feet above the ground and with an initial velocity of v_0 feet per second. A ball is thrown directly upward from ground level with an initial velocity of 64 feet per second. Find the time interval during which the ball has a height of more than 48 feet.
more than 1 s but less than 3 s

80. **HEIGHT OF A PROJECTILE** A ball is thrown directly upward from a height of 32 feet above the ground with an initial velocity of 80 feet per second. Find the time interval during which the ball will be more than 96 feet above the ground. (*Hint:* See Exercise 79.)
more than 1 s but less than 4 s

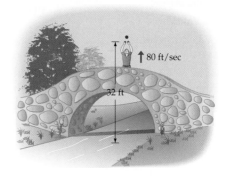

80 ft/sec

32 ft

━━━ PREPARE FOR SECTION 1.6 ━━━

81. Solve $1820 = k(28)$ for k. [1.1]
65

82. Solve $20 = \dfrac{k}{1.5^2}$ for k. [1.1]
45

83. Evaluate $k\dfrac{3}{5^2}$ given that $k = 225$. [P.1]
27

84. Evaluate $k\dfrac{4.5 \cdot 32}{8^2}$ given that $k = 12.5$. [P.1]
28.125

85. If the length of each side of a square is doubled, what effect does this have on its area? [P.1/P.2]
The area becomes 4 times as large.

86. If the radius of a cylinder is tripled, does this triple the volume of the cylinder? [P.1/P.2]
No. The volume becomes 9 times as large.

PROJECTS
---

1. TRIANGLES In any triangle, the sum of the lengths of the two shorter sides must be greater than the length of the longest side. Find all possible values of x if a triangle has sides of lengths

a. $x, x + 5$, and $x + 9$ **b.** $x, x^2 + x$, and $2x^2 + x$

c. $\dfrac{1}{x + 2}, \dfrac{1}{x + 1}$, and $\dfrac{1}{x}$

2. FAIR COINS A coin is considered a **fair** coin if it has an equal chance of landing heads up or tails up. To decide whether a coin is a fair coin, a statistician tosses it 1000 times and records the number of tails t. The statistician is prepared to state that the coin is a fair coin if

$$\left| \frac{t - 500}{15.81} \right| \le 2.33$$

a. Determine what values of t will cause the statistician to state that the coin is a fair coin.

b. Pick a coin and test it according to the criteria above to see whether it is a fair coin.

SECTION **1.6**   # VARIATION AND APPLICATIONS

- DIRECT VARIATION
- INVERSE VARIATION
- JOINT VARIATION AND COMBINED VARIATION

• DIRECT VARIATION

Many real-life situations involve variables that are related by a type of equation called a **variation.** For example, a stone thrown into a pond generates circular ripples whose circumference and diameter are increasing. The equation $C = \pi d$ expresses the relationship between the circumference C of a circle and its diameter d. If d increases, then C increases. The circumference C is said to *vary directly* as the diameter d.

> Ⓟ   **Definition of Direct Variation**
>
> The variable y **varies directly** as the variable x, or y is **directly proportional** to x, if and only if
>
> $$y = kx$$
>
> where k is a constant called the **constant of proportionality** or the **variation constant.**

Direct variations occur in many daily applications. For example, suppose the cost of a newspaper is 50 cents. The cost C to purchase n newspapers is directly proportional to the number n. That is, $C = 50n$. In this example the variation constant is 50.

To solve a problem that involves a variation, we typically write a general equation that relates the variables and then use given information to solve for the variation constant.

Alternative to Example 1
Some colleges are on the semester system, whereas other colleges use the quarter system. When a student transfers from one college to another, it is sometimes necessary to translate between the semester and quarter systems. The number of semester hours completed is directly proportional to the number of quarter hours completed. If a student whose record shows 45 quarter hours is credited with completing 30 semester hours, how many semester hours credit will a student have if the student completes 240 quarter hours?
- **160 semester hours**

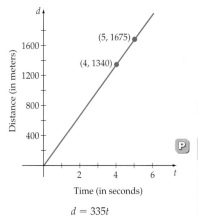

$$d = 335t$$

FIGURE 1.15

Alternative to Example 2
The distance s that a ball rolls down an inclined plane is directly proportional to the square of the time t. If the ball rolls 5 feet in 1 second, how far will it roll in 4 seconds?
- **80 ft**

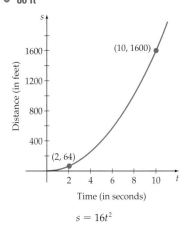

$$s = 16t^2$$

FIGURE 1.16

EXAMPLE 1   Solve a Direct Variation

The distance sound travels varies directly as the time it travels. If sound travels 1340 meters in 4 seconds, find the distance sound will travel in 5 seconds.

Solution

Write an equation that relates the distance d to the time t. Because d varies directly as t, our equation is $d = kt$. Because $d = 1340$ when $t = 4$, we obtain

$$1340 = k \cdot 4 \qquad \text{which implies} \qquad k = \frac{1340}{4} = 335$$

Therefore, the specific equation that relates the distance d sound travels in t seconds is $d = 335t$. To find the distance sound travels in 5 seconds, replace t with 5 to produce

$$d = 335(5) = 1675$$

Under the same conditions, sound will travel 1675 meters in 5 seconds. See **Figure 1.15.**

▶ **TRY EXERCISE 22, PAGE 151**

Direct Variation as the *n*th Power

If y **varies directly as the *n*th power** of x, then

$$y = kx^n$$

where k is a constant.

EXAMPLE 2   Solve a Variation of the Form $y = kx^2$

The distance s that an object falls from rest (neglecting air resistance) varies directly as the square of the time t that it has been falling. If an object falls 64 feet in 2 seconds, how far will it fall in 10 seconds?

Solution

Because s varies directly as the square of t, $s = kt^2$. The variable s is 64 when t is 2, so

$$64 = k \cdot 2^2 \qquad \text{which implies} \qquad k = \frac{64}{4} = 16$$

The specific equation that relates the distance s an object falls in t seconds is $s = 16t^2$. Letting $t = 10$ yields

$$s = 16(10^2) = 16(100) = 1600$$

Under the same conditions, the object will fall 1600 feet in 10 seconds. See **Figure 1.16.**

▶ **TRY EXERCISE 26, PAGE 151**

• INVERSE VARIATION

Two variables also can vary *inversely*.

Ⓟ **Definition of Inverse Variation**

The variable y **varies inversely** as the variable x, or y is **inversely proportional** to x, if and only if

$$y = \frac{k}{x}$$

where k is the variation constant.

In 1661, Robert Boyle made a study of the *compressibility* of gases. **Figure 1.17** shows that he used a J-shaped tube to demonstrate the inverse relationship between the volume of a gas at a given temperature and the applied pressure. The J-shaped tube on the left shows that the volume of a gas at normal atmospheric pressure is 60 milliliters. If the pressure is doubled by adding mercury (Hg), as shown in the middle tube, the volume of the gas is halved to 30 milliliters. Tripling the pressure decreases the volume of the gas to 20 milliliters, as shown in the tube at the right.

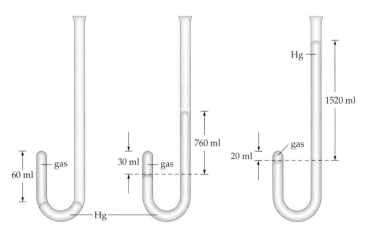

FIGURE 1.17

Alternative to Example 3
The speed v of a gear varies inversely as the number of teeth t. If a gear that has 48 teeth makes 20 revolutions per minute, how many revolutions per minute will a gear that has 30 teeth make?
● **32 revolutions**

EXAMPLE 3   Solve an Inverse Variation

Boyle's Law states that the volume V of a sample of gas (at a constant temperature) varies inversely as the pressure P. The volume of a gas in a J-shaped tube is 75 milliliters when the pressure is 1.5 atmospheres. Find the volume of the gas when the pressure is increased to 2.5 atmospheres.

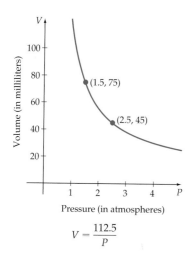

$$V = \frac{112.5}{P}$$

FIGURE 1.18

take note

Because the volume V varies inversely as the pressure P, the function $V = \frac{112.5}{P}$ is a decreasing function, as shown in Figure 1.18.

Solution

The volume V varies inversely as the pressure P, so $V = \frac{k}{P}$. The volume V is 75 milliliters when the pressure is 1.5 atmospheres, so

$$75 = \frac{k}{1.5} \quad \text{and} \quad k = (75)(1.5) = 112.5$$

Thus $V = \frac{112.5}{P}$. When the pressure is 2.5 atmospheres, we have

$$V = \frac{112.5}{2.5} = 45 \text{ milliliters}$$

See **Figure 1.18.**

▶ **TRY EXERCISE 30, PAGE 151**

Many real-world situations can be modeled by inverse variations that involve a power.

Inverse Variation as the *n*th Power

If y varies inversely as the **nth power** of x, then

$$y = \frac{k}{x^n}$$

where k is a constant and $n > 0$.

? QUESTION Consider the variation $y = \frac{k}{x}$, with $k > 0$. What happens to y as x increases?

Alternative to Example 4

The decibel level of music measures 120 decibels at a distance of 8 feet from a speaker. What is the decibel level of this music at a distance of 32 feet from the same speaker?

● **7.5 dB**

EXAMPLE 4   Solve an Inverse Variation Involving a Power

The intensity of music, measured in decibels (dB), is inversely proportional to the square of the distance from the music source to a listener. During a party, the decibel level of the music measured 100 decibels at a distance of 12 feet from a loud speaker. What was the decibel level of the music for a dancer who was only 10 feet from the speaker?

Continued ▶

? ANSWER As x increases, y decreases.

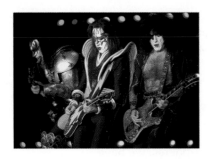

Solution

The decibel level L is inversely proportional to the square of the distance d between the loud speaker and a listener. The general variation is given by

$$L = \frac{k}{d^2}$$

We are given that $L = 100$ decibels when $d = 12$ feet. Substituting these values into the preceding variation allows us to solve for the variation constant k.

$$100 = \frac{k}{12^2}$$

$$k = 12^2(100)$$

$$= 14{,}400$$

The specific variation formula is

$$L = \frac{14{,}400}{d^2}$$

When $d = 10$ feet, the decibel level of the music is

$$L = \frac{14{,}400}{10^2}$$

$$= 144$$

At a distance of 10 feet from the speaker, the decibel level of the music is 144 decibels.

▶ **TRY EXERCISE 32, PAGE 152**

● **JOINT VARIATION AND COMBINED VARIATION**

Some variations involve more than two variables.

P   **Definition of Joint Variation**

The variable z **varies jointly** as the variables x and y if and only if

$$z = kxy$$

where k is a constant.

Alternative to Example 5
The cost of a concrete patio varies jointly as the area of the patio and the depth of the patio. It costs $500 for a patio with an area of 80 square feet and a depth of 4 inches. Find the cost of a patio with an area of 144 square feet and a depth of 6 inches.
● **$1350**

EXAMPLE 5   **Solve a Joint Variation**

The cost of insulating the ceiling of a house varies jointly as the thickness of the insulation and the area of the ceiling. It costs $175 to insulate a 2100-square-foot ceiling with insulation that is 4 inches thick. Find the cost of insulating a 2400-square-foot ceiling with insulation that is 6 inches thick.

Solution

Because the cost C varies jointly as the area A of the ceiling and the thickness T of the insulation, we know $C = kAT$. Using the fact that $C = 175$ when $A = 2100$ and $T = 4$ gives us

$$175 = k(2100)(4) \qquad \text{which implies} \qquad k = \frac{175}{(2100)(4)} = \frac{1}{48}$$

Consequently, the specific formula for C is $C = \dfrac{1}{48}AT$. Now, when $A = 2400$ and $T = 6$, we have

$$C = \frac{1}{48}(2400)(6) = 300$$

The cost of insulating the 2400-square-foot ceiling with 6-inch insulation is $300.

▶ **TRY EXERCISE 34, PAGE 152**

Combined variations involve more than one type of variation.

Alternative to Example 6

The volume of a given mass of a gas varies directly as the temperature T and inversely as the pressure P. If the volume of the gas is 220 cm³ when $T = 40°C$ and $P = 20$ kg/cm², what is the volume when $T = 35°C$ and $P = 10$ kg/cm²?

◉ **385 cm³**

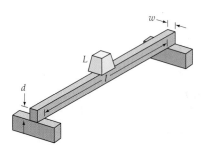

FIGURE 1.19

EXAMPLE 6 **Solve a Combined Variation**

The weight that a horizontal beam with a rectangular cross section can safely support varies jointly as the width and square of the depth of the cross section and inversely as the length of the beam. See **Figure 1.19**. If a 4-inch by 4-inch beam 10 feet long safely supports a load of 256 pounds, what load L can be safely supported by a beam made of the same material and with a width w of 4 inches, a depth d of 6 inches, and a length l of 16 feet?

Solution

The general variation equation is $L = k\dfrac{wd^2}{l}$. Using the given data yields

$$256 = k\frac{4(4^2)}{10}$$

Solving for k produces $k = 40$, so the specific formula for L is

$$L = 40\frac{wd^2}{l}$$

Substituting 4 for w, 6 for d, and 16 for l gives

$$L = 40\frac{4(6^2)}{16} = 360 \text{ pounds}$$

▶ **TRY EXERCISE 38, PAGE 152**

TOPICS FOR DISCUSSION

1. The area A of a trapezoid varies jointly as the product of its height h and the sum of its bases b and B. State an equation that represents this variation. Given that $A = 15$ square inches when $h = 6$ inches, $b = 2$ inches, and $B = 3$ inches, explain how you would determine the value of the variation constant.

2. Given that the variation constant $k > 0$ and that A varies directly as b, then A _____ when b increases, and A _____ when b decreases.

3. Given that the variation constant $k > 0$ and that S varies inversely as d, then S _____ when d increases, and S _____ when d decreases.

4. The volume V of a right circular cylinder varies jointly as the square of the radius r and the height h. Tell what happens to V when

   a. h is tripled   b. r is tripled

   c. r is doubled and h is decreased to $\dfrac{1}{2}h$

5. Give some examples of real situations where one quantity varies inversely as a second quantity.

EXERCISE SET 1.6   —Suggested Assignment: Exercises 1–37, odd.

In Exercises 1 to 12, write an equation that represents the relationship between the given variables. Use k as the variation constant.

1. d varies directly as t.
   $d = kt$

2. r varies directly as the square of s.
   $r = ks^2$

3. y varies inversely as x. $y = \dfrac{k}{x}$

4. p is inversely proportional to q. $p = \dfrac{k}{q}$

5. m varies jointly as n and p.
   $m = knp$

6. t varies jointly as r and the cube of s.
   $t = krs^3$

7. V varies jointly as l, w, and h.
   $V = klwh$

8. u varies directly as v and inversely as the square of w. $u = \dfrac{kv}{w^2}$

9. A is directly proportional to the square of s.
   $A = ks^2$

10. A varies jointly as h and the square of r.
    $A = khr^2$

11. F varies jointly as m_1 and m_2 and inversely as the square of d. $F = \dfrac{km_1 m_2}{d^2}$

12. T varies jointly as t and r and the square of a.
    $T = ktra^2$

In Exercises 13 to 20, write the equation that expresses the relationship between the variables, and then use the given data to solve for the variation constant.

13. y varies directly as x, and $y = 64$ when $x = 48$. $y = kx, k = \dfrac{4}{3}$

14. m is directly proportional to n, and $m = 92$ when $n = 23$.
    $m = kn, k = 4$

15. r is directly proportional to the square of t, and $r = 144$ when $t = 108$. $r = kt^2, k = \dfrac{1}{81}$

16. C varies directly as r, and $C = 94.2$ when $r = 15$.
    $C = kr, k = 6.28$

17. T varies jointly as r and the square of s, and $T = 210$ when $r = 30$ and $s = 5$. $T = krs^2, k = \dfrac{7}{25}$

18. u varies directly as v and inversely as the square root of w, and $u = 0.04$ when $v = 8$ and $w = 0.04$. $u = \dfrac{kv}{\sqrt{w}}, k = 0.001$

19. V varies jointly as l, w, and h, and $V = 240$ when $l = 8$, $w = 6$, and $h = 5$.
    $V = klwh, k = 1$

20. t varies directly as the cube of r and inversely as the square root of s, and $t = 10$ when $r = 5$ and $s = 0.09$. $t = \dfrac{kr^3}{\sqrt{s}}, k = 0.024$

21. CHARLES'S LAW *Charles's Law* states that the volume V occupied by a gas (at a constant pressure) is directly proportional to its absolute temperature T. An experiment with a balloon shows that the volume of the balloon is 0.85 liter at 270 K (absolute temperature).[4] What will the volume of the balloon be when its temperature is 324 K?
1.02 l

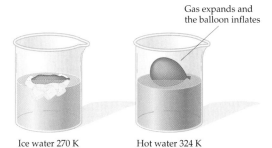

Gas expands and
the balloon inflates

Ice water 270 K   Hot water 324 K

▶ **22. HOOKE'S LAW** *Hooke's Law* states that the distance a spring stretches varies directly as the weight on the spring. A weight of 80 pounds stretches a spring 6 inches. How far will a weight of 100 pounds stretch the spring?
7.5 in.

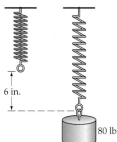

6 in.

80 lb

23. SEMESTER HOURS VS. QUARTER HOURS A student plans to transfer from a college that uses the quarter system to a college that uses the semester system. The number of semester hours a student receives credit for is directly proportional to the number of quarter hours the student has earned. A student with 51 quarter hours is given credit for 34 semester hours. How many semester hours credit should a student receive if the student has completed 93 quarter hours?
62 semester hours

24. PRESSURE AND DEPTH The pressure a liquid exerts at a given point on a submarine is directly proportional to the depth of the point below the surface of the liquid. If the pressure at a depth of 3 feet is 187.5 pounds per square foot, find the pressure at a depth of 7 feet.
437.5 lb/ft²

---

[4]Absolute temperature is measured on the Kelvin scale. A unit (called a kelvin) on the Kelvin scale is the same measure as a degree on the Celsius scale; however, 0 on the Kelvin scale corresponds to $-273°C$ on the Celsius scale.

25. AMOUNT OF JUICE CONTAINED IN A GRAPEFRUIT The amount of juice in a grapefruit is directly proportional to the cube of its diameter. A grapefruit with a 4-inch diameter contains 6 fluid ounces of juice. How much juice is contained in a grapefruit with a 5-inch diameter? Round to the nearest tenth of a fluid ounce.
11.7 fl oz

▶ **26. MOTORCYCLE JUMP** The range of a projectile is directly proportional to the square of its velocity. If a motorcyclist can make a jump of 140 feet by coming off a ramp at 60 mph, find the distance the motorcyclist could expect to jump if the speed coming off the ramp were increased to 65 mph. Round to the nearest tenth of a foot.
164.3 ft

27. PERIOD OF A PENDULUM The period T of a pendulum (the time it takes the pendulum to make one complete oscillation) varies directly as the square root of its length L. A pendulum 3 feet long has a period of 1.8 seconds.

a. Find the period of a pendulum that is 10 feet long. Round to the nearest tenth of a second.
3.3 s

b. What is the length of a pendulum that *beats seconds* (that is, has a 2-second period)? Round to the nearest tenth of a foot.
3.7 ft

28. AREA OF A PROJECTED PICTURE The area of a projected picture on a movie screen varies directly as the square of the distance from the projector to the screen. If a distance of 20 feet produces a picture with an area of 64 square feet, what distance produces an area of 100 square feet?
25 ft

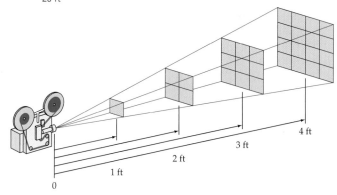

4 ft

3 ft

2 ft

1 ft

0

29. SPEED OF A BICYCLE GEAR The speed of a bicycle gear, in revolutions per minute, is inversely proportional to the number of teeth on the gear. If a gear with 64 teeth has a speed of 30 revolutions per minute, what will be the speed of a gear with 48 teeth?
40 revolutions/min

▶ **30. VIBRATION OF A GUITAR STRING** The frequency of vibration of a guitar string under constant tension varies inversely as the length of the string. A guitar string with a length of 20 inches has a frequency of 144 vibrations per

second. Find the frequency of a guitar string with a length of 18 inches. Assume the tension is the same for both strings.
160 vibrations/s

31. DECIBELS The loudness, measured in decibels, of a stereo speaker is inversely proportional to the square of the distance of the listener from the speaker. The loudness is 28 decibels at a distance of 8 feet. What is the loudness when the listener is 4 feet from the speaker?
112 decibels

▶ **32. ILLUMINATION** The illumination a source of light provides is inversely proportional to the square of the distance from the source. If the illumination at a distance of 10 feet from the source is 50 footcandles, what is the illumination at a distance of 15 feet from the source? Round to the nearest tenth of a footcandle.
22.2 footcandles

33. VOLUME RELATIONSHIPS The volume V of a right circular cone varies jointly as the square of the radius r and the height h. Tell what happens to V when

  a. r is tripled
    9 times larger
  b. h is tripled
    3 times larger
  c. both r and h are tripled
    27 times larger

▶ **34. SAFE LOAD** The load L that a horizontal beam can safely support varies jointly as the width w and the square of the depth d. If a beam with width 2 inches and depth 6 inches safely supports up to 200 pounds, how many pounds can a beam of the same length that has width 4 inches and depth 4 inches be expected to support? Round to the nearest pound.
178 lb

35. IDEAL GAS LAW The *Ideal Gas Law* states that the volume V of a gas varies jointly as the number of moles of gas n and the absolute temperature T and inversely as the pressure P. What happens to V when n is tripled and P is reduced by a factor of one-half?
6 times larger

36. MAXIMUM LOAD The maximum load a cylindrical column of circular cross section can support varies directly as the fourth power of the diameter and inversely as the square of the height. If a column 2 feet in diameter and 10 feet high supports up to 6 tons, how much of a load does a column 3 feet in diameter and 14 feet high support?
≈15.5 tons

37. EARNED RUN AVERAGE A pitcher's earned run average (ERA) is directly proportional to the number of earned runs the pitcher has allowed and is inversely proportional to the number of innings the pitcher has pitched. During the 2002 season, Randy Johnson of the Arizona Diamondbacks had an ERA of 2.32. He allowed 67 earned runs in 260 innings. During the same 2002 season, Tom Glavine of the Atlanta Braves allowed 74 earned runs in 224.2 innings. What was Glavine's ERA for the 2002 season? Round to the nearest hundredth. (*Source:* MLB.com)
2.97

▶ **38. SAFE LOAD** The load L a horizontal beam can safely support varies jointly as the width w and the square of the depth d and inversely as the length l. If a 12-foot beam with width 4 inches and depth 8 inches safely supports 800 pounds, how many pounds can a 16-foot beam that has width 3.5 inches and depth 6 inches be expected to support? ≈295 lb

39. FORCE, SPEED, AND RADIUS RELATIONSHIPS The force needed to keep a car from skidding on a curve varies jointly as the weight of the car and the square of its speed and inversely as the radius of the curve. It takes 2800 pounds of force to keep an 1800-pound car from skidding on a curve with radius 425 feet at 45 mph. What force is needed to keep the same car from skidding when it takes a similar curve with radius 450 feet at 55 mph? Round to the nearest ten pounds.
3950 lb

--- *CONNECTING CONCEPTS* ---

40. STIFFNESS OF A BEAM A cylindrical log is to be cut so that it will yield a beam that has a rectangular cross section of depth d and width w. The stiffness of a beam of given length is directly proportional to the width and the cube of the depth. The diameter of the log is 18 inches.

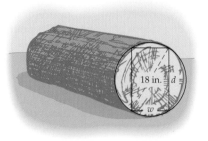

What depth will yield the "stiffest" beam, $d = 10$ inches, $d = 12$ inches, $d = 14$ inches, or $d = 16$ inches?

$d = 16$ in.

41. KEPLER'S THIRD LAW *Kepler's Third Law* states that the time T needed for a planet to make one complete revolution about the sun is directly proportional to the $\frac{3}{2}$ power of the average distance d between the planet and the sun. The earth, which averages 93 million miles from the sun, completes one revolution in 365 days. Find the average distance from the sun to Mars if Mars completes one revolution about the sun in 686 days. Round to the nearest million miles.

142 million mi

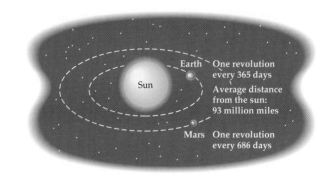

PROJECTS

1. A DIRECT VARIATION FORMULA If $f(x)$ varies directly as x, prove that $f(x_2) = f(x_1)\frac{x_2}{x_1}$. Use this formula to solve the following direct variation without solving for the variation constant. The distance a spring stretches varies directly as the force applied. An experiment shows that a force of 17 kilograms stretches the spring 8.5 centimeters. How far will a 22-kilogram force stretch the spring?

2. AN INVERSE VARIATION FORMULA Given that $f(x)$ varies inversely as x, prove that $f(x_2) = f(x_1)\frac{x_1}{x_2}$. Use this formula to solve the following inverse variation *without* solving for the variation constant. The volume of a gas varies inversely as pressure (assuming the temperature remains constant). An experiment shows that a particular gas has a volume of 2.4 liters under a pressure of 280 grams per square centimeter. What volume will the gas have when a pressure of 330 grams per square centimeter is applied?

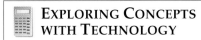

EXPLORING CONCEPTS WITH TECHNOLOGY

Use a Graphing Calculator to Solve Equations

Most graphing calculators can be used to solve equations. The following example shows how to solve an equation using the **solve(** feature that is available on a TI-83 graphing calculator.

The calculator display below indicates that the solution of $2x - 17 = 0$ is 8.5.

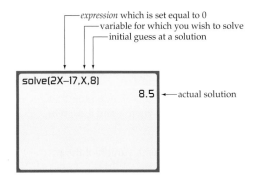

The calculator display on page 153 was produced by the following keystrokes. Press $\boxed{\text{2nd}}$ [catalog] S (scroll down to **solve(**) $\boxed{\text{ENTER}}$. Now enter 2 $\boxed{\text{X,T,}\Theta\text{,}n}$ $\boxed{-}$ 17 $\boxed{,}$ $\boxed{\text{X,T,}\Theta\text{,}n}$ $\boxed{,}$ 8 $\boxed{)}$ $\boxed{\text{ENTER}}$. In this example, the 8.5 represents the solution of $2x - 17 = 0$ that is close to our initial guess of 8. Because $2x - 17 = 0$ has only one solution, we are finished. Note that the **solve(** feature can only be used to solve equations of the form

$$Expression = 0$$

Also, you are required to indicate the variable you wish to solve for, and you must enter an initial guess. In the preceding display we entered X as the variable and 8 as our initial guess.

The **solve(** feature can only be used to find *real* solutions. Also, the **solve(** feature finds only one solution each time the solution procedure is applied. If you know that an equation has two real solutions, then you need to apply the solution procedure twice. Each time you must enter an initial guess that is close to the solution you are trying to find. The calculator display below indicates that the solutions of $2x^2 - x - 15 = 0$ are 3 and -2.5. To find these solutions, we first used the **solve(** feature with an initial guess of 2, and we then used the **solve(** feature with an initial guess of -1.

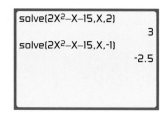

The following chapters will illustrate additional techniques and calculator procedures that can be used to solve equations.

CHAPTER 1 SUMMARY

1.1 Linear and Absolute Value Equations

- A number is said to satisfy an equation if substituting the number for the variable results in an equation that is a true statement. To solve an equation means to find all values of the variable that satisfy the equation. These values that make the equation true are called solutions or roots of the equation. Equivalent equations have the same solution(s).

- A linear equation in the single variable x is an equation that can be written in the form $ax + b = 0$, where a and b are real numbers, with $a \neq 0$.

- The solution set of $|ax + b| = c, a \neq 0$, is the union of the solution sets of $ax + b = c$ and $ax + b = -c$.

1.2 Formulas and Applications

- A formula is an equation that expresses known relationships between two or more variables. Application problems are best solved by using the guidelines developed in this section.

1.3 Quadratic Equations

- A quadratic equation in x is an equation that can be written in the form $ax^2 + bx + c = 0$, where $a \neq 0$. If the quadratic polynomial in a quadratic equation is factorable over the set of integers, then the equation can be solved by factoring and using the zero product property. Every quadratic equation can be solved by completing the square or by using the quadratic formula.

- **The Quadratic Formula**

  If $ax^2 + bx + c = 0$, $a \neq 0$, then $x = \dfrac{-b \pm \sqrt{b^2 - 4ac}}{2a}$.

1.4 Other Types of Equations

- **The Power Principle**

  If P and Q are algebraic expressions and n is a positive integer, then every solution of $P = Q$ is a solution of $P^n = Q^n$.

- An equation is said to be quadratic in form if it can be written in the form $au^2 + bu + c = 0$, where $a \neq 0$ and u is an algebraic expression.

1.5 Inequalities

- The set of all solutions of an inequality is the solution set of the inequality. Equivalent inequalities have the same

solution set. To solve an inequality, use the properties of inequalities or the critical value method.

- An inequality of the form $|ax + b| > c$, $a \neq 0$, is an absolute value inequality. The inequality symbol $>$ can be replaced by $<$, $\leq$, or $\geq$.

1.6 Variation and Applications

- The variable y varies directly as the variable x if and only if $y = kx$, where k is a constant called the variation constant.

- The variable y varies inversely as the variable x if and only if $y = \dfrac{k}{x}$, where k is the variation constant.

- The variable z varies jointly as the variables x and y if and only if $z = kxy$, where k is the variation constant.

CHAPTER 1 TRUE/FALSE EXERCISES

In Exercises 1 to 10, answer true or false. If the statement is false, state a reason or give an example to show that the statement is false.

1. If $x^2 = 9$, then $x = 3$.
   False; $(-3)^2 = 9$.

2. The equations
   $$x = \sqrt{12 - x} \qquad \text{and} \qquad x^2 = 12 - x$$
   are equivalent equations.
   False; one has solution set $\{3\}$, and the other has solution set $\{3, -4\}$.

3. Adding the same constant to each side of a given equation produces an equation that is equivalent to the given equation.
   True

4. If $a > b$, then $-a < -b$.
   True

5. If $a \neq 0$, $b \neq 0$, and $a > b$, then $\dfrac{1}{a} > \dfrac{1}{b}$.
   False; $100 > 1$ but $\dfrac{1}{100} \not> \dfrac{1}{1}$.

6. The discriminant of $ax^2 + bx + c = 0$ is $\sqrt{b^2 - 4ac}$.
   False; the discriminant is $b^2 - 4ac$.

7. If $\sqrt{a} + \sqrt{b} = c$, then $a + b = c^2$.
   False; $\sqrt{1} + \sqrt{1} = 1 + 1 = 2$ but $1 + 1 = 2 \neq 2^2$.

8. The solution set of $|x - a| < b$ with $b > 0$ is given by the interval $(a - b, a + b)$.
   True

9. The only quadratic equation that has roots of 4 and -4 is $x^2 - 16 = 0$.
   False; $3x^2 - 48 = 0$ has roots of 4 and -4.

10. Every quadratic equation $ax^2 + bx + c = 0$ with real coefficients such that $ac < 0$ has two distinct real roots.
    True

CHAPTER 1 REVIEW EXERCISES

In Exercises 1 to 28, solve each equation.

1. $x - 2(5x - 3) = -3(-x + 4)$ $\dfrac{3}{2}$ [1.1]

2. $3x - 5(2x - 7) = -4(5 - 2x)$ $\dfrac{11}{3}$ [1.1]

3. $\dfrac{4x}{3} - \dfrac{4x - 1}{6} = \dfrac{1}{2}$ $\dfrac{1}{2}$ [1.1]

4. $\dfrac{3x}{4} - \dfrac{2x - 1}{8} = \dfrac{3}{2}$ $\dfrac{11}{4}$ [1.1]

5. $\dfrac{x}{x + 2} + \dfrac{1}{4} = 5$ $-\dfrac{38}{15}$ [1.4]

6. $\dfrac{y - 1}{y + 1} - 1 = \dfrac{2}{y}$ $-\dfrac{1}{2}$ [1.4]

7. $x^2 - 5x + 6 = 0$ $3, 2$ [1.3]

8. $6x^2 + x - 12 = 0$ $\dfrac{4}{3}, -\dfrac{3}{2}$ [1.3]

9. $3x^2 - x - 1 = 0$ $\dfrac{1 \pm \sqrt{13}}{6}$ [1.3]

10. $x^2 - x + 1 = 0$ $\dfrac{1}{2} \pm \dfrac{\sqrt{3}}{2}i$ [1.3]

11. $3x^3 - 5x^2 = 0$ $0, \dfrac{5}{3}$ [1.4]

12. $2x^3 - 8x = 0$ $0, \pm 2$ [1.4]

13. $6x^4 - 23x^2 + 20 = 0$ $\dfrac{\pm 2\sqrt{3}}{3}, \dfrac{\pm\sqrt{10}}{2}$ [1.4]

14. $3x + 16\sqrt{x} - 12 = 0$ $\dfrac{4}{9}$ [1.4]

15. $\sqrt{x^2 - 15} = \sqrt{-2x}$ $-5, 3$ [1.4]

16. $\sqrt{x^2 - 24} = \sqrt{2x}$ $6, -4$ [1.4]

17. $\sqrt{3x + 4} + \sqrt{x - 3} = 5$ 4 [1.4]

18. $\sqrt{2x + 2} - \sqrt{x + 2} = \sqrt{x - 6}$ 7 [1.4]

19. $\sqrt{4 - 3x} - \sqrt{5 - x} = \sqrt{5 + x}$ -4 [1.4]

20. $\sqrt{3x + 9} - \sqrt{2x + 4} = \sqrt{x + 1}$ 0 [1.4]

21. $\dfrac{1}{(y + 3)^2} = 1$ $-2, -4$ [1.4]

22. $\dfrac{1}{(2s - 5)^2} = 4$ $\dfrac{11}{4}, \dfrac{9}{4}$ [1.4]

23. $|x - 3| = 2$ $5, 1$ [1.1]

24. $|x + 5| = 4$ $-1, -9$ [1.1]

25. $|2x + 1| = 5$ $2, -3$ [1.1]

26. $|3x - 7| = 8$ $5, -\dfrac{1}{3}$ [1.1]

27. $(x + 2)^{1/2} + x(x + 2)^{3/2} = 0$ $-2, -1$ [1.4]

28. $x^2(3x - 4)^{1/4} + (3x - 4)^{5/4} = 0$ $1, -4, \dfrac{4}{3}$ [1.4]

In Exercises 29 to 44, solve each inequality. Express your solution sets by using interval notation.

29. $-3x + 4 \geq -2$ $(-\infty, 2]$ [1.5]

30. $-2x + 7 \leq 5x + 1$ $\left[\dfrac{6}{7}, \infty\right)$ [1.5]

31. $x^2 + 3x - 10 \leq 0$
$[-5, 2]$ [1.5]

32. $x^2 - 2x - 3 > 0$
$(-\infty, -1) \cup (3, \infty)$ [1.5]

33. $61 \leq \dfrac{9}{5}C + 32 \leq 95$
$\left[\dfrac{145}{9}, 35\right]$ [1.5]

34. $30 < \dfrac{5}{9}(F - 32) < 65$
$(86, 149)$ [1.5]

35. $x^3 - 7x^2 + 12x \leq 0$
$(-\infty, 0] \cup [3, 4]$ [1.5]

36. $x^3 + 4x^2 - 21x > 0$
$(-7, 0) \cup (3, \infty)$ [1.5]

37. $\dfrac{x + 3}{x - 4} > 0$
$(-\infty, -3) \cup (4, \infty)$ [1.5]

38. $\dfrac{x(x - 5)}{x + 7} \leq 0$
$(-\infty, -7) \cup [0, 5]$ [1.5]

39. $\dfrac{2x}{3 - x} \leq 10$
$\left(-\infty, \dfrac{5}{2}\right] \cup (3, \infty)$ [1.5]

40. $\dfrac{x}{5 - x} \geq 1$
$\left[\dfrac{5}{2}, 5\right)$ [1.5]

41. $|3x - 4| < 2$ $\left(\dfrac{2}{3}, 2\right)$ [1.5]

42. $|2x - 3| \geq 1$
$(-\infty, 1] \cup [2, \infty)$ [1.5]

43. $0 < |x - 2| < 1$
$(1, 2) \cup (2, 3)$ [1.5]

44. $0 < |x - a| < b$ $(b > 0)$
$(a - b, a) \cup (a, a + b)$ [1.5]

In Exercises 45 to 50, solve each equation for the indicated unknown.

45. $V = \pi r^2 h$, for h
$h = \dfrac{V}{\pi r^2}$ [1.2]

46. $P = \dfrac{A}{1 + rt}$, for t
$t = \dfrac{A - P}{Pr}$ [1.2]

47. $A = \dfrac{h}{2}(b_1 + b_2)$, for b_1
$b_1 = \dfrac{2A - hb_2}{h}$ [1.2]

48. $P = 2(l + w)$, for w
$w = \dfrac{P - 2l}{2}$ [1.2]

49. $e = mc^2$, for m $m = \dfrac{e}{c^2}$ [1.2]

50. $F = G\dfrac{m_1 m_2}{s^2}$, for m_1
$m_1 = \dfrac{Fs^2}{Gm_2}$ [1.2]

51. UNKNOWN NUMBER One-half of a number minus one-fourth of the number is four more than one-fifth of the number. What is the number?
80 [1.2]

52. RECTANGULAR REGION The length of a rectangle is 9 feet less than twice the width of the rectangle. The perimeter of the rectangle is 54 feet. Find the width and the length.
width = 12 ft by length = 15 ft [1.2]

53. DISTANCE TO AN ISLAND A motorboat left a harbor and traveled to an island at an average rate of 8 knots. The average speed on the return trip was 6 knots. If the total trip took 7 hours, how far is it from the harbor to the island?
24 nautical mi [1.2]

54. PRICE OF SUBSCRIPTION The price of a magazine subscription rose 5% this year. If the subscription now costs $21, how much did the subscription cost last year?
$20.00 [1.2]

55. INVESTMENT A total of $5500 was deposited into two simple interest accounts. On one account the annual simple interest rate is 4%, and on the second account the annual simple interest rate is 6%. The amount of interest earned for 1 year was $295. How much was invested in each account?
$1750 in the 4% account, $3750 in the 6% account [1.2]

56. INDIVIDUAL PRICE A calculator and a battery together sell for $21. The price of the calculator is $20 more than the price of the battery. Find the price of the calculator and the price of the battery.
Price of calculator is $20.50. Price of battery is $0.50. [1.2]

57. MAINTENANCE COST Eighteen owners share the maintenance cost of a condominium complex. If six more units are sold, the maintenance cost will be reduced by $12 per month for each of the present owners. What is the total monthly maintenance cost for the condominium complex?
$864 [1.2]

58. RECTANGULAR REGION The perimeter of a rectangle is 40 inches and its area is 96 square inches. Find the length and the width of the rectangle.
length = 12 in. by width = 8 in., or length = 8 in. by width = 12 in. [1.2]

59. CONSTRUCTION OF A WALL A mason can build a wall in 9 hours less than an apprentice. Together they can build the wall in 6 hours. How long would it take the apprentice, working alone, to build the wall?
18 h [1.4]

60. COMMERCE An art show brought in $33,196 on the sale of 4526 tickets. The adult tickets sold for $8 and the student tickets sold for $2. How many of each type of ticket were sold?
4024 adult tickets, 502 student tickets [1.2]

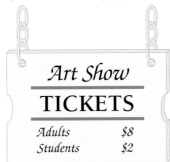

61. DIAMETER OF A CONE As sand is poured from a chute, it forms a right circular cone whose height is one-fourth the diameter of the base. What is the diameter of the base when the cone has a volume of 144 cubic feet?
≈ 13 ft [1.2]

62. REVENUE A manufacturer of calculators finds that the monthly revenue R from a particular style of calculator is given by $R = 72x - 2x^2$, where x is the price in dollars of each calculator. Find the interval, in terms of x, for which the monthly revenue is greater than $576. (12, 24)
The revenue is greater than $576 when the price is between $12 and $24. [1.5]

63. CONSUMER SPENDING The price of a pair of Revo sunglasses and the price of a pair of Bolle sunglasses differ by more than $48. The price of the Revo sunglasses is $218.

a. Write an absolute value inequality that expresses the relationship between the price B, in dollars, of the Bolle sunglasses and the price, in dollars, of the Revo sunglasses.
$|B - 218| > 48$ [1.5]

b. Use interval notation to describe the price range, in dollars, that is possible for the Bolle sunglasses.
$(0, 170) \cup (266, \infty)$ [1.5]

64. CONSUMER SPENDING Ronda wants to rent one of two apartments. There is less than $150 difference between the monthly rental fees of the apartments. One of the apartments rents for $575 per month. What is the range of possible monthly rental fees for the other apartment?
more than $425 but less than $725 [1.5]

65. SHIPPING REQUIREMENTS Federal Express (FedEx) will only ship packages for which the length is less than or equal to 119 inches and the length plus the girth is less than or equal to 165 inches. The length of a package is defined as the length of the longest side and the girth is defined as twice the width plus twice the height of the package. If a box has a length of 42 inches and a width of 38 inches, determine the possible range of heights h for this package if you wish to ship it by FedEx. (*Source:* http://www.iship.com)
$0 < h \le 23.5$ in. [1.5]

66. COURSE GRADE An average of 68 to 79 in a biology class receives a C grade. A student has test scores of 82, 72, 64, and 95 on four tests. Find the range of scores on the fifth test that will give the student a C grade for the course.
[27, 82] [1.5]

67. BASKETBALL DIMENSIONS A basketball is to have a circumference of 29.5 inches to 30.0 inches. Find the acceptable range of diameters for the basketball. Round results to the nearest hundredth of an inch.
9.39 to 9.55 in. [1.5]

68. POPULATION DENSITY The population density D, in people per square mile, of a city is related to the horizontal distance x, in miles, from the center of the city by the equation

$$D = -45x^2 + 190x + 200, \qquad 0 < x < 5$$

Describe the region of the city in which the population density exceeds 300 people per square mile. Round critical values to the nearest tenth of a mile.
more than 0.6 mi but less than 3.6 mi from the city center [1.5]

69. ACCELERATION The acceleration due to gravity on the surface of a planetary body is directly proportional to the mass of the body and inversely proportional to the square of its radius. If the acceleration due to gravity is 9.8 meters per second squared on Earth, whose radius is 6,370,000 meters and whose mass is 5.98×10^{26} grams, find the acceleration due to gravity on the moon, whose radius is 1,740,000 meters and whose mass is 7.46×10^{24} grams. Round to the nearest hundredth of a meter per second squared.
1.64 m/s² [1.6]

70. LOAD ON A COLUMN The maximum safe load that a cylindrical column of circular cross section can support varies directly as the fourth power of the diameter and inversely as the square of the height. If a column 1.5 feet in diameter and 8 feet high safely supports 4 tons, how much of a load can a column 4 feet in diameter and 12 feet high safely support? Round to the nearest tenth of a ton.
89.9 tons [1.6]

CHAPTER 1 TEST

1. Solve: $3(2x - 5) + 1 = -2(x - 5)$
3 [1.1]

2. Solve: $|x - 3| = 8$
$-5, 11$ [1.1]

3. Solve $6x^2 - 13x - 8 = 0$ by factoring and applying the zero product property. $-\dfrac{1}{2}, \dfrac{8}{3}$ [1.3]

4. Solve $2x^2 - 8x + 1 = 0$ by completing the square. $\dfrac{4 \pm \sqrt{14}}{2}$ [1.3]

5. Use the quadratic formula to solve $3x^2 - 5x - 1 = 0$. $\dfrac{5 \pm \sqrt{37}}{6}$ [1.3]

6. Determine the discriminant of $2x^2 + 3x + 1 = 0$ and state the number of real solutions of the equation.
discriminant: 1; two real solutions [1.3]

7. Solve $ax - c = c(x - d)$ for x. $x = \dfrac{c - cd}{a - c}, a \neq c$ [1.2]

8. Solve: $\sqrt{x - 2} - 1 = \sqrt{3 - x}$ 3 [1.4]

9. Solve: $3x^{2/3} + 10x^{1/3} - 8 = 0$ $\dfrac{8}{27}, -64$ [1.4]

10. Solve: $\dfrac{3}{x + 2} - \dfrac{3}{4} = \dfrac{5}{x + 2} - \dfrac{14}{3}$ [1.4]

11. a. Solve the compound inequality:

$$2x - 5 \leq 11 \qquad \text{or} \qquad -3x + 2 > 14$$

Write the solution set using set-builder notation.
$\{x \,|\, x \leq 8\}$ [1.5]

b. Solve the compound inequality:

$$2x - 1 < 9 \qquad \text{and} \qquad -3x + 1 \leq 7$$

Write the solution set using interval notation.
$[-2, 5)$ [1.5]

12. Solve:

$$\dfrac{x^2 + x - 12}{x + 1} \geq 0$$

Write the solution set using interval notation.
$[-4, -1) \cup [3, \infty)$ [1.5]

13. According to the National Collegiate Athletic Association (NCAA), the length x of a football, in inches, must satisfy the following inequality. (*Source:* http://www.infoplease.com.)

$$\left| x - 11\dfrac{5}{32} \right| \leq \dfrac{9}{32}$$

Find the acceptable range of lengths for an NCAA football.
from $10\dfrac{7}{8}$ in. to $11\dfrac{7}{16}$ in. [1.5]

14. A boat has a speed of 5 mph in still water. The boat can travel 21 miles with the current in the same time in which it can travel 9 miles against the current. Find the rate of the current.
2 mph [1.2]

15. A radiator contains 6 liters of a 20% antifreeze solution. How much should be drained and replaced with pure antifreeze to produce a 50% antifreeze solution?
2.25 l [1.2]

16. A worker can cover a parking lot with asphalt in 10 hours. With the help of an assistant, the work can be done in 6 hours. How long would it take the assistant, working alone, to cover the parking lot with asphalt?
15 h [1.4]

17. You can rent a car for the day from Company A for $28 plus $0.10 a mile. Company B charges $20 plus $0.18 a mile. At what point, in terms of miles driven per day, is it cheaper to rent from Company A?
more than 100 mi [1.5]

18. A football field is built in the shape of a parabolic mound so that water will drain off the field. A model for the parabolic contour of the field is

$$h = -0.0002348x^2 + 0.0375x$$

where h is the height of the field, in feet, at a distance of x feet from one sideline. Describe the portion of the field for which $h > 6$ inches. Round your results to the nearest tenth of a foot.
more than 14.7 ft but less than 145.0 ft from a side line [1.5]

19. The population density D, in people per square mile, of a city is related to the horizontal distance x, in miles, from the center of the city by the equation

$$D = \dfrac{4500x}{2x^2 + 25}, \qquad 0 < x < 12$$

Describe the region of the city in which the population density exceeds 200 people per square mile.
more than 1.25 mi but less than 10 mi from the city center [1.5]

20. A meteorite approaching the moon has a velocity that varies inversely as the square root of its distance from the center of the moon. If the meteorite has a velocity of 4 miles per second at 3000 miles from the center of the moon, find the velocity of the meteorite when it is 2500 miles from the center of the moon. Round to the nearest tenth of a mile per second.
4.4 mi/s [1.6]

CUMULATIVE REVIEW EXERCISES

1. Evaluate: $4 + 3(-5)$
-11 [P.1]

2. Write 0.00017 in scientific notation.
1.7×10^{-4} [P.2]

3. Perform the indicated operations and simplify:
$(3x - 5)^2 - (x + 4)(x - 4)$
$8x^2 - 30x + 41$ [P.3]

4. Factor: $8x^2 + 19x - 15$
$(8x - 5)(x + 3)$ [P.4]

5. Simplify: $\dfrac{7x - 3}{x - 4} - 5 \dfrac{2x + 17}{x - 4}$ [P.5]

6. Simplify: $a^{2/3} \cdot a^{1/4}$
$a^{11/12}$ [P.2]

7. Find: $(2 + 5i)(2 - 5i)$
29 [P.6]

8. Solve: $2(3x - 4) + 5 = 17$ $\dfrac{10}{3}$ [1.1]

9. Solve $2x^2 - 4x = 3$ by using the quadratic formula.
$\dfrac{2 \pm \sqrt{10}}{2}$ [1.3]

10. Solve: $|2x - 6| = 4$
$1, 5$ [1.1]

11. Solve: $x = 3 + \sqrt{9 - x}$
5 [1.4]

12. Factor to solve: $x^3 - 36x = 0$
$-6, 0, 6$ [1.4]

13. Solve: $2x^4 - 11x^2 + 15 = 0$ $\pm\sqrt{3}, \pm\dfrac{\sqrt{10}}{2}$ [1.4]

14. Solve the compound inequality
$$3x - 1 > 2 \quad \text{or} \quad -3x + 5 \geq 8$$
Write the solution set using set-builder notation.
$\{x \mid x \leq -1 \text{ or } x > 1\}$ [1.5]

15. Solve $|x - 6| \geq 2$. Write the solution set using interval notation.
$(-\infty, 4] \cup [8, \infty)$ [1.5]

16. Solve $\dfrac{x - 2}{2x - 3} \geq 4$. Write the solution set using set-builder notation. $\left\{ x \mid \dfrac{10}{7} \leq x < \dfrac{3}{2} \right\}$ [1.5]

17. A fence built around the border of a rectangular field measures a total of 200 feet. If the length of the field is 16 feet longer than the width, find the dimensions of the field.
length 58 ft, width 42 ft [1.2]

18. The revenue, in dollars, earned by selling x inkjet printers is given by $R = 200x - 0.004x^2$. The cost, in dollars, of manufacturing x inkjet printers is $C = 65x + 320,000$. How many printers should be manufactured and sold to earn a profit of at least \$600,000?
9475 to 24,275 printers [1.5]

19. An average score of 80 or above, but less than 90, in a history class receives a B grade. Rebecca has scores of 86, 72, and 94 on three tests. Find the range of scores she could receive on the fourth test that would give her a B grade for the course. Assume that the highest test score she can receive is 100.
68 to 100 [1.5]

20. A highway patrol department estimates that the cost of ticketing p percent of the speeders who travel on a freeway is given by
$$C = \frac{600p}{100 - p}, \qquad 0 < p < 100$$
where C is in thousands of dollars. If the highway patrol department plans to fund its program to ticket speeding drivers with \$100,000 to \$180,000, what is the range of the percent of speeders the department can expect to ticket? Round your percents to the nearest 0.1%.
between 14.3% and 23.1% [1.5]

CHAPTER 2

FUNCTIONS AND GRAPHS

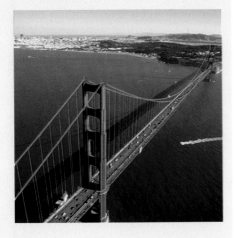

Functions as Models

The Golden Gate Bridge spans the Golden Gate Strait, which is the entrance to the San Francisco Bay from the Pacific Ocean. Designed by Joseph Strass, the Golden Gate Bridge is a *suspension* bridge. A *quadratic function,* one of the topics of this chapter, can be used to model a cable of this bridge. See **Exercise 74 on page 226.**

Strass had many skeptics who did not believe the bridge could be built. Nonetheless, the bridge opened on May 27, 1937, a little over 4 years after construction began. When it was completed, Strass composed the following poem.

The Mighty Task Is Done

At last the mighty task is done;
Resplendent in the western sun;
The Bridge looms mountain high.

On its broad decks in rightful pride,
The world in swift parade shall ride
Throughout all time to be.

Launched midst a thousand hopes and fears,
Damned by a thousand hostile sneers,
Yet ne'er its course was stayed.
But ask of those who met the foe,
Who stood alone when faith was low,
Ask them the price they paid.
High overhead its lights shall gleam,
Far, far below life's restless stream,
Unceasingly shall flow....

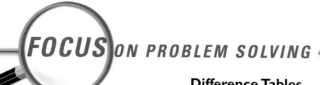

Difference Tables

When devising a plan to solve a problem, it may be helpful to organize information in a table. One particular type of table that can be used to discern some patterns is called a *difference table.* For instance, suppose that we want to determine the number of square tiles in the tenth figure of a pattern whose first four figures are

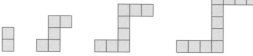

We begin by creating a difference table by listing the number of tiles in each figure and the differences between the numbers of tiles on the next line.

Tiles	2		5		8		11
Differences		3		3		3	

From the difference table, note that each succeeding figure has three more tiles. Therefore, we can find the number of tiles in the tenth figure by extending the difference table.

Tiles	2		5		8		11		14		17		20		23		26		29
Differences		3		3		3		3		3		3		3		3		3	

There are 29 tiles in the tenth figure.

Sometimes the first differences are not constant, as was the case for the preceding example. In this case we find the second differences. For instance, consider the pattern at the right.

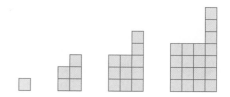

The difference table is shown below.

Tiles	1		5		11		19
First differences		4		6		8	
Second differences			2		2		

In this case the first differences are not constant, but the second differences are constant. With this information we can determine the number of tiles in succeeding figures.

Tiles	1		5		11		19		29		41		55		71		89		109
First differences		4		6		8		10		12		14		16		18		20	
Second differences			2		2		2		2		2		2		2		2		

In this case there are 109 tiles in the tenth figure.

If second differences are not constant, try the third differences.[1] If third differences are not constant, try fourth differences, and so on.

---

[1] Not all lists of numbers will end with a difference row of constants. For instance, consider 1, 1, 2, 3, 5, 8, 13, 21, 34,....

A TWO-DIMENSIONAL COORDINATE SYSTEM AND GRAPHS

- CARTESIAN COORDINATE SYSTEMS
- THE DISTANCE AND MIDPOINT FORMULAS
- GRAPH OF AN EQUATION
- INTERCEPTS
- CIRCLES, THEIR EQUATIONS, AND THEIR GRAPHS

---

take note

Abscissa comes from the same root word as scissors. An open pair of scissors looks like an x.

MATH MATTERS

The concepts of *analytic geometry* developed over an extended period of time, culminating in 1637 with the publication of two works: *Discourse on the Method for Rightly Directing One's Reason and Searching for Truth in the Sciences* by René Descartes (1596–1650) and *Introduction to Plane and Solid Loci* by Pierre de Fermat. Each of these works was an attempt to integrate the study of geometry with the study of algebra. Of the two mathematicians, Descartes is usually given most of the credit for developing analytic geometry. In fact, Descartes became so famous in La Haye, the city in which he was born, that it was renamed La Haye-Descartes.

● CARTESIAN COORDINATE SYSTEMS

Each point on a coordinate axis is associated with a number called its **coordinate.** Each point on a flat, two-dimensional surface, called a **coordinate plane** or *xy*-plane, is associated with an **ordered pair** of numbers called **coordinates** of the point. Ordered pairs are denoted by (a, b), where the real number a is the **x-coordinate** or **abscissa** and the real number b is the **y-coordinate** or **ordinate.**

The coordinates of a point are determined by the point's position relative to a horizontal coordinate axis called the **x-axis** and a vertical coordinate axis called the **y-axis.** The axes intersect at the point $(0, 0)$, called the **origin.** In **Figure 2.1,** the axes are labeled such that positive numbers appear to the right of the origin on the *x*-axis and above the origin on the *y*-axis. The four regions formed by the axes are called **quadrants** and are numbered counterclockwise. This two-dimensional coordinate system is referred to as a **Cartesian coordinate system** in honor of René Descartes.

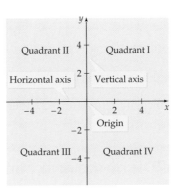

FIGURE 2.1

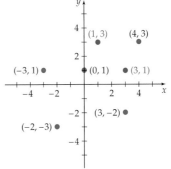

FIGURE 2.2

To **plot a point** $P(a, b)$ means to draw a dot at its location in the coordinate plane. In **Figure 2.2** we have plotted the points $(4, 3)$, $(-3, 1)$, $(-2, -3)$, $(3, -2)$, $(0, 1)$, $(1, 3)$, and $(3, 1)$. The order in which the coordinates of an ordered pair are listed is important. **Figure 2.2** shows that $(1, 3)$ and $(3, 1)$ do not denote the same point.

 Data often are displayed in visual form as a set of points called a *scatter diagram* or *scatter plot*. For instance, the scatter diagram in **Figure 2.3** shows the number of Internet virus incidents from 1993 to 2003. The point whose coordinates are approximately $(7, 21{,}000)$ means that in the year 2000 there were approximately 21,000 Internet virus incidents. The line segments that connect the points in **Figure 2.3** help illustrate trends.

INSTRUCTOR NOTE

The **P** symbol means that a Microsoft PowerPoint® slide of that figure is available. These slides are available on the *ClassPrep CD* and can also be downloaded from our website at **math.college.hmco.com/ instructors.** These slides can also be printed as transparency masters.

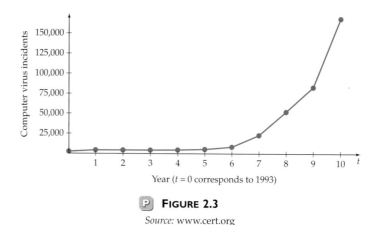

P **FIGURE 2.3**

Source: www.cert.org

take note

The notation (a, b) was used earlier to denote an interval on a one-dimensional number line. In this section, (a, b) denotes an ordered pair in a two-dimensional plane. This should not cause confusion in future sections because as each mathematical topic is introduced, it will be clear whether a one-dimensional or a two-dimensional coordinate system is involved.

❓ QUESTION If the trend in **Figure 2.3** continues, will the number of virus incidents in 2004 be more or less than 200,000?

In some instances, it is important to know when two ordered pairs are equal.

Equality of Ordered Pairs

The ordered pairs (a, b) and (c, d) are equal if and only if $a = c$ and $b = d$.

For instance, if $(3, y) = (x, -2)$, then $x = 3$ and $y = -2$.

● THE DISTANCE AND MIDPOINT FORMULAS

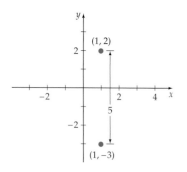

FIGURE 2.4

The Cartesian coordinate system makes it possible to combine the concepts of algebra and geometry into a branch of mathematics called *analytic geometry.*

The distance between two points on a horizontal line is the absolute value of the difference between the x-coordinates of the two points. The distance between two points on a vertical line is the absolute value of the difference between the y-coordinates of the two points. For example, as shown in **Figure 2.4,** the distance d between the points with coordinates $(1, 2)$ and $(1, -3)$ is $d = |2 - (-3)| = 5$.

If two points are not on a horizontal or vertical line, then a *distance formula* for the distance between the two points can be developed as follows.

The distance between the points $P_1(x_1, y_1)$ and $P_2(x_2, y_2)$ in **Figure 2.5** is the length of the hypotenuse of a right triangle whose sides are horizontal and verti-

❓ ANSWER More. The increase between 2002 and 2003 was more than 70,000. If this trend continues, the increase between 2003 and 2004 will be at least 70,000 more than 150,000. That is, the number of virus incidents in 2004 will be at least 220,000.

To review **PYTHAGOREAN THEOREM,** *see p. 110.*

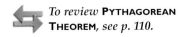

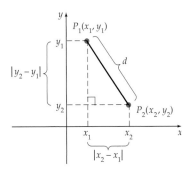

FIGURE 2.5

cal line segments that measure $|x_2 - x_1|$ and $|y_2 - y_1|$, respectively. Applying the Pythagorean Theorem to this triangle produces

$$d^2 = |x_2 - x_1|^2 + |y_2 - y_1|^2$$
$$d = \sqrt{|x_2 - x_1|^2 + |y_2 - y_1|^2}$$ • The square root theorem. Because *d* is nonnegative, the negative root is not listed.
$$= \sqrt{(x_2 - x_1)^2 + (y_2 - y_1)^2}$$ • Because $|x_2 - x_1|^2 = (x_2 - x_1)^2$ and $|y_2 - y_1|^2 = (y_2 - y_1)^2$

Thus we have established the following theorem.

The Distance Formula

The distance d between the points $P_1(x_1, y_1)$ and $P_2(x_2, y_2)$ is

$$d = \sqrt{(x_2 - x_1)^2 + (y_2 - y_1)^2}$$

The distance d between the points whose coordinates are $P_1(x_1, y_1)$ and $P_2(x_2, y_2)$ is denoted by $d(P_1, P_2)$. To find the distance $d(P_1, P_2)$ between the points $P_1(-3, 4)$ and $P_2(7, 2)$, we apply the distance formula with $x_1 = -3$, $y_1 = 4$, $x_2 = 7$, and $y_2 = 2$.

$$d(P_1, P_2) = \sqrt{(x_2 - x_1)^2 + (y_2 - y_1)^2}$$
$$= \sqrt{[7 - (-3)]^2 + (2 - 4)^2}$$
$$= \sqrt{104} = 2\sqrt{26} \approx 10.2$$

The **midpoint** M of a line segment is the point on the line segment that is equidistant from the endpoints $P_1(x_1, y_1)$ and $P_2(x_2, y_2)$ of the segment. See **Figure 2.6.**

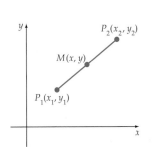

FIGURE 2.6

The Midpoint Formula

The midpoint M of the line segment from $P_1(x_1, y_1)$ to $P_2(x_2, y_2)$ is given by

$$\left(\frac{x_1 + x_2}{2}, \frac{y_1 + y_2}{2} \right)$$

The midpoint formula states that the x-coordinate of the midpoint of a line segment is the *average* of the x-coordinates of the endpoints of the line segment and that the y-coordinate of the midpoint of a line segment is the *average* of the y-coordinates of the endpoints of the line segment.

The midpoint M of the line segment connecting $P_1(-2, 6)$ and $P_2(3, 4)$ is

$$M = \left(\frac{x_1 + x_2}{2}, \frac{y_1 + y_2}{2} \right) = \left(\frac{(-2) + 3}{2}, \frac{6 + 4}{2} \right) = \left(\frac{1}{2}, 5 \right)$$

Alternative to Example 1
Find the midpoint and the length of the line
segment connecting the points whose
coordinates are $P_1(6, -5)$ and $P_2(-3, -1)$.

- $\left(\dfrac{3}{2}, -3\right)$; $\sqrt{97}$

EXAMPLE 1   **Find the Midpoint and Length of a Line Segment**

Find the midpoint and the length of the line segment connecting the points whose coordinates are $P_1(-4, 3)$ and $P_2(4, -2)$.

Solution

$$\text{Midpoint} = \left(\frac{x_1 + x_2}{2}, \frac{y_1 + y_2}{2}\right)$$
$$= \left(\frac{-4 + 4}{2}, \frac{3 + (-2)}{2}\right)$$
$$= \left(0, \frac{1}{2}\right)$$

$$d(P_1, P_2) = \sqrt{(x_2 - x_1)^2 + (y_2 - y_1)^2}$$
$$= \sqrt{(4 - (-4))^2 + (-2 - 3)^2} = \sqrt{(8)^2 + (-5)^2}$$
$$= \sqrt{64 + 25} = \sqrt{89}$$

▶ **TRY EXERCISE 6, PAGE 174**

● GRAPH OF AN EQUATION

The equations below are equations in two variables.

$$y = 3x^3 - 4x + 2 \qquad x^2 + y^2 = 25 \qquad y = \frac{x}{x + 1}$$

The solution of an equation in two variables is an ordered pair (x, y) whose coordinates satisfy the equation. For instance, the ordered pairs $(3, 4)$, $(4, -3)$, and $(0, 5)$ are some of the solutions of $x^2 + y^2 = 25$. Generally, there are an infinite number of solutions of an equation in two variables. These solutions can be displayed in a *graph*.

INSTRUCTOR NOTE
For $x = -3, -2, -1, 0, 1, 2, 3$, ask
students to find the ordered-pair
solutions of
a. $y = 3x - 2$
b. $y = x^2 + 1$
c. $y = |x| - x$
- **a.** $(-3, -11), (-2, -8), (-1, -5),$ $(0, -2), (1, 1), (2, 4), (3, 7)$
- **b.** $(-3, 10), (-2, 5), (-1, 2), (0, 1),$ $(1, 2), (2, 5), (3, 10)$
- **c.** $(-3, 6), (-2, 4), (-1, 2), (0, 0),$ $(1, 0), (2, 0), (3, 0)$

Graph of an Equation

The **graph of an equation** in the two variables x and y is the set of all points whose coordinates satisfy the equation.

Consider $y = 2x - 1$. Substituting various values of x into the equation and solving for y produces some of the ordered pairs of the equation. It is convenient to record the results in a table similar to the one shown on the following page. The graph of the ordered pairs is shown in **Figure 2.7.**

x	y = 2x − 1	y	(x, y)
−2	2(−2) − 1	−5	(−2, −5)
−1	2(−1) − 1	−3	(−1, −3)
0	2(0) − 1	−1	(0, −1)
1	2(1) − 1	1	(1, 1)
2	2(2) − 1	3	(2, 3)

Choosing some noninteger values of x produces more ordered pairs to graph, such as $\left(-\dfrac{3}{2}, -4\right)$ and $\left(\dfrac{5}{2}, 4\right)$, as shown in **Figure 2.8.** Using still other values of x would result in more and more ordered pairs being graphed. The result would be so many dots that the graph would appear as the straight line shown in **Figure 2.9,** which is the graph of $y = 2x - 1$.

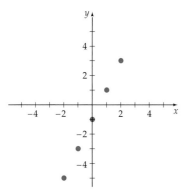

FIGURE 2.7

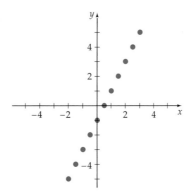

FIGURE 2.8

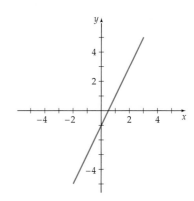

FIGURE 2.9

Alternative to Example 2
Exercise 28, page 174.

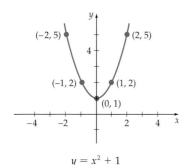

$y = x^2 + 1$

FIGURE 2.10

EXAMPLE 2   **Draw a Graph by Plotting Points**

Graph: $-x^2 + y = 1$

Solution

Solve the equation for y.

$$y = x^2 + 1$$

Select values of x and use the equation to calculate y. Choose enough values of x so that an accurate graph can be drawn. Plot the points and draw a curve through them. See **Figure 2.10.**

x	y = x² + 1	y	(x, y)
−2	(−2)² + 1	5	(−2, 5)
−1	(−1)² + 1	2	(−1, 2)
0	(0)² + 1	1	(0, 1)
1	(1)² + 1	2	(1, 2)
2	(2)² + 1	5	(2, 5)

▶ **TRY EXERCISE 26, PAGE 175**

MATH MATTERS

Maria Agnesi (1718–1799) wrote *Foundations of Analysis for the Use of Italian Youth*, one of the most successful textbooks of the 18th century. The French Academy authorized a translation into French in 1749, noting that "there is no other book, in any language, which would enable a reader to penetrate as deeply, or as rapidly, into the fundamental concepts of analysis." A curve that she discusses in her text is given by the equation $y = \dfrac{a^3}{x^2 + a^2}$.

Unfortunately, due to a translation error from Italian to English, the curve became known as the "witch of Agnesi."

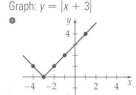

$$y = \frac{a^3}{x^2 + a^2}$$

INTEGRATING TECHNOLOGY

Some graphing calculators, such as the *TI-83*, have a TABLE feature that allows you to create a table similar to the one shown in Example 2. Enter the equation to be graphed, the first value for x, and the increment (the difference between successive values of x). For instance, entering $y_1 = x^2 + 1$, an initial value of x as -2, and an increment of 1 yields a display similar to the one in **Figure 2.11**. Changing the initial value to -6 and the increment to 2 gives the table in **Figure 2.12**.

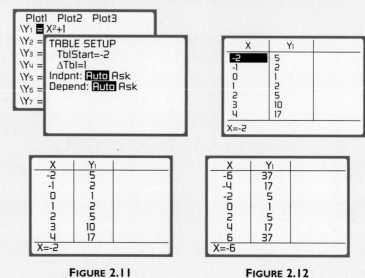

FIGURE 2.11   **FIGURE 2.12**

With some calculators, you may scroll through the table by using the up- or down-arrow keys. In this way, you can determine many more ordered pairs of the graph.

Alternative to Example 3
Graph: $y = |x + 3|$

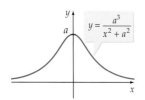

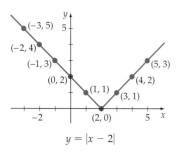

(−3, 5)
(−2, 4)
(−1, 3)
(0, 2)
(1, 1)
(2, 0)
(3, 1)
(4, 2)
(5, 3)

$$y = |x - 2|$$

FIGURE 2.13

EXAMPLE 3   Graph by Plotting Points

Graph: $y = |x - 2|$

Solution

This equation is already solved for y, so start by choosing an x value and using the equation to determine the corresponding y value. For example, if $x = -3$, then $y = |(-3) - 2| = |-5| = 5$. Continuing in this manner produces the following table:

When x is	−3	−2	−1	0	1	2	3	4	5
y is	5	4	3	2	1	0	1	2	3

Now plot the points listed in the table. Connecting the points forms a V shape, as shown in **Figure 2.13**.

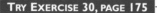

▶ TRY EXERCISE 30, PAGE 175

Alternative to Example 4
Graph: $2y + 2 = |x - 1|$

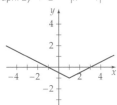

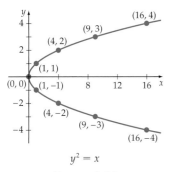

$y^2 = x$

FIGURE 2.14

EXAMPLE 4   **Graph by Plotting Points**

Graph: $y^2 = x$

Solution

Solve the equation for y.

$$y^2 = x$$
$$y = \pm\sqrt{x}$$

Choose several x values, and use the equation to determine the corresponding y values.

When x is	0	1	4	9	16
y is	0	±1	±2	±3	±4

Plot the points as shown in **Figure 2.14.** The graph is a *parabola*.

▶ **TRY EXERCISE 32, PAGE 175**

INTEGRATING TECHNOLOGY

A graphing calculator or computer graphing software can be used to draw the graphs in Examples 3 and 4. These graphing utilities graph a curve in much the same way as you would, by selecting values of x and calculating the corresponding values of y. A curve is then drawn through the points.

If you use a graphing utility to graph $y = |x - 2|$, you will need to use the *absolute value* function that is built into the utility. The equation you enter will look similar to Y₁=abs(X–2).

To graph the equation in Example 4, you will enter two equations. The equations you enter will be similar to

$$Y_1 = \sqrt{(X)}$$
$$Y_2 = -\sqrt{(X)}$$

The graph of the first equation will be the top half of the parabola; the graph of the second equation will graph the bottom half.

● **INTERCEPTS**

Any point that has an x- or a y-coordinate of zero is called an **intercept** of the graph of an equation because it is at these points that the graph intersects the x- or the y-axis.

> **Definition of x-Intercepts and y-Intercepts**
>
> If $(x_1, 0)$ satisfies an equation, then the point $(x_1, 0)$ is called an **x-intercept** of the graph of the equation.
>
> If $(0, y_1)$ satisfies an equation, then the point $(0, y_1)$ is called a **y-intercept** of the graph of the equation.

To find the x-intercepts of the graph of an equation, let $y = 0$, and solve the equation for x. To find the y-intercepts of the graph of an equation, let $x = 0$, and solve the equation for y.

Alternative to Example 5 Find the x- and y-intercepts for $y = x^2 + 3x - 4$.
• The x-intercepts are $(-4, 0)$ and $(1, 0)$. The y-intercept is $(0, -4)$.

EXAMPLE 5   **Find x- and y-Intercepts**

Find the x- and y-intercepts of the graph of $y = x^2 - 2x - 3$.

Algebraic Solution

To find the y-intercept, let $x = 0$ and solve for y.

$$y = 0^2 - 2(0) - 3 = -3$$

To find the x-intercepts, let $y = 0$ and solve for x.

$$0 = x^2 - 2x - 3$$
$$0 = (x - 3)(x + 1)$$
$$(x - 3) = 0 \quad \text{or} \quad (x + 1) = 0$$
$$x = 3 \quad \text{or} \quad x = -1$$

Because $y = -3$ when $x = 0$, $(0, -3)$ is a y-intercept. Because $x = 3$ or -1 when $y = 0$, $(3, 0)$ and $(-1, 0)$ are x-intercepts. **Figure 2.15** confirms that these three points are intercepts.

Visualize the Solution

The graph of $y = x^2 - 2x - 3$ is shown below. Observe that the graph intersects the x-axis at $(-1, 0)$ and $(3, 0)$, the x-intercepts. The graph also intersects the y-axis at $(0, -3)$, the y-intercept.

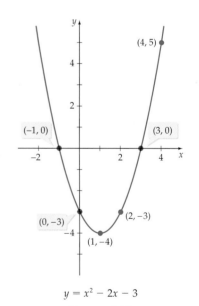

$$y = x^2 - 2x - 3$$

FIGURE 2.15

▶ **TRY EXERCISE 40, PAGE 175**

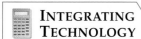
INTEGRATING TECHNOLOGY

In Example 5 it was possible to find the x-intercepts by solving a quadratic equation. In some instances, however, solving an equation to find the intercepts may be very difficult. In these cases, a graphing calculator can be used to estimate the x-intercepts.

The x-intercepts of the graph of $y = x^3 + x + 4$ can be estimated using the INTERCEPT feature of a TI-83 calculator. The keystrokes and some sample screens for this procedure are shown below.

Press $\boxed{\text{Y=}}$. Now enter X^3+X+4. Press $\boxed{\text{ZOOM}}$ and select the standard viewing window.

Press $\boxed{\text{2nd}}$ CALC to access the CALCULATE menu. The y-coordinate of an x-intercept is zero. Therefore, select 2:zero. Press $\boxed{\text{ENTER}}$.

The "Left Bound?" shown on the bottom of the screen means to move the cursor until it is to the left of an x-intercept. Press $\boxed{\text{ENTER}}$.

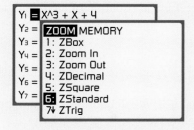

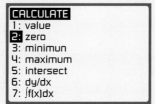

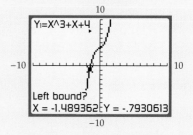

The "Right Bound?" shown on the bottom of the screen means to move the cursor until it is to the right of the desired x-intercept. Press $\boxed{\text{ENTER}}$.

"Guess?" is shown on the bottom of the screen. Move the cursor until it is approximately on the x-intercept. Press $\boxed{\text{ENTER}}$.

The "Zero" shown on the bottom of the screen means that the value of y is 0 when $x = -1.378797$. The x-intercept is about $(-1.378797, 0)$.

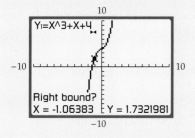

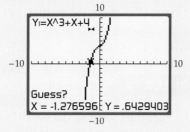

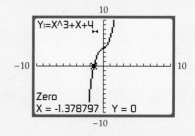

● CIRCLES, THEIR EQUATIONS, AND THEIR GRAPHS

Frequently you will sketch graphs by plotting points. However, some graphs can be sketched merely by recognizing the form of the equation. A *circle* is an example of a curve whose graph you can sketch after you have inspected its equation.

Definition of a Circle

A **circle** is the set of points in a plane that are a fixed distance from a specified point. The distance is the **radius** of the circle, and the specified point is the **center** of the circle.

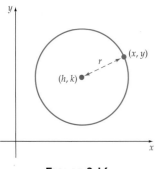

FIGURE 2.16

The standard form of the equation of a circle is derived by using this definition. To derive the standard form, we use the distance formula. **Figure 2.16** is a circle with center (h, k) and radius r. The point (x, y) is on the circle if and only if it is a distance of r units from the center (h, k). Thus (x, y) is on the circle if and only if

$$\sqrt{(x - h)^2 + (y - k)^2} = r$$
$$(x - h)^2 + (y - k)^2 = r^2 \qquad \bullet \text{ Square each side.}$$

Standard Form of the Equation of a Circle

The **standard form of the equation of a circle** with center at (h, k) and radius r is

$$(x - h)^2 + (y - k)^2 = r^2$$

For example, the equation $(x - 3)^2 + (y + 1)^2 = 4$ is the equation of a circle. The standard form of the equation is

$$(x - 3)^2 + (y - (-1))^2 = 2^2$$

from which it can be determined that $h = 3$, $k = -1$, and $r = 2$. Thus the graph is a circle centered at $(3, -1)$ with a radius of 2.

If a circle is centered at the origin $(0, 0)$ (that is, if $h = 0$ and $k = 0$), then the standard form of the equation of the circle simplifies to

$$x^2 + y^2 = r^2$$

For example, the graph of $x^2 + y^2 = 9$ is a circle with center at the origin and radius of 3.

> ❓ **QUESTION** What are the radius and the coordinates of the center of the circle with equation $x^2 + (y - 2)^2 = 10$?

Alternative to Example 6
Find the standard form of the equation of the circle that has center $C(6, -3)$ and contains the point $P(4, 1)$.
○ $(x - 6)^2 + (y + 3)^2 = 20$

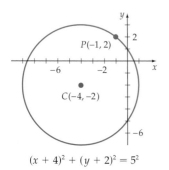

$(x + 4)^2 + (y + 2)^2 = 5^2$

FIGURE 2.17

EXAMPLE 6   **Find the Standard Form of the Equation of a Circle**

Find the standard form of the equation of the circle that has center $C(-4, -2)$ and contains the point $P(-1, 2)$.

Solution

See the graph of the circle in **Figure 2.17.** Because the point P is on the circle, the radius r of the circle must equal the distance from C to P. Thus

$$r = \sqrt{(-1 - (-4))^2 + (2 - (-2))^2}$$
$$= \sqrt{9 + 16} = \sqrt{25} = 5$$

Using the standard form with $h = -4$, $k = -2$, and $r = 5$, we obtain

$$(x + 4)^2 + (y + 2)^2 = 5^2$$

▶ **TRY EXERCISE 64, PAGE 175**

❓ **ANSWER** The radius is $\sqrt{10}$ and the coordinates of the center are $(0, 2)$.

INSTRUCTOR NOTE
Here are some questions to ask students
about the equation of a circle.

1. What is the radius and what are the
coordinates of the center of the circle
whose equation is
a. $(x - 1)^2 + (y + 3)^2 = 4$?
b. $x^2 + y^2 = 5$?
● **a. 2; (1, −3)**
● **b. √5̄; (0, 0)**

2. What is the standard form of the
equation of a circle with radius 3 and
with center $(-2, 4)$?
● **$(x + 2)^2 + (y − 4)^2 = 9$**

If we rewrite $(x + 4)^2 + (y + 2)^2 = 5^2$ by squaring and combining like terms, we produce

$$x^2 + 8x + 16 + y^2 + 4y + 4 = 25$$
$$x^2 + y^2 + 8x + 4y - 5 = 0$$

This form of the equation is known as the **general form of the equation of a circle.** By completing the square, it is always possible to write the general form $x^2 + y^2 + Ax + By + C = 0$ in the standard form

$$(x - h)^2 + (y - k)^2 = s$$

for some number s. If $s > 0$, the graph is a circle with radius $r = \sqrt{s}$. If $s = 0$, the graph is the point (h, k), and if $s < 0$, the equation has no real solutions and there is no graph.

Alternative to Example 7
Find the center and the radius of the circle
that is given by
$x^2 + y^2 + 6x + 8y - 11 = 0$.
● **center: (−3, −4); radius: 6**

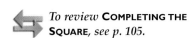

To review **COMPLETING THE SQUARE,** *see p. 105.*

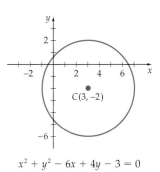

$x^2 + y^2 - 6x + 4y - 3 = 0$

FIGURE 2.18

EXAMPLE 7 **Find the Center and Radius of a Circle by Completing the Square**

Find the center and the radius of the circle that is given by

$$x^2 + y^2 - 6x + 4y - 3 = 0$$

Solution

First rearrange and group the terms as shown.

$$(x^2 - 6x) + (y^2 + 4y) = 3$$

Now complete the square of $(x^2 - 6x)$ and $(y^2 + 4y)$.

$$(x^2 - 6x + 9) + (y^2 + 4y + 4) = 3 + 9 + 4 \qquad \bullet \text{ Add 9 and 4 to each side of the equation.}$$

$$(x - 3)^2 + (y + 2)^2 = 16$$
$$(x - 3)^2 + (y - (-2))^2 = 4^2$$

This equation is the standard form of the equation of a circle and indicates that the graph of the original equation is a circle centered at $(3, -2)$ with radius 4. See **Figure 2.18.**

 TRY EXERCISE 66, PAGE 175

TOPICS FOR DISCUSSION

1. The distance formula states that the distance d between the points $P_1(x_1, y_1)$ and $P_2(x_2, y_2)$ is $d = \sqrt{(x_2 - x_1)^2 + (y_2 - y_1)^2}$. Can the distance formula also be written as follows? Explain.

$$d = \sqrt{(x_1 - x_2)^2 + (y_1 - y_2)^2}$$

2. Does the equation $(x - 3)^2 + (y + 4)^2 = -6$ have a graph that is a circle? Explain.

3. Explain why the graph of $|x| + |y| = 1$ does not contain any points that have

   a. a y-coordinate that is greater than 1 or less than -1

   b. an x-coordinate that is greater than 1 or less than -1

4. Discuss the graph of $xy = 0$.

5. Explain how to determine the x- and y-intercepts of a graph defined by an equation (without using the graph).

EXERCISE SET 2.1

—*Suggested Assignment: Exercises 1, 3, 5–89, every other odd; 97–102.*
—*Answers to Exercises 1–2, 3a, 25–48, and 77–86 are on pages AA2–AA3.*

In Exercises 1 and 2, plot the points whose coordinates are given on a Cartesian coordinate system.

1. $(2, 4), (0, -3), (-2, 1), (-5, -3)$

2. $(-3, -5), (-4, 3), (0, 2), (-2, 0)$

3. **HEALTH** A study at the Ohio State University measured the changes in heart rates of students doing stepping exercises. Students stepped onto a platform that was approximately 11 inches high at a rate of 14 steps per minute. The heart rate, in beats per minute, before and after the exercise is given in the table below.

Before	After	Before	After
63	84	96	141
72	99	69	93
87	111	81	96
90	129	75	90
90	108	84	90

a. Draw a scatter diagram for these data.

b. For these students, what is the average increase in heart rate?
   23.4 beats/min

4. **AVERAGE INCOME** The following graph, based on data from the Bureau of Economic Analysis, shows per capita personal income in the United States.

a. From the data, does it appear that per capita personal income is increasing, decreasing, or remaining the same?
   increasing

b. If per capita personal income continues to increase by the same percent as the percent increase between 2001 and 2002, what will be the per capita income in 2004?
   $31,900

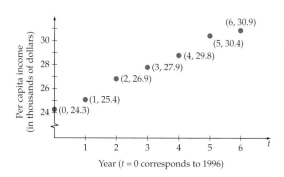

Year ($t = 0$ corresponds to 1996)

In Exercises 5 to 16, find the distance between the points whose coordinates are given.

5. $(6, 4), (-8, 11)$
   $7\sqrt{5}$

▶ 6. $(-5, 8), (-10, 14)$
   $\sqrt{61}$

7. $(-4, -20), (-10, 15)$
   $\sqrt{1261}$

8. $(40, 32), (36, 20)$
   $4\sqrt{10}$

9. $(5, -8), (0, 0)$
   $\sqrt{89}$

10. $(0, 0), (5, 13)$
   $\sqrt{194}$

11. $(\sqrt{3}, \sqrt{8}), (\sqrt{12}, \sqrt{27})$
   $\sqrt{38 - 12\sqrt{6}}$

12. $(\sqrt{125}, \sqrt{20}), (6, 2\sqrt{5})$
   $5\sqrt{5} - 6$ or $\sqrt{161 - 60\sqrt{5}}$

13. $(a, b), (-a, -b)$
   $2\sqrt{a^2 + b^2}$

14. $(a - b, b), (a, a + b)$
   $\sqrt{a^2 + b^2}$

15. $(x, 4x), (-2x, 3x)$ given that $x < 0$
   $-x\sqrt{10}$

16. $(x, 4x), (-2x, 3x)$ given that $x > 0$
   $x\sqrt{10}$ (since $x > 0, \sqrt{x^2} = x$)

17. Find all points on the x-axis that are 10 units from $(4, 6)$. (*Hint:* First write the distance formula with $(4, 6)$ as one of the points and $(x, 0)$ as the other point.)
   $(12, 0), (-4, 0)$

18. Find all points on the y-axis that are 12 units from $(5, -3)$.
   $(0, -3 + \sqrt{119}), (0, -3 - \sqrt{119})$

In Exercises 19 to 24, find the midpoint of the line segment with the following endpoints.

19. $(1, -1), (5, 5)$
   $(3, 2)$

20. $(-5, -2), (6, 10)$ $\left(\dfrac{1}{2}, 4\right)$

21. $(6, -3), (6, 11)$
$(6, 4)$

22. $(4, 7), (-10, 7)$
$(-3, 7)$

23. $(1.75, 2.25), (-3.5, 5.57)$
$(-0.875, 3.91)$

24. $(-8.2, 10.1), (-2.4, -5.7)$
$(-5.3, 2.2)$

In Exercises 25 to 38, graph each equation by plotting points that satisfy the equation.

25. $x - y = 4$

▶ **26.** $2x + y = -1$

27. $y = 0.25x^2$

28. $3x^2 + 2y = -4$

29. $y = -2|x - 3|$

▶ **30.** $y = |x + 3| - 2$

31. $y = x^2 - 3$

▶ **32.** $y = x^2 + 1$

33. $y = \dfrac{1}{2}(x - 1)^2$

34. $y = 2(x + 2)^2$

35. $y = x^2 + 2x - 8$

36. $y = x^2 - 2x - 8$

37. $y = -x^2 + 2$

38. $y = -x^2 - 1$

In Exercises 39 to 48, find the x- and y-intercepts of the graph of each equation. Use the intercepts and additional points as needed to draw the graph of the equation.

39. $2x + 5y = 12$ $(6, 0), \left(0, \dfrac{12}{5}\right)$

▶ **40.** $3x - 4y = 15$ $(5, 0), \left(0, -\dfrac{15}{4}\right)$

41. $x = -y^2 + 5$
$(5, 0), \left(0, \pm\sqrt{5}\right)$

42. $x = y^2 - 6$
$(-6, 0), \left(0, \pm\sqrt{6}\right)$

43. $x = |y| - 4$
$(-4, 0), (0, \pm 4)$

44. $x = y^3 - 2$
$(-2, 0), \left(0, \sqrt[3]{2}\right)$

45. $x^2 + y^2 = 4$
$(\pm 2, 0), (0, \pm 2)$

46. $x^2 = y^2$
$(0, 0)$

47. $|x| + |y| = 4$
$(\pm 4, 0), (0, \pm 4)$

48. $|x - 4y| = 8$
$(\pm 8, 0), (0, \pm 2)$

In Exercises 49 to 56, determine the center and radius of the circle with the given equation.

49. $x^2 + y^2 = 36$
center $(0, 0)$, radius 6

50. $x^2 + y^2 = 49$
center $(0, 0)$, radius 7

51. $(x - 1)^2 + (y - 3)^2 = 49$
center $(1, 3)$, radius 7

52. $(x - 2)^2 + (y - 4)^2 = 25$
center $(2, 4)$, radius 5

53. $(x + 2)^2 + (y + 5)^2 = 25$
center $(-2, -5)$, radius 5

54. $(x + 3)^2 + (y + 5)^2 = 121$
center $(-3, -5)$, radius 11

55. $(x - 8)^2 + y^2 = \dfrac{1}{4}$

center $(8, 0)$, radius $\dfrac{1}{2}$

56. $x^2 + (y - 12)^2 = 1$

center $(0, 12)$, radius 1

In Exercises 57 to 64, find an equation of a circle that satisfies the given conditions. Write your answer in standard form.

57. Center $(4, 1)$, radius $r = 2$
$(x - 4)^2 + (y - 1)^2 = 2^2$

58. Center $(5, -3)$, radius $r = 4$
$(x - 5)^2 + (y + 3)^2 = 4^2$

59. Center $\left(\dfrac{1}{2}, \dfrac{1}{4}\right)$, radius $r = \sqrt{5}$
$\left(x - \dfrac{1}{2}\right)^2 + \left(y - \dfrac{1}{4}\right)^2 = \left(\sqrt{5}\right)^2$

60. Center $\left(0, \dfrac{2}{3}\right)$, radius $r = \sqrt{11}$
$(x - 0)^2 + \left(y - \dfrac{2}{3}\right)^2 = \left(\sqrt{11}\right)^2$

61. Center $(0, 0)$, passing through $(-3, 4)$
$(x - 0)^2 + (y - 0)^2 = 5^2$

62. Center $(0, 0)$, passing through $(5, 12)$
$(x - 0)^2 + (y - 0)^2 = 13^2$

63. Center $(1, 3)$, passing through $(4, -1)$
$(x - 1)^2 + (y - 3)^2 = 5^2$

▶ **64.** Center $(-2, 5)$, passing through $(1, 7)$
$(x + 2)^2 + (y - 5)^2 = \left(\sqrt{13}\right)^2$

In Exercises 65 to 72, find the center and the radius of the graph of the circle. The equations of the circles are written in the general form.

65. $x^2 + y^2 - 6x + 5 = 0$
center $(3, 0)$, radius 2

▶ **66.** $x^2 + y^2 - 6x - 4y + 12 = 0$
center $(3, 2)$, radius 1

67. $x^2 + y^2 - 14x + 8y + 56 = 0$
center $(7, -4)$, radius 3

68. $x^2 + y^2 - 10x + 2y + 25 = 0$
center $(5, -1)$, radius 1

69. $4x^2 + 4y^2 + 4x - 63 = 0$ center $\left(-\dfrac{1}{2}, 0\right)$, radius 4

70. $9x^2 + 9y^2 - 6y - 17 = 0$ center $\left(0, \dfrac{1}{3}\right)$, radius $\sqrt{2}$

71. $x^2 + y^2 - x + 3y - \dfrac{15}{4} = 0$ center $\left(\dfrac{1}{2}, -\dfrac{3}{2}\right)$, radius $\dfrac{5}{2}$

72. $x^2 + y^2 + 3x - 5y + \dfrac{25}{4} = 0$ center $\left(-\dfrac{3}{2}, \dfrac{5}{2}\right)$, radius $\dfrac{3}{2}$

73. Find an equation of a circle that has a diameter with endpoints $(2, 3)$ and $(-4, 11)$. Write your answer in standard form.
$(x + 1)^2 + (y - 7)^2 = 25$

74. Find an equation of a circle that has a diameter with endpoints $(7, -2)$ and $(-3, 5)$. Write your answer in standard form. $(x - 2)^2 + \left(y - \dfrac{3}{2}\right)^2 = \left(\dfrac{\sqrt{149}}{2}\right)^2$

75. Find an equation of a circle that has its center at $(7, 11)$ and is tangent to the x-axis. Write your answer in standard form.
$(x - 7)^2 + (y - 11)^2 = 121$

76. Find an equation of a circle that has its center at $(-2, 3)$ and is tangent to the y-axis. Write your answer in standard form.
$(x + 2)^2 + (y - 3)^2 = 2^2$

CONNECTING CONCEPTS

In Exercises 77 to 86, graph the set of all points whose x- and y-coordinates satisfy the given conditions.

77. $x = 1, y \geq 1$

78. $y = -3, x \geq -2$

79. $y \leq 3$

80. $x \geq 2$

81. $xy \geq 0$

82. $|y| \geq 1, \dfrac{x}{y} \leq 0$

83. $|x| = 2, |y| = 3$

84. $|x| = 4, |y| = 1$

85. $|x| \leq 2, y \geq 2$

86. $x \geq 1, |y| \leq 3$

In Exercises 87 to 90, find the other endpoint of the line segment that has the given endpoint and midpoint.

87. Endpoint $(5, 1)$, midpoint $(9, 3)$
$(13, 5)$

88. Endpoint $(4, -6)$, midpoint $(-2, 11)$
$(-8, 28)$

89. Endpoint $(-3, -8)$, midpoint $(2, -7)$
$(7, -6)$

90. Endpoint $(5, -4)$, midpoint $(0, 0)$
$(-5, 4)$

91. Find a formula for the set of all points (x, y) for which the distance from (x, y) to $(3, 4)$ is 5.
$x^2 - 6x + y^2 - 8y = 0$

92. Find a formula for the set of all points (x, y) for which the distance from (x, y) to $(-5, 12)$ is 13.
$x^2 + 10x + y^2 - 24y = 0$

93. Find a formula for the set of all points (x, y) for which the sum of the distances from (x, y) to $(4, 0)$ and from (x, y) to $(-4, 0)$ is 10.
$9x^2 + 25y^2 = 225$

94. Find a formula for the set of all points for which the absolute value of the difference of the distances from (x, y) to $(0, 4)$ and from (x, y) to $(0, -4)$ is 6.
$-9x^2 + 7y^2 = 63$

95. Find an equation of a circle that is tangent to both axes, has its center in the second quadrant, and has a radius of 3.
$(x + 3)^2 + (y - 3)^2 = 3^2$

96. Find an equation of a circle that is tangent to both axes, has its center in the third quadrant, and has a diameter of $\sqrt{5}$.
$\left(x + \dfrac{\sqrt{5}}{2}\right)^2 + \left(y + \dfrac{\sqrt{5}}{2}\right)^2 = \left(\dfrac{\sqrt{5}}{2}\right)^2$

PREPARE FOR SECTION 2.2

97. Evaluate $x^2 + 3x - 4$ when $x = -3$. [P.3]
-4

98. From the set of ordered pairs $A = \{(-3, 2), (-2, 4), (-1, 1), (0, 4), (2, 5)\}$, create two new sets, D and R, where D is the set of the first coordinates of the ordered pairs of A and R is the set of the second coordinates of the ordered pairs of A. [P.1]
$D = \{-3, -2, -1, 0, 2\}, R = \{1, 2, 4, 5\}$

99. Find the length of the line segment connecting $P_1(-4, 1)$ and $P_2(3, -2)$. [2.1]
$\sqrt{58}$

100. For what values of x is $\sqrt{2x - 6}$ a real number? [P.6/1.5]
$x \geq 3$

101. For what values of x is $\dfrac{x + 3}{x^2 - x - 6}$ not a real number? [P.5]
$-2, 3$

102. If $a = 3x + 4$ and $a = 6x - 5$, find the value of a. [1.1]
13

PROJECTS

1. VERIFY A GEOMETRIC THEOREM Use the midpoint formula and the distance formula to prove that the midpoint M of the hypotenuse of a right triangle is equidistant from each of the vertices of the triangle. (*Hint:* Label the vertices of the triangle as shown in the figure at the right.)

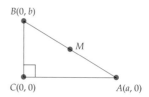

2. **SOLVE A QUADRATIC EQUATION GEOMETRICALLY** In the 17th century, Descartes (and others) solved equations by using both algebra and geometry. This project outlines the method Descartes used to solve certain quadratic equations.

a. Consider the equation $x^2 = 2ax + b^2$. Construct a right triangle ABC with $d(A, C) = a$ and $d(C, B) = b$. Now draw a circle with center at A and radius a. Let P be the point at which the circle intersects the hypotenuse of the right triangle and Q the point at which an extension of the hypotenuse intersects the circle. Your drawing should be similar to the one at the right.

b. Show that a solution of the equation $x^2 = 2ax + b^2$ is $d(Q, B)$.

c. Show that $d(P, B)$ is a solution of the equation $x^2 = -2ax + b^2$.

d. Construct a line parallel to AC and passing through B. Let S and T be the points at which the line intersects the circle. Show that $d(S, B)$ and $d(T, B)$ are solutions of the equation $x^2 = 2ax - b^2$.

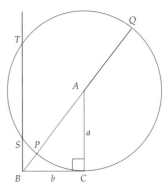

SECTION 2.2

INTRODUCTION TO FUNCTIONS

- **RELATIONS**
- **FUNCTIONS**
- **FUNCTIONAL NOTATION**
- **IDENTIFYING FUNCTIONS**
- **GRAPHS OF FUNCTIONS**
- **THE GREATEST INTEGER FUNCTION (FLOOR FUNCTION)**
- **APPLICATIONS**

TABLE 2.1

Score	Grade
[90, 100]	A
[80, 90)	B
[70, 80)	C
[60, 70)	D
[0, 60)	F

● RELATIONS

In many situations in science, business, and mathematics, a correspondence exists between two sets. The correspondence is often defined by a *table*, an *equation*, or a *graph*, each of which can be viewed from a mathematical perspective as a set of ordered pairs. In mathematics, any set of ordered pairs is called a **relation.**

Table 2.1 defines a correspondence between a set of percent scores and a set of letter grades. For each score from 0 to 100, there corresponds only one letter grade. The score 94% corresponds to the letter grade of A. Using ordered-pair notation, we record this correspondence as (94, A).

The *equation* $d = 16t^2$ indicates that the distance d that a rock falls (neglecting air resistance) corresponds to the time t that it has been falling. For each nonnegative value t, the equation assigns only one value for the distance d. According to this equation, in 3 seconds a rock will fall 144 feet, which we record as (3, 144). Some of the other ordered pairs determined by $d = 16t^2$ are (0, 0), (1, 16), (2, 64), and (2.5, 100).

$$\text{Equation:} \qquad d = 16t^2$$
$$\text{If } t = 3, \text{ then } \quad d = 16(3)^2 = 144$$

The *graph* in **Figure 2.19** defines a correspondence between the length of a pendulum and the time it takes the pendulum to complete one oscillation. For each nonnegative pendulum length, the graph yields only one time. According to the graph, a pendulum length of 2 feet yields an oscillation time of 1.6 seconds, and a length of 4 feet yields an oscillation time of 2.2 seconds, where the time is measured to the nearest tenth of a second. These results can be recorded as the ordered pairs (2, 1.6) and (4, 2.2).

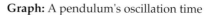

Graph: A pendulum's oscillation time

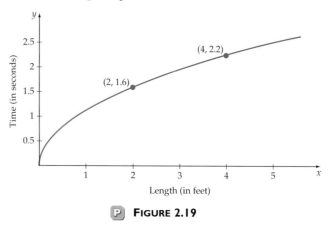

P **FIGURE 2.19**

● FUNCTIONS

The preceding table, equation, and graph each determines a special type of relation called a *function*.

MATH MATTERS

It is generally agreed among historians that Leonhard Euler (1707–1783) was the first person to use the word *function*. His definition of function occurs in his book *Introduction to Analysis of the Infinite*, published in 1748. Euler contributed to many areas of mathematics and was one of the most prolific expositors of mathematics.

Definition of a Function

A **function** is a set of ordered pairs in which no two ordered pairs have the same first coordinate and different second coordinates.

Although every function is a relation, not every relation is a function. For instance, consider (94, A) from the grading correspondence. The first coordinate, 94, is paired with a second coordinate of A. It would not make sense to have 94 paired with A, (94, A), and 94 paired with B, (94, B). The same first coordinate would be paired with two different second coordinates. This would mean that two students with the same score received different grades, one student an A and the other a B!

Functions may have ordered pairs with the same second coordinate. For instance, (94, A) and (95, A) are both ordered pairs that belong to the function defined by **Table 2.1.** A function may have different first coordinates and the same second coordinate.

The equation $d = 16t^2$ represents a function because for each value of t there is only one value of d. Not every equation, however, represents a function. For instance, $y^2 = 25 - x^2$ does not represent a function. The ordered pairs $(-3, 4)$ and $(-3, -4)$ are both solutions of the equation. But these ordered pairs do not satisfy the definition of a function; there are two ordered pairs with the same first coordinate but *different* second coordinates.

❓ QUESTION Does the set $\{(0, 0), (1, 0), (2, 0), (3, 0), (4, 0)\}$ define a function?

The **domain** of a function is the set of all the first coordinates of the ordered pairs. The **range** of a function is the set of all the second coordinates. In the func-

❓ ANSWER Yes. There are no two ordered pairs with the same first coordinate that have different second coordinates.

tion determined by the grading correspondence in **Table 2.1,** the domain is the interval [0, 100]. The range is {A, B, C, D, F}. In a function, each domain element is paired with one and only one range element.

If a function is defined by an equation, the variable that represents elements of the domain is the **independent variable.** The variable that represents elements of the range is the **dependent variable.** In the free-fall experiment, we used the equation $d = 16t^2$. The elements of the domain represented the time the rock fell, and the elements of the range represented the distance the rock fell. Thus, in $d = 16t^2$, the independent variable is t and the dependent variable is d.

The specific letters used for the independent and the dependent variable are not important. For example, $y = 16x^2$ represents the same function as $d = 16t^2$. Traditionally, x is used for the independent variable and y for the dependent variable. Anytime we use the phrase "y is a function of x" or a similar phrase with different letters, the variable that follows "function of" is the independent variable.

● FUNCTIONAL NOTATION

Functions can be named by using a letter or a combination of letters, such as f, g, A, log, or tan. If x is an element of the domain of f, then $f(x)$, which is read "f of x" or "the value of f at x," is the element in the range of f that corresponds to the domain element x. The notation "f" and the notation "$f(x)$" mean different things. "f" is the name of the function, whereas "$f(x)$" is the value of the function at x. Finding the value of $f(x)$ is referred to as *evaluating f at x.* To evaluate $f(x)$ at $x = a$, substitute a for x, and simplify.

INSTRUCTOR NOTE
Emphasize to students that f and $f(x)$ are not the same. f is the name of the function; $f(x)$ is the value of the function at x.

Alternative to Example 1
Let $f(x) = 2x^2 - 2$, and evaluate.
a. $f(-1)$
● **0**
b. $f(2a)$
● $8a^2 - 2$
c. $2f(a)$
● $4a^2 - 4$
d. $f(b - 3)$
● $2b^2 - 12b + 16$
e. $f(b) - f(3)$
● $2b^2 - 18$

EXAMPLE 1   Evaluate Functions

Let $f(x) = x^2 - 1$, and evaluate.

a. $f(-5)$ **b.** $f(3b)$ **c.** $3f(b)$ **d.** $f(a + 3)$ **e.** $f(a) + f(3)$

Solution

a. $f(-5) = (-5)^2 - 1 = 25 - 1 = 24$ • Substitute -5 for x, and simplify.

b. $f(3b) = (3b)^2 - 1 = 9b^2 - 1$ • Substitute $3b$ for x, and simplify.

c. $3f(b) = 3(b^2 - 1) = 3b^2 - 3$ • Substitute b for x, and simplify.

d. $f(a + 3) = (a + 3)^2 - 1$ • Substitute $a + 3$ for x.
$= a^2 + 6a + 8$ • Simplify.

e. $f(a) + f(3) = (a^2 - 1) + (3^2 - 1)$ • Substitute a for x; substitute 3 for x.
$= a^2 + 7$ • Simplify.

▶ TRY EXERCISE 2, PAGE 190

take note

In Example 1, observe that
$$f(3b) \neq 3f(b)$$
and that
$$f(a + 3) \neq f(a) + f(3)$$

Piecewise-defined functions are functions represented by more than one expression. The function shown below is an example of a piecewise-defined function.

$$f(x) = \begin{cases} 2x, & x < -2 \\ x^2, & -2 \leq x < 1 \\ 4 - x, & x \geq 1 \end{cases}$$

• This function is made up of different pieces, $2x$, x^2, and $4 - x$, depending on the value of x.

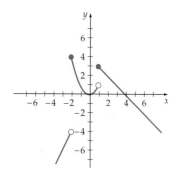

FIGURE 2.20

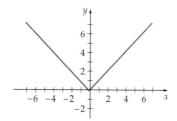

FIGURE 2.21

The expression that is used to evaluate this function depends on the value of x. For instance, to find $f(-3)$, we note that $-3 < -2$ and therefore use the expression $2x$ to evaluate the function.

$$f(-3) = 2(-3) = -6 \qquad \text{• When } x < -2, \text{ use the expression } 2x.$$

Here are some additional instances of evaluating this function:

$$f(-1) = (-1)^2 = 1 \qquad \text{• When } x \text{ satisfies } -2 \leq x < 1,$$
$$\text{use the expression } x^2.$$

$$f(4) = 4 - 4 = 0 \qquad \text{• When } x \geq 1, \text{ use the expression } 4 - x.$$

The graph of this function is shown in **Figure 2.20.** Note the use of the open and closed circles at the endpoints of the intervals. These circles are used to show the evaluation of the function at the endpoints of each interval. For instance, because -2 is in the interval $-2 \leq x < 1$, the value of the function at -2 is 4 $[f(-2) = (-2)^2 = 4]$. Therefore a closed dot is placed at $(-2, 4)$. Similarly, when $x = 1$, because 1 is in the interval $x \geq 1$, the value of the function at 1 is 3 $(f(1) = 4 - 1 = 3)$.

 QUESTION Evaluate the function f defined at the bottom of page 179 when $x = 0.5$.

The absolute value function is another example of a piecewise-defined function. Below is the definition of this function, which is sometimes abbreviated $\text{abs}(x)$. Its graph **(Figure 2.21)** is shown at the left.

$$\text{abs}(x) = \begin{cases} -x, & x < 0 \\ x, & x \geq 0 \end{cases}$$

Alternative to Example 2

Let $f(x) = \begin{cases} -x, & x < -2 \\ x^2 - 2, & -2 \leq x \leq 1 \\ x + 1, & x > 1 \end{cases}$

Find **a.** $f(-3)$ **b.** $f(4)$ **c.** $f(0)$

- **a.** 3
- **b.** 5
- **c.** −2

EXAMPLE 2   **Evaluate a Piecewise-Defined Function**

The number of monthly spam email attacks is shown in **Figure 2.22.**

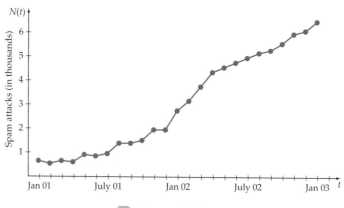

P **FIGURE 2.22**

Source: www.brightmail.com

 ANSWER   0.5 is in the interval $-2 \leq x < 1$. Therefore, $f(0.5) = 0.5^2 = 0.25$.

The data in the graph can be approximated by

$$N(t) = \begin{cases} 24.68t^2 - 170.47t + 957.73, & 0 \le t < 17 \\ 196.9t + 1164.6, & 17 \le t \le 26 \end{cases}$$

where $N(t)$ is the number of spam attacks in thousands for month t, where $t = 0$ corresponds to January 2001. Use this function to estimate, to the nearest hundred thousand, the number of monthly spam attacks for the following months.

a.   October 2001   **b.**   December 2002

Solution

a.   The month October 2001 corresponds to $t = 9$. Because $t = 9$ is in the interval $0 \le t < 17$, evaluate $24.68t^2 - 170.47t + 957.73$ at $t = 9$.

$$24.68t^2 - 170.47t + 957.73$$
$$24.68(9)^2 - 170.47(9) + 957.73 = 1422.58$$

There were approximately 1,423,000 spam attacks in October 2001.

b.   The month December 2002 corresponds to $t = 23$. Because $t = 23$ is in the interval $17 \le t \le 26$, evaluate $196.9t + 1164.6$ at 23.

$$196.9t + 1164.6$$
$$196.9(23) + 1164.6 = 5693.3$$

There were approximately 5,693,000 spam attacks in December 2002.

▶ **TRY EXERCISE 10, PAGE 191**

TRY EXERCISE 10, PAGE 191

● **IDENTIFYING FUNCTIONS**

Recall that although every function is a relation, not every relation is a function. In the next example we examine four relations to determine which are functions.

EXAMPLE 3   **Identify Functions**

Which relations define y as a function of x?

a. $\{(2, 3), (4, 1), (4, 5)\}$ **b.** $3x + y = 1$ **c.** $-4x^2 + y^2 = 9$

d.   The correspondence between the x values and the y values in **Figure 2.23.**

Solution

a.   There are two ordered pairs, $(4, 1)$ and $(4, 5)$, with the same first coordinate and different second coordinates. This set does not define y as a function of x.

b.   Solving $3x + y = 1$ for y yields $y = -3x + 1$. Because $-3x + 1$ is a unique real number for each x, this equation defines y as a function of x.

Continued ▶

Alternative to Example 3
Which relations define y as a function of x?
a. $\{(3, 4), (6, 7), (3, 6)\}$
● **No**
b. $x + 3y = -6$
● **Yes**
c. $x^2 + y^2 = 16$
● **No**
d.   The correspondence between the x-values and the y-values in the accompanying figure.

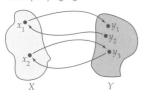

● **No**

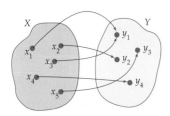

FIGURE 2.23

Chapter 2 — Functions and Graphs (page 182)

c. Solving $-4x^2 + y^2 = 9$ for y yields $y = \pm\sqrt{4x^2 + 9}$. The right side $\pm\sqrt{4x^2 + 9}$ produces two values of y for each value of x. For example, when $x = 0$, $y = 3$ or $y = -3$. Thus $-4x^2 + y^2 = 9$ does not define y as a function of x.

d. Each x is paired with one and only one y. The correspondence in **Figure 2.23** defines y as a function of x.

▶ TRY EXERCISE 14, PAGE 191

take note

You may indicate the domain of a function using set notation or interval notation. For instance, the domain of $f(x) = \sqrt{x - 3}$ may be given in each of the following ways:

Set notation: $\{x \mid x \geq 3\}$
Interval notation: $[3, \infty)$

Sometimes the domain of a function is stated explicitly. For example, each of f, g, and h below is given by an equation, followed by a statement that indicates the domain of the function.

$$f(x) = x^2, x > 0 \qquad g(t) = \frac{1}{t^2 + 4}, 0 \leq t \leq 5 \qquad h(x) = x^2, x = 1, 2, 3$$

Although f and h have the same equation, they are different functions because they have different domains. If the domain of a function is not explicitly stated, then its domain is determined by the following convention.

Domain of a Function

Unless otherwise stated, the domain of a function is the set of all real numbers for which the function makes sense and yields real numbers.

Alternative to Example 4
Determine the domain of each function. Write the answer in interval notation.

a. $f(x) = \dfrac{x + 3}{x - 2}$
○ $(-\infty, 2) \cup (2, \infty)$
b. $g(x) = \sqrt{x - 4}$
○ $[4, \infty)$

c. $V(r) = \dfrac{4}{3}r^3$, where $V(r)$ is the volume of a sphere whose radius is r units.
○ $(0, \infty)$

EXAMPLE 4   Determine the Domain of a Function

Determine the domain of each function.

a. $G(t) = \dfrac{1}{t - 4}$ b. $f(x) = \sqrt{x + 1}$

c. $A(s) = s^2$, where $A(s)$ is the area of a square whose sides are s units.

Solution

a. The number 4 is not an element of the domain because G is undefined when the denominator $t - 4$ equals 0. The domain of G is all real numbers except 4. In interval notation the domain is $(-\infty, 4) \cup (4, \infty)$.

b. The radical $\sqrt{x + 1}$ is a real number only when $x + 1 \geq 0$ or when $x \geq -1$. Thus, in set notation, the domain of f is $\{x \mid x \geq -1\}$.

c. Because s represents the length of the side of a square, s must be positive. In interval notation the domain of A is $(0, \infty)$.

▶ TRY EXERCISE 28, PAGE 191

● GRAPHS OF FUNCTIONS

If a is an element of the domain of a function, then $(a, f(a))$ is an ordered pair that belongs to the function.

Graph of a Function

The **graph of a function** is the graph of all the ordered pairs that belong to the function.

Alternative to Example 5
Exercise 42, page 191.

EXAMPLE 5   **Graph a Function by Plotting Points**

Graph each function. State the domain and the range of each function.

a. $f(x) = |x - 1|$ b. $n(x) = \begin{cases} 2, & \text{if } x \le 1 \\ x, & \text{if } x > 1 \end{cases}$

Solution

a.   The domain of f is the set of all real numbers. Write the function as $y = |x - 1|$. Evaluate the function for several domain values. We have used $x = -3, -2, -1, 0, 1, 2, 3$, and 4.

x	−3	−2	−1	0	1	2	3	4
y = |x − 1|	4	3	2	1	0	1	2	3

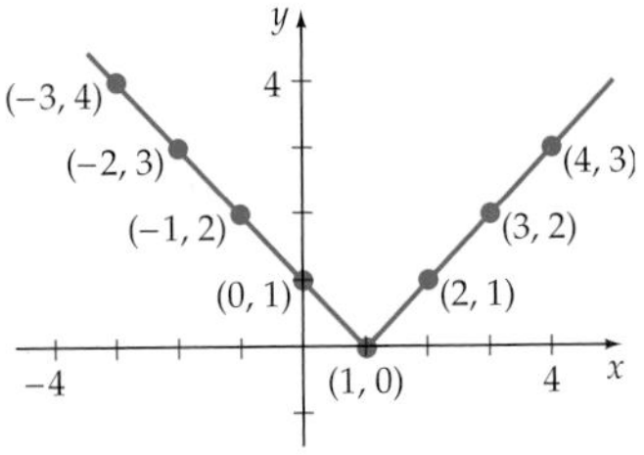

Plot the points determined by the ordered pairs. Connect the points to form the graph in **Figure 2.24.**

     Because $|x - 1| \ge 0$, we can conclude that the graph of f extends from a height of 0 upward, so the range is $\{y \mid y \ge 0\}$.

b.   The domain is the union of the inequalities $x \le 1$ and $x > 1$. Thus the domain of n is the set of all real numbers. For $x \le 1$, graph $n(x) = 2$. This results in the horizontal ray in **Figure 2.25.** The solid circle indicates that the point $(1, 2)$ *is* part of the graph. For $x > 1$, graph $n(x) = x$. This produces the second ray in **Figure 2.25.** The open circle indicates that the point $(1, 1)$ *is not* part of the graph.

     Examination of the graph shows that it includes only points whose y values are greater than 1. Thus the range of n is $\{y \mid y > 1\}$.

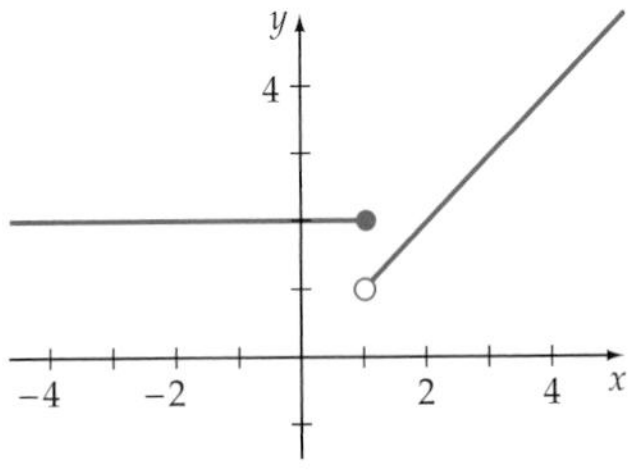

Graph (Figure 2.24):

Points: $(-3, 4)$, $(-2, 3)$, $(-1, 2)$, $(0, 1)$, $(1, 0)$, $(2, 1)$, $(3, 2)$, $(4, 3)$

$f(x) = |x - 1|$

FIGURE 2.24

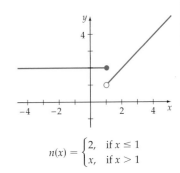

$n(x) = \begin{cases} 2, & \text{if } x \le 1 \\ x, & \text{if } x > 1 \end{cases}$

FIGURE 2.25

▶ **TRY EXERCISE 40, PAGE 191**

INTEGRATING TECHNOLOGY

A graphing utility also can be used to draw the graph of a function. For instance, to graph $f(x) = x^2 - 1$, you will enter an equation similar to Y₁=x²–1. The graph is shown in **Figure 2.26.**

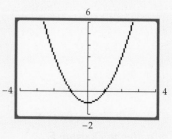

FIGURE 2.26

The definition that a function is a set of ordered pairs in which no two ordered pairs that have the same first coordinate have different second coordinates implies that any vertical line intersects the graph of a function at no more than one point. This is known as the *vertical line test.*

The Vertical Line Test for Functions

A graph is the graph of a function if and only if no vertical line intersects the graph at more than one point.

Alternative to Example 6

Which of the following graphs are graphs of functions?

a.

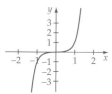

● **Yes**

b.

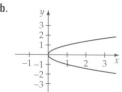

● **No**

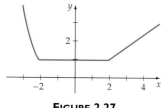

FIGURE 2.27

EXAMPLE 6   **Apply the Vertical Line Test**

Which of the following graphs are graphs of functions?

a.

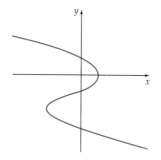

b.

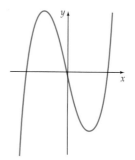

Solution

a. This graph *is not* the graph of a function because some vertical lines intersect the graph in more than one point.

b. This graph *is* the graph of a function because every vertical line intersects the graph in at most one point.

▶ **TRY EXERCISE 50, PAGE 192**

Consider the graph in **Figure 2.27.** As a point on the graph moves from left to right, this graph falls for values of $x \leq -2$, it remains the same height from

$x = -2$ to $x = 2$, and it rises for $x \geq 2$. The function represented by the graph is said to be *decreasing* on the interval $(-\infty, -2]$, *constant* on the interval $[-2, 2]$, and *increasing* on the interval $[2, \infty)$.

Definition of Increasing, Decreasing, and Constant Functions

If a and b are elements of an interval I that is a subset of the domain of a function f, then

- f is **increasing** on I if $f(a) < f(b)$ whenever $a < b$.
- f is **decreasing** on I if $f(a) > f(b)$ whenever $a < b$.
- f is **constant** on I if $f(a) = f(b)$ for all a and b.

Recall that a function is a relation in which no two ordered pairs that have the same first coordinate have different second coordinates. This means that given any x, there is only one y that can be paired with that x. A **one-to-one function** satisfies the additional condition that given any y, there is only one x that can be paired with that given y. In a manner similar to applying the vertical line test, we can apply a *horizontal line test* to identify one-to-one functions.

Horizontal Line Test for a One-To-One Function

If every horizontal line intersects the graph of a function at most once, then the graph is the graph of a one-to-one function.

For example, some horizontal lines intersect the graph in **Figure 2.28** at more than one point. It is *not* the graph of a one-to-one function. Every horizontal line intersects the graph in **Figure 2.29** at most once. This is the graph of a one-to-one function.

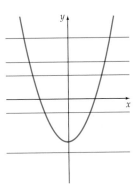

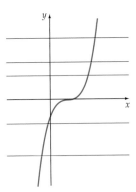

FIGURE 2.28

Some horizontal lines intersect this graph at more than one point. It is *not* the graph of a one-to-one function.

FIGURE 2.29

Every horizontal line intersects this graph at most once. It is the graph of a one-to-one function.

• THE GREATEST INTEGER FUNCTION (FLOOR FUNCTION)

take note

The greatest integer function is an important function that is often used in advanced mathematics and also in computer science.

To this point, the graphs of the functions have not had any breaks or gaps. These functions whose graphs can be drawn without lifting the pencil off the paper are called *continuous functions*. The graphs of some functions do have breaks or *discontinuities*. One such function is the **greatest integer function** or **floor function**. This function is denoted by various symbols such as $[\![x]\!]$, $\lfloor x \rfloor$, and $\text{int}(x)$.

The value of the greatest integer function at x is the greatest integer that is less than or equal to x. For instance,

$$\lfloor -1.1 \rfloor = -2 \qquad [\![-3]\!] = -3 \qquad \text{int}\left(\frac{5}{2}\right) = 2 \qquad \lfloor 5 \rfloor = 5 \qquad [\![\pi]\!] = 3$$

INTEGRATING TECHNOLOGY

Many graphing calculators use the notation $\text{int}(x)$ for the greatest integer function. Here is a screen from a TI-83 Plus.

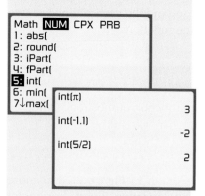

❓ QUESTION Evaluate. **a.** $\text{int}\left(-\frac{3}{2}\right)$ **b.** $\lfloor 2 \rfloor$

To graph the floor function, first observe that the value of the floor function is constant between any two consecutive integers. For instance, between the integers 1 and 2, we have

$$\text{int}(1.1) = 1 \qquad \text{int}(1.35) = 1 \qquad \text{int}(1.872) = 1 \qquad \text{int}(1.999) = 1$$

Between -3 and -2, we have

$$\text{int}(-2.98) = -3 \qquad \text{int}(-2.4) = -3 \qquad \text{int}(-2.35) = -3 \qquad \text{int}(-2.01) = -3$$

Using this property of the floor function, we can create a table of values and then graph the floor function.

x	y = int(x)
$-5 \le x < 4$	-5
$-4 \le x < -3$	-4
$-3 \le x < -2$	-3
$-2 \le x < -1$	-2
$-1 \le x < 0$	-1
$0 \le x < 1$	0
$1 \le x < 2$	1
$2 \le x < 3$	2
$3 \le x < 4$	3
$4 \le x < 5$	4

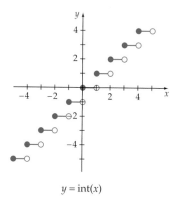

$y = \text{int}(x)$

FIGURE 2.30

The graph of the floor function has discontinuities (breaks) whenever x is an integer. The domain of the floor function is the set of real numbers; the range is the set of integers. Because the graph appears to be a series of steps, sometimes the floor function is referred to as a **step function**.

❓ ANSWER **a.** Because -2 is the greatest integer that is less than $-\frac{3}{2}$, $\text{int}\left(-\frac{3}{2}\right) = -2$.

b. Because 2 is the greatest integer less than or *equal* to 2, $\lfloor 2 \rfloor = 2$.

┌─────────────────────┐
│ INTEGRATING   │
│ TECHNOLOGY   │
└─────────────────────┘

Many graphing calculators use the notation int(x) for the floor function. The screens at the left are from a TI-83 Plus graphing calculator.

A graphing calculator also can be used to graph the floor function. The graph in **Figure 2.31** was drawn in "connected" mode. This graph does not show the discontinuities that occur whenever x is an integer.

The graph in **Figure 2.32** was constructed by graphing the floor function in "dot" mode. In this case the discontinuities at the integers are apparent.

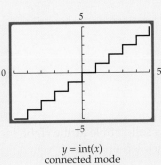

$y = \text{int}(x)$
connected mode

FIGURE 2.31

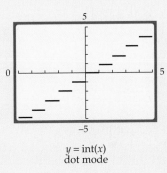

$y = \text{int}(x)$
dot mode

FIGURE 2.32

Alternative to Example 7
A telephone call costs 9 cents a minute for the first minute or any part of the minute. Each additional minute or part of a minute costs 8 cents. If x is the length of the call in minutes, then the cost of the call in dollars is given by
$C(x) = 0.09 - 0.08 \, \text{int}(1 - x)$, $x > 0$.
a. Evaluate $C(3)$ and $C(3.5)$.
● **$C(3) = \$0.25$, $C(3.5) = \$0.33$**
b. Graph $y = C(x)$ for $0 < x \le 4$.

● *(graph)*
```
C(x)
0.35
0.30        ●——○
0.25      ●——○
0.20
0.15   ●——○
0.10 ○——○
0.05
     0  1  2  3  4  x
```

EXAMPLE 7

Use the Greatest Integer Function to Model Expenses

The cost of parking in a garage is $3 for the first hour or any part of the hour and $2 for each additional hour or any part of the hour thereafter. If x is the time in hours that you park your car, then the cost is given by

$$C(x) = 3 - 2 \, \text{int}(1 - x), \quad x > 0$$

a. Evaluate $C(2)$ and $C(2.5)$.   **b.** Graph $y = C(x)$ for $0 < x \le 5$.

Solution

a. $C(2) = 3 - 2 \, \text{int}(1 - 2)$ $C(2.5) = 3 - 2 \, \text{int}(1 - 2.5)$
$ = 3 - 2 \, \text{int}(-1)$ $ = 3 - 2 \, \text{int}(-1.5)$
$ = 3 - 2(-1)$ $ = 3 - 2(-2)$
$ = \$5$ $ = \$7$

b. To graph $C(x)$ for $0 < x \le 5$, consider the value of $\text{int}(1 - x)$ for each of the intervals $0 < x \le 1, 1 < x \le 2, 2 < x \le 3, 3 < x \le 4$, and $4 < x \le 5$. For instance, when $0 < x \le 1, 0 \le 1 - x < 1$. Thus $\text{int}(1 - x) = 0$ when $0 < x \le 1$. Now consider $1 < x \le 2$. When $1 < x \le 2, 1 \le 1 - x < 2$. Thus $\text{int}(1 - x) = 1$ when $1 < x \le 2$. Applying the same reasoning to

Continued ▶

each of the other intervals gives the following table of values and the corresponding graph of C.

x	C(x) = 3 − 2 int(1 − x)
0 < x ≤ 1	3
1 < x ≤ 2	5
2 < x ≤ 3	7
3 < x ≤ 4	9
4 < x ≤ 5	11

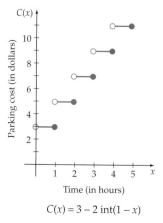

$C(x) = 3 - 2 \text{ int}(1 - x)$

FIGURE 2.33

Because $C(1) = 3$, $C(2) = 5$, $C(3) = 7$, $C(4) = 9$, and $C(5) = 11$, we can use a solid circle at the right endpoint of each "step" and an open circle at each left endpoint.

▶ **TRY EXERCISE 48, PAGE 192**

 INTEGRATING TECHNOLOGY

Example 7 illustrates that a graphing calculator may not produce a graph that is a good representation of a function. You may be required to *make adjustments* in the MODE, SET UP, or WINDOW of the graphing calculator so that it will produce a better representation of the function. Some graphs may also require some *fine tuning*, such as open or solid circles at particular points, to accurately represent the function.

● **APPLICATIONS**

Alternative to Example 8
A boat was purchased for $38,000. Assuming that the boat depreciates at a constant rate of $7000 per year *(straight-line depreciation)* for the first 5 years, write the value *v* of the boat as a function of time, and calculate the value of the boat 2 years after purchase.
● $v(t) = 38,000 - 7000t, 0 \le t \le 5$; $v(2) = $24,000$

EXAMPLE 8   **Solve an Application**

A car was purchased for $16,500. Assuming the car depreciates at a constant rate of $2200 per year (*straight-line depreciation*) for the first 7 years, write the value *v* of the car as a function of time, and calculate the value of the car 3 years after purchase.

Solution

Let *t* represent the number of years that have passed since the car was purchased. Then 2200*t* is the amount that the car has depreciated after *t* years. The value of the car at time *t* is given by

$$v(t) = 16,500 - 2200t, \quad 0 \le t \le 7$$

When $t = 3$, the value of the car is

$$v(3) = 16{,}500 - 2200(3) = 16{,}500 - 6600 = \$9900$$

▶ **TRY EXERCISE 66, PAGE 193**

Often in applied mathematics, formulas are used to determine the functional relationship that exists between two variables.

Alternative to Example 9

An airport is 15 miles north of a broadcasting tower. An airplane takes off and flies east at 450 mph. Express the ground distance d between the airplane and the tower as a function of time, given that the airplane has been flying for t hours.

● $d(t) = \sqrt{202{,}500t^2 + 225}$

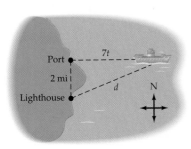

FIGURE 2.34

EXAMPLE 9   **Solve an Application**

A lighthouse is 2 miles south of a port. A ship leaves port and sails east at a rate of 7 mph. Express the distance d between the ship and the lighthouse as a function of time, given that the ship has been sailing for t hours.

Solution

Draw a diagram and label it as shown in **Figure 2.34.** Note that because distance = (rate)(time) and the rate is 7, in t hours the ship has sailed a distance of $7t$.

$$[d(t)]^2 = (7t)^2 + 2^2 \qquad \bullet \textbf{ The Pythagorean Theorem}$$
$$[d(t)]^2 = 49t^2 + 4$$
$$d(t) = \sqrt{49t^2 + 4} \qquad \bullet \textbf{ The } \pm \textbf{ sign is not used because}$$
$$\qquad\qquad\qquad\qquad\qquad\quad \textbf{\textit{d} must be nonnegative.}$$

▶ **TRY EXERCISE 72, PAGE 194**

Alternative to Example 10

Exercise 76, page 195.

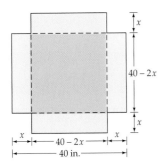

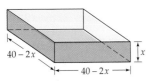

FIGURE 2.35

EXAMPLE 10   **Solve an Application**

An open box is to be made from a square piece of cardboard that measures 40 inches on each side. To construct the box, squares that measure x inches on each side are cut from each corner of the cardboard as shown in **Figure 2.35.**

a. Express the volume V of the box as a function of x.

b. Determine the domain of V.

Solution

a. The length l of the box is $40 - 2x$. The width w is also $40 - 2x$. The height of the box is x. The volume V of a box is the product of its length, its width, and its height. Thus

$$V = (40 - 2x)^2 x$$

b. The squares that are cut from each corner require x to be larger than 0 inches but less than 20 inches. Thus the domain is $\{x \mid 0 < x < 20\}$.

▶ **TRY EXERCISE 68, PAGE 193**

TOPICS FOR DISCUSSION

1. Discuss the definition of *function*. Give some examples of relationships that are functions and some that are not functions.

2. What is the difference between the domain and range of a function?

3. How many y-intercepts can a function have? How many x-intercepts can a function have?

4. Discuss how the vertical line test is used to determine whether or not a graph is the graph of a function. Explain why the vertical line test works.

5. What is the domain of $f(x) = \dfrac{\sqrt{1-x}}{x^2 - 9}$? Explain.

6. Is 2 in the range of $g(x) = \dfrac{6x - 5}{3x + 1}$? Explain the process you used to make your decision.

7. Suppose that f is a function and that $f(a) = f(b)$. Does this imply that $a = b$? Explain your answer.

EXERCISE SET 2.2

—Suggested Assignment: Exercises 1–89, every other odd; 91, 93, 95, 103–108.
—Answers to Exercises 39–47, 85–90, and 101–102 are on pages AA3–AA4.

In Exercises 1 to 8, evaluate each function.

1. Given $f(x) = 3x - 1$, find

   a. $f(2)$ 5

   b. $f(-1)$ -4

   c. $f(0)$ -1

   d. $f\left(\dfrac{2}{3}\right)$ 1

   e. $f(k)$ $3k - 1$

   f. $f(k + 2)$ $3k + 5$

▶ 2. Given $g(x) = 2x^2 + 3$, find

   a. $g(3)$ 21

   b. $g(-1)$ 5

   c. $g(0)$ 3

   d. $g\left(\dfrac{1}{2}\right)$ $\dfrac{7}{2}$

   e. $g(c)$ $2c^2 + 3$

   f. $g(c + 5)$ $2c^2 + 20c + 53$

3. Given $A(w) = \sqrt{w^2 + 5}$, find

   a. $A(0)$ $\sqrt{5}$

   b. $A(2)$ 3

   c. $A(-2)$ 3

   d. $A(4)$ $\sqrt{21}$

   e. $A(r + 1)$ $\sqrt{r^2 + 2r + 6}$

   f. $A(-c)$ $\sqrt{c^2 + 5}$

4. Given $J(t) = 3t^2 - t$, find

   a. $J(-4)$ 52

   b. $J(0)$ 0

   c. $J\left(\dfrac{1}{3}\right)$ 0

   d. $J(-c)$ $3c^2 + c$

   e. $J(x + 1)$ $3x^2 + 5x + 2$

   f. $J(x + h)$ $3x^2 + 6xh + 3h^2 - x - h$

5. Given $f(x) = \dfrac{1}{|x|}$, find

   a. $f(2)$ $\dfrac{1}{2}$

   b. $f(-2)$ $\dfrac{1}{2}$

   c. $f\left(\dfrac{-3}{5}\right)$ $\dfrac{5}{3}$

   d. $f(2) + f(-2)$ 1

   e. $f(c^2 + 4)$ $\dfrac{1}{c^2 + 4}$

   f. $f(2 + h)$ $\dfrac{1}{|2 + h|}$

6. Given $T(x) = 5$, find

   a. $T(-3)$ 5

   b. $T(0)$ 5

   c. $T\left(\dfrac{2}{7}\right)$ 5

   d. $T(3) + T(1)$ 10

   e. $T(x + h)$ 5

   f. $T(3k + 5)$ 5

7. Given $s(x) = \dfrac{x}{|x|}$, find

   a. $s(4)$ 1

   b. $s(5)$ 1

   c. $s(-2)$ -1

   d. $s(-3)$ -1

   e. $s(t), t > 0$ 1

   f. $s(t), t < 0$ -1

8. Given $r(x) = \dfrac{x}{x + 4}$, find

   a. $r(0)$ 0

   b. $r(-1)$ $-\dfrac{1}{3}$

   c. $r(-3)$ -3

d. $r\left(\dfrac{1}{2}\right)$ **e.** $r(0.1)$ **f.** $r(10,000)$

$\dfrac{1}{9}$ $\dfrac{1}{41}$ $\dfrac{2500}{2501}$

In Exercises 9 and 10, evaluate each piecewise-defined function for the indicated values.

9. $P(x) = \begin{cases} 3x + 1, & \text{if } x < 2 \\ -x^2 + 11, & \text{if } x \geq 2 \end{cases}$

  a. $P(-4)$ **b.** $P(\sqrt{5})$

    -11 6

  c. $P(c), \quad c < 2$ **d.** $P(k + 1), \quad k \geq 1$

    $3c + 1$ $-k^2 - 2k + 10$

10. $Q(t) = \begin{cases} 4, & \text{if } 0 \leq t \leq 5 \\ -t + 9, & \text{if } 5 < t \leq 8 \\ \sqrt{t - 7}, & \text{if } 8 < t \leq 11 \end{cases}$

  a. $Q(0)$ **b.** $Q(e), \quad 6 < e < 7$

    4 $-e + 9$

  c. $Q(n), \quad 1 < n < 2$ **d.** $Q(m^2 + 7), \quad 1 < m \leq 2$

    4 m since $m > 0$

In Exercises 11 to 20, identify the equations that define y as a function of x.

11. $2x + 3y = 7$ **12.** $5x + y = 8$

  Yes   Yes

13. $-x + y^2 = 2$ **14.** $x^2 - 2y = 2$

  No   Yes

15. $y = 4 \pm \sqrt{x}$ **16.** $x^2 + y^2 = 9$

  No   No

17. $y = \sqrt[3]{x}$ **18.** $y = |x| + 5$

  Yes   Yes

19. $y^2 = x^2$ **20.** $y^3 = x^3$

  No   Yes

In Exercises 21 to 26, identify the sets of ordered pairs (x, y) that define y as a function of x.

21. $\{(2, 3), (5, 1), (-4, 3), (7, 11)\}$

  Yes

22. $\{(5, 10), (3, -2), (4, 7), (5, 8)\}$

  No

23. $\{(4, 4), (6, 1), (5, -3)\}$

  Yes

24. $\{(2, 2), (3, 3), (7, 7)\}$

  Yes

25. $\{(1, 0), (2, 0), (3, 0)\}$

  Yes

26. $\left\{\left(-\dfrac{1}{3}, \dfrac{1}{4}\right), \left(-\dfrac{1}{4}, \dfrac{1}{3}\right), \left(\dfrac{1}{4}, \dfrac{2}{3}\right)\right\}$

  Yes

In Exercises 27 to 38, determine the domain of the function represented by the given equation.

27. $f(x) = 3x - 4$ **28.** $f(x) = -2x + 1$

  all real numbers   all real numbers

29. $f(x) = x^2 + 2$ **30.** $f(x) = 3x^2 + 1$

  all real numbers   all real numbers

31. $f(x) = \dfrac{4}{x + 2}$ **32.** $f(x) = \dfrac{6}{x - 5}$

  $\{x \,|\, x \neq -2\}$ $\{x \,|\, x \neq 5\}$

33. $f(x) = \sqrt{7 + x}$ **34.** $f(x) = \sqrt{4 - x}$

  $\{x \,|\, x \geq -7\}$ $\{x \,|\, x \leq 4\}$

35. $f(x) = \sqrt{4 - x^2}$ **36.** $f(x) = \sqrt{12 - x^2}$

  $\{x \,|\, -2 \leq x \leq 2\}$ $\{x \,|\, -2\sqrt{3} \leq x \leq 2\sqrt{3}\}$

37. $f(x) = \dfrac{1}{\sqrt{x + 4}}$ **38.** $f(x) = \dfrac{1}{\sqrt{5 - x}}$

  $\{x \,|\, x > -4\}$ $\{x \,|\, x < 5\}$

In Exercises 39 to 46, graph each function. Insert solid circles or hollow circles where necessary to indicate the true nature of the function.

39. $f(x) = \begin{cases} |x|, & \text{if } x \leq 1 \\ 2, & \text{if } x > 1 \end{cases}$

40. $g(x) = \begin{cases} -4, & \text{if } x \leq 0 \\ x^2 - 4, & \text{if } 0 < x \leq 1 \\ -x, & \text{if } x > 1 \end{cases}$

41. $J(x) = \begin{cases} 4, & \text{if } x \leq -1 \\ x^2, & \text{if } -1 < x < 1 \\ -x + 5, & \text{if } x \geq 1 \end{cases}$

42. $K(x) = \begin{cases} 1, & \text{if } x \leq -2 \\ x^2 - 4, & \text{if } -2 < x < 2 \\ \dfrac{1}{2}x, & \text{if } x \geq 2 \end{cases}$

43. $L(x) = \left\llbracket \dfrac{1}{3}x \right\rrbracket \quad$ for $-6 \leq x \leq 6$

44. $M(x) = \llbracket x \rrbracket + 2 \quad$ for $0 \leq x \leq 4$

45. $N(x) = \text{int}(-x) \quad$ for $-3 \leq x \leq 3$

46. $P(x) = \text{int}(x) + x \quad$ for $0 \leq x \leq 4$

47. FIRST-CLASS MAIL In 2003, the cost to mail a first-class letter is given by

$$C(w) = 0.37 - 0.34 \, \text{int}(1 - w), \quad w > 0$$

where C is in dollars and w is the weight of the letter in ounces.

  a. What is the cost to mail a letter that weighs 2.8 ounces?

    $C(2.8) = \$1.05$

  b. Graph C for $0 < w \leq 5$.

► **48.** **INCOME TAX** The amount of federal income tax $T(x)$ a person owed in 2003 is given by

$$T(x) = \begin{cases} 0.10x, & 0 \leq x < 6000 \\ 0.15(x - 6000) + 600, & 6000 \leq x < 27{,}950 \\ 0.27(x - 27{,}950) + 3892.50, & 27{,}950 \leq x < 67{,}700 \\ 0.30(x - 67{,}700) + 14{,}625, & 67{,}700 \leq x < 141{,}250 \\ 0.35(x - 141{,}250) + 36{,}690, & 141{,}250 \leq x < 307{,}050 \\ 0.386(x - 307{,}050) + 94{,}720, & x \geq 307{,}050 \end{cases}$$

where x is the adjusted gross income tax of the taxpayer.

a. What is the domain of this function?
$[0, \infty)$

b. Find the income tax owed by a taxpayer whose adjusted gross income was $31,250.
$4783.50

c. Find the income tax owed by a taxpayer whose adjusted gross income was $72,000.
$15,915

49. Use the vertical line test to determine which of the following graphs are graphs of functions.
a, b, and d.

a.
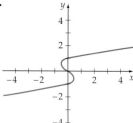

b.
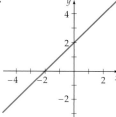

c.
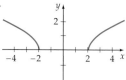

d.
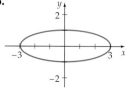

► **50.** Use the vertical line test to determine which of the following graphs are graphs of functions.
a. and d.

a.

b.

c.
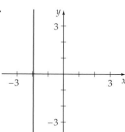

d.
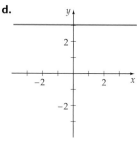

In Exercises 51 to 60, use the indicated graph to identify the intervals over which the function is increasing, constant, or decreasing.

51.
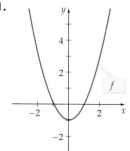

decreasing on $(-\infty, 0]$; increasing on $[0, \infty)$

52.
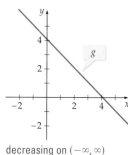

decreasing on $(-\infty, \infty)$

53.
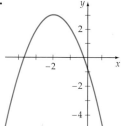

increasing on $(-\infty, \infty)$

54.
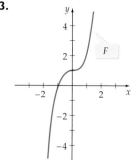

increasing on $(-\infty, 2]$;
decreasing on $[2, \infty)$

55.
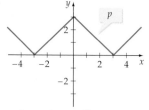

decreasing on $(-\infty, -3]$;
increasing on $[-3, 0]$;
decreasing on $[0, 3]$; increasing on $[3, \infty)$

56.
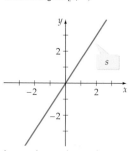

increasing on $(-\infty, \infty)$

c.
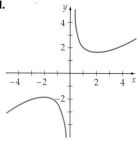

d.
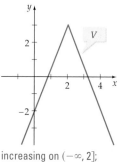

57.

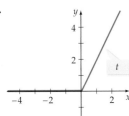

constant on $(-\infty, 0]$; increasing on $[0, \infty)$

58.

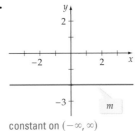

constant on $(-\infty, \infty)$

59.

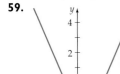

decreasing on $(-\infty, 0]$; constant on $[0, 1]$; increasing on $[1, \infty)$

60.

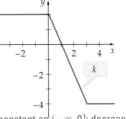

constant on $(-\infty, 0]$; decreasing on $[0, 3]$; constant on $[3, \infty)$

61. Use the horizontal line test to determine which of the following functions are one-to-one. *g and F*

  f as shown in Exercise 51
  g as shown in Exercise 52
  F as shown in Exercise 53
  V as shown in Exercise 54
  p as shown in Exercise 55

62. Use the horizontal line test to determine which of the following functions are one-to-one. *s*

  s as shown in Exercise 56
  t as shown in Exercise 57
  m as shown in Exercise 58
  r as shown in Exercise 59
  k as shown in Exercise 60

63. A rectangle has a length of *l* feet and a perimeter of 50 feet.

  a. Write the width *w* of the rectangle as a function of its length.
  $w = 25 - l$

  b. Write the area *A* of the rectangle as a function of its length.
  $A = 25l - l^2$

64. The sum of two numbers is 20. Let *x* represent one of the numbers.

  a. Write the second number *y* as a function of *x*.
  $y = 20 - x$

  b. Write the product *P* of the two numbers as a function of *x*.
  $P = 20x - x^2$

65. DEPRECIATION A bus was purchased for \$80,000. Assuming the bus depreciates at a rate of \$6500 per year (*straight-line depreciation*) for the first 10 years, write the value *v* of the bus as a function of the time *t* (measured in years) for $0 \le t \le 10$.
$v(t) = 80,000 - 6500t, 0 \le t \le 10$

▶ **66. DEPRECIATION** A boat was purchased for \$44,000. Assuming the boat depreciates at a rate of \$4200 per year (*straight-line depreciation*) for the first 8 years, write the value *v* of the boat as a function of the time *t* (measured in years) for $0 \le t \le 8$.
$v(t) = 44,000 - 4200t, 0 \le t \le 8$

67. COST, REVENUE, AND PROFIT A manufacturer produces a product at a cost of \$22.80 per unit. The manufacturer has a fixed cost of \$400.00 per day. Each unit retails for \$37.00. Let *x* represent the number of units produced in a 5-day period.

  a. Write the total cost *C* as a function of *x*.
  $C(x) = 2000 + 22.80x$

  b. Write the revenue *R* as a function of *x*.
  $R(x) = 37.00x$

  c. Write the profit *P* as a function of *x*. (*Hint:* The profit function is given by $P(x) = R(x) - C(x)$.)
  $P(x) = 14.20x - 2000$

▶ **68. VOLUME OF A BOX** An open box is to be made from a square piece of cardboard having dimensions 30 inches by 30 inches by cutting out squares of area x^2 from each corner, as shown in the figure.

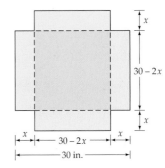

  a. Express the volume *V* of the box as a function of *x*.
  $V = 900x - 120x^2 + 4x^3$

  b. State the domain of *V*.
  $0 < x < 15$

69. HEIGHT OF AN INSCRIBED CYLINDER A cone has an altitude of 15 centimeters and a radius of 3 centimeters. A right circular cylinder of radius *r* and height *h* is inscribed in the cone as shown in the figure. Use similar triangles to write *h* as a function of *r*.
$h = 15 - 5r$

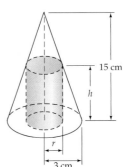

70. VOLUME OF WATER Water is flowing into a conical drinking cup that has an altitude of 4 inches and a radius of 2 inches, as shown in the figure.

a. Write the radius r of the water as a function of its depth h. $r = \dfrac{1}{2}h$

b. Write the volume V of the water as a function of its depth h. $V = \dfrac{1}{12}\pi h^3$

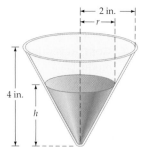

71. DISTANCE FROM A BALLOON For the first minute of flight, a hot air balloon rises vertically at a rate of 3 meters per second. If t is the time in seconds that the balloon has been airborne, write the distance d between the balloon and a point on the ground 50 meters from the point of lift-off as a function of t.
$d = \sqrt{(3t)^2 + 50^2}$

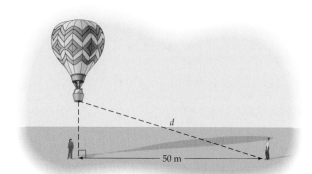

72. TIME FOR A SWIMMER An athlete swims from point A to point B at the rate of 2 mph and runs from point B to point C at a rate of 8 mph. Use the dimensions in the figure to write the time t required to reach point C as a function of x.
$t = \dfrac{\sqrt{1 + x^2}}{2} + \dfrac{3 - x}{8}$ h

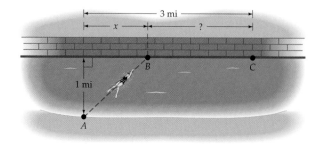

73. DISTANCE BETWEEN SHIPS At 12:00 noon Ship A is 45 miles due south of ship B and is sailing north at a rate of 8 mph. Ship B is sailing east at a rate of 6 mph. Write the distance d between the ships as a function of the time t, where $t = 0$ represents 12:00 noon. $d = \sqrt{(45 - 8t)^2 + (6t)^2}$

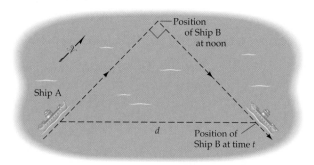

74. AREA A rectangle is bounded by the x- and y-axes and the graph of $y = -\dfrac{1}{2}x + 4$.

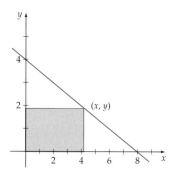

a. Find the area of the rectangle as a function of x. $A(x) = -\dfrac{1}{2}x^2 + 4x$

b. Complete the table below.

x	Area
1	3.5
2	6
4	8
6	6
7	3.5

c. What is the domain of this function?
(0, 8)

75. AREA A piece of wire 20 centimeters long is cut at a point x centimeters from the left end. The left-hand piece is formed into the shape of a circle and the right-hand piece is formed into a square.

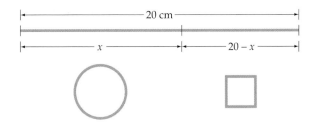

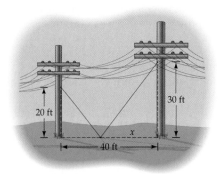

a. Find the area enclosed by the two figures as a function of x.
$$L(x) = \left(\frac{1}{4\pi} + \frac{1}{16}\right)x^2 - \frac{5}{2}x + 25$$

b. Complete the table below. Round the area to the nearest hundredth.

x	Total Area Enclosed
0	25
4	17.27
8	14.09
12	15.46
16	21.37
20	31.83

c. What is the domain of this function?
$[0, 20]$

76. AREA A triangle is bounded by the x- and y-axes and must pass through $P(2, 2)$, as shown below.

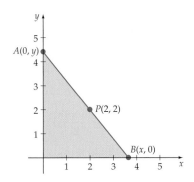

a. Find the area of the triangle as a function of x. (*Suggestion:* The slope of the line between points A and P equals the slope of the line between P and B.) $A(x) = \dfrac{x^2}{x-2}$

b. What is the domain of the function you found in part **a.**?
$(2, \infty)$

77. LENGTH Two guy wires are attached to utility poles that are 40 feet apart, as shown in the following diagram.

a. Find the total length of the two guy wires as a function of x.
$$A(x) = \sqrt{900 + x^2} + \sqrt{400 + (40 - x)^2}$$

b. Complete the table below. Round the length to the nearest hundredth.

x	Total Length of Wires
0	74.72
10	67.68
20	64.34
30	64.79
40	70

c. What is the domain of this function?
$(0, 40)$

78. SALES VS. PRICE A business finds that the number of feet f of pipe it can sell per week is a function of the price p in cents per foot as given by

$$f(p) = \frac{320,000}{p + 25}, \quad 40 \le p \le 90$$

Complete the following table by evaluating f (to the nearest hundred feet) for the indicated values of p.
4900, 4300, 3800, 3200, 2800

p	40	50	60	75	90
$f(p)$					

79. MODEL YIELD The yield Y of apples per tree is related to the amount x of a particular type of fertilizer applied (in pounds per year) by the function

$$Y(x) = 400[1 - 5(x - 1)^{-2}], \quad 5 \le x \le 20$$

Complete the following table by evaluating Y (to the nearest apple) for the indicated applications.
275, 375, 385, 390, 394

x	5	10	12.5	15	20
$Y(x)$					

80. MODEL COST A manufacturer finds that the cost C in dollars of producing x items of a product is given by

$$C(x) = \left(225 + 1.4\sqrt{x}\right)^2, \quad 100 \le x \le 1000$$

Complete the following table by evaluating C (to the nearest dollar) for the indicated numbers of items.
57,121, 59,927, 65,692, 69,348, 72,507

x	100	200	500	750	1000
$C(x)$					

81. If $f(x) = x^2 - x - 5$ and $f(c) = 1$, find c.
$c = -2$ or $c = 3$

82. If $g(x) = -2x^2 + 4x - 1$ and $g(c) = -4$, find c.
$c = \dfrac{2 \pm \sqrt{10}}{2}$

83. Determine whether 1 is in the range of $f(x) = \dfrac{x-1}{x+1}$.
1 is not in the range of f.

84. Determine whether 0 is in the range of $g(x) = \dfrac{1}{x-3}$.
0 is not in the range of $g(x)$.

In Exercises 85 to 90, use a graphing utility.

85. Graph $f(x) = \dfrac{[\![x]\!]}{|x|}$ for $-4.7 \le x \le 4.7$ and $x \ne 0$.

86. Graph $f(x) = \dfrac{[\![2x]\!]}{|x|}$ for $-4 \le x \le 4$ and $x \ne 0$.

87. Graph: $f(x) = x^2 - 2|x| - 3$

88. Graph: $f(x) = x^2 - |2x - 3|$

89. Graph: $f(x) = |x^2 - 1| - |x - 2|$

90. Graph: $f(x) = |x^2 - 2x| - 3$

CONNECTING CONCEPTS

The notation $f(x)\big|_a^b$ is used to denote the difference $f(b) - f(a)$. That is,

$$f(x)\big|_a^b = f(b) - f(a)$$

In Exercises 91 to 94, evaluate $f(x)\big|_a^b$ for the given function f and the indicated values of a and b.

91. $f(x) = x^2 - x; f(x)\big|_2^3$
4

92. $f(x) = -3x + 2; f(x)\big|_4^7$
-9

93. $f(x) = 2x^3 - 3x^2 - x; f(x)\big|_0^2$
2

94. $f(x) = \sqrt{8 - x}; f(x)\big|_0^8$
$-2\sqrt{2}$

In Exercises 95 to 98, each function has two or more independent variables.

95. Given $f(x, y) = 3x + 5y - 2$, find

a. $f(1, 7)$
36

b. $f(0, 3)$
13

c. $f(-2, 4)$
12

d. $f(4, 4)$
30

e. $f(k, 2k)$
$13k - 2$

f. $f(k + 2, k - 3)$
$8k - 11$

96. Given $g(x, y) = 2x^2 - |y| + 3$, find

a. $g(3, -4)$
17

b. $g(-1, 2)$
3

c. $g(0, -5)$
-2

d. $g\left(\dfrac{1}{2}, -\dfrac{1}{4}\right)$
$\dfrac{13}{4}$

e. $g(c, 3c), c > 0$
$2c^2 - 3c + 3, (|3c| = 3c$ since $c > 0)$

f. $g(c + 5, c - 2), c < 0$
$2c^2 + 21c + 51$

97. AREA OF A TRIANGLE The area of a triangle with sides a, b, and c is given by the function

$$A(a, b, c) = \sqrt{s(s - a)(s - b)(s - c)}$$

where s is the semiperimeter

$$s = \dfrac{a + b + c}{2}$$

Find $A(5, 8, 11)$.
$4\sqrt{21}$

98. COST OF A PAINTER The cost in dollars to hire a house painter is given by the function

$$C(h, g) = 15h + 14g$$

where h is the number of hours it takes to paint the house and g is the number of gallons of paint required to paint the house. Find $C(18, 11)$.
$424

A *fixed point* of a function is a number a such that $f(a) = a$. In Exercises 99 and 100, find all fixed points for the given function.

99. $f(x) = x^2 + 3x - 3$
1, −3

100. $g(x) = \dfrac{x}{x + 5}$
0, −4

In Exercises 101 and 102, sketch the graph of the piecewise-defined function.

101. $s(x) = \begin{cases} 1 & \text{if } x \text{ is an integer} \\ 2 & \text{if } x \text{ is not an integer} \end{cases}$

102. $v(x) = \begin{cases} 2x - 2 & \text{if } x \neq 3 \\ 1 & \text{if } x = 3 \end{cases}$

PREPARE FOR SECTION 2.3

103. Find the distance on a real number line between the points whose coordinates are −2 and 5. [P.1]
7

104. Find the product of a nonzero number and its negative reciprocal. [P.5]
−1

105. Given the points $P_1(-3, 4)$ and $P_2(2, -4)$, evaluate $\dfrac{y_2 - y_1}{x_2 - x_1}$.
[P.1] $-\dfrac{8}{5}$

106. Solve $y - 3 = -2(x - 3)$ for y. [1.1]
$y = -2x + 9$

107. Solve $3x - 5y = 15$ for y. [1.1] $y = \dfrac{3}{5}x - 3$

108. Given $y = 3x - 2(5 - x)$, find the value of x for which $y = 0$. [1.1]
2

PROJECTS

1. **DAY OF THE WEEK** A formula known as Zeller's Congruence makes use of the greatest integer function $[\![x]\!]$ to determine the day of the week on which a given day fell or will fall. To use Zeller's Congruence, we first compute the integer z given by

$$z = \left[\!\!\left[\frac{13m - 1}{5} \right]\!\!\right] + \left[\!\!\left[\frac{y}{4} \right]\!\!\right] + \left[\!\!\left[\frac{c}{4} \right]\!\!\right] + d + y - 2c$$

The variables c, y, d, and m are defined as follows:

$c =$ the century
$y =$ the year of the century
$d =$ the day of the month
$m =$ the month, using 1 for March, 2 for April, . . . , 10 for December. January and February are assigned the values 11 and 12 of the previous year.

For example, for the date September 12, 2001, we use $c = 20$, $y = 1$, $d = 12$, and $m = 7$. The remainder of z divided by 7 gives the day of the week. A remainder of 0 represents a Sunday, a remainder of 1 a Monday, . . . , and a remainder of 6 a Saturday.

a. Verify that December 7, 1941 was a Sunday.

b. Verify that January 1, 2010 will fall on a Friday.

c. Determine on what day of the week Independence Day (July 4, 1776) fell.

d. Determine on what day of the week you were born.

| SECTION **2.3** | **LINEAR FUNCTIONS** |

The following function has many applications.

Definition of a Linear Function

A function of the form

$$f(x) = mx + b, \quad m \neq 0$$

where m and b are real numbers, is a **linear function** of x.

● SLOPES OF LINES

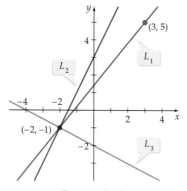

FIGURE 2.36

The graph of $f(x) = mx + b$, or $y = mx + b$, is a nonvertical straight line.

The graphs shown in **Figure 2.36** are the graphs of $f(x) = mx + b$ for various values of m. The graphs intersect at the point $(-2, -1)$, but they differ in *steepness*. The steepness of a line is called the *slope* of the line and is denoted by the symbol m. The slope of a line is the ratio of the change in the y values of any two points on the line to the change in the x values of the same two points. For example, the graph of the line L_1 in **Figure 2.36** passes through the points $(-2, -1)$ and $(3, 5)$. The change in the y values is determined by subtracting the two y-coordinates.

$$\text{Change in } y = 5 - (-1) = 6$$

The change in the x values is determined by subtracting the two x-coordinates.

$$\text{Change in } x = 3 - (-2) = 5$$

The slope m of L_1 is the ratio of the change in the y values of the two points to the change in the x values of the two points. That is,

$$m = \frac{\text{change in } y}{\text{change in } x} = \frac{6}{5}$$

Because the slope of a nonvertical line can be calculated by using any two arbitrary points on the line, we have the following formula.

Slope of a Nonvertical Line

The **slope** m of the line passing through the points $P_1(x_1, y_1)$ and $P_2(x_2, y_2)$ with $x_1 \neq x_2$ is given by

$$m = \frac{y_2 - y_1}{x_2 - x_1}$$

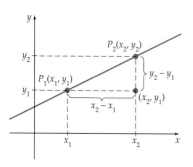

FIGURE 2.37

Because the numerator $y_2 - y_1$ is the vertical **rise** and the denominator $x_2 - x_1$ is the horizontal **run** from P_1 to P_2, slope is often referred to as the *rise over the run* or the *change in y divided by the change in x*. See **Figure 2.37**. Lines that have a positive slope slant upward from left to right. Lines that have a negative slope slant downward from left to right.

Alternative to Example 1
Find the slope of the line passing through
the points whose coordinates are given.
a. $(3, 4)$ and $(5, 10)$
⊙ $m = 3$
b. $(-4, -3)$ and $(1, -2)$
⊙ $m = \dfrac{1}{5}$

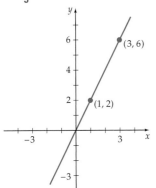

FIGURE 2.38

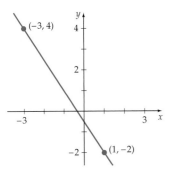

FIGURE 2.39

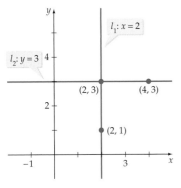

FIGURE 2.40

EXAMPLE 1   **Find the Slope of a Line**

Find the slope of the line passing through the points whose coordinates are given.

a. $(1, 2)$ and $(3, 6)$ **b.** $(-3, 4)$ and $(1, -2)$

Solution

a.   The slope of the line passing through $(1, 2)$ and $(3, 6)$ is

$$m = \frac{y_2 - y_1}{x_2 - x_1} = \frac{6 - 2}{3 - 1} = \frac{4}{2} = 2$$

Because $m > 0$, the line slants upward from left to right. See **Figure 2.38**.

b.   The slope of the line passing through $(-3, 4)$ and $(1, -2)$ is

$$m = \frac{y_2 - y_1}{x_2 - x_1} = \frac{-2 - 4}{1 - (-3)} = \frac{-6}{4} = -\frac{3}{2}$$

Because $m < 0$, the line slants downward from left to right. See **Figure 2.39**.

▶ **TRY EXERCISE 2, PAGE 207**

The definition of slope does not apply to vertical lines. Consider, for example, the points $(2, 1)$ and $(2, 3)$ on the vertical line l_1 in **Figure 2.40**. Applying the definition of slope to this line produces

$$m = \frac{3 - 1}{2 - 2}$$

which is undefined because it requires division by zero. Because division by zero is undefined, we say that the slope of any vertical line is undefined.

Every point on the vertical line through $(a, 0)$ has an x-coordinate of a. The equation of the vertical line through $(a, 0)$ is $x = a$. See **Figure 2.41**.

❓ QUESTION Is the graph of a vertical line the graph of a function?

All horizontal lines have 0 slope. For example, the line l_2 through $(2, 3)$ and $(4, 3)$ in **Figure 2.40** is a horizontal line. Its slope is given by

$$m = \frac{3 - 3}{4 - 2} = \frac{0}{2} = 0$$

When computing the slope of a line, it does not matter which point we label P_1 and which P_2 because

$$\frac{y_2 - y_1}{x_2 - x_1} = \frac{y_1 - y_2}{x_1 - x_2}$$

❓ ANSWER   No. For example, the vertical line passing through $x = 2$ contains the ordered pairs $(2, 3)$ and $(2, -5)$. Thus there are two ordered pairs with the same first coordinate but different second coordinates.

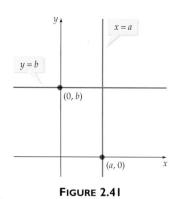

FIGURE 2.41

In functional notation, the points P_1 and P_2 can be represented by

$$(x_1, f(x_1)) \qquad \text{and} \qquad (x_2, f(x_2))$$

In this notation, the slope formula

$$m = \frac{y_2 - y_1}{x_2 - x_1} \qquad \text{is expressed as} \qquad m = \frac{f(x_2) - f(x_1)}{x_2 - x_1} \qquad (1)$$

If $m = 0$, then $f(x) = mx + b$ can be written as $f(x) = b$, or $y = b$. The graph of $y = b$ is the horizontal line through $(0, b)$. See **Figure 2.41**. Because every point on the graph of $y = b$ has a y-coordinate of b, the function $f(x) = b$ is called a **constant function.**

Horizontal Lines and Vertical Lines

The graph of $x = a$ is a vertical line through $(a, 0)$.

The graph of $y = b$ is a horizontal line through $(0, b)$.

The equation $f(x) = mx + b$ is called the **slope-intercept form** of the equation of a line because of the following theorem.

Slope-Intercept Form

The graph of $f(x) = mx + b$ is a line with slope m and y-intercept $(0, b)$.

Proof   The slope of the graph of $f(x) = mx + b$ is given by Equation (1).

$$\frac{f(x_2) - f(x_1)}{x_2 - x_1} = \frac{(mx_2 + b) - (mx_1 + b)}{x_2 - x_1} = \frac{m(x_2 - x_1)}{x_2 - x_1} = m, \quad x_1 \neq x_2$$

The y-intercept of the graph of $f(x) = mx + b$ is found by letting $x = 0$.

$$f(0) = m(0) + b = b$$

Thus $(0, b)$ is the y-intercept, and m is the slope, of the graph of $f(x) = mx + b$.   ◆

If a function is written in the form $f(x) = mx + b$, then its graph can be drawn by first plotting the y-intercept $(0, b)$ and then using the slope m to determine another point on the line.

Alternative to Example 2
Graph: $f(x) = -3x + 4$

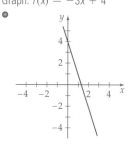

EXAMPLE 2   Graph a Linear Function

Graph: $f(x) = 2x - 1$

Solution

The equation $y = 2x - 1$ is in slope-intercept form, with $b = -1$ and $m = 2$. Thus the y-intercept is $(0, -1)$, and the slope is 2. Write the slope as

$$m = \frac{2}{1} = \frac{\text{change in } y}{\text{change in } x}$$

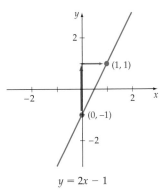

$y = 2x - 1$

FIGURE 2.42

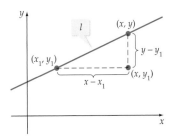

The slope of line l is $m = \dfrac{y - y_1}{x - x_1}$.

FIGURE 2.43

To graph the equation, first plot the y-intercept, and then use the slope to plot a second point. This second point is 2 units up (change in y) and 1 unit to the right (change in x) of the y-intercept. See **Figure 2.42.**

▶ TRY EXERCISE 16, PAGE 208

● FIND THE EQUATION OF A LINE

We can find an equation of a line provided we know its slope and at least one point on the line. **Figure 2.43** suggests that if (x_1, y_1) is a point on a line l of slope m, and (x, y) is *any other* point on the line, then

$$\frac{y - y_1}{x - x_1} = m, \quad x \neq x_1$$

Multiplying each side by $x - x_1$ produces $y - y_1 = m(x - x_1)$. This equation is called the **point-slope form** of the equation of line l.

Point-Slope Form

The graph of

$$y - y_1 = m(x - x_1)$$

is a line that has slope m and passes through (x_1, y_1).

Alternative to Example 3

Find the equation of the line with slope $\dfrac{2}{3}$ that passes through $(-3, 4)$.

● $y = \dfrac{2}{3}x + 6$

take note

To determine an equation of a nonvertical line that passes through two points, first determine the slope of the line and then use the coordinates of either one of the points in the point-slope form.

EXAMPLE 3   **Use the Point-Slope Form**

Find an equation of the line with slope -3 that passes through $(-1, 4)$.

Solution

Use the point-slope form with $m = -3$, $x_1 = -1$, and $y_1 = 4$.

$$y - y_1 = m(x - x_1)$$
$$y - 4 = -3[x - (-1)] \quad \text{• Substitute.}$$
$$y - 4 = -3x - 3 \quad \text{• Solve for y.}$$
$$y = -3x + 1 \quad \text{• Slope-intercept form}$$

▶ TRY EXERCISE 28, PAGE 208

An equation of the form $Ax + By = C$, where A, B, and C are real numbers and both A and B are not zero, is called the **general form of the equation of a line.** For example, the equation $y = -3x + 1$ in Example 3 can be written in general form as $3x + y = 1$.

take note

It is not always possible to solve a linear equation in general form for y in terms of x. For instance, the linear equation $x = 4$ is in general form with $A = 1$, $B = 0$, and $C = 4$.

One way to graph a linear equation that is written in general form is to first solve the equation for y in terms of x. For instance, to graph $3x - 2y = 4$, solve for y.

$$3x - 2y = 4$$
$$-2y = -3x + 4$$
$$y = \frac{3}{2}x - 2$$

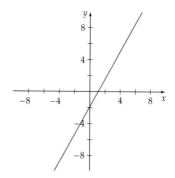

FIGURE 2.44

The y-intercept is $(0, -2)$ and the slope is $\frac{3}{2}$. The graph is shown in **Figure 2.44.**

By solving a first-degree equation, the specific relationship between an element of the domain and an element of the range of a linear function can be determined.

EXAMPLE 4   **Find the Value in the Domain of f for which $f(x) = b$**

Find the value x in the domain of $f(x) = 3x - 4$ for which $f(x) = 5$.

Algebraic Solution

Alternative to Example 4

Find the value of x in the domain of $f(x) = 5x + 12$ for which $f(x) = 2$.

● $x = -2$

$$f(x) = 3x - 4$$
$$5 = 3x - 4 \qquad \text{• Replace } f(x) \text{ by 5 and solve for } x.$$
$$9 = 3x$$
$$3 = x$$

When $x = 3$, $f(x) = 5$. This means that 3 in the domain of f is paired with 5 in the range of f. Another way of stating this is that the ordered pair $(3, 5)$ is an element of f.

Visualize the Solution

By graphing $y = 5$ and $f(x) = 3x - 4$, we can see that $f(x) = 5$ when $x = 3$.

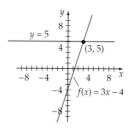

▶ **TRY EXERCISE 42, PAGE 208**

Although we are mainly concerned with linear functions in this section, the following theorem applies to all functions. It illustrates a powerful relationship between the real solutions of $f(x) = 0$ and the x-intercepts of the graph of $y = f(x)$.

Real Solutions and x-Intercepts Theorem

For every function f, the real number c is a solution of $f(x) = 0$ if and only if $(c, 0)$ is an x-intercept of the graph of $y = f(x)$.

❓ **QUESTION** Is $(-2, 0)$ an x-intercept of $f(x) = x^3 - x + 6$?

The real solutions and x-intercepts theorem tells us that we can find real solutions of $f(x) = 0$ by graphing. The following example illustrates the theorem for a linear function of x.

❓ **ANSWER** Yes. $f(-2) = (-2)^3 - (-2) + 6 = 0$

EXAMPLE 5   **Verify the Real Solutions and x-Intercepts Theorem**

Let $f(x) = -2x + 6$. Find the real solution of $f(x) = 0$ and then graph $f(x)$.
Compare the solution of $f(x) = 0$ with the x-intercept of the graph of f.

Algebraic Solution

To find the real solution of $f(x) = 0$, replace $f(x)$ by $-2x + 6$ and solve
for x.

$$f(x) = 0$$
$$-2x + 6 = 0$$
$$-2x = -6$$
$$x = 3$$

The x-coordinate of the x-intercept is 3. The real solution of $f(x) = 0$ is 3.

Alternative to Example 5
Let $f(x) = 2x + 4$. Find the real solution
of $f(x) = 0$ and then graph $y = f(x)$.
Compare the solution of $f(x) = 0$ with the
x-intercept of the graph of f.
● **The real solution of $f(x) = 0$ is**
$x = -2$, which is the x-coordinate of
the x-intercept, $(-2, 0)$.

▶ TRY EXERCISE 46, PAGE 208

Visualize the Solution

Graph $f(x) = -2x + 6$ (see
Figure 2.45).

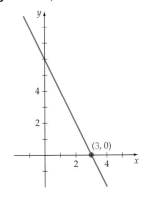

FIGURE 2.45
The x-intercept is $(3, 0)$.

EXAMPLE 6   **Solve $f_1(x) = f_2(x)$**

Let $f_1(x) = 2x - 1$ and $f_2(x) = -x + 11$. Find the values x for which $f_1(x) = f_2(x)$.

Algebraic Solution

$$f_1(x) = f_2(x)$$
$$2x - 1 = -x + 11$$
$$3x = 12$$
$$x = 4$$

When $x = 4$, $f_1(x) = f_2(x)$.

Alternative to Example 6
Let $f_1(x) = \dfrac{3}{2}x + 6$ and $f_2(x) = -2x - 1$.
Find the value of x for which $f_1(x) = f_2(x)$.

● **$x = -2$. Note that the point of**
intersection is $(-2, 3)$.

▶ TRY EXERCISE 50, PAGE 208

Visualize the Solution

The graphs of $y = f_1(x)$ and
$y = f_2(x)$ are shown on the
same coordinate axes (see
Figure 2.46). Note that the
point of intersection is $(4, 7)$.

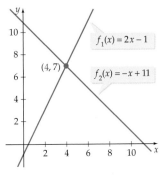

FIGURE 2.46

• APPLICATIONS

Alternative to Example 7
Exercise 58, page 209.

EXAMPLE 7 Find a Linear Model of Data

The bar graph in **Figure 2.47** is based on data from the Nevada Department of Motor Vehicles. The graph illustrates the distance (in feet) a car travels between the time (in seconds) a driver recognizes an emergency and the time the brakes are applied.

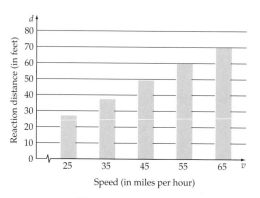

P **FIGURE 2.47**

a. Find a linear function that models the reaction distance in terms of the speed of the car by using the ordered pairs $(25, 27)$ and $(55, 60)$.

b. What reaction distance does the model predict for a car traveling at 50 miles per hour?

Solution

a. First, calculate the slope of the line. Then use the point-slope formula to find the equation of the line.

$$m = \frac{d_2 - d_1}{v_2 - v_1} = \frac{60 - 27}{55 - 25} = \frac{33}{30} = 1.1 \qquad \bullet \textbf{ Find the slope.}$$

$$d - d_1 = m(v - v_1) \qquad \bullet \textbf{ Use the point-slope formula.}$$

$$d - 27 = 1.1(v - 25) \qquad \bullet \, d_1 = 27,\, v_1 = 25,\, m = 1.1.$$

$$d = 1.1v - 0.5$$

In functional notation, the linear model is $d(v) = 1.1v - 0.5$.

b. To find the reaction distance for a car traveling at 50 miles per hour, evaluate $d(v)$ when $v = 50$.

$$d(v) = 1.1v - 0.5$$
$$d(50) = 1.1(50) - 0.5$$
$$= 54.5$$

The reaction distance is 54.5 feet.

▶ **TRY EXERCISE 56, PAGE 209**

If a manufacturer produces x units of a product that sells for p dollars per unit, then the **cost function** C, the **revenue function** R, and the **profit function** P are defined as follows:

$$C(x) = \text{cost of producing and selling } x \text{ units}$$

$$R(x) = xp = \text{revenue from the sale of } x \text{ units at } p \text{ dollars each}$$

$$P(x) = \text{profit from selling } x \text{ units}$$

Because profit equals the revenue less the cost, we have

$$P(x) = R(x) - C(x)$$

The value of x for which $R(x) = C(x)$ is called the **break-even point.** At the break-even point, $P(x) = 0$.

Alternative to Example 8

A manufacturer finds that the costs to manufacture and sell a calendar are $15,000 plus $2 per calendar.
a. Determine the profit function, P, given that x calendars are manufactured and sold at $12 each.
○ **$P(x) = 10x - 15,000$, $x \geq 0$ and x is an integer**
b. Determine the break-even point.
○ **1500 calendars**

EXAMPLE 8   **Find the Profit Function and the Break-even Point**

A manufacturer finds that the costs incurred in the manufacture and sale of a particular type of calculator are $180,000 plus $27 per calculator.

a.   Determine the profit function P, given that x calculators are manufactured and sold at $59 each.

b.   Determine the break-even point.

Solution

a.   The cost function is $C(x) = 27x + 180,000$. The revenue function is $R(x) = 59x$. Thus the profit function is

$$P(x) = R(x) - C(x)$$
$$= 59x - (27x + 180,000)$$
$$= 32x - 180,000, \quad x \geq 0 \text{ and } x \text{ is an integer}$$

b.   At the break-even point, $R(x) = C(x)$.

$$59x = 27x + 180,000$$
$$32x = 180,000$$
$$x = 5625$$

The manufacturer will break even when 5625 calculators are sold.

▶ **TRY EXERCISE 66, PAGE 211**

take note

The graphs of C, R, and P are shown below. Observe that the graphs of C and R intersect at the break-even point, where $x = 5625$ and $P(5625) = 0$.

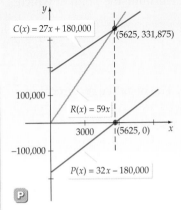

● **PARALLEL AND PERPENDICULAR LINES**

Two nonintersecting lines in a plane are **parallel.** All vertical lines are parallel to each other. All horizontal lines are parallel to each other.

Two lines are **perpendicular** if and only if they intersect and form adjacent angles each of which measures 90°. In a plane, vertical and horizontal lines are perpendicular to one another.

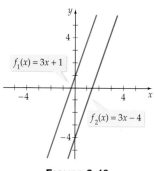

FIGURE 2.48

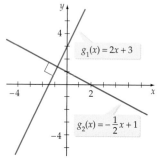

FIGURE 2.49

Parallel and Perpendicular Lines

Let l_1 be the graph of $f_1(x) = m_1 x + b$ and l_2 be the graph of $f_2(x) = m_2 x + b$. Then

- l_1 and l_2 are parallel if and only if $m_1 = m_2$.

- l_1 and l_2 are perpendicular if and only if $m_1 = -\dfrac{1}{m_2}$.

The graphs of $f_1(x) = 3x + 1$ and $f_2(x) = 3x - 4$ are shown in **Figure 2.48.** Because $m_1 = m_2 = 3$, the lines are parallel.

If $m_1 = -\dfrac{1}{m_2}$, then m_1 and m_2 are negative reciprocals of each other. The graphs

of $g_1(x) = 2x + 3$ and $g_2(x) = -\dfrac{1}{2}x + 1$ are shown in **Figure 2.49.** Because 2

and $-\dfrac{1}{2}$ are negative reciprocals of each other, the lines are perpendicular. The

symbol $\rceil$ indicates an angle of 90°. In **Figure 2.49** it is used to indicate that the lines are perpendicular.

Alternative to Example 9
A rock is whirled horizontally in a circular counterclockwise path with radius 4 feet, about the origin, O. When the string breaks, the rock travels on a linear path perpendicular to the radius $\overline{OP}$ and hits a wall located at $y = 9$ feet. If the string breaks when the rock is at $P(2$ feet, $2\sqrt{3}$ feet$)$, determine the point at which the rock hits the wall.

● $(8 - 9\sqrt{3}$ feet, 9 feet$)$

EXAMPLE 9   Determine a Point of Impact

A rock attached to a string is whirled horizontally in a circular counterclockwise path about the origin. When the string breaks, the rock travels on a linear path perpendicular to the radius $\overline{OP}$ and hits a wall located at

$$y = x + 12 \tag{2}$$

If the string breaks when the rock is at $P(4, 3)$, determine the point at which the rock hits the wall. See **Figure 2.50.**

Solution

The slope of the radius from $(0, 0)$ to $(4, 3)$ is $\dfrac{3}{4}$. The negative reciprocal of $\dfrac{3}{4}$

is $-\dfrac{4}{3}$. Therefore, the linear path of the rock is given by

$$y - 3 = -\frac{4}{3}(x - 4)$$

$$y = -\frac{4}{3}x + \frac{25}{3} \tag{3}$$

To find the point at which the rock hits the wall, set the right side of Equation (2) equal to the right side of Equation (3) and solve for x. This is the procedure explained in Example 6.

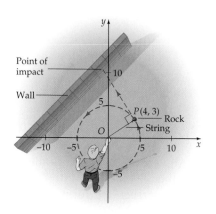

Ⓟ **FIGURE 2.50**

$$-\frac{4}{3}x + \frac{25}{3} = x + 12$$

$$-4x + 25 = 3x + 36 \qquad \bullet \text{ Multiply all terms by 3.}$$

$$-7x = 11$$

$$x = -\frac{11}{7}$$

For every point on the wall, x and y are related by $y = x + 12$. Therefore, substituting $-\frac{11}{7}$ for x in $y = x + 12$ yields $y = -\frac{11}{7} + 12 = \frac{73}{7}$, and the rock hits the wall at $\left(-\frac{11}{7}, \frac{73}{7}\right)$.

▶ **TRY EXERCISE 78, PAGE 212**

TOPICS FOR DISCUSSION

1. Can the graph of a linear function contain points in only one quadrant? only two quadrants? only four quadrants?

2. Is a "break-even point" a point or a number? Explain.

3. Some perpendicular lines do not have the property that their slopes are negative reciprocals of each other. Characterize these lines.

4. Does the real solutions and x-intercepts theorem apply only to linear functions?

5. Explain why the function $f(x) = x$ is referred to as the identity function.

EXERCISE SET 2.3

—*Suggested Assignment: Exercises 1–91, every other odd; 93, 95–100.*
—*Answers to Exercises 15–26 are on pages AA4–AA5.*

In Exercises 1 to 10, find the slope of the line that passes through the given points.

1. $(3, 4)$ and $(1, 7)$ $-\frac{3}{2}$

 2. $(-2, 4)$ and $(5, 1)$ $-\frac{3}{7}$

3. $(4, 0)$ and $(0, 2)$ $-\frac{1}{2}$

4. $(-3, 4)$ and $(2, 4)$ 0

5. $(0, 0)$ and $(0, 4)$
    The line does not have slope.

6. $(0, 0)$ and $(3, 0)$
    0

7. $(-3, 4)$ and $(-4, -2)$ 6

8. $(-5, -1)$ and $(-3, 4)$ $\frac{5}{2}$

9. $\left(-4, \frac{1}{2}\right)$ and $\left(\frac{7}{3}, \frac{7}{2}\right)$ $\frac{9}{19}$

10. $\left(\frac{1}{2}, 4\right)$ and $\left(\frac{7}{4}, 2\right)$ $-\frac{8}{5}$

In Exercises 11 to 14, find the slope of the line that passes through the given points.

11. $(3, f(3))$ and $(3 + h, f(3 + h))$ $\frac{f(3 + h) - f(3)}{h}$

12. $(-2, f(-2 + h))$ and $(-2 + h, f(-2 + h))$ 0

13. $(0, f(0))$ and $(h, f(h))$ $\frac{f(h) - f(0)}{h}$

14. $(a, f(a))$ and $(a + h, f(a + h))$ $\frac{f(a + h) - f(a)}{h}$

In Exercises 15 to 26, graph y as a function of x by finding the slope and y-intercept of each line.

15. $y = 2x - 4$

▶ 16. $y = -x + 1$

17. $y = -\dfrac{1}{3}x + 4$

18. $y = \dfrac{2}{3}x - 2$

19. $y = 3$

20. $y = x$

21. $y = 2x$

22. $y = -3x$

23. $2x + y = 5$

24. $x - y = 4$

25. $4x + 3y - 12 = 0$

26. $2x + 3y + 6 = 0$

In Exercises 27 to 38, find the equation of the indicated line. Write the equation in the form y = mx + b.

27. y-intercept $(0, 3)$, slope 1
$y = x + 3$

▶ 28. y-intercept $(0, 5)$, slope -2
$y = -2x + 5$

29. y-intercept $\left(0, \dfrac{1}{2}\right)$, slope $\dfrac{3}{4}$ $y = \dfrac{3}{4}x + \dfrac{1}{2}$

30. y-intercept $\left(0, \dfrac{3}{4}\right)$, slope $-\dfrac{2}{3}$ $y = -\dfrac{2}{3}x + \dfrac{3}{4}$

31. y-intercept $(0, 4)$, slope 0
$y = (0)x + 4 = 4$

32. y-intercept $(0, -1)$, slope $\dfrac{1}{2}$
$y = \dfrac{1}{2}x - 1$

33. Through $(-3, 2)$, slope -4
$y = -4x - 10$

34. Through $(-5, -1)$, slope -3
$y = -3x - 16$

35. Through $(3, 1)$ and $(-1, 4)$ $y = -\dfrac{3}{4}x + \dfrac{13}{4}$

36. Through $(5, -6)$ and $(2, -8)$ $y = \dfrac{2}{3}x - \dfrac{28}{3}$

37. Through $(7, 11)$ and $(2, -1)$ $y = \dfrac{12}{5}x - \dfrac{29}{5}$

38. Through $(-5, 6)$ and $(-3, -4)$
$y = -5x - 19$

39. Find the value of x in the domain of $f(x) = 2x + 3$ for which $f(x) = -1$.
-2

40. Find the value of x in the domain of $f(x) = 4 - 3x$ for which $f(x) = 7$.
-1

41. Find the value of x in the domain of $f(x) = 1 - 4x$ for which $f(x) = 3$.
$-\dfrac{1}{2}$

▶ 42. Find the value of x in the domain of $f(x) = \dfrac{2x}{3} + 2$ for which $f(x) = 4$.
3

43. Find the value of x in the domain of $f(x) = 3 - \dfrac{x}{2}$ for which $f(x) = 5$.
-4

44. Find the value of x in the domain of $f(x) = 4x - 3$ for which $f(x) = -2$.
$\dfrac{1}{4}$

In Exercises 45 to 48, find the solution f(x) = 0. Verify that the solution of f(x) = 0 is the same as the x-coordinate of the x-intercept of the graph of y = f(x).

45. $f(x) = 3x - 12$
4

▶ 46. $f(x) = -2x - 4$
-2

47. $f(x) = \dfrac{1}{4}x + 5$
-20

48. $f(x) = -\dfrac{1}{3}x + 2$
6

In Exercises 49 to 52, solve $f_1(x) = f_2(x)$ by an algebraic method and by graphing.

49. $f_1(x) = 4x + 5$ $f_2(x) = x + 6$ $\dfrac{1}{3}$

▶ 50. $f_1(x) = -2x - 11$ $f_2(x) = 3x + 7$ $-\dfrac{18}{5}$

51. $f_1(x) = 2x - 4$ $f_2(x) = -x + 12$ $\dfrac{16}{3}$

52. $f_1(x) = \dfrac{1}{2}x + 5$ $f_2(x) = \dfrac{2}{3}x - 7$ 72

53. **OCEANOGRAPHY** The graph below shows the relationship between the speed of sound in water and the temperature of the water. Find the slope of this line, and write a sentence that explains the meaning of the slope in the context of this problem. $m = 2.875$. The value of the slope indicates that the speed of sound in water increases 2.875 ft/s for a one-degree increase in temperature.

54. **COMPUTER SCIENCE** The graph on the following page shows the relationship between the time, in seconds, it takes to download a file and the size of the file in megabytes. Find the slope of the line between the two points shown on the graph. Write a sentence that states the meaning of the slope in the context of this problem. $m = 0.04$. The value of the slope indicates that the file is being downloaded at 0.04 megabyte per second.

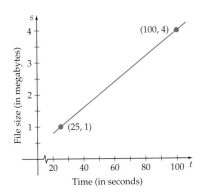

55. AUTOMOTIVE TECHNOLOGY The table below shows the EPA fuel economy values for selected two-seater cars for the 2003 model year. (*Source:* www.fueleconomy.gov.)

EPA Fuel Economy Values for Selected Two-Seater Cars

Car	City mpg	Highway mpg
Audi, TT Roadster	20	29
BMW, Z8	13	21
Ferrari, 360 Spider	11	16
Lamborghini, L-174	9	13
Lotus, Esprit V8	15	22
Maserati, Spider GT	11	17

a. Using the data for the Lamborghini and the Audi, find a linear function that predicts highway miles per gallon in terms of city miles per gallon. Round the slope to the nearest hundredth.
$H(c) = 1.45c$

b. Using your model, predict the highway miles per gallon for a Porsche Boxer, whose city fuel efficiency is 18 miles per gallon. Round to the nearest whole number.
26 mpg

▶ **56.** CONSUMER CREDIT The amount of revolving consumer credit (such as credit cards and department store cards) for the years 1997 to 2003 is given in the table below. (*Source:* www.nber.org, Board of Governor's of the Federal Reserve System.)

Year	Consumer Credit (in billions of $)
1997	531.0
1998	562.5
1999	598.0
2000	667.4
2001	701.3
2002	712.0
2003	725.0

a. Using the data for 1997 and 2003, find a linear model that predicts the amount of revolving consumer credit (in billions) for year t. Round the slope to the nearest tenth.
$C(t) = 32.3t - 64,038.7$

b. Using this model, in what year would consumer credit first exceed $850 billion?
2008

57. LABOR MARKET According to the Bureau of Labor Statistics (BLS), there were 38,000 desktop publishing jobs in the United States in the year 2000. The BLS projects that there will be 63,000 desktop publishing jobs in 2010.

a. Using the BLS data, find the number of desktop publishing jobs as a linear function of the year.
$N(t) = 2500t - 4,962,000$

b. Using your model, in what year will the number of desktop publishing jobs first exceed 60,000?
2008

58. POTTERY A piece of pottery is removed from a kiln and allowed to cool in a controlled environment. The temperature (in degrees Fahrenheit) of the pottery after it is removed from the kiln for various times (in minutes) is shown in the table below.

Time, min	Temperature, °F
15	2200
20	2150
30	2050
60	1750

a. Find a linear model for the temperature of the pottery after t minutes.
$T(t) = -10t + 2350$

b. Explain the meaning of the slope of this line in the context of the problem. The value of the slope means that the temperature is decreasing at a rate of 10 degrees per minute.

c. Assuming temperature continues to decrease at the same rate, what will be the temperature of the pottery in 3 hours?
550°F

59. LUMBER INDUSTRY For a log, the number of board-feet (bf) that can be obtained from the log depends on the diameter, in inches, of the log and its length. The table below shows the number of board-feet of lumber that can be obtained from a log that is 32 feet long.

Diameter, inches	bf
16	180
18	240
20	300
22	360

a. Find a linear model for the number of board-feet as a function of tree diameter.
$B(d) = 30d - 300$

b. Write a sentence explaining the meaning of the slope of this line in the context of the problem.
The value of the slope means that a 1-inch increase in the diameter of a log 32 ft long results in an increase of 30 board-feet of lumber that can be obtained from the log.

c. Using this model, how many board-feet of lumber can be obtained from a log 32 feet long with a diameter of 19 inches?
270 board-feet

60. ECOLOGY The rate at which water evaporates from a certain reservoir depends on air temperature. The table below shows the number of acre-feet (af) of water per day that evaporate from the reservoir for various temperatures in degrees Fahrenheit.

Temperature, °F	af
40	800
60	1640
70	2060
85	2690

a. Find a linear model for the number of acre-feet of water that evaporate as a function of temperature.
$E(T) = 42T - 880$

b. Write a sentence that explains the meaning of the slope of this line in the context of this problem.
The value of the slope means that an additional 42 acre-feet of water evaporate for a one degree increase in temperature.

c. Assuming that water continues to evaporate at the same rate, how many acre-feet of water will evaporate per day when the temperature is 75°F?
2270 acre-feet

61. CYCLING SPEEDS Michelle and Amanda start from the same place on a cycling course. Michelle is riding at 15 miles per hour and Amanda is cycling at 12 miles per hour. The graphs below show the total distance traveled by each cyclist and the total distance between Michelle and Amanda after t hours. Which graphs represent which distances? line A: Michelle; line B: Amanda; line C: distance between Michelle and Amanda

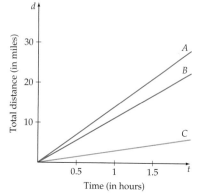

62. TEMPERATURE The graph below shows the temperature changes, in degrees Fahrenheit, over a 12-hour period at a weather station.

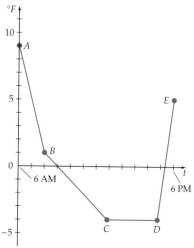

a. How many degrees per hour did the temperature change between A and B?
−4°F

b. Between which two points did the temperature change most rapidly?
D and E

c. Between which two points was the temperature constant?
C and D

63. HEALTH Framingham Heart Study is an ongoing research project that is attempting to identify risk factors associated with heart disease. Selected blood pressure data from that study is shown in the table at the right.

Selected Framingham Blood Pressure Statistics

Diastolic	Systolic
100	135
88	154
80	110
70	110
80	114
108	180
85	135
75	115

a. Find the equation of a linear model of this data, given that the graph of the line passes through $P_1(70, 110)$ and $P_2(108, 180)$.
$y = 1.842x - 18.947$

b. What systolic blood pressure does the model you found in part **a.** predict for a diastolic pressure of 90?
147

64. HEALTH The table on the following page shows average remaining lifetime, by age, of all people in the United States in 1997. (*Source:* National Institutes of Health)

Average Remaining Lifetime by Age in the United States

Current Age	Remaining Years
0	76.5
15	62.3
35	43.4
65	17.7
75	11.2

a. Find the equation of a linear model of this data, given that the graph of the line passes through $(0, 76.5)$ and $(75, 11.2)$.
$y = -0.87x + 76.5$

b. Based on your model, what is the average remaining lifetime of a person whose current age is 25?
55 years

In Exercises 65 to 68, determine the profit function for the given revenue function and cost function. Also determine the break-even point.

65. $R(x) = 92.50x; C(x) = 52x + 1782$
$P(x) = 40.50x - 1782$, $x = 44$, the break-even point

▶ **66.** $R(x) = 124x; C(x) = 78.5x + 5005$
$P(x) = 45.5x - 5005$, $x = 110$, the break-even point

67. $R(x) = 259x; C(x) = 180x + 10,270$
$P(x) = 79x - 10,270$, $x = 130$, the break-even point

68. $R(x) = 14,220x; C(x) = 8010x + 1,602,180$
$P(x) = 6210x - 1,602,180$, $x = 258$, the break-even point

69. MARGINAL COST In business, *marginal cost* is a phrase used to represent the rate of change or slope of a cost function that relates the cost C to the number of units x produced. If a cost function is given by $C(x) = 8x + 275$, find

a. $C(0)$ **b.** $C(1)$ **c.** $C(10)$ **d.** marginal cost
275 283 355 8

70. MARGINAL REVENUE In business, *marginal revenue* is a phrase used to represent the rate of change or slope of a revenue function that relates the revenue R to the number of units x sold. If a revenue function is given by the function $R(x) = 210x$, find

a. $R(0)$ **b.** $R(1)$ **c.** $R(10)$ **d.** marginal revenue
0 210 2100 210

71. BREAK-EVEN POINT FOR A RENTAL TRUCK A rental company purchases a truck for $19,500. The truck requires an average of $6.75 per day in maintenance.

a. Find the linear function that expresses the total cost C of owning the truck after t days.
$C(t) = 19,500.00 + 6.75t$

b. The truck rents for $55.00 a day. Find the linear function that expresses the revenue R when the truck has been rented for t days.
$R(t) = 55.00t$

c. The profit after t days, $P(t)$, is given by the function $P(t) = R(t) - C(t)$. Find the linear function $P(t)$.
$P(t) = 48.25t - 19,500.00$

d. Use the function $P(t)$ that you obtained in **c.** to determine how many days it will take the company to break even on the purchase of the truck. Assume that the truck is always in use.
approximately 405 days

72. BREAK-EVEN POINT FOR A PUBLISHER A magazine company had a profit of $98,000 per year when it had 32,000 subscribers. When it obtained 35,000 subscribers, it had a profit of $117,500. Assume that the profit P is a linear function of the number of subscribers s.

a. Find the function P.
$P(s) = 6.5s - 110,000$

b. What will the profit be if the company obtains 50,000 subscribers?
$P(50,000) = \$215,000$

c. What is the number of subscribers needed to break even?
$s \approx 16,924$ subscribers

In Exercises 73 to 76, find the equation of the indicated line. Write the equation in the form $y = mx + b$.

73. Through $(1, 3)$ and parallel to $3x + 4y = -24$
$y = -\dfrac{3}{4}x + \dfrac{15}{4}$

74. Through $(2, -1)$ and parallel to $x + y = 10$ $y = -x + 1$

75. Through $(1, 2)$ and perpendicular to $x + y = 4$ $y = x + 1$

76. Through $(-3, 4)$ and perpendicular to $2x - y = 7$
$y = -\dfrac{1}{2}x + \dfrac{5}{2}$

77. POINT OF IMPACT A rock attached to a string is whirled horizontally, in a counterclockwise circular path with radius 5 feet, about the origin. When the string breaks, the rock travels on a linear path perpendicular to the radius $\overline{OP}$ and hits a wall located at $y = 10$ feet.

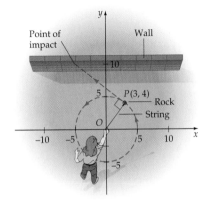

If the string breaks when the rock is at $P(3$ feet, 4 feet$)$, find the x-coordinate of the point at which the rock hits the wall.
$x = -5$

▶ **78.** POINT OF IMPACT A rock attached to a string is whirled horizontally, in a counterclockwise circular path with radius 4 feet, about the origin. When the string breaks, the rock travels on a linear path perpendicular to the radius $\overline{OP}$ and hits a wall located at $y = 14$ feet. If the string breaks when the rock is at $P(\sqrt{15}$ feet, 1 foot$)$, find the x-coordinate of the point at which the rock hits the wall.

$$x = \frac{2}{\sqrt{15}} \approx 0.52$$

79. SLOPE OF A SECANT LINE The graph of $y = x^2 + 1$ is shown below with $P(2, 5)$ and $Q(2 + h, [2 + h]^2 + 1)$ points on the graph.

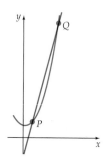

a. If $h = 1$, determine the coordinates of Q and the slope of the line PQ.
   $Q = (3, 10), m = 5$

b. If $h = 0.1$, determine the coordinates of Q and the slope of the line PQ.
   $Q = (2.1, 5.41), m = 4.1$

c. If $h = 0.01$, determine the coordinates of Q and the slope of the line PQ.
   $Q = (2.01, 5.0401), m = 4.01$

d. As h approaches 0, what value does the slope of the line PQ seem to be approaching?
   4

e. Verify that the slope of the line passing through $(2, 5)$ and $(2 + h, [2 + h]^2 + 1)$ is $4 + h$.

80. SLOPE OF A SECANT LINE The graph of $y = 3x^2$ is shown below with $P(-1, 3)$ and $Q(-1 + h, 3[-1 + h]^2)$ points on the graph.

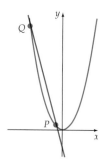

a. If $h = 1$, determine the coordinates of Q and the slope of the line PQ.
   $Q(0, 0), m = -3$

b. If $h = 0.1$, determine the coordinates of Q and the slope of the line PQ.
   $Q(-0.9, 2.43), m = -5.7$

c. If $h = 0.01$, determine the coordinates of Q and the slope of the line PQ.
   $Q(-0.99, 2.9403), m = -5.97$

d. As h approaches 0, what value does the slope of the line PQ seem to be approaching?
   -6

e. Verify that the slope of the line passing through $(-1, 3)$ and $(-1 + h, 3[-1 + h]^2)$ is $-6 + 3h$.
   $x_1 = -1, y_1 = 3, x_2 = -1 + h, y_2 = 3[-1 + h]^2, m = -6 + 3h$

81. Verify that the slope of the line passing through (x, x^2) and $(x + h, [x + h]^2)$ is $2x + h$.

82. Verify that the slope of the line passing through $(x, 4x^2)$ and $(x + h, 4[x + h]^2)$ is $8x + 4h$.

CONNECTING CONCEPTS

83. THE TWO-POINT FORM Use the point-slope form to derive the following equation, which is called the two-point form.

$$y - y_1 = \left(\frac{y_2 - y_1}{x_2 - x_1}\right)(x - x_1)$$

84. THE INTERCEPT FORM Use the two-point form from Exercise 83 to show that the line with intercepts $(a, 0)$ and $(0, b)$, $a \neq 0$ and $b \neq 0$, has the equation

$$\frac{x}{a} + \frac{y}{b} = 1$$

In Exercises 85 and 86, use the two-point form to find an equation of the line that passes through the indicated points. Write your answers in slope-intercept form.

85. $(5, 1), (4, 3)$
   $y = -2x + 11$

86. $(2, 7), (-1, 6)$
   $y = \frac{1}{3}x + \frac{19}{3}$

In Exercises 87 to 90, use the equation from Exercise 84 (called the intercept form) to write an equation of the line with the indicated intercepts.

87. x-intercept $(3, 0)$, y-intercept $(0, 5)$
   $5x + 3y = 15$

88. x-intercept $(-2, 0)$, y-intercept $(0, 7)$
   $-7x + 2y = 14$

89. x-intercept $(a, 0)$, y-intercept $(0, 3a)$, point on the line $(5, 2)$, $a \neq 0$
$3x + y = 17$

90. x-intercept $(-b, 0)$, y-intercept $(0, 2b)$, point on the line $(-3, 10)$, $b \neq 0$
$-2x + y = 16$

91. Verify that the slope of the line passing through $(1, 3)$ and $(1 + h, 3[1 + h]^3)$ is $9 + 9h + 3h^2$.

92. Find the two points on the circle given by $x^2 + y^2 = 25$ such that the slope of the radius from $(0, 0)$ to each point is 0.5. The points are $\left(2\sqrt{5}, \sqrt{5}\right)$ and $\left(-2\sqrt{5}, -\sqrt{5}\right)$.

93. Find a point $P(x, y)$ on the graph of the equation $y = x^2$ such that the slope of the line through the point $(3, 9)$ and P is $\dfrac{15}{2}$. $\left(\dfrac{9}{2}, \dfrac{81}{4}\right)$

94. Determine whether there is a point $P(x, y)$ on the graph of the equation $y = \sqrt{x + 1}$ such that the slope of the line through the point $(3, 2)$ and P is $\dfrac{3}{8}$. $\left(-\dfrac{5}{9}, \dfrac{2}{3}\right)$

PREPARE FOR SECTION 2.4

95. Factor: $3x^2 + 10x - 8$ [P.4]
$(3x - 2)(x + 4)$

96. Complete the square of $x^2 - 8x$. Write the resulting trinomial as the square of a binomial. [1.3]
$x^2 - 8x + 16 = (x - 4)^2$

97. Find $f(-3)$ for $f(x) = 2x^2 - 5x - 7$. [2.2]
26

In Exercises 98 and 99, solve for x.

98. $2x^2 - x = 1$ [1.3] $-\dfrac{1}{2}, 1$

99. $x^2 + 3x - 2 = 0$ [1.3] $\dfrac{-3 \pm \sqrt{17}}{2}$

100. Suppose that $h = -16t^2 + 64t + 5$. Find two values of t for which $h = 53$. [1.3] 1, 3

PROJECTS

1. VISUAL INSIGHT

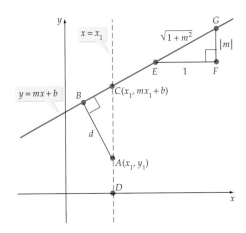

The distance d between the point $A(x_1, y_1)$ and the line given by $y = mx + b$ is $d = \dfrac{|mx_1 + b - y_1|}{\sqrt{1 + m^2}}$.

Write a paragraph that explains how to make use of the figure above to verify the formula for the distance d.

2. VERIFY GEOMETRIC THEOREMS

a. Prove that in any triangle, the line segment that joins the midpoints of two sides of the triangle is parallel to the third side. (*Hint:* Assign coordinates to the vertices of the triangle as shown in the figure at the left below.)

b. Prove that in any square, the diagonals are perpendicular bisectors of each other. (*Hint:* Assign coordinates to the vertices of the square as shown in the figure at the right below.)

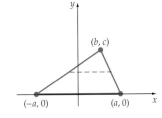

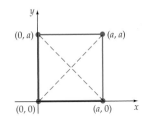

SECTION 2.4 · QUADRATIC FUNCTIONS

Some applications can be modeled by a *quadratic function*.

Definition of a Quadratic Function

A **quadratic function** of x is a function that can be represented by an equation of the form

$$f(x) = ax^2 + bx + c$$

where a, b, and c are real numbers and $a \neq 0$.

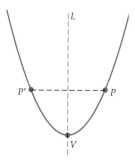

FIGURE 2.51

The graph of $f(x) = ax^2 + bx + c$ is a *parabola*. The graph opens up if $a > 0$, and it opens down if $a < 0$. The **vertex of a parabola** is the lowest point on a parabola that opens up or the highest point on a parabola that opens down. Point V is the vertex of the parabola in **Figure 2.51**.

The graph of $f(x) = ax^2 + bx + c$ is *symmetric* with respect to a vertical line through its vertex.

Definition of Symmetry with Respect to a Line

A graph is **symmetric with respect to a line** L if for each point P on the graph there is a point P' on the graph such that the line L is the perpendicular bisector of the line segment PP'.

> **take note**
>
> The axis of symmetry is a line. When asked to determine the axis of symmetry, the answer is an equation, not just a number.

In **Figure 2.51**, the parabola is symmetric with respect to the line L. The line L is called the **axis of symmetry**. The points P and P' are reflections or images of each other with respect to the axis of symmetry.

If $b = 0$ and $c = 0$, then $f(x) = ax^2 + bx + c$ simplifies to $f(x) = ax^2$. The graph of $f(x) = ax^2$ ($a \neq 0$) is a parabola with its vertex at the origin, and the y-axis is its axis of symmetry. The graph of $f(x) = ax^2$ can be constructed by plotting a few points and drawing a smooth curve that passes through these points, with the origin as the vertex and the y-axis as its axis of symmetry. The graphs of $f(x) = x^2$, $g(x) = 2x^2$, and $h(x) = -\dfrac{1}{2}x^2$ are shown in **Figure 2.52**.

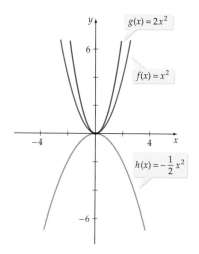

FIGURE 2.52

take note

The equation $z = x^2 - y^2$ defines z as a quadratic function of x and y. You might think that the graph of every quadratic function is a parabola. However, the graph of $z = x^2 - y^2$ is the saddle shown in the figure below. You will study quadratic functions involving two or more independent variables in calculus.

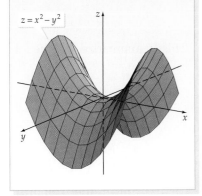

$z = x^2 - y^2$

Standard Form of Quadratic Functions

Every quadratic function f given by $f(x) = ax^2 + bx + c$ can be written in the **standard form of a quadratic function:**

$$f(x) = a(x - h)^2 + k, \quad a \neq 0$$

The graph of f is a parabola with vertex (h, k). The parabola opens up if $a > 0$, and it opens down if $a < 0$. The vertical line $x = h$ is the axis of symmetry of the parabola.

The standard form is useful because it readily gives information about the vertex of the parabola and its axis of symmetry. For example, note that the graph of $f(x) = 2(x - 4)^2 - 3$ is a parabola. The coordinates of the vertex are $(4, -3)$, and the line $x = 4$ is its axis of symmetry. Because a is the positive number 2, the parabola opens upward.

EXAMPLE 1 **Find the Standard Form of a Quadratic Function**

Use the technique of completing the square to find the standard form of $g(x) = 2x^2 - 12x + 19$. Sketch the graph.

Solution

$$
\begin{aligned}
g(x) &= 2x^2 - 12x + 19 \\
&= 2(x^2 - 6x) + 19 && \bullet \text{ Factor 2 from the variable terms.} \\
&= 2(x^2 - 6x + 9 - 9) + 19 && \bullet \text{ Complete the square.} \\
&= 2(x^2 - 6x + 9) - 2(9) + 19 && \bullet \text{ Regroup.} \\
&= 2(x - 3)^2 - 18 + 19 && \bullet \text{ Factor and simplify.} \\
&= 2(x - 3)^2 + 1 && \bullet \text{ Standard form}
\end{aligned}
$$

The vertex is $(3, 1)$. The axis of symmetry is $x = 3$. Because $a > 0$, the parabola opens up. See **Figure 2.53.**

▶ **TRY EXERCISE 10, PAGE 222**

Alternative to Example 1
Use the technique of completing the square to find the standard form of
$f(x) = 2x^2 - 4x - 1$.
● $f(x) = 2(x - 1)^2 - 3$

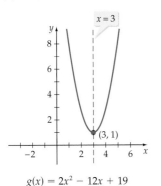

$g(x) = 2x^2 - 12x + 19$

FIGURE 2.53

● **VERTEX OF A PARABOLA**

We can write $f(x) = ax^2 + bx + c$ in standard form by completing the square of $ax^2 + bx + c$. This will allow us to derive a general expression for the x- and y-coordinates of the graph of $f(x) = ax^2 + bx + c$.

$$
\begin{aligned}
f(x) &= ax^2 + bx + c \\
&= a\left(x^2 + \frac{b}{a}x\right) + c && \bullet \text{ Factor } a \text{ from } ax^2 + bx. \\
&= a\left(x^2 + \frac{b}{a}x + \frac{b^2}{4a^2}\right) + c - \frac{b^2}{4a} && \bullet \text{ Complete the square by adding and} \\
& && \quad \text{subtracting } \left(\frac{1}{2} \cdot \frac{b}{a}\right)^2 = \frac{b^2}{4a^2}. \\
&= a\left(x + \frac{b}{2a}\right)^2 + \frac{4ac - b^2}{4a} && \bullet \text{ Factor and simplify.}
\end{aligned}
$$

Thus $f(x) = ax^2 + bx + c$ in standard form is $f(x) = a\left(x + \dfrac{b}{2a}\right)^2 + \dfrac{4ac - b^2}{4a}$. Comparing this last expression with $f(x) = a(x - h)^2 + k$, we see that the coordinates of the vertex are $\left(-\dfrac{b}{2a}, \dfrac{4ac - b^2}{4a}\right)$.

Note that by evaluating $f(x) = a\left(x + \dfrac{b}{2a}\right)^2 + \dfrac{4ac - b^2}{4a}$ at $x = -\dfrac{b}{2a}$, we have

$$f(x) = a\left(x + \frac{b}{2a}\right)^2 + \frac{4ac - b^2}{4a}$$

$$f\left(-\frac{b}{2a}\right) = a\left(-\frac{b}{2a} + \frac{b}{2a}\right)^2 + \frac{4ac - b^2}{4a} = a(0) + \frac{4ac - b^2}{4a}$$

$$= \frac{4ac - b^2}{4a}$$

That is, the y-coordinate of the vertex is $f\left(-\dfrac{b}{2a}\right)$. This is summarized by the following formula.

Vertex Formula

The coordinates of the vertex of $f(x) = ax^2 + bx + c$ are $\left(-\dfrac{b}{2a}, f\left(-\dfrac{b}{2a}\right)\right)$.

The vertex formula can be used to write the standard form of the equation of a parabola. We have

$$h = -\frac{b}{2a} \qquad \text{and} \qquad k = f\left(-\frac{b}{2a}\right)$$

Alternative to Example 2
Use the vertex formula to find the vertex and standard form of $f(x) = x^2 - 4x + 7$.
● vertex: (2, 3); standard form: $f(x) = (x - 2)^2 + 3$

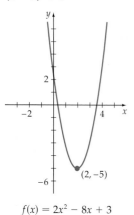

$f(x) = 2x^2 - 8x + 3$

FIGURE 2.54

EXAMPLE 2   **Find the Vertex and Standard Form of a Quadratic Function**

Use the vertex formula to find the vertex and standard form of $f(x) = 2x^2 - 8x + 3$. See **Figure 2.54.**

Solution

$$f(x) = 2x^2 - 8x + 3 \qquad \bullet\ a = 2,\ b = -8,\ c = 3$$

$$h = -\frac{b}{2a} = -\frac{-8}{2(2)} = 2 \qquad \bullet\ \textbf{x-coordinate of the vertex}$$

$$k = f\left(-\frac{b}{2a}\right) = 2(2)^2 - 8(2) + 3 = -5 \qquad \bullet\ \textbf{y-coordinate of the vertex}$$

The vertex is $(2, -5)$. Substituting into the standard form equation $f(x) = a(x - h)^2 + k$ yields the standard form $f(x) = 2(x - 2)^2 - 5$.

▶ **TRY EXERCISE 20, PAGE 223**

● MAXIMUM AND MINIMUM OF A QUADRATIC FUNCTION

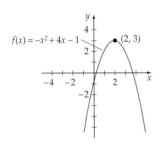

$f(x) = -x^2 + 4x - 1$ (2, 3)

Note from Example 2 that the graph of the parabola opens up, and the vertex is the *lowest* point on the graph of the parabola. Therefore, the y-coordinate of the vertex is the *minimum* value of that function. This information can be used to determine the range of $f(x) = 2x^2 - 8x + 3$. The range is $\{y \mid y \geq -5\}$. Similarly, if the graph of a parabola opened down, the vertex would be the *highest* point on the graph, and the y-coordinate of the vertex would be the *maximum* value of the function. For instance, the maximum value of $f(x) = -x^2 + 4x - 1$, graphed at the left, is 3, the y-coordinate of the vertex. The range of the function is $\{y \mid y \leq 3\}$. For the function in Example 2 and the function whose graph is shown at the left, the domain is the set of real numbers.

EXAMPLE 3   Find the Range of $f(x) = ax^2 + bx + c$

Find the range of $f(x) = -2x^2 - 6x - 1$. Determine the values of x for which $f(x) = 3$.

Algebraic Solution

To find the range of f, determine the y-coordinate of the vertex of the graph of f.

$$f(x) = -2x^2 - 6x - 1$$
• $a = -2, b = -6,$
  $c = -1$

$$h = -\frac{b}{2a} = -\frac{-6}{2(-2)} = -\frac{3}{2}$$
• Find the x-coordinate of the vertex.

$$k = f\left(-\frac{3}{2}\right) = -2\left(-\frac{3}{2}\right)^2 - 6\left(-\frac{3}{2}\right) - 1 = \frac{7}{2}$$
• Find the y-coordinate of the vertex.

The vertex is $\left(-\dfrac{3}{2}, \dfrac{7}{2}\right)$. Because the parabola opens down, $\dfrac{7}{2}$ is the maximum value of f. Therefore, the range of f is $\left\{y \mid y \leq \dfrac{7}{2}\right\}$.

    To determine the values of x for which $f(x) = 3$, replace $f(x)$ by $-2x^2 - 6x - 1$ and solve for x.

$$f(x) = 3$$
$$-2x^2 - 6x - 1 = 3$$
• Replace $f(x)$ by $-2x^2 - 6x - 1$.
$$-2x^2 - 6x - 4 = 0$$
• Solve for x.
$$-2(x + 1)(x + 2) = 0$$
• Factor.
$$x + 1 = 0 \text{ or } x + 2 = 0$$
• Use the Principle of Zero Products to solve for x.
$$x = -1 \qquad x = -2$$

The values of x for which $f(x) = 3$ are -1 and -2.

Visualize the Solution

The graph of f is shown below. The vertex of the graph is $\left(-\dfrac{3}{2}, \dfrac{7}{2}\right)$. Note that the line $y = 3$ intersects the graph of f when $x = -2$ and when $x = -1$.

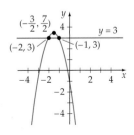

Alternative to Example 3 Find the range of $f(x) = 3x^2 - 12x + 13$. Determine the values of x for which $f(x) = 28$.
● The range is $\{y \mid y \geq 1\}$. The values of x for which $f(x) = 28$ are -1 and 5.

▶ **TRY EXERCISE 32, PAGE 223**

The following theorem can be used to determine the maximum value or the minimum value of a quadratic function.

> ### Maximum or Minimum Value of a Quadratic Function
>
> If $a > 0$, then the vertex (h, k) is the lowest point on the graph of $f(x) = a(x - h)^2 + k$, and the y-coordinate k of the vertex is the **minimum value** of the function f. See **Figure 2.55a.**
>
> If $a < 0$, then the vertex (h, k) is the highest point on the graph of $f(x) = a(x - h)^2 + k$, and the y-coordinate k is the **maximum value** of the function f. See **Figure 2.55b.**
>
> In either case, the maximum or minimum is achieved when $x = h$.

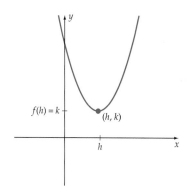

a. k is the minimum value of f.

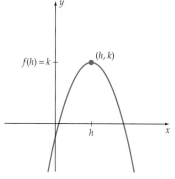

b. k is the maximum value of f.

FIGURE 2.55

Alternative to Example 4

Find the maximum or minimum value of each quadratic function. State whether the value is a maximum or a minimum.

a. $f(x) = \dfrac{1}{2}x^2 - 4x - 3$

- The minimum value is -11.

b. $g(x) = -4x^2 + 8x - 10$

- The maximum value is -6.

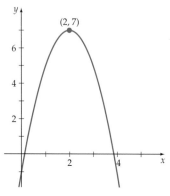

$F(x) = -2x^2 + 8x - 1$

FIGURE 2.56

EXAMPLE 4 Find the Maximum or Minimum of a Quadratic Function

Find the maximum or minimum value of each quadratic function. State whether the value is a maximum or a minimum.

a. $F(x) = -2x^2 + 8x - 1$ **b.** $G(x) = x^2 - 3x + 1$

Solution

The maximum or minimum value of a quadratic function is the y-coordinate of the vertex of the graph of the function.

a. $h = -\dfrac{b}{2a} = -\dfrac{8}{2(-2)} = 2$ • **x-coordinate of the vertex**

$k = F\left(-\dfrac{b}{2a}\right) = -2(2)^2 + 8(2) - 1 = 7$ • **y-coordinate of the vertex**

Because $a < 0$, the function has a maximum value but no minimum value. The maximum value is 7. See **Figure 2.56.**

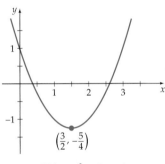

$G(x) = x^2 - 3x + 1$

FIGURE 2.57

b. $h = -\dfrac{b}{2a} = -\dfrac{-3}{2(1)} = \dfrac{3}{2}$ • **x-coordinate of the vertex**

$k = G\left(-\dfrac{b}{2a}\right) = \left(\dfrac{3}{2}\right)^2 - 3\left(\dfrac{3}{2}\right) + 1$

$= -\dfrac{5}{4}$ • **y-coordinate of the vertex**

Because $a > 0$, the function has a minimum value but no maximum value. The minimum value is $-\dfrac{5}{4}$. See **Figure 2.57**.

▶ **TRY EXERCISE 36, PAGE 223**

● **APPLICATIONS**

Alternative to Example 5
A home owner is enclosing a rectangular plot of ground for a garden. The home owner has 64 feet of fencing material to place around the perimeter of the garden. What dimensions would give the garden a maximum area?
● **16 ft by 16 ft**

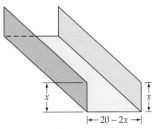

P **FIGURE 2.58**

EXAMPLE 5   **Find the Maximum of a Quadratic Function**

A long sheet of tin 20 inches wide is to be made into a trough by bending up two sides until they are perpendicular to the bottom. How many inches should be turned up so that the trough will achieve its maximum carrying capacity?

Solution

The trough is shown in **Figure 2.58**. If x is the number of inches to be turned up on each side, then the width of the base is $20 - 2x$ inches. The maximum carrying capacity of the trough will occur when the cross-sectional area is a maximum. The cross-sectional area $A(x)$ is given by

$$A(x) = x(20 - 2x) \qquad \text{• Area = (length)(width)}$$
$$= -2x^2 + 20x$$

To find the point at which A obtains its maximum value, find the x-coordinate of the vertex of the graph of A. Using the vertex formula with $a = -2$ and $b = 20$, we have

$$x = -\dfrac{b}{2a} = -\dfrac{20}{2(-2)} = 5$$

Therefore, the maximum carrying capacity will be achieved when 5 inches are turned up. See **Figure 2.59**.

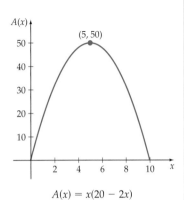

$A(x) = x(20 - 2x)$

FIGURE 2.59

▶ **TRY EXERCISE 46, PAGE 223**

Alternative to Example 6

A mining company has determined that the cost in dollars (c) per ton of mining a mineral is given by $c(x) = 0.2x^2 - 2x + 12$, where x is the number of tons of the mineral that is mined. Find the number of tons of the mineral that should be mined to minimize the cost. What is the minimum cost?

● **To minimize the cost, 5 tons should be mined. The minimum cost per ton is $7.**

EXAMPLE 6 **Solve a Business Application**

The owners of a travel agency have determined that they can sell all 160 tickets for a tour if they charge $8 (their cost) for each ticket. For each $0.25 increase in the price of a ticket, they estimate they will sell 1 ticket less. A business manager determines that their cost function is $C(x) = 8x$ and that the customer's price per ticket is

$$p(x) = 8 + 0.25(160 - x) = 48 - 0.25x$$

where x represents the number of tickets sold. Determine the maximum profit and the cost per ticket that yields the maximum profit.

Solution

The profit from selling x tickets is $P(x) = R(x) - C(x)$, where P, R, and C are the profit function, the revenue function, and the cost function as defined in Section 2.3. Thus

$$\begin{aligned} P(x) &= R(x) - C(x) \\ &= x[p(x)] - C(x) \\ &= x(48 - 0.25x) - 8x \\ &= 40x - 0.25x^2 \end{aligned}$$

The graph of the profit function is a parabola that opens down. Thus the maximum profit occurs when

$$x = -\frac{b}{2a} = -\frac{40}{2(-0.25)} = 80$$

The maximum profit is determined by evaluating $P(x)$ with $x = 80$.

$$P(80) = 40(80) - 0.25(80)^2 = 1600$$

The maximum profit is $1600.

To find the price per ticket that yields the maximum profit, we evaluate $p(x)$ with $x = 80$.

$$p(80) = 48 - 0.25(80) = 28$$

Thus the travel agency can expect a maximum profit of $1600 when 80 people take the tour at a ticket price of $28 per person. The graph of the profit function is shown in **Figure 2.60.**

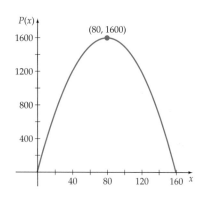

$$P(x) = 40x - 0.25x^2$$

FIGURE 2.60

❓ **QUESTION** In **Figure 2.60,** why have we shown only the portion of the graph that lies in quadrant I?

▶ **TRY EXERCISE 68, PAGE 225**

❓ **ANSWER** Since x represents the number of tickets sold, x must be greater than or equal to zero but less than or equal to 160. $P(x)$ is nonnegative for $0 \le x \le 160$.

Alternative to Example 7
The height of a ball thrown upward at an initial speed of 64 ft/s from a platform 50 ft above the ground is given by the function $s(t) = -16t^2 + 64t + 50$, where $s(t)$ is measured in feet above ground level and t is the time in seconds.

a. Determine the time it takes the ball to attain its maximum height.

⊙ **2 s**

b. Determine the maximum height the ball attains.

⊙ **114 ft**

c. Determine the time it takes the ball to hit the ground. Round to the nearest hundredth of a second.

⊙ **4.67 s**

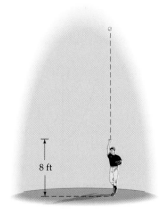

FIGURE 2.61

  To review **QUADRATIC FORMULA**, *see p. 107.*

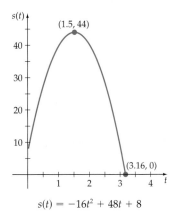

$s(t) = -16t^2 + 48t + 8$

FIGURE 2.62

EXAMPLE 7   **Solve a Projectile Application**

In **Figure 2.61,** a ball is thrown vertically upward with an initial velocity of 48 feet per second. If the ball started its flight at a height of 8 feet, then its height s at time t can be determined by $s(t) = -16t^2 + 48t + 8$, where $s(t)$ is measured in feet above ground level and t is the number of seconds of flight.

a.   Determine the time it takes the ball to attain its maximum height.

b.   Determine the maximum height the ball attains.

c.   Determine the time it takes the ball to hit the ground.

Solution

a.   The graph of $s(t) = -16t^2 + 48t + 8$ is a parabola that opens downward. See **Figure 2.62.** Therefore, s will attain its maximum value at the vertex of its graph. Using the vertex formula with $a = -16$ and $b = 48$, we get

$$t = -\frac{b}{2a} = -\frac{48}{2(-16)} = \frac{3}{2}$$

Therefore, the ball attains its maximum height $1\frac{1}{2}$ seconds into its flight.

b.   When $t = \frac{3}{2}$, the height of the ball is

$$s\left(\frac{3}{2}\right) = -16\left(\frac{3}{2}\right)^2 + 48\left(\frac{3}{2}\right) + 8 = 44 \text{ feet}$$

c.   The ball will hit the ground when its height $s(t) = 0$. Therefore, solve $-16t^2 + 48t + 8 = 0$ for t.

$$-16t^2 + 48t + 8 = 0$$
$$-2t^2 + 6t + 1 = 0 \qquad \bullet \text{ Divide each side by 8.}$$
$$t = \frac{-(6) \pm \sqrt{6^2 - 4(-2)(1)}}{2(-2)} \qquad \bullet \text{ Use the quadratic formula.}$$
$$= \frac{-6 \pm \sqrt{44}}{-4} = \frac{-3 \pm \sqrt{11}}{-2}$$

Using a calculator to approximate the positive root, we find that the ball will hit the ground in $t \approx 3.16$ seconds. This is also the value of the t-coordinate of the t-intercept in **Figure 2.62.**

▶ **TRY EXERCISE 70, PAGE 225**

TOPICS FOR DISCUSSION

1.   Does the graph of every quadratic function of the form

$$f(x) = ax^2 + bx + c$$

have a y-intercept? If so, what are the coordinates of the y-intercept?

2. The graph of $f(x) = -x^2 + 6x + 11$ has a vertex of $(3, 20)$. Is this vertex point the highest point or the lowest point on the graph of f?

3. A tutor states that the graph of $f(x) = ax^2 + bx + c$ $(a \neq 0)$ is a parabola and that its axis of symmetry is $y = -\dfrac{b}{2a}$. Do you agree?

4. Every quadratic function of the form $f(x) = ax^2 + bx + c$ has a domain of all real numbers. Do you agree?

5. A classmate states that the graph of every quadratic function of the form

$$f(x) = ax^2 + bx + c$$

must contain points from at least two quadrants. Do you agree?

EXERCISE SET 2.4

—Suggested Assignment: Exercises 1–73, every other odd; 75, 77, 79, 89–94.
—Answers to Exercises 9–18 and 25–28 are on page AA5.

In Exercises 1 to 8, match each graph in *a.* through *h.* with the proper quadratic function.

1. $f(x) = x^2 - 3$
d

2. $f(x) = x^2 + 2$
f

3. $f(x) = (x - 4)^2$
b

4. $f(x) = (x + 3)^2$
h

5. $f(x) = -2x^2 + 2$
g

6. $f(x) = -\dfrac{1}{2}x^2 + 3$
e

7. $f(x) = (x + 1)^2 + 3$
c

8. $f(x) = -2(x - 2)^2 + 2$
a

e.
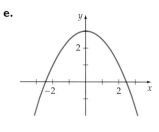

f.
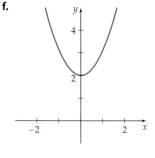

a.
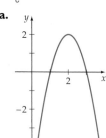

b.
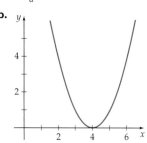

g.
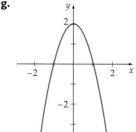

h.
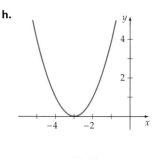

c.
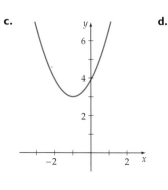

d.
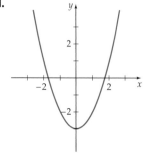

In Exercises 9 to 18, use the method of completing the square to find the standard form of the quadratic function, and then sketch its graph. Label its vertex and axis of symmetry.

9. $f(x) = x^2 + 4x + 1$

▶ **10.** $f(x) = x^2 + 6x - 1$

11. $f(x) = x^2 - 8x + 5$

12. $f(x) = x^2 - 10x + 3$

13. $f(x) = x^2 + 3x + 1$

14. $f(x) = x^2 + 7x + 2$

15. $f(x) = -x^2 + 4x + 2$ **16.** $f(x) = -x^2 - 2x + 5$

17. $f(x) = -3x^2 + 3x + 7$ **18.** $f(x) = -2x^2 - 4x + 5$

In Exercises 19 to 28, use the vertex formula to determine the vertex of the graph of the function and write the function in standard form.

vertex: $(3, -9)$, $f(x) = (x - 3)^2 - 9$

19. $f(x) = x^2 - 10x$ ▶ **20.** $f(x) = x^2 - 6x$
vertex: $(5, -25)$, $f(x) = (x - 5)^2 - 25$

21. $f(x) = x^2 - 10$ **22.** $f(x) = x^2 - 4$
vertex: $(0, -10)$, $f(x) = x^2 - 10$ vertex: $(0, -4)$, $f(x) = x^2 - 4$

23. $f(x) = -x^2 + 6x + 1$ **24.** $f(x) = -x^2 + 4x + 1$
vertex: $(3, 10)$, $f(x) = -(x - 3)^2 + 10$ vertex: $(2, 5)$, $f(x) = -(x - 2)^2 + 5$

25. $f(x) = 2x^2 - 3x + 7$ **26.** $f(x) = 3x^2 - 10x + 2$
Answer is on p. AA5.   Answer is on p. AA5.

27. $f(x) = -4x^2 + x + 1$ **28.** $f(x) = -5x^2 - 6x + 3$
Answer is on p. AA5.   Answer is on p. AA5.

29. Find the range of $f(x) = x^2 - 2x - 1$. Determine the values of x in the domain of f for which $f(x) = 2$.
$\{y\,|\,y \geq -2\}$, -1 and 3

30. Find the range of $f(x) = -x^2 - 6x - 2$. Determine the values of x in the domain of f for which $f(x) = 3$.
$\{y\,|\,y \leq 7\}$, -5 and -1

31. Find the range of $f(x) = -2x^2 + 5x - 1$. Determine the values of x in the domain of f for which $f(x) = 2$. $\left\{y\,\middle|\,y \leq \dfrac{17}{8}\right\}$, 1 and $\dfrac{3}{2}$

▶ **32.** Find the range of $f(x) = 2x^2 + 6x - 5$. Determine the values of x in the domain of f for which $f(x) = 15$. $\left\{y\,\middle|\,y \geq -\dfrac{19}{2}\right\}$, -5 and 2

33. Is 3 in the range of $f(x) = x^2 + 3x + 6$? Explain your answer. No, $3 \in \left\{y\,\middle|\,y \leq \dfrac{15}{4}\right\}$

34. Is -2 in the range of $f(x) = -2x^2 - x + 1$? Explain your answer. Yes, $-2 \in \left\{y\,\middle|\,y \leq \dfrac{9}{8}\right\}$

In Exercises 35 to 44, find the maximum or minimum value of the function. State whether this value is a maximum or a minimum.

35. $f(x) = x^2 + 8x$ ▶ **36.** $f(x) = -x^2 - 6x$
-16, minimum 9, maximum

37. $f(x) = -x^2 + 6x + 2$ **38.** $f(x) = -x^2 + 10x - 3$
11, maximum 22, maximum

39. $f(x) = 2x^2 + 3x + 1$ $-\dfrac{1}{8}$, minimum   **40.** $f(x) = 3x^2 + x - 1$ $-\dfrac{13}{12}$, minimum

41. $f(x) = 5x^2 - 11$ **42.** $f(x) = 3x^2 - 41$
-11, minimum -41, minimum

43. $f(x) = -\dfrac{1}{2}x^2 + 6x + 17$

35, maximum

44. $f(x) = -\dfrac{3}{4}x^2 - \dfrac{2}{5}x + 7$ $\dfrac{529}{75} = 7\dfrac{4}{75}$, maximum

45. HEIGHT OF AN ARCH The height of an arch is given by the equation

$$h(x) = -\frac{3}{64}x^2 + 27, \quad -24 \leq x \leq 24$$

where $|x|$ is the horizontal distance in feet from the center of the arch.

a. What is the maximum height of the arch?
27 ft

b. What is the height of the arch 10 feet to the right of center? $22\dfrac{5}{16}$ ft

c. How far from the center is the arch 8 feet tall?
$\approx$20.1 ft from the center

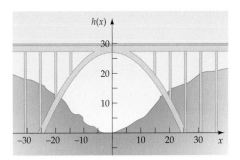

46. The sum of the length l and the width w of a rectangular area is 240 meters.

a. Write w as a function of l.
$w = 240 - l$

b. Write the area A as a function of l.
$A = 240l - l^2$

c. Find the dimensions that produce the greatest area.
$l = 120$ and $w = 120$ produce the greatest area

47. RECTANGULAR ENCLOSURE A veterinarian uses 600 feet of chain-link fencing to enclose a rectangular region and also to subdivide the region into two smaller rectangular regions by placing a fence parallel to one of the sides, as shown in the figure.

a. Write the width w as a function of the length l. $w = \dfrac{600 - 2l}{3}$

b. Write the total area A as a function of l. $A = 200l - \dfrac{2}{3}l^2$

c. Find the dimensions that produce the greatest enclosed area. $w = 100$ ft, $l = 150$ ft

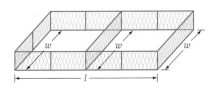

48. RECTANGULAR ENCLOSURE A farmer uses 1200 feet of fence to enclose a rectangular region and also to subdivide the region into three smaller rectangular regions by placing the fences parallel to one of the sides. Find the dimensions that produce the greatest enclosed area.

$w = 150$ ft and $l = 300$ ft

49. TEMPERATURE FLUCTUATIONS The temperature $T(t)$, in degrees Fahrenheit, during the day can be modeled by the equation $T(t) = -0.7t^2 + 9.4t + 59.3$, where t is the number of hours after 6:00 A.M.

a. At what time is the temperature a maximum? Round to the nearest minute.

12:43 P.M.

b. What is the maximum temperature? Round to the nearest degree.

91°F

50. LARVAE SURVIVAL Soon after insect larvae are hatched, they must begin to search for food. The survival rate of the larvae depends on many factors, but the temperature of the environment is one of the most important. For a certain species of insect, a model of the number of larvae, $N(T)$, that survive this searching period is given by

$$N(T) = -0.6T^2 + 32.1T - 350$$

where T is the temperature in degrees Celsius.

a. At what temperature will the maximum number of larvae survive? Round to the nearest degree.

27°C

b. What is the maximum number of surviving larvae? Round to the nearest whole number.

79 larvae

c. Find the x-intercepts, to the nearest whole number, for the graph of this function.

(15, 0) and (38, 0)

d. Write a sentence that describes the meaning of the x-intercepts in the context of this problem.

When the temperature is less than 15°C or greater than 38°C, none of the larvae survive.

51. REAL ESTATE The number of California homes that have sold for over $1,000,000 between 1989 and 2002 can be modeled by

$$N(t) = 1.43t^2 - 11.44t + 47.68$$

where $N(t)$ is the number (in hundreds) of homes that were sold in year t, with $t = 0$ corresponding to 1989. According to this model, in what year were the least number of million-dollar homes sold? How many million-dollar homes, to the nearest hundred, were sold that year?

1993, 2500 homes

52. GEOLOGY In June 2001, Mt. Etna in Sicily, Italy erupted, sending volcanic bombs (a mass of molten lava ejected from the volcano) into the air. A model of the height h, in meters, of a volcanic bomb above the crater of the volcano t seconds after the eruption is given by $h(t) = -9.8t^2 + 100t$. Find the maximum height of a volcanic bomb above the crater for this eruption. Round to the nearest meter.

255 m

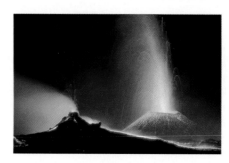

53. SPORTS For a serve to be legal in tennis, the ball must be at least 3 feet high when it is 39 feet from the server, and it must land in a spot that is less than 60 feet from the server. Does the path of a ball given by $h(x) = -0.002x^2 - 0.03x + 8$, where $h(x)$ is the height of the ball (in feet) x feet from the server, satisfy the conditions of a legal serve?

Yes

54. SPORTS A pitcher releases a baseball 6 feet above the ground at a speed of 132 feet per second (90 miles per hour) toward home plate which is 60.5 feet away. The height $h(x)$, in feet, of the ball x feet from home plate can be approximated by $h(x) = -0.0009x^2 + 6$. To be considered a strike, the ball must cross home plate and be at least 2.5 feet high and less than 5.4 feet high. Assuming the ball crosses home plate, is this particular pitch a strike? Explain.

Yes

55. AUTOMOTIVE ENGINEERING The fuel efficiency for a certain midsize car is given by

$$E(v) = -0.018v^2 + 1.476v + 3.4$$

where $E(v)$ is the fuel efficiency in miles per gallon for a car traveling v miles per hour.

a. What speed will yield the maximum fuel efficiency? Round to the nearest mile per hour.

41 mph

b. What is the maximum fuel efficiency for this car? Round to the nearest mile per gallon.

34 mpg

56. SPORTS Some football fields are built in a parabolic mound shape so that water will drain off the field. A model for the shape of a certain field is given by

$$h(x) = -0.0002348x^2 + 0.0375x$$

where $h(x)$ is the height, in feet, of the field at a distance of x feet from one sideline. Find the maximum height of the field. Round to the nearest tenth of a foot.
1.5 ft

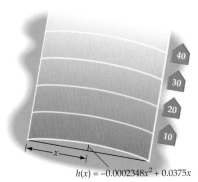

$h(x) = -0.0002348x^2 + 0.0375x$

In Exercises 57 to 60, determine the y- and x-intercepts (if any) of the quadratic function.   *y*-intercept (0, 0);
x-intercepts (0, 0) and (4, 0)

57. $f(x) = x^2 + 6x$ **58.** $f(x) = -x^2 + 4x$
y-intercept (0, 0); *x*-intercepts (0, 0) and (−6, 0)

59. $f(x) = -3x^2 + 5x - 6$ **60.** $f(x) = 2x^2 + 3x + 4$
y-intercept (0, −6); no *x*-intercepts   *y*-intercept (0, 4); no *x*-intercepts

In Exercises 61 and 62, determine the number of units x that produce a maximum revenue for the given revenue function. Also determine the maximum revenue.
675 units yield a maximum revenue of $273,375.

61. $R(x) = 296x - 0.2x^2$ **62.** $R(x) = 810x - 0.6x^2$
740 units yield a maximum revenue of $109,520.

In Exercises 63 and 64, determine the number of units x that produce a maximum profit for the given profit function. Also determine the maximum profit.

63. $P(x) = -0.01x^2 + 1.7x - 48$
85 units yield a maximum profit of $24.25.

64. $P(x) = -\dfrac{x^2}{14,000} + 1.68x - 4000$
11,760 units yield a maximum profit of $5878.40.

In Exercises 65 and 66, determine the profit function for the given revenue function and cost function. Also determine the break-even point(s).

65. $R(x) = x(102.50 - 0.1x)$; $C(x) = 52.50x + 1840$
$P(x) = -0.1x^2 + 50x - 1840$, break-even points: $x = 40$ and $x = 460$

66. $R(x) = x(210 - 0.25x)$; $C(x) = 78x + 6399$
$P(x) = -0.25x^2 + 132x - 6399$, break-even points: $x = 54$ and $x = 474$

67. TOUR COST A charter bus company has determined that the cost of providing x people a tour is

$$C(x) = 180 + 2.50x$$

A full tour consists of 60 people. The ticket price per person is $15 plus $0.25 for each unsold ticket. Determine

a. the revenue function   **b.** the profit function
$R(x) = -0.25x^2 + 30.00x$ $P(x) = -0.25x^2 + 27.50x - 180$

c. the company's maximum profit
$576.25

d. the number of ticket sales that yields the maximum profit
55 tickets

▶ **68. DELIVERY COST** An air freight company has determined that the cost, in dollars, of delivering x parcels per flight is

$$C(x) = 2025 + 7x$$

The price per parcel, in dollars, the company charges to send x parcels is

$$p(x) = 22 - 0.01x$$

Determine

a. the revenue function   **b.** the profit function
$R(x) = -0.01x^2 + 22x$ $P(x) = -0.01x^2 + 15x - 2025$

c. the company's maximum profit
$3600

d. the price per parcel that yields the maximum profit
$14.50

e. the minimum number of parcels the air freight company must ship to break even
150 parcels

69. PROJECTILE If the initial velocity of a projectile is 128 feet per second, then its height h in feet is a function of time t in seconds given by the equation $h(t) = -16t^2 + 128t$.

a. Find the time t when the projectile achieves its maximum height.
$t = 4$ s

b. Find the maximum height of the projectile.
256 ft

c. Find the time t when the projectile hits the ground.
$t = 8$ s

▶ **70. PROJECTILE** The height in feet of a projectile with an initial velocity of 64 feet per second and an initial height of 80 feet is a function of time t in seconds given by

$$h(t) = -16t^2 + 64t + 80$$

a. Find the maximum height of the projectile.
The vertex (2, 144) gives us the maximum height of 144 ft.

b. Find the time t when the projectile achieves its maximum height.
$t = 2$ s

c. Find the time t when the projectile has a height of 0 feet.
height of 0 ft at $t = 5$ s

71. FIRE MANAGEMENT The height of a stream of water from the nozzle of a fire hose can be modeled by

$$y(x) = -0.014x^2 + 1.19x + 5$$

where $y(x)$ is the height, in feet, of the stream x feet from the firefighter. What is the maximum height that the stream of water from this nozzle can reach? Round to the nearest foot.
30 ft

72. OLYMPIC SPORTS In 1988, Louise Ritter of the United States set the women's Olympic record for the high jump. A mathematical model that approximates her jump is given by

$$h(t) = -204.8t^2 + 256t$$

where $h(t)$ is her height in inches t seconds after beginning her jump. Find the maximum height of her jump.
80 in.

73. NORMAN WINDOW A Norman window has the shape of a rectangle surmounted by a semicircle. The exterior perimeter of the window shown in the figure is 48 feet. Find the height h and the radius r that will allow the maximum amount of light to enter the window. (*Hint:* Write the area of the window as a quadratic function of the radius r.) $r = \dfrac{48}{4 + \pi} \approx 6.72$ ft, $h = r \approx 6.72$ ft

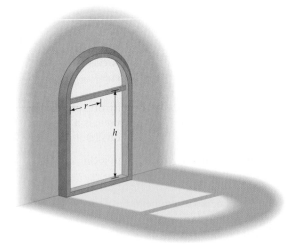

74. GOLDEN GATE BRIDGE The suspension cables of the main span of the Golden Gate Bridge are in the shape of a parabola. If a coordinate system is drawn as shown, find the quadratic function that models a suspension cable for the main span of the bridge. $f(x) = 0.000112018x^2 + 6$

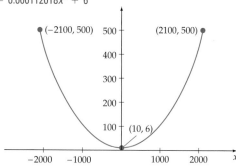

CONNECTING CONCEPTS

75. Let $f(x) = x^2 - (a + b)x + ab$, where a and b are real numbers.

   a. Show that the x-intercepts are $(a, 0)$ and $(b, 0)$.

   b. Show that the minimum value of the function occurs at the x-value of the midpoint of the line segment defined by the x-intercepts.

76. Let $f(x) = ax^2 + bx + c$, where $a, b,$ and c are real numbers.

   a. What conditions must be imposed on the coefficients so that f has a maximum?
   $a < 0$, b and c any real numbers

   b. What conditions must be imposed on the coefficients so that f has a minimum?
   $a > 0$, b and c any real numbers

   c. What conditions must be imposed on the coefficients so that the graph of f intersects the x-axis?
   $b^2 - 4ac > 0$

77. Find the quadratic function of x whose graph has a minimum at $(2, 1)$ and passes through $(0, 4)$. $f(x) = \dfrac{3}{4}x^2 - 3x + 4$

78. Find the quadratic function of x whose graph has a maximum at $(-3, 2)$ and passes through $(0, -5)$.
$f(x) = -\dfrac{7}{9}x^2 - \dfrac{14}{3}x - 5$

79. AREA OF A RECTANGLE A wire 32 inches long is bent so that it has the shape of a rectangle. The length of the rectangle is x and the width is w.

   a. Write w as a function of x.
   $w = 16 - x$

   b. Write the area A of the rectangle as a function of x.
   $A = 16x - x^2$

80. Maximize Area Use the function A from **b.** in Exercise 79 to prove that the area A is greatest if the rectangle is a square.

81. Show that the function $f(x) = x^2 + bx - 1$ has a real zero for any value b.
The discriminant is $b^2 - 4(1)(-1) = b^2 + 4$, which is positive for all b.

82. Show that the function $g(x) = -x^2 + bx + 1$ has a real zero for any value b.
The discriminant is $b^2 - 4(-1)(1) = b^2 + 4 > 0$.

83. What effect does increasing the constant c have on the graph of $f(x) = ax^2 + bx + c$?
increases the height of each point on the graph by c units

84. If $a > 0$, what effect does decreasing the coefficient a have on the graph of $f(x) = ax^2 + bx + c$?
shrinks the graph of the parabola toward the x-axis

85. Find two numbers whose sum is 8 and whose product is a maximum.
4, 4

86. Find two numbers whose difference is 12 and whose product is a minimum.
$-6, 6$

87. Verify that the slope of the line passing through (x, x^3) and $(x + h, [x + h]^3)$ is $3x^2 + 3xh + h^2$.

88. Verify that the slope of the line passing through $(x, 4x^3 + x)$ and $(x + h, 4[x + h]^3 + [x + h])$ is given by $12x^2 + 12xh + 4h^2 + 1$.

PREPARE FOR SECTION 2.5

89. For the graph of the parabola whose equation is $f(x) = x^2 + 4x - 6$, what is the equation of the axis of symmetry? [2.4] $x = -2$

90. For $f(x) = \dfrac{3x^4}{x^2 + 1}$, show that $f(-3) = f(3)$. [2.2]

91. For $f(x) = 2x^3 - 5x$, show that $f(-2) = -f(2)$. [2.2]

92. Let $f(x) = x^2$ and $g(x) = x + 3$. Find $f(a) - g(a)$ for $a = -2, -1, 0, 1, 2$. [2.2] $3, -1, -3, -3, -1$

93. What is the midpoint of the line segment between $P(-a, b)$ and $Q(a, b)$? [2.1] $(0, b)$

94. What is the midpoint of the line segment between $P(-a, -b)$ and $Q(a, b)$? [2.1] $(0, 0)$

PROJECTS

1. **The Cubic Formula** Write an essay on the development of the cubic formula. An excellent source of information is the chapter "Cardano and the Solution of the Cubic" in *Journey Through Genius*, by William Dunham (New York: Wiley, 1990).

2. **Simpson's Rule** In calculus a procedure known as *Simpson's Rule* is often used to approximate the area under a curve. The figure at the right shows the graph of a parabola that passes through $P_0(-h, y_0)$, $P_1(0, y_1)$, and $P_2(h, y_2)$. The equation of the parabola is of the form $y = Ax^2 + Bx + C$. Using calculus procedures, we can show that the area bounded by the parabola, the x-axis, and the vertical lines $x = -h$ and $x = h$ is

$$\frac{h}{3}(2Ah^2 + 6C)$$

Use algebra to show that $y_0 + 4y_1 + y_2 = 2Ah^2 + 6C$, from which we can deduce that the area of the bounded region can also be written as

$$\frac{h}{3}(y_0 + 4y_1 + y_2)$$

(*Hint:* Evaluate $Ax^2 + Bx + C$ at $x = -h$, $x = 0$, and $x = h$ to determine values of y_0, y_1, and y_2, respectively. Then compute $y_0 + 4y_1 + y_2$.)

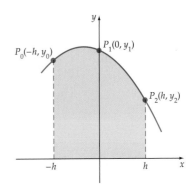

SECTION 2.5   PROPERTIES OF GRAPHS

● SYMMETRY

The graph in **Figure 2.63** is symmetric with respect to the line *l*. Note that the graph has the property that if the paper is folded along the dotted line *l*, the point A' will coincide with the point A, the point B' will coincide with the point B, and the point C' will coincide with the point C. One part of the graph is a *mirror image* of the rest of the graph across the line *l*.

A graph is **symmetric with respect to the y-axis** if, whenever the point given by (x, y) is on the graph, then $(-x, y)$ is also on the graph. The graph in **Figure 2.64** is symmetric with respect to the y-axis. A graph is **symmetric with respect to the x-axis** if, whenever the point given by (x, y) is on the graph, then $(x, -y)$ is also on the graph. The graph in **Figure 2.65** is symmetric with respect to the x-axis.

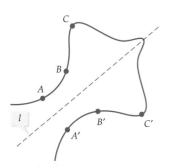

P **FIGURE 2.63**

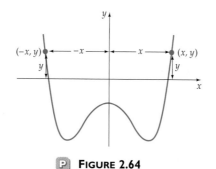

P **FIGURE 2.64**
Symmetry with respect to the y-axis

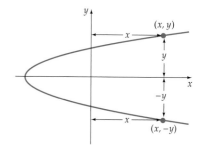

P **FIGURE 2.65**
Symmetry with respect to the x-axis

Tests for Symmetry with Respect to a Coordinate Axis

The graph of an equation is symmetric with respect to

- the y-axis if the replacement of x with $-x$ leaves the equation unaltered.
- the x-axis if the replacement of y with $-y$ leaves the equation unaltered.

❓ QUESTION Which of the graphs below, I, II, or III, is **a.** symmetric with respect to the x-axis? **b.** symmetric with respect to the y-axis?

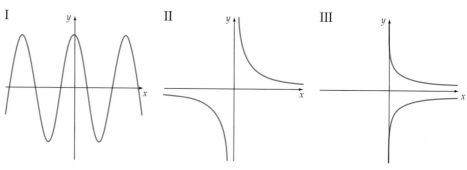

❓ ANSWER **a.** I is symmetric with respect to the y-axis.
b. III is symmetric with respect to the x-axis.

Alternative to Example 1
Determine whether the graph of the given equation has symmetry with respect to either the *x*- or the *y*-axis.
a. $x + y^2 = 4$
• **symmetric with respect to the *x*-axis**
b. $|x| + y = 4$
• **symmetric with respect to the *y*-axis**

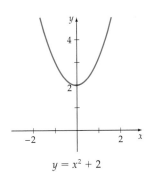

$$y = x^2 + 2$$

FIGURE 2.66

| EXAMPLE 1 | Determine Symmetries of a Graph |

Determine whether the graph of the given equation has symmetry with respect to either the *x*- or the *y*-axis.

a. $y = x^2 + 2$ **b.** $x = |y| - 2$

Solution

a. The equation $y = x^2 + 2$ *is unaltered* by the replacement of x with $-x$. That is, the simplification of $y = (-x)^2 + 2$ yields the original equation $y = x^2 + 2$. Thus the graph of $y = x^2 + 2$ is symmetric with respect to the *y*-axis. However, the equation $y = x^2 + 2$ *is altered* by the replacement of y with $-y$. That is, the simplification of $-y = x^2 + 2$, which is $y = -x^2 - 2$, *does not* yield the original equation $y = x^2 + 2$. The graph of $y = x^2 + 2$ is not symmetric with respect to the *x*-axis. See **Figure 2.66.**

b. The equation $x = |y| - 2$ *is altered* by the replacement of x with $-x$. That is, the simplification of $-x = |y| - 2$, which is $x = -|y| + 2$, *does not* yield the original equation $x = |y| - 2$. This implies that the graph of $x = |y| - 2$ is not symmetric with respect to the *y*-axis. However, the equation $x = |y| - 2$ *is unaltered* by the replacement of y with $-y$. That is, the simplification of $x = |-y| - 2$ yields the original equation $x = |y| - 2$. The graph of $x = |y| - 2$ is symmetric with respect to the *x*-axis. See **Figure 2.67.**

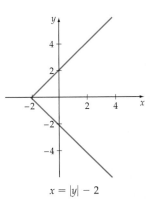

$$x = |y| - 2$$

FIGURE 2.67

▶ **TRY EXERCISE 14, PAGE 238**

Symmetry with Respect to a Point

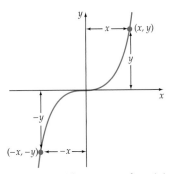

P **FIGURE 2.68**

A graph is **symmetric with respect to a point** Q if for each point P on the graph there is a point P' on the graph such that Q is the midpoint of the line segment PP'.

The graph in **Figure 2.68** is symmetric with respect to the point Q. For any point P on the graph, there exists a point P' on the graph such that Q is the midpoint of $P'P$.

When we discuss symmetry with respect to a point, we frequently use the origin. A graph is symmetric with respect to the origin if, whenever the point given by (x, y) is on the graph, then $(-x, -y)$ is also on the graph. The graph in **Figure 2.69** is symmetric with respect to the origin.

Test for Symmetry with Respect to the Origin

The graph of an equation is symmetric with respect to the origin if the replacement of x with $-x$ and of y with $-y$ leaves the equation unaltered.

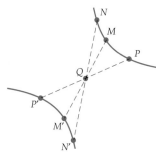

Symmetry with respect to the origin

P **FIGURE 2.69**

Alternative to Example 3
Determine whether each function is even,
odd, or neither.
a. $h(x) = 4x^5 + 5x$
⊙ **odd**
b. $f(x) = |3x|$
⊙ **even**
c. $g(x) = x^3 + 3x^2$
⊙ **neither**

EXAMPLE 3 **Identify Even or Odd Functions**

Determine whether each function is even, odd, or neither.

a. $f(x) = x^3$ **b.** $F(x) = |x|$ **c.** $h(x) = x^4 + 2x$

Solution

Replace x with $-x$ and simplify.

a. $f(-x) = (-x)^3 = -x^3 = -(x^3) = -f(x)$
Because $f(-x) = -f(x)$, this function is an odd function.

b. $F(-x) = |-x| = |x| = F(x)$
Because $F(-x) = F(x)$, this function is an even function.

c. $h(-x) = (-x)^4 + 2(-x) = x^4 - 2x$
This function is neither an even nor an odd function because

$$h(-x) = x^4 - 2x,$$

which is not equal to either $h(x)$ or $-h(x)$.

▶ **TRY EXERCISE 44, PAGE 238**

The following properties are a result of the tests for symmetry:

- The graph of an even function is symmetric with respect to the y-axis.
- The graph of an odd function is symmetric with respect to the origin.

The graph of f in **Figure 2.73** is symmetric with respect to the y-axis. It is the graph of an even function. The graph of g in **Figure 2.74** is symmetric with respect to the origin. It is the graph of an odd function. The graph of h in **Figure 2.75** is not symmetric with respect to the y-axis and is not symmetric with respect to the origin. It is neither an even nor an odd function.

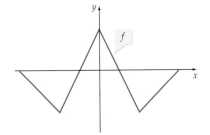

FIGURE 2.73
The graph of an even function is symmetric with respect to the y-axis.

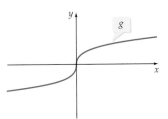

FIGURE 2.74
The graph of an odd function is symmetric with respect to the origin.

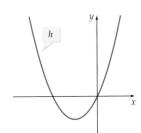

FIGURE 2.75
If the graph of a function is not symmetric to the y-axis or to the origin, then the function is neither even nor odd.

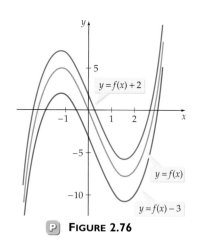

P **FIGURE 2.76**

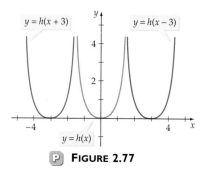

P **FIGURE 2.77**

• TRANSLATIONS OF GRAPHS

The shape of a graph may be exactly the same as the shape of another graph; only their positions in the xy-plane may differ. For example, the graph of $y = f(x) + 2$ is the graph of $y = f(x)$ with each point moved up vertically 2 units. The graph of $y = f(x) - 3$ is the graph of $y = f(x)$ with each point moved down vertically 3 units. See **Figure 2.76**.

The graphs of $y = f(x) + 2$ and $y = f(x) - 3$ in **Figure 2.76** are called *vertical translations* of the graph of $y = f(x)$.

Vertical Translations

If f is a function and c is a positive constant, then the graph of

- $y = f(x) + c$ is the graph of $y = f(x)$ shifted up *vertically* c units.
- $y = f(x) - c$ is the graph of $y = f(x)$ shifted down *vertically* c units.

In **Figure 2.77**, the graph of $y = h(x + 3)$ is the graph of $y = h(x)$ with each point shifted to the left horizontally 3 units. Similarly, the graph of $y = h(x - 3)$ is the graph of $y = h(x)$ with each point shifted to the right horizontally 3 units.

The graphs of $y = h(x + 3)$ and $y = h(x - 3)$ in **Figure 2.77** are called *horizontal translations* of the graph of $y = h(x)$.

Horizontal Translations

If f is a function and c is a positive constant, then the graph of

- $y = f(x + c)$ is the graph of $y = f(x)$ shifted left *horizontally* c units.
- $y = f(x - c)$ is the graph of $y = f(x)$ shifted right *horizontally* c units.

INTEGRATING TECHNOLOGY

A graphing calculator can be used to draw the graphs of a *family* of functions. For instance, $f(x) = x^2 + c$ constitutes a family of functions with **parameter** c. The only feature of the graph that changes is the value of c.

A graphing calculator can be used to produce the graphs of a family of curves for specific values of the parameter. The LIST feature of the calculator can be used. For instance, to graph $f(x) = x^2 + c$ for $c = -2, 0$, and 1, we will create a list and use that list to produce the family of curves. The keystrokes for a TI-83 calculator are given below.

2nd { -2 , 0 , 1 2nd } STO 2nd L1

Now use the Y= key to enter

Y= X x² + 2nd L1 ZOOM 6

INSTRUCTOR NOTE

The graphing calculator example at the right shows how lists can be used to graph vertical translations. Horizontal translations can be accomplished in a similar manner. For instance,

2nd {−3, 0, 3 2nd} STO 2nd L2 stores −3, 0, and 3 in L2.

Now use the Y= key and enter

Y=(X−2nd L2)x² ZOOM 6.

This will produce horizontal translations of $y = (x - k)^2$.

Sample screens for the keystrokes and graphs are shown here. You can use similar keystrokes for Exercises 75–82 of this section.

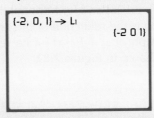

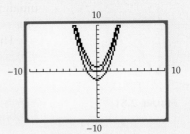

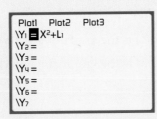

Alternative to Example 4
Exercise 60, page 239.

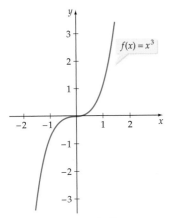

FIGURE 2.78

EXAMPLE 4   **Graph by Using Translations**

Use vertical and horizontal translations of the graph of $f(x) = x^3$, shown in **Figure 2.78,** to graph

a. $g(x) = x^3 - 2$ b. $h(x) = (x + 1)^3$

Solution

a. The graph of $g(x) = x^3 - 2$ is the graph of $f(x) = x^3$ shifted down vertically 2 units. See **Figure 2.79.**

b. The graph of $h(x) = (x + 1)^3$ is the graph of $f(x) = x^3$ shifted to the left horizontally 1 unit. See **Figure 2.80.**

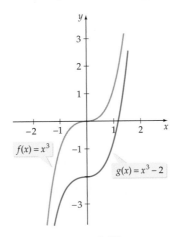

FIGURE 2.79

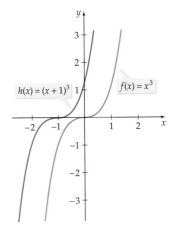

FIGURE 2.80

▶ **TRY EXERCISE 58, PAGE 239**

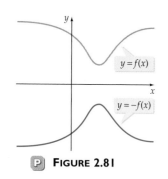

P **FIGURE 2.81**

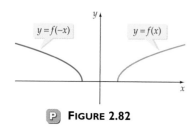

P **FIGURE 2.82**

• REFLECTIONS OF GRAPHS

The graph of $y = -f(x)$ cannot be obtained from the graph of $y = f(x)$ by a combination of vertical and/or horizontal shifts. **Figure 2.81** illustrates that the graph of $y = -f(x)$ is the reflection of the graph of $y = f(x)$ across the x-axis.

The graph of $y = f(-x)$ is the reflection of the graph of $y = f(x)$ across the y-axis as, shown in **Figure 2.82.**

Reflections

The graph of

- $y = -f(x)$ is the graph of $y = f(x)$ reflected across the x-axis.
- $y = f(-x)$ is the graph of $y = f(x)$ reflected across the y-axis.

EXAMPLE 5   Graph by Using Reflections

Alternative to Example 5
Exercise 64, page 239.

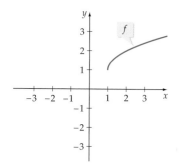

FIGURE 2.83

Use reflections of the graph of $f(x) = \sqrt{x - 1} + 1$, shown in **Figure 2.83,** to graph

a. $g(x) = -\left(\sqrt{x - 1} + 1\right)$ **b.** $h(x) = \sqrt{-x - 1} + 1$

Solution

a.   Because $g(x) = -f(x)$, the graph of g is the graph of f reflected across the x-axis. See **Figure 2.84.**

b.   Because $h(x) = f(-x)$, the graph of h is the graph of f reflected across the y-axis. See **Figure 2.85.**

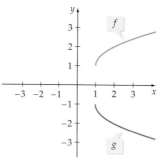

FIGURE 2.84

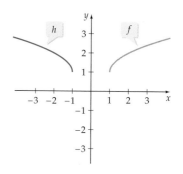

FIGURE 2.85

▶ **TRY EXERCISE 68, PAGE 240**

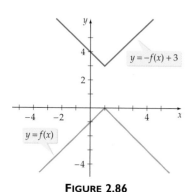

FIGURE 2.86

Some graphs of functions can be constructed by using a combination of translations and reflections. For instance, the graph of $y = -f(x) + 3$ in **Figure 2.86** was obtained by reflecting the graph of $y = f(x)$ in **Figure 2.86** across the x-axis and then shifting that graph up vertically 3 units.

• COMPRESSING AND STRETCHING OF GRAPHS

The graph of the equation $y = c \cdot f(x)$ for $c \neq 1$ vertically compresses or stretches the graph of $y = f(x)$. To determine the points on the graph of $y = c \cdot f(x)$, multiply each y-coordinate of the points on the graph of $y = f(x)$ by c. For example, **Figure 2.87** shows that the graph of $y = \frac{1}{2}|x|$ can be obtained by plotting points that have a y-coordinate that is one-half of the y-coordinate of those found on the graph of $y = |x|$.

If $0 < c < 1$, then the graph of $y = c \cdot f(x)$ is obtained by *compressing* the graph of $y = f(x)$. **Figure 2.87** illustrates the vertical compressing of the graph of $y = |x|$ toward the x-axis to form the graph of $y = \frac{1}{2}|x|$.

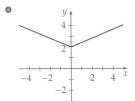

P **FIGURE 2.87**

If $c > 1$, then the graph of $y = c \cdot f(x)$ is obtained by *stretching* the graph of $y = f(x)$. For example, if $f(x) = |x|$, then we obtain the graph of

$$y = 2f(x) = 2|x|$$

by stretching the graph of f away from the x-axis. See **Figure 2.88**.

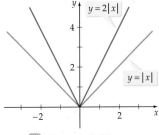

P **FIGURE 2.88**

P **Vertical Stretching and Compressing of Graphs**

If f is a function and c is a positive constant, then

- if $c > 1$, the graph of $y = c \cdot f(x)$ is the graph of $y = f(x)$ *stretched* vertically by a factor of c away from the x-axis.

- if $0 < c < 1$, the graph of $y = c \cdot f(x)$ is the graph of $y = f(x)$ *compressed* vertically by a factor of c toward the x-axis.

Alternative to Example 6

Graph: $G(x) = \frac{1}{2}|x| + 2$

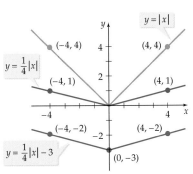

FIGURE 2.89

EXAMPLE 6   **Graph by Using Vertical Compressing and Shifting**

Graph: $H(x) = \frac{1}{4}|x| - 3$

Solution

The graph of $y = |x|$ has a V shape that has its lowest point at $(0, 0)$ and passes through $(4, 4)$ and $(-4, 4)$. The graph of $y = \frac{1}{4}|x|$ is a compressing of the graph of $y = |x|$. The y-coordinates of the ordered pairs $(0, 0)$, $(4, 1)$, and $(-4, 1)$ are obtained by multiplying the y-coordinates of the ordered pairs $(0, 0)$, $(4, 4)$, and $(-4, 4)$ by $\frac{1}{4}$. To find the points on the graph of H, we still need to subtract 3 from each y-coordinate. Thus the graph of H is a V shape that has its lowest point at $(0, -3)$ and passes through $(4, -2)$ and $(-4, -2)$. See **Figure 2.89**.

▶ **TRY EXERCISE 70, PAGE 240**

Some functions can be graphed by using a horizontal compressing or stretching of a given graph. The procedure makes use of the following concept.

Ⓟ **Horizontal Compressing and Stretching of Graphs**

If f is a function and c is a positive constant, then

- if $c > 1$, the graph of $y = f(c \cdot x)$ is the graph of $y = f(x)$ *compressed* horizontally by a factor of $\dfrac{1}{c}$ toward the y-axis.

- if $0 < c < 1$, the graph of $y = f(c \cdot x)$ is the graph of $y = f(x)$ *stretched* horizontally by a factor of $\dfrac{1}{c}$ away from the y-axis.

If the point (x, y) is on the graph of $y = f(x)$, then the graph of $y = f(cx)$ will contain the point $\left(\dfrac{1}{c}x, y\right)$.

Alternative to Example 7
Exercise 74, page 240.

E X A M P L E 7   **Graph by Using Horizontal Compressing and Stretching**

Use the graph of $y = f(x)$ shown in **Figure 2.90** to graph

a. $y = f(2x)$ **b.** $y = f\left(\dfrac{1}{3}x\right)$

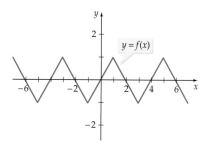

$y = f(x)$

FIGURE 2.90

Solution

a. Because $2 > 1$, the graph of $y = f(2x)$ is a horizontal compression of the graph of $y = f(x)$ by a factor of $\dfrac{1}{2}$. For example, the point $(2, 0)$ on the graph of $y = f(x)$ becomes the point $(1, 0)$ on the graph of $y = f(2x)$. See **Figure 2.91**.

b. Since $0 < \dfrac{1}{3} < 1$, the graph of $y = f\left(\dfrac{1}{3}x\right)$ is a horizontal stretching of the graph of $y = f(x)$ by a factor of 3. For example, the point $(1, 1)$ on the graph of $y = f(x)$ becomes the point $(3, 1)$ on the graph of $y = f\left(\dfrac{1}{3}x\right)$.

See **Figure 2.92.**

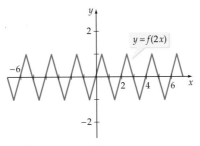

FIGURE 2.91

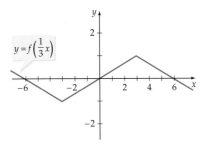

FIGURE 2.92

 TRY EXERCISE 72, PAGE 240

TOPICS FOR DISCUSSION

1. Discuss the meaning of symmetry of a graph with respect to a line. How do you determine whether a graph has symmetry with respect to the x-axis? with respect to the y-axis?

2. Discuss the meaning of symmetry of a graph with respect to a point. How do you determine whether a graph has symmetry with respect to the origin?

3. What does it mean to reflect a graph across the x-axis or across the y-axis?

4. Explain how the graphs of $y_1 = 2x^3 - x^2$ and $y_2 = 2(-x)^3 - (-x)^2$ are related.

5. Given the graph of $y_3 = f(x)$, explain how to obtain the graph of $y_4 = f(x - 3) + 1$.

6. The graph of the *step function* $y_5 = [\![x]\!]$ has steps that are 1 unit wide. Determine how wide the steps are in the graph of $y_6 = \left[\!\left[\dfrac{1}{3}x\right]\!\right]$.

EXERCISE SET 2.5

—Suggested Assignment: Exercises 1–77, every other odd, and 87–92.
—Answers to Exercises 1–12, 31–42, 57–60, 63, 64, 67–79, and 80–84 are on pages AA6–AA8.

In Exercises 1 to 6, plot the image of the given point with respect to
a. **the y-axis. Label this point A.**
b. **the x-axis. Label this point B.**
c. **the origin. Label this point C.**

1. $P(5, -3)$ **2.** $Q(-4, 1)$ **3.** $R(-2, 3)$

4. $S(-5, 3)$ **5.** $T(-4, -5)$ **6.** $U(5, 1)$

In Exercises 7 and 8, sketch a graph that is symmetric to the given graph with respect to the x-axis.

7.
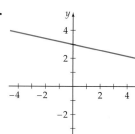

8.
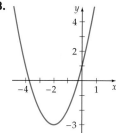

In Exercises 9 and 10, sketch a graph that is symmetric to the given graph with respect to the y-axis.

9.
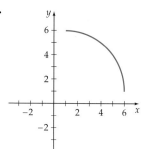

10.
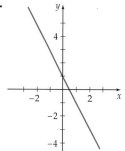

In Exercises 11 and 12, sketch a graph that is symmetric to the given graph with respect to the origin.

11.
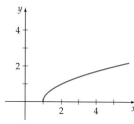

12.
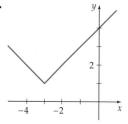

In Exercises 13 to 21, determine whether the graph of each equation is symmetric with respect to the a. x-axis, b. y-axis.

13. $y = 2x^2 - 5$
a. No b. Yes

▶ **14.** $x = 3y^2 - 7$
a. Yes b. No

15. $y = x^3 + 2$
a. No b. No

16. $y = x^5 - 3x$
a. No b. No

17. $x^2 + y^2 = 9$
a. Yes b. Yes

18. $x^2 - y^2 = 10$
a. Yes b. Yes

19. $x^2 = y^4$
a. Yes b. Yes

20. $xy = 8$
a. No b. No

21. $|x| - |y| = 6$
a. Yes b. Yes

In Exercises 22 to 30, determine whether the graph of each equation is symmetric with respect to the origin.

22. $y = x + 1$
No

23. $y = 3x - 2$
No

▶ **24.** $y = x^3 - x$
Yes

25. $y = -x^3$
Yes

26. $y = \dfrac{9}{x}$
Yes

27. $x^2 + y^2 = 10$
Yes

28. $x^2 - y^2 = 4$
Yes

29. $y = \dfrac{x}{|x|}$
Yes

30. $|y| = |x|$
Yes

In Exercises 31 to 42, graph the given equations. Label each intercept. Use the concept of symmetry to confirm that the graph is correct.

31. $y = x^2 - 1$
$(\pm 1, 0), (0, -1)$

32. $x = y^2 - 1$
$(-1, 0), (0, \pm 1)$

33. $y = x^3 - x$
$(\pm 1, 0), (0, 0)$

34. $y = -x^3$
$(0, 0)$

35. $xy = 4$
no intercepts

36. $xy = -8$
no intercepts

37. $y = 2|x - 4|$
$(4, 0), (0, 8)$

38. $y = |x - 2| - 1$
$(3, 0), (1, 0); (0, 1)$

39. $y = (x - 2)^2 - 4$
$(0, 0), (4, 0); (0, 1)$

40. $y = (x - 1)^2 - 4$
$(-1, 0), (3, 0); (0, -3)$

41. $y = x - |x|$
$(a, 0), a \geq 0; (0, 0)$

42. $|y| = |x|$
$(0, 0)$

In Exercises 43 to 56, identify whether the given function is an even function, an odd function, or neither.

43. $g(x) = x^2 - 7$
even

▶ **44.** $h(x) = x^2 + 1$
even

45. $F(x) = x^5 + x^3$
odd

46. $G(x) = 2x^5 - 10$
neither

47. $H(x) = 3|x|$
even

48. $T(x) = |x| + 2$
even

49. $f(x) = 1$
even

50. $k(x) = 2 + x + x^2$
neither

51. $r(x) = \sqrt{x^2 + 4}$
even

52. $u(x) = \sqrt{3 - x^2}$
even

53. $s(x) = 16x^2$
even

54. $v(x) = 16x^2 + x$
neither

55. $w(x) = 4 + \sqrt[3]{x}$ **56.** $z(x) = \dfrac{x^3}{x^2 + 1}$
     neither
                                        odd

57. Use the graph of f to sketch the graph of

a. $y = f(x) + 3$ **b.** $y = f(x - 3)$

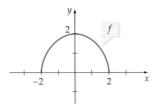

▶ **58.** Use the graph of g to sketch the graph of

a. $y = g(x) - 2$ **b.** $y = g(x - 3)$

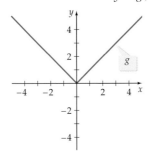

59. Use the graph of f to sketch the graph of

a. $y = f(x + 2)$ **b.** $y = f(x) + 2$

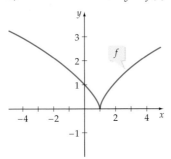

60. Use the graph of g to sketch the graph of

a. $y = g(x - 1)$ **b.** $y = g(x) - 1$

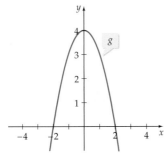

61. Let f be a function such that $f(-2) = 5$, $f(0) = -2$, and $f(1) = 0$. Give the coordinates of three points on the graph of

a. $y = f(x + 3)$ **b.** $y = f(x) + 1$
     $(-5, 5), (-3, -2), (-2, 0)$ $(-2, 6), (0, -1), (1, 1)$

62. Let g be a function such that $g(-3) = -1$, $g(1) = -3$, and $g(4) = 2$. Give the coordinates of three points on the graph of

a. $y = g(x - 2)$ **b.** $y = g(x) - 2$
     $(-1, -1), (3, -3), (6, 2)$ $(-3, -3), (1, -5), (4, 0)$

63. Use the graph of f to sketch the graph of

a. $y = f(-x)$ **b.** $y = -f(x)$

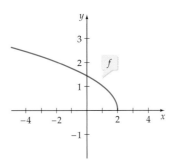

64. Use the graph of g to sketch the graph of

a. $y = -g(x)$ **b.** $y = g(-x)$

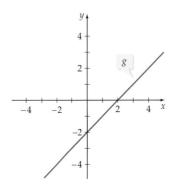

65. Let f be a function such that $f(-1) = 3$ and $f(2) = -4$. Give the coordinates of two points on the graph of

a. $y = f(-x)$ **b.** $y = -f(x)$
     $(1, 3), (-2, -4)$ $(-1, -3), (2, 4)$

66. Let g be a function such that $g(4) = -5$ and $g(-3) = 2$. Give the coordinates of two points on the graph of

a. $y = -g(x)$ **b.** $y = g(-x)$.
     $(4, 5), (-3, -2)$ $(-4, -5), (3, 2)$

67. Use the graph of F to sketch the graph of

a. $y = -F(x)$ **b.** $y = F(-x)$

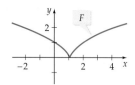

68. Use the graph of E to sketch the graph of

a. $y = -E(x)$ **b.** $y = E(-x)$

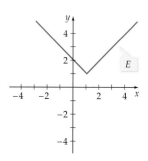

69. Use the graph of $m(x) = x^2 - 2x - 3$ to sketch the graph of $y = -\dfrac{1}{2}m(x) + 3$.

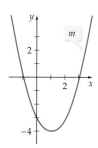

70. Use the graph of $n(x) = -x^2 - 2x + 8$ to sketch the graph of $y = \dfrac{1}{2}n(x) + 1$.

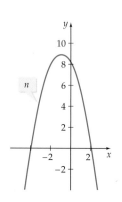

71. Use the graph of $y = f(x)$ to sketch the graph of

a. $y = f(2x)$ **b.** $y = f\left(\dfrac{1}{3}x\right)$

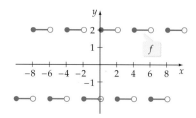

72. Use the graph of $y = g(x)$ to sketch the graph of

a. $y = g(2x)$ **b.** $y = g\left(\dfrac{1}{2}x\right)$

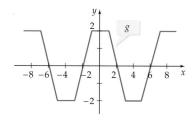

73. Use the graph of $y = h(x)$ to sketch the graph of

a. $y = h(2x)$ **b.** $y = h\left(\dfrac{1}{2}x\right)$

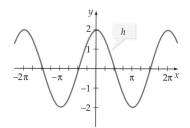

74. Use the graph of $y = j(x)$ to sketch the graph of

a. $y = j(2x)$ **b.** $y = j\left(\dfrac{1}{3}x\right)$

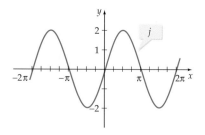

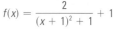 **In Exercises 75 to 82, use a graphing utility.**

75. On the same coordinate axes, graph
$$G(x) = \sqrt[3]{x} + c$$
for $c = 0, -1$, and 3.

76. On the same coordinate axes, graph
$$H(x) = \sqrt[3]{x + c}$$
for $c = 0, -1$, and 3.

77. On the same coordinate axes, graph
$$J(x) = |2(x + c) - 3| - |x + c|$$
for $c = 0, -1$, and 2.

78. On the same coordinate axes, graph
$$K(x) = |x - 1| - |x| + c$$
for $c = 0, -1$, and 2.

79. On the same coordinate axes, graph
$$L(x) = cx^2$$
for $c = 1, \dfrac{1}{2}$, and 2.

80. On the same coordinate axes, graph
$$M(x) = c\sqrt{x^2 - 4}$$
for $c = 1, \dfrac{1}{3}$, and 3.

81. On the same coordinate axes, graph
$$S(x) = c(|x - 1| - |x|)$$
for $c = 1, \dfrac{1}{4}$, and 4.

82. On the same coordinate axes, graph
$$T(x) = c\left(\dfrac{x}{|x|}\right)$$
for $c = 1, \dfrac{2}{3}$, and $\dfrac{3}{2}$.

83. Graph $V(x) = [\![cx]\!], 0 \le x \le 6$, for each value of c.

   a. $c = 1$ **b.** $c = \dfrac{1}{2}$ **c.** $c = 2$

84. Graph $W(x) = [\![cx]\!] - cx, 0 \le x \le 6$, for each value of c.

   a. $c = 1$ **b.** $c = \dfrac{1}{3}$ **c.** $c = 3$

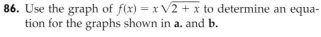

CONNECTING CONCEPTS

85. Use the graph of $f(x) = 2/(x^2 + 1)$ to determine an equation for the graphs shown in **a.** and **b.**

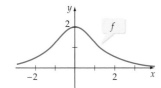

86. Use the graph of $f(x) = x\sqrt{2 + x}$ to determine an equation for the graphs shown in **a.** and **b.**

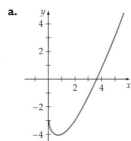

a.

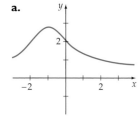

$$f(x) = \dfrac{2}{(x + 1)^2 + 1} + 1$$

b.

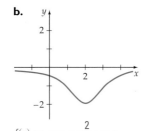

$$f(x) = -\dfrac{2}{(x - 2)^2 + 1}$$

a.

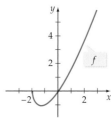

$$f(x) = (x - 2)\sqrt{x} - 3$$

b.

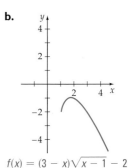

$$f(x) = (3 - x)\sqrt{x - 1} - 2$$

PREPARE FOR SECTION 2.6
---

87. Subtract: $(2x^2 + 3x - 4) - (x^2 + 3x - 5)$ [P.3]
$x^2 + 1$

88. Multiply: $(3x^2 - x + 2)(2x - 3)$ [P.3]
$6x^3 - 11x^2 + 7x - 6$

In Exercises 89 and 90, find each of the following for $f(x) = 2x^2 - 5x + 2$.

89. $f(3a)$ [2.2]
$18a^2 - 15a + 2$

90. $f(2 + h)$ [2.2]
$2h^2 + 3h$

In Exercises 91 and 92, find the domain of each function.

91. $F(x) = \dfrac{x}{x - 1}$ [2.2] all real numbers except $x = 1$

92. $r(x) = \sqrt{2x - 8}$ [2.2] $[4, \infty)$

PROJECTS
---

1. **DIRICHLET FUNCTION** We owe our present-day definition of a function to the German mathematician Peter Gustav Dirichlet (1805–1859). He created the following unusual function, which is now known as the *Dirichlet function*.

$$f(x) = \begin{cases} 0, & \text{if } x \text{ is a rational number} \\ 1, & \text{if } x \text{ is an irrational number} \end{cases}$$

Answer the following questions about the Dirichlet function.

a. What is its domain?   **b.** What is its range?

c. What are its x-intercepts?

d. What is its y-intercept?

e. Is it an even or an odd function?

f. Explain why a graphing calculator cannot be used to produce an accurate graph of the function.

g. Write a sentence or two that describes its graph.

2. **ISOLATED POINT** Consider the function given by

$$y = \sqrt{(x - 1)^2(x - 2)} + 1$$

Verify that the point $(1, 1)$ is a solution of the equation. Now use a graphing utility to graph the function. Does your graph include the isolated point at $(1, 1)$, as shown at the right? If the graphing utility you used failed to include the point $(1, 1)$, explain at least one reason for the omission of this isolated point.

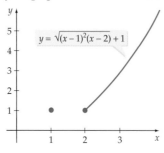

$y = \sqrt{(x-1)^2(x-2)} + 1$

3. **A LINE WITH A HOLE** The function

$$f(x) = \frac{(x - 2)(x + 1)}{(x - 2)}$$

graphs as a line with a y-intercept of 1, a slope of 1, and a hole at $(2, 3)$. Use a graphing utility to graph f. Explain why a graphing utility might not show the hole at $(2, 3)$.

4. **FINDING A COMPLETE GRAPH** Use a graphing utility to graph the function $f(x) = 3x^{5/3} - 6x^{4/3} + 2$ for $-2 \le x \le 10$. Compare your graph with the graph below. Does your graph include the part to the left of the y-axis? If not, how might you enter the function in such a way that the graphing utility you used would include this part?

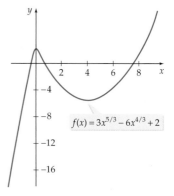

$f(x) = 3x^{5/3} - 6x^{4/3} + 2$

THE ALGEBRA OF FUNCTIONS

● OPERATIONS ON FUNCTIONS

Functions can be defined in terms of other functions. For example, the function defined by $h(x) = x^2 + 8x$ is the sum of

$$f(x) = x^2 \quad \text{and} \quad g(x) = 8x$$

Thus, if we are given any two functions f and g, we can define the four new functions $f + g$, $f - g$, fg, and $\dfrac{f}{g}$ as follows.

Operations on Functions

For all values of x for which both $f(x)$ and $g(x)$ are defined, we define the following functions.

Sum	$(f + g)(x) = f(x) + g(x)$
Difference	$(f - g)(x) = f(x) - g(x)$
Product	$(fg)(x) = f(x) \cdot g(x)$
Quotient	$\left(\dfrac{f}{g}\right)(x) = \dfrac{f(x)}{g(x)}, \quad g(x) \neq 0$

Domain of $f + g$, $f - g$, fg, f/g

For the given functions f and g, the domains of $f + g$, $f - g$, and $f \cdot g$ consist of all real numbers formed by the intersection of the domains of f and g. The domain of $\dfrac{f}{g}$ is the set of all real numbers formed by the intersection of the domains of f and g, except for those real numbers x such that $g(x) = 0$.

Alternative to Example 1

If $f(x) = x^2 - 25$ and $g(x) = \sqrt{x + 3}$, find the domains of $f + g$, $f - g$, fg, and $\dfrac{f}{g}$.

● The domain of $f + g$, $f - g$, and fg is $\{x \mid x \geq -3\}$. The domain of $\dfrac{f}{g}$ is $\{x \mid x > -3\}$.

EXAMPLE 1   **Determine the Domain of a Function**

If $f(x) = \sqrt{x - 1}$ and $g(x) = x^2 - 4$, find the domain of $f + g$, of $f - g$, of fg, and of $\dfrac{f}{g}$.

Solution

Note that f has the domain $\{x \mid x \geq 1\}$ and g has the domain of all real numbers. Therefore, the domain of $f + g$, $f - g$, and fg is $\{x \mid x \geq 1\}$. Because $g(x) = 0$ when $x = -2$ or $x = 2$, neither -2 nor 2 is in the domain of $\dfrac{f}{g}$. The domain of $\dfrac{f}{g}$ is $\{x \mid x \geq 1 \text{ and } x \neq 2\}$.

▶ **TRY EXERCISE 10, PAGE 251**

Alternative to Example 2
Let $f(x) = x^2 + 2$ and $g(x) = 3x - 1$.
Find
a. $(f + g)(3)$
 19
b. $(fg)(4)$
 198
c. $\left(\dfrac{f}{g}\right)(-1)$

 $-\dfrac{3}{4}$

EXAMPLE 2 **Evaluate Functions**

Let $f(x) = x^2 - 9$ and $g(x) = 2x + 6$. Find

a. $(f + g)(5)$ **b.** $(fg)(-1)$ **c.** $\left(\dfrac{f}{g}\right)(4)$

Solution

a. $(f + g)(x) = f(x) + g(x) = (x^2 - 9) + (2x + 6) = x^2 + 2x - 3$
Therefore, $(f + g)(5) = (5)^2 + 2(5) - 3 = 25 + 10 - 3 = 32$.

b. $(fg)(x) = f(x) \cdot g(x) = (x^2 - 9)(2x + 6) = 2x^3 + 6x^2 - 18x - 54$
Therefore, $(fg)(-1) = 2(-1)^3 + 6(-1)^2 - 18(-1) - 54$
$$= -2 + 6 + 18 - 54 = -32.$$

c. $\left(\dfrac{f}{g}\right)(x) = \dfrac{f(x)}{g(x)} = \dfrac{x^2 - 9}{2x + 6} = \dfrac{(x+3)(x-3)}{2(x+3)} = \dfrac{x - 3}{2}, \quad x \neq -3$
Therefore, $\left(\dfrac{f}{g}\right)(4) = \dfrac{4 - 3}{2} = \dfrac{1}{2}$.

▶ **TRY EXERCISE 14, PAGE 251**

● **THE DIFFERENCE QUOTIENT**

take note

The difference quotient is an important concept that plays a fundamental role in calculus.

The expression
$$\frac{f(x + h) - f(x)}{h}, \quad h \neq 0$$

is called the **difference quotient** of f. It enables us to study the manner in which a function changes in value as the independent variable changes.

Alternative to Example 3
Determine the difference quotient of
$f(x) = 2x^2 + 5x - 3$.
 $4x + 2h + 5$

EXAMPLE 3 **Determine a Difference Quotient**

Determine the difference quotient of $f(x) = x^2 + 7$.

Solution

$\dfrac{f(x + h) - f(x)}{h} = \dfrac{[(x + h)^2 + 7] - [x^2 + 7]}{h}$ • Apply the difference quotient.

$= \dfrac{[x^2 + 2xh + h^2 + 7] - [x^2 + 7]}{h}$

$= \dfrac{x^2 + 2xh + h^2 + 7 - x^2 - 7}{h}$

$= \dfrac{2xh + h^2}{h} = \dfrac{h(2x + h)}{h} = 2x + h$

▶ **TRY EXERCISE 30, PAGE 251**

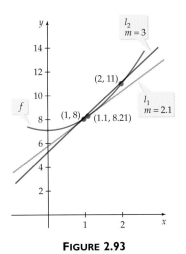

FIGURE 2.93

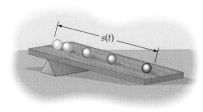

FIGURE 2.94

The difference quotient $2x + h$ of $f(x) = x^2 + 7$ from Example 3 is the slope of the secant line through the points

$$(x, f(x)) \qquad \text{and} \qquad (x + h, f(x + h))$$

For instance, let $x = 1$ and $h = 1$. Then the difference quotient is

$$2x + h = 2(1) + 1 = 3$$

This is the slope of the secant line l_2 through $(1, 8)$ and $(2, 11)$, as shown in **Figure 2.93.** If we let $x = 1$ and $h = 0.1$, then the difference quotient is

$$2x + h = 2(1) + 0.1 = 2.1$$

This is the slope of the secant line l_1 through $(1, 8)$ and $(1.1, 8.21)$.

The difference quotient

$$\frac{f(x + h) - f(x)}{h}$$

can be used to compute *average velocities*. In such cases it is traditional to replace f with s (for distance), the variable x with the variable a (for the time at the start of an observed interval of time), and the variable h with Δt (read as "delta t"), where Δt is the difference between the time at the end of an interval and the time at the start of the interval. For example, if an experiment is observed over the time interval from $t = 3$ seconds to $t = 5$ seconds, then the time interval is denoted as $[3, 5]$ with $a = 3$ and $\Delta t = 5 - 3 = 2$. Thus if the distance traveled by a ball that rolls down a ramp is given by $s(t)$, where t is the time in seconds after the ball is released (see **Figure 2.94**), then the **average velocity** of the ball over the interval $t = a$ to $t = a + \Delta t$ is the difference quotient

$$\frac{s(a + \Delta t) - s(a)}{\Delta t}$$

Alternative to Example 4
The distance traveled by a ball rolling down a ramp is given by $s(t) = 6t^2$, where t is the time in seconds after the ball is released, and $s(t)$ is measured in feet. Evaluate the average velocity of the ball for each time interval.
a. $[2, 3]$
○ **30 ft/s**
b. $[2, 2.5]$
○ **27 ft/s**
c. $[2, 2.1]$
○ **24.6 ft/s**
d. $[2, 2.001]$
○ **24.006 ft/s**

EXAMPLE 4 **Evaluate Average Velocities**

The distance traveled by a ball rolling down a ramp is given by $s(t) = 4t^2$, where t is the time in seconds after the ball is released, and $s(t)$ is measured in feet. Evaluate the average velocity of the ball for each time interval.

a. $[3, 5]$ **b.** $[3, 4]$ **c.** $[3, 3.5]$ **d.** $[3, 3.01]$

Solution

a. In this case, $a = 3$ and $\Delta t = 2$. Thus the average velocity over this interval is

$$\frac{s(a + \Delta t) - s(a)}{\Delta t} = \frac{s(3 + 2) - s(3)}{2} = \frac{s(5) - s(3)}{2} = \frac{100 - 36}{2}$$

$$= 32 \text{ feet per second}$$

b. Let $a = 3$ and $\Delta t = 4 - 3 = 1$.

$$\frac{s(a + \Delta t) - s(a)}{\Delta t} = \frac{s(3 + 1) - s(3)}{1} = \frac{s(4) - s(3)}{1} = \frac{64 - 36}{1}$$

$$= 28 \text{ feet per second}$$

Continued ▶

c. Let $a = 3$ and $\Delta t = 3.5 - 3 = 0.5$.

$$\frac{s(a + \Delta t) - s(a)}{\Delta t} = \frac{s(3 + 0.5) - s(3)}{0.5} = \frac{49 - 36}{0.5} = 26 \text{ feet per second}$$

d. Let $a = 3$ and $\Delta t = 3.01 - 3 = 0.01$.

$$\frac{s(a + \Delta t) - s(a)}{\Delta t} = \frac{s(3 + 0.01) - s(3)}{0.01} = \frac{36.2404 - 36}{0.01}$$

$$= 24.04 \text{ feet per second}$$

▶ **TRY EXERCISE 72, PAGE 253**

● COMPOSITION OF FUNCTIONS

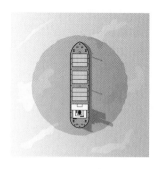

Composition of functions is another way in which functions can be combined. This method of combining functions uses the output of one function as the input for a second function.

Suppose that the spread of oil from a leak in a tanker can be approximated by a circle with the tanker at its center. The radius r (in feet) of the spill t hours after the leak begins is given by $r(t) = 150\sqrt{t}$. The area of the spill is the area of a circle and is given by the formula $A(r) = \pi r^2$. To find the area of the spill 4 hours after the leak begins, we first find the radius of the spill and then use that number to find the area of the spill.

$$r(t) = 150\sqrt{t} \qquad\qquad\qquad A(r) = \pi r^2$$
$$r(4) = 150\sqrt{4} \quad \bullet\, t = 4 \text{ hours} \qquad A(300) = \pi(300^2) \quad \bullet\, r = 300 \text{ feet}$$
$$= 150(2) \qquad\qquad\qquad\qquad = 90{,}000\pi$$
$$= 300 \qquad\qquad\qquad\qquad\quad \approx 283{,}000$$

The area of the spill after 4 hours is approximately 283,000 square feet.

There is an alternative way to solve this problem. Because the area of the spill depends on the radius and the radius depends on the time, there is a relationship between area and time. We can determine this relationship by evaluating the formula for the area of a circle using $r(t) = 150\sqrt{t}$. This will give the area of the spill as a function of time.

$$A(r) = \pi r^2$$
$$A[r(t)] = \pi[r(t)]^2 \qquad\quad \bullet \text{ Replace } r \text{ by } r(t).$$
$$= \pi\left[150\sqrt{t}\,\right]^2 \qquad \bullet\, r(t) = 150\sqrt{t}$$
$$A(t) = 22{,}500\pi t \qquad\qquad \bullet \text{ Simplify.}$$

The area of the spill as a function of time is $A(t) = 22{,}500\pi t$. To find the area of the oil spill after 4 hours, evaluate this function at $t = 4$.

$$A(t) = 22{,}500\pi t$$
$$A(4) = 22{,}500\pi(4) \qquad \bullet\, t = 4 \text{ hours}$$
$$= 90{,}000\pi$$
$$\approx 283{,}000$$

This is the same result we calculated earlier.

The function $A(t) = 22{,}500\pi t$ is referred to as the *composition* of A with r. The notation $A \circ r$ is used to denote this composition of functions. That is,

$$(A \circ r)(t) = 22{,}500\pi t$$

Definition of the Composition of Two Functions

Let f and g be two functions such that $g(x)$ is in the domain of f for all x in the domain of g. Then the composition of the two functions, denoted by $f \circ g$, is the function whose value at x is given by $(f \circ g)(x) = f[g(x)]$.

The function defined by $(f \circ g)(x)$ is also called the *composite* of f and g. We read $(f \circ g)(x)$ as "f circle g of x" and $f[g(x)]$ as "f of g of x."

Consider the functions $f(x) = 2x - 1$ and $g(x) = x^2 - 3$. The expression $(f \circ g)(-1)$ (or, equivalently, $f[g(-1)]$) means to evaluate the function f at $g(-1)$.

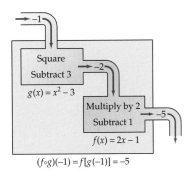

$$g(x) = x^2 - 3$$
$$g(-1) = (-1)^2 - 3 \qquad \text{• Evaluate } g \text{ at } -1.$$
$$= -2$$

$$f(x) = 2x - 1$$
$$f(-2) = 2(-2) - 1 = -5 \qquad \text{• Evaluate } f \text{ at } g(-1) = -2.$$

A graphical depiction of the composition $(f \circ g)(-1)$ would look something like **Figure 2.95.**

FIGURE 2.95

The requirement in the definition of the composition of two functions that $g(x)$ be in the domain of f for all x in the domain of g is important. For instance, let

$$f(x) = \frac{1}{x - 1} \qquad \text{and} \qquad g(x) = 3x - 5$$

When $x = 2$,

$$g(2) = 3(2) - 5 = 1$$
$$f[g(2)] = f(1) = \frac{1}{1 - 1} = \frac{1}{0} \qquad \text{• Undefined}$$

In this case, $g(2)$ is not in the domain of f. Thus the composition $(f \circ g)(x)$ is not defined at 2.

We can find a general expression for $f[g(x)]$ by evaluating f at $g(x)$. For instance, using $f(x) = 2x - 1$ and $g(x) = x^2 - 3$ as in **Figure 2.95,** we have

$$f(x) = 2x - 1$$
$$f[g(x)] = 2[g(x)] - 1 \qquad \text{• Replace } x \text{ by } g(x).$$
$$= 2[x^2 - 3] - 1 \qquad \text{• Replace } g(x) \text{ by } x^2 - 3.$$
$$= 2x^2 - 7 \qquad \text{• Simplify.}$$

In general, the composition of functions is not a commutative operation. That is, $(f \circ g)(x) \neq (g \circ f)(x)$. To verify this, we will compute the composition

$(g \circ f)(x) = g[f(x)]$, again using the functions $f(x) = 2x - 1$ and $g(x) = x^2 - 3$.

$$g(x) = x^2 - 3$$
$$g[f(x)] = [f(x)]^2 - 3 \qquad \text{• Replace } x \text{ by } f(x).$$
$$= [2x - 1]^2 - 3 \qquad \text{• Replace } f(x) \text{ by } 2x - 1.$$
$$= 4x^2 - 4x - 2 \qquad \text{• Simplify.}$$

Thus $f[g(x)] = 2x^2 - 7$, which is not equal to $g[f(x)] = 4x^2 - 4x - 2$. Therefore, $(f \circ g)(x) \neq (g \circ f)(x)$ and composition is not a commutative operation.

> **❓ QUESTION**   Let $f(x) = x - 1$ and $g(x) = x + 1$. Then $f[g(x)] = g[f(x)]$. (You should verify this statement.) Does this contradict the statement we made that composition is not a commutative operation?

Alternative to Example 5
If $f(x) = 2x^2 + 3x + 1$ and
$g(x) = 4x - 5$, find
a. $(g \circ f)(x)$
◉ $8x^2 + 12x - 1$
b. $(f \circ g)(x)$
◉ $32x^2 - 68x + 36$

EXAMPLE 5   **Form Composite Functions**

If $f(x) = x^2 - 3x$ and $g(x) = 2x + 1$, find

a. $(g \circ f)$ **b.** $(f \circ g)$

Solution

a.
$$(g \circ f) = g[f(x)] = 2(f(x)) + 1 \qquad \text{• Substitute } f(x) \text{ for } x \text{ in } g.$$
$$= 2(x^2 - 3x) + 1 \qquad \text{• } f(x) = x^2 - 3x$$
$$= 2x^2 - 6x + 1$$

b.
$$(f \circ g) = f[g(x)] = (g(x))^2 - 3(g(x)) \qquad \text{• Substitute } g(x) \text{ for } x \text{ in } f.$$
$$= (2x + 1)^2 - 3(2x + 1) \qquad \text{• } g(x) = 2x + 1$$
$$= 4x^2 - 2x - 2$$

▶ **TRY EXERCISE 38, PAGE 252**

INSTRUCTOR NOTE
Here is an example to test students'
understanding of how the composition of
functions may require adjustments to the
domains of the given functions. Let
$f(x) = 2x + 3$ and $g(x) = \dfrac{1}{x + 1}$. What
value of x must be excluded from the
domain of f so that $g[f(x)]$ can always be
evaluated?
◉ -2

Note that in this example $(f \circ g) \neq (g \circ f)$. In general, the composition of functions is not a commutative operation.

Caution   Some care must be used when forming the composition of functions. For instance, if $f(x) = x + 1$ and $g(x) = \sqrt{x - 4}$, then

$$(g \circ f)(2) = g[f(2)] = g(3) = \sqrt{3 - 4} = \sqrt{-1}$$

which is not a real number. We can avoid this problem by imposing suitable restrictions on the domain of f so that the range of f is part of the domain of g. If the

---

❓ ANSWER   No. When we say that composition is not a commutative operation, we mean that generally, given any two functions, $(f \circ g)(x) \neq (g \circ f)(x)$. However, there may be particular instances in which $(f \circ g)(x) = (g \circ f)(x)$. It turns out that these particular instances are quite important, as we shall see later.

domain of f is restricted to $[3, \infty)$, then the range of f is $[4, \infty)$. But this is precisely the domain of g. Note that $2 \notin [3, \infty)$, and thus we avoid the problem of $(g \circ f)(2)$ not being a real number.

To evaluate $(f \circ g)(c)$ for some constant c, you can use either of the following methods.

Method 1   First evaluate $g(c)$. Then substitute this result for x in $f(x)$.

Method 2   First determine $f[g(x)]$ and then substitute c for x.

Alternative to Example 6
Evaluate $(f \circ g)(-2)$, where $f(x) = x + 3$ and $g(x) = 2x^2 - 9$.
● 2

EXAMPLE 6   **Evaluate a Composite Function**

Evaluate $(f \circ g)(3)$, where $f(x) = 2x - 7$ and $g(x) = x^2 + 4$.

Solution

Method 1 $(f \circ g)(3) = f[g(3)]$

$\qquad\qquad\qquad = f[(3)^2 + 4]$ • Evaluate $g(3)$.

$\qquad\qquad\qquad = f(13)$

$\qquad\qquad\qquad = 2(13) - 7 = 19$ • Substitute 13 for x in f.

Method 2 $(f \circ g)(x) = 2[g(x)] - 7$ • Form $f[g(x)]$.

$\qquad\qquad\qquad = 2[x^2 + 4] - 7$

$\qquad\qquad\qquad = 2x^2 + 1$

$\qquad (f \circ g)(3) = 2(3)^2 + 1 = 19$ • Substitute 3 for x.

▶ **TRY EXERCISE 50, PAGE 252**

> **take note**
>
> In Example 6, both Method 1 and Method 2 produce the same result. Although Method 2 is longer, it is the better method if you must evaluate $(f \circ g)(x)$ for several values of x.

Figures 2.96 and **2.97** graphically illustrate the difference between Method 1 and Method 2.

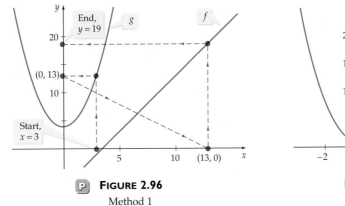

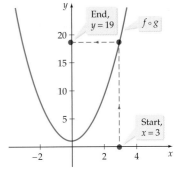

FIGURE 2.96
Method 1

FIGURE 2.97
Method 2

Alternative to Example 7
Exercise 70, page 253.

EXAMPLE 7

Use a Composite Function to Solve an Application

A graphic artist has drawn a 3-inch by 2-inch rectangle on a computer screen. The artist has been scaling the size of the rectangle for t seconds in such a way that the upper right corner of the original rectangle is moving to the right at the rate of 0.5 inch per second and downward at the rate of 0.2 inch per second. See **Figure 2.98.**

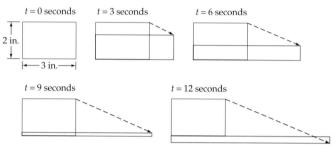

FIGURE 2.98

a. Write the length l and the width w of the scaled rectangles as functions of t.

b. Write the area A of the scaled rectangle as a function of t.

c. Find the intervals on which A is an increasing function for $0 \le t \le 14$. Also find the intervals on which A is a decreasing function.

d. Find the value of t (where $0 \le t \le 14$) that maximizes $A(t)$.

Solution

a. Because *distance = rate · time*, we see that the change in l is given by $0.5t$. Therefore, the length at any time t is $l = 3 + 0.5t$. For $0 \le t \le 10$, the width is given by $w = 2 - 0.2t$. For $10 < t \le 14$, the width is $w = -2 + 0.2t$. In either case the width can be determined by finding $w = |2 - 0.2t|$. (The absolute value symbol is needed to keep the width positive for $10 < t \le 14$.)

b. $A = lw = (3 + 0.5t)|2 - 0.2t|$

c. Use a graphing utility to determine that A is increasing on $[0, 2]$ and on $[10, 14]$ and that A is decreasing on $[2, 10]$. See **Figure 2.99.**

d. The highest point on the graph of A occurs when $t = 14$ seconds. See **Figure 2.99.**

▶ **TRY EXERCISE 66, PAGE 252**

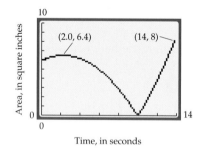

$A = (3 + 0.5t)|2 - 0.2t|$

FIGURE 2.99

You may be inclined to think that if the area of a rectangle is decreasing, then its perimeter is also decreasing, but this is not always the case. For example, the area of the scaled rectangle in Example 7 was shown to decrease on $[2, 10]$ even though its perimeter is always increasing. See Exercise 68 in Exercise Set 2.6.

TOPICS FOR DISCUSSION

1. The domain of $f + g$ consists of all real numbers formed by the *union* of the domain of f and the domain of g. Do you agree?

2. Given $f(x) = 3x - 2$ and $g(x) = \dfrac{1}{3}x + \dfrac{2}{3}$, determine $f \circ g$ and $g \circ f$. Does this show that composition of functions is a commutative operation?

3. A tutor states that the difference quotient of $f(x) = x^2$ and the difference quotient of $g(x) = x^2 + 4$ are the same. Do you agree?

4. A classmate states that the difference quotient of any linear function $f(x) = mx + b$ is always m. Do you agree?

5. When we use a difference quotient to determine an average velocity, we generally replace the variable h with the variable Δt. What does Δt represent?

EXERCISE SET 2.6

—Suggested Assignment: Exercises 1–77, every other odd, and 83–88.
—Answers to Exercises 1–12 are on pages AA8–AA9.

In Exercises 1 to 12, use the given functions f and g to find $f + g$, $f - g$, fg, and $\dfrac{f}{g}$. State the domain of each.

1. $f(x) = x^2 - 2x - 15$, $g(x) = x + 3$

2. $f(x) = x^2 - 25$, $g(x) = x - 5$

3. $f(x) = 2x + 8$, $g(x) = x + 4$

4. $f(x) = 5x - 15$, $g(x) = x - 3$

5. $f(x) = x^3 - 2x^2 + 7x$, $g(x) = x$

6. $f(x) = x^2 - 5x - 8$, $g(x) = -x$

7. $f(x) = 2x^2 + 4x - 7$, $g(x) = 2x^2 + 3x - 5$

8. $f(x) = 6x^2 + 10$, $g(x) = 3x^2 + x - 10$

9. $f(x) = \sqrt{x - 3}$, $g(x) = x$

▶ 10. $f(x) = \sqrt{x - 4}$, $g(x) = -x$

11. $f(x) = \sqrt{4 - x^2}$, $g(x) = 2 + x$

12. $f(x) = \sqrt{x^2 - 9}$, $g(x) = x - 3$

In Exercises 13 to 28, evaluate the indicated function, where $f(x) = x^2 - 3x + 2$ and $g(x) = 2x - 4$.

13. $(f + g)(5)$ 18

▶ 14. $(f + g)(-7)$ 54

15. $(f + g)\left(\dfrac{1}{2}\right)$ $-\dfrac{9}{4}$

16. $(f + g)\left(\dfrac{2}{3}\right)$ $-\dfrac{20}{9}$

17. $(f - g)(-3)$ 30

18. $(f - g)(24)$ 462

19. $(f - g)(-1)$ 12

20. $(f - g)(0)$ 6

21. $(fg)(7)$ 300

22. $(fg)(-3)$ −200

23. $(fg)\left(\dfrac{2}{5}\right)$ $-\dfrac{384}{125}$

24. $(fg)(-100)$ −2,101,608

25. $\left(\dfrac{f}{g}\right)(-4)$ $-\dfrac{5}{2}$

26. $\left(\dfrac{f}{g}\right)(11)$ 5

27. $\left(\dfrac{f}{g}\right)\left(\dfrac{1}{2}\right)$ $-\dfrac{1}{4}$

28. $\left(\dfrac{f}{g}\right)\left(\dfrac{1}{4}\right)$ $-\dfrac{3}{8}$

In Exercises 29 to 36, find the difference quotient of the given function.

29. $f(x) = 2x + 4$ 2

▶ 30. $f(x) = 4x - 5$ 4

31. $f(x) = x^2 - 6$ $2x + h$

32. $f(x) = x^2 + 11$ $2x + h$

33. $f(x) = 2x^2 + 4x - 3$
$4x + 2h + 4$

34. $f(x) = 2x^2 - 5x + 7$
$4x + 2h - 5$

35. $f(x) = -4x^2 + 6$
$-8x - 4h$

36. $f(x) = -5x^2 - 4x$
$-10x - 5h - 4$

In Exercises 37 to 48, find $g \circ f$ and $f \circ g$ for the given functions f and g.

37. $f(x) = 3x + 5$, $g(x) = 2x - 7$
$(g \circ f)(x) = 6x + 3$, $(f \circ g)(x) = 6x - 16$

▶ **38.** $f(x) = 2x - 7$, $g(x) = 3x + 2$
$(g \circ f)(x) = 6x - 19$, $(f \circ g)(x) = 6x - 3$

39. $f(x) = x^2 + 4x - 1$, $g(x) = x + 2$
$(g \circ f)(x) = x^2 + 4x + 1$, $(f \circ g)(x) = x^2 + 8x + 11$

40. $f(x) = x^2 - 11x$, $g(x) = 2x + 3$
$(g \circ f)(x) = 2x^2 - 22x + 3$, $(f \circ g)(x) = 4x^2 - 10x - 24$

41. $f(x) = x^3 + 2x$, $g(x) = -5x$
$(g \circ f)(x) = -5x^3 - 10x$, $(f \circ g)(x) = -125x^3 - 10x$

42. $f(x) = -x^3 - 7$, $g(x) = x + 1$
$(g \circ f)(x) = -x^3 - 6$, $(f \circ g)(x) = -x^3 - 3x^2 - 3x - 8$

43. $f(x) = \dfrac{2}{x + 1}$, $g(x) = 3x - 5$
$(g \circ f)(x) = \dfrac{1 - 5x}{x + 1}$, $(f \circ g)(x) = \dfrac{2}{3x - 4}$

44. $f(x) = \sqrt{x + 4}$, $g(x) = \dfrac{1}{x}$
$(g \circ f)(x) = \dfrac{\sqrt{x + 4}}{x + 4}$, $(f \circ g)(x) = \dfrac{\sqrt{x + 4x^2}}{x}$

45. $f(x) = \dfrac{1}{x^2}$, $g(x) = \sqrt{x - 1}$
$(g \circ f)(x) = \dfrac{\sqrt{1 - x^2}}{|x|}$, $(f \circ g)(x) = \dfrac{1}{x - 1}$

46. $f(x) = \dfrac{6}{x - 2}$, $g(x) = \dfrac{3}{5x}$
$(g \circ f)(x) = \dfrac{x - 2}{10}$, $(f \circ g)(x) = \dfrac{30x}{3 - 10x}$

47. $f(x) = \dfrac{3}{|5 - x|}$, $g(x) = -\dfrac{2}{x}$
$(g \circ f)(x) = -\dfrac{2|5 - x|}{3}$, $(f \circ g)(x) = \dfrac{3|x|}{|5x + 2|}$

48. $f(x) = |2x + 1|$, $g(x) = 3x^2 - 1$
$(g \circ f)(x) = 12x^2 + 12x + 2$, $(f \circ g)(x) = |6x^2 - 1|$

In Exercises 49 to 64, evaluate each composite function, where $f(x) = 2x + 3, g(x) = x^2 - 5x$, and $h(x) = 4 - 3x^2$.

49. $(g \circ f)(4)$ 66

▶ **50.** $(f \circ g)(4)$ −5

51. $(f \circ g)(-3)$ 51

52. $(g \circ f)(-1)$ −4

53. $(g \circ h)(0)$ −4

54. $(h \circ g)(0)$ 4

55. $(f \circ f)(8)$ 41

56. $(f \circ f)(-8)$ −23

57. $(h \circ g)\left(\dfrac{2}{5}\right)$ $-\dfrac{3848}{625}$

58. $(g \circ h)\left(-\dfrac{1}{3}\right)$ $-\dfrac{44}{9}$

59. $(g \circ f)(\sqrt{3})$ $6 + 2\sqrt{3}$

60. $(f \circ g)(\sqrt{2})$ $7 - 10\sqrt{2}$

61. $(g \circ f)(2c)$ $16c^2 + 4c - 6$

62. $(f \circ g)(3k)$ $18k^2 - 30k + 3$

63. $(g \circ h)(k + 1)$
$9k^4 + 36k^3 + 45k^2 + 18k - 4$

64. $(h \circ g)(k - 1)$
$-3k^4 + 42k^3 - 183k^2 + 252k - 104$

65. **WATER TANK** A water tank has the shape of a right circular cone, with height 16 feet and radius 8 feet. Water is running into the tank so that the radius r (in feet) of the surface of the water is given by $r = 1.5t$, where t is the time (in minutes) that the water has been running.

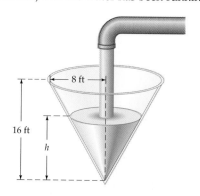

a. The area A of the surface of the water is $A = \pi r^2$. Find $A(t)$ and use it to determine the area of the surface of the water when $t = 2$ minutes.
$A(t) = \pi(1.5t)^2$, $A(2) = 9\pi$ ft$^2 \approx 28.27$ ft^2

b. The volume V of the water is given by $V = \dfrac{1}{3}\pi r^2 h$. Find $V(t)$ and use it to determine the volume of the water when $t = 3$ minutes. (*Hint:* The height of the water in the cone is always twice the radius of the water.)
$V(t) = 2.25\pi t^3$, $V(3) = 60.75\pi$ ft$^3 \approx 190.85$ ft^3

66. a. $l = |3 - 0.5t|$
b. $A = lw = |3 - 0.5t||2 - 0.2t|$
$= |(3 - 0.5t)(2 - 0.2t)|$
c. A is increasing on $[6, 8]$ and on $[10, 14]$; A is decreasing on $[0, 6]$ and on $[8, 10]$.
d. The highest point on the graph of A occurs when $t = 0$ s.

▶ **66.** 🖩 **SCALING A RECTANGLE** Work Example 7 of this section with the scaling as follows. The upper right corner of the original rectangle is pulled to the *left* at 0.5 inch per second and downward at 0.2 inch per second.

67. **TOWING A BOAT** A boat is towed by a rope that runs through a pulley that is 4 feet above the point where the rope is tied to the boat. The length (in feet) of the rope from the boat to the pulley is given by $s = 48 - t$, where t is the time in seconds that the boat has been in tow. The horizontal distance from the pulley to the boat is d.

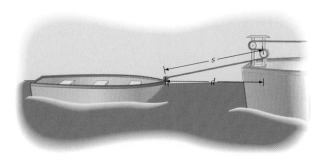

a. Find $d(t)$.   **b.** Evaluate $s(35)$ and $d(35)$.
$d(t) = \sqrt{(48 - t)^2 - 4^2}$ $s(35) = 13$ ft, $d(35) \approx 12.37$ ft

68. ▦ PERIMETER OF A SCALED RECTANGLE Show by a graph that the perimeter

$$P = 2(3 + 0.5t) + 2|2 - 0.2t|$$

of the scaled rectangle in Example 7 of this section is an increasing function over $0 \le t \le 14$.
Answer on page AA9.

69. CONVERSION FUNCTIONS The function $F(x) = \dfrac{x}{12}$ converts x inches to feet. The function $Y(x) = \dfrac{x}{3}$ converts x feet to yards. Explain the meaning of $(Y \circ F)(x)$.
$(Y \circ F)(x)$ converts x inches to yards.

70. CONVERSION FUNCTIONS The function $F(x) = 3x$ converts x yards to feet. The function $I(x) = 12x$ converts x feet to inches. Explain the meaning of $(I \circ F)(x)$.
$(I \circ F)(x) = I(F(x))$ converts x yards to inches.

71. ● CONCENTRATION OF A MEDICATION The concentration $C(t)$ (in milligrams per liter) of a medication in a patient's blood is given by the data in the following table.

Concentration of Medication in Patient's Blood

t hours	C(t) mg/l
0	0
0.25	47.3
0.50	78.1
0.75	94.9
1.00	99.8
1.25	95.7
1.50	84.4
1.75	68.4
2.00	50.1
2.25	31.6
2.50	15.6
2.75	4.3

The **average rate of change** of the concentration over the time interval from $t = a$ to $t = a + \Delta t$ is

$$\frac{C(a + \Delta t) - C(a)}{\Delta t}$$

Use the data in the table to evaluate the average rate of change for each of the following time intervals.

a. $[0, 1]$ (*Hint*: In this case, $a = 0$ and $\Delta t = 1$.) Compare this result to the slope of the line through $(0, C(0))$ and $(1, C(1))$.
99.8; This is identical to the slope of the line through $(0, C(0))$ and $(1, C(1))$.

b. $[0, 0.5]$ **c.** $[1, 2]$ **d.** $[1, 1.5]$ **e.** $[1, 1.25]$
156.2   −49.7   −30.8   −16.4

f. The data in the table can be modeled by the function $Con(t) = 25t^3 - 150t^2 + 225t$. Use $Con(t)$ to verify that the average rate of change over $[1, 1 + \Delta t]$ is $-75(\Delta t) + 25(\Delta t)^2$. What does the average rate of change over $[1, 1 + \Delta t]$ seem to approach as Δt approaches 0? 0

▶ **72.** BALL ROLLING ON A RAMP The distance traveled by a ball rolling down a ramp is given by $s(t) = 6t^2$, where t is the time in seconds after the ball is released, and $s(t)$ is measured in feet. The ball travels 6 feet in 1 second and it travels 24 feet in 2 seconds. Use the difference quotient for average velocity given on page 245 to evaluate the average velocity for each of the following time intervals.

a. $[2, 3]$ (*Hint*: In this case, $a = 2$ and $\Delta t = 1$.) Compare this result to the slope of the line through $(2, s(2))$ and $(3, s(3))$.
30; This is identical to the slope of the line through $(2, s(2))$ and $(3, s(3))$.

b. $[2, 2.5]$ **c.** $[2, 2.1]$ **d.** $[2, 2.01]$ **e.** $[2, 2.001]$
27 ft/s   24.6 ft/s   24.06 ft/s   24.006 ft/s

f. Verify that the average velocity over $[2, 2 + \Delta t]$ is $24 + 6(\Delta t)$. What does the average velocity seem to approach as Δt approaches 0?
24 ft/s

CONNECTING CONCEPTS

In Exercises 73 to 76, show that $(f \circ g)(x) = (g \circ f)(x)$.

73. $f(x) = 2x + 3$; $g(x) = 5x + 12$

74. $f(x) = 4x - 2$; $g(x) = 7x - 4$

75. $f(x) = \dfrac{6x}{x - 1}$; $g(x) = \dfrac{5x}{x - 2}$

76. $f(x) = \dfrac{5x}{x + 3}$; $g(x) = -\dfrac{2x}{x - 4}$

In Exercises 77 to 82, show that

$$(g \circ f)(x) = x \quad \text{and} \quad (f \circ g)(x) = x$$

77. $f(x) = 2x + 3, \quad g(x) = \dfrac{x - 3}{2}$

78. $f(x) = 4x - 5, \quad g(x) = \dfrac{x + 5}{4}$

79. $f(x) = \dfrac{4}{x + 1}, \quad g(x) = \dfrac{4 - x}{x}$

80. $f(x) = \dfrac{2}{1 - x}, \quad g(x) = \dfrac{x - 2}{x}$

81. $f(x) = x^3 - 1, \quad g(x) = \sqrt[3]{x + 1}$

82. $f(x) = -x^3 + 2, \quad g(x) = \sqrt[3]{2 - x}$

PREPARE FOR SECTION 2.7

In Exercises 83 and 84, find the slope and y-intercept of the graph of the equation.

83. $y = -\dfrac{x}{3} + 4$ [2.3] slope: $-\dfrac{1}{3}$; y-intercept: $(0, 4)$

84. $3x - 4y = 12$ [2.3] slope: $\dfrac{3}{4}$; y-intercept: $(0, -3)$

85. Find the equation of the line that has a slope of -0.45 and a y-intercept of $(0, 2.3)$. [2.3] $y = -0.45x + 2.3$

86. Find the equation of the line that passes through $P(3, -4)$ and has a slope of $-\dfrac{2}{3}$. [2.3] $y = -\dfrac{2}{3}x - 2$

87. If $f(x) = 3x^2 + 4x - 1$, find $f(2)$. [2.2] 19

88. You are given $P_1(2, -1)$ and $P_2(4, 14)$. If $f(x) = x^2 - 3$, find $|f(x_1) - y_1| + |f(x_2) - y_2|$. [2.2] 3

PROJECTS

1.   **A GRAPHING UTILITY PROJECT** For any two different real numbers x and y, the larger of the two numbers is given by

$$\text{Maximum}(x, y) = \frac{x + y}{2} + \frac{|x - y|}{2} \qquad (1)$$

a. Verify Equation (1) for $x = 5$ and $y = 9$.

b. Verify Equation (1) for $x = 201$ and $y = 80$.

For any two different functional values $f(x)$ and $g(x)$, the larger of the two is given by

$$\text{Maximum}(f(x), g(x)) = \frac{f(x) + g(x)}{2} + \frac{|f(x) - g(x)|}{2} \qquad (2)$$

To illustrate how we might make use of Equation (2), consider the functions $y_1 = x^2$ and $y_2 = \sqrt{x}$ on the interval from Xmin $= -1$ to Xmax $= 6$. The graphs of y_1 and y_2 are shown at the right.

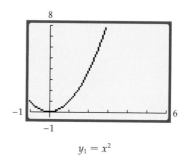

$y_1 = x^2$

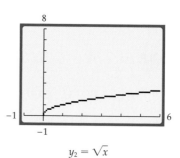

$y_2 = \sqrt{x}$

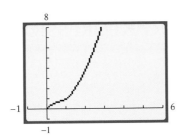

$$y_3 = (y_1 + y_2)/2 + (\text{abs }(y_1 - y_2))/2$$

Now consider the function

$$y_3 = (y_1 + y_2)/2 + (\text{abs}(y_1 - y_2))/2$$

where "abs" represents the absolute value function. The graph of y_3 is shown above.

c. Write a sentence or two that explains why the graph of y_3 is as shown.

d. What is the domain of y_1? of y_2? of y_3? Write a sentence that explains how to determine the domain of y_3, given the domain of y_1 and the domain of y_2.

e. Determine a formula for the function Minimum$(f(x), g(x))$.

2. THE NEVER-NEGATIVE FUNCTION The author J. D. Murray describes a function f_+ that is defined in the following manner.[2]

$$f_+ = \begin{cases} f & \text{if } f \geq 0 \\ 0 & \text{if } f < 0 \end{cases}$$

We will refer to this function as a **never-negative** function. Never-negative functions can be graphed by using Equation (2) in Project 1. For example, if we let $g(x) = 0$, then Equation (2) simplifies to

$$\text{Maximum}(f(x), 0) = \frac{f(x)}{2} + \frac{|f(x)|}{2} \qquad (3)$$

The graph of $y = \text{Maximum}(f(x), 0)$ is the graph of $y = f(x)$ provided that $f(x) \geq 0$, and it is the graph of $y = 0$ provided that $f(x) < 0$.

An Application The mosquito population per acre of a large resort is controlled by spraying on a monthly basis. A biologist has determined that the mosquito population can be approximated by the never-negative function M_+ with

$$M(t) = -35{,}400(t - \text{int}(t))^2 + 35{,}400(t - \text{int}(t)) - 4000$$

Here t represents the month, and $t = 0$ corresponds to June 1, 2004.

a. Use a graphing utility to graph M for $0 \leq t \leq 3$.

b. Use a graphing utility to graph M_+ for $0 \leq t \leq 3$.

c. Write a sentence or two that explains how the graph of M_+ differs from the graph of M.

d. What is the maximum mosquito population per acre for $0 \leq t \leq 3$? When does this maximum population occur?

e. Explain when would be the best time to visit the resort, provided that you wished to minimize your exposure to mosquitos.

[2]*Mathematical Biology* (New York: Springer-Verlag, 1989), p. 101.

MODELING DATA USING REGRESSION

● LINEAR REGRESSION MODELS

The data in the table below show the population of a few states and the number of professional sports teams (Major League Baseball, National Football League, National Basketball Association, Women's National Basketball Association, National Hockey League) in those states.

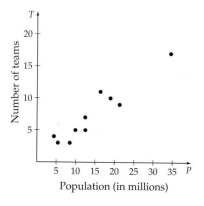

Number of Professional Sports Teams for Selected States

State	Population (in millions)	Number of Teams
California	34.5	17
Florida	16.4	11
New York	19.0	10
Texas	21.3	9
Pennsylvania	12.3	7
Illinois	12.5	5
Michigan	10	5
Colorado	4.4	4
New Jersey	8.5	3
Wisconsin	5.4	3

Source: Bureau of Census, 50States.com.

Although there is no one line that passes through every point, we could find an approximate linear model of these data. For instance, the line shown in **Figure 2.100** in blue approximates the data better than the line shown in red. However, as **Figure 2.101** shows, there are many other lines we could have drawn that seem to approximate the data.

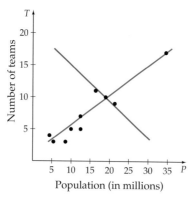

FIGURE 2.100

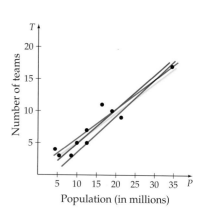

FIGURE 2.101

To find the line that "best" approximates the data, **regression analysis** is used. This analysis produces the linear function whose graph is called the **line of best fit** or the **least-squares regression line**.[3]

Definition of the Least-Squares Regression Line

The **least-squares regression line** is the line that minimizes the sum of the squares of the vertical deviations of all data points from the line.

To help understand this definition, consider the data set $S = \{(1, 2), (2, 3), (3, 3), (4, 4), (5, 7)\}$ as shown in **Figure 2.102.** As we will show later, the least-squares line for this data set is $y = 1.1x + 0.5$. If we evaluate this function at the x-coordinates of the data set S, we obtain the set of ordered pairs $T = \{(1, 1.6), (2, 2.7), (3, 3.8), (4, 4.9), (5, 6)\}$. The vertical deviations are the differences between the y-coordinates in S and the y-coordinates in T. From the definition, we must calculate the sum of the squares of these deviations.

$$(2 - 1.6)^2 + (3 - 2.7)^2 + (3 - 3.8)^2 + (4 - 4.9)^2 + (7 - 6)^2 = 2.7$$

Because $y = 1.1x + 0.5$ is the least squares regression line, for no other line is the sum of the squares of the deviations less than 2.7. For instance, if we consider the equation $y = 1.25x + 0.75$, which is the equation of the line through the two points $P_1(1, 2)$ and $P_2(5, 7)$ of the data set as shown in **Figure 2.103,** the sum of the squared deviations is larger than 2.7.

$$(2 - 2)^2 + (3 - 3.25)^2 + (3 - 4.5)^2 + (4 - 5.75)^2 + (7 - 7)^2 = 5.375$$

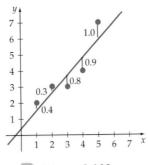

P **FIGURE 2.102**

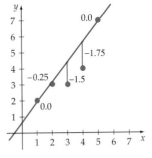

P **FIGURE 2.103**

---

[3]The least-squares regression line is also called the *least-squares line* and the *regression line*.

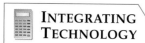

INTEGRATING
TECHNOLOGY

The equations used to calculate a regression line are somewhat cumbersome. Fortunately, these equations are preprogrammed into most graphing calculators. We will now illustrate the technique for a TI-83 calculator using data set S given on page 257.

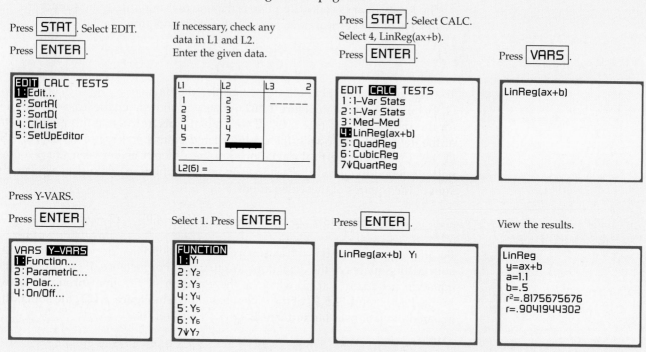

Press STAT. Select EDIT.

Press ENTER.

If necessary, check any data in L1 and L2. Enter the given data.

Press STAT. Select CALC. Select 4, LinReg(ax+b). Press ENTER.

Press VARS.

Press Y-VARS.

Press ENTER.

Select 1. Press ENTER.

Press ENTER.

View the results.

From the last screen, the equation of the regression line is $y = 1.1x + 0.5$. Your last screen may not look exactly like ours. The information provided on our screen requires that DiagnosticsOn be enabled. This is accomplished using the following keystrokes:

2ND CATALOG (Scroll to DiagnosticsOn) ENTER

With DiagnosticsOn enabled, besides the values for the regression equation, two other values, r^2 and r, are given. We will discuss these values later in this section.

If you used the keystrokes we have shown above, the regression line will be stored in Y1. This is helpful if you wish to graph the regression line. However, if it is not necessary to graph the regression line, then instead of pressing VARS at step 4, just press ENTER. The result will be the last screen showing the results of the regression calculations.

EXAMPLE 1   Find a Regression Equation

Find the regression equation for the data on the population of a state and the number of professional sports teams in that state. How many sports teams are predicted for North Carolina, whose population is approximately 8.2 million? Round to the nearest whole number.

Alternative to Example 1

A study was conducted to determine whether a score on a placement test could predict the success of a student in a statistics course. The results for six students are given in the table.

Test Score	20	25	28	31	32	35
Average in course	58	71	72	84	80	87

Find the linear regression equation for these data. What average score does the model predict for a student who scores 34 on the placement test?

● $y = 1.91x + 20.88$; 86

Solution

Using your calculator, enter the data from the table. Then have the calculator produce the values for the regression equation. Your results should be similar to those shown at the right. The equation of the regression line is

$$y = 0.4704143697x + 0.6119206457$$

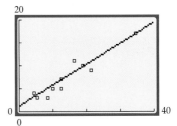
```
LinReg
y=ax+b
a=.4704143697
b=.6119206457
r²=.9031742558
r=.9503548052
```

To find the number of sports teams the regression equation predicts for North Carolina, evaluate the regression equation for $x = 8.2$.

$$y = 0.4704143697x + 0.6119206457$$
$$= 0.4704143697(8.2) + 0.6119206457$$
$$\approx 4.46$$

The equation predicts that North Carolina should have 4 sports teams.

▶ **TRY EXERCISE 18, PAGE 264**

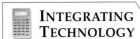

INTEGRATING TECHNOLOGY

If you followed the steps we gave on page 258 and stored the regression equation in Y1, then you can evaluate the regression equation using the following keystrokes:

| VARS | ▶ | ENTER | ENTER |

| (8.2) | ENTER |

● **CORRELATION COEFFICIENT AND COEFFICIENT OF DETERMINATION**

The scatter plot of a state's population and the corresponding number of professional sports teams is shown in **Figure 2.104,** along with the graph of the regression line. Note that the slope of the regression line is positive. This indicates that as a state's population increases, the number of teams increases. Note also that for these data the value of r on the regression calculation screen was positive, $r \approx 0.9504$.

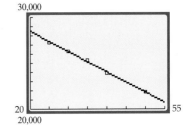

FIGURE 2.104

---

take note

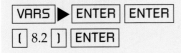

The data for the Corvette were created assuming that the condition of the car was excellent. The only variable that changed was the odometer reading.

```
LinReg
y=ax+b
a=-223.0405405
b=32959.45946
r²=.9912312349
r=-.9956059637
```

Now consider the data in the table below, which shows the trade-in value of a 2001 Corvette for various odometer readings.

Trade-in Value of 2001 Corvette Coupe, April 2003

Odometer Reading, in thousands	Trade-in Value
25	27,200
30	26,325
35	25,475
40	23,900
50	21,750

Source: Kelley Blue Book Web site, April 2003.

The scatter diagram below is based on the trade-in value table. The graph of the regression line is also shown.

In this case the slope of the regression line is negative. This means that as the odometer reading increases, the trade-in value of the car decreases. Note also that the value of r is negative, $r \approx -0.996$.

Linear Correlation Coefficient

The **linear correlation coefficient** r is a measure of how close the points of a data set can be modeled by a straight line. If $r = -1$, then the points of the data set can be modeled *exactly* by a straight line with negative slope. If $r = 1$, then the data set can be modeled *exactly* by a straight line with positive slope. For all data sets, $-1 \leq r \leq 1$.

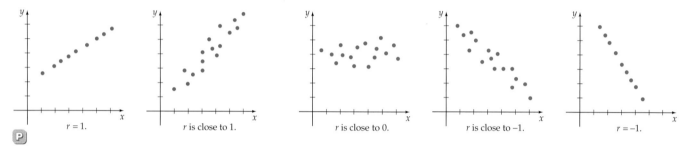

| $r = 1$. | r is close to 1. | r is close to 0. | r is close to -1. | $r = -1$. |

If $r \neq 1$ or $r \neq -1$, then the data set *cannot* be modeled exactly by a straight line. The further the value of r is from 1 or -1 (or in other words, the closer the value of r to zero), the more the ordered pairs of the data set deviate from a straight line.

The graphs below show the points of the data sets and the graphs of the regression lines for the state population/sports teams data and the odometer reading/trade-in data. Note the values of r and the closeness of the data points to the regression lines.

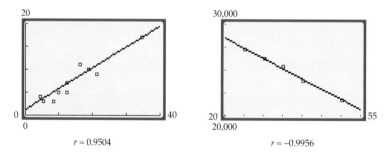

$r \approx 0.9504$ $r \approx -0.9956$

A researcher calculates a regression line to determine a relationship between two variables. The researcher wants to know whether a change in one variable produces a predictable change in the second variable. The value of r^2 tells the researcher the extent of that relationship.

Coefficient of Determination

The **coefficient of determination** is r^2. It measures the proportion of the variation in the dependent variable that is explained by the regression line.

For the population/sports team data, $r^2 \approx 0.90$. This means that approximately 90% of the total variation in the dependent variable (number of teams) can be attributed to the state population. This also means that population alone does not predict with certainty the number of sports teams. Other factors, such as climate, are also involved in the number of sports teams.

? QUESTION What is the coefficient of determination for the odometer reading/trade-in value data (see page 259), and what is its significance?

● QUADRATIC REGRESSION MODELS

To this point our focus has been *linear* regression equations. However, there may be a nonlinear relationship between two quantities. The accompanying scatter diagram to the left suggests that a quadratic function might be a better model of the data than a linear model. As we proceed through this text, various functional models will be discussed.

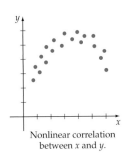

Nonlinear correlation between x and y.

Alternative to Example 2
Exercise 30, page 266.

EXAMPLE 2 **Find a Quadratic Regression Model**

The data in the table below were collected on five successive Saturdays. They show the average number of cars entering a shopping center parking lot. The value of t is the number of minutes after 9:00 A.M. The value of N is the number of cars that entered the parking lot in the 10 minutes prior to the value of t. Find a regression model for this data.

Average Number of Cars Entering a Shopping Center Parking Lot

t	N	t	N
20	70	140	301
40	135	160	298
60	178	180	284
80	210	200	286
100	260	220	260
120	280	240	195

Solution

1. **Construct a scatter diagram for these data.** Enter the data into your calculator as explained on page 258.

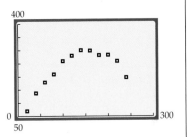

From the scatter diagram, it appears that there is a nonlinear relationship between the variables.

Continued ▶

? ANSWER $r^2 \approx 0.991$. This means that 99.1% of the total variation in trade-in value can be attributed to the odometer reading.

2. **Find the regression equation.** Try a quadratic regression model. For a TI-83 calculator, press $\boxed{\text{STAT}}$ $\blacktriangleright$ $\boxed{\text{2ND}}$ CALC 5 $\boxed{\text{ENTER}}$.

```
QuadReg
y=ax²+bx+c
a=-.0124881369
b=3.904433067
c=-7.25
R²=.9840995401
```

---

take note

In the case of nonlinear regression calculations, the value of r is not shown on a TI-83 graphing calculator. In these cases, the coefficient of determination is used to determine how well the data fit the model.

---

3. **Examine the coefficient of determination.** The coefficient of determination is approximately 0.984. Because this number is fairly close to 1, the regression equation $y = -0.0124881369x^2 + 3.904433067x - 7.25$ provides a good model of the data.

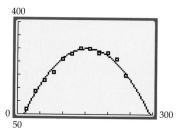

▶ **TRY EXERCISE 32, PAGE 267**

```
LinReg
y=ax+b
a=.6575174825
b=144.2727273
r²=.4193509866
r=.6475731515
```

For Example 2, we could have calculated the *linear* regression line for the data. The results are shown at the left. Note that the coefficient of determination for this calculation is approximately 0.419. Because this number is less than the coefficient of determination for the quadratic model, we choose a quadratic model of the data rather than a linear model.

Now for a final note: The regression line equation does not *prove* that the changes in the dependent variable are *caused* by the independent variable. For instance, suppose various cities throughout the United States were randomly selected and the numbers of gas stations (independent variable) and restaurants (dependent variable) were recorded in a table. If we calculated the regression equation for these data, we would find that r would be close to 1. However, this does not mean that gas stations *cause* restaurants to be built. The primary cause is that there are fewer gas stations and restaurants in cities with small populations and greater numbers of gas stations and restaurants in cities with large populations.

 TOPICS FOR DISCUSSION

1. What is the purpose of calculating the equation of a regression line?

2. Discuss the implications of the following correlation coefficients: $r = -1$, $r = 0$, and $r = 1$.

3. Discuss the coefficient of determination and what its value says about a data set.

4. What are the implications of $r^2 = 1$ for a nonlinear regression equation?

EXERCISE SET 2.7   —*Suggested Assignment: Exercises 1–35, odd.*

    Use a graphing calculator for this Exercise Set.

In Exercises 1 to 4, determine whether the scatter diagram suggests a linear relationship between x and y, a nonlinear relationship between x and y, or no linear relationship between x and y.

1.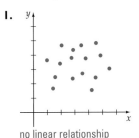
no linear relationship

2.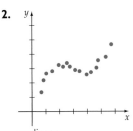
nonlinear

3.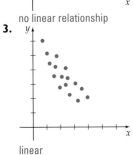
linear

4.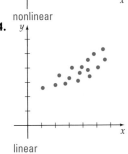
linear

In Exercises 5 and 6, determine for which scatter diagram, A or B, the coefficient of determination is closer to 1.

5.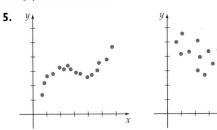
FIGURE A   FIGURE B

6.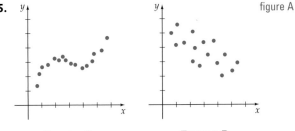
FIGURE A   FIGURE B

In Exercises 7 to 12, find the linear regression equation for the given set.

7. $\{(2, 6), (3, 6), (4, 8), (6, 11), (8, 18)\}$
$y = 2.00862069x + 0.5603448276$

8. $\{(2, -3), (3, -4), (4, -9), (5, -10), (7, -12)\}$
$y = -1.918918919x + 0.4594594595$

9. $\{(-3, 11.8), (-1, 9.5), (0, 8.6), (2, 8.7), (5, 5.4)\}$
$y = -0.7231182796x + 9.233870968$

10. $\{(-7, -11.7), (-5, -9.8), (-3, -8.1), (1, -5.9), (2, -5.7)\}$
$y = 0.6591216216x - 6.658108108$

11. $\{(1.3, -4.1), (2.6, -0.9), (5.4, 1.2), (6.2, 7.6), (7.5, 10.5)\}$
$y = 2.222641509x - 7.364150943$

12. $\{(-1.5, 8.1), (-0.5, 6.2), (3.0, -2.3), (5.4, -7.1), (6.1, -9.6)\}$
$y = -2.301587302x + 4.813968254$

In Exercises 13 to 16, find a quadratic model of the given data.

13. $\{(1, -1), (2, 1), (4, 8), (5, 14), (6, 25)\}$
$y = 1.095779221x^2 - 2.69642857x + 1.136363636$

14. $\{(-2, -5), (-1, 0), (0, 1), (1, 4), (2, 4)\}$
$y = -0.5714285714x^2 + 2.2x + 1.942857143$

15. $\{(1.5, -2.2), (2.2, -4.8), (3.4, -11.2), (5.1, -20.6), (6.3, -28.7)\}$
$y = -0.2987274717x^2 - 3.20998141x + 3.416463667$

16. $\{(-2, -1), (-1, -3.1), (0, -2.9), (1, 0.8), (2, 6.8), (3, 15.9)\}$
$y = 1.414285714x^2 + 1.954285714x - 2.705714286$

In Exercises 17 to 32, determine a regression model of the data.

17. ARCHEOLOGY The data below show the length, in centimeters, of the humerus and the total wingspan, in centimeters, of several pterosaurs, which are extinct flying reptiles of the order Pterosauria. (*Source: Southwest Educational Development Laboratory.*)

Pterosaur Data

Humerus	Wingspan	Humerus	Wingspan
24	600	20	500
32	750	27	570
22	430	15	300
17	370	15	310
13	270	9	240
4.4	68	4.4	55
3.2	53	2.9	50
1.5	24		

a. Compute the linear regression equation for these data.
$y = 23.55706665x - 24.4271215$

b. On the basis of this model, what is the projected wingspan of the pterosaur *Quetzalcoatlus northropi*, which is thought to have been the largest of the prehistoric birds, if its humerus is 54 centimeters? 1247.7 cm

▶ **18.** CONSUMER SCIENCE The table below shows the trade-in value for a 2-door, 1996 Ford Explorer in excellent condition for various odometer readings in thousands of miles. (*Source:* Kelley Blue Book web site, May–June 2000 Edition)

Trade-in Value of 1996 Ford Explorer, May 2000

Odometer	Trade-in	Odometer	Trade-in
45	11,635	70	9,710
50	11,435	75	9,460
60	10,735	80	8,985
68	10,060	95	8,260

a. Compute the linear regression equation for these data. $y = -72.06131724x + 14926.16191$

b. On the basis of this model, what is the expected trade-in value of a similar Ford Explorer with 55,000 miles on the odometer? $10,963

19. BOTANY The data in the table below are based on a study by R. A. Fisher of various flowers of the iris family. The width, in centimeters, and length, in centimeters, of the petal for selected flowers are shown in the table.

Iris Petal Data

Width	Length	Width	Length
2	14	24	56
23	51	10	36
20	52	19	51
13	45	16	47
17	45	14	47
16	31	17	45
14	47	16	31

a. Compute the linear regression equation for these data. $y = 1.671510024x + 16.32830605$

b. On the basis of this model, what is the estimated length of an iris petal if the iris has a petal width of 18 centimeters? 46.4 cm

20. BOTANY The study by R. A. Fisher (see Exercise 19) also included the width, in centimeters, and length, in centimeters, of the sepal for these flowers. Some of the data are shown below.

Iris Sepal Data

Width	Length	Width	Length
33	50	31	67
31	69	36	46
30	65	27	58
28	57	33	63
25	49	32	70
31	48	25	63
32	70	25	63

a. Compute the linear correlation coefficient for these data. $r = -0.0631510113$

b. On the basis of the value of the linear correlation coefficient, is a linear model of the data reasonable? No

21. HEALTH The body mass index (BMI) of a person is a measure of the person's ideal body weight. The table below shows the BMI for different weights for a person 5 feet 6 inches tall. (*Source:* San Diego *Union-Tribune*, May 31, 2000.)

BMI Data for Person 5′ 6″ Tall

Weight (lb)	BMI	Weight (lb)	BMI
110	17	160	25
120	19	170	27
125	20	180	29
135	21	190	30
140	22	200	32
145	23	205	33
150	24	215	34

a. Compute the linear regression equation for these data. $y = 0.1628623408x - 0.6875682232$

b. On the basis of the model, what is the estimated BMI for a person 5 feet 6 inches tall whose weight is 158 pounds? 25

22. **HEALTH** The BMI (see Exercise 21) of a person depends on height as well as weight. The table below shows the changes in BMI for a 150-pound person as height (in inches) changes. (*Source:* San Diego *Union-Tribune*, May 31, 2000.)

BMI Data for 150-Pound Person

Height (in.)	BMI	Height (in.)	BMI
60	29	71	21
62	27	72	20
64	25	73	19
66	24	74	19
67	23	75	18
68	23	76	18
70	21		

a. Compute the linear regression equation for these data.
$y = -0.6800298805x + 69.05129482$

b. On the basis of the model, what is the estimated BMI for a 150-pound person who is 5 feet 8 inches tall?
23

23. **INDUSTRIAL ENGINEERING** Permanent-magnet direct-current motors are used in a variety of industrial applications. For these motors to be effective, there must be a strong linear relationship between the current (in amps, A) supplied to the motor and the resulting torque (in newton-centimeters, N-cm) produced by the motor. A randomly selected motor is chosen from a production line and tested, with the following results.

Direct-Current Motor Data at 12 Volts

Current, in A	Torque, in N-cm	Current, in A	Torque, in N-cm
7.3	9.4	8.5	8.6
11.9	2.8	7.9	4.3
5.6	5.6	14.5	9.5
14.2	4.9	12.7	8.3
7.9	7.0	10.6	4.7

Based on the data in this table, is the chosen motor effective? Explain.
No, because the linear correlation coefficient is close to 0.

24. **HEALTH SCIENCES** The average remaining lifetime for men in the United States is given in the table below. (*Source:* National Institutes of Health.)

Average Remaining Lifetime for Men

Age	Years	Age	Years
0	73.6	65	15.9
15	59.4	75	9.9
35	40.8		

Based on the data in this table, is there a strong correlation between a man's age and the average remaining lifetime for that man? Explain.
Yes, because the linear correlation coefficient is close to −1.

25. **HEALTH SCIENCES** The average remaining lifetime for women in the United States is given in the table below. (*Source:* National Institutes of Health.)

Average Remaining Lifetime for Women

Age	Years	Age	Years
0	79.4	65	19.2
15	65.1	75	12.1
35	45.7		

a. Based on the data in this table, is there a strong correlation between a woman's age and the average remaining lifetime for that woman?
Yes, there is a strong linear correlation.

b. Compute the linear regression equation for these data.
$y = -0.9033088235x + 78.62573529$

c. On the basis of the model, what is the estimated remaining lifetime of a woman of age 25? 56 yrs

26. **BIOLOGY** The table below gives the body lengths, in centimeters, and the highest observed flying speeds, in meters per second, of various animals.

Species	Length	Flying speed
Horsefly	1.3	6.6
Hummingbird	8.1	11.2
Dragonfly	8.5	10.0
Willow warbler	11	12.0
Common pintail	56	22.8

Based on these data, what is the flying speed of a Whimbrel whose length is 41 centimeters? Round to the nearest whole number. (*Source:* Based on data from Leiva, *Algebra 2: Explorations and Applications*, p. 76, McDougall Littell, Boston; copyright 1997.) 19 m/s

27. ⬤ **AUTOMOTIVE TECHNOLOGY** The data in the table below show the horsepower and EPA fuel economy rating for *Car and Driver* magazine's 10 best cars for 2003.

Car	Horsepower	EPA
Acura RSX	160	27
BMW 3-series/M3	184	21
Cheverolet Corvette	350	19
Ford Focus	110	28
Honda Accord	160	26
Infiniti G35	260	20
Mazda 6 S	220	20
Nissan 350Z	287	20
Porsche Boxster	228	19
Subaru Impreza WRX	227	20

Find the linear coefficient of determination for these data, and write a sentence that explains the meaning of the coefficient of determination in the context of this problem. (*Source:* www.caranddriver.com.)
See answer at bottom of page.

28. HEALTH The table below shows the number of calories burned in 1 hour when running at various speeds.

Running Speed (mph)	Calories Burned
10	1126
10.9	1267
5	563
5.2	633
6	704
6.7	774
7	809
8	950
8.6	985
9	1056
7.5	880

a. Are the data positively or negatively correlated?
positively

b. How many calories does this model predict a person will burn who runs at 9.5 mph for 1 hour? Round to the nearest whole number. 1098 calories

29. BIOLOGY The survival of certain larvae after hatching depends on the temperature (in degrees Celsius) of the surrounding environment. The table below shows the number of larvae that survive at various temperatures. Find a quadratic model of these data.
$y = -0.6328671329x^2 + 33.6160839x - 379.4405594$

Larvae Surviving for Various Temperatures

Temp.	Number Surviving	Temp.	Number Surviving
20	40	26	68
21	47	27	67
22	52	28	64
23	61	29	62
24	64	30	61
25	64		

30. METEOROLOGY The temperature at various times on a summer day at a resort in southern California is given in the following table. The variable t is the number of minutes after 6:00 A.M., and the variable T is the temperature in degrees Fahrenheit.

Temperatures at a Resort

Time, t	Temp., T	Time, t	Temp., T
20	59	240	86
40	65	280	88
80	71	320	86
120	78	360	85
160	81	400	80
200	83		

a. Find a quadratic model for these data.
$T = -0.0004093949t^2 + 0.2265681259t + 55.57907207$

b. Use the model to predict the temperature at 1:00 P.M.
78.5°F

31. AUTOMOTIVE ENGINEERING The fuel efficiency, in miles per gallon, for a certain midsize car at various speeds, in miles per hour, is given in the table below.

Fuel Efficiency of a Midsize Car

mph	mpg	mph	mpg
25	29	55	31
30	32	60	28
35	33	65	24
40	35	70	19
45	34	75	17
50	33		

27. $r^2 \approx 0.667$. The coefficient of determination means that approximately 66.7% of the variation in EPA mileage estimates can be attributed to the horsepower of a car.

a. Find a quadratic model for these data.
   $y = -0.0165034965x^2 + 1.366713287x + 5.685314685$

b. Use the model to predict the fuel efficiency of this car when it is traveling at a speed of 50 mph. 32.8 mpg

▶ **32.** **BIOLOGY** The data in the table at the right show the oxygen consumption, in milliliters per minute, of a bird flying level at various speeds in kilometers per hour.

a. Find a quadratic model for these data.
   $y = 0.05208x^2 - 3.56026x + 82.32999$

b. Use the model to determine the speed at which the bird has minimum oxygen consumption. ≈34 km/h

Oxygen Consumption

Speed	Consumption
20	32
25	27
28	22
35	21
42	26
50	34

33. a. 5 lb: $s = 0.6130952381t^2 - 0.0714285714t + 0.1071428571$
10 lb: $s = 0.6091269841t^2 - 0.0011904762t - 0.3$
15 lb: $s = 0.5922619048t^2 + 0.3571428571t - 1.520833333$

CONNECTING CONCEPTS

33. PHYSICS Galileo (1564–1642) studied the acceleration due to gravity by allowing balls of various weights to roll down an incline. This allowed him to time the descent of a ball more accurately than by just dropping the ball. The data in the table show some possible results of such an experiment using balls of different masses. Time, t, is measured in seconds; distance, s, is measured in centimeters.

Distance Traveled for Balls of Various Weights

5-Pound Ball		10-Pound Ball		15-Pound Ball	
t	s	t	s	t	s
2	2	3	5	3	5
4	10	6	22	5	15
6	22	9	49	7	30
8	39	12	87	9	49
10	61	15	137	11	75
12	86	18	197	13	103
14	120			15	137
16	156				

a. Find a quadratic model for each of the balls.

b. ✎ On the basis of a similar experiment, Galileo concluded that if air resistance is excluded, all falling objects fall with the same acceleration. Explain how one could make such a conclusion from the regression equations.
All the regression equations are approximately the same. Therefore, the equations of motion of the three masses are the same.

34. ● **ASTRONOMY** In 1929, Edwin Hubble published a paper that revolutionized astronomy ("A Relationship Between Distance and Radial Velocity Among Extra-Galactic Nebulae," *Proceedings of the National Academy of Science*, 168). His paper dealt with the distance an extragalactic nebula was from the Milky Way galaxy and the nebula's velocity with respect to the Milky Way. The data are given in the table below. Distance is measured in megaparsecs (1 megaparsec equals 1.918×10^{19} miles), and velocity (called the *recession velocity*) is measured in kilometers per second. A negative velocity means the nebula is moving toward the Milky Way; a positive velocity means the nebula is moving away from the Milky Way.

Recession Velocities

Distance	Velocity	Distance	Velocity
0.032	170	0.9	650
0.034	290	0.9	150
0.214	−130	0.9	500
0.263	−70	1.0	920
0.275	−185	1.1	450
0.275	−220	1.1	500
0.45	200	1.4	500
0.5	290	1.7	960
0.5	270	2.0	500
0.63	200	2.0	850
0.8	300	2.0	800
0.9	−30	2.0	1090

a. Find the linear regression model for these data.
$y = 454.1584409x - 40.78364910$

b. On the basis of this model, what is the recession velocity of a nebula that is 1.5 megaparsecs from the Milky Way? 640 km/s

35. The data in the table at the right were collected on five successive Saturdays. They show the average number of cars entering a shopping center parking lot. The value of t is the number of minutes after 9:00 A.M. The value of N is the number of cars that entered the parking lot in the 10 minutes prior to the value of t. Does a linear model or a quadratic regression model better fit these data? Explain. quadratic; r^2 is closer to 1 for the quadratic model.

Average Number of Cars Entering a Parking Lot

t	N	t	N
20	70	140	301
40	135	160	298
60	178	180	284
80	210	200	286
100	260	220	260
120	280	240	195

PROJECTS

MEDIAN–MEDIAN LINE Another linear model of data is called the **median–median line**. This line employs *summary points* calculated using the medians of subsets of the independent and dependent variables. The **median** of a data set is the middle number or the average of the two middle numbers for a data set arranged in numerical order. For instance, to find the median of {8, 12, 6, 7, 9}, first arrange the data in numerical order.

$$6, 7, 8, 9, 12$$

The median is 8, the number in the middle. To find the median of {15, 12, 20, 9, 13, 10}, arrange the numbers in numerical order.

$$9, 10, 12, 13, 15, 20$$

The median is 12.5, the average of the two middle numbers.

$$\text{Median} = \frac{12 + 13}{2} = 12.5$$

The median–median line is determined by dividing a data set into three equal groups. (If the set cannot be divided into three equal groups, the first and third groups should be equal. For instance, if there are 11 data points, divide the set into groups of 4, 3, and 4.) The slope of the median–median line is the slope of the line through the x-medians and y-medians of the first and third sets of points. The median–median line passes through the average of the x- and y-medians of all three sets.

A graphing calculator can be used to find the median–median line. This line, along with the linear regression line, is shown in the next column for the data in the accompanying table.

I. Find the median–median line for the data in Exercise 17 on page 263.

2. Find the median–median line for the data in Exercise 18 on page 264.

x	y
2	3
3	5
4	4
5	7
6	8
7	9
8	12
9	12
10	14
11	15
12	14

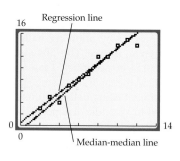

3. Consider the data set {(1, 3), (2, 5), (3, 7), (4, 9), (5, 11), (6, 13), (7, 15), (8, 17)}.

a. Find the linear regression line for these data.

b. Find the median–median line for these data.

c. What conclusion might you draw from the answers to parts **a.** and **b.**?

4. For this exercise, use the data in the table in Project 1.

a. Calculate the median–median line and the linear regression line.

b. Change the entry (12, 14) to (12, 1) and then recalculate the median–median line and the linear regression line.

c. Explain why there is more change in the linear regression line than in the median–median line.

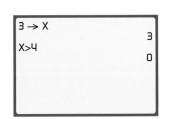

Exploring Concepts with Technology

Graphing Piecewise Functions with a Graphing Calculator

A graphing calculator can be used to graph piecewise functions by including as part of the function the interval on which each piece of the function is defined. The method is based on the fact that a graphing calculator "evaluates" inequalities. For purposes of this Exploration, we will use keystrokes for a TI-83 calculator.

For instance, store 3 in **X** by pressing 3 [STO▶] [X,T,Θ,n] [ENTER]. Now enter the inequality $x > 4$ by pressing [X,T,Θ,n] [2ND] TEST 3 4 [ENTER]. Your screen should look like the one at the left. Note that the value of the inequality is 0. This occurs because the calculator replaced **X** by 3 and then determined whether the inequality $3 > 4$ was true or false. The calculator expresses the fact that the inequality is false by placing a zero on the screen. If we repeat the sequence of steps above, except that we store 5 in **X** instead of 3, the calculator will determine that the inequality is true and place a 1 on the screen.

This property of calculators is used to graph piecewise functions. Graphs of these functions work best when Dot mode rather than Connected mode is used. To switch to Dot mode, select [MODE], use the arrow keys to highlight [DOT], and then press [ENTER].

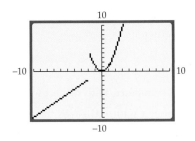

Now we will graph the piecewise function defined by $f(x) = \begin{cases} x, & x \le -2 \\ x^2, & x > -2 \end{cases}$.

Enter the function[4] as Y₁=X*(X≤-2)+X²*(X>-2) and graph this in the standard viewing window. Note that you are multiplying each piece of the function by its domain. The graph will appear as shown at the left.

To understand how the graph is drawn, we will consider two values of x, -8 and 2, and evaluate Y₁ for each of these values.

Y₁=X*(X≤-2)+X²*(X>-2)

$= -8(-8 \le -2) + (-8)^2(-8 > -2)$

$= -8(1) + 64(0) = -8$ • When $x = -8$, the value assigned to $-8 \le -2$ is 1; the value assigned to $-8 > -2$ is 0.

Y₁=X*(X≤-2)+X²*(X>-2)

$= 2(2 \le -2) + 2^2(2 > -2)$

$= 2(0) + 4(1) = 4$ • When $x = 2$, the value assigned to $2 \le -2$ is 0; the value assigned to $2 > -2$ is 1.

In a similar manner, for any value of x for which $x \le -2$, the value assigned to (X≤-2) is 1 and the value assigned to (X>-2) is 0. Thus Y₁=X*1+X²*0=X on that interval. This means that only the $f(x) = x$ piece of the function is graphed. When $x > -2$, the value assigned to (X≤-2) is 0 and the value assigned to (X>-2) is 1. Thus Y₁=X*0+X²*1=X² on that interval. This means that only the $f(x) = x^2$ piece of the function is graphed on that interval.

[4]Note that pressing [2ND] TEST will display the inequality menu.

1. Graph: $f(x) = \begin{cases} x^2, & x < 2 \\ -x, & x \geq 2 \end{cases}$

2. Graph: $f(x) = \begin{cases} x^2 - x, & x < 2 \\ -x + 4, & x \geq 2 \end{cases}$

3. Graph: $f(x) = \begin{cases} -x^2 + 1, & x < 0 \\ x^2 - 1, & x \geq 0 \end{cases}$

4. Graph: $f(x) = \begin{cases} x^3 - 4x, & x < 1 \\ x^2 - x + 2, & x \geq 1 \end{cases}$

CHAPTER 2 SUMMARY

2.1 A Two-Dimensional Coordinate System and Graphs

- *The Distance Formula* The distance d between the points represented by (x_1, y_1) and (x_2, y_2) is

$$d = \sqrt{(x_2 - x_1)^2 + (y_2 - y_1)^2}$$

- The midpoint of the line segment from $P_1(x_1, y_1)$ to $P_2(x_2, y_2)$ is

$$\left(\frac{x_1 + x_2}{2}, \frac{y_1 + y_2}{2} \right)$$

- The standard form of the equation of a circle with center at (h, k) and radius r is $(x - h)^2 + (y - k)^2 = r^2$.

2.2 Introduction to Functions

- *Definition of a Function* A function is a set of ordered pairs in which no two ordered pairs that have the same first coordinate have different second coordinates.

- A graph is the graph of a function if and only if no vertical line intersects the graph at more than one point. If every horizontal line intersects the graph of a function at most once, then the graph is the graph of a one-to-one function.

2.3 Linear Functions

- A function is a linear function of x if it can be written in the form $f(x) = mx + b$, where m and b are real numbers and $m \neq 0$.

- The slope m of the line passing through the points $P_1(x_1, y_1)$ and $P_2(x_2, y_2)$ with $x_1 \neq x_2$ is given by

$$m = \frac{y_2 - y_1}{x_2 - x_1}$$

- The graph of the equation $f(x) = mx + b$ has slope m and y-intercept $(0, b)$.

- Two nonvertical lines are parallel if and only if their slopes are equal. Two lines with slopes m_1 and m_2 are perpendicular if and only if $m_1 = -\dfrac{1}{m_2}$.

2.4 Quadratic Functions

- A quadratic function of x is a function that can be represented by an equation of the form $f(x) = ax^2 + bx + c$, where a, b, and c are real numbers and $a \neq 0$.

- The vertex of the graph of $f(x) = ax^2 + bx + c$ is

$$\left(-\frac{b}{2a}, f\left(-\frac{b}{2a} \right) \right)$$

- Every quadratic function $f(x) = ax^2 + bx + c$ can be written in the standard form $f(x) = a(x - h)^2 + k$, $a \neq 0$. The graph of f is a parabola with vertex (h, k). The parabola is symmetric with respect to the vertical line $x = h$, which is called the axis of symmetry of the parabola. The parabola opens up if $a > 0$; it opens down if $a < 0$.

2.5 Properties of Graphs

- The graph of an equation is symmetric with respect to

  the y-axis if the replacement of x with $-x$ leaves the equation unaltered.

  the x-axis if the replacement of y with $-y$ leaves the equation unaltered.

  the origin if the replacement of x with $-x$ and y with $-y$ leaves the equation unaltered.

- If f is a function and c is a positive constant, then

  $y = f(x) + c$ is the graph of $y = f(x)$ shifted up *vertically* c units

  $y = f(x) - c$ is the graph of $y = f(x)$ shifted down *vertically* c units

  $y = f(x + c)$ is the graph of $y = f(x)$ shifted left *horizontally* c units

  $y = f(x - c)$ is the graph of $y = f(x)$ shifted right *horizontally* c units

- The graph of

  $y = -f(x)$ is the graph of $y = f(x)$ reflected across the x-axis.

$y = f(-x)$ is the graph of $y = f(x)$ reflected across the y-axis.

- If $a > 1$, then the graph of $y = f(ax)$ is a horizontal compressing of $y = f(x)$.

- If $0 < a < 1$, then the graph of $y = f(ax)$ is a horizontal stretching of the graph of $y = f(x)$.

2.6 The Algebra of Functions

- For all values of x for which both $f(x)$ and $g(x)$ are defined, we define the following functions.

  Sum $(f + g)(x) = f(x) + g(x)$

  Difference $(f - g)(x) = f(x) - g(x)$

  Product $(fg)(x) = f(x) \cdot g(x)$

  Quotient $\left(\dfrac{f}{g}\right)(x) = \dfrac{f(x)}{g(x)}, \quad g(x) \neq 0$

- The expression

$$\frac{f(x + h) - f(x)}{h}, \quad h \neq 0$$

is called the difference quotient of f. The difference quotient is an important function because it can be used to compute the *average rate of change* of f over the time interval $[x, x + h]$.

- For the functions f and g, the composite function, or composition, of f by g is given by $(g \circ f)(x) = g[f(x)]$ for all x in the domain of f such that $f(x)$ is in the domain of g.

2.7 Modeling Data Using Regression

- Regression analysis is used to find a mathematical model of collected data.

- The least-squares regression line is the line that minimizes the sum of the squares of the vertical deviations of all data points from the line.

- The linear correlation coefficient r is a measure of how closely the points of a data set can be modeled by a straight line. If $r = -1$, then the points of the data set can be modeled *exactly* by a straight line with negative slope. If $r = 1$, then the data set can be modeled *exactly* by a straight line with positive slope. For all data sets, $-1 \leq r \leq 1$.

- The coefficient of determination is r^2. It measures the percent of the total variation in the dependent variable that is explained by the regression line.

- It is possible to find both linear and nonlinear mathematical models of data.

CHAPTER 2 TRUE/FALSE EXERCISES

In Exercises 1 to 14, answer true or false. If the statement is false, give an example or a reason to show that the statement is false.

1. Let f be any function. Then $f(a) = f(b)$ implies that $a = b$.
   False. Let $f(x) = x^2$. Then $f(3) = f(-3) = 9$, but $3 \neq -3$.

2. If f and g are two functions, then $(f \circ g)(x) = (g \circ f)(x)$.
   False. Consider $f(x) = x + 1$ and $g(x) = x^2 - 2$.

3. If f is not a one-to-one function, then there are at least two numbers u and v in the domain of f for which $f(u) = f(v)$. True

4. Let f be a function such that $f(x) = f(x + 4)$ for all real numbers x. If $f(2) = 3$, then $f(18) = 3$. True

5. For all functions f, $[f(x)]^2 = f[f(x)]$.
   False. Let $f(x) = 3x$. $[f(x)]^2 = 9x^2$, whereas $f[f(x)] = f(3x) = 3(3x) = 9x$.

6. Let f be any function. Then for all a and b in the domain of f such that $f(b) \neq 0$ and $b \neq 0$,
$$\frac{f(a)}{f(b)} = \frac{a}{b}$$
   False. Let $f(x) = x^2$. Then $f(1) = 1$, $f(2) = 4$. Thus $\dfrac{f(2)}{f(1)} = 4 \neq \dfrac{2}{1}$.

7. The **identity function** $f(x) = x$ is its own inverse. True

8. If f is a function, then $f(a + b) = f(a) + f(b)$ for all real numbers a and b in the domain of f.
   False. Let $f(x) = |x|$. Then $f(-1 + 3) = f(2) = 2$. $f(-1) + f(3) = 1 + 3 = 4$.

9. If f is defined by $f(x) = |x|$, then $f(ab) = f(a)f(b)$ for all real numbers a and b. True

10. If f is a one-to-one function and a and b are real numbers in the domain of f with $a < b$, then $f(a) \neq f(b)$. True

11. The coordinates of a point on the graph of $y = f(x)$ are (a, b). If k is a positive constant, then (a, kb) are the coordinates of a point on the graph of $y = kf(x)$. True

12. For every function f, the real number c is a solution of $f(x) = 0$ if and only if $(c, 0)$ is an x-intercept of the graph of $y = f(x)$. True

13. The domain of every polynomial function is the set of real numbers. True

14. If the linear coefficient of determination is 0.8, then the slope of the regression line is positive.
   False. The coefficient of determination is r^2 and therefore nonnegative.

CHAPTER 2 REVIEW EXERCISES

—Answers to Exercises 15–20, 41–42, and 51–68 are on pages AA9–AA10.

In Exercises 1 and 2, find the distance between the points whose coordinates are given.

1. $(-3, 2)$ $(7, 11)$
$\sqrt{181}$ [2.1]

2. $(5, -4)$ $(-3, -8)$
$\sqrt{80} = 4\sqrt{5}$ [2.1]

In Exercises 3 and 4, find the midpoint of the line segment with the given endpoints.

3. $(2, 8)$ $(-3, 12)$
$\left(-\frac{1}{2}, 10\right)$ [2.1]

4. $(-4, 7)$ $(8, -11)$
$(2, -2)$ [2.1]

In Exercises 5 and 6, determine the center and radius of the circle with the given equation.

5. $(x - 3)^2 + (y + 4)^2 = 81$ center $(3, -4)$, radius 9 [2.1]

6. $x^2 + y^2 + 10x + 4y + 20 = 0$ center $(-5, -2)$, radius 3 [2.1]

In Exercises 7 and 8, find the equation in standard form of the circle that satisfies the given conditions.

7. Center $C = (2, -3)$, radius $r = 5$
$(x - 2)^2 + (y + 3)^2 = 5^2$ [2.1]

8. Center $C = (-5, 1)$, passing through $(3, 1)$
$(x + 5)^2 + (y - 1)^2 = 8^2$, radius $= |-5 - (3)| = 8$ [2.1]

9. If $f(x) = 3x^2 + 4x - 5$, find

a. $f(1)$ 2
b. $f(-3)$ 10
c. $f(t)$ $3t^2 + 4t - 5$
d. $f(x + h)$ $3x^2 + 6xh + 3h^2 + 4x + 4h - 5$
e. $3f(t)$ $9t^2 + 12t - 15$
f. $f(3t)$ $27t^2 + 12t - 5$ [2.2]

10. If $g(x) = \sqrt{64 - x^2}$, find

a. $g(3)$ $\sqrt{55}$
b. $g(-5)$ $\sqrt{39}$
c. $g(8)$ 0
d. $g(-x)$ $\sqrt{64 - x^2}$
e. $2g(t)$ $2\sqrt{64 - t^2}$
f. $g(2t)$ $2\sqrt{16 - t^2}$ [2.2]

11. If $f(x) = x^2 + 4x$ and $g(x) = x - 8$, find

a. $(f \circ g)(3)$ 5
b. $(g \circ f)(-3)$ −11
c. $(f \circ g)(x)$ $x^2 - 12x + 32$
d. $(g \circ f)(x)$ $x^2 + 4x - 8$ [2.6]

12. If $f(x) = 2x^2 + 7$ and $g(x) = |x - 1|$, find

a. $(f \circ g)(-5)$ 79
b. $(g \circ f)(-5)$ 56
c. $(f \circ g)(x)$ $2x^2 - 4x + 9$
d. $(g \circ f)(x)$ $2x^2 + 6$ [2.6]

13. If $f(x) = 4x^2 - 3x - 1$, find the difference quotient
$$\frac{f(x + h) - f(x)}{h}$$
$8x + 4h - 3$ [2.6]

14. If $g(x) = x^3 - x$, find the difference quotient
$$\frac{g(x + h) - g(x)}{h}$$
$3x^2 + 3xh + h^2 - 1$ [2.6]

In Exercises 15 to 20, sketch the graph of f. Find the interval(s) in which f is a. increasing, b. constant, c. decreasing.

15. $f(x) = |x - 3| - 2$ [2.2]
16. $f(x) = x^2 - 5$ [2.2]
17. $f(x) = |x + 2| - |x - 2|$ [2.2]
18. $f(x) = [\![x + 3]\!]$ [2.2]
19. $f(x) = \frac{1}{2}x - 3$ [2.2]
20. $f(x) = \sqrt[3]{x}$ [2.2]

In Exercises 21 to 24, determine the domain of the function represented by the given equation.

21. $f(x) = -2x^2 + 3$
Domain: $\{x \mid x \text{ is a real number}\}$ [2.2]

22. $f(x) = \sqrt{6 - x}$
Domain: $\{x \mid x \le 6\}$ [2.2]

23. $f(x) = \sqrt{25 - x^2}$
Domain: $\{x \mid -5 \le x \le 5\}$ [2.2]

24. $f(x) = \frac{3}{x^2 - 2x - 15}$
Domain: $\{x \mid x \ne -3, x \ne 5\}$ [2.2]

In Exercises 25 and 26, find the slope-intercept form of the equation of the line through the two points.

25. $(-1, 3)$ $(4, -7)$
$y = -2x + 1$ [2.3]

26. $(0, 0)$ $(7, 11)$ $y = \frac{11}{7}x$ [2.3]

27. Find the slope-intercept form of the equation of the line that is parallel to the graph of $3x - 4y = 8$ and passes through $(2, 11)$. $y = \frac{3}{4}x + \frac{19}{2}$ [2.3]

28. Find the slope-intercept form of the equation of the line that is perpendicular to the graph of $2x = -5y + 10$ and passes through $(-3, -7)$. $y = \frac{5}{2}x + \frac{1}{2}$ [2.3]

In Exercises 29 to 34, use the method of completing the square to write each quadratic equation in its standard form.

29. $f(x) = x^2 + 6x + 10$
$f(x) = (x + 3)^2 + 1$ [2.4]

30. $f(x) = 2x^2 + 4x + 5$
$f(x) = 2(x + 1)^2 + 3$ [2.4]

31. $f(x) = -x^2 - 8x + 3$
$f(x) = -(x + 4)^2 + 19$ [2.4]

32. $f(x) = 4x^2 - 6x + 1$
$f(x) = 4\left(x - \frac{3}{4}\right)^2 - \frac{5}{4}$ [2.4]

33. $f(x) = -3x^2 + 4x - 5$
$f(x) = -3\left(x - \frac{2}{3}\right)^2 - \frac{11}{3}$ [2.4]

34. $f(x) = x^2 - 6x + 9$
$f(x) = (x - 3)^2 + 0$ [2.4]

In Exercises 35 to 38, find the vertex of the graph of the quadratic function.

35. $f(x) = 3x^2 - 6x + 11$
$(1, 8)$ [2.4]

36. $h(x) = 4x^2 - 10$
$(0, -10)$ [2.4]

37. $k(x) = -6x^2 + 60x + 11$
$(5, 161)$ [2.4]

38. $m(x) = 14 - 8x - x^2$
$(-4, 30)$ [2.4]

39. Use the formula
$$d = \frac{|mx_1 + b - y_1|}{\sqrt{1 + m^2}}$$
$\frac{4\sqrt{5}}{5}$ [2.3]

to find the distance from the point $(1, 3)$ to the line given by $y = 2x - 3$.

40. A freight company has determined that its cost per delivery of delivering x parcels is

$$C(x) = 1050 + 0.5x$$

The price it charges to send a parcel is $13.00 per parcel. Determine

a. the revenue function $R = 13x$

b. the profit function $P = 12.5x - 1050$

c. the minimum number of parcels the company must ship to break even $x = 84$ [2.3]

In Exercises 41 and 42, sketch a graph that is symmetric to the given graph with respect to the a. x-axis, b. y-axis, c. origin.

41.

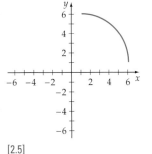

[2.5]

42.

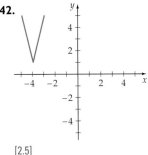

[2.5]

In Exercises 43 to 50, determine whether the graph of each equation is symmetric with respect to the a. x-axis, b. y-axis, c. origin.

43. $y = x^2 - 7$
symmetric to the y-axis [2.5]

44. $x = y^2 + 3$
symmetric to the x-axis [2.5]

45. $y = x^3 - 4x$
symmetric to the origin [2.5]

46. $y^2 = x^2 + 4$
symmetric to the x-axis, the y-axis, and the origin [2.5]

47. $\dfrac{x^2}{3^2} + \dfrac{y^2}{4^2} = 1$ symmetric to the x-axis, the y-axis, and the origin [2.5]

48. $xy = 8$
symmetric to the origin [2.5]

49. $|y| = |x|$ symmetric to the x-axis, the y-axis, and the origin [2.5]

50. $|x + y| = 4$
symmetric to the origin [2.5]

In Exercises 51 to 56, sketch the graph of g. a. Find the domain and the range of g. b. State whether g is even, odd, or neither even nor odd.

51. $g(x) = -x^2 + 4$ [2.5]

52. $g(x) = -2x - 4$ [2.5]

53. $g(x) = |x - 2| + |x + 2|$ [2.5]   **54.** $g(x) = \sqrt{16 - x^2}$ [2.5]

55. $g(x) = x^3 - x$ [2.5]

56. $g(x) = 2[\![x]\!]$ [2.5]

In Exercises 57 to 62, first write the quadratic function in standard form, and then make use of translations to graph the function.

57. $F(x) = x^2 + 4x - 7$ [2.5]   **58.** $A(x) = x^2 - 6x - 5$ [2.5]

59. $P(x) = 3x^2 - 4$ [2.5]   **60.** $G(x) = 2x^2 - 8x + 3$ [2.5]

61. $W(x) = -4x^2 - 6x + 6$ [2.5] **62.** $T(x) = -2x^2 - 10x$ [2.5]

63. On the same set of coordinate axes, sketch the graph of $p(x) = \sqrt{x} + c$ for $c = 0, -1$, and 2. [2.5]

64. On the same set of coordinate axes, sketch the graph of $q(x) = \sqrt{x + c}$ for $c = 0, -1$, and 2. [2.5]

65. On the same set of coordinate axes, sketch the graph of $r(x) = c\sqrt{9 - x^2}$ for $c = 1, \dfrac{1}{2}$, and -2. [2.5]

66. On the same set of coordinate axes, sketch the graph of $s(t) = [\![cx]\!]$ for $c = 1, \dfrac{1}{4}$, and 4. [2.2]

In Exercises 67 and 68, graph each piecewise-defined function.

67. $f(x) = \begin{cases} x, & \text{if } x \le 0 \\ \dfrac{1}{2}x, & \text{if } x > 0 \end{cases}$ [2.2]

68. $g(x) = \begin{cases} -2, & \text{if } x < -3 \\ \dfrac{2}{3}x, & \text{if } -3 \le x \le 3 \\ 2, & \text{if } x > 3 \end{cases}$ [2.2]

In Exercises 69 and 70, use the given functions f and g to find $f + g, f - g, fg$, and $\dfrac{f}{g}$. State the domain of each.

69. $f(x) = x^2 - 9, \quad g(x) = x + 3$
Answer on page AA10. [2.6]

70. $f(x) = x^3 + 8, \quad g(x) = x^2 - 2x + 4$
Answer on page AA10. [2.6]

71. Find two numbers whose sum is 50 and whose product is a maximum.   25, 25 [2.4]

72. Find two numbers whose difference is 10 and the sum of whose squares is a minimum.   −5 and 5 [2.4]

73. The distance traveled by a ball rolling down a ramp is given by $s(t) = 3t^2$, where t is the time in seconds after the ball is released and $s(t)$ is measured in feet. Evaluate the average velocity of the ball for each of the following time intervals.

a. [2, 4]   18 ft/s
b. [2, 3]   15 ft/s
c. [2, 2.5]   13.5 ft/s
d. [2, 2.01]   12.03 ft/s

e. What appears to be the average velocity of the ball for the time interval $[2, 2 + \Delta t]$ as Δt approaches 0?   12 ft/s [2.4]

74. The distance traveled by a ball that is pushed down a ramp is given by $s(t) = 2t^2 + t$, where t is the time in seconds after the ball is released and $s(t)$ is measured in feet.

Evaluate the average velocity of the ball for each of the following time intervals.

a. [3, 5]   **b.** [3, 4]   **c.** [3, 3.5]   **d.** [3, 3.01]
   17 ft/s   15 ft/s   14 ft/s   13.02 ft/s

e. What appears to be the average velocity of the ball for the time interval [3, 3 + Δt] as Δt approaches 0?
13 ft/s [2.4]

75. COMPUTER SCIENCE A test of an Internet service provider showed the following download times (in seconds) for files of various sizes (in kilobytes).

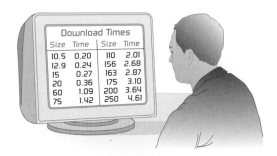

Download Times

Size	Time	Size	Time
10.5	0.20	110	2.01
12.9	0.24	156	2.68
15	0.27	163	2.87
20	0.36	175	3.10
60	1.09	200	3.64
75	1.42	250	4.61

a. Find a linear regression model for these data.
$y = 0.0180247x + 0.0005005$

b. Judging on the basis of the value of r, is a linear model of these data a reasonable model? Explain.
Yes. $r \approx 0.999$, which is very close to 1.

c. On the basis of the model, what is the expected download time of a file that is 100 kilobytes in size? Round to the nearest tenth of a second. 1.8 s [2.7]

76. PHYSICS The rate at which water will escape from the bottom of a can depends on a number of factors, including the height of the water, the size of the hole, and the diameter of the can. The table below shows the height (in millimeters) of water in a can after t seconds.

Water Escaping a Ruptured Can

Height	Time	Height	Time
0	180	60	93
10	163	70	81
20	147	80	70
30	133	90	60
40	118	100	50
50	105	110	48

a. Find the quadratic regression model for these data.
$y = 0.0047952048x^2 - 1.756843157x + 180.4065934$

b. On the basis of this model, will the can ever empty?
No

c. Explain why there seems to be a contradiction between the model and reality, in that we know the can will eventually run out of water.
The regression line is a model of the data and is not based on physical principles. [2.7]

CHAPTER 2 TEST

1. Find the midpoint and the length of the line segment with endpoints $(-2, 3)$ and $(4, -1)$.
midpoint (1, 1); length $2\sqrt{13}$ [2.1]

2. Determine the x- and y-intercepts, and then graph the equation $x = 2y^2 - 4$. [2.1]
Answer on page AA11.

3. Graph the equation $y = |x + 2| + 1$. [2.1]
Answer on page AA11.

4. Find the center and radius of the circle that has the general form $x^2 - 4x + y^2 + 2y - 4 = 0$.
center (2, −1); radius 3 [2.1]

5. Determine the domain of the function
$$f(x) = -\sqrt{x^2 - 16}$$
domain $\{x \mid x \geq 4 \text{ or } x \leq -4\}$ [2.2]

6. Graph $f(x) = -2|x - 2| + 1$. Identify the intervals over which the function is

a. increasing

b. constant

c. decreasing [2.2]
Answers on page AA11.

7. An air freight company has determined that its cost per flight of delivering x parcels is
$$C(x) = 875 + 0.75x$$
The price it charges to send a parcel is $12.00 per parcel. Determine

a. the revenue function $R = 12.00x$

b. the profit function $P = 11.25x - 875$

c. the minimum number of parcels the company must ship to break even $x = 78$ [2.4]

8. Use the graph of $f(x) = |x|$ to graph $y = -f(x + 2) - 1$. [2.5]
Answer on page AA11.

9. Classify each of the following as either an even function, an odd function, or neither an even nor an odd function.

a. $f(x) = x^4 - x^2$ **b.** $f(x) = x^3 - x$
even   odd

c. $f(x) = x - 1$
neither [2.5]

10. Find the slope-intercept form of the equation of the line that passes through $(4, -2)$ and is perpendicular to the graph of $3x - 2y = 4$. $y = -\dfrac{2}{3}x + \dfrac{2}{3}$ [2.3]

11. Find the maximum or minimum value of the function $f(x) = x^2 - 4x - 8$. State whether this value is a maximum or a minimum value. -12, minimum [2.4]

12. Let $f(x) = x^2 - 1$ and $g(x) = x - 2$. Find $(f + g)$ and (f/g). $x^2 + x - 3;\ \dfrac{x^2 - 1}{x - 2}, x \neq 2$ [2.6]

13. Find the difference quotient of the function
$$f(x) = x^2 + 1 \quad 2x + h \text{ [2.6]}$$

14. Evaluate $(f \circ g)(x)$, where
$$f(x) = x^2 - 2x \quad \text{and} \quad g(x) = 2x + 5$$
$4x^2 + 16x + 15$ [2.6]

15. The distance traveled by a ball rolling down a ramp is given by $s(t) = 5t^2$, where t is the time in seconds after the ball is released and $s(t)$ is measured in feet. Evaluate the average velocity of the ball for each of the following time intervals.

a. $[2, 3]$ **b.** $[2, 2.5]$ **c.** $[2, 2.01]$
25 ft/s   22.5 ft/s   20.05 ft/s [2.6]

16. The table below shows the percent of water and the number of calories in various canned soups to which 100 grams of water are added.

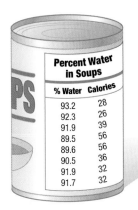

% Water	Calories
93.2	28
92.3	26
91.9	39
89.5	56
89.6	56
90.5	36
91.9	32
91.7	32

a. Find the linear regression line for these data.
$y = -7.98245614x + 767.122807$

b. Using the linear model from part **a.**, find the expected number of calories in a soup that is 89% water. Round to the nearest whole number. 57 calories [2.7]

CUMULATIVE REVIEW EXERCISES

1. What property of real numbers is demonstrated by $3(a + b) = 3(b + a)$? Commutative Property of Addition [P.1]

2. Which of the numbers -3, $-\dfrac{2}{3}$, $\dfrac{6}{\pi}$, 0, $\sqrt{16}$ and $\sqrt{2}$ are not rational numbers? $\dfrac{6}{\pi}, \sqrt{2}$ [P.1]

In Exercises 3 to 8, simplify the expression.

3. $3 + 4(2x - 9)$
$8x - 33$ [P.1]

4. $(-4xy^2)^3(-2x^2y^4)$
$128x^5y^{10}$ [P.2]

5. $\dfrac{24a^4b^3}{18a^4b^5}$ $\dfrac{4}{3b^2}$ [P.2]

6. $(2x + 3)(3x - 7)$
$6x^2 - 5x - 21$ [P.3]

7. $\dfrac{x^2 + 6x - 27}{x^2 - 9}$ $\dfrac{x + 9}{x + 3}$ [P.5]

8. $\dfrac{\dfrac{4}{2x - 1} - \dfrac{2}{x - 1}}{\dfrac{-2}{(2x - 1)(x - 1)}}$ [P.5]

In Exercises 9 to 14, solve for x.

9. $6 - 2(2x - 4) = 14$
0 [1.1]

10. $x^2 - x - 1 = 0$
$\dfrac{1 \pm \sqrt{5}}{2}$ [1.3]

11. $(2x - 1)(x + 3) = 4$ $-\dfrac{7}{2}, 1$ [1.3]

12. $3x + 2y = 15$ $x = -\dfrac{2}{3}y + 5$ [1.1]

13. $x^4 - x^2 - 2 = 0$
$\pm\sqrt{2}, \pm i$ [1.4]

14. $3x - 1 < 5x + 7$
$x > -4$ [1.5]

15. Find the distance between the points $P_1(-2, -4)$ and $P_2(2, -3)$. $\sqrt{17}$ [2.1]

16. Given $G(x) = 2x^3 - 4x - 7$, find $G(-2)$. -15 [2.2]

17. Find the equation of the line between the points $P_1(2, -3)$ and $P_2(-2, -1)$. $y = -\dfrac{1}{2}x - 2$ [2.3]

18. How many ounces of pure water must be added to 60 ounces of an 8% salt solution to make a 3% salt solution? 100 oz [1.1]

19. The path of a tennis ball during a serve is given by $h(x) = -0.002x^2 - 0.03x + 8$. For a serve to be legal in tennis, the ball must be at least 3 feet high when it is 39 feet from the server, and it must land in a spot that is less than 60 feet from the server. Does the path of a ball given by $h(x) = -0.002x^2 - 0.03x + 8$, where $h(x)$ is the height of the ball in feet x feet from the server, satisfy the conditions of a legal serve? Yes [2.4]

20. A patient with a fever is given a medication to reduce the fever. The equation $T = -0.04t + 104$ models the temperature T, in degrees Fahrenheit, t minutes after taking the medication. What is the rate, in degrees per minute, at which the patient's temperature is decreasing? 0.04°F/min [2.3]

POLYNOMIAL AND RATIONAL FUNCTIONS

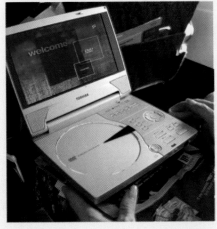

DVD players have become very popular in the last few years. More than 31 million DVD players have been sold as of January 2002.

Production Cost and Average Cost

In this chapter you will study polynomial and rational functions. These types of functions have many practical applications. For instance, they can be used to model production costs and average costs associated with the manufacture of DVD players.

The cost, in dollars, of producing x DVD players is given by the polynomial function

$$C(x) = 0.001x^2 + 101x + 245,000$$

The average cost per DVD player is given by the rational function

$$\overline{C}(x) = \frac{C(x)}{x} = \frac{0.001x^2 + 101x + 245,000}{x}$$

The following graph of $\overline{C}$ shows that the minimum average cost per DVD player is obtained by producing 15,652 DVD players.

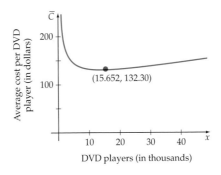

Average cost per DVD player (in dollars)

(15.652, 132.30)

DVD players (in thousands)

Additional average cost applications are given in **Exercises 53 and 54 on page 342.**

VIDEO & DVD

SSG

WWW

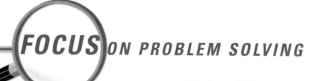

Find and Use Clues to Narrow the Search

The game of Clue is a classic whodunit game. At the beginning of the game you are informed that Mr. Boddy has been murdered! It is your job to find and use clues to determine the murderer, the weapon, and the room in which the murder was committed. Was it Miss Scarlet in the billiard room with the revolver? Or did Professor Plum commit the murder in the conservatory with the rope? There are six suspects, six possible murder weapons, and nine rooms in Mr. Boddy's mansion. There are a total of $6 \times 6 \times 9 = 324$ possible solutions to each game.

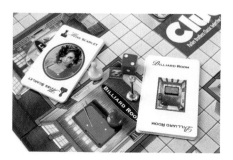

In this chapter you will often need to find the zeros of a polynomial function. Finding the zeros of a polynomial function can be more complicated than solving a game of Clue. After all, any real or complex number is a possible zero. Quite often the zeros of a polynomial function are found by using several theorems to narrow the search. In most cases no single theorem can be used to find the zeros of a given polynomial function, but by combining the results of several theorems, we are often able to gather enough clues to find the zeros. In **Exercise 52, page 317,** you will apply several theorems from this chapter to find the zeros of a polynomial function.

THE REMAINDER THEOREM AND THE FACTOR THEOREM

If $P(x)$ is a polynomial, then the values of x for which $P(x)$ is equal to 0 are called the **zeros** of $P(x)$. For instance, -1 is a zero of $P(x) = 2x^3 - x + 1$ because

$$P(-1) = 2(-1)^3 - (-1) + 1$$
$$= -2 + 1 + 1$$
$$= 0$$

❓ QUESTION Is 0 a zero of $P(x) = 2x^3 - x + 1$?

Much of the work in this chapter concerns finding the zeros of a polynomial. Sometimes the zeros of a polynomial $P(x)$ are determined by dividing $P(x)$ by another polynomial.

● DIVISION OF POLYNOMIALS

take note

Recall that a fraction bar acts as a grouping symbol. Division of a polynomial by a monomial is an application of the distributive property.

To divide a polynomial by a monomial, divide each term of the polynomial by the monomial. For instance,

$$\frac{16x^3 - 8x^2 + 12x}{4x} = \frac{16x^3}{4x} - \frac{8x^2}{4x} + \frac{12x}{4x}$$

• Divide each term in the numerator by the denominator.

$$= 4x^2 - 2x + 3$$

• Simplify.

To divide a polynomial by a binomial, we use a method similar to that used to divide whole numbers. For instance, consider $(6x^3 - 16x^2 + 23x - 5) \div (3x - 2)$.

INSTRUCTOR NOTE

It may help some students understand the division of polynomials process if you first divide two whole numbers, such as $7345 \div 3$.

$$3x - 2 \overline{)6x^3 - 16x^2 + 23x - 5}$$

$$\begin{array}{r} 2x^2 \\ 3x - 2 \overline{)6x^3 - 16x^2 + 23x - 5} \\ \underline{6x^3 - 4x^2} \\ -12x^2 + 23x \end{array}$$

• Think $\dfrac{6x^3}{3x} = 2x^2$.

• Multiply: $2x^2(3x - 2) = 6x^3 - 4x^2$

• Subtract and bring down the next term, $23x$.

$$\begin{array}{r} 2x^2 - 4x \\ 3x - 2 \overline{)6x^3 - 16x^2 + 23x - 5} \\ \underline{6x^3 - 4x^2} \\ -12x^2 + 23x \\ \underline{-12x^2 + 8x} \\ 15x - 5 \end{array}$$

• Think $\dfrac{-12x^2}{3x} = -4x$.

• Multiply: $-4x(3x - 2) = -12x^2 + 8x$

• Subtract and bring down the next term, -5.

❓ ANSWER No. $P(0) = 2(0)^3 - 0 + 1 = 1$. Because $P(0) \neq 0$, we know that 0 is not a zero of $P(x)$.

$$\begin{array}{r} 2x^2 - 4x + 5 \\ 3x - 2 \overline{)6x^3 - 16x^2 + 23x - 5} \\ \underline{6x^3 - 4x^2} \\ -12x^2 + 23x \\ \underline{-12x^2 + 8x} \\ 15x - 5 \\ \underline{15x - 10} \\ 5 \end{array}$$

- Think $\dfrac{15x}{3x} = 5$.
- Multiply: $5(3x - 2) = 15x - 10$
- Subtract to produce the remainder, 5.

Thus $(6x^3 - 16x^2 + 23x - 5) \div (3x - 2) = 2x^2 - 4x + 5$ with a remainder of 5.

Although there is nothing wrong with writing the answer as we did above, it is more common to write the answer as the quotient plus the remainder divided by the divisor. (See the Take Note at the left.) Using this method, we write

$$\underbrace{\frac{6x^3 - 16x^2 + 23x - 5}{3x - 2}}_{} = 2x^2 - 4x + 5 + \frac{5 \leftarrow \text{Remainder}}{3x - 2 \leftarrow \text{Divisor}}$$

take note

$\dfrac{20}{3}$ written as a mixed number is

$6\dfrac{2}{3}$. Recall, however, that $6\dfrac{2}{3}$

means $6 + \dfrac{2}{3}$, which is in the form

$quotient + \dfrac{remainder}{divisor}$.

In this example, $6x^3 - 16x^2 + 23x - 5$ is called the **dividend**, $3x - 2$ is the **divisor**, $2x^2 - 4x + 5$ is the **quotient**, and 5 is the **remainder**. In every division, the dividend is equal to the product of the quotient and divisor, plus the remainder. That is,

$$\underbrace{6x^3 - 16x^2 + 23x - 5}_{\text{Dividend}} = \underbrace{(2x^2 - 4x + 5)}_{\text{quotient}} \cdot \underbrace{(3x - 2)}_{\text{divisor}} + \underbrace{5}_{\text{remainder}}$$

Before dividing polynomials, make sure that each polynomial is written in descending order. In some cases, it is helpful to insert a 0 in the dividend for a missing term (one whose coefficient is 0) so that like terms align in the same column. This is demonstrated in Example 1.

? QUESTION What is the first step you should perform to find the quotient of $(2x + 1 + x^2) \div (x - 1)$?

Alternative to Example 1
Exercise 6, page 287.

EXAMPLE 1   **Divide Polynomials**

Divide: $\dfrac{-5x^2 - 8x + x^4 + 3}{x - 3}$

Solution
Write the numerator in descending order. Then divide.

$$\frac{-5x^2 - 8x + x^4 + 3}{x - 3} = \frac{x^4 - 5x^2 - 8x + 3}{x - 3}$$

? ANSWER Write the dividend in descending order as $x^2 + 2x + 1$.

$$
\begin{array}{r}
x^3 + 3x^2 + \ 4x + \ 4 \\
x - 3 \overline{)x^4 + 0x^3 - 5x^2 - \ 8x + \ 3} \\
\underline{x^4 - 3x^3} \\
3x^3 - 5x^2 \\
\underline{3x^3 - 9x^2} \\
4x^2 - \ 8x \\
\underline{4x^2 - 12x} \\
4x + \ 3 \\
\underline{4x - 12} \\
15
\end{array}
$$

• Inserting $0x^3$ for the missing term helps align like terms in the same column.

Thus $\dfrac{-5x^2 - 8x + x^4 + 3}{x - 3} = x^3 + 3x^2 + 4x + 4 + \dfrac{15}{x - 3}$.

▶ **TRY EXERCISE 2, PAGE 287**

A procedure called **synthetic division** can expedite the division process. To apply the synthetic division procedure, the divisor must be a polynomial of the form $x - c$, where c is a constant. In the synthetic division procedure, the variables that occur in the polynomials are not listed. To understand how synthetic division is performed, examine the following **long division** on the left and the related synthetic division on the right.

Long Division

$$
\begin{array}{r}
4x^2 + 3x + \ 8 \\
x - 2 \overline{)4x^3 - 5x^2 + 2x - 10} \\
\underline{4x^3 - 8x^2} \\
3x^2 + 2x \\
\underline{3x^2 - 6x} \\
8x - 10 \\
\underline{8x - 16} \\
6
\end{array}
$$

Coefficients of the quotient

Remainder

Synthetic Division

$$
\begin{array}{r|rrrr}
2 & 4 & -5 & 2 & -10 \\
  &   & 8 & 6 & 16 \\
\hline
  & 4 & 3 & 8 & 6
\end{array}
$$

First row
Second row
Third row
Coefficients of the quotient
Remainder

In the long division above, the dividend is $4x^3 - 5x^2 + 2x - 10$, and the divisor is $x - 2$. Because the divisor is of the form $x - c$, with $c = 2$, the division can be performed by the synthetic division procedure. Observe that in the accompanying synthetic division

1. The constant c is listed as the first number in the first row, followed by the coefficients of the dividend.

2. The first number in the third row is the leading coefficient of the dividend.

3. Each number in the second row is determined by computing the product of c and the number in the third row of the preceding column.

4. Each of the numbers in the third row, other than the first number, is determined by adding the numbers directly above it.

The following explanation illustrates the steps used to find the quotient and remainder of $(2x^3 - 8x + 7) \div (x + 3)$ by using synthetic division. The divisor $x + 3$ is written in $x - c$ form as $x - (-3)$, which indicates that $c = -3$. The dividend $2x^3 - 8x + 7$ is missing an x^2 term. If we insert $0x^2$ for the missing term, the dividend becomes $2x^3 + 0x^2 - 8x + 7$.

Coefficients of the dividend

$$-3 \begin{array}{|cccc} 2 & 0 & -8 & 7 \end{array}$$
$$\quad\;\; 2$$

- Write the constant c, -3, followed by the coefficients of the dividend. Bring down the first coefficient in the first row, 2, as the first number of the third row.

$$-3 \begin{array}{|cccc} 2 & 0 & -8 & 7 \\ & -6 & & \\ 2 & -6 & & \end{array}$$

- Multiply c times the first number in the third row, 2, to produce the first number of the second row, -6. Add the 0 and the -6 to produce the next number of the third row, -6.

$$-3 \begin{array}{|cccc} 2 & 0 & -8 & 7 \\ & -6 & 18 & \\ 2 & -6 & 10 & \end{array}$$

- Multiply c times the second number in the third row, -6, to produce the next number of the second row, 18. Add the -8 and the 18 to produce the next number of the third row, 10.

$$-3 \begin{array}{|cccc} 2 & 0 & -8 & 7 \\ & -6 & 18 & -30 \\ 2 & -6 & 10 & -23 \end{array}$$

- Multiply c times the third number in the third row, 10, to produce the next number of the second row, -30. Add the 7 and the -30 to produce the last number of the third row, -23.

Coefficients of the quotient   Remainder

take note

$2x^2 - 6x + 10 + \dfrac{-23}{x + 3}$

can also be written as m

$2x^2 - 6x + 10 - \dfrac{23}{x + 3}$

The last number in the bottom row, -23, is the remainder. The other numbers in the bottom row are the coefficients of the quotient. The quotient of a synthetic division always has a degree that is *one less* than the degree of the dividend. Thus the quotient in this example is $2x^2 - 6x + 10$. The results of the above synthetic division can be expressed in **fractional form** as

$$\frac{2x^3 - 8x + 7}{x + 3} = 2x^2 - 6x + 10 + \frac{-23}{x + 3}$$

or as

$$2x^3 - 8x + 7 = (x + 3)(2x^2 - 6x + 10) - 23$$

In Example 2 we illustrate the compact form of synthetic division, obtained by condensing the process explained above.

Alternative to Example 2
Exercise 14, page 287.

EXAMPLE 2   **Use Synthetic Division to Divide Polynomials**

Use synthetic division to divide $x^4 - 4x^2 + 7x + 15$ by $x + 4$.

Solution
Because the divisor is $x + 4$, we perform synthetic division with $c = -4$.

$$-4 \begin{array}{|ccccc} 1 & 0 & -4 & 7 & 15 \\ & -4 & 16 & -48 & 164 \\ 1 & -4 & 12 & -41 & 179 \end{array}$$

The quotient is $x^3 - 4x^2 + 12x - 41$, and the remainder is 179.

$$\frac{x^4 - 4x^2 + 7x + 15}{x + 4} = x^3 - 4x^2 + 12x - 41 + \frac{179}{x + 4}$$

▶ **TRY EXERCISE 12, PAGE 287**

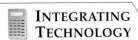

INTEGRATING TECHNOLOGY

A TI-82/83 synthetic-division program called SYDIV is available on the Internet at math.college.hmco.com. The program prompts you to enter the degree of the dividend, the coefficients of the dividend, and the constant c from the divisor $x - c$. For instance, to perform the synthetic division in Example 2, enter 4 for the degree of the dividend, followed by the coefficients 1, 0, –4, 7, and 15. See **Figure 3.1**. Press ENTER followed by –4 to produce the display in **Figure 3.2**. Press ENTER to produce the display in **Figure 3.3**. Press ENTER again to produce the display in **Figure 3.4**.

```
prgmSYDIV
DEGREE? 4
DIVIDEND COEF
?1
?0
?-4
?7
?15
```

FIGURE 3.1

```
C? -4
```

FIGURE 3.2

```
COEF OF QUOTIENT
                1
               -4
               12
              -41
```

FIGURE 3.3

```
REMAINDER
                179
QUIT? PRESS 1
NEW C? PRESS 2
```

FIGURE 3.4

● THE REMAINDER THEOREM

The following theorem shows that synthetic division can be used to determine the value $P(c)$ for a given polynomial P and constant c.

⬤P The Remainder Theorem

If a polynomial $P(x)$ is divided by $x - c$, then the remainder equals $P(c)$.

The following example illustrates the Remainder Theorem by showing that the remainder of $(x^2 + 9x - 16) \div (x - 3)$ is the same as $P(x) = x^2 + 9x - 16$ evaluated at $x = 3$.

Let $x = 3$ and $P(x) = x^2 + 9x - 16$.

Then $P(3) = (3)^2 + 9(3) - 16$

$\qquad = 9 + 27 - 16$

$\qquad = 20$

$$\begin{array}{r} x + 12 \\ x - 3\overline{)x^2 + 9x - 16} \\ \underline{x^2 - 3x} \\ 12x - 16 \\ \underline{12x - 36} \\ 20 \end{array}$$

$P(3)$ is equal to the remainder of $P(x)$ divided by $(x - 3)$.

In Example 3 we use synthetic division and the Remainder Theorem to evaluate a polynomial function.

EXAMPLE 3   Use the Remainder Theorem to Evaluate a Polynomial Function

Let $P(x) = 2x^3 + 3x^2 + 2x - 2$. Use the Remainder Theorem to find $P(c)$ for $c = -2$ and $c = \dfrac{1}{2}$.

Alternative to Example 3
Exercise 18, page 287.

Algebraic Solution

Perform synthetic division with $c = -2$ and $c = \dfrac{1}{2}$ and examine the remainders.

$$
\begin{array}{r|rrrr}
-2 & 2 & 3 & 2 & -2 \\
   &   & -4 & 2 & -8 \\
\hline
   & 2 & -1 & 4 & -10
\end{array}
$$

The remainder is -10. Therefore, $P(-2) = -10$.

$$
\begin{array}{r|rrrr}
\frac{1}{2} & 2 & 3 & 2 & -2 \\
   &   & 1 & 2 & 2 \\
\hline
   & 2 & 4 & 4 & 0
\end{array}
$$

The remainder is 0. Therefore, $P\left(\dfrac{1}{2}\right) = 0$.

Visualize the Solution

A graph of P shows that the points $(-2, -10)$ and $\left(\dfrac{1}{2}, 0\right)$ are on the graph.

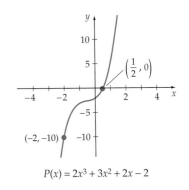

$P(x) = 2x^3 + 3x^2 + 2x - 2$

▶ **TRY EXERCISE 26, PAGE 287**

Using the Remainder Theorem to evaluate a polynomial function is often faster than evaluating the polynomial function by direct substitution. For instance, to evaluate $P(x) = x^5 - 10x^4 + 35x^3 - 50x^2 + 24x$ by substituting 7 for x, we must do the following work.

$$
\begin{aligned}
P(7) &= (7)^5 - 10(7)^4 + 35(7)^3 - 50(7)^2 + 24(7) \\
&= 16{,}807 - 10(2401) + 35(343) - 50(49) + 24(7) \\
&= 16{,}807 - 24{,}010 + 12{,}005 - 2450 + 168 \\
&= 2520
\end{aligned}
$$

take note

Because $P(x)$ has a constant term of 0, we must include 0 as the last number in the first row of the synthetic division at the right.

Using the Remainder Theorem to perform the above evaluation requires only the following work.

$$
\begin{array}{r|rrrrrr}
7 & 1 & -10 & 35 & -50 & 24 & 0 \\
  &   & 7 & -21 & 98 & 336 & 2520 \\
\hline
  & 1 & -3 & 14 & 48 & 360 & 2520 \leftarrow P(7)
\end{array}
$$

● THE FACTOR THEOREM

Note from Example 3 that $P\left(\dfrac{1}{2}\right) = 0$. Recall that $\dfrac{1}{2}$ is a zero of P because $P(x) = 0$ when $x = \dfrac{1}{2}$.

INSTRUCTOR NOTE
Point out that although the Factor Theorem
provides a method of *testing* whether
$(x - c)$ is a factor of a polynomial, it does
not provide a procedure for *detecting* such
a factor.

The following theorem is a direct result of the Remainder Theorem. It points out the important relationship between a zero of a given polynomial function and a factor of the polynomial function.

Ⓟ **The Factor Theorem**

A polynomial function $P(x)$ has a factor $(x - c)$ if and only if $P(c) = 0$. That is, $(x - c)$ is a factor of $P(x)$ if and only if c is a zero of P.

Alternative to Example 4
Exercise 40, page 287.

EXAMPLE 4   **Apply the Factor Theorem**

Use synthetic division and the Factor Theorem to determine whether $(x + 5)$ or $(x - 2)$ is a factor of $P(x) = x^4 + x^3 - 21x^2 - x + 20$.

Solution

$$
\begin{array}{r|rrrrr}
-5 & 1 & 1 & -21 & -1 & 20 \\
   &   & -5 & 20 & 5 & -20 \\
\hline
   & 1 & -4 & -1 & 4 & 0
\end{array}
$$

The remainder of 0 indicates that $(x + 5)$ is a factor of $P(x)$.

$$
\begin{array}{r|rrrrr}
2 & 1 & 1 & -21 & -1 & 20 \\
  &   & 2 & 6 & -30 & -62 \\
\hline
  & 1 & 3 & -15 & -31 & -42
\end{array}
$$

The remainder of -42 indicates that $(x - 2)$ is not a factor of $P(x)$.

▶ **TRY EXERCISE 36, PAGE 287**

❓ **QUESTION** Is -5 a zero of $P(x)$ given in Example 4?

Here is a summary of the important role played by the remainder in the division of a polynomial by $(x - c)$.

Ⓟ **The Remainder of a Polynomial Division**

In the division of the polynomial function $P(x)$ by $(x - c)$, the remainder is

- equal to $P(c)$.

- 0 if and only if $(x - c)$ is a factor of P.

- 0 if and only if c is a zero of P.

Also, if c is a real number, then the remainder of $P(x) \div (x - c)$ is 0 if and only if $(c, 0)$ is an x-intercept of the graph of P.

❓ **ANSWER** Yes. Because $(x + 5)$ is a factor of $P(x)$, the Factor Theorem states that $P(-5) = 0$, and thus -5 is a zero of $P(x)$.

• REDUCED POLYNOMIALS

In Example 4 we determined that $(x + 5)$ is a factor of the polynomial function $P(x) = x^4 + x^3 - 21x^2 - x + 20$ and that the quotient of $x^4 + x^3 - 21x^2 - x + 20$ divided by $(x + 5)$ is $Q(x) = x^3 - 4x^2 - x + 4$. Thus

$$P(x) = (x + 5)(x^3 - 4x^2 - x + 4)$$

The quotient $Q(x) = x^3 - 4x^2 - x + 4$ is called a **reduced polynomial** or a **depressed polynomial** of $P(x)$ because it is a factor of $P(x)$ and its degree is 1 less than the degree of $P(x)$. Reduced polynomials will play an important role in Sections 3.3 and 3.4.

Alternative to Example 5
Exercise 58, page 288.

EXAMPLE 5   **Find a Reduced Polynomial**

Verify that $(x - 3)$ is a factor of $P(x) = 2x^3 - 3x^2 - 4x - 15$, and write $P(x)$ as the product of $(x - 3)$ and the reduced polynomial $Q(x)$.

Solution

$$
\begin{array}{r|rrrr}
3 & 2 & -3 & -4 & -15 \\
  &   & 6 & 9 & 15 \\
\hline
  & 2 & 3 & 5 & 0
\end{array}
$$

↑
Coefficients of the
reduced polynomial $Q(x)$

Thus $(x - 3)$ and the reduced polynomial $2x^2 + 3x + 5$ are both factors of $P(x)$. That is,

$$P(x) = 2x^3 - 3x^2 - 4x - 15 = (x - 3)(2x^2 + 3x + 5)$$

▶ **TRY EXERCISE 56, PAGE 288**

TOPICS FOR DISCUSSION

1. Explain the meaning of the phrase *zero of a polynomial.*

2. If $P(x)$ is a polynomial of degree 3, what is the degree of the quotient of $\dfrac{P(x)}{x - c}$?

3. Discuss how the Remainder Theorem can be used to determine whether a number is a zero of a polynomial.

4. A zero of $P(x) = x^3 - x^2 - 14x + 24$ is -4. Discuss how this information and the Factor Theorem can be used to solve $x^3 - x^2 - 14x + 24 = 0$.

5. Discuss the advantages and disadvantages of using synthetic division rather than substitution to evaluate a polynomial function at $x = c$.

EXERCISE SET 3.1   —*Suggested Assignment: Exercises 1–67, odd; 73–78, all.*

In Exercises 1 to 10, use long division to divide the first polynomial by the second.

1. $5x^3 + 6x^2 - 17x + 20$, $x + 3$ $5x^2 - 9x + 10 - \dfrac{10}{x + 3}$

▶ 2. $6x^3 + 15x^2 - 8x + 2$, $x + 4$ $6x^2 - 9x + 28 - \dfrac{110}{x + 4}$

3. $x^4 - 5x^2 + 3x - 1$, $x - 2$ $x^3 + 2x^2 - x + 1 + \dfrac{1}{x - 2}$

4. $x^4 - 5x^3 + x - 4$, $x - 1$ $x^3 - 4x^2 - 4x - 3 - \dfrac{7}{x - 1}$

5. $x^2 + x^3 - 2x - 5$, $x - 3$ $x^2 + 4x + 10 + \dfrac{25}{x - 3}$

6. $4x + 3x^2 + x^3 - 5$, $x - 2$ $x^2 + 5x + 14 + \dfrac{23}{x - 2}$

7. $x^4 + 3x^3 - 5x + 3x^2 - 1$, $x - 4$ $x^3 + 7x^2 + 31x + 119 + \dfrac{475}{x - 4}$

8. $2x^4 + x^3 - 5x^2 + 2x - 8$, $x + 4$ $2x^3 - 7x^2 + 23x - 90 + \dfrac{352}{x + 4}$

9. $x^5 + x^4 - 2x^3 + 2x^2 - 3x - 7$, $x - 1$ $x^4 + 2x^3 + 2x - 1 - \dfrac{8}{x - 1}$

10. $x^5 - 2x^4 - x^3 + 3x^2 - 5x + 8$, $x + 4$ $x^4 - 6x^3 + 23x^2 - 89x + 351 - \dfrac{1396}{x + 4}$

In Exercises 11 to 24, use synthetic division to divide the first polynomial by the second.

11. $4x^3 - 5x^2 + 6x - 7$, $x - 2$ $4x^2 + 3x + 12 + \dfrac{17}{x - 2}$

▶ 12. $5x^3 + 6x^2 - 8x + 1$, $x - 5$ $5x^2 + 31x + 147 + \dfrac{736}{x - 5}$

13. $4x^3 - 2x + 3$, $x + 1$ $4x^2 - 4x + 2 + \dfrac{1}{x + 1}$

14. $6x^3 - 4x^2 + 17$, $x + 3$ $6x^2 - 22x + 66 - \dfrac{181}{x + 3}$

15. $x^5 - 10x^3 + 5x - 1$, $x - 4$ $x^4 + 4x^3 + 6x^2 + 24x + 101 + \dfrac{403}{x - 4}$

16. $6x^4 - 2x^3 - 3x^2 - x$, $x - 5$ $6x^3 + 28x^2 + 137x + 684 + \dfrac{3420}{x - 5}$

17. $x^5 - 1$, $x - 1$ $x^4 + x^3 + x^2 + x + 1$

18. $x^4 + 1$, $x + 1$ $x^3 - x^2 + x - 1 + \dfrac{2}{x + 1}$

19. $8x^3 - 4x^2 + 6x - 3$, $x - \dfrac{1}{2}$ $8x^2 + 6$

20. $12x^3 + 5x^2 + 5x + 6$, $x + \dfrac{3}{4}$ $12x^2 - 4x + 8$

21. $x^8 + x^6 + x^4 + x^2 + 4$, $x - 2$ $x^7 + 2x^6 + 5x^5 + 10x^4 + 21x^3 + 42x^2 + 85x + 170 + \dfrac{344}{x - 2}$

22. $-x^7 - x^5 - x^3 - x - 5$, $x + 1$ $-x^6 + x^5 - 2x^4 + 2x^3 - 3x^2 + 3x - 4 - \dfrac{1}{x + 1}$

23. $x^6 + x - 10$, $x + 3$ $x^5 - 3x^4 + 9x^3 - 27x^2 + 81x - 242 + \dfrac{716}{x + 3}$

24. $2x^5 - 3x^4 - 5x^2 - 10$, $x - 4$ $2x^4 + 5x^3 + 20x^2 + 75x + 300 + \dfrac{1190}{x - 4}$

In Exercises 25 to 34, use the Remainder Theorem to find P(c).

25. $P(x) = 3x^3 + x^2 + x - 5, c = 2$ 25

▶ 26. $P(x) = 2x^3 - x^2 + 3x - 1, c = 3$ 53

27. $P(x) = 4x^4 - 6x^2 + 5, c = -2$ 45

28. $P(x) = 6x^3 - x^2 + 4x, c = -3$ −183

29. $P(x) = -2x^3 - 2x^2 - x - 20, c = 10$ −2230

30. $P(x) = -x^3 + 3x^2 + 5x + 30, c = 8$ −250

31. $P(x) = -x^4 + 1, c = 3$ −80

32. $P(x) = x^5 - 1, c = 1$ 0

33. $P(x) = x^4 - 10x^3 + 2, c = 3$ −187

34. $P(x) = x^5 + 20x^2 - 1, c = -5$ −2626

In Exercises 35 to 44, use synthetic division and the Factor Theorem to determine whether the given binomial is a factor of P(x).

35. $P(x) = x^3 + 2x^2 - 5x - 6, x - 2$ Yes

▶ 36. $P(x) = x^3 + 4x^2 - 27x - 90, x + 6$ Yes

37. $P(x) = 2x^3 + x^2 - 3x - 1, x + 1$ No

38. $P(x) = 3x^3 + 4x^2 - 27x - 36, x - 4$ No

39. $P(x) = x^4 - 25x^2 + 144, x + 3$ Yes

40. $P(x) = x^4 - 25x^2 + 144, x - 3$ Yes

41. $P(x) = x^5 + 2x^4 - 22x^3 - 50x^2 - 75x, x - 5$ Yes

42. $P(x) = 9x^4 - 6x^3 - 23x^2 - 4x + 4, x + 1$ Yes

43. $P(x) = 16x^4 - 8x^3 + 9x^2 + 14x + 4, x - \dfrac{1}{4}$ No

44. $P(x) = 10x^4 + 9x^3 - 4x^2 + 9x + 6, x + \dfrac{1}{2}$ Yes

In Exercises 45 to 54, use synthetic division to show that c is a zero of $P(x)$.

45. $P(x) = 3x^3 - 8x^2 - 10x + 28, c = 2$

46. $P(x) = 4x^3 - 10x^2 - 8x + 6, c = 3$

47. $P(x) = x^4 - 1, c = 1$

48. $P(x) = x^3 + 8, c = -2$

49. $P(x) = 3x^4 + 8x^3 + 10x^2 + 2x - 20, c = -2$

50. $P(x) = x^4 - 2x^2 - 100x - 75, c = 5$

51. $P(x) = 2x^3 - 18x^2 - 50x + 66, c = 11$

52. $P(x) = 2x^4 - 34x^3 + 70x^2 - 153x + 45, c = 15$

53. $P(x) = 3x^2 - 8x + 4, c = \dfrac{2}{3}$

54. $P(x) = 5x^2 + 12x + 4, c = -\dfrac{2}{5}$

In Exercises 55 to 58, verify that the given binomial is a factor of $P(x)$, and write $P(x)$ as the product of the binomial and its reduced polynomial $Q(x)$.

55. $P(x) = x^3 + x^2 + x - 14, x - 2$ $(x - 2)(x^2 + 3x + 7)$

▶ **56.** $P(x) = x^4 + 5x^3 + 3x^2 - 5x - 4, x + 1$
$(x + 1)(x^3 + 4x^2 - x - 4)$

57. $P(x) = x^4 - x^3 - 9x^2 - 11x - 4, x - 4$
$(x - 4)(x^3 + 3x^2 + 3x + 1)$

58. $P(x) = 2x^5 - x^4 - 7x^3 + x^2 + 7x - 10, x - 2$
$(x - 2)(2x^4 + 3x^3 - x^2 - x + 5)$

59. **COST OF A WEDDING** The average cost of a wedding, in dollars, is modeled by

$$C(t) = 38t^2 + 291t + 15{,}208$$

where $t = 0$ represents the year 1990 and $0 \le t \le 12$. Use the Remainder Theorem to estimate the average cost of a wedding in

a. 1998. $19,968

b. 2001. $23,007

60. **SELECTION OF BRIDESMAIDS** A bride-to-be has several girlfriends, but she has decided to have only five bridesmaids, including the maid of honor. The number of different ways n girlfriends can be chosen and assigned a position, such as maid of honor, first matron, second matron, and so on, is given by the polynomial function

$$P(n) = n^5 - 10n^4 + 35n^3 - 50n^2 + 24n, \quad n \ge 5$$

a. Use the Remainder Theorem to determine the number of ways the bride can select her bridesmaids if she chooses from $n = 7$ girlfriends. 2520

b. Evaluate $P(n)$ for $n = 7$ by substituting 7 for n. How does this result compare with the result obtained in part **a.**? 2520; They are the same.

61. **SELECTION OF CARDS** The number of ways you can select three cards from a stack of n cards, in which the order of selection is important, is given by

$$P(n) = n^3 - 3n^2 + 2n, \quad n \ge 3$$

a. Use the Remainder Theorem to determine the number of ways you can select three cards from a stack of $n = 8$ cards. 336

b. Evaluate $P(n)$ for $n = 8$ by substituting 8 for n. How does this result compare with the result obtained in part **a.**? 336; They are the same.

62. **ROCKET LAUNCH** A model rocket is projected upward from an initial height of 4 feet with an initial velocity of 158 feet per second. The height of the rocket, in feet, is given by $s = -16t^2 + 158t + 4$, where $0 \le t \le 9.9$ seconds. Use the Remainder Theorem to determine the height of the rocket at

a. $t = 5$ seconds. 394 ft

b. $t = 8$ seconds. 244 ft

63. **HOUSE OF CARDS** The number of cards C needed to build a house of cards with r rows (levels) is given by the function $C(r) = 1.5r^2 + 0.5r$.

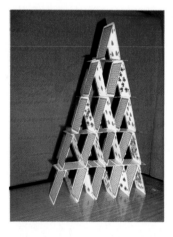

Use the Remainder Theorem to determine the number of cards needed to build a house of cards with

a. $r = 8$ rows. 100 cards

b. $r = 20$ rows. 610 cards

64. **ELECTION OF CLASS OFFICERS** The number of ways a class of n students can elect a president, a vice president, a secretary, and a treasurer is given by the function

$P(n) = n^4 - 6n^3 + 11n^2 - 6n$, where $n \geq 4$. Use the Remainder Theorem to determine the number of ways the class can elect officers if the class consists of

a. $n = 12$ students. 11,880 ways

b. $n = 24$ students. 255,024 ways

65. POPULATION DENSITY OF A CITY The population density D, in people per square mile, of a city is related to the distance x, in miles, from the center of the city by $D = -45x^2 + 190x + 200$, $0 < x < 5$. Use the Remainder Theorem to determine the population density of the city at a distance of

a. $x = 2$ miles. 400 people/mi²

b. $x = 4$ miles. 240 people/mi²

66. VOLUME OF A SOLID The volume of the solid at the right is given by $V(x) = x^3 + 3x^2$.

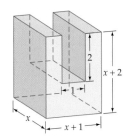

Use the Remainder Theorem to determine the volume of the solid if

a. $x = 7$ inches. 490 in³

b. $x = 11$ inches. 1694 in³

67. VOLUME OF A SOLID The volume of the following solid is given by $V(x) = x^3 + x^2 + 10x - 8$.

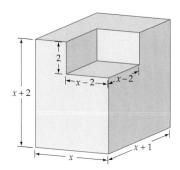

Use the Remainder Theorem to determine the volume of the solid if

a. $x = 6$ inches. 304 in³

b. $x = 9$ inches. 892 in³

CONNECTING CONCEPTS

68. Use the Factor Theorem to show that for any positive integer n, $P(x) = x^n - 1$ has $x - 1$ as a factor. $P(1) = (1)^n - 1 = 0$.
Thus, by the Factor Theorem, $(x - 1)$ is a factor of $P(x)$ for any positive integer n.

69. Find the remainder of $5x^{48} + 6x^{10} - 5x + 7$ divided by $x - 1$. 13

70. Find the remainder of $18x^{80} - 6x^{50} + 4x^{20} - 2$ divided by $x + 1$. 14

71. Determine whether i is a zero of $P(x) = x^3 - 3x^2 + x - 3$. Yes

72. Determine whether $-2i$ is a zero of $P(x) = x^4 - 2x^3 + x^2 - 8x - 12$. Yes

---

PREPARE FOR SECTION 3.2

73. Find the minimum value of $P(x) = x^2 - 4x + 6$. [2.4] 2

74. Find the maximum value of $P(x) = -2x^2 - x + 1$. [2.4] $\frac{9}{8}$

75. Find the interval on which $P(x) = x^2 + 2x + 7$ is increasing. [2.4] $[-1, \infty)$

76. Find the interval on which $P(x) = -2x^2 + 4x + 5$ is decreasing. [2.4] $[1, \infty)$

77. Factor: $x^4 - 5x^2 + 4$ [P.4] $(x + 1)(x - 1)(x + 2)(x - 2)$

78. Find the x-intercepts of the graph of $P(x) = 6x^2 - x - 2$. [2.4] $\left(\frac{2}{3}, 0\right), \left(-\frac{1}{2}, 0\right)$

PROJECTS

I.   **HORNER'S POLYNOMIAL FORM** William Horner (1786–1837) devised a method of writing a polynomial in a form that does not involve any exponents other than 1. For instance, $4x^4 + 2x^3 - 5x^2 + 7x - 11$ can be written in each of the following forms.

$4x^4 + 2x^3 - 5x^2 + 7x - 11$

$= (4x^3 + 2x^2 - 5x + 7)x - 11$

• Factor an x from the first four terms.

$= [(4x^2 + 2x - 5)x + 7]x - 11$

• Factor an x from the first three terms inside the innermost parentheses.

$= \{[(4x + 2)x - 5]x + 7\}x - 11$

• Factor an x from the first two terms inside the innermost parentheses.

Horner's form, $\{[(4x + 2)x - 5]x + 7\}x - 11$, is easier to evaluate than the descending exponent form, $4x^4 + 2x^3 - 5x^2 + 7x - 11$. Horner's form is sometimes used by computer programmers to make their programs run faster.

a. Let $P(x) = 3x^5 - 4x^4 + 5x^3 - 2x^2 + 3x - 8$. Find $P(6)$ by direct substitution. $P(6) = 19{,}162$

b. Use Horner's method to write $P(x)$ in a form that does not involve any exponents other than 1. Now use this form to evaluate $P(6)$. Which was easier to perform, the evaluation in part **a.** or in part **b.**?
$P(x) = (\{[(3x - 4)x + 5]x - 2\}x + 3)x - 8$; 19,162; part **b.**

POLYNOMIAL FUNCTIONS OF HIGHER DEGREE

- **FAR-LEFT AND FAR-RIGHT BEHAVIOR**
- **MAXIMUM AND MINIMUM VALUES**
- **REAL ZEROS OF A POLYNOMIAL FUNCTION**
- **EVEN AND ODD POWERS OF $(x - c)$ THEOREM**
- **A PROCEDURE FOR GRAPHING POLYNOMIAL FUNCTIONS**

Table 3.1 summarizes information developed in Chapter 2 about graphs of polynomial functions of degree 0, 1, or 2.

TABLE 3.1

Polynomial Function $P(x)$	Graph
$P(x) = a$ (degree 0)	Horizontal line through $(0, a)$
$P(x) = ax + b$ (degree 1), $a \neq 0$	Line with y-intercept $(0, b)$ and slope a.
$P(x) = ax^2 + bx + c$ (degree 2), $a \neq 0$	Parabola with vertex $\left(-\dfrac{b}{2a}, P\left(-\dfrac{b}{2a}\right)\right)$

Polynomial functions of degree 3 or higher can be graphed by the technique of plotting points; however, some additional knowledge about polynomial functions will make graphing easier.

All polynomial functions have graphs that are **smooth continuous curves.** The terms *smooth* and *continuous* are defined rigorously in calculus, but for the

take note

The general form of a polynomial is given by $a_nx^n + a_{n-1}x^{n-1} + \cdots + a_0$. In this text the coefficients $a_n, a_{n-1}, \ldots, a_0$ are all real numbers unless specifically stated otherwise.

present, a smooth curve is a curve that does not have sharp corners such as that shown in **Figure 3.5a.** A continuous curve does not have a break or hole such as those shown in **Figure 3.5b.**

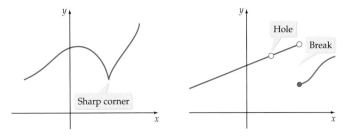

a. Continuous, but not smooth   **b.** Not continuous

FIGURE 3.5

● FAR-LEFT AND FAR-RIGHT BEHAVIOR

take note

The leading term of a polynomial function in x is the nonzero term that contains the largest power of x. The leading coefficient of a polynomial function is the coefficient of the leading term.

The graph of a polynomial function may have several up and down fluctuations; however, the graph of every polynomial function eventually will increase or decrease without bound as $|x|$ becomes large. The **leading term** a_nx^n is said to be the **dominate term** of the polynomial function $P(x) = a_nx^n + a_{n-1}x^{n-1} + \cdots + a_1x + a_0$ because as $|x|$ becomes large, the absolute value of a_nx^n will be much larger than the absolute value of any of the other terms. Because of this condition, you can determine the **far-left and far-right behavior** of the polynomial by examining the **leading coefficient** a_n and the degree n of the polynomial.

Table 3.2 indicates the far-left and far-right behavior of a polynomial function $P(x)$ with leading term a_nx^n.

TABLE 3.2   Far-Right and Far-Left Behavior of the Graph of a Polynomial Function with Leading Term a_nx^n

P		*n* is even	*n* is odd
	$a_n > 0$	Up to far left and up to far right	Down to far left and up to far right
	$a_n < 0$	Down to far left and down to far right	Up to far left and down to far right

Alternative to Example 1

Exercise 4, page 301.

EXAMPLE 1   Determine the Far-Left and Far-Right Behavior of a Polynomial Function

Examine the leading term to determine the far-left and far-right behavior of the graph of each polynomial function.

a. $P(x) = x^3 - x$

b. $S(x) = \dfrac{1}{2}x^4 - \dfrac{5}{2}x^2 + 2$

c. $T(x) = -2x^3 + x^2 + 7x - 6$

d. $U(x) = 9 + 8x^2 - x^4$

Continued ▶

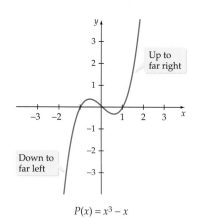

$P(x) = x^3 - x$

FIGURE 3.6

Solution

a. Because $a_n = 1$ is *positive* and $n = 3$ is *odd*, the graph of P goes down to its far left and up to its far right. See **Figure 3.6.**

b. Because $a_n = \dfrac{1}{2}$ is *positive* and $n = 4$ is *even*, the graph of S goes up to its far left and up to its far right. See **Figure 3.7.**

c. Because $a_n = -2$ is *negative* and $n = 3$ is *odd*, the graph of T goes up to its far left and down to its far right. See **Figure 3.8.**

d. The leading term of $U(x)$ is $-x^4$ and the leading coefficient is -1. Because $a_n = -1$ is *negative* and $n = 4$ is *even*, the graph of U goes down to its far left and down to its far right. See **Figure 3.9.**

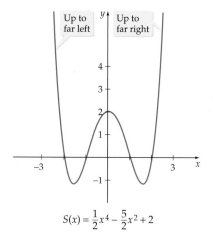

$S(x) = \dfrac{1}{2}x^4 - \dfrac{5}{2}x^2 + 2$

FIGURE 3.7

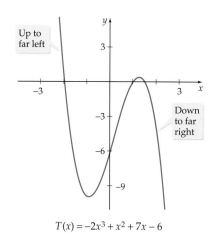

$T(x) = -2x^3 + x^2 + 7x - 6$

FIGURE 3.8

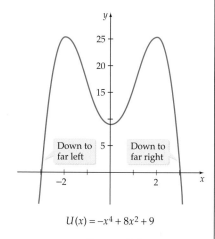

$U(x) = -x^4 + 8x^2 + 9$

FIGURE 3.9

▶ **TRY EXERCISE 2, PAGE 301**

● **MAXIMUM AND MINIMUM VALUES**

Figure 3.10 illustrates the graph of a polynomial function of degree 3 with two **turning points,** points at which the function changes from an increasing function to a decreasing function, or vice versa. In general, the graph of a polynomial function of degree n has at most $n - 1$ turning points.

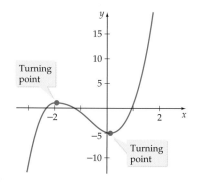

$P(x) = 2x^3 + 5x^2 - x - 5$

FIGURE 3.10

Turning points can be related to the concepts of maximum and minimum values of a function. These concepts were introduced in the discussion of graphs of second-degree equations in two variables earlier in the text. Recall that the minimum value of a function f is the smallest range value of f. It is often called the **absolute minimum.** The maximum value of a function f is the largest range value of f. The maximum value of a function is also called the **absolute maximum.** For the function whose graph is shown in **Figure 3.11,** the y value of point E is the absolute minimum. There are no y values less than y_5.

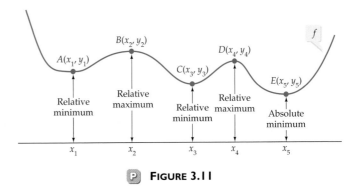

Now consider y_1, the y value of turning point A in **Figure 3.11.** It is not the smallest y value of every point on the graph of f; however, it is the smallest y value if we *localize* our field of view to a small open interval containing x_1. It is for this reason that we refer to y_1 as a **local minimum,** or **relative minimum,** of f. The y value of point C is also a relative minimum of f.

The function does not have an absolute maximum because it goes up both to its far left and to its far right. The y value of point B is a relative maximum, as is the y value of point D. The formal definitions of **relative maximum** and **relative minimum** are presented below.

Relative Minimum and Relative Maximum

If there is an open interval I containing c on which

- $f(c) \le f(x)$ for all x in I, then $f(c)$ is a **relative minimum** of f.

- $f(c) \ge f(x)$ for all x in I, then $f(c)$ is a **relative maximum** of f.

❓ **QUESTION**   Is the absolute minimum y_5 shown in **Figure 3.11** also a relative minimum of f?

❓ **ANSWER**   Yes, the absolute minimum y_5 also satisfies the requirements of a relative minimum.

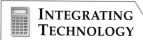

INTEGRATING TECHNOLOGY

A graphing utility can estimate the minimum and maximum values of a function. To use a TI-83 calculator to estimate the relative maximum of

$$P(x) = 0.3x^3 - 2.8x^2 + 6.4x + 2$$

use the following steps:

1. Enter the function in the Y = menu. Choose your window settings.

2. Select 4:maximum from the $\boxed{\text{CALC}}$ menu, which is located above the $\boxed{\text{TRACE}}$ key. The graph of Y1 is displayed.

3. PRESS ◄ or ► repeatedly to select an x-value that is to the left of the relative maximum point. Press $\boxed{\text{ENTER}}$. A left bound is displayed in the bottom left corner.

4. Press ► repeatedly to select an x-value that is to the right of the relative maximum point. Press $\boxed{\text{ENTER}}$. A right bound is displayed in the bottom left corner.

5. The word **Guess?** is now displayed in the bottom left corner. Press ◄ repeatedly to move to a point near the maximum point. Press $\boxed{\text{ENTER}}$.

6. The cursor appears on the relative maximum point and the coordinates of the relative maximum point are displayed. In this example, the y value 6.312608 is the approximate relative maximum of the function P. *Note:* If your window settings, bounds, or your guess are different from those shown below, then your final results may differ slightly from the final results shown below in step 6.

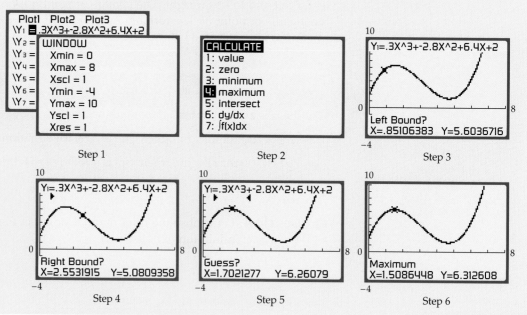

The following example illustrates the role a maximum may play in an application.

Alternative to Example 2

Exercise 50, page 303.

EXAMPLE 2   **Solve an Application**

A rectangular piece of cardboard measures 12 inches by 16 inches. An open box is formed by cutting congruent squares that measure x inches by x inches from each of the corners of the cardboard and folding up the sides as shown below.

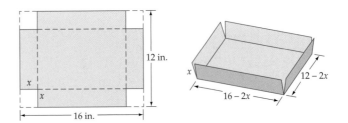

a.   Express the volume V of the box as a function of x.

b.   Determine (to the nearest tenth of an inch) the x value that maximizes the volume.

Solution

a.   The height, width, and length of the open box are x, $12 - 2x$, and $16 - 2x$. The volume is given by

$$V(x) = x(12 - 2x)(16 - 2x)$$
$$= 4x^3 - 56x^2 + 192x$$

b.   Use a graphing utility to graph $y = V(x)$. The graph is shown in **Figure 3.12.**

Note that we are interested only in the part of the graph for which $0 < x < 6$. This is so because the length of each side of the box must be positive. In other words,

$$x > 0, \quad 12 - 2x > 0 \quad \text{and} \quad 16 - 2x > 0$$
$$x < 6 \qquad\qquad x < 8$$

The domain of V is the intersection of the solution sets of the three inequalities. Thus the domain is $\{x \mid 0 < x < 6\}$.

Now use a graphing utility to find that V attains its maximum of about 194.06736 when $x \approx 2.3$. See **Figure 3.13.**

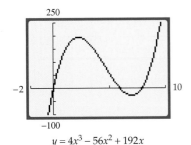

$y = 4x^3 - 56x^2 + 192x$

FIGURE 3.12

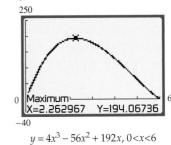

$y = 4x^3 - 56x^2 + 192x, \ 0 < x < 6$

FIGURE 3.13

INTEGRATING TECHNOLOGY

A TI graphing calculator program is available that simulates the construction of a box by cutting out squares from each corner of a rectangular piece of cardboard. This program, CUTOUT, can be found on our website at
math.college.hmco.com

▶ **TRY EXERCISE 48, PAGE 302**

● REAL ZEROS OF A POLYNOMIAL FUNCTION

Sometimes the real zeros of a polynomial function can be determined by using the factoring procedures developed in previous chapters. We illustrate this concept in the next example.

EXAMPLE 3   Factor to Find the Real Zeros of a Polynomial Function

Factor to find the three real zeros of $P(x) = x^3 + 3x^2 - 4x$.   *Alternative to Example 3*
Exercise 24, page 302.

Algebraic Solution

$P(x)$ can be factored as shown below.

$$P(x) = x^3 + 3x^2 - 4x$$
$$= x(x^2 + 3x - 4) \qquad \bullet \text{ Factor out the common factor } x.$$
$$= x(x - 1)(x + 4) \qquad \bullet \text{ Factor the trinomial } x^2 + 3x - 4.$$

The real zeros of $P(x)$ are $x = 0$, $x = 1$, and $x = -4$.

Visualize the Solution

The graph of $P(x)$ has x-intercepts at $(0, 0)$, $(1, 0)$, and $(-4, 0)$.

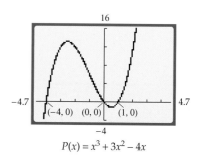

$P(x) = x^3 + 3x^2 - 4x$

▶ **TRY EXERCISE 22, PAGE 302**

The graph of every polynomial function P is a smooth continuous curve, and if the value of P changes sign on an interval, then $P(c)$ must equal zero for at least one real number c in the interval. This result is known as the *Zero Location Theorem*.

INSTRUCTOR NOTE
The Zero Location Theorem is a special case of the Intermediate Value Theorem (IVT), which states that if f is continuous on $[a, b]$ and $f(a) \neq f(b)$, then on $[a, b]$, f takes on every value between $f(a)$ and $f(b)$. You may wish to discuss the IVT with your students and explain that the Zero Location Theorem is a *corollary* of the IVT because it follows directly from the IVT.

The Zero Location Theorem

Let $P(x)$ be a polynomial function and let a and b be two distinct real numbers. If $P(a)$ and $P(b)$ have opposite signs, then there is at least one real number c between a and b such that $P(c) = 0$.

For instance, if the value of P is negative at $x = a$ and positive at $x = b$, then there is at least one real number c between a and b such that $P(c) = 0$. See **Figure 3.14**.

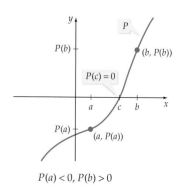

$P(a) < 0, P(b) > 0$

FIGURE 3.14

EXAMPLE 4   **Apply the Zero Location Theorem**

Use the Zero Location Theorem to verify that $S(x) = x^3 - x - 2$ has a real zero between 1 and 2.

Alternative to Example 4
Exercise 30, page 302.

Algebraic Solution

Use synthetic division to evaluate S for $x = 1$ and $x = 2$. If S changes sign between these two values, then S has a real zero between 1 and 2.

$$
\begin{array}{r|rrrr}
1 & 1 & 0 & -1 & -2 \\
  &   & 1 & 1 & 0 \\
\hline
  & 1 & 1 & 0 & -2
\end{array}
$$

• $S(1)$ is negative.

$$
\begin{array}{r|rrrr}
2 & 1 & 0 & -1 & -2 \\
  &   & 2 & 4 & 6 \\
\hline
  & 1 & 2 & 3 & 4
\end{array}
$$

• $S(2)$ is positive.

The graph of S is continuous because S is a polynomial function. Also, $S(1)$ is negative and $S(2)$ is positive. Thus the Zero Location Theorem indicates that there is a real zero between 1 and 2.

Visualize the Solution

The graph of S crosses the x-axis between $x = 1$ and $x = 2$. Thus S has a real zero between 1 and 2.

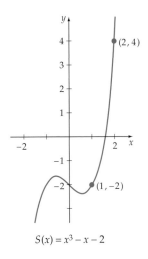

$S(x) = x^3 - x - 2$

▶ **TRY EXERCISE 28, PAGE 302**

TRY EXERCISE 28, PAGE 302

The following theorem summarizes important relationships among the real zeros of a polynomial function, the x-intercepts of its graph, and its factors that can be written in the form $(x - c)$, where c is a real number.

INSTRUCTOR NOTE
To fully understand the concepts in this chapter, the student will need to know that the four statements marked by the bullets are equivalent.

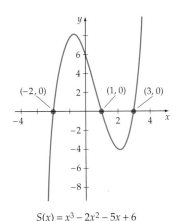

$S(x) = x^3 - 2x^2 - 5x + 6$

FIGURE 3.15

Ⓟ **Polynomial Functions, Real Zeros, Graphs, and Factors $(x - c)$**

If P is a polynomial function and c is a real number, then all the following statements are equivalent in the sense that if any one statement is true, then they are all true, and if any one statement is false, then they are all false.

• $(x - c)$ is a factor of P.

• $x = c$ is a real solution of $P(x) = 0$.

• $x = c$ is a real zero of P.

• $(c, 0)$ is an x-intercept of the graph of $y = P(x)$.

Sometimes it is possible to make use of the preceding theorem and a graph of a polynomial function to find factors of a function. For example, the graph of

$$S(x) = x^3 - 2x^2 - 5x + 6$$

is shown in **Figure 3.15.** The x-intercepts are $(-2, 0)$, $(1, 0)$, and $(3, 0)$. Hence -2, 1, and 3 are zeros of S, and $[x - (-2)]$, $(x - 1)$, and $(x - 3)$ are all factors of S.

● EVEN AND ODD POWERS OF $(x - c)$ THEOREM

Use a graphing utility to graph $P(x) = (x + 3)(x - 4)^2$. Compare your graph with **Figure 3.16.** Examine the graph near the x-intercepts $(-3, 0)$ and $(4, 0)$. Observe that the graph of P

● crosses the x-axis at $(-3, 0)$.

● intersects the x-axis but does not cross the x-axis at $(4, 0)$.

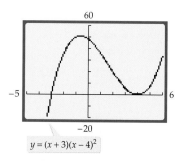

$y = (x + 3)(x - 4)^2$

FIGURE 3.16

The following theorem can be used to determine at which x-intercepts the graph of a polynomial function will cross the x-axis and at which x-intercepts the graph will intersect but not cross the x-axis.

Even and Odd Powers of $(x - c)$ Theorem

If c is a real number and the polynomial function $P(x)$ has $(x - c)$ as a factor exactly k times, then the graph of P will

● intersect but not cross the x-axis at $(c, 0)$, provided k is an even positive integer.

● cross the x-axis at $(c, 0)$, provided k is an odd positive integer.

Alternative to Example 5
Exercise 36, page 302.

EXAMPLE 5 **Apply the Even and Odd Powers of $(x - c)$ Theorem**

Determine where the graph of $P(x) = (x + 3)(x - 2)^2(x - 4)^3$ crosses the x-axis and where the graph intersects but does not cross the x-axis.

Solution

The exponents of the factors $(x + 3)$ and $(x - 4)$ are odd integers. Therefore, the graph of P will cross the x-axis at the x-intercepts $(-3, 0)$ and $(4, 0)$.

The exponent of the factor $(x - 2)$ is an even integer. Therefore, the graph of P will intersect but not cross the x-axis at $(2, 0)$.

Use a graphing utility to check these results.

▶ **TRY EXERCISE 34, PAGE 302**

● A PROCEDURE FOR GRAPHING POLYNOMIAL FUNCTIONS

You may find that you can sketch the graph of a polynomial function just by plotting several points; however, the following procedure will help you sketch the graph of many polynomial functions in an efficient manner.

To *review* **FACTORING OF POLYNOMIALS**, *see Section P.4, p. 44.*

A Procedure for Graphing Polynomial Functions

$$P(x) = a_n x^n + a_{n-1} x^{n-1} + \cdots + a_1 x + a_0, \quad a_n \neq 0$$

To graph P:

1. *Determine the far-left and the far-right behavior.* Examine the leading coefficient $a_n x^n$ to determine the far-left and the far-right behavior of the graph.

2. *Find the y-intercept.* Determine the y-intercept by evaluating $P(0)$.

3. *Find the x-intercept(s) and determine the behavior of the graph near the x-intercept(s).* If possible, find the x-intercepts by factoring. If $(x - c)$, where c is a real number, is a factor of P, then $(c, 0)$ is an x-intercept of the graph. Use the Even and Odd Powers of $(x - c)$ Theorem to determine where the graph crosses the x-axis and where the graph intersects but does not cross the x-axis.

4. *Find additional points on the graph.* Find a few additional points (in addition to the intercepts).

5. *Check for symmetry.*

   a. The graph of an even function is symmetric with respect to the y-axis.

   b. The graph of an odd function is symmetric with respect to the origin.

6. *Sketch the graph.* Use all the information obtained above to sketch the graph of the polynomial function. The graph should be a smooth continuous curve that passes through the points determined in steps 2 to 4. The graph should have a maximum of $n - 1$ turning points.

Alternative to Example 6
Exercise 44, page 302.

EXAMPLE 6   Graph a Polynomial Function

Sketch the graph of $P(x) = x^3 - 4x^2 + 4x$.

Solution

Step 1   *Determine the far-left and the far-right behavior.* The leading term is $1x^3$. Because the leading coefficient 1 is positive and the degree of the polynomial 3 is odd, the graph of P goes down to its far left and up to its far right.

Step 2   *Find the y-intercept.* $P(0) = 0^3 - 4(0)^2 + 4(0) = 0$. The y-intercept is $(0, 0)$.

Continued ▶

Step 3 *Find the x-intercept(s) and determine the behavior of the graph near the x-intercept(s).* Try to factor $x^3 - 4x^2 + 4x$.

$$x^3 - 4x^2 + 4x = x(x^2 - 4x + 4)$$
$$= x(x - 2)(x - 2)$$
$$= x(x - 2)^2$$

Because $(x - 2)$ is a factor of P, the point $(2, 0)$ is an x-intercept of the graph of P. Because x is a factor of P (think of x as $x - 0$), the point $(0, 0)$ is an x-intercept of the graph of P. Applying the Even and Odd Powers of $(x - c)$ Theorem allows us to determine that the graph of P crosses the x-axis at $(0, 0)$ and intersects but does not cross the x-axis at $(2, 0)$.

Step 4 *Find additional points on the graph.*

x	P(x)
−1	−9
0.5	1.125
1	1
3	3

Step 5 *Check for symmetry.* The function P is not an even or an odd function, so the graph of P is *not* symmetric to either the y-axis or the origin.

Step 6 *Sketch the graph.*

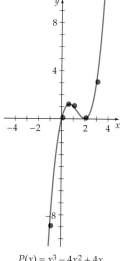

$$P(x) = x^3 - 4x^2 + 4x$$

 ▶ **TRY EXERCISE 42, PAGE 302**

TOPICS FOR DISCUSSION

1. Give an example of a polynomial function and of a function that is not a polynomial function.

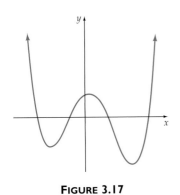

FIGURE 3.17

2. Is it possible for the graph of the polynomial function shown in **Figure 3.17** to be the graph of a polynomial function of odd degree? If so, explain how. If not, explain why not.

3. Explain the difference between a relative minimum and an absolute minimum.

4. Discuss how the Zero Location Theorem can be used to find a real zero of a polynomial function.

5. Let $P(x)$ be a polynomial function with real coefficients. Explain the relationships among the real zeros of the polynomial function, the x-coordinates of the x-intercepts of the graph of the polynomial function, and the solutions of the equation $P(x) = 0$.

EXERCISE SET 3.2

—Suggested Assignment: Exercises 1–61, odd; 65–70, all.
—Answer graphs to Exercises 15–20 and 41–46 are on page AA11.

In Exercises 1 to 8, examine the leading term and determine the far-left and far-right behavior of the graph of the polynomial function.

1. $P(x) = 3x^4 - 2x^2 - 7x + 1$
   up to the far left, up to the far right

▶ 2. $P(x) = -2x^3 - 6x^2 + 5x - 1$
   up to the far left, down to the far right

3. $P(x) = 5x^5 - 4x^3 - 17x^2 + 2$
   down to the far left, up to the far right

4. $P(x) = -6x^4 - 3x^3 + 5x^2 - 2x + 5$
   down to the far left, down to the far right

5. $P(x) = 2 - 3x - 4x^2$
   down to the far left, down to the far right

6. $P(x) = -16 + x^4$
   up to the far left, up to the far right

7. $P(x) = \frac{1}{2}(x^3 + 5x^2 - 2)$

   down to the far left, up to the far right

8. $P(x) = -\frac{1}{4}(x^4 + 3x^2 - 2x + 6)$

   down to the far left, down to the far right

9. The following graph is the graph of a third-degree (cubic) polynomial function. What does the far-left and far-right behavior of the graph say about the leading coefficient a? $a < 0$

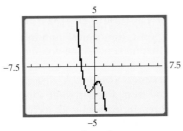

$P(x) = ax^3 + bx^2 + cx + d$

10. The following graph is the graph of a fourth-degree (quartic) polynomial function. What does the far-left and far-right behavior of the graph say about the leading coefficient a? $a < 0$

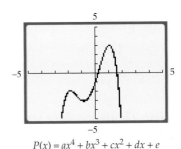

$P(x) = ax^4 + bx^3 + cx^2 + dx + e$

In Exercises 11 to 14, state the vertex of the graph of the function and use your knowledge of the vertex of a parabola to find the maximum or minimum of each function.

11. $P(x) = x^2 + 4x - 1$ Vertex is $(-2, -5)$, minimum is -5.

12. $P(x) = x^2 + 6x + 1$ Vertex is $(-3, -8)$, minimum is -8.

13. $P(x) = -x^2 - 8x + 1$ Vertex is $(-4, 17)$, maximum is 17.

14. $P(x) = -2x^2 + 8x - 1$ Vertex is $(2, 7)$, maximum is 7.

In Exercises 15 to 20, use a graphing utility to graph each polynomial. Use the maximum and minimum features of the graphing utility to estimate, to the nearest tenth, the coordinates of the points where $P(x)$ has a relative maximum or a relative minimum. For each point, indicate whether the y value is a relative maximum or a relative minimum. The number in parentheses to the

right of the polynomial is the total number of relative maxima and minima.

15. $P(x) = x^3 + x^2 - 9x - 9$ (2) relative maximum $y \approx 5.0$ at $x \approx -2.1$, relative minimum $y \approx -16.9$ at $x \approx 1.4$

16. $P(x) = x^3 + 4x^2 - 4x - 16$ (2) relative maximum $y \approx 5.0$ at $x \approx -3.1$, relative minimum $y \approx -16.9$ at $x \approx 0.4$

17. $P(x) = x^3 - 3x^2 - 24x + 3$ (2) relative maximum $y \approx 31.0$ at $x \approx -2.0$, relative minimum $y \approx -77.0$ at $x \approx 4.0$

18. $P(x) = -2x^3 - 3x^2 + 12x + 1$ (2) relative maximum $y \approx 8.0$ at $x \approx 1.0$, relative minimum $y \approx -19.0$ at $x \approx -2.0$

19. $P(x) = x^4 - 4x^3 - 2x^2 + 12x - 5$ (3) relative maximum $y \approx 2.0$ at $x \approx 1.0$, relative minima $y \approx -14.0$ at $x \approx -1.0$ and $y \approx -14.0$ at $x \approx 3.0$

20. $P(x) = x^4 - 10x^2 + 9$ (3) relative maximum $y \approx 9.0$ at $x \approx 0.0$, relative minima $y \approx -16.0$ at $x \approx -2.2$ and $y \approx -16.0$ at $x \approx 2.2$

In Exercises 21 to 26, find the real zeros of each polynomial function by factoring. The number in parentheses to the right of each polynomial indicates the number of real zeros of the given polynomial function.

21. $P(x) = x^3 - 2x^2 - 15x$ (3) $-3, 0, 5$

▶ **22.** $P(x) = x^3 - 6x^2 + 8x$ (3) $0, 2, 4$

23. $P(x) = x^4 - 13x^2 + 36$ (4) $-3, -2, 2, 3$

24. $P(x) = 4x^4 - 37x^2 + 9$ (4) $-3, -\dfrac{1}{2}, \dfrac{1}{2}, 3$

25. $P(x) = x^5 - 5x^3 + 4x$ (5) $-2, -1, 0, 1, 2$

26. $P(x) = x^5 - 25x^3 + 144x$ (5) $-4, -3, 0, 3, 4$

In Exercises 27 to 32, use the Zero Location Theorem to verify that P has a zero between a and b.

27. $P(x) = 2x^3 + 3x^2 - 23x - 42$; $a = 3, b = 4$

▶ **28.** $P(x) = 4x^3 - x^2 - 6x + 1$; $a = 0, b = 1$

29. $P(x) = 3x^3 + 7x^2 + 3x + 7$; $a = -3, b = -2$

30. $P(x) = 2x^3 - 21x^2 - 2x + 25$; $a = 1, b = 2$

31. $P(x) = 4x^4 + 7x^3 - 11x^2 + 7x - 15$; $a = 1, b = 1\dfrac{1}{2}$

32. $P(x) = 5x^3 - 16x^2 - 20x + 64$; $a = 3, b = 3\dfrac{1}{2}$

In Exercises 33 to 40, determine the x-intercepts of the graph of P. For each x-intercept, use the Even and Odd Powers of (x − c) Theorem to determine whether the graph of P crosses the x-axis or intersects but does not cross the x-axis.

33. $P(x) = (x - 1)(x + 1)(x - 3)$
crosses the x-axis at $(-1, 0)$, $(1, 0)$, and $(3, 0)$

▶ **34.** $P(x) = (x + 2)(x - 6)^2$
crosses the x-axis at $(-2, 0)$; intersects but does not cross at $(6, 0)$

35. $P(x) = -(x - 3)^2(x - 7)^5$
crosses the x-axis at $(7, 0)$; intersects but does not cross at $(3, 0)$

36. $P(x) = (x + 2)^3(x - 6)^{10}$
crosses the x-axis at $(-2, 0)$; intersects but does not cross at $(6, 0)$

37. $P(x) = (2x - 3)^4(x - 1)^{15}$
crosses the x-axis at $(1, 0)$; intersects but does not cross at $\left(\dfrac{3}{2}, 0\right)$

38. $P(x) = (5x + 10)^6(x - 2.7)^5$
crosses the x-axis at $(2.7, 0)$; intersects but does not cross at $(-2, 0)$

39. $P(x) = x^3 - 6x^2 + 9x$
crosses the x-axis at $(0, 0)$; intersects but does not cross at $(3, 0)$

40. $P(x) = x^4 + 3x^3 + 4x^2$
intersects but does not cross the x-axis at $(0, 0)$

In Exercises 41 to 46, sketch the graph of the polynomial function.

41. $P(x) = x^3 - x^2 - 2x$

▶ **42.** $P(x) = x^3 + 2x^2 - 3x$

43. $P(x) = -x^3 - 2x^2 + 5x + 6$ (*Hint:* In factored form $P(x) = (x + 3)(x + 1)(x - 2)$.)

44. $P(x) = -x^3 - 3x^2 + x + 3$ (*Hint:* In factored form $P(x) = (x + 3)(x + 1)(x - 1)$.)

45. $P(x) = x^4 - 4x^3 + 2x^2 + 4x - 3$ (*Hint:* In factored form $P(x) = (x + 1)(x - 1)^2(x - 3)$.)

46. $P(x) = x^4 - 6x^3 + 8x^2$

47. **CONSTRUCTION OF A BOX** A company constructs boxes from rectangular pieces of cardboard that measure 10 inches by 15 inches. An open box is formed by cutting squares that measure x inches by x inches from each corner of the cardboard and folding up the sides, as shown in the following figure.

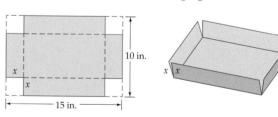

a. Express the volume V of the box as a function of x.
$V(x) = x(15 - 2x)(10 - 2x) = 4x^3 - 50x^2 + 150x$

b. Determine (to the nearest hundredth of an inch) the x value that maximizes the volume of the box. 1.96 in.

▶ **48.** **MAXIMIZING VOLUME** A closed box is to be constructed from a rectangular sheet of cardboard that measures 18 inches by 42 inches. The box is made by cutting rectangles that measure x inches by $2x$ inches from two of the corners and by cutting two squares that measure x inches by x inches from the top and from the bottom of the rectangle, as shown in the following figure. What value of x (to the nearest thousandth of an inch) will produce a box with maximum volume? 3.571 in.

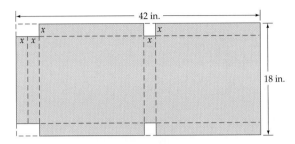

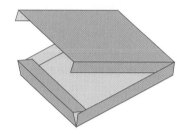

49. **MAXIMIZING VOLUME** An open box is to be constructed from a rectangular sheet of cardboard that measures 16 inches by 22 inches. To assemble the box, make the four cuts shown in the figure below and then fold on the dashed lines. What value of x (to the nearest thousandth of an inch) will produce a box with maximum volume? 2.137 in.

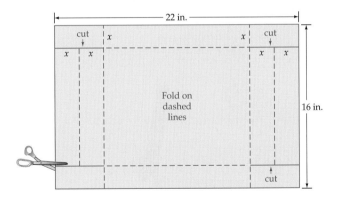

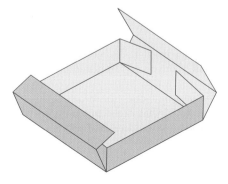

50. **PROFIT** A software company produces a computer game. The company has determined that its profit P, in dollars, from the manufacture and sale of x games is given by

$$P(x) = -0.000001x^3 + 96x - 98,000$$

where $0 < x \leq 9000$.

a. What is the maximum profit, to the nearest thousand dollars, the company can expect from the sale of its games? $264,000

b. How many games, to the nearest unit, does the company need to produce and sell to obtain the maximum profit? 5657 games

51. **ADVERTISING EXPENSES** A company manufactures digital cameras. The company estimates that the profit from camera sales is

$$P(x) = -0.02x^3 + 0.01x^2 + 1.2x - 1.1$$

where P is the profit in millions of dollars and x is the amount, in hundred-thousands of dollars, spent on advertising.

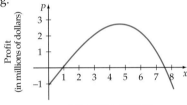

Advertising expenses
(in hundred-thousands of dollars)

Determine the amount, rounded to the nearest thousand dollars, the company needs to spend on advertising if it is to generate the maximum profit. $464,000

52. **DIVORCE RATE** The divorce rate for a given year is defined as the number of divorces per thousand population. The function

$$D(t) = 0.00001807t^4 - 0.001406t^3 + 0.02884t^2$$
$$- 0.003466t + 2.1148$$

approximates the U.S. divorce rate for the years 1960 ($t = 0$) to 1999 ($t = 39$). Use $D(t)$ and a graphing utility to estimate

a. the year during which the U.S. divorce rate reached its absolute maximum for the period from 1960 to 1999. 1981

b. the absolute minimum divorce rate, rounded to the nearest 0.1, during the period from 1960 to 1999. 2.1 divorces per thousand population

53. **MARRIAGE RATE** The marriage rate for a given year is defined as the number of marriages per thousand population. The function

$$M(t) = -0.00000115t^4 + 0.000252t^3$$
$$- 0.01827t^2 + 0.4438t + 9.1829$$

approximates the U.S. marriage rate for the years 1900 ($t = 0$) to 1999 ($t = 99$).

U.S. Marriage Rate, 1900–1999

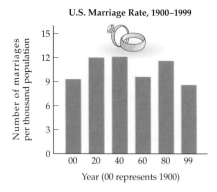

Year (00 represents 1900)

Use $M(t)$ and a graphing utility to estimate

a. during what year the U.S. marriage rate reached its maximum for the period from 1900 to 1999. 1918

b. the relative minimum marriage rate, rounded to the nearest 0.1, during the period from 1950 to 1970. 9.5 marriages per thousand population

54. **GAZELLE POPU-LATION** A herd of 204 African gazelles is introduced into a wild animal park. The popula- 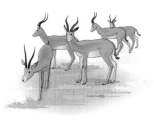 tion of the gazelles, $P(t)$, after t years is given by $P(t) = -0.7t^3 + 18.7t^2 - 69.5t + 204$, where $0 < t \le 18$.

a. Use a graph of P to determine the absolute minimum gazelle population (rounded to the nearest single gazelle) that is attained during this time period. 134 gazelles

b. Use a graph of P to determine the absolute maximum gazelle population (rounded to the nearest single gazelle) that is attained during this time period. 1013 gazelles

55. **MEDICATION LEVEL** Pseudoephedrine hydrochloride is an allergy medication. The function
$$L(t) = 0.03t^4 + 0.4t^3 - 7.3t^2 + 23.1t$$
where $0 \le t \le 5$, models the level of pseudoephedrine hydrochloride, in milligrams, in the bloodstream of a patient t hours after 30 milligrams of the medication have been taken.

a. Use a graphing utility and the function $L(t)$ to determine the maximum level of pseudoephedrine hydrochloride in the patient's bloodstream. Round your result to the nearest 0.01 milligram. 20.69 mg

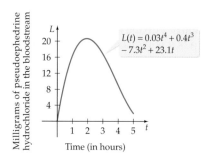

b. At what time t, to the nearest minute, is this maximum level of pseudoephedrine hydrochloride reached? 118 min

56. 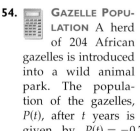 **SQUIRREL POPULATION** The population P of squirrels in a wilderness area is given by
$$P(t) = 0.6t^4 - 13.7t^3 + 104.5t^2 - 243.8t + 360,$$
where $0 \le t \le 12$ years.

a. What is the absolute minimum number of squirrels (rounded to the nearest single squirrel) attained on the interval $0 \le t \le 12$? 185 squirrels

b. The absolute maximum of P is attained at the endpoint, where $t = 12$. What is this absolute maximum (rounded to the nearest single squirrel)? 1250 squirrels

57. 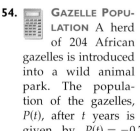 **BEAM DEFLECTION** The deflection D, in feet, of an 8-foot beam that is center loaded is given by
$$D(x) = (-0.0025)(4x^3 - 3 \cdot 8x^2), \quad 0 < x \le 4$$
where x is the distance, in feet, from one end of the beam.

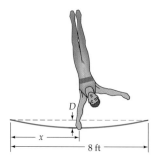

a. Determine the deflection of the beam when $x = 3$ feet. Round to the nearest hundredth of an inch. 3.24 in.

b. At what point does the beam achieve its maximum deflection? What is the maximum deflection? Round to the nearest hundredth of an inch. 4 ft from an end; 3.84 in.

c. What is the deflection at $x = 5$ feet? 3.24 in.

58. ENGINEERING A cylindrical log with a diameter of 22 inches is to be cut so that it will yield a beam that has a rectangular cross section of depth d and width w.

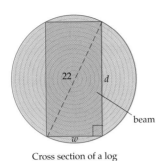

Cross section of a log

An engineer has determined that the stiffness S of the resulting beam is given by $S = 1.15wd^2$, where $0 < w < 22$ inches. Find the width and the depth that will maximize the stiffness of the beam. Round each result to the nearest hundredth of an inch. (*Hint:* Use the Pythagorean Theorem to solve for d^2 in terms of w^2.) $w = 12.70$ in.; $d = 17.96$ in.

CONNECTING CONCEPTS

59. Use a graph of $P(x) = x^3 - x - 25$ to determine between which two consecutive integers P has a real zero. between 3 and 4

60. Use a graph of the polynomial function $P(x) = 4x^4 - 12x^3 + 13x^2 - 12x + 9$ to determine between which two consecutive integers P has a real zero. between 1 and 2

61. The point $(2, 0)$ is on the graph of $P(x)$. What point must be on the graph of $P(x - 3)$? $(5, 0)$

62. The point $(3, 5)$ is on the graph of $P(x)$. What point must be on the graph of $P(x + 1) - 2$? $(2, 3)$

63. Explain how to use the graph of $y = x^3$ to produce the graph of $P(x) = (x - 2)^3 + 1$. Shift the graph of $y = x^3$ horizontally two units to the right and vertically upward 1 unit.

64. Consider the following conjecture. Let $P(x)$ be a polynomial function. If a and b are real numbers such that $a < b$, $P(a) > 0$, and $P(b) > 0$, then $P(x)$ does not have a real zero between a and b. Is this conjecture true or false? Support your answer. False. Consider $P(x) = x^2$, $a = -1$, and $b = 1$. Then $a < b$, $P(a) > 0$, and $P(b) > 0$; however, $P(x)$ has a zero between a and b.

PREPARE FOR SECTION 3.3

65. Find the zeros of $P(x) = 6x^2 - 25x + 14$. [1.3/2.4] $\dfrac{2}{3}, \dfrac{7}{2}$

66. Use synthetic division to divide $2x^3 + 3x^2 + 4x - 7$ by $x + 2$. [3.1] $2x^2 - x + 6 - \dfrac{19}{x + 2}$

67. Use synthetic division to divide $3x^4 - 21x^2 - 3x - 5$ by $x - 3$. [3.1] $3x^3 + 9x^2 + 6x + 15 + \dfrac{40}{x - 3}$

68. List all natural numbers that are factors of 12. [P.1] 1, 2, 3, 4, 6, 12

69. List all integers that are factors of 27. [P.1] $\pm 1, \pm 3, \pm 9, \pm 27$

70. Given $P(x) = 4x^3 - 3x^2 - 2x + 5$, find $P(-x)$. [2.5] $P(-x) = -4x^3 - 3x^2 + 2x + 5$

PROJECTS

1. A student thinks that $P(n) = n^3 - n$ is always a multiple of 6 for all natural numbers n. What do you think? Provide a mathematical argument to show that the student is correct or a counterexample to show that the student is wrong.

The student is correct. The polynomial function $P(n) = n^3 - n$ can be written in factored form as $P(n) = n(n - 1)(n + 1)$. In this form it is easy to see that $P(n)$ is the product of three consecutive natural numbers, one of which must be an even number and one of which must be a multiple of three. Thus $P(n)$ must be a multiple of 6 for any natural number n.

ZEROS OF POLYNOMIAL FUNCTIONS

• MULTIPLE ZEROS OF A POLYNOMIAL FUNCTION

Recall that if $P(x)$ is a polynomial function, then the values of x for which $P(x)$ is equal to 0 are called the *zeros* of $P(x)$ or the **roots** of the equation $P(x) = 0$. A zero of a polynomial function may be a **multiple zero**. For example, $P(x) = x^2 + 6x + 9$ can be expressed in factored form as $(x + 3)(x + 3)$. Setting each factor equal to zero yields $x = -3$ in both cases. Thus $P(x) = x^2 + 6x + 9$ has a zero of -3 that occurs twice. The following definition will be most useful when we are discussing multiple zeros.

> **Definition of Multiple Zeros of a Polynomial Function**
>
> If a polynomial function $P(x)$ has $(x - r)$ as a factor exactly k times, then r is a **zero of multiplicity k** of the polynomial function $P(x)$.

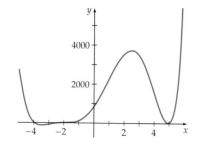

$P(x) = (x - 5)^2(x + 2)^3(x + 4)$

FIGURE 3.18

The graph of the polynomial function

$$P(x) = (x - 5)^2(x + 2)^3(x + 4)$$

is shown in **Figure 3.18.** This polynomial function has

- 5 as a zero of multiplicity 2.
- -2 as a zero of multiplicity 3.
- -4 as a zero of multiplicity 1.

A zero of multiplicity 1 is generally referred to as a **simple zero.**

When searching for the zeros of a polynomial function, it is important that we know how many zeros to expect. This question is answered completely in Section 3.4. For the work in this section, the following result is valuable.

> **Number of Zeros of a Polynomial Function**
>
> A polynomial function P of degree n has at most n zeros, where each zero of multiplicity k is counted k times.

• THE RATIONAL ZERO THEOREM

The rational zeros of polynomial functions with integer coefficients can be found with the aid of the following theorem.

P **The Rational Zero Theorem**

take note

The Rational Zero Theorem is one of the most important theorems of this chapter. It enables us to narrow the search for rational zeros to a finite list.

If $P(x) = a_n x^n + a_{n-1} x^{n-1} + \cdots + a_1 x + a_0$ has *integer* coefficients ($a_n \neq 0$) and $\dfrac{p}{q}$ is a rational zero (in lowest terms) of P, then

- p is a factor of the constant term a_0 and
- q is a factor of the leading coefficient a_n.

The Rational Zero Theorem often is used to make a list of all possible rational zeros of a polynomial function. The list consists of all rational numbers of the form $\dfrac{p}{q}$, where p is an integer factor of the constant term a_0 and q is an integer factor of the leading coefficient a_n.

Alternative to Example 1
Exercise 12, page 316.

EXAMPLE 1 **Apply the Rational Zero Theorem**

Use the Rational Zero Theorem to list all possible rational zeros of

$$P(x) = 4x^4 + x^3 - 40x^2 + 38x + 12$$

Solution

List all integers p that are factors of 12 and all integers q that are factors of 4.

$$p: \quad \pm 1, \pm 2, \pm 3, \pm 4, \pm 6, \pm 12$$
$$q: \quad \pm 1, \pm 2, \pm 4$$

Form all possible rational numbers using ± 1, ± 2, ± 3, ± 4, ± 6, and ± 12 for the numerator and ± 1, ± 2, and ± 4 for the denominator. By the Rational Zero Theorem, the possible rational zeros are

$$\pm 1, \pm \frac{1}{2}, \pm \frac{1}{4}, \pm 2, \pm 3, \pm \frac{3}{2}, \pm \frac{3}{4}, \pm 4, \pm 6, \pm 12$$

It is not necessary to list a factor that is already listed in reduced form. For example, $\pm \dfrac{6}{4}$ is not listed because it is equal to $\pm \dfrac{3}{2}$.

take note

The Rational Zero Theorem gives the *possible* rational zeros of a polynomial function. That is, if P has a rational zero, then it must be one indicated by the theorem. However, P may not have any rational zeros. In the case of the polynomial function in Example 1, the only rational zeros are $-\dfrac{1}{4}$ and 2. The remaining rational numbers in the list are not zeros of P.

▶ **TRY EXERCISE 10, PAGE 316**

❓ **QUESTION** If $P(x) = a_n x^n + a_{n-1} x^{n-1} + \cdots + a_1 x + a_0$ has integer coefficients and a leading coefficient of $a_n = 1$, must all the rational zeros of P be integers?

❓ **ANSWER** Yes. By the Rational Zero Theorem, the rational zeros of P are of the form $\dfrac{p}{q}$, where p is an integer factor of a_0 and q is an integer factor of a_n. Thus $q = \pm 1$ and $\dfrac{p}{q} = \dfrac{p}{\pm 1} = \pm p$.

• UPPER AND LOWER BOUNDS FOR REAL ZEROS

A real number b is called an **upper bound** of the zeros of the polynomial function P if no zero is greater than b. A real number b is called a **lower bound** of the zeros of P if no zero is less than b. The following theorem is often used to find positive upper bounds and negative lower bounds for the real zeros of a polynomial function.

Ⓟ **Upper- and Lower-Bound Theorem**

Let $P(x)$ be a polynomial function with real coefficients. Use synthetic division to divide $P(x)$ by $x - b$, where b is a nonzero real number.

Upper bound   **a.** If $b > 0$ and the leading coefficient of P is positive, then b is an upper bound for the real zeros of P provided none of the numbers in the bottom row of the synthetic division are negative.

b. If $b > 0$ and the leading coefficient of P is negative, then b is an upper bound for the real zeros of P provided none of the numbers in the bottom row of the synthetic division are positive.

Lower bound   If $b < 0$ and the numbers in the bottom row of the synthetic division alternate in sign (the number zero can be considered positive or negative as needed to produce an alternating sign pattern), then b is a lower bound for the real zeros of P.

Upper and lower bounds are not unique. For example, if b is an upper bound for the real zeros of P, then any number greater than b is also an upper bound. Likewise, if a is a lower bound for the real zeros of P, then any number less than a is also a lower bound.

Alternative to Example 2
Exercise 20, page 316.

EXAMPLE 2   **Find Upper and Lower Bounds**

According to the Upper- and Lower-Bound Theorem, what is the smallest positive integer that is an upper bound and the largest negative integer that is a lower bound of the real zeros of $P(x) = 2x^3 + 7x^2 - 4x - 14$?

Solution

To find the smallest positive-integer upper bound, use synthetic division with $1, 2, \ldots,$ as test values.

```
1 | 2   7   -4   -14        2 | 2   7   -4   -14
  |     2    9    5           |     4   22    36
  -----------------           -----------------
    2   9    5   -9             2  11   18    22     • No negative numbers
```

Thus 2 is the smallest positive-integer upper bound.

take note

When you check for bounds, you do not need to limit your choices to the possible zeros given by the Rational Zero Theorem. For instance, in Example 2 the integer -4 is a lower bound; however, -4 is not one of the possible zeros of P as given by the Rational Zero Theorem.

Now find the largest negative-integer lower bound.

```
-1 | 2   7   -4  -14        -2 | 2   7   -4  -14
   |    -2  -5    9            |    -4  -6   20
   ------------------          ------------------
     2   5   -9   -5            2   3  -10    6

-3 | 2   7   -4  -14        -4 | 2   7   -4  -14
   |    -6  -3   21            |    -8   4    0
   ------------------          ------------------
     2   1   -7    7            2  -1    0  -14
```

• **Alternating signs**

Thus -4 is the largest negative-integer lower bound.

▶ **TRY EXERCISE 18, PAGE 316**

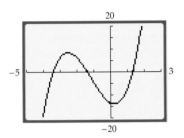

$P(x) = 2x^3 + 7x^2 - 4x - 14$

FIGURE 3.19

🖩 **INTEGRATING TECHNOLOGY**

You can use the Upper- and Lower-Bound Theorem to determine Xmin (the lower bound) and Xmax (the upper bound) for the viewing window of a graphing utility. This will ensure that all the real zeros, which are the x-coordinates of the x-intercepts of the polynomial function, will be shown. Note in **Figure 3.19** that the zeros of $P(x) = 2x^3 + 7x^2 - 4x - 14$ are between -4 (a lower bound) and 2 (an upper bound).

• DESCARTES' RULE OF SIGNS

MATH MATTERS

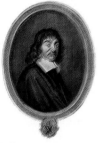

Descartes' Rule of Signs first appeared in his *La Géométrie* (1673). Although a proof of Descartes' Rule of Signs is beyond the scope of this course, we can see that a polynomial function with no variations in sign cannot have a positive zero. For instance, consider $P(x) = x^3 + x^2 + x + 1$. Each term of P is positive for any positive value of x. Thus P is never zero for $x > 0$.

Descartes' Rule of Signs is another theorem that is often used to obtain information about the zeros of a polynomial function. In Descartes' Rule of Signs, the number of **variations in sign** of the coefficients of $P(x)$ or $P(-x)$ refers to sign changes of the coefficients from positive to negative or from negative to positive that we find when we examine successive terms of the function. The terms are assumed to appear in order of descending powers of x. For example, the polynomial function

$$P(x) = +3x^4 - 5x^3 - 7x^2 + x - 7$$

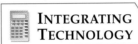

has three variations in sign. The polynomial function

$$P(-x) = +3(-x)^4 - 5(-x)^3 - 7(-x)^2 + (-x) - 7$$
$$= +\ 3x^4\ +\ 5x^3\ -\ 7x^2\ -\ x\ -\ 7$$

has one variation in sign.

Terms that have a coefficient of 0 are not counted as variations in sign and may be ignored. For example,

$$P(x) = -x^5 + 4x^2 + 1$$

has one variation in sign.

P **Descartes' Rule of Signs**

Let $P(x)$ be a polynomial function with real coefficients and with the terms arranged in order of decreasing powers of x.

1. The number of positive real zeros of $P(x)$ is equal to the number of variations in sign of $P(x)$, or to that number decreased by an even integer.

2. The number of negative real zeros of $P(x)$ is equal to the number of variations in sign of $P(-x)$, or to that number decreased by an even integer.

Alternative to Example 3
Exercise 30, page 316.

EXAMPLE 3 **Apply Descartes' Rule of Signs**

Use Descartes' Rule of Signs to determine both the number of possible positive and the number of possible negative real zeros of each polynomial function.

a. $P(x) = x^4 - 5x^3 + 5x^2 + 5x - 6$ **b.** $P(x) = 2x^5 + 3x^3 + 5x^2 + 8x + 7$

INSTRUCTOR NOTE
A real application of some of the concepts in this chapter can be found in "A Genuine Application of Synthetic Division, Descartes' Rule of Signs, and All That Stuff," by Dwight D. Freund [*The College Mathematics Journal*, vol. 26, no. 2 (March 1995)].

Solution

a.
$$P(x) = +x^4 - 5x^3 + 5x^2 + 5x - 6$$
$$\underbrace{\qquad}_{1}\ \underbrace{\qquad}_{2}\qquad \underbrace{\qquad}_{3}$$

There are three variations in sign. By Descartes' Rule of Signs, there are either three or one positive real zeros. Now examine the variations in sign of $P(-x)$.

$$P(-x) = x^4 + 5x^3 + 5x^2 - 5x - 6$$
$$\underbrace{\qquad}_{1}$$

There is one variation in sign of $P(-x)$. By Descartes' Rule of Signs, there is one negative real zero.

b. $P(x) = 2x^5 + 3x^3 + 5x^2 + 8x + 7$ has no variation in sign, so there are no positive real zeros.

$$P(-x) = -2x^5 - 3x^3 + 5x^2 - 8x + 7$$
$$\underbrace{\qquad}_{1}\ \underbrace{\qquad}_{2}\ \underbrace{\qquad}_{3}$$

$P(-x)$ has three variations in sign, so there are either three or one negative real zeros.

▶ **TRY EXERCISE 28, PAGE 316**

❓ **QUESTION** If $P(x) = ax^2 + bx + c$ has two variations in sign, must $P(x)$ have two positive real zeros?

❓ **ANSWER** No. According to Descartes' Rule of Signs, $P(x)$ will have either two positive real zeros or no positive real zeros.

In applying Descartes' Rule of Signs, we count each zero of multiplicity k as k zeros. For instance,

$$P(x) = x^2 - 10x + 25$$

has two variations in sign. Thus, by Descartes' Rule of Signs, $P(x)$ must have either two or no positive real zeros. Factoring $P(x)$ produces $(x - 5)^2$, from which it can be observed that 5 is a positive zero of multiplicity 2.

● ZEROS OF A POLYNOMIAL FUNCTION

⒫ Guidelines for Finding the Zeros of a Polynomial Function with Integer Coefficients

1. *Gather general information.* Determine the degree n of the polynomial function. The number of distinct zeros of the polynomial function is at most n. Apply Descartes' Rule of Signs to find the possible number of positive zeros and also the possible number of negative zeros.

2. *Check suspects.* Apply the Rational Zero Theorem to list rational numbers that are possible zeros. Use synthetic division to test numbers in your list. If you find an upper or a lower bound, then eliminate from your list any number that is greater than the upper bound or less than the lower bound.

3. *Work with the reduced polynomials.* Each time a zero is found, you obtain a reduced polynomial.

   ● If a reduced polynomial is of degree 2, find its zeros either by factoring or by applying the quadratic formula.

   ● If the degree of a reduced polynomial is 3 or greater, repeat the above steps for this polynomial.

Example 4 illustrates the procedure discussed in the above guidelines.

Alternative to Example 4
Exercise 40, page 316.

EXAMPLE 4   **Find the Zeros of a Polynomial Function**

Find the zeros of $P(x) = 3x^4 + 23x^3 + 56x^2 + 52x + 16$.

Solution

1. *Gather general information.* The degree of P is 4. Thus the number of zeros of P is at most 4. By Descartes' Rule of Signs, there are no positive zeros, and there are either four, two, or no negative zeros.

2. *Check suspects.* By the Rational Zero Theorem, the possible negative rational zeros of P are

$$\frac{p}{q}: \quad -1, -2, -4, -8, -16, -\frac{1}{3}, -\frac{2}{3}, -\frac{4}{3}, -\frac{8}{3}, -\frac{16}{3}$$

Continued ▶

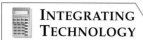

INTEGRATING TECHNOLOGY

If you have a graphing utility, you can produce a graph similar to the one below. By looking at the x-intercepts of the graph, you can reject as possible zeros some of the values suggested by the Rational Zero Theorem. This will reduce the amount of work that is necessary to find the zeros of the polynomial function.

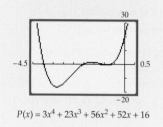

$P(x) = 3x^4 + 23x^3 + 56x^2 + 52x + 16$

Use synthetic division to test the possible rational zeros. The following work shows that -4 is a zero of P.

$$
\begin{array}{r|rrrrr}
-4 & 3 & 23 & 56 & 52 & 16 \\
   &   & -12 & -44 & -48 & -16 \\
\hline
   & 3 & 11 & 12 & 4 & 0 \\
\end{array}
$$

Coefficients of the first reduced polynomial

3. *Work with the reduced polynomials.* Because -4 is a zero, $(x + 4)$ and the first reduced polynomial $(3x^3 + 11x^2 + 12x + 4)$ are both factors of P. Thus

$$P(x) = (x + 4)(3x^3 + 11x^2 + 12x + 4)$$

All remaining zeros of P must be zeros of $3x^3 + 11x^2 + 12x + 4$. The Rational Zero Theorem indicates that the only possible negative rational zeros of $3x^3 + 11x^2 + 12x + 4$ are

$$\frac{p}{q}: \quad -1, -2, -4, -\frac{1}{3}, -\frac{2}{3}, -\frac{4}{3}$$

Synthetic division is again used to test possible zeros.

$$
\begin{array}{r|rrrr}
-2 & 3 & 11 & 12 & 4 \\
   &   & -6 & -10 & -4 \\
\hline
   & 3 & 5 & 2 & 0 \\
\end{array}
$$

Coefficients of the second reduced polynomial

Because -2 is a zero, $(x + 2)$ is also a factor of P. Thus

$$P(x) = (x + 4)(x + 2)(3x^2 + 5x + 2)$$

The remaining zeros of P must be zeros of $3x^2 + 5x + 2$.

$$3x^2 + 5x + 2 = 0$$
$$(3x + 2)(x + 1) = 0$$
$$x = -\frac{2}{3} \quad \text{and} \quad x = -1$$

The zeros of $P(x) = 3x^4 + 23x^3 + 56x^2 + 52x + 16$ are -4, -2, $-\dfrac{2}{3}$, and -1.

▶ **TRY EXERCISE 38, PAGE 316**

● **APPLICATIONS OF POLYNOMIAL FUNCTIONS**

In the following example we make use of an upper bound to eliminate several of the possible zeros that are given by the Rational Zero Theorem.

Alternative to Example 5
If 560 glasses are used to form a triangular pyramid, how many levels are in the pyramid?
● **14 levels**

EXAMPLE 5 Solve an Application

Glasses can be stacked to form a triangular pyramid.

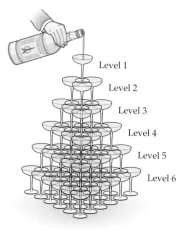

The total number of glasses in one of these pyramids is given by

$$T = \frac{1}{6}(k^3 + 3k^2 + 2k)$$

where k is the number of levels in the pyramid. If 220 glasses are used to form a triangular pyramid, how many levels are in the pyramid?

Solution

We need to solve $220 = \frac{1}{6}(k^3 + 3k^2 + 2k)$ for k. Multiplying each side of the equation by 6 produces $1320 = k^3 + 3k^2 + 2k$, which can be written as $k^3 + 3k^2 + 2k - 1320 = 0$. The number 1320 has many natural number divisors, but we can eliminate many of these by showing that 12 is an upper bound.

$$
\begin{array}{r|rrrr}
12 & 1 & 3 & 2 & -1320 \\
   &   & 12 & 180 & 2184 \\
\hline
   & 1 & 15 & 182 & 864
\end{array}
$$

No number in the bottom row is negative. Thus 12 is an upper bound.

The only natural number divisors of 1320 that are less than 12 are 1, 2, 3, 4, 5, 6, 8, 10, and 11. The following synthetic division shows that 10 is a zero of $k^3 + 3k^2 + 2k - 1320$.

$$
\begin{array}{r|rrrr}
10 & 1 & 3 & 2 & -1320 \\
   &   & 10 & 130 & 1320 \\
\hline
   & 1 & 13 & 132 & 0
\end{array}
$$

The pyramid has 10 levels. There is no need to seek additional solutions, because the number of levels is uniquely determined by the number of glasses.

take note

The reduced polynomial $k^2 + 13k + 132$ has zeros of $k = \dfrac{-13 \pm i\sqrt{359}}{2}$. These zeros are not solutions of this application because the number of levels must be a natural number.

▶ **TRY EXERCISE 72, PAGE 319**

The procedures developed in this section will not find all solutions of every polynomial equation. However, a graphing utility can be used to estimate the real solutions of any polynomial equation. In Example 6 we utilize a graphing utility to solve an application.

Alternative to Example 6

A farmer plans to construct a silo with a cylindrical base topped by a hemisphere. The height of the cylindrical base is to be 20 feet and the volume of the silo needs to be 864π cubic feet. Determine the length of the radius r.

● **6 ft**

EXAMPLE 6   **Use a Graphing Utility to Solve an Application**

A CO_2 (carbon dioxide) cartridge for a paintball rifle has the shape of a right circular cylinder with a hemisphere at each end. The cylinder is 4 inches long, and the volume of the cartridge is 2π cubic inches (approximately 6.3 cubic inches). In the figure at the right, the common interior radius of the cylinder and the hemispheres is denoted by x. Use a graphing utility to estimate, to the nearest hundredth of an inch, the length of the radius x.

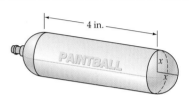

Solution

The volume of the cartridge is equal to the volume of the two hemispheres plus the volume of the cylinder. Recall that the volume of a sphere of radius x is given by $\dfrac{4}{3}\pi x^3$. Therefore, the volume of a hemisphere is $\dfrac{1}{2}\left(\dfrac{4}{3}\pi x^3\right)$.

The volume of a right circular cylinder is $\pi x^2 h$, where x is the radius of the base and h is the height of the cylinder. Thus the volume V of the cartridge is given by

$$V = \frac{1}{2}\left(\frac{4}{3}\pi x^3\right) + \frac{1}{2}\left(\frac{4}{3}\pi x^3\right) + \pi x^2 h$$

$$= \frac{4}{3}\pi x^3 + \pi x^2 h$$

Replacing V with 2π and h with 4 yields

$$2\pi = \frac{4}{3}\pi x^3 + 4\pi x^2$$

$$2 = \frac{4}{3}x^3 + 4x^2 \qquad \text{• Divide by } \pi.$$

$$3 = 2x^3 + 6x^2 \qquad \text{• Multiply by } \frac{3}{2}.$$

Here are two methods that can be used to solve

$$3 = 2x^3 + 6x^2 \tag{1}$$

for x with the aid of a graphing utility.

1. **Intersection Method**   Use a graphing utility to graph $y = 2x^3 + 6x^2$ and $y = 3$ on the same screen, with $x > 0$. The x-coordinate of the point of intersection of the two graphs is the desired solution. The graphs intersect at $x \approx 0.64$ inch. See the following figures.

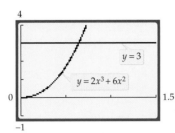

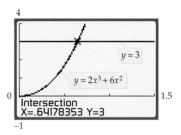

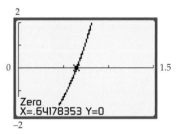

The length of the radius is approximately 0.64 inch.

2. **Intercept Method** Rewrite Equation (1) as $2x^3 + 6x^2 - 3 = 0$. Graph $y = 2x^3 + 6x^2 - 3$ with $x > 0$. Use a graphing utility to find the x-intercept of the graph. This method also shows that $x \approx 0.64$ inch.

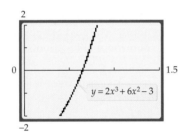

The length of the radius is approximately 0.64 inch.

▶ **TRY EXERCISE 68, PAGE 318**

👥 📝 TOPICS FOR DISCUSSION

1. What is a multiple zero of a polynomial function? Give an example of a polynomial function that has -2 as a multiple zero.

2. Discuss how the Rational Zero Theorem is used.

3. Let $P(x)$ be a polynomial function with real coefficients. Explain why $(a, 0)$ is an x-intercept of the graph of $P(x)$ if a is a real zero of $P(x)$.

4. Let $P(x)$ be a polynomial function with integer coefficients. Suppose that the Rational Zero Theorem is applied to $P(x)$ and that after testing each possible rational zero, it is determined that $P(x)$ has no rational zeros. Does this mean that all of the zeros of $P(x)$ are irrational numbers?

EXERCISE SET 3.3 —Suggested Assignment: Exercises 1–71, odds; 79–84, all.

In Exercises 1 to 6, find the zeros of the polynomial function and state the multiplicity of each zero.

1. $P(x) = (x - 3)^2(x + 5)$ 3 (multiplicity 2), -5 (multiplicity 1)

2. $P(x) = (x + 4)^3(x - 1)^2$ -4 (multiplicity 3), 1 (multiplicity 2)

3. $P(x) = x^2(3x + 5)^2$ 0 (multiplicity 2), $-\dfrac{5}{3}$ (multiplicity 2)

4. $P(x) = x^3(2x + 1)(3x - 12)^2$ 0 (multiplicity 3), $-\dfrac{1}{2}$ (multiplicity 1), 4 (multiplicity 2)

5. $P(x) = (x^2 - 4)(x + 3)^2$
2 (multiplicity 1), -2 (multiplicity 1), -3 (multiplicity 2)

6. $P(x) = (x + 4)^3(x^2 - 9)^2$
-4 (multiplicity 3), 3 (multiplicity 2), -3 (multiplicity 2)

In Exercises 7 to 16, use the Rational Zero Theorem to list possible rational zeros for each polynomial function.

7. $P(x) = x^3 + 3x^2 - 6x - 8$ $\pm 1, \pm 2, \pm 4, \pm 8$

8. $P(x) = x^3 - 19x - 30$ $\pm 1, \pm 2, \pm 3, \pm 5, \pm 6, \pm 10, \pm 15, \pm 30$

9. $P(x) = 2x^3 + x^2 - 25x + 12$
$\pm 1, \pm 2, \pm 3, \pm 4, \pm 6, \pm 12, \pm\dfrac{1}{2}, \pm\dfrac{3}{2}$

▶ **10.** $P(x) = 3x^3 + 11x^2 - 6x - 8$
$\pm 1, \pm 2, \pm 4, \pm 8, \pm\dfrac{1}{3}, \pm\dfrac{2}{3}, \pm\dfrac{4}{3}, \pm\dfrac{8}{3}$

11. $P(x) = 6x^4 + 23x^3 + 19x^2 - 8x - 4$
$\pm 1, \pm 2, \pm 4, \pm\dfrac{1}{2}, \pm\dfrac{1}{3}, \pm\dfrac{2}{3}, \pm\dfrac{4}{3}, \pm\dfrac{1}{6}$

12. $P(x) = 2x^3 + 9x^2 - 2x - 9$
$\pm 1, \pm 3, \pm 9, \pm\dfrac{1}{2}, \pm\dfrac{3}{2}, \pm\dfrac{9}{2}$

13. $P(x) = 4x^4 - 12x^3 - 3x^2 + 12x - 7$
$\pm 1, \pm 7, \pm\dfrac{1}{2}, \pm\dfrac{7}{2}, \pm\dfrac{1}{4}, \pm\dfrac{7}{4}$

14. $P(x) = x^5 - x^4 - 7x^3 + 7x^2 - 12x - 12$
$\pm 1, \pm 2, \pm 3, \pm 4, \pm 6, \pm 12$

15. $P(x) = x^5 - 32$ $\pm 1, \pm 2, \pm 4, \pm 8, \pm 16, \pm 32$

16. $P(x) = x^4 - 1$ ± 1

In Exercises 17 to 26, find the smallest positive integer and the largest negative integer that, by the Upper- and Lower-Bound Theorem, are upper and lower bounds for the real zeros of each polynomial function.

17. $P(x) = x^3 + 3x^2 - 6x - 6$ upper bound 2, lower bound -5

▶ **18.** $P(x) = x^3 - 19x - 28$ upper bound 5, lower bound -5

19. $P(x) = 2x^3 + x^2 - 25x + 10$ upper bound 4, lower bound -4

20. $P(x) = 3x^3 + 11x^2 - 6x - 9$ upper bound 2, lower bound -5

21. $P(x) = 6x^4 + 23x^3 + 19x^2 - 8x - 4$
upper bound 1, lower bound -4

22. $P(x) = -2x^3 - 9x^2 + 2x + 9$ upper bound 1, lower bound -5

23. $P(x) = -4x^4 + 12x^3 + 3x^2 - 12x + 7$
upper bound 4, lower bound -2

24. $P(x) = x^5 - x^4 - 7x^3 + 7x^2 - 12x - 12$
upper bound 4, lower bound -3

25. $P(x) = x^5 - 32$ upper bound 2, lower bound -1

26. $P(x) = x^4 - 1$ upper bound 1, lower bound -1

In Exercises 27 to 36, use Descartes' Rule of Signs to state the number of possible positive and negative real zeros of each polynomial function.

27. $P(x) = x^3 + 3x^2 - 6x - 8$
one positive zero, two or no negative zeros

▶ **28.** $P(x) = x^3 - 19x - 30$
one positive zero, two or no negative zeros

29. $P(x) = 2x^3 + x^2 - 25x + 12$
two or no positive zeros, one negative zero

30. $P(x) = 3x^3 + 11x^2 - 6x - 8$
one positive zero, two or no negative zeros

31. $P(x) = 6x^4 + 23x^3 + 19x^2 - 8x - 4$
one positive zero, three or one negative zeros

32. $P(x) = 2x^3 + 9x^2 - 2x - 9$
one positive zero, two or no negative zeros

33. $P(x) = 4x^4 - 12x^3 - 3x^2 + 12x - 7$
three or one positive zeros, one negative zero

34. $P(x) = x^5 - x^4 - 7x^3 + 7x^2 - 12x - 12$
three or one positive zeros, two or no negative zeros

35. $P(x) = x^5 - 32$ one positive zero, no negative zeros

36. $P(x) = x^4 - 1$ one positive zero, one negative zero

In Exercises 37 to 58, find the zeros of each polynomial function. If a zero is a multiple zero, state its multiplicity.

37. $P(x) = x^3 + 3x^2 - 6x - 8$ $2, -1, -4$

▶ **38.** $P(x) = x^3 - 19x - 30$ $5, -2, -3$

39. $P(x) = 2x^3 + x^2 - 25x + 12$ $3, -4, \dfrac{1}{2}$

40. $P(x) = 3x^3 + 11x^2 - 6x - 8$ $1, -4, -\dfrac{2}{3}$

41. $P(x) = 6x^4 + 23x^3 + 19x^2 - 8x - 4$ $\dfrac{1}{2}, -\dfrac{1}{3}, -2$ (multiplicity 2)

42. $P(x) = 2x^3 + 9x^2 - 2x - 9$ $1, -1, -\dfrac{9}{2}$

43. $P(x) = 2x^4 - 9x^3 - 2x^2 + 27x - 12$ $\frac{1}{2}, 4, \sqrt{3}, -\sqrt{3}$

44. $P(x) = 3x^3 - x^2 - 6x + 2$ $\frac{1}{3}, \sqrt{2}, -\sqrt{2}$

45. $P(x) = x^3 - 8x^2 + 8x + 24$ $6, 1 + \sqrt{5}, 1 - \sqrt{5}$

46. $P(x) = x^3 - 7x^2 - 7x + 69$ $-3, 5 + \sqrt{2}, 5 - \sqrt{2}$

47. $P(x) = 2x^4 - 19x^3 + 51x^2 - 31x + 5$ $5, \frac{1}{2}, 2 + \sqrt{3}, 2 - \sqrt{3}$

48. $P(x) = 4x^4 - 35x^3 + 71x^2 - 4x - 6$ $3, -\frac{1}{4}, 3 + \sqrt{7}, 3 - \sqrt{7}$

49. $P(x) = 3x^6 - 10x^5 - 29x^4 + 34x^3 + 50x^2 - 24x - 24$
$1, -1, -2, -\frac{2}{3}, 3 + \sqrt{3}, 3 - \sqrt{3}$

50. $P(x) = 2x^4 + 3x^3 - 4x^2 - 3x + 2$
$-2, -1, \frac{1}{2}, 1$

51. $P(x) = x^3 - 3x - 2$
$2, -1$ (multiplicity 2)

52. $P(x) = 3x^4 - 4x^3 - 11x^2 + 16x - 4$ $-2, \frac{1}{3}, 1, 2$

53. $P(x) = x^4 - 5x^2 - 2x$ $0, -2, 1 + \sqrt{2}, 1 - \sqrt{2}$

54. $P(x) = x^3 - 2x + 1$ $1, \dfrac{-1 + \sqrt{5}}{2}, \dfrac{-1 - \sqrt{5}}{2}$

55. $P(x) = x^4 + x^3 - 3x^2 - 5x - 2$ -1 (multiplicity 3), 2

56. $P(x) = 6x^4 - 17x^3 - 11x^2 + 42x$ $-\dfrac{3}{2}, 0, 2, \dfrac{7}{3}$

57. $P(x) = 2x^4 - 17x^3 + 4x^2 + 35x - 24$ $-\dfrac{3}{2}, 1$ (multiplicity 2), 8

58. $P(x) = x^5 + 5x^4 + 10x^3 + 10x^2 + 5x + 1$ -1 (multiplicity 5)

59. FIND THE DIMENSIONS A cube measures n inches on each edge. If a slice 2 inches thick is cut from one face of the cube, the resulting solid has a volume of 567 cubic inches. Find n. $n = 9$ in.

60. FIND THE DIMENSIONS A cube measures n units on each edge. If a slice 1 inch thick is cut from one face of the cube, and then a slice 3 inches thick is cut from another face of the cube as shown, the resulting solid has a volume of 1560 cubic inches. Find the dimensions of the original cube. 13 in. on each edge

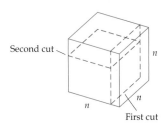

61. DIMENSIONS OF A SOLID For what value of x will the volume of the following solid be 112 cubic inches? $x = 4$ in.

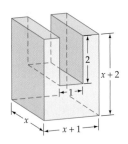

62. DIMENSIONS OF A BOX The length of a rectangular box is 1 inch more than twice the height of the box, and the width is 3 inches more than the height. If the volume of the box is 126 cubic inches, find the dimensions of the box. 3 in. by 7 in. by 6 in.

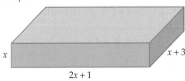

63. PIECES AND CUTS One straight cut through a thick piece of cheese produces two pieces. Two straight cuts can produce a maximum of four pieces. Three straight cuts can produce a maximum of eight pieces.

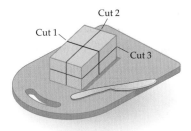

You might be inclined to think that every additional cut doubles the previous number of pieces. However, for four straight cuts, you get a maximum of 15 pieces. The maximum number of pieces P that can be produced by n straight cuts is given by

$$P(n) = \frac{n^3 + 5n + 6}{6}$$

a. Use the above function to determine the maximum number of pieces that can be produced by five straight cuts. 26 pieces

b. What is the fewest number of straight cuts that are needed to produce 64 pieces? 7 cuts

64. 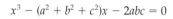 INSCRIBED QUADRILATERAL Isaac Newton discovered that if a quadrilateral with sides of lengths a, b, c, and x is inscribed in a semicircle with diameter x, then the lengths of the sides are related by the following equation.

$$x^3 - (a^2 + b^2 + c^2)x - 2abc = 0$$

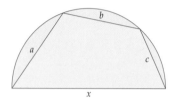

Given $a = 6$, $b = 5$, and $c = 4$, find x. Round to the nearest hundredth. 10.04

65. CANNONBALL STACKS Cannonballs can be stacked to form a pyramid with a square base. The total number of cannonballs T in one of these square pyramids is

$$T = \frac{1}{6}(2n^3 + 3n^2 + n)$$

where n is the number of rows (levels). If 140 cannonballs are used to form a square pyramid, how many rows are in the pyramid? 7 rows

66. ADVERTISING EXPENSES A company manufactures digital cameras. The company estimates that the profit from camera sales is

$$P(x) = -0.02x^3 + 0.01x^2 + 1.2x - 1.1$$

where P is the profit in millions of dollars and x is the amount, in hundred-thousands of dollars, spent on advertising.

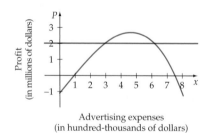

Advertising expenses
(in hundred-thousands of dollars)

Determine the minimum amount, rounded to the nearest thousand dollars, the company needs to spend on advertising if it is to receive a profit of $2,000,000. $293,000

67. COST CUTTING At the present time, a nutrition bar in the shape of a rectangular solid measures 0.75 inch by 1 inch by 5 inches.

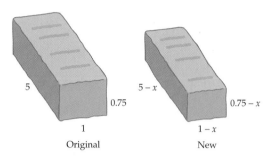

To reduce costs the manufacturer has decided to decrease each of the dimensions of the nutrition bar by x inches. What value of x, rounded to the nearest thousandth of an inch, will produce a new nutrition bar with a volume that is 0.75 cubic inch less than the present bar's volume? $x = 0.084$ in.

▶ 68. PROPANE TANK DIMENSIONS A propane tank has the shape of a circular cylinder with a hemisphere at each end. The cylinder is 6 feet long and the volume of the tank is 9π cubic feet. Find, to the nearest thousandth of a foot, the length of the radius x. 1.098 ft

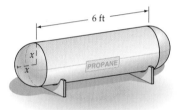

69. DIVORCE RATE The divorce rate for a given year is defined as the number of divorces per thousand population. The polynomial function

$$D(t) = 0.00001807t^4 - 0.001406t^3 + 0.02884t^2 - 0.003466t + 2.1148$$

approximates the U.S. divorce rate for the years 1960 ($t = 0$) to 1999 ($t = 39$). Use $D(t)$ and a graphing utility to determine during what years the U.S. divorce rate attained a level of 5.0. 1977 and 1986

70. MEDICATION LEVEL Pseudoephedrine hydrochloride is an allergy medication. The polynomial function

$$L(t) = 0.03t^4 + 0.4t^3 - 7.3t^2 + 23.1t$$

where $0 \le t \le 5$, models the level of pseudoephedrine hydrochloride, in milligrams, in the bloodstream of a patient t hours after 30 milligrams of the medication have been taken.

At what times, to the nearest minute, does the level of pseudoephedrine hydrochloride in the bloodstream reach 12 milligrams? After 39 min and after 3 h 38 min

71. 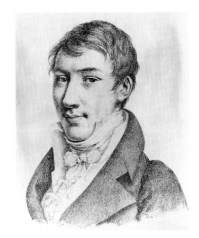 **WEIGHT AND HEIGHT OF GIRAFFES** A veterinarian at a wild animal park has determined that the average weight w, in pounds, of an adult male giraffe is closely approximated by the function

$$w = 8.3h^3 - 307.5h^2 + 3914h - 15{,}230$$

where h is the giraffe's height in feet, and $15 \leq h \leq 18$. Use the above function to estimate the height of a giraffe that weighs 3150 pounds. Round to the nearest tenth of a foot. 16.9 ft

▶ **72.** **SELECTION OF CARDS** The number of ways one can select three cards from a group of n cards (the order of the selection matters), where $n \geq 3$, is given by $P(n) = n^3 - 3n^2 + 2n$. For a certain card trick a magician has determined that there are exactly 504 ways to choose three cards from a given group. How many cards are in the group? 9 cards

73. **DIGITS OF PI** In 1999, Professor Yasumasa Kanada of the University of Tokyo used a supercomputer to compute 206,158,430,000 digits of

pi (π). (*Source: Guinness World Records 2001*, Bantam Books, p. 252.) Computer scientists often try to find mathematical models that approximate the time a computer program takes to complete a calculation or mathematical procedure. Procedures for which the completion time can be closely modeled by a polynomial are called *polynomial time procedures*. Here is an example. A student finds that the time, in seconds, required to compute $n \times 10{,}000$ digits of pi on a personal computer using the mathematical program MAPLE is closely approximated by

$$T(n) = 0.23245n^3 + 0.53797n^2$$
$$+ 7.88932n - 8.53299$$

a. Evaluate $T(n)$ to estimate how long, to the nearest second, the computer takes to compute 50,000 digits of pi. 73 s

b. About how many digits of pi can the computer compute in 5 minutes? Round to the nearest thousand digits. 93,000 digits

---

CONNECTING CONCEPTS

74. If p is a prime number, prove that $\sqrt{p}$ is an irrational number. (*Hint:* Start with the equation $x = \sqrt{p}$, and square each side to produce the equivalent equation $x^2 = p$, which can be written as $x^2 - p = 0$. Then apply the Rational Zero Theorem to show that $P(x) = x^2 - p$ has no rational zeros.)

The mathematician Augustin Louis Cauchy (1789–1857) proved the following theorem, which can be used to quickly establish a bound B for *all* the zeros (both real and complex) of a given polynomial function.

Cauchy's Bound Theorem

Let $P(x) = a_n x^n + a_{n-1}x^{n-1} + \cdots + a_1 + a_0$ be a polynomial function with complex coefficients. The absolute value of each zero of P is less than

$$B = \left(\frac{\text{maximum of } (|a_{n-1}|, |a_{n-2}|, \cdots, |a_1|, |a_0|)}{|a_n|} + 1 \right)$$

In Exercises 75 to 78, a polynomial function and its zeros are given. For each polynomial function, apply Cauchy's Bound Theorem to determine the bound B for the polynomial and determine whether the absolute value of each of the given zeros is less than B. (*Hint:* $|a + bi| = \sqrt{a^2 + b^2}$)

75. $P(x) = 2x^3 - 5x^2 - 28x + 15$, zeros: $-3, \dfrac{1}{2}, 5$
$B = 15$. The absolute value of each zero is less than B.

76. $P(x) = x^3 - 5x^2 + 2x + 8$, zeros: $-1, 2, 4$
$B = 9$. The absolute value of each zero is less than B.

77. $P(x) = x^4 - 2x^3 + 9x^2 + 2x - 10$,
zeros: $1 + 3i, 1 - 3i, 1, -1$
$B = 11$. The absolute value of each zero is less than B.

78. $P(x) = x^4 - 4x^3 + 14x^2 - 4x + 13$,
zeros: $2 + 3i, 2 - 3i, i, -i$
$B = 15$. The absolute value of each zero is less than B.

PREPARE FOR SECTION 3.4
---

79. What is the conjugate of $3 - 2i$? [P.6] $3 + 2i$

80. What is the conjugate of $2 + i\sqrt{5}$? [P.6] $2 - i\sqrt{5}$

81. Find $(x - 1)(x - 3)(x - 4)$. [P.3] $x^3 - 8x^2 + 19x - 12$

82. Find $[x - (2 + i)][x - (2 - i)]$. [P.3/P.6] $x^2 - 4x + 5$

83. Solve: $x^2 + 9 = 0$ [1.3] $-3i, 3i$

84. Solve: $x^2 - x + 5 = 0$ [1.3] $\dfrac{1}{2} - \dfrac{1}{2}i\sqrt{19}, \dfrac{1}{2} + \dfrac{1}{2}i\sqrt{19}$

PROJECTS
---

1.   **RELATIONSHIPS BETWEEN ZEROS AND COEFFICIENTS**
Consider the polynomial function

$$P(x) = x^n + C_1 x^{n-1} + C_2 x^{n-2} + \cdots + C_n$$

with zeros $r_1, r_2, r_3, \ldots, r_n$. The following equations illustrate important relationships between the zeros of the polynomial function and the coefficients of the polynomial.

- The sum of the zeros.

$$r_1 + r_2 + r_3 + \cdots + r_{n-1} + r_n = -C_1$$

- The sum of the products of the zeros taken two at a time.

$$r_1 r_2 + r_1 r_3 + \cdots + r_{n-2} r_n + r_{n-1} r_n = C_2$$

- The sum of the products of the zeros taken three at a time.

$$r_1 r_2 r_3 + r_1 r_2 r_4 + \cdots + r_{n-2} r_{n-1} r_n = -C_3$$

$$\vdots$$

- The product of the zeros.

$$r_1 r_2 r_3 r_4 \cdots r_{n-1} r_n = (-1)^n C_n$$

a. Show that each of the previous equations holds true for the polynomial function

$$P(x) = x^3 - 6x^2 + 11x - 6$$

which has zeros of 1, 2, and 3.

b. Create a polynomial function of degree 4 with four real zeros. Illustrate that each of the above equations holds true for your polynomial function. (*Hint:* The polynomial function

$$P(x) = (x - a)(x - b)(x - c)(x - d)$$

has a, b, c, and d as zeros.) Responses will vary.

SECTION 3.4   # THE FUNDAMENTAL THEOREM OF ALGEBRA

- THE FUNDAMENTAL THEOREM OF ALGEBRA
- THE NUMBER OF ZEROS OF A POLYNOMIAL FUNCTION
- THE CONJUGATE PAIR THEOREM
- FIND A POLYNOMIAL FUNCTION WITH GIVEN ZEROS

• THE FUNDAMENTAL THEOREM OF ALGEBRA

The German mathematician Carl Friedrich Gauss (1777–1855) was the first to prove that every polynomial function has at least one complex zero. This concept is so basic to the study of algebra that it is called the **Fundamental Theorem of Algebra.** The proof of the Fundamental Theorem is beyond the scope of this text; however, it is important to understand the theorem and its consequences. As you consider each of the following theorems, keep in mind that the terms *complex coefficients* and *complex zeros* include real coefficients and real zeros because the set of real numbers is a subset of the set of complex numbers.

MATH MATTERS

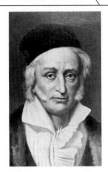

Carl Friedrich Gauss (1777–1855) has often been referred to as the Prince of Mathematics. His work covered topics in algebra, calculus, analysis, probability, number theory, non-Euclidean geometry, astronomy, and physics, to name but a few. The following quote by Eric Temple Bell gives credence to the fact that Gauss was one of the greatest mathematicians of all time. "Archimedes, Newton, and Gauss, these three, are in a class by themselves among the great mathematicians, and it is not for ordinary mortals to attempt to range them in order of merit."*

*Men of Mathematics, by E. T. Bell, New York, Simon and Schuster, 1937.

The Fundamental Theorem of Algebra

If $P(x)$ is a polynomial function of degree $n \geq 1$ with complex coefficients, then $P(x)$ has at least one complex zero.

THE NUMBER OF ZEROS OF A POLYNOMIAL FUNCTION

Let $P(x)$ be a polynomial function of degree $n \geq 1$ with complex coefficients. The Fundamental Theorem implies that $P(x)$ has a complex zero—say, c_1. The Factor Theorem implies that

$$P(x) = (x - c_1)Q(x)$$

where $Q(x)$ is a polynomial of degree one less than the degree of $P(x)$. Recall that the polynomial $Q(x)$ is called a *reduced polynomial*. Assuming that the degree of $Q(x)$ is 1 or more, the Fundamental Theorem implies that it also must have a zero. A continuation of this reasoning process leads to the following theorem.

The Linear Factor Theorem

If $P(x)$ is a polynomial function of degree $n \geq 1$ with leading coefficient $a_n \neq 0$,

$$P(x) = a_n x^n + a_{n-1} x^{n-1} + \cdots + a_1 x^1 + a_0$$

then $P(x)$ has exactly n linear factors

$$P(x) = a_n(x - c_1)(x - c_2) \cdots (x - c_n)$$

where $c_1, c_2, \ldots, c_n$ are complex numbers.

The following theorem follows directly from the Linear Factor Theorem.

The Number of Zeros of a Polynomial Function Theorem

If $P(x)$ is a polynomial function of degree $n \geq 1$, then $P(x)$ has exactly n complex zeros, provided each zero is counted according to its multiplicity.

The Linear Factor Theorem and the Number of Zeros of a Polynomial Function Theorem are referred to as **existence theorems.** They state that an nth degree polynomial will have n linear factors and n complex zeros, but they do not provide any information on how to determine the linear factors or the zeros. In Example 1 we make use of previously developed methods to actually find the linear factors and zeros of some polynomial functions.

Alternative to Example 1
Exercise 4, page 327.

EXAMPLE I   **Find the Zeros and Linear Factors of a Polynomial Function**

Find all the zeros of each of the following polynomial functions, and write each polynomial as a product of linear factors.

a. $P(x) = x^4 - 4x^3 + 8x^2 - 16x + 16$

b. $S(x) = x^4 - 6x^3 + 10x^2 + 2x - 15$

Solution

a. We know that $P(x)$ will have four zeros and four linear factors. The possible rational zeros are $\pm 1, \pm 2, \pm 4, \pm 8, \pm 16$. Synthetic division can be used to show that 2 is a zero of multiplicity 2.

$$
\begin{array}{r|rrrrr}
2 & 1 & -4 & 8 & -16 & 16 \\
  &   & 2 & -4 & 8 & -16 \\
\hline
  & 1 & -2 & 4 & -8 & 0 \\
\end{array}
$$

$$
\begin{array}{r|rrrr}
2 & 1 & -2 & 4 & -8 \\
  &   & 2 & 0 & 8 \\
\hline
  & 1 & 0 & 4 & 0 \\
\end{array}
$$

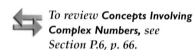

To review **Concepts Involving Complex Numbers,** *see Section P.6, p. 66.*

The final reduced polynomial is $x^2 + 4$. The zeros of $x^2 + 4$ can be found by solving $x^2 + 4 = 0$, as shown below.

$$x^2 + 4 = 0$$
$$x^2 = -4$$
$$x = \pm\sqrt{-4}$$
$$x = \pm 2i$$

Thus the four zeros of $P(x)$ are $2, 2, -2i$, and $2i$. The linear factored form of $P(x)$ is

$$P(x) = (x - 2)(x - 2)[x - (-2i)][x - 2i]$$

or

$$P(x) = (x - 2)^2(x + 2i)(x - 2i)$$

b. We know that $S(x)$ will have four zeros and four linear factors. The possible rational zeros are $\pm 1, \pm 3, \pm 5, \pm 15$. Synthetic division can be used to show that 3 and -1 are zeros of $S(x)$.

$$
\begin{array}{r|rrrrr}
3 & 1 & -6 & 10 & 2 & -15 \\
  &   & 3 & -9 & 3 & 15 \\
\hline
  & 1 & -3 & 1 & 5 & 0 \\
\end{array}
$$

$$
\begin{array}{r|rrrr}
-1 & 1 & -3 & 1 & 5 \\
   &   & -1 & 4 & -5 \\
\hline
   & 1 & -4 & 5 & 0 \\
\end{array}
$$

The final reduced polynomial is $x^2 - 4x + 5$. We can find the remaining zeros by using the quadratic formula to solve $x^2 - 4x + 5 = 0$.

$$x = \frac{-(-4) \pm \sqrt{(-4)^2 - 4(1)(5)}}{2(1)}$$

$$= \frac{4 \pm \sqrt{-4}}{2}$$

$$= 2 \pm i$$

Thus the four zeros of $S(x)$ are $3, -1, 2 + i$, and $2 - i$. The linear factored form of $S(x)$ is

$$S(x) = (x - 3)[x - (-1)][x - (2 + i)][x - (2 - i)]$$

or $\qquad S(x) = (x - 3)(x + 1)(x - 2 - i)(x - 2 + i)$

▶ **TRY EXERCISE 2, PAGE 327**

● THE CONJUGATE PAIR THEOREM

You may have noticed that the complex zeros of the polynomial function in Example 1 were complex conjugates. The following theorem shows that this is not a coincidence.

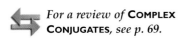
For a review of **COMPLEX CONJUGATES,** *see p. 69.*

The Conjugate Pair Theorem

If $a + bi$ ($b \neq 0$) is a complex zero of a polynomial function *with real coefficients*, then the conjugate $a - bi$ is also a complex zero of the polynomial function.

Alternative to Example 2
Exercise 14, page 327.

EXAMPLE 2 Use the Conjugate Pair Theorem to Find Zeros

Find all the zeros of $P(x) = x^4 - 4x^3 + 14x^2 - 36x + 45$ given that $2 + i$ is a zero.

Solution

Because the coefficients are real numbers and $2 + i$ is a zero, the Conjugate Pair Theorem implies that $2 - i$ also must be a zero. Using synthetic division with $2 + i$ and then $2 - i$, we have

```
2 + i | 1    -4        14      -36         45
       |      2 + i    -5       18 + 9i    -45
       ──────────────────────────────────────
         1    -2 + i    9      -18 + 9i      0     • The coefficients of the
                                                     reduced polynomial
2 - i | 1    -2 + i     9      -18 + 9i
       |      2 - i     0        18 - 9i
       ──────────────────────────────────────
         1     0        9        0                • The coefficients of the
                                                     next reduced polynomial
```

The resulting reduced polynomial is $x^2 + 9$, which has $3i$ and $-3i$ as zeros. Therefore, the four zeros of $x^4 - 4x^3 + 14x^2 - 36x + 45$ are $2 + i, 2 - i, 3i$, and $-3i$.

▶ **TRY EXERCISE 12, PAGE 327**

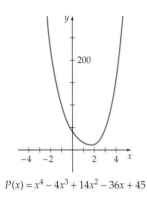

$P(x) = x^4 - 4x^3 + 14x^2 - 36x + 45$

FIGURE 3.20

Alternative to Example 3
Exercise 18, page 327.

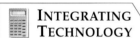
INTEGRATING TECHNOLOGY

Many graphing calculators can be used to do computations with complex numbers. The following TI-83 screen display shows that the product of $3 - 5i$ and $-7 - 5i$ is $-46 + 20i$. The i symbol is located above the decimal point key.

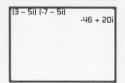

A graph of $P(x) = x^4 - 4x^3 + 14x^2 - 36x + 45$ is shown in **Figure 3.20**. Because the polynomial in Example 2 is a fourth-degree polynomial and because we have verified that $P(x)$ has four imaginary solutions, it comes as no surprise that the graph does not intersect the x-axis.

When performing synthetic division with complex numbers, it is helpful to write the coefficients of the given polynomial as complex coefficients. For instance, -10 can be written as $-10 + 0i$. This technique is illustrated in the next example.

EXAMPLE 3   Apply the Conjugate Pair Theorem

Find all the zeros of $P(x) = x^5 - 10x^4 + 65x^3 - 184x^2 + 274x - 204$ given that $3 - 5i$ is a zero.

Solution

Because the coefficients are real numbers and $3 - 5i$ is a zero, $3 + 5i$ also must be a zero. Use synthetic division to produce

$3 - 5i$	1	$-10 + 0i$	$65 + 0i$	$-184 + 0i$	$274 + 0i$	-204
		$3 - 5i$	$-46 + 20i$	$157 - 35i$	$-256 + 30i$	204
$3 + 5i$	1	$-7 - 5i$	$19 + 20i$	$-27 - 35i$	$18 + 30i$	0
		$3 + 5i$	$-12 - 20i$	$21 + 35i$	$-18 - 30i$	
	1	-4	7	-6	0	

Descartes' Rule of Signs can be used to show that the reduced polynomial $x^3 - 4x^2 + 7x - 6$ has three or one positive zeros and no negative zeros. Using the Rational Zero Theorem, we have

$$\frac{p}{q} = 1, 2, 3, 6$$

Use synthetic division to determine that 2 is a zero.

2	1	-4	7	-6
		2	-4	6
	1	-2	3	0

Use the quadratic formula to solve $x^2 - 2x + 3 = 0$.

$$x = \frac{-(-2) \pm \sqrt{(-2)^2 - 4(1)(3)}}{2(1)} = \frac{2 \pm \sqrt{-8}}{2} = \frac{2 \pm 2\sqrt{2}i}{2} = 1 \pm \sqrt{2}i$$

The zeros of $P(x) = x^5 - 10x^4 + 65x^3 - 184x^2 + 274x - 204$ are $3 - 5i$, $3 + 5i$, 2, $1 + \sqrt{2}i$, and $1 - \sqrt{2}i$.

▶ **TRY EXERCISE 16, PAGE 327**

❓ QUESTION Is it possible for a third-degree polynomial function with real coefficients to have two real zeros and one complex zero?

❓ ANSWER No. Because the coefficients of the polynomial are real numbers, the complex zeros of the polynomial function must occur as conjugate pairs.

Recall that the real zeros of a polynomial function P are the x-coordinates of the x-intercepts of the graph of P. This important connection between the real zeros of a polynomial function and the x-intercepts of the graph of the polynomial function is the basis for using a graphing utility to solve equations. Careful analysis of the graph of a polynomial function and your knowledge of the properties of polynomial functions can be used to solve many polynomial equations.

Alternative to Example 4
Exercise 26, page 327.

EXAMPLE 4   **Solve a Polynomial Equation**

 Solve: $x^4 - 5x^3 + 4x^2 + 3x + 9 = 0$

Solution

Let $P(x) = x^4 - 5x^3 + 4x^2 + 3x + 9$. The x-intercepts of the graph of P are the real solutions of the equation. Use a graphing utility to graph P. See **Figure 3.21.**

From the graph, it appears that $(3, 0)$ is an x-intercept and the only x-intercept. Because the graph of P intersects but does not cross the x-axis at $(3, 0)$, we know that 3 is a multiple zero of P with an even multiplicity.

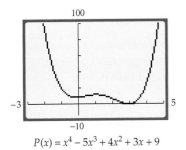

$$P(x) = x^4 - 5x^3 + 4x^2 + 3x + 9$$

FIGURE 3.21

```
3 | 1   -5    4    3    9       • Coefficients of P
  |       3   -6   -6   -9
  ------------------------
    1   -2   -2   -3    0       • The remainder is zero. Thus 3 is a zero.
```

By the Number of Zeros Theorem, there are three more zeros of P. Use synthetic division to show that 3 is also a zero of the reduced polynomial $x^3 - 2x^2 - 2x - 3$.

```
3 | 1   -2   -2   -3       • Coefficients of reduced polynomial
  |       3    3    3
  --------------------
    1    1    1    0       • The remainder is zero. Thus 3 is a zero
                            of multiplicity 2.
```

We now have 3 as a double root of the original equation, and from the last line of the preceding synthetic division, the remaining solutions must be solutions of $x^2 + x + 1 = 0$. Use the quadratic formula to solve this equation.

$$x = \frac{-1 \pm \sqrt{1^2 - 4(1)(1)}}{2(1)} = \frac{-1 \pm \sqrt{-3}}{2} = \frac{-1 \pm i\sqrt{3}}{2}$$

The solutions of $x^4 - 5x^3 + 4x^2 + 3x + 9 = 0$ are $3, 3, -\dfrac{1}{2} + \dfrac{\sqrt{3}}{2}i$, and $-\dfrac{1}{2} - \dfrac{\sqrt{3}}{2}i$.

▶ **TRY EXERCISE 24, PAGE 327**

● FIND A POLYNOMIAL FUNCTION WITH GIVEN ZEROS

Many of the problems in this section and in Section 3.3 dealt with the process of finding the zeros of a given polynomial function. Example 5 considers the reverse process, finding a polynomial function when the zeros are given.

Alternative to Example 5
Exercise 44, page 327.

EXAMPLE 5   **Determine a Polynomial Function Given Its Zeros**

Find each polynomial function.

a. A polynomial function of degree 3 that has 1, 2, and -3 as zeros

b. A polynomial function of degree 4 that has real coefficients and zeros $2i$ and $3 - 7i$

Solution

a. Because 1, 2, and -3 are zeros, $(x - 1)$, $(x - 2)$, and $(x + 3)$ are factors. The product of these factors produces a polynomial function that has the indicated zeros.

$$P(x) = (x - 1)(x - 2)(x + 3) = (x^2 - 3x + 2)(x + 3) = x^3 - 7x + 6$$

b. By the Conjugate Pair Theorem, the polynomial function also must have $-2i$ and $3 + 7i$ as zeros. The product of the factors $x - 2i$, $x - (-2i)$, $x - (3 - 7i)$, and $x - (3 + 7i)$ produces the desired polynomial function.

$$P(x) = (x - 2i)(x + 2i)[x - (3 - 7i)][x - (3 + 7i)]$$
$$= (x^2 + 4)(x^2 - 6x + 58)$$
$$= x^4 - 6x^3 + 62x^2 - 24x + 232$$

▶ **TRY EXERCISE 42, PAGE 327**

A polynomial function that has a given set of zeros is not unique. For example, $P(x) = x^3 - 7x + 6$ has zeros 1, 2, and -3, but so does any nonzero multiple of $P(x)$, such as $S(x) = 2x^3 - 14x + 12$. This concept is illustrated in **Figure 3.22.** The graphs of the two polynomial functions are different, but they have the same x-intercepts.

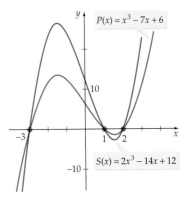

$P(x) = x^3 - 7x + 6$

$S(x) = 2x^3 - 14x + 12$

FIGURE 3.22

 TOPICS FOR DISCUSSION

1. What is the Fundamental Theorem of Algebra, and why is this theorem so important?

2. Let $P(x)$ be a polynomial function of degree n with real coefficients. Discuss the number of *possible* real zeros of this polynomial function. Include in your discussion the cases when n is even and when n is odd.

3. Consider the graph of a polynomial function in **Figure 3.23.** Is it possible that the degree of the polynomial is 3? Explain.

4. If two polynomial functions have exactly the same zeros, do the graphs of the polynomial functions look exactly the same?

5. Does the graph of every polynomial function have at least one x-intercept?

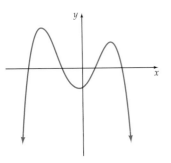

FIGURE 3.23

EXERCISE SET 3.4 —Suggested Assignment: Exercises 1–45, odd; 53–58, all.

In Exercises 1 to 10, find all the zeros of the polynomial function and write the polynomial as a product of linear factors. (Hint: First determine the rational zeros.)

1. $P(x) = x^4 + x^3 - 2x^2 + 4x - 24$
$2, -3, 2i, -2i; P(x) = (x-2)(x+3)(x-2i)(x+2i)$

▶ **2.** $P(x) = x^3 - 3x^2 + 7x - 5$
$1, 1-2i, 1+2i; P(x) = (x-1)(x-1+2i)(x-1-2i)$

3. $P(x) = 2x^4 + x^3 + 39x^2 + 136x - 78$
$\frac{1}{2}, -3, 1+5i, 1-5i; P(x) = \left(x-\frac{1}{2}\right)(x+3)(x-1-5i)(x-1+5i)$

4. $P(x) = x^3 - 13x^2 + 65x - 125$
$5, 4+3i, 4-3i; P(x) = (x-5)(x-4-3i)(x-4+3i)$

5. $P(x) = x^5 - 9x^4 + 34x^3 - 58x^2 + 45x - 13$
$1 \text{ (multiplicity 3)}, 3+2i, 3-2i; P(x) = (x-1)^3(x-3-2i)(x-3+2i)$

6. $P(x) = x^4 - 4x^3 + 53x^2 - 196x + 196$
$2 \text{ (multiplicity 2)}, 7i, -7i; P(x) = (x-2)^2(x-7i)(x+7i)$

7. $P(x) = 2x^4 - x^3 - 15x^2 + 23x + 15$
Answer on page AA11.

8. $P(x) = 3x^4 - 17x^3 - 39x^2 + 337x + 116$
Answer on page AA11.

9. $P(x) = 2x^4 - 14x^3 + 33x^2 - 46x + 40$
Answer on page AA11.

10. $P(x) = 3x^4 - 10x^3 + 15x^2 + 20x - 8$
$-1, \frac{1}{3}, 2+2i, 2-2i; P(x) = (x+1)\left(x-\frac{1}{3}\right)(x-2-2i)(x-2+2i)$

In Exercises 11 to 22, use the given zero to find the remaining zeros of each polynomial function.

11. $P(x) = 2x^3 - 5x^2 + 6x - 2$; $1+i$ $1-i, \frac{1}{2}$

▶ **12.** $P(x) = 3x^3 - 29x^2 + 92x + 34$; $5+3i$ $5-3i, -\frac{1}{3}$

13. $P(x) = x^3 + 3x^2 + x + 3$; $-i$ $i, -3$

14. $P(x) = x^4 - 6x^3 + 71x^2 - 146x + 530$; $2+7i$
$2-7i, 1+3i, 1-3i$

15. $P(x) = x^4 - 4x^3 + 14x^2 - 4x + 13$; $2-3i$ $2+3i, i, -i$

▶ **16.** $P(x) = x^5 - 6x^4 + 22x^3 - 64x^2 + 117x - 90$; $3i$
$-3i, 2, 2+i, 2-i$

17. $P(x) = x^4 - 4x^3 + 19x^2 - 30x + 50$; $1+3i$
$1-3i, 1+2i, 1-2i$

18. $P(x) = x^5 - x^4 - 4x^3 - 4x^2 - 5x - 3$; i
$-i, 3, -1 \text{ (multiplicity 2)}$

19. $P(x) = x^5 - 3x^4 + 7x^3 - 13x^2 + 12x - 4$; $-2i$
$2i, 1 \text{ (multiplicity 3)}$

20. $P(x) = x^4 - 8x^3 + 18x^2 - 8x + 17$; i $-i, 4+i, 4-i$

21. $P(x) = x^4 - 17x^3 + 112x^2 - 333x + 377$; $5+2i$

22. $P(x) = 2x^5 - 8x^4 + 61x^3 - 99x^2 + 12x + 182$; $1-5i$
21. $5-2i, \frac{7}{2}+\frac{\sqrt{3}}{2}i, \frac{7}{2}-\frac{\sqrt{3}}{2}i$ **22.** $1+5i, -1, \frac{3}{2}+\frac{\sqrt{5}}{2}i, \frac{3}{2}-\frac{\sqrt{5}}{2}i$

In Exercises 23 to 30, use a graph and your knowledge of the zeros of polynomial functions to determine the exact values of all the solutions of each equation.

23. $2x^3 - x^2 + x - 6 = 0$ $\frac{3}{2}, -\frac{1}{2}+\frac{\sqrt{7}}{2}i, -\frac{1}{2}-\frac{\sqrt{7}}{2}i$

▶ **24.** $4x^3 + 3x^2 + 16x + 12 = 0$ $-\frac{3}{4}, -2i, 2i$

25. $24x^3 - 62x^2 - 7x + 30 = 0$ $-\frac{2}{3}, \frac{3}{4}, \frac{5}{2}$

26. $12x^3 - 52x^2 + 27x + 28 = 0$ $-\frac{1}{2}, \frac{4}{3}, \frac{7}{2}$

27. $x^4 - 4x^3 + 5x^2 - 4x + 4 = 0$ $-i, i, 2 \text{ (multiplicity 2)}$

28. $x^4 + 4x^3 + 8x^2 + 16x + 16 = 0$ $-2 \text{ (multiplicity 2)}, 2i, -2i$

29. $x^4 + 4x^3 - 2x^2 - 12x + 9 = 0$
$-3 \text{ (multiplicity 2)}, 1 \text{ (multiplicity 2)}$

30. $x^4 + 3x^3 - 6x^2 - 28x - 24 = 0$ $3, -2 \text{ (multiplicity 3)}$

In Exercises 31 to 40, find a polynomial function of lowest degree with integer coefficients that has the given zeros.

31. $4, -3, 2$
$P(x) = x^3 - 3x^2 - 10x + 24$

32. $-1, 1, -5$
$P(x) = x^3 + 5x^2 - x - 5$

33. $3, 2i, -2i$
$P(x) = x^3 - 3x^2 + 4x - 12$

34. $0, i, -i$
$P(x) = x^3 + x$

35. $3+i, 3-i, 2+5i, 2-5i$
$P(x) = x^4 - 10x^3 + 63x^2 - 214x + 290$

36. $2+3i, 2-3i, -5, 2$ $P(x) = x^4 - x^3 - 9x^2 + 79x - 130$

37. $P(x) = x^5 - 22x^4 + 212x^3 - 1012x^2 + 2251x - 1830$

37. $6+5i, 6-5i, 2, 3, 5$

38. $\frac{1}{2}, 4-i, 4+i$
$P(x) = 2x^3 - 17x^2 + 42x - 17$

39. $\frac{3}{4}, 2+7i, 2-7i$
$P(x) = 4x^3 - 19x^2 + 224x - 159$

40. $\frac{1}{4}, -\frac{1}{5}, i, -i$
$P(x) = 20x^4 - x^3 + 19x^2 - x - 1$

In Exercises 41 to 46, find a polynomial function $P(x)$ that has the indicated zeros.

41. Zeros: $2-5i, -4$; degree 3 $P(x) = x^3 + 13x + 116$

▶ **42.** Zeros: $3+2i, 7$; degree 3 $P(x) = x^3 - 13x^2 + 55x - 91$

43. Zeros: $4+3i, 5-i$; degree 4
$P(x) = x^4 - 18x^3 + 131x^2 - 458x + 650$

44. Zeros: $i, 3-5i$; degree 4
$P(x) = x^4 - 6x^3 + 35x^2 - 6x + 34$

45. Zeros: $-2, 1, 3, 1+4i, 1-4i$; degree 5
$P(x) = x^5 - 4x^4 + 16x^3 - 18x^2 - 97x + 102$

46. Zeros: $-5, 3 \text{ (multiplicity 2)}, 2+i, 2-i$; degree 5
$P(x) = x^5 - 5x^4 - 12x^3 + 124x^2 - 285x - 225$

CONNECTING CONCEPTS

In Exercises 47 to 50, find a polynomial function $P(x)$ with real coefficients that has the indicated zeros and satisfies the given conditions.

47. Zeros: $-1, 2, 3$; degree 3; $P(1) = 12$
$P(x) = 3x^3 - 12x^2 + 3x + 18$

48. Zeros: $3i, 2$; degree 3; $P(3) = 27$ $P(x) = \dfrac{3}{2}x^3 - 3x^2 + \dfrac{27}{2}x - 27$

49. Zeros: $3, -5, 2 + i$; degree 4; $P(1) = 48$
$P(x) = -2x^4 + 4x^3 + 36x^2 - 140x + 150$

50. Zeros: $\dfrac{1}{2}, 1 - i$; degree 3; $P(4) = 140$
$P(x) = 4x^3 - 10x^2 + 12x - 4$

51. Verify that $P(x) = x^3 - x^2 - ix^2 - 9x + 9 + 9i$ has $1 + i$ as a zero and that its conjugate $1 - i$ is not a zero. Explain why this does not contradict the Conjugate Pair Theorem. The Conjugate Pair Theorem does not apply because some of the coefficients of the polynomial are not real numbers.

52. Verify that $P(x) = x^3 - x^2 - ix^2 - 20x + ix + 20i$ has a zero of i and that its conjugate $-i$ is not a zero. Explain why this does not contradict the Conjugate Pair Theorem. The Conjugate Pair Theorem does not apply because some of the coefficients of the polynomial are not real numbers.

PREPARE FOR SECTION 3.5

53. Simplify: $\dfrac{x^2 - 9}{x^2 - 2x - 15}$ [P.5] $\dfrac{x - 3}{x - 5}$

54. Evaluate $\dfrac{x + 4}{x^2 - 2x - 5}$ for $x = -1$. [P.1] $-\dfrac{3}{2}$

55. Evaluate $\dfrac{2x^2 + 4x - 5}{x + 6}$ for $x = -3$. [P.1] $\dfrac{1}{3}$

56. For what values of x does the denominator of $\dfrac{x^2 - x - 5}{2x^3 + x^2 - 15x}$ equal zero? [1.4] $x = 0, -3, \dfrac{5}{2}$

57. Determine the degree of the numerator and the degree of the denominator of $\dfrac{x^3 + 3x^2 - 5}{x^2 - 4}$. [P.3]
degree of numerator: 3; degree of denominator: 2

58. Write $\dfrac{x^3 + 2x^2 - x - 11}{x^2 - 2x}$ in $Q(x) + \dfrac{R(x)}{x^2 - 2x}$ form. [3.1]
$x + 4 + \dfrac{7x - 11}{x^2 - 2x}$

PROJECTS

1. **INVESTIGATE THE ROOTS OF A CUBIC EQUATION** Hieronimo Cardano, using a technique he learned from Nicolo Tartaglia, was able to solve some cubic equations.

a. Show that the cubic equation $x^3 + bx^2 + cx + d = 0$ can be transformed into the "reduced" cubic $y^3 + my = n$, where m and n are constants, depending on b, c, and d, by using the substitution $x = y - \dfrac{b}{3}$.

b. Cardano then showed that a solution of the reduced cubic is given by
$$\sqrt[3]{\dfrac{n}{2} + \sqrt{\dfrac{n^2}{4} + \dfrac{m^3}{27}}} - \sqrt[3]{-\dfrac{n}{2} + \sqrt{\dfrac{n^2}{4} + \dfrac{m^3}{27}}}$$
Use Cardano's procedure to solve the equation $x^3 - 6x^2 + 20x - 33 = 0$.
See the Instructor's Solutions Manual.

GRAPHS OF RATIONAL FUNCTIONS AND THEIR APPLICATIONS

● VERTICAL AND HORIZONTAL ASYMPTOTES

If $P(x)$ and $Q(x)$ are polynomials, then the function F given by

$$F(x) = \frac{P(x)}{Q(x)}$$

is called a **rational function.** The domain of F is the set of all real numbers except those for which $Q(x) = 0$. For example, let

$$F(x) = \frac{x^2 - x - 5}{2x^3 + x^2 - 15x}$$

Setting the denominator equal to zero, we have

$$2x^3 + x^2 - 15x = 0$$
$$x(2x - 5)(x + 3) = 0$$

The denominator is 0 for $x = 0$, $x = \dfrac{5}{2}$, and $x = -3$. Thus the domain of F is the set of all real numbers except 0, $\dfrac{5}{2}$, and -3.

The graph of $G(x) = \dfrac{x + 1}{x - 2}$ is given in **Figure 3.24.** The graph shows that G has the following properties:

- The graph has an x-intercept at $(-1, 0)$ and a y-intercept at $\left(0, -\dfrac{1}{2}\right)$.

- The graph does not exist when $x = 2$.

Note the behavior of the graph as x takes on values that are close to 2 but *less* than 2. Mathematically, we say that "x approaches 2 from the left."

x	1.9	1.95	1.99	1.995	1.999
$G(x)$	-29	-59	-299	-599	-2999

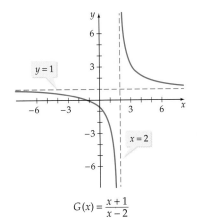

$$G(x) = \frac{x + 1}{x - 2}$$

FIGURE 3.24

From this table and the graph, it appears that as x approaches 2 from the left, the functional values $G(x)$ decrease without bound.

- In this case, we say that "$G(x)$ approaches negative infinity."

Now observe the behavior of the graph as x takes on values that are close to 2 but *greater* than 2. Mathematically, we say that "x approaches 2 from the right."

x	2.1	2.05	2.01	2.005	2.001
$G(x)$	31	61	301	601	3001

From this table and the graph, it appears that as x approaches 2 from the right, the functional values $G(x)$ increase without bound.

- In this case, we say that "$G(x)$ approaches positive infinity."

Now consider the values of $G(x)$ as x *increases* without bound. The following table gives values of $G(x)$ for selected values of x.

x	1000	5000	10,000	50,000	100,000
G(x)	1.00301	1.00060	1.00030	1.00006	1.00003

- As x increases without bound, the values of $G(x)$ become closer to 1.

Now let the values of x *decrease* without bound. The table below gives the values of $G(x)$ for selected values of x.

x	−1000	−5000	−10,000	−50,000	−100,000
G(x)	0.997006	0.999400	0.999700	0.999940	0.999970

- As x decreases without bound, the values of $G(x)$ become closer to 1.

When we are discussing graphs that increase or decrease without bound, it is convenient to use mathematical notation. The notation

$$f(x) \rightarrow \infty \quad \text{as} \quad x \rightarrow a^+$$

means that the functional values $f(x)$ increase without bound as x approaches a from the right. Recall that the symbol ∞ does not represent a real number but is used merely to describe the concept of a variable taking on larger and larger values without bound. See **Figure 3.25a.**

The notation

$$f(x) \rightarrow \infty \quad \text{as} \quad x \rightarrow a^-$$

means that the function values $f(x)$ increase without bound as x approaches a from the left. See **Figure 3.25b.**

The notation

$$f(x) \rightarrow -\infty \quad \text{as} \quad x \rightarrow a^+$$

means that the functional values $f(x)$ decrease without bound as x approaches a from the right. See **Figure 3.25c.**

The notation

$$f(x) \rightarrow -\infty \quad \text{as} \quad x \rightarrow a^-$$

means that the functional values $f(x)$ decrease without bound as x approaches a from the left. See **Figure 3.25d.**

Each graph in **Figure 3.25** approaches a vertical line through $(a, 0)$ as $x \rightarrow a^+$ or a^-. The line is said to be a *vertical asymptote* of the graph.

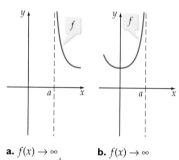

a. $f(x) \rightarrow \infty$
as $x \rightarrow a^+$

b. $f(x) \rightarrow \infty$
as $x \rightarrow a^-$

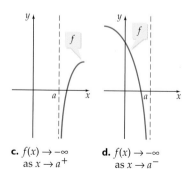

c. $f(x) \rightarrow -\infty$
as $x \rightarrow a^+$

d. $f(x) \rightarrow -\infty$
as $x \rightarrow a^-$

FIGURE 3.25

Definition of a Vertical Asymptote

The line $x = a$ is a **vertical asymptote** of the graph of a function F provided

$$F(x) \to \infty \quad \text{or} \quad F(x) \to -\infty$$

as x approaches a from either the left or right.

In **Figure 3.24,** the line $x = 2$ is a vertical asymptote of the graph of G. Note that the graph of G in **Figure 3.24** also approaches the horizontal line $y = 1$ as $x \to \infty$ and as $x \to -\infty$. The line $y = 1$ is a *horizontal asymptote* of the graph of G.

Definition of a Horizontal Asymptote

The line $y = b$ is a **horizontal asymptote** of the graph of a function F provided

$$F(x) \to b \quad \text{as} \quad x \to \infty \quad \text{or} \quad x \to -\infty$$

Figure 3.26 illustrates some of the ways in which the graph of a rational function may approach its horizontal asymptote. It is common practice to display the asymptotes of the graph of a rational function by using dashed lines. Although a rational function may have several vertical asymptotes, it can have at most one horizontal asymptote. The graph may intersect its horizontal asymptote.

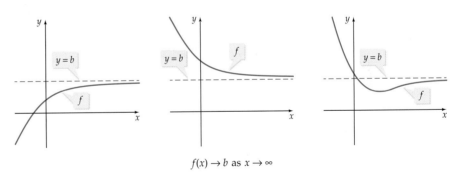

$$f(x) \to b \text{ as } x \to \infty$$

FIGURE 3.26

? QUESTION Can a graph of a rational function cross its vertical asymptote? Why or why not?

Geometrically, a line is an asymptote of a curve if the distance between the line and a point $P(x, y)$ on the curve approaches zero as the distance between the origin and the point P increases without bound.

? ANSWER No. If $x = a$ is a vertical asymptote of a rational function R, then $R(a)$ is undefined.

Vertical asymptotes of the graph of a rational function can be found by using the following theorem.

INSTRUCTOR NOTE

Stress that the Theorem on Vertical Asymptotes is valid only for rational functions whose numerator and denominator have no common factor.

Theorem on Vertical Asymptotes

If the real number a is a zero of the denominator $Q(x)$, then the graph of $F(x) = P(x)/Q(x)$, where $P(x)$ and $Q(x)$ have no common factors, has the vertical asymptote $x = a$.

Alternative to Example 1
Exercise 4, page 341.

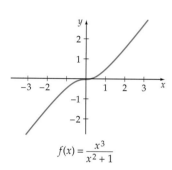

$$f(x) = \frac{x^3}{x^2 + 1}$$

FIGURE 3.27

EXAMPLE 1 **Find the Vertical Asymptotes of a Rational Function**

Find the vertical asymptotes of each rational function.

a. $f(x) = \dfrac{x^3}{x^2 + 1}$ **b.** $g(x) = \dfrac{x}{x^2 - x - 6}$

Solution

a. To find the vertical asymptotes, determine the real zeros of the denominator. The denominator $x^2 + 1$ has no real zeros, so the graph of f has no vertical asymptotes. See **Figure 3.27.**

b. The denominator $x^2 - x - 6 = (x - 3)(x + 2)$ has zeros of 3 and -2. The numerator has no common factors with the denominator, so $x = 3$ and $x = -2$ are both vertical asymptotes of the graph of g, as shown in **Figure 3.28.**

▶ **TRY EXERCISE 2, PAGE 341**

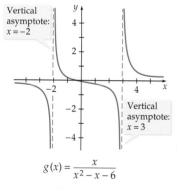

$$g(x) = \frac{x}{x^2 - x - 6}$$

FIGURE 3.28

The following theorem indicates that a horizontal asymptote can be determined by examining the leading terms of the numerator and the denominator of a rational function.

Theorem on Horizontal Asymptotes

Let $$F(x) = \frac{a_n x^n + a_{n-1} x^{n-1} + \cdots + a_1 x + a_0}{b_m x^m + b_{m-1} x^{m-1} + \cdots + b_1 x + b_0}$$

be a rational function with numerator of degree n and denominator of degree m.

1. If $n < m$, then the x-axis, which is the line given by $y = 0$, is the horizontal asymptote of the graph of F.

2. If $n = m$, then the line given by $y = a_n/b_m$ is the horizontal asymptote of the graph of F.

3. If $n > m$, the graph of F has no horizontal asymptote.

Alternative to Example 2
Exercise 8, page 341.

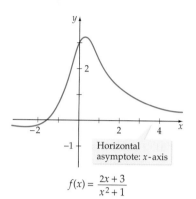

$$f(x) = \frac{2x+3}{x^2+1}$$

FIGURE 3.29

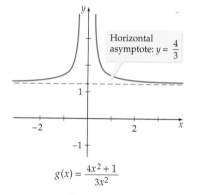

$$g(x) = \frac{4x^2+1}{3x^2}$$

FIGURE 3.30

EXAMPLE 2 Find the Horizontal Asymptote of a Rational Function

Find the horizontal asymptote of each rational function.

a. $f(x) = \dfrac{2x+3}{x^2+1}$ b. $g(x) = \dfrac{4x^2+1}{3x^2}$ c. $h(x) = \dfrac{x^3+1}{x-2}$

Solution

a. The degree of the numerator $2x + 3$ is less than the degree of the denominator $x^2 + 1$. By the Theorem on Horizontal Asymptotes, the x-axis is the horizontal asymptote of f. See the graph of f in **Figure 3.29.**

b. The numerator $4x^2 + 1$ and the denominator $3x^2$ of g are both of degree 2. By the Theorem on Horizontal Asymptotes, the line $y = \dfrac{4}{3}$ is the horizontal asymptote of g. See the graph of g in **Figure 3.30.**

c. The degree of the numerator $x^3 + 1$ is larger than the degree of the denominator $x - 2$, so by the Theorem on Horizontal Asymptotes, the graph of h has no horizontal asymptotes.

▶ **TRY EXERCISE 6, PAGE 341**

The proof of the Theorem on Horizontal Asymptotes makes use of the technique employed in the following verification. To verify that

$$y = \frac{5x^2 + 4}{3x^2 + 8x + 7}$$

has a horizontal asymptote of $y = \dfrac{5}{3}$, divide the numerator and the denominator by the largest power of the variable x (x^2 in this case).

$$y = \frac{\dfrac{5x^2 + 4}{x^2}}{\dfrac{3x^2 + 8x + 7}{x^2}} = \frac{5 + \dfrac{4}{x^2}}{3 + \dfrac{8}{x} + \dfrac{7}{x^2}}, \quad x \neq 0$$

As x increases without bound or decreases without bound, the fractions $\dfrac{4}{x^2}, \dfrac{8}{x}$, and $\dfrac{7}{x^2}$ approach zero. Thus

$$y \to \frac{5 + 0}{3 + 0 + 0} = \frac{5}{3} \quad \text{as} \quad x \to \pm\infty$$

and hence the line $y = \dfrac{5}{3}$ is a horizontal asymptote of the graph.

• A Sign Property of Rational Functions

The zeros and vertical asymptotes of a rational function F divide the x-axis into intervals. In each interval, $F(x)$ is positive for all x in the interval or $F(x)$ is negative for all x in the interval. For example, consider the rational function

$$g(x) = \frac{x + 1}{x^2 + 2x - 3}$$

which has vertical asymptotes of $x = -3$ and $x = 1$ and a zero of -1. These three numbers divide the x-axis into the four intervals $(-\infty, -3)$, $(-3, -1)$, $(-1, 1)$, and $(1, \infty)$. Note in **Figure 3.31** that the graph of g is negative for all x such that $x < -3$, positive for all x such that $-3 < x < -1$, negative for all x such that $-1 < x < 1$, and positive for all x such that $x > 1$.

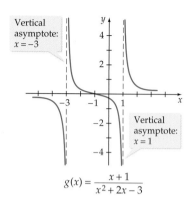

Vertical asymptote: $x = -3$

Vertical asymptote: $x = 1$

$$g(x) = \frac{x + 1}{x^2 + 2x - 3}$$

FIGURE 3.31

• A General Graphing Procedure

If $F(x) = P(x)/Q(x)$, where $P(x)$ and $Q(x)$ are polynomials that have no common factors, then the following general procedure offers useful guidelines for graphing F.

(P) **General Procedure for Graphing Rational Functions That Have No Common Factors**

1. *Asymptotes*   Find the real zeros of the denominator $Q(x)$. For each zero a, draw the dashed line $x = a$. Each line is a vertical asymptote of the graph of F. Also graph any horizontal asymptotes.

2. *Intercepts*   Find the real zeros of the numerator $P(x)$. For each real zero c, plot the point $(c, 0)$. Each such point is an x-intercept of the graph of F. For each x-intercept use the even and odd powers of $(x - c)$ to determine if the graph crosses the x-axis at the intercept or if the graph intersects but does not cross the x-axis. Also evaluate $F(0)$. Plot $(0, F(0))$, the y-intercept of the graph of F.

3. *Symmetry*   Use the tests for symmetry to determine whether the graph of the function has symmetry with respect to the y-axis or symmetry with respect to the origin.

4. *Additional points*   Plot some points that lie in the intervals between and beyond the vertical asymptotes and the x-intercepts.

5. *Behavior near asymptotes*   If $x = a$ is a vertical asymptote, determine whether $F(x) \to \infty$ or $F(x) \to -\infty$ as $x \to a^-$ and also as $x \to a^+$.

6. *Complete the sketch*   Use all the information obtained above to sketch the graph of F.

Alternative to Example 3
Exercise 12, page 341.

INSTRUCTOR NOTE

Example 3 shows how graphing technology can be used in conjunction with the analytical concepts that were discussed in this section. The idea is that technology is useful for displaying graphs and that analytical concepts can be used to ensure that the graph reflects what was intended and that no errors were made when entering the function. If the intercepts, symmetry, and asymptotes that are determined analytically are not reflected in the graph, then either the expression was entered incorrectly or the analysis was performed incorrectly.

EXAMPLE 3   **Graph a Rational Function**

Sketch a graph of $f(x) = \dfrac{2x^2 - 18}{x^2 + 3}$.

Solution

Asymptotes   The denominator $x^2 + 3$ has no real zeros, so the graph of f has no vertical asymptotes. The numerator and denominator both are of degree 2. The leading coefficients are 2 and 1, respectively. By the Theorem on Horizontal Asymptotes, the graph of f has a horizontal asymptote of

$$y = \frac{2}{1} = 2.$$

Intercepts   The zeros of the numerator occur when $2x^2 - 18 = 0$ or, solving for x, when $x = -3$ and $x = 3$. Therefore, the x-intercepts are $(-3, 0)$ and $(3, 0)$. The factored numerator is $2(x + 3)(x - 3)$. Each linear factor has an exponent of 1, an odd number. Thus the graph crosses the x-axis at its x-intercepts. To find the y-intercept, evaluate f when $x = 0$. This gives $y = -6$. Therefore, the y-intercept is $(0, -6)$.

Symmetry   Below we show that $f(-x) = f(x)$, which means that f is an even function and therefore its graph is symmetric with respect to the y-axis.

$$f(-x) = \frac{2(-x)^2 - 18}{(-x)^2 + 3} = \frac{2x^2 - 18}{x^2 + 3} = f(x)$$

Additional Points   The intervals determined by the x-intercepts are $x < -3$, $-3 < x < 3$, and $x > 3$. Generally, it is necessary to determine points in all intervals. However, because f is an even function, its graph is symmetric with respect to the y-axis. The following table lists a few points for $x > 0$. Symmetry can be used to locate corresponding points for $x < 0$.

x	1	2	6
$f(x)$	-4	$-\dfrac{10}{7} \approx -1.43$	$\dfrac{18}{13} \approx 1.38$

Behavior Near Asymptotes   As x increases or decreases without bound, $f(x)$ approaches the horizontal asymptote $y = 2$.

To determine whether the graph of f intersects the horizontal asymptote at any point, solve the equation $f(x) = 2$.

There are no solutions of $f(x) = 2$ because

$$\frac{2x^2 - 18}{x^2 + 3} = 2 \quad \text{implies} \quad 2x^2 - 18 = 2x^2 + 6 \quad \text{implies} \quad -18 = 6$$

This is not possible. Thus the graph of f does not intersect the horizontal asymptote but approaches it from below as x increases or decreases without bound.

Continued ▶

Complete the Sketch   Use the summary in **Table 3.3,** to the left, to finish the sketch. The completed graph is shown in **Figure 3.32.**

TABLE 3.3

Vertical Asymptote	None
Horizontal Asymptote	$y = 2$
x-Intercepts	crosses at $(-3, 0)$, crosses at $(3, 0)$
y-Intercept	$(0, -6)$
Additional Points	$(1, -4), (2, -1.43),$ $(6, 1.38)$

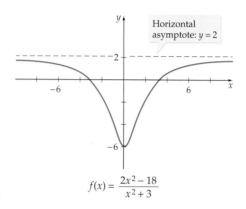

$$f(x) = \frac{2x^2 - 18}{x^2 + 3}$$

FIGURE 3.32

▶ **TRY EXERCISE 10, PAGE 341**

Alternative to Example 4
Exercise 28, page 341.

EXAMPLE 4   **Graph a Rational Function**

Sketch a graph of $h(x) = \dfrac{x^2 + 1}{x^2 + x - 2}$.

Solution

Asymptotes   The denominator $x^2 + x - 2 = (x + 2)(x - 1)$ has zeros -2 and 1; because there are no common factors of the numerator and the denominator, the lines $x = -2$ and $x = 1$ are vertical asymptotes.
 The numerator and denominator both are of degree 2. The leading coefficients of the numerator and denominator are both 1. Thus h has the horizontal asymptote $y = \dfrac{1}{1} = 1$.

Intercepts   The numerator $x^2 + 1$ has no real zeros, so the graph of h has no x-intercepts. Because $h(0) = -0.5$, h has the y-intercept $(0, -0.5)$.

Symmetry   By applying the tests for symmetry, we can determine that the graph of h is not symmetric with respect to the origin or to the y-axis.

Additional Points   The intervals determined by the vertical asymptotes are $(-\infty, -2)$, $(-2, 1)$, and $(1, \infty)$. Plot a few points from each interval.

x	−5	−3	−1	0.5	2	3	4
h(x)	$\dfrac{13}{9}$	$\dfrac{5}{2}$	−1	−1	$\dfrac{5}{4}$	1	$\dfrac{17}{18}$

The graph of h will intersect the horizontal asymptote $y = 1$ exactly once. This can be determined by solving the equation $h(x) = 1$.

$$\frac{x^2 + 1}{x^2 + x - 2} = 1$$

$$x^2 + 1 = x^2 + x - 2 \qquad \bullet \text{ Multiply both sides by } x^2 + x - 2.$$

$$1 = x - 2$$

$$3 = x$$

The only solution is $x = 3$. Therefore, the graph of h intersects the horizontal asymptote at $(3, 1)$.

Behavior Near Asymptotes As x approaches -2 from the left, the denominator $(x + 2)(x - 1)$ approaches 0 but remains positive. The numerator $x^2 + 1$ approaches 5, which is positive, so the quotient $h(x)$ increases without bound. Stated in mathematical notation,

$$h(x) \to \infty \quad \text{as} \quad x \to -2^-$$

Similarly, it can be determined that

$$h(x) \to -\infty \quad \text{as} \quad x \to -2^+$$
$$h(x) \to -\infty \quad \text{as} \quad x \to 1^-$$
$$h(x) \to \infty \quad \text{as} \quad x \to 1^+$$

Complete the Sketch Use the summary in **Table 3.4** to obtain the graph sketched in **Figure 3.33**.

TABLE 3.4

Vertical Asymptote	$x = -2, x = 1$
Horizontal Asymptote	$y = 1$
x-Intercepts	None
y-Intercept	$(0, -0.5)$
Additional Points	$(-5, 1.\overline{4}), (-3, 2.5),$ $(-1, -1), (0.5, -1),$ $(2, 1.25), (3, 1),$ $(4, 0.9\overline{4})$

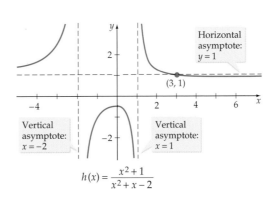

FIGURE 3.33

▶ TRY EXERCISE 26, PAGE 341

● SLANT ASYMPTOTES

Some rational functions have an asymptote that is neither vertical nor horizontal, but slanted.

Theorem on Slant Asymptotes

The rational function given by $F(x) = P(x)/Q(x)$, where $P(x)$ and $Q(x)$ have no common factors, has a **slant asymptote** if the degree of the polynomial $P(x)$ in the numerator is one greater than the degree of the polynomial $Q(x)$ in the denominator.

To find the slant asymptote, divide $P(x)$ by $Q(x)$ and write $F(x)$ in the form

$$F(x) = \frac{P(x)}{Q(x)} = (mx + b) + \frac{r(x)}{Q(x)}$$

where the degree of $r(x)$ is less than the degree of $Q(x)$. Because

$$\frac{r(x)}{Q(x)} \to 0 \quad \text{as} \quad x \to \pm\infty$$

we know that $F(x) \to mx + b$ as $x \to \pm\infty$.

The line represented by $y = mx + b$ is the slant asymptote of the graph of F.

Alternative to Example 5
Exercise 34, page 341.

EXAMPLE 5   **Find the Slant Asymptote of a Rational Function**

Find the slant asymptote of $f(x) = \dfrac{2x^3 + 5x^2 + 1}{x^2 + x + 3}$.

Solution

Because the degree of the numerator $2x^3 + 5x^2 + 1$ is exactly one larger than the degree of the denominator $x^2 + x + 3$ and f is in simplest form, f has a slant asymptote. To find the asymptote, divide $2x^3 + 5x^2 + 1$ by $x^2 + x + 3$.

$$
\begin{array}{r}
2x + 3 \\
x^2 + x + 3\overline{\smash{)}2x^3 + 5x^2 + 0x + 1} \\
\underline{2x^3 + 2x^2 + 6x\phantom{{}+ 1}} \\
3x^2 - 6x + 1 \\
\underline{3x^2 + 3x + 9} \\
-9x - 8
\end{array}
$$

Therefore,

$$f(x) = \frac{2x^3 + 5x^2 + 1}{x^2 + x + 3} = 2x + 3 + \frac{-9x - 8}{x^2 + x + 3}$$

and the line given by $y = 2x + 3$ is the slant asymptote for the graph of f.
Figure 3.34 shows the graph of f and its slant asymptote.

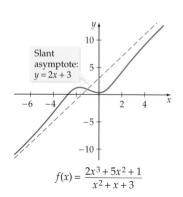

Slant asymptote: $y = 2x + 3$

$f(x) = \dfrac{2x^3 + 5x^2 + 1}{x^2 + x + 3}$

FIGURE 3.34

▶ **TRY EXERCISE 32, PAGE 341**

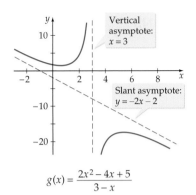

$$g(x) = \frac{2x^2 - 4x + 5}{3 - x}$$

FIGURE 3.35

The function f in Example 5 does not have a vertical asymptote because the denominator $x^2 + x + 3$ does not have any real zeros. However, the function

$$g(x) = \frac{2x^2 - 4x + 5}{3 - x}$$

has both a slant asymptote and a vertical asymptote. The vertical asymptote is $x = 3$, and the slant asymptote is $y = -2x - 2$. **Figure 3.35** shows the graph of g and its asymptotes.

● GRAPH RATIONAL FUNCTIONS THAT HAVE A COMMON FACTOR

If a rational function has a numerator and denominator that have a common factor, then you should reduce the rational function to lowest terms before you apply the general procedure for sketching the graph of a rational function.

Alternative to Example 6
Exercise 50, page 342.

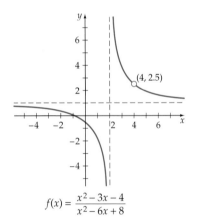

$$f(x) = \frac{x^2 - 3x - 4}{x^2 - 6x + 8}$$

FIGURE 3.36

EXAMPLE 6   Graph a Rational Function That Has a Common Factor

Sketch the graph of $f(x) = \dfrac{x^2 - 3x - 4}{x^2 - 6x + 8}$.

Solution

Factor the numerator and denominator to obtain

$$f(x) = \frac{x^2 - 3x - 4}{x^2 - 6x + 8} = \frac{(x + 1)(x - 4)}{(x - 2)(x - 4)}, \quad x \neq 2, x \neq 4$$

Thus for all x values other than $x = 4$, the graph of f is the same as the graph of

$$G(x) = \frac{x + 1}{x - 2}$$

Figure 3.24 on page 329 shows a graph of G. The graph of f will be the same as this graph, except that it will have an open circle at $(4, 2.5)$ to indicate that it is undefined at $x = 4$. See the graph of f in **Figure 3.36**. The height of the open circle was found by evaluating the resulting reduced rational function $G(x) = \dfrac{x + 1}{x - 2}$ at $x = 4$.

▶ **TRY EXERCISE 48, PAGE 342**

❓ QUESTION Does $F(x) = \dfrac{x^2 - x - 6}{x^2 - 9}$ have a vertical asymptote at $x = 3$?

❓ ANSWER No. $F(x) = \dfrac{x^2 - x - 6}{x^2 - 9} = \dfrac{(x - 3)(x + 2)}{(x - 3)(x + 3)} = \dfrac{x + 2}{x + 3}$, $x \neq 3$. As $x \to 3$,

$F(x) \to \dfrac{5}{6}$.

• APPLICATIONS OF RATIONAL FUNCTIONS

Alternative to Example 7
Exercise 54, page 342.

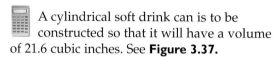

EXAMPLE 7   Solve an Application

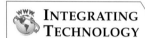 **INTEGRATING TECHNOLOGY**

A Web applet is available to explore the relationship between the radius of a cylinder with a given volume and the surface area of the cylinder. This applet, CYLINDER, can be found on our website at

math.college.hmco.com

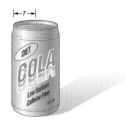

A cylindrical soft drink can is to be constructed so that it will have a volume of 21.6 cubic inches. See **Figure 3.37.**

a. Write the total surface area A of the can as a function of r, where r is the radius of the can in inches.

b. Use a graphing utility to estimate the value of r (to the nearest tenth of an inch) that produces the minimum surface area.

FIGURE 3.37

Solution

a. The formula for the volume of a cylinder is $V = \pi r^2 h$, where r is the radius and h is the height. Because we are given that the volume is 21.6 cubic inches, we have

$$21.6 = \pi r^2 h$$

$$\frac{21.6}{\pi r^2} = h \qquad \text{• Solve for } h.$$

The surface area of the cylinder is given by

$$A = 2\pi r^2 + 2\pi rh$$

$$A = 2\pi r^2 + 2\pi r\left(\frac{21.6}{\pi r^2}\right) \qquad \text{• Substitute for } h.$$

$$A = 2\pi r^2 + \frac{2(21.6)}{r} \qquad \text{• Simplify.}$$

$$A = \frac{2\pi r^3 + 43.2}{r} \qquad\qquad\qquad (1)$$

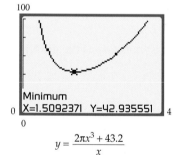

$$y = \frac{2\pi x^3 + 43.2}{x}$$

FIGURE 3.38

b. Use Equation (1) with $y = A$ and $x = r$ and a graphing utility to determine that A is a minimum when $r \approx 1.5$ inches. See **Figure 3.38.**

▶ **TRY EXERCISE 56, PAGE 342**

🧑‍🤝‍🧑 📝 TOPICS FOR DISCUSSION

1. What is a rational function? Give examples of functions that are rational functions and of functions that are not rational functions.

2. Does the graph of every rational function have at least one vertical asymptote? If so, explain why. If not, give an example of a rational function without a vertical asymptote.

3. Does the graph of every rational function have a horizontal asymptote? If so, explain why. If not, give an example of a rational function without a horizontal asymptote.

4. Can the graph of a polynomial function have a vertical asymptote? a horizontal asymptote?

EXERCISE SET 3.5

—Suggested Assignment: Exercises 1–61, odd.
—Answer graphs to Exercises 9–30 and 35–52 are on pages AA12–AA13.

In Exercises 1 to 4, find all vertical asymptotes of each rational function.

1. $F(x) = \dfrac{2x - 1}{x^2 + 3x}$

   $x = 0, x = -3$

▶2. $F(x) = \dfrac{3x^2 + 5}{x^2 - 4}$

   $x = 2, x = -2$

3. $F(x) = \dfrac{x^2 + 11}{6x^2 - 5x - 4}$

   $x = -\dfrac{1}{2}, x = \dfrac{4}{3}$

4. $F(x) = \dfrac{3x - 5}{x^3 - 8}$

   $x = 2$

In Exercises 5 to 8, find the horizontal asymptote of each rational function.

5. $F(x) = \dfrac{4x^2 + 1}{x^2 + x + 1}$ $y = 4$

▶6. $F(x) = \dfrac{3x^3 - 27x^2 + 5x - 11}{x^5 - 2x^3 + 7}$ $y = 0$

7. $F(x) = \dfrac{15{,}000x^3 + 500x - 2000}{700 + 500x^3}$ $y = 30$

8. $F(x) = 6000\left(1 - \dfrac{25}{(x + 5)^2}\right)$ $y = 6000$

In Exercises 9 to 30, determine the vertical and horizontal asymptotes and sketch the graph of the rational function F. Label all intercepts and asymptotes.

9. $F(x) = \dfrac{1}{x + 4}$

   $x = -4, y = 0$

▶10. $F(x) = \dfrac{1}{x - 2}$

   $x = 2, y = 0$

11. $F(x) = \dfrac{-4}{x - 3}$

   $x = 3, y = 0$

12. $F(x) = \dfrac{-3}{x + 2}$

   $x = -2, y = 0$

13. $F(x) = \dfrac{4}{x}$

   $x = 0, y = 0$

14. $F(x) = \dfrac{-4}{x}$

   $x = 0, y = 0$

15. $F(x) = \dfrac{x}{x + 4}$

   $x = -4, y = 1$

16. $F(x) = \dfrac{x}{x - 2}$

   $x = 2, y = 1$

17. $F(x) = \dfrac{x + 4}{2 - x}$

   $x = 2, y = -1$

18. $F(x) = \dfrac{x + 3}{1 - x}$

   $x = 1, y = -1$

19. $F(x) = \dfrac{1}{x^2 - 9}$

   $x = 3, x = -3, y = 0$

20. $F(x) = \dfrac{-2}{x^2 - 4}$

   $x = 2, x = -2, y = 0$

21. $F(x) = \dfrac{1}{x^2 + 2x - 3}$

   $x = -3, x = 1, y = 0$

22. $F(x) = \dfrac{1}{x^2 - 2x - 8}$

   $x = 4, x = -2, y = 0$

23. $F(x) = \dfrac{x^2}{x^2 + 4x + 4}$

   $x = -2, y = 1$

24. $F(x) = \dfrac{2x^2}{x^2 - 1}$

   $x = -1, x = 1, y = 2$

25. $F(x) = \dfrac{10}{x^2 + 2}$

   no vertical asymptote; $y = 0$

▶26. $F(x) = \dfrac{x^2}{x^2 - 6x + 9}$

   $x = 3, y = 1$

27. $F(x) = \dfrac{2x^2 - 2}{x^2 - 9}$

   $x = 3, x = -3, y = 2$

28. $F(x) = \dfrac{6x^2 - 5}{2x^2 + 6}$

   no vertical asymptote; $y = 3$

29. $F(x) = \dfrac{x^2 + x + 4}{x^2 + 2x - 1}$

   $x = -1 + \sqrt{2}, x = -1 - \sqrt{2},$
   $y = 1$

30. $F(x) = \dfrac{2x^2 - 14}{x^2 - 6x + 5}$

   $x = 5, x = 1, y = 2$

In Exercises 31 to 34, find the slant asymptote of each rational function.

31. $F(x) = \dfrac{3x^2 + 5x - 1}{x + 4}$ $y = 3x - 7$

▶32. $F(x) = \dfrac{x^3 - 2x^2 + 3x + 4}{x^2 - 3x + 5}$ $y = x + 1$

33. $F(x) = \dfrac{x^3 - 1}{x^2}$ $y = x$

34. $F(x) = \dfrac{4000 + 20x + 0.0001x^2}{x}$ $y = 0.0001x + 20$

In Exercises 35 to 44, determine the vertical and slant asymptotes and sketch the graph of the rational function F.

35. $F(x) = \dfrac{x^2 - 4}{x}$

$x = 0, y = x$

36. $F(x) = \dfrac{x^2 + 10}{2x}$

$x = 0, y = \dfrac{1}{2}x$

37. $F(x) = \dfrac{x^2 - 3x - 4}{x + 3}$

$x = -3, y = x - 6$

38. $F(x) = \dfrac{x^2 - 4x - 5}{2x + 5}$

$y = \dfrac{1}{2}x - \dfrac{13}{4}$ $x = -\dfrac{5}{2}$,

39. $F(x) = \dfrac{2x^2 + 5x + 3}{x - 4}$

$x = 4, y = 2x + 13$

40. $F(x) = \dfrac{4x^2 - 9}{x + 3}$

$x = -3, y = 4x - 12$

41. $F(x) = \dfrac{x^2 - x}{x + 2}$

$x = -2, y = x - 3$

42. $F(x) = \dfrac{x^2 + x}{x - 1}$

$x = 1, y = x + 2$

43. $F(x) = \dfrac{x^3 + 1}{x^2 - 4}$

$x = 2, x = -2, y = x$

44. $F(x) = \dfrac{x^3 - 1}{3x^2}$

$x = 0, y = \dfrac{1}{3}x$

In Exercises 45 to 52, sketch the graph of the rational function F. (*Hint:* First examine the numerator and denominator to determine whether there are any common factors.)

45. $F(x) = \dfrac{x^2 + x}{x + 1}$

46. $F(x) = \dfrac{x^2 - 3x}{x - 3}$

47. $F(x) = \dfrac{2x^3 + 4x^2}{2x + 4}$

▶ 48. $F(x) = \dfrac{x^2 - x - 12}{x^2 - 2x - 8}$

49. $F(x) = \dfrac{-2x^3 + 6x}{2x^2 - 6x}$

50. $F(x) = \dfrac{x^3 + 3x^2}{x(x + 3)(x - 1)}$

51. $F(x) = \dfrac{x^2 - 3x - 10}{x^2 + 4x + 4}$

52. $F(x) = \dfrac{2x^2 + x - 3}{x^2 - 2x + 1}$

53. **AVERAGE COST OF GOLF BALLS** The cost, in dollars, of producing x golf balls is given by

$$C(x) = 0.43x + 76,000$$

The average cost per golf ball is given by

$$\overline{C}(x) = \dfrac{C(x)}{x} = \dfrac{0.43x + 76,000}{x}$$

a. Find the average cost of producing 1000, 10,000, and 100,000 golf balls. $76.43, $8.03, $1.19

b. What is the equation of the horizontal asymptote of the graph of $\overline{C}$? Explain the significance of the horizontal asymptote as it relates to this application. $y = 0.43$. As the number of golf balls produced increases, the average cost per ball approaches $.43.

54. **AVERAGE COST OF CD PLAYERS** The cost, in dollars, of producing x CD players is given by

$$C(x) = 0.001x^2 + 54x + 175,000$$

The average cost per CD player is given by

$$\overline{C}(x) = \dfrac{C(x)}{x} = \dfrac{0.001x^2 + 54x + 175,000}{x}$$

a. Find the average cost of producing 1000, 10,000, and 100,000 CD players. $230, $81.50, $155.75

b. What is the minimum average cost per CD player? How many CD players should be produced to minimize the average cost per CD player? ≈$80.46; ≈13,229 CD players

55. **DESALINIZATION** The cost C, in dollars, to remove $p\%$ of the salt in a tank of seawater is given by

$$C(p) = \dfrac{2000p}{100 - p}, \quad 0 \le p < 100$$

a. Find the cost of removing 40% of the salt. $1333.33

b. Find the cost of removing 80% of the salt. $8000

c. Sketch the graph of C. Answer on page AA13.

▶ 56. PRODUCTION COSTS The cost, in dollars, of producing x cellular telephones is given by

$$C(x) = 0.0006x^2 + 9x + 401,000$$

The average cost per telephone is

$$\overline{C}(x) = \dfrac{C(x)}{x} = \dfrac{0.0006x^2 + 9x + 401,000}{x}$$

a. Find the average cost per telephone when 1000, 10,000, and 100,000 telephones are produced. $410.60, $55.10, $73.01

b. What is the minimum average cost per telephone? How many cellular telephones should be produced to minimize the average cost per telephone? $40.02; 25,852 telephones

57. 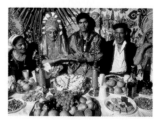 **WEDDING EXPENSES** The function $C(t) = 17t^2 + 128t + 5900$ models the average cost of a wedding reception, and the function $W(t) = 38t^2 + 291t + 15,208$ models the average cost of a wedding, where $t = 0$ represents the year 1990 and $0 \le t \le 12$. The rational function

$$R(t) = \dfrac{C(t)}{W(t)} = \dfrac{17t^2 + 128t + 5900}{38t^2 + 291t + 15,208}$$

gives the relative cost of the reception compared to the cost of a wedding.

a. Use $R(t)$ to estimate the relative cost of the reception compared to the cost of a wedding for the years $t = 0$, $t = 7$, and $t = 12$. Round your results to the nearest tenth of a percent.
$R(0) \approx 38.8\%$, $R(7) \approx 39.9\%$, $R(12) \approx 40.9\%$

b. According to the function $R(t)$, what percent of the total cost of a wedding, to the nearest tenth of a percent, will the cost of the reception approach as the years go by?
$\approx 44.7\%$

58. **INCOME TAX THEORY** The economist Arthur Laffer conjectured that if taxes were increased starting from very low levels, then the tax revenue received by the government would increase. But as tax rates continued to increase, there would be a point at which the tax revenue would start to decrease. The underlying concept was that if taxes were increased too much, people would not work as hard because much of their additional income would be taken from them by the increase in taxes. Laffer illustrated his concept by drawing a curve similar to the following.

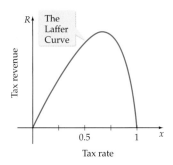

Laffer's curve shows that if the tax rate is 0%, the tax revenue will be $0, and if the tax rate is 100%, the tax revenue also will be $0. Laffer assumed that most people would not work if all their income went for taxes.

Most economists agree with Laffer's basic concept, but there is much disagreement about the equation of the actual tax revenue curve R and the tax rate x that will maximize the government's tax revenues.

a. Assume that Laffer's curve is given by
$$R(x) = \frac{-6.5(x^3 + 2x^2 - 3x)}{x^2 + x + 1}$$
where R is measured in trillions of dollars. Use a graphing utility to determine the tax rate x, to the nearest tenth of a percent, that would produce the maximum tax revenue. (*Hint:* Use a domain of $[0, 1]$ and a range of $[0, 4]$.) $\approx 39.7\%$

b. Assume that Laffer's curve is given by
$$R(x) = \frac{-1500(x^3 + 2x^2 - 3x)}{x^2 + x + 400}$$
where R is measured in trillions of dollars. Use a graphing utility to determine the tax rate x, to the nearest tenth of a percent, that would produce the maximum tax revenue. $\approx 53.5\%$

59. **A POPULATION MODEL** The population of a suburb, in thousands, is given by
$$P(t) = \frac{420t}{0.6t^2 + 15}$$
where t is the time in years after June 1, 1996.

a. Find the population of the suburb for $t = 1, 4$, and 10 years. 26,923, 68,293, 56,000

b. In what year will the population of the suburb reach its maximum? 2001

c. What will happen to the population as $t \to \infty$?
The population will approach 0.

60. **A MEDICATION MODEL** The rational function
$$M(t) = \frac{0.5t + 400}{0.04t^2 + 1}$$
models the number of milligrams of medication in the bloodstream of a patient t hours after 400 milligrams of the medication have been injected into the patient's bloodstream.

a. Find $M(5)$ and $M(10)$. Round to the nearest milligram.
201 mg, 81 mg

b. What will M approach as $t \to \infty$? 0 mg

61. **MINIMIZING SURFACE AREA** A cylindrical soft drink can is to be made so that it will have a volume of 354 milliliters. If r is the radius of the can in centimeters, then the total surface area A of the can is given by the rational function
$$A(r) = \frac{2\pi r^3 + 708}{r}$$

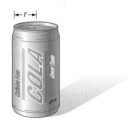

a. Graph A and use the graph to estimate (to the nearest tenth of a centimeter) the value of r that produces the minimum value of A. 3.8 cm
Answer on page AA13.

b. Does the graph of A have a slant asymptote? No

c. Explain the meaning of the following statement as it applies to the graph of A.

As the radius r increases without bound, the surface area approaches twice the area of a circle with radius r. As $r \to \infty$, $A \to 2\pi r^2$.

62. RESISTORS IN PARALLEL The electronic circuit at the right shows two resistors connected in parallel.

One resistor has a resistance of R_1 ohms and the other has a resistance of R_2 ohms. The total resistance for the circuit, measured in ohms, is given by the formula

$$R_T = \frac{R_1 R_2}{R_1 + R_2}$$

Assume R_1 has a fixed resistance of 10 ohms.

a. Compute R_T for $R_2 = 2$ ohms and for $R_2 = 20$ ohms. $\frac{5}{3}$ ohms, $\frac{20}{3}$ ohms

b. What happens to R_T as $R_2 \to \infty$? $R_T \to 10$ ohms

---

CONNECTING CONCEPTS

63. Determine the point at which the graph of

$$F(x) = \frac{2x^2 + 3x + 4}{x^2 + 4x + 7}$$

intersects its horizontal asymptote. $(-2, 2)$

64. Determine the point at which the graph of

$$F(x) = \frac{3x^3 + 2x^2 - 8x - 12}{x^2 + 4}$$

intersects its slant asymptote. $(-1, -1)$

65. Determine the two points at which the graph of

$$F(x) = \frac{x^3 + x^2 + 4x + 1}{x^3 + 1}$$

intersects its horizontal asymptote. $(0, 1)$ and $(-4, 1)$

66. Give an example of a rational function that intersects its slant asymptote at two points.

Answers will vary; however, $F(x) = \dfrac{x^4 + 2x^3 + x^2 - 4}{x^2}$ is one example.

PROJECTS

1. PARABOLIC ASYMPTOTES It can be shown that the rational function $F(x) = R(x)/S(x)$, where $R(x)$ and $S(x)$ have no common factors, has a parabolic asymptote provided the degree of $R(x)$ is *two* greater than the degree of $S(x)$. For instance, the rational function

$$F(x) = \frac{x^3 + 2}{x + 1}$$

has a parabolic asymptote given by $y = x^2 - x + 1$.

a. Use a graphing utility to graph $F(x)$ and the parabola given by $y = x^2 - x + 1$ in the same viewing window. Does the parabola appear to be an asymptote for the graph of F? Explain. Yes. As $x \to \infty$ and as $x \to -\infty$, the graph of F approaches the graph of the parabola.

b. Write a paragraph that explains how to determine the equation of the parabolic asymptote for a rational func-

tion $F(x) = R(x)/S(x)$, where $R(x)$ and $S(x)$ have no common factors and the degree of $R(x)$ is two greater than the degree of $S(x)$. Divide $R(x)$ by $S(x)$ to find the quotient of $Q(x)$. The equation $y = Q(x)$ is the equation of the parabolic asymptote.

c. What is the equation of the parabolic asymptote for the rational function $G(x) = \dfrac{x^4 + x^2 + 2}{x^2 - 1}$? Use a graphing utility to graph $G(x)$ and the parabolic asymptote in the same viewing window. Does the parabola appear to be an asymptote for the graph of G? $y = x^2 + 2$; yes

d. Create a rational function that has $y = x^2 + x + 2$ as its parabolic asymptote. Explain the procedure you used to create your rational function. Answers will vary.

Finding Zeros of a Polynomial Using *Mathematica*

Computer algebra systems (CAS) are computer programs that are used to solve equations, graph functions, simplify algebraic expressions, and help us perform many other mathematical tasks. In this exploration, we will demonstrate how to use one of these programs, *Mathematica*, to find zeros of a polynomial function.

Recall that a zero of a function P is a number x for which $P(x) = 0$. The idea behind finding a zero of a polynomial function by using a CAS is to solve the polynomial equation $P(x) = 0$ for x.

Two commands in *Mathematica* that can be used to solve an equation are **Solve** and **NSolve**. (*Mathematica* is sensitive about syntax (the way in which an expression is typed). You *must* use upper-case and lower-case letters as we indicate.) **Solve** will attempt to find an *exact* solution of the equation; **NSolve** attempts to find *approximate* solutions. Here are some examples.

To find the exact values of the zeros of $P(x) = x^3 + 5x^2 + 11x + 15$, input the following. *Note:* The two equals signs are necessary.

$$\text{Solve}[x^3+5x^2+11x+15==0]$$

Press $\boxed{\text{Enter}}$. The result should be

$$\{\{x->-3\}, \{x->-1-2\ I\}, \{x->-1+2\ I\}\}$$

Thus the three zeros of P are -3, $-1 - 2i$, and $-1 + 2i$.

To find the approximate values of the zeros of $P(x) = x^4 - 3x^3 + 4x^2 + x - 4$, input the following.

$$\text{NSolve}[x^4-3x^3+4x^2+x-4==0]$$

Press $\boxed{\text{Enter}}$. The result should be

$$\{\{x->-0.821746\}, \{x->1.2326\}, \{x->1.29457-1.50771\ I\},$$

$$\{x->1.29457+1.50771\ I\}\}$$

The four zeros are (approximately) -0.821746, 1.2326, $1.29457 - 1.50771i$, and $1.29457 + 1.50771i$.

Not all polynomial equations can be solved exactly. This means that **Solve** will not always give solutions with *Mathematica*. Consider the two examples below.

Input	NSolve[x^5–3x^3+2x^2–5==0]
Output	{{x->-1.80492}, {x->-1.12491}, {x->0.620319-1.03589 I}, {x->0.620319+1.03589 I}, {x->1.68919}}

These are the approximate zeros of the polynomial.

Input	Solve[x^5–3x^3+2x^2–5==0]
Output	{ToRules[Roots[$2x^2-3x^3+x^5==5$]]}

In this case, no exact solution could be found. In general, there are no formulas like the quadratic formula, for instance, that yield exact solutions for fifth- or higher-degree polynomial equations.

Use *Mathematica* (or another CAS) to find the zeros of each of the following polynomial functions.

1. $P(x) = x^4 - 3x^3 + x - 5$

2. $P(x) = 3x^3 - 4x^2 + x - 3$

3. $P(x) = 4x^5 - 3x^3 + 2x^2 - x + 2$

4. $P(x) = -3x^4 - 6x^3 + 2x - 8$

CHAPTER 3 SUMMARY

3.1 The Remainder Theorem and the Factor Theorem

- *The Remainder Theorem*   If a polynomial function $P(x)$ is divided by $(x - c)$, then the remainder equals $P(c)$.

- *The Factor Theorem*   A polynomial function $P(x)$ has a factor $(x - c)$ if and only if $P(c) = 0$.

3.2 Polynomial Functions of Higher Degree

- Characteristics and properties used in graphing polynomial functions include:

  1. Continuity—Polynomial functions are smooth continuous curves.

  2. Leading term test—Determines the behavior of the graph of a polynomial function at the far right and at the far left.

  3. The real zeros of the function determine the x-intercepts.

- *Relative Minimum and Relative Maximum*   If there is an open interval I containing c on which

  $f(c) \leq f(x)$ for all x in I, then $f(c)$ is a relative minimum of f.

  $f(c) \geq f(x)$ for all x in I, then $f(c)$ is a relative maximum of f.

- *The Zero Location Theorem*   Let $P(x)$ be a polynomial function. If $a < b$, and if $P(a)$ and $P(b)$ have opposite signs, then there is at least one real number c between a and b such that $P(c) = 0$.

3.3 Zeros of Polynomial Functions

- Values of x that satisfy $P(x) = 0$ are called zeros of P.

- *Definition of Multiple Zeros of a Polynomial*   If a polynomial function $P(x)$ has $(x - r)$ as a factor exactly k times, then r is said to be a zero of multiplicity k of the polynomial function $P(x)$.

- *The Rational Zero Theorem*   If

$$P(x) = a_n x^n + a_{n-1} x^{n-1} + \cdots + a_1 x + a_0, \ a_n \neq 0$$

has integer coefficients, and $\dfrac{p}{q}$ (where p and q have no common factors) is a rational zero of P, then p is a factor of a_0 and q is a factor of a_n.

- *Upper- and Lower-Bound Theorem*
Let $P(x)$ be a polynomial function with real coefficients. Use synthetic division to divide $P(x)$ by $x - b$, where b is a nonzero real number.

Upper Bound

a. If $b > 0$ and the leading coefficient of P is positive, then b is an upper bound for the real zeros of P provided none of the numbers in the bottom row of the synthetic division are negative.

b. If $b > 0$ and the leading coefficient of P is negative, then b is an upper bound for the real zeros of P provided none of the numbers in the bottom row of the synthetic division are positive.

Lower Bound   If $b < 0$ and the numbers in the bottom row of the synthetic division of P by $x - b$ alternate in sign, then b is a lower bound for the real zeros of P.

- *Descartes' Rule of Signs*   Let $P(x)$ be a polynomial function with real coefficients and with terms arranged in order of decreasing powers of x.

  1. The number of positive real zeros of $P(x)$ is equal to the number of variations in sign of $P(x)$, or is equal to that number decreased by an even integer.

  2. The number of negative real zeros of $P(x)$ is equal to the number of variations in sign of $P(-x)$ or is equal to that number decreased by an even integer.

- The zeros of some polynomial functions with integer coefficients can be found by using the guidelines stated on page 311.

3.4 The Fundamental Theorem of Algebra

- *The Fundamental Theorem of Algebra*   If $P(x)$ is a polynomial function of degree $n \geq 1$ with complex coefficients, then $P(x)$ has at least one complex zero.

- *The Conjugate Pair Theorem*   If $a + bi$ ($b \neq 0$) is a complex zero of the polynomial function $P(x)$, with real coefficients, then the conjugate $a - bi$ is also a complex zero of the polynomial function.

3.5 Graphs of Rational Functions and Their Applications

• If $P(x)$ and $Q(x)$ are polynomials, then the function F given by

$$F(x) = \frac{P(x)}{Q(x)}$$

is called a rational function.

• *General Procedure for Graphing Rational Functions That Have No Common Factors*

1. Find the real zeros of the denominator. For each zero a, the vertical line $x = a$ will be a vertical asymptote. Use the Theorem on Horizontal Asymptotes to determine if the function has a horizontal asymptote. Graph the horizontal asymptote.

2. Find the real zeros of the numerator. For each real zero a, plot $(a, 0)$. These points are the x-intercepts. The y-intercept of the graph of $F(x)$ is the point $(0, F(0))$.

3. Use the tests for symmetry to determine whether the graph has symmetry with respect to the y-axis or to the origin.

4. Find additional points that lie in the intervals between the x-intercepts and the vertical asymptotes.

5. Determine the behavior of the graph near the asymptotes.

6. Use the information obtained in the above steps to sketch the graph.

• *Theorem on Slant Asymptotes* The rational function given by $F(x) = P(x)/Q(x)$, where $P(x)$ and $Q(x)$ have no common factors, has a slant asymptote if the degree of the polynomial $P(x)$ in the numerator is one greater than the degree of the polynomial $Q(x)$ in the denominator.

CHAPTER 3 TRUE/FALSE EXERCISES

In Exercises 1 to 12, answer true or false. If the statement is false, explain why the statement is false or give an example to show that the statement is false.

1. The complex zeros of a polynomial function with complex coefficients always occur in conjugate pairs.
False; $P(x) = x - i$ has a zero of i, but it does not have a zero of $-i$.

2. Descartes' Rule of Signs indicates that the polynomial function $P(x) = x^3 - x^2 + x - 1$ must have three positive zeros. False; Descartes' Rule of Signs indicates that $P(x) = x^3 - x^2 + x - 1$ has three or one positive zeros. In fact, P has only one positive zero.

3. The polynomial $2x^5 + x^4 - 7x^3 - 5x^2 + 4x + 10$ has two variations in sign.
True

4. If 4 is an upper bound of the zeros of the polynomial function P, then 5 is also an upper bound of the zeros of P.
True

5. The graph of every rational function has a vertical asymptote. False; $F(x) = \dfrac{x}{x^2 + 1}$ does not have a vertical asymptote.

6. The graph of the rational function $F(x) = \dfrac{x^2 - 4x + 4}{x^2 - 5x + 6}$ has a vertical asymptote of $x = 2$.
False; $F(x) = \dfrac{(x - 2)^2}{(x - 3)(x - 2)} = \dfrac{x - 2}{x - 3}$, $x \neq 2$. The graph of F has a hole at $x = 2$.

7. If 7 is a zero of the polynomial function P, then $x - 7$ is a factor of P. True

8. According to the Zero Location Theorem, the polynomial function $P(x) = x^3 + 6x - 2$ has a real zero between 0 and 1. True

9. Every fourth-degree polynomial function with complex coefficients has exactly four complex zeros, provided each zero is counted according to its multiplicity. True

10. The graph of a rational function can have at most one horizontal asymptote. True

11. Descartes' Rule of Signs indicates that the polynomial function $P(x) = x^3 + 2x^2 + 4x - 7$ does have a positive zero. True

12. Every polynomial function has at least one real zero.
False; $P(x) = x^2 + 1$ does not have a real zero.

CHAPTER 3 REVIEW EXERCISES
—Answer graphs to Exercises 15–20 and 47–54 are on pages AA13–AA14.

In Exercises 1 to 6, use synthetic division to divide the first polynomial by the second.

1. $4x^3 - 11x^2 + 5x - 2, x - 3$ $4x^2 + x + 8 + \dfrac{22}{x-3}$ [3.1]

2. $5x^3 - 18x + 2, x - 1$ $5x^2 + 5x - 13 - \dfrac{11}{x-1}$ [3.1]

3. $3x^3 - 5x + 1, x + 2$ $3x^2 - 6x + 7 - \dfrac{13}{x+2}$ [3.1]

4. $2x^3 + 7x^2 + 16x - 10, x - \dfrac{1}{2}$ $2x^2 + 8x + 20$ [3.1]

5. $3x^3 - 10x^2 - 36x + 55, x - 5$ $3x^2 + 5x - 11$ [3.1]

6. $x^4 + 9x^3 + 6x^2 - 65x - 63, x + 7$ $x^3 + 2x^2 - 8x - 9$ [3.1]

In Exercises 7 to 10, use the Remainder Theorem to find $P(c)$.

7. $P(x) = x^3 + 2x^2 - 5x + 1, c = 4$ 77 [3.1]

8. $P(x) = -4x^3 - 10x + 8, c = -1$ 22 [3.1]

9. $P(x) = 6x^4 - 12x^2 + 8x + 1, c = -2$ 33 [3.1]

10. $P(x) = 5x^5 - 8x^4 + 2x^3 - 6x^2 - 9, c = 3$ 558 [3.1]

In Exercises 11 to 14, use synthetic division to show that c is a zero of the given polynomial function. *The verifications in Exercises 11–14 make use of the concepts from Section 3.1.*

11. $P(x) = x^3 + 2x^2 - 26x + 33, c = 3$

12. $P(x) = 2x^4 + 8x^3 - 8x^2 - 31x + 4, c = -4$

13. $P(x) = x^5 - x^4 - 2x^2 + x + 1, c = 1$

14. $P(x) = 2x^3 + 3x^2 - 8x + 3, c = \dfrac{1}{2}$

In Exercises 15 to 20, graph the polynomial function.

15. $P(x) = x^3 - x$ [3.2]

16. $P(x) = -x^3 - x^2 + 8x + 12$ [3.2]

17. $P(x) = x^4 - 6$ [3.2]

18. $P(x) = x^5 - x$ [3.2]

19. $P(x) = x^4 - 10x^2 + 9$ [3.2]

20. $P(x) = x^5 - 5x^3$ [3.2]

In Exercises 21 to 26, use the Rational Zero Theorem to list all possible rational zeros for each polynomial function.

21. $P(x) = x^3 - 7x - 6$ $\pm 1, \pm 2, \pm 3, \pm 6$ [3.3]

22. $P(x) = 2x^3 + 3x^2 - 29x - 30$
$\pm 1, \pm 2, \pm 3, \pm 5, \pm 6, \pm 10, \pm 15, \pm 30, \pm \dfrac{1}{2}, \pm \dfrac{3}{2}, \pm \dfrac{5}{2}, \pm \dfrac{15}{2}$ [3.3]

23. $P(x) = 15x^3 - 91x^2 + 4x + 12$
Answer on page AA14.

24. $P(x) = x^4 - 12x^3 + 52x^2 - 96x + 64$
$\pm 1, \pm 2, \pm 4, \pm 8, \pm 16, \pm 32, \pm 64$ [3.3]

25. $P(x) = x^3 + x^2 - x - 1$
± 1 [3.3]

26. $P(x) = 6x^5 + 3x - 2$ $\pm 1, \pm 2, \pm \dfrac{1}{6}, \pm \dfrac{1}{3}, \pm \dfrac{1}{2}, \pm \dfrac{2}{3}$ [3.3]

In Exercises 27 to 30, use Descartes' Rule of Signs to state the number of possible positive and negative real zeros of each polynomial function.

27. $P(x) = x^3 + 3x^2 + x + 3$
no positive real zeros and three or one negative real zeros [3.3]

28. $P(x) = x^4 - 6x^3 - 5x^2 + 74x - 120$
three or one positive real zeros, one negative real zero [3.3]

29. $P(x) = x^4 - x - 1$
one positive real zero and one negative real zero [3.3]

30. $P(x) = x^5 - 4x^4 + 2x^3 - x^2 + x - 8$
five, three, or one positive real zeros, no negative real zeros [3.3]

In Exercises 31 to 36, find the zeros of the polynomial function.

31. $P(x) = x^3 + 6x^2 + 3x - 10$ $1, -2, -5$ [3.3]

32. $P(x) = x^3 - 10x^2 + 31x - 30$ $2, 5, 3$ [3.3]

33. $P(x) = 6x^4 + 35x^3 + 72x^2 + 60x + 16$
-2 (multiplicity 2), $-\dfrac{1}{2}, -\dfrac{4}{3}$ [3.3]

34. $P(x) = 2x^4 + 7x^3 + 5x^2 + 7x + 3$ $-\dfrac{1}{2}, -3, i, -i$ [3.4]

35. $P(x) = x^4 - 4x^3 + 6x^2 - 4x + 1$ 1 (multiplicity 4) [3.3]

36. $P(x) = 2x^3 - 7x^2 + 22x + 13$ $-\dfrac{1}{2}, 2 + 3i, 2 - 3i$ [3.4]

In Exercises 37 and 38, use the given zero to find the remaining zeros of each polynomial function.

37. $P(x) = x^4 - 4x^3 + 6x^2 - 4x - 15; 1 - 2i$ $-1, 3, 1 + 2i$ [3.4]

38. $P(x) = x^4 - x^3 - 17x^2 + 55x - 50; 2 + i$ $-5, 2, 2 - i$ [3.4]

39. Find a third-degree polynomial function with integer coefficients and zeros of 4, -3, and $\dfrac{1}{2}$.
$P(x) = 2x^3 - 3x^2 - 23x + 12$ [3.4]

40. Find a fourth-degree polynomial function with zeros of 2, -3, i, and $-i$.
$P(x) = x^4 + x^3 - 5x^2 + x - 6$ [3.4]

41. Find a fourth-degree polynomial function with real coefficients that has zeros of 1, 2, and $5i$.
$P(x) = x^4 - 3x^3 + 27x^2 - 75x + 50$ [3.4]

42. Find a fourth-degree polynomial function with real coefficients that has -2 as a zero of multiplicity 2 and also has $1 + 3i$ as a zero. $P(x) = x^4 + 2x^3 + 6x^2 + 32x + 40$ [3.4]

In Exercises 43 to 46, find the vertical, horizontal, and slant asymptotes for each rational function.

43. vertical asymptote: $x = -2$, horizontal asymptote: $y = 3$ [3.5]

43. $f(x) = \dfrac{3x + 5}{x + 2}$ **44.** $f(x) = \dfrac{2x^2 + 12x + 2}{x^2 + 2x - 3}$

44. vertical asymptotes: $x = -3$, $x = 1$, horizontal asymptote: $y = 2$ [3.5]

45. $f(x) = \dfrac{2x^2 + 5x + 11}{x + 1}$ **46.** $f(x) = \dfrac{6x^2 - 1}{2x^2 + x + 7}$

vertical asymptote: $x = -1$,
slant asymptote: $y = 2x + 3$ [3.5]

no vertical asymptote, horizontal
asymptote: $y = 3$ [3.5]

In Exercises 47 to 54, graph each rational function.

47. $f(x) = \dfrac{3x - 2}{x}$ [3.5]   **48.** $f(x) = \dfrac{x + 4}{x - 2}$ [3.5]

49. $f(x) = \dfrac{6}{x^2 + 2}$ [3.5]   **50.** $f(x) = \dfrac{4x^2}{x^2 + 1}$ [3.5]

51. $f(x) = \dfrac{2x^3 - 4x + 6}{x^2 - 4}$ [3.5]   **52.** $f(x) = \dfrac{x}{x^3 - 1}$ [3.5]

53. $f(x) = \dfrac{3x^2 - 6}{x^2 - 9}$ [3.5]   **54.** $f(x) = \dfrac{-x^3 + 6}{x^2}$ [3.5]

55. AVERAGE COST OF SKATEBOARDS The cost, in dollars, of producing x skateboards is given by

$$C(x) = 5.75x + 34{,}200$$

The average cost per skateboard is given by

$$\overline{C}(x) = \dfrac{C(x)}{x} = \dfrac{5.75x + 34{,}200}{x}$$

a. Find the average cost per skateboard, to the nearest cent, of producing 5000 and 50,000 skateboards.
$12.59, $6.43

b. What is the equation of the horizontal asymptote of the graph of $\overline{C}$? Explain the significance of the horizontal asymptote as it relates to this application. $y = 5.75$. As the number of skateboards produced increases, the average cost per skateboard approaches $5.75. [3.5]

56. FOOD TEMPERATURE The temperature F, in degrees Fahrenheit, of a dessert placed in a freezer for t hours is given by the rational function

$$F(t) = \dfrac{60}{t^2 + 2t + 1}, \quad t \geq 0$$

a. Find the temperature of the dessert after it has been in the freezer for 1 hour. 15°F

b. Find the temperature of the dessert after 4 hours.
2.4°F

c. What temperature will the dessert approach as $t \to \infty$?
0°F [3.5]

57. **PHYSIOLOGY** One of Poiseuille's Laws states that the resistance R encountered by blood flowing through a blood vessel is given by

$$R(r) = C\dfrac{L}{r^4}$$

where C is a positive constant determined by the viscosity of the blood, L is the length of the blood vessel, and r is its radius.

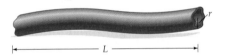

a. Explain the meaning of $R(r) \to \infty$ as $r \to 0$.
As the radius of the blood vessel approaches 0, the resistance gets larger.

b. Explain the meaning of $R(r) \to 0$ as $r \to \infty$.
As the radius of the blood vessel gets larger, the resistance approaches zero. [3.5]

CHAPTER 3 TEST

1. Use synthetic division to divide:

$$(3x^3 + 5x^2 + 4x - 1) \div (x + 2)$$
$3x^2 - x + 6 - \dfrac{13}{x + 2}$ [3.1]

2. Use the Remainder Theorem to find $P(-2)$ if

$$P(x) = -3x^3 + 7x^2 + 2x - 5 \quad 43 \text{ [3.1]}$$

3. Show that $x - 1$ is a factor of

$$x^4 - 4x^3 + 7x^2 - 6x + 2$$
The verification for Exercise 3 makes use of the concepts from Section 3.1.

4. Examine the leading term of the function given by the equation $P(x) = -3x^3 + 2x^2 - 5x + 2$ and determine the far-left and far-right behavior of the graph of P.
up to the far left and down to the far right [3.2]

5. Find the real solutions of $3x^3 + 7x^2 - 6x = 0$. $0, \dfrac{2}{3}, -3$ [3.2]

6. Use the Zero Location Theorem to verify that

$$P(x) = 2x^3 - 3x^2 - x + 1$$

has a zero between 1 and 2. $P(1) < 0$, $P(2) > 0$. Therefore, by the Zero Location Theorem, the continuous polynomial function P has a zero between 1 and 2. [3.2]

7. Find the zeros of

$$P(x) = (x^2 - 4)^2(2x - 3)(x + 1)^3$$

and state the multiplicity of each. 2 (multiplicity 2), -2 (multiplicity 2), $\dfrac{3}{2}$ (multiplicity 1), -1 (multiplicity 3) [3.3]

8. Use the Rational Zero Theorem to list the possible rational zeros of $\pm 1, \pm 3, \pm\dfrac{1}{2}, \pm\dfrac{3}{2}, \pm\dfrac{1}{3}, \pm\dfrac{1}{6}$ [3.3]

$$P(x) = 6x^3 - 3x^2 + 2x - 3$$

9. Find, by using the Upper- and Lower-Bound Theorem, the smallest positive integer and the largest negative integer that are upper and lower bounds for the real zeros of the polynomial function

$$P(x) = 2x^4 + 5x^3 - 23x^2 - 38x + 24$$

upper bound 4, lower bound -5 [3.3]

10. Use Descartes' Rule of Signs to state the number of possible positive and negative real zeros of

$$P(x) = x^4 - 3x^3 + 2x^2 - 5x + 1$$

4, 2, or 0 positive zeros, no negative zero [3.3]

11. Find the zeros of $P(x) = 2x^3 - 3x^2 - 11x + 6$ $\dfrac{1}{2}, 3, -2$ [3.3]

12. Given that $2 + 3i$ is a zero of

$$P(x) = 6x^4 - 5x^3 + 12x^2 + 207x + 130$$

find the remaining zeros. $2 - 3i, -\dfrac{2}{3}, -\dfrac{5}{2}$ [3.4]

13. Find all the zeros of

$$P(x) = x^5 - 6x^4 + 14x^3 - 14x^2 + 5x$$

0, 1 (multiplicity 2), $2 + i$, $2 - i$ [3.4]

14. Find a polynomial of smallest degree that has real coefficients and zeros $1 + i$, 3, and 0.
$P(x) = x^4 - 5x^3 + 8x^2 - 6x$ [3.4]

15. Find all vertical asymptotes of the graph of

$$f(x) = \frac{3x^2 - 2x + 1}{x^2 - 5x + 6}$$

vertical asymptotes: $x = 3$, $x = 2$ [3.5]

16. Find the horizontal asymptote of the graph of

$$f(x) = \frac{3x^2 - 2x + 1}{2x^2 - 1}$$

horizontal asymptote: $y = \dfrac{3}{2}$ [3.5]

17. Graph $f(x) = \dfrac{x^2 - 1}{x^2 - 2x - 3}$. Use an open circle to show the hole in the graph of f. [3.5]
Answer on page AA14.

18. Graph $f(x) = \dfrac{2x^2 + 2x + 1}{x + 1}$ and label the slant asymptote with its equation. [3.5]
Answer on page AA14.

19. The rational function

$$w(t) = \frac{70t + 120}{t + 40}, \quad t \geq 0$$

models Rene's typing speed, in words per minute, after t hours of typing lessons.

a. Find $w(1)$, $w(10)$, and $w(20)$. Round to the nearest word per minute. 5 words/min, 16 words/min, 25 words/min

b. What will Rene's typing speed approach as $t \to \infty$? 70 words/min [3.5]

20. 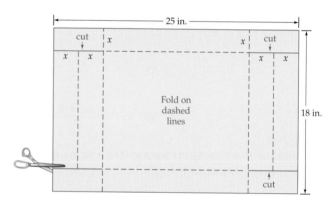 **MAXIMIZING VOLUME** You are to construct an open box from a rectangular sheet of cardboard that measures 18 inches by 25 inches. To assemble the box, make the four cuts shown in the figure below and then fold on the dashed lines. What value of x (to the nearest 0.01 inch) will produce a box with maximum volume? What is the maximum volume (to the nearest 0.1 cubic inch)? 2.42 in., 487.9 in³ [3.3]

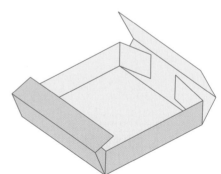

CUMULATIVE REVIEW EXERCISES

1. Write $\dfrac{3 + 4i}{1 - 2i}$ in $a + bi$ form. $-1 + 2i$ [P.6]

2. Use the quadratic formula to solve $x^2 - x - 1 = 0$.
$\dfrac{1 \pm \sqrt{5}}{2}$ [1.3]

3. Solve: $\sqrt{2x + 5} - \sqrt{x - 1} = 2$
2, 10 [1.4]

4. Solve: $|x - 3| \le 11$
$\{x \mid -8 \le x \le 14\}$ [1.5]

5. Find the distance between the points $(2, 5)$ and $(7, -11)$.
$\sqrt{281}$ [2.1]

6. Explain how to use the graph of $y = x^2$ to produce the graph of $y = (x - 2)^2 + 4$.
Translate the graph of $y = x^2$ to the right 2 units and 4 units up. [2.5]

7. Find the difference quotient for the function $P(x) = x^2 - 2x - 3$. $2x + h - 2$ [2.6]

8. Given $f(x) = 2x^2 + 5x - 3$ and $g(x) = 4x - 7$, find $(f \circ g)(x)$. $32x^2 - 92x + 60$ [2.6]

9. Given $f(x) = x^3 - 2x + 7$ and $g(x) = x^2 - 3x - 4$, find $(f - g)(x)$. $x^3 - x^2 + x + 11$ [2.6]

10. Use synthetic division to divide $(4x^4 - 2x^2 - 4x - 5)$ by $(x + 2)$. $4x^3 - 8x^2 + 14x - 32 + \dfrac{59}{x + 2}$ [3.1]

11. Use the Remainder Theorem to find $P(3)$ for $P(x) = 2x^4 - 3x^2 + 4x - 6$. 141 [3.1]

12. Determine the far-right behavior of the graph of $P(x) = -3x^4 - x^2 + 7x - 6$. The graph goes down. [3.2]

13. Determine the relative maximum of the polynomial function $P(x) = -3x^3 - x^2 + 4x - 1$. Round to the nearest ten thousandth. 0.3997 [3.2]

14. Use the Rational Zero Theorem to list all possible rational zeros of $P(x) = 3x^4 - 4x^3 - 11x^2 + 16x - 4$.
$\pm 1, \pm 2, \pm 4, \pm \dfrac{1}{3}, \pm \dfrac{2}{3}, \pm \dfrac{4}{3}$ [3.3]

15. Use Descartes' Rule of Signs to state the number of possible positive and negative real zeros of $P(x) = x^3 + x^2 + 2x + 4$.
zero positive real zeros, three or one negative real zeros [3.3]

16. Find all zeros of $P(x) = x^3 + x + 10$.
$-2, 1 + 2i, 1 - 2i$ [3.4]

17. Find a polynomial function of smallest degree that has real coefficients and -2 and $3 + i$ as zeros.
$P(x) = x^3 - 4x^2 - 2x + 20$ [3.4]

18. Write $P(x) = x^3 - 2x^2 + 9x - 18$ as a product of linear factors. $(x - 2)(x + 3i)(x - 3i)$ [3.4]

19. Determine the vertical and horizontal asymptotes of the graph of $F(x) = \dfrac{4x^2}{x^2 + x - 6}$.
vertical asymptotes: $x = -3$, $x = 2$; horizontal asymptote: $y = 4$ [3.5]

20. Find the equation of the slant asymptote for the graph of $F(x) = \dfrac{x^3 + 4x^2 + 1}{x^2 + 4}$. $y = x + 4$ [3.5]

EXPONENTIAL AND LOGARITHMIC FUNCTIONS

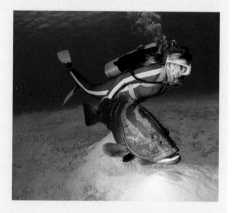

Modeling Data with an Exponential Function

The following table shows the time, in hours, before the body of a scuba diver, wearing a 5-millimeter-thick wet suit, reaches hypothermia (95°F) for various water temperatures.

Water Temperature, °F	Time, hours
36	1.5
41	1.8
46	2.6
50	3.1
55	4.9

Source: Data extracted from the *American Journal of Physics,* vol. 71, no. 4 (April 2003), Fig. 3, p. 336.

The following function, which is an example of an exponential function, closely models the data in the table:

$$T(F) = 0.1509(1.0639)^F$$

In this function F represents the Fahrenheit temperature of the water, and T represents the time in hours. A diver can use the function to determine the time it takes to reach hypothermia for water temperatures that are not included in the table. See **Exercise 21, page 445.** The function $T(F)$ was determined by using exponential regression, which is one of the topics in Section 4.7.

VIDEO & DVD

SSG
WWW

Use Two Methods to Solve and Compare Results

Sometimes it is possible to solve a problem in two or more ways. In such situations it is recommended that you use at least two methods to solve the problem, and compare your results. Here is an example of an application that can be solved in more than one way.

Example

In a league of eight basketball teams, each team plays every other team in the league exactly once. How many league games will take place?

Solution

Method 1: *Use an analytic approach.* Each of the eight teams must play the other seven teams. Using this information, you might be tempted to conclude that there will be $8 \cdot 7 = 56$ games, but this result is too large because it counts each game between two individual teams as two different games. Thus the number of league games will be

$$\frac{8 \cdot 7}{2} = \frac{56}{2} = 28$$

Method 2: *Make an organized list.* Use the letters A, B, C, D, E, F, G, and H to represent the eight teams. Use the notation AB to represent the game between team A and team B. Do not include BA in your list because it represents the same game between team A and team B.

AB	AC	AD	AE	AF	AG	AH
	BC	BD	BE	BF	BG	BH
		CD	CE	CF	CG	CH
			DE	DF	DG	DH
				EF	EG	EH
					FG	FH
						GH

The list shows that there will be 28 league games.

The procedure of using two different solution methods and comparing results is employed often in this chapter. For instance, see **Example 2, page 409.** In this example, a solution is found by applying algebraic procedures and also by graphing. Notice that both methods produce the same result.

INVERSE FUNCTIONS

• INTRODUCTION TO INVERSE FUNCTIONS

Consider the "doubling" function $f(x) = 2x$ that doubles every input. Some of the ordered pairs of this function are

$$\left\{ (-4, -8), (-1.5, -3), (1, 2), \left(\frac{5}{3}, \frac{10}{3} \right), (7, 14) \right\}$$

Now consider the "halving" function $g(x) = \frac{1}{2}x$ that takes one-half of every input. Some of the ordered pairs of this function are

$$\left\{ (-8, -4), (-3, -1.5), (2, 1), \left(\frac{10}{3}, \frac{5}{3} \right), (14, 7) \right\}$$

Observe that the coordinates of the ordered pairs of g are the reverse of the coordinates of the ordered pairs of f. This is always the case for f and g. Here are two more examples.

$$f(5) = 2(5) = 10 \qquad\qquad g(10) = \frac{1}{2}(10) = 5$$

Ordered pair: (5, 10)   **Ordered pair: (10, 5)**

$$f(a) = 2(a) = 2a \qquad\qquad g(2a) = \frac{1}{2}(2a) = a$$

Ordered pair: (a, 2a)   **Ordered pair: (2a, a)**

For these functions, f and g are called *inverse functions* of one another.

Inverse Function

If the coordinates of the ordered pairs of a function g are the reverse of the coordinates of the ordered pairs of a function f, then g is said to be the **inverse function** of f.

---

take note

It is important to remember the information in the paragraph at the right. If f is a function and g is the inverse of f, then

Domain of g = range of f

and

Range of g = domain of f

Because the coordinates of the ordered pairs of the inverse function g are the reverse of the coordinates of the ordered pairs of the function f, the domain of g is the range of f, and the range of g is the domain of f.

Not all functions have an inverse that is a function. Consider, for instance, the "square" function $S(x) = x^2$. Some of the ordered pairs of S are

$$\{(-3, 9), (-1, 1), (0, 0), (1, 1), (3, 9), (5, 25)\}$$

If we reverse the coordinates of the ordered pairs, we have

$$\{(9, -3), (1, -1), (0, 0), (1, 1), (9, 3), (25, 5)\}$$

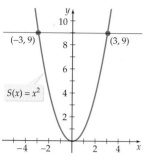

FIGURE 4.1

This set of ordered pairs is not a function because there are ordered pairs, for instance $(9, -3)$ and $(9, 3)$, with the same first coordinate and different second coordinates. In this case, S has an inverse *relation* but not an inverse *function*.

A graph of S is shown in **Figure 4.1**. Note that $x = -3$ and $x = 3$ produce the same value of y. Thus the graph of S fails the horizontal line test, and therefore S is not a one-to-one function. This observation is used in the following theorem.

> **Condition for an Inverse Function**
>
> A function f has an inverse function if and only if f is a one-to-one function.

Recall that increasing functions or decreasing functions are one-to-one functions. Thus we can state the following theorem.

> **Alternative Condition for an Inverse Function**
>
> If f is an increasing function or a decreasing function, then f has an inverse function.

? QUESTION Which of the functions graphed below has an inverse function?

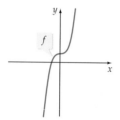
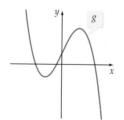
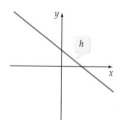

INSTRUCTOR NOTE

After introducing the notation for inverse functions, give students an example such as $f(2) = 12$ and ask them to find $f^{-1}(12)$.

take note

$f^{-1}(x)$ does not mean $\dfrac{1}{f(x)}$. For

$f(x) = 2x$, $f^{-1}(x) = \dfrac{1}{2}x$ but

$\dfrac{1}{f(x)} = \dfrac{1}{2x}$.

If a function g is the inverse of a function f, we usually denote the inverse function by f^{-1} rather than g. For the doubling and halving functions f and g discussed on page 355, we write

$$f(x) = 2x \qquad f^{-1}(x) = \frac{1}{2}x$$

● **GRAPHS OF INVERSE FUNCTIONS**

Because the coordinates of the ordered pairs of the inverse of a function f are the reverse of the coordinates of f, we can use them to create a graph of f^{-1}.

? ANSWER The graph of f is the graph of an increasing function. Therefore, f is a one-to-one function and has an inverse function. The graph of h is the graph of a decreasing function. Therefore, h is a one-to-one function and has an inverse function. The graph of g is not the graph of a one-to-one function. g does not have an inverse function.

Alternative to Example 1
Exercise 12, page 364.

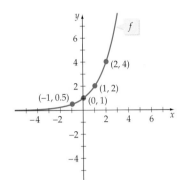

FIGURE 4.2

EXAMPLE 1 Sketch the Graph of the Inverse of a Function

Sketch the graph of f^{-1} given that f is the function shown in **Figure 4.2.**

Solution

Because the graph of f passes through $(-1, 0.5)$, $(0, 1)$, $(1, 2)$, and $(2, 4)$, the graph of f^{-1} must pass through $(0.5, -1)$, $(1, 0)$, $(2, 1)$, and $(4, 2)$. Plot the points and then draw a smooth graph through the points, as shown in **Figure 4.3.**

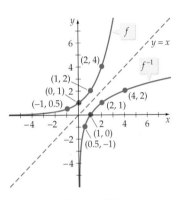

FIGURE 4.3

▶ **TRY EXERCISE 10, PAGE 364**

The graph from the solution to Example 1 is shown again in **Figure 4.4.** Note that the graph of f^{-1} is symmetric to the graph of f with respect to the graph of $y = x$. If the graph were folded along the dashed line, the graph of f would lie on top of the graph of f^{-1}. This is a characteristic of all graphs of functions and their inverses. In **Figure 4.5,** although S does not have an inverse that is a function, the graph of the inverse relation S^{-1} is symmetric to S with respect to the graph of $y = x$.

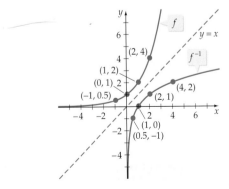

FIGURE 4.4

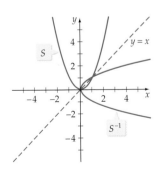

FIGURE 4.5

● COMPOSITION OF A FUNCTION AND ITS INVERSE

Observe the effect, as shown below, of taking the composition of functions that are inverses of one another.

INSTRUCTOR NOTE
It may help some students if you show them other instances of reversing operations. For example, if you take the number 7, add 5, and then subtract 5, you are back to 7.

$$f(x) = 2x \qquad\qquad g(x) = \frac{1}{2}x$$

$$f[g(x)] = 2\left[\frac{1}{2}x\right] \quad \bullet \text{ Replace } x \qquad g[f(x)] = \frac{1}{2}[2x] \quad \bullet \text{ Replace } x$$
$$\qquad\qquad\qquad\qquad\quad \text{by } g(x). \qquad\qquad\qquad\qquad\qquad\quad \text{by } f(x).$$

$$f[g(x)] = x \qquad\qquad\qquad\qquad g[f(x)] = x$$

This property of the composition of inverse functions always holds true. When taking the composition of inverse functions, the inverse function reverses the effect of the original function. For the two functions above, f doubles a number, and g halves a number. If you double a number and then take one-half of the result, you are back to the original number.

take note

If we think of a function as a machine, then the Composition of Inverse Functions Property can be represented as shown below. Take any input x for f. Use the output of f as the input for f^{-1}. The result is the original input, x.

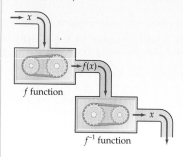

f function

f^{-1} function

Composition of Inverse Functions Property

If f is a one-to-one function, then f^{-1} is the inverse function of f if and only if

$$(f \circ f^{-1})(x) = f[f^{-1}(x)] = x \qquad \text{for all } x \text{ in the domain of } f^{-1}$$

and

$$(f^{-1} \circ f)(x) = f^{-1}[f(x)] = x \qquad \text{for all } x \text{ in the domain of } f.$$

EXAMPLE 2 Use the Composition of Inverse Functions Property

Use composition of functions to show that $f^{-1}(x) = 3x - 6$ is the inverse function of $f(x) = \frac{1}{3}x + 2$.

Solution

We must show that $f[f^{-1}(x)] = x$ and $f^{-1}[f(x)] = x$.

$$f(x) = \frac{1}{3}x + 2 \qquad\qquad f^{-1}(x) = 3x - 6$$

$$f[f^{-1}(x)] = \frac{1}{3}[3x - 6] + 2 \qquad f^{-1}[f(x)] = 3\left[\frac{1}{3}x + 2\right] - 6$$

$$f[f^{-1}(x)] = x \qquad\qquad\qquad f^{-1}[f(x)] = x$$

Alternative to Example 2
Use composition of functions to show that
$f^{-1}(x) = \frac{2}{3}x + 4$ is the inverse function
of $f(x) = \frac{3}{2}x - 6$.

▶ **TRY EXERCISE 20, PAGE 365**

INTEGRATING TECHNOLOGY

In the standard viewing window of a calculator, the distance between two tic marks on the x-axis is not equal to the distance between two tic marks on the y-axis. As a result, the graph of $y = x$ does not appear to bisect the first and third quadrants. See **Figure 4.6.** This anomaly is important if a graphing calculator is being used to check whether two functions are inverses of one another. Because the graph of $y = x$ does not appear to bisect the first and third quadrants, the graphs of f and f^{-1} will not appear to be symmetric about the graph of $y = x$. The graphs of $f(x) = \dfrac{1}{3}x + 2$ and $f^{-1}(x) = 3x - 6$ from Example 2 are shown in **Figure 4.7.** Notice that the graphs do not appear to be quite symmetric about the graph of $y = x$.

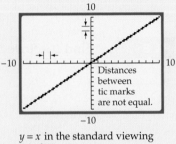

$y = x$ in the standard viewing window

FIGURE 4.6

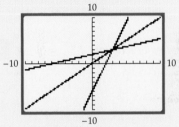

f, f^{-1}, and $y = x$ in the standard viewing window

FIGURE 4.7

To get a better view of a function and its inverse, it is necessary to use the SQUARE viewing window, as in **Figure 4.8.** In this window, the distance between two tic marks on the x-axis is equal to the distance between two tic marks on the y-axis.

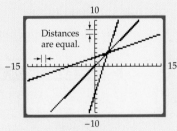

f, f^{-1}, and $y = x$ in a square viewing window

FIGURE 4.8

● FIND AN INVERSE FUNCTION

If a one-to-one function f is defined by an equation, then we can use the following method to find the equation for f^{-1}.

take note

If the ordered pairs of f are given by (x, y), then the ordered pairs of f^{-1} are given by (y, x). That is, x and y are interchanged. This is the reason for Step 2 at the right.

Steps for Finding the Inverse of a Function

To find the equation of the inverse f^{-1} of the one-to-one function f:

1. Substitute y for $f(x)$.

2. Interchange x and y.

3. Solve, if possible, for y in terms of x.

4. Substitute $f^{-1}(x)$ for y.

Alternative to Example 3

Find the inverse of $f(x) = \dfrac{1}{3}x - 6$.

● $f^{-1}(x) = 3x + 18$

EXAMPLE 3 Find the Inverse of a Function

Find the inverse of $f(x) = 3x + 8$.

Solution

$$f(x) = 3x + 8$$
$$y = 3x + 8 \qquad \text{• Replace } f(x) \text{ by } y.$$
$$x = 3y + 8 \qquad \text{• Interchange } x \text{ and } y.$$
$$x - 8 = 3y \qquad \text{• Solve for } y.$$
$$\frac{x - 8}{3} = y$$
$$\frac{1}{3}x - \frac{8}{3} = f^{-1}(x) \qquad \text{• Replace } y \text{ by } f^{-1}(x).$$

The inverse function is given by $f^{-1}(x) = \dfrac{1}{3}x - \dfrac{8}{3}$.

▶ **TRY EXERCISE 28, PAGE 365**

Alternative to Example 4

Find the inverse of $f(x) = \dfrac{x - 1}{x}$, $x \neq 0$.

● $f^{-1}(x) = -\dfrac{1}{x - 1}$, $x \neq 1$

EXAMPLE 4 Find the Inverse of a Function

Find the inverse of $f(x) = \dfrac{2x + 1}{x}$, $x \neq 0$.

Solution

$$f(x) = \frac{2x + 1}{x}$$

$$y = \frac{2x + 1}{x}$$ • **Replace f(x) by y.**

$$x = \frac{2y + 1}{y}$$ • **Interchange x and y.**

$$xy = 2y + 1$$ • **Solve for y.**

$$xy - 2y = 1$$

$$y(x - 2) = 1$$ • **Factor the left side.**

$$y = \frac{1}{x - 2}$$

$$f^{-1}(x) = \frac{1}{x - 2}, x \neq 2$$ • **Replace y by f⁻¹(x).**

▶ **TRY EXERCISE 34, PAGE 365**

❓ **QUESTION**   If f is a one-to-one function and $f(4) = 5$, what is $f^{-1}(5)$?

The graph of $f(x) = x^2 + 4x + 3$ is shown in **Figure 4.9a.** The function f is not a one-to-one function and therefore does not have an inverse function. However, the function given by $G(x) = x^2 + 4x + 3$, shown in **Figure 4.9b,** for which the domain is restricted to $\{x \mid x \geq -2\}$, is a one-to-one function and has an inverse function G^{-1}. This is shown in Example 5.

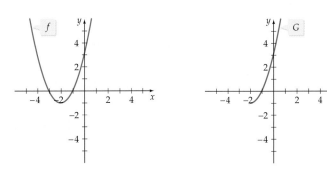

FIGURE 4.9a   **FIGURE 4.9b**

❓ **ANSWER**   Because f^{-1} is the inverse function of f, the coordinates of the ordered pairs of f^{-1} are the reverse of the coordinates of the ordered pairs of f. Therefore, $f^{-1}(5) = 4$.

Alternative to Example 5
Find the inverse of $H(x) = x^2 - 6x + 2$,
where the domain of H is $\{x \mid x \geq 3\}$.
● $H^{-1}(x) = \sqrt{x + 7} + 3,\ x \geq -7$

> ***take note***
>
> Recall that the range of a function
> f is the domain of f^{-1}, and the
> domain of f is the range of f^{-1}.

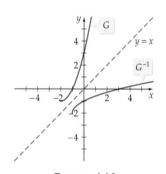

FIGURE 4.10

EXAMPLE 5   Find the Inverse of a Function with a Restricted Domain

Find the inverse of $G(x) = x^2 + 4x + 3$, where the domain of G is $\{x \mid x \geq -2\}$.

Solution

$$G(x) = x^2 + 4x + 3$$
$$y = x^2 + 4x + 3 \qquad \text{• Replace } G(x) \text{ by } y.$$
$$x = y^2 + 4y + 3 \qquad \text{• Interchange } x \text{ and } y.$$
$$x = (y^2 + 4y + 4) - 4 + 3 \qquad \text{• Solve for } y \text{ by completing the square of } y^2 + 4y.$$
$$x = (y + 2)^2 - 1 \qquad \text{• Factor.}$$
$$x + 1 = (y + 2)^2 \qquad \text{• Add 1 to each side of the equation.}$$
$$\sqrt{x + 1} = \sqrt{(y + 2)^2} \qquad \text{• Take the square root of each side of the equation.}$$
$$\pm\sqrt{x + 1} = y + 2 \qquad \text{• Recall that if } a^2 = b, \text{ then } a = \pm\sqrt{b}.$$
$$\pm\sqrt{x + 1} - 2 = y$$

Because the domain of G is $\{x \mid x \geq -2\}$, the range of G^{-1} is $\{y \mid y \geq -2\}$. This means that we must choose the positive value of $\pm\sqrt{x + 1}$. Thus $G^{-1}(x) = \sqrt{x + 1} - 2$. See **Figure 4.10.**

▶ **TRY EXERCISE 40, PAGE 365**

● **APPLICATION**

There are practical applications of finding the inverse of a function. Here is one in which a shirt size in the United States is converted to a shirt size in Italy. Finding the inverse function gives the function that converts a shirt size in Italy to a shirt size in the United States.

Alternative to Example 6
Exercise 46, page 365.

EXAMPLE 6   Solve an Application

 The function $IT(x) = 2x + 8$ converts a men's shirt size x in the United States to the equivalent shirt size in Italy.

a. Use IT to determine the equivalent Italian shirt size for a size 16.5 U.S. shirt.

b. Find IT^{-1} and use IT^{-1} to determine the U.S. men's shirt size that is equivalent to an Italian shirt size of 36.

Solution

a. $IT(16.5) = 2(16.5) + 8 = 33 + 8 = 41$

A size 16.5 U.S. shirt is equivalent to a size 41 Italian shirt.

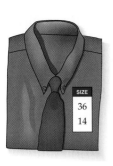

b. To find the inverse function, begin by substituting y for $IT(x)$.

$$IT(x) = 2x + 8$$
$$y = 2x + 8$$
$$x = 2y + 8 \qquad \text{• Interchange } x \text{ and } y.$$
$$x - 8 = 2y \qquad \text{• Solve for } y.$$
$$\frac{x - 8}{2} = y$$

In inverse notation, the above equation can be written as

$$IT^{-1}(x) = \frac{x - 8}{2} \qquad \text{or} \qquad IT^{-1}(x) = \frac{1}{2}x - 4$$

Substitute 36 for x to find the equivalent U.S. shirt size.

$$IT^{-1}(36) = \frac{1}{2}(36) - 4 = 18 - 4 = 14$$

A size 36 Italian shirt is equivalent to a size 14 U.S. shirt.

▶ **TRY EXERCISE 50, PAGE 366**

INTEGRATING TECHNOLOGY

Some graphing utilities can be used to draw the graph of the inverse of a function without the user having to find the inverse function. For instance, **Figure 4.11** shows the graph of $f(x) = 0.1x^3 - 4$. The graphs of f and f^{-1} are both shown in **Figure 4.12**, along with the graph of $y = x$. Note that the graph of f^{-1} is the reflection of the graph of f with respect to the graph of $y = x$. The display shown in **Figure 4.12** was produced on a TI-83 graphing calculator by using the DrawInv command, which is in the DRAW menu.

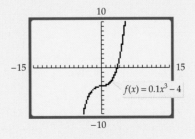

FIGURE 4.11

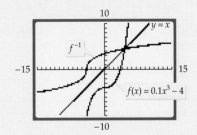

FIGURE 4.12

 TOPICS FOR DISCUSSION

1. If $f(x) = 3x + 1$, what are the values of $f^{-1}(2)$ and $[f(2)]^{-1}$?

2. How are the domain and range of a one-to-one function f related to the domain and range of the inverse function of f?

3. How is the graph of the inverse of a function f related to the graph of f?

4. The function $f(x) = -x$ is its own inverse. Find at least two other functions that are their own inverses.

5. What are the steps in finding the inverse of a one-to-one function?

EXERCISE SET 4.1

—*Suggested Assignment: Exercises 1–59, odd; 69–74, all.*
—*Answer graphs to Exercises 9–16 are on page AA14.*

In Exercises 1 to 4, assume that the given function has an inverse function.

1. Given $f(3) = 7$, find $f^{-1}(7)$.   3

2. Given $g(-3) = 5$, find $g^{-1}(5)$.   −3

3. Given $h^{-1}(-3) = -4$, find $h(-4)$.   −3

4. Given $f^{-1}(7) = 0$, find $f(0)$.   7

5. If 3 is in the domain of f^{-1}, find $f[f^{-1}(3)]$.   3

6. If f is a one-to-one function and $f(0) = 5$, $f(1) = 2$, and $f(2) = 7$, find:

     a. $f^{-1}(5)$ **b.** $f^{-1}(2)$
        0   1

7. The domain of the inverse function f^{-1} is the _____ of f.
range

8. The range of the inverse function f^{-1} is the _____ of f.
domain

In Exercises 9 to 16, draw the graph of the inverse relation. Is the inverse relation a function?

9.

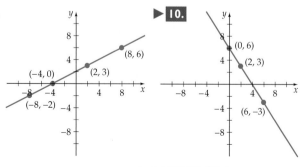

▶ **10.**

11.

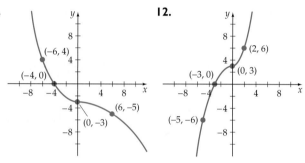

12.

13.

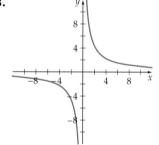

14.

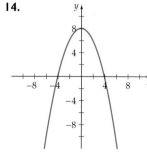

15.

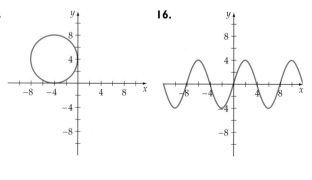

16.

In Exercises 17 to 22, use composition of functions to determine whether *f* and *g* are inverses of one another.

17. $f(x) = 4x$; $g(x) = \dfrac{x}{4}$ Yes

18. $f(x) = 3x$; $g(x) = \dfrac{1}{3x}$ No

19. $f(x) = 4x - 1$; $g(x) = \dfrac{1}{4}x + \dfrac{1}{4}$ Yes

▶ **20.** $f(x) = \dfrac{1}{2}x - \dfrac{3}{2}$; $g(x) = 2x + 3$ Yes

21. $f(x) = -\dfrac{1}{2}x - \dfrac{1}{2}$; $g(x) = -2x + 1$ No

22. $f(x) = 3x + 2$; $g(x) = \dfrac{1}{3}x - \dfrac{2}{3}$ Yes

In Exercises 23 to 26, find the inverse of the function. If the function does not have an inverse function, write "no inverse function."

23. $\{(-3, 1), (-2, 2), (1, 5), (4, -7)\}$ $\{(1, -3), (2, -2), (5, 1), (-7, 4)\}$

24. $\{(-5, 4), (-2, 3), (0, 1), (3, 2), (7, 11)\}$
$\{(4, -5), (3, -2), (1, 0), (2, 3), (11, 7)\}$

25. $\{(0, 1), (1, 2), (2, 4), (3, 8), (4, 16)\}$
$\{(1, 0), (2, 1), (4, 2), (8, 3), (16, 4)\}$

26. $\{(1, 0), (10, 1), (100, 2), (1000, 3), (10{,}000, 4)\}$
$\{(0, 1), (1, 10), (2, 100), (3, 1000), (4, 10{,}000)\}$

In Exercises 27 to 44, find $f^{-1}(x)$. State any restrictions on the domain of $f^{-1}(x)$.

27. $f(x) = 2x + 4$ $f^{-1}(x) = \dfrac{1}{2}x - 2$

▶ **28.** $f(x) = 4x - 8$ $f^{-1}(x) = \dfrac{1}{4}x + 2$

29. $f(x) = 3x - 7$ $f^{-1}(x) = \dfrac{1}{3}x + \dfrac{7}{3}$

30. $f(x) = -3x - 8$ $f^{-1}(x) = -\dfrac{1}{3}x - \dfrac{8}{3}$

31. $f(x) = -2x + 5$ $f^{-1}(x) = -\dfrac{1}{2}x + \dfrac{5}{2}$

32. $f(x) = -x + 3$ $f^{-1}(x) = -x + 3$

33. $f(x) = \dfrac{2x}{x - 1}$, $x \neq 1$ $f^{-1}(x) = \dfrac{x}{x - 2}$, $x \neq 2$

▶ **34.** $f(x) = \dfrac{x}{x - 2}$, $x \neq 2$ $f^{-1}(x) = \dfrac{2x}{x - 1}$, $x \neq 1$

35. $f(x) = \dfrac{x - 1}{x + 1}$, $x \neq -1$ $f^{-1}(x) = \dfrac{x + 1}{1 - x}$, $x \neq 1$

36. $f(x) = \dfrac{2x - 1}{x + 3}$, $x \neq -3$ $f^{-1}(x) = \dfrac{3x + 1}{2 - x}$, $x \neq 2$

37. $f(x) = x^2 + 1$, $x \geq 0$ $f^{-1}(x) = \sqrt{x - 1}$, $x \geq 1$

38. $f(x) = x^2 - 4$, $x \geq 0$ $f^{-1}(x) = \sqrt{x + 4}$, $x \geq -4$

39. $f(x) = \sqrt{x - 2}$, $x \geq 2$ $f^{-1}(x) = x^2 + 2$, $x \geq 0$

▶ **40.** $f(x) = \sqrt{4 - x}$, $x \leq 4$ $f^{-1}(x) = -x^2 + 4$, $x \geq 0$

41. $f(x) = x^2 + 4x$, $x \geq -2$ $f^{-1}(x) = \sqrt{x + 4} - 2$, $x \geq -4$

42. $f(x) = x^2 - 6x$, $x \leq 3$ $f^{-1}(x) = -\sqrt{x + 9} + 3$, $x \geq -9$

43. $f(x) = x^2 + 4x - 1$, $x \leq -2$
$f^{-1}(x) = -\sqrt{x + 5} - 2$, $x \geq -5$

44. $f(x) = x^2 - 6x + 1$, $x \geq 3$ $f^{-1}(x) = \sqrt{x + 8} + 3$, $x \geq -8$

45. **GEOMETRY** The volume of a cube is given by $V(x) = x^3$, where x is the measure of the length of a side of the cube. Find $V^{-1}(x)$ and explain what it represents. $V^{-1}(x) = \sqrt[3]{x}$. V^{-1} finds the length of a side of a cube given the volume.

46. **UNIT CONVERSIONS** The function $f(x) = 12x$ converts feet, x, into inches, $f(x)$. Find $f^{-1}(x)$ and explain what it determines. $f^{-1}(x) = \dfrac{x}{12}$. f^{-1} converts x inches into feet.

47. **UNIT CONVERSIONS** A conversion function such as the one in Exercise 46 converts a measurement in one unit into another unit. Is a conversion function always a one-to-one function? Does a conversion function always have an inverse function? Explain your answer. See answer below.

47. Yes. Yes. A conversion function is a nonconstant linear function. All nonconstant linear functions have inverses that are also functions.

48. **GRADING SCALE** Does the grading scale function given below have an inverse function? Explain your answer. No. It is not a one-to-one function. For a given grade, there is more than one score that can be associated with that grade.

Score	Grade
90–100	A
80–89	B
70–79	C
60–69	D
0–59	F

49. **FASHION** The function $s(x) = 2x + 24$ can be used to convert a U.S. women's shoe size into an Italian women's shoe size. Determine the function $s^{-1}(x)$ that can be used to convert an Italian women's shoe size to its equivalent U.S. shoe size. $s^{-1}(x) = \dfrac{1}{2}x - 12$

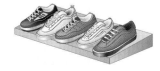

▶ **50.** ⬤ **FASHION** The function $K(x) = 1.3x - 4.7$ converts a men's shoe size in the United States to the equivalent shoe size in the United Kingdom. Determine the function $K^{-1}(x)$ that can be used to convert a United Kingdom men's shoe size to its equivalent U.S. shoe size. $K^{-1}(x) = \dfrac{x + 4.7}{1.3}$

51. 🖊 **COMPENSATION** The monthly earnings $E(s)$, in dollars, of a software sales executive is given by $E(s) = 0.05s + 2500$, where s is the value, in dollars, of the software sold by the executive during the month. Find $E^{-1}(s)$, and explain how the executive could use this function. $E^{-1}(s) = 20s - 50,000$. From the monthly earnings s, the executive can find $E^{-1}(s)$, the value of the software sold.

52. 🖊 ⬤ **POSTAGE** Does the first-class postage rate function given below have an inverse function? Explain your answer. No. It is not a one-to-one function. For a given cost, there is more than one weight that can be associated with that cost.

Weight (in ounces)	Cost
$0 < w \le 1$	$.37
$1 < w \le 2$	$.60
$2 < w \le 3$	$.83
$3 < w \le 4$	$1.06

53. **INTERNET COMMERCE** Functions and their inverses can be used to create secret codes that are used to secure business transactions made over the Internet. Let $A = 10$, $B = 11, \ldots$, and $Z = 35$. Let $f(x) = 2x - 1$ define a coding function. Code the word MATH (M—22, A—10, T—29, H—17), which is 22102917, by finding $f(22102917)$. Now find the inverse of f and show that applying f^{-1} to the output of f returns the original word.

44205833; $f^{-1}(x) = \dfrac{1}{2}x + \dfrac{1}{2}$; $f^{-1}(44205833) = 22102917$

54. **CRYPTOGRAPHY** A friend is using the letter-number correspondence in Exercise 53 and the coding function $f(x) = 2x + 3$. Suppose this friend sends you the coded message 5658602671. Decode this message. STUDY

In Exercises 55 to 60, answer the question without finding the equation of the linear function.

55. 🖊 Suppose that f is a linear function, $f(2) = 7$, and $f(5) = 12$. If $f(4) = c$, then is c less than 7, between 7 and 12, or greater than 12? Explain your answer. Because the function is increasing and 4 is between 2 and 5, c must be between 7 and 12.

56. 🖊 Suppose that f is a linear function, $f(1) = 13$, and $f(4) = 9$. If $f(3) = c$, then is c less than 9, between 9 and 13, or greater than 13? Explain your answer. Because the function is decreasing and 3 is between 1 and 4, c must be between 9 and 13.

57. Suppose that f is a linear function, $f(2) = 3$, and $f(5) = 9$. Between which two numbers is $f^{-1}(6)$? between 2 and 5

58. Suppose that f is a linear function, $f(5) = -1$, and $f(9) = -3$. Between which two numbers is $f^{-1}(-2)$? between 5 and 9

59. Suppose that g is a linear function, $g^{-1}(3) = 4$, and $g^{-1}(7) = 8$. Between which two numbers is $g(5)$? between 3 and 7

60. Suppose that g is a linear function, $g^{-1}(-2) = 5$, and $g^{-1}(0) = -3$. Between which two numbers is $g(0)$? between -2 and 0

CONNECTING CONCEPTS

In Exercises 61 and 62, find the inverse of the given function.

61. $f(x) = ax + b, \quad a \ne 0$ $f^{-1}(x) = \dfrac{x - b}{a}, \quad a \ne 0$

62. $f(x) = ax^2 + bx + c, \quad a \ne 0, \quad x \ge -\dfrac{b}{2a}$
Answer on bottom of page.

63. Use a graph of $f(x) = -x + 3$ to explain why f is its own inverse. The reflection of f across the line given by $y = x$ yields f. Thus f is its own inverse.

64. Use a graph of $f(x) = \sqrt{16 - x^2}$, with $0 \le x \le 4$, to explain why f is its own inverse. The reflection of f across the line given by $y = x$ yields f. Thus f is its own inverse.

Only one-to-one functions have inverses that are functions. In Exercises 65 to 68, determine if the given function is a one-to-one function.

65. $p(t) = \sqrt{9 - t}$ Yes

66. $v(t) = \sqrt{16 + t}$ Yes

67. $F(x) = |x| + x$ No

68. $T(x) = |x^2 - 6|, \quad x \ge 0$ No

62. $f^{-1}(x) = \dfrac{-b + \sqrt{b^2 + 4ax - 4ac}}{2a}, \quad a \ne 0, x \ge \dfrac{4ac - b^2}{4a}$

PREPARE FOR SECTION 4.2

69. Evaluate: 2^3 [P.2] 8

70. Evaluate: 3^{-4} [P.2] $\dfrac{1}{81}$

71. Evaluate: $\dfrac{2^2 + 2^{-2}}{2}$ [P.2/P.5] $\dfrac{17}{8}$

72. Evaluate: $\dfrac{3^2 - 3^{-2}}{2}$ [P.2/P.5] $\dfrac{40}{9}$

73. Evaluate $f(x) = 10^x$ for $x = -1, 0, 1,$ and 2. [P.2]
$\dfrac{1}{10}, 1, 10,$ and 100

74. Evaluate $f(x) = \left(\dfrac{1}{2}\right)^x$ for $x = -1, 0, 1,$ and 2. [P.2]
$2, 1, \dfrac{1}{2},$ and $\dfrac{1}{4}$

PROJECTS

I. **INTERSECTION POINTS FOR THE GRAPHS OF f AND f^{-1}** For each of the following, graph f and its inverse.

i. $f(x) = 2x - 4$

ii. $f(x) = -x + 2$

iii. $f(x) = x^3 + 1$

iv. $f(x) = x - 3$

v. $f(x) = -3x + 2$

vi. $f(x) = \dfrac{1}{x}$

a. Do the graphs of a function and its inverse always intersect? No

b. If the graphs of a function and its inverse intersect at one point, what is true about the coordinates of the point of intersection? They are equal.

c. Can the graphs of a function and its inverse intersect at more than one point? Yes. Consider the function $f(x) = x$.

SECTION 4.2

EXPONENTIAL FUNCTIONS AND THEIR APPLICATIONS

- EXPONENTIAL FUNCTIONS
- GRAPHS OF EXPONENTIAL FUNCTIONS
- THE NATURAL EXPONENTIAL FUNCTION
- APPLICATIONS OF EXPONENTIAL FUNCTIONS

EXPONENTIAL FUNCTIONS

In 1965, Gordon Moore, one of the cofounders of Intel Corporation, observed that the maximum number of transistors that could be placed on a microprocessor seemed to be doubling every 18 to 24 months. **Table 4.1** below shows how the maximum number of transistors on various Intel processors has changed over time. (*Source:* Intel Museum home page.)

TABLE 4.1

Year	1971	1979	1983	1985	1990	1993	1995	1998	2000
Number of transistors per microprocessor (in thousands)	2.3	31	110	280	1200	3100	5500	14,000	42,000

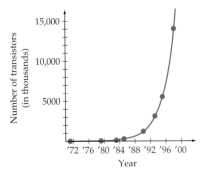

FIGURE 4.13

Moore's Law

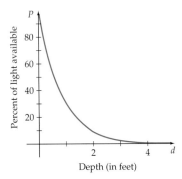

FIGURE 4.14

The curve that approximately passes through the points is a mathematical model of the data. See **Figure 4.13.** The model is based on an *exponential* function.

When light enters water, the intensity of the light decreases with the depth of the water. The graph in **Figure 4.14** shows a model, for Lake Michigan, of the decrease in the percentage of available light as the depth of the water increases. This model is also based on an exponential function.

Definition of an Exponential Function

The **exponential function with base b** is defined by

$$f(x) = b^x$$

where $b > 0$, $b \neq 1$, and x is a real number.

The base b of $f(x) = b^x$ is required to be positive. If the base were a negative number, the value of the function would be a complex number for some values of x. For instance, if $b = -4$ and $x = \dfrac{1}{2}$, then $f\left(\dfrac{1}{2}\right) = (-4)^{1/2} = 2i$. To avoid complex number values of a function, the base of any exponential function must be a nonnegative number. Also, b is defined such that $b \neq 1$ because $f(x) = 1^x = 1$ is a constant function.

In the following examples we evaluate $f(x) = 2^x$ at $x = 3$ and $x = -2$.

$$f(3) = 2^3 = 8 \qquad f(-2) = 2^{-2} = \frac{1}{2^2} = \frac{1}{4}$$

To evaluate the exponential function $f(x) = 2^x$ at an irrational number such as $x = \sqrt{2}$, we use a rational approximation of $\sqrt{2}$, such as 1.4142, and a calculator to obtain an approximation of the function. For instance, if $f(x) = 2^x$, then $f(\sqrt{2}) = 2^{\sqrt{2}} \approx 2^{1.4142} \approx 2.6651$.

Alternative to Example 1

Evaluate $f(x) = 4^x$ at $x = 3$, $x = -2$, and $x = \sqrt{2}$.

● $f(3) = 64$, $f(-2) = \dfrac{1}{16}$,

$f(\sqrt{2}) = 4^{\sqrt{2}} \approx 7.10299$

EXAMPLE 1   **Evaluate an Exponential Function**

Evaluate $f(x) = 3^x$ at $x = 2$, $x = -4$, and $x = \pi$.

Solution

$$f(2) = 3^2 = 9$$

$$f(-4) = 3^{-4} = \frac{1}{3^4} = \frac{1}{81}$$

$$f(\pi) = 3^\pi \approx 3^{3.1415927} \approx 31.54428 \qquad \text{• Evaluate with the aid of a calculator.}$$

▶ **TRY EXERCISE 2, PAGE 376**

● **GRAPHS OF EXPONENTIAL FUNCTIONS**

The graph of $f(x) = 2^x$ is shown in **Figure 4.15.** The coordinates of some of the points on the curve are given in **Table 4.2.**

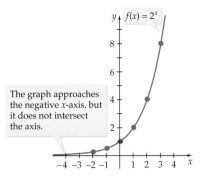

FIGURE 4.15

TABLE 4.2

x	$y = f(x) = 2^x$	(x, y)
−2	$f(-2) = 2^{-2} = \dfrac{1}{4}$	$\left(-2, \dfrac{1}{4}\right)$
−1	$f(-1) = 2^{-1} = \dfrac{1}{2}$	$\left(-1, \dfrac{1}{2}\right)$
0	$f(0) = 2^0 = 1$	$(0, 1)$
1	$f(1) = 2^1 = 2$	$(1, 2)$
2	$f(2) = 2^2 = 4$	$(2, 4)$
3	$f(3) = 2^3 = 8$	$(3, 8)$

Note the following properties of the graph of the exponential function $f(x) = 2^x$.

- The y-intercept is $(0, 1)$.

- The graph passes through $(1, 2)$.

- As x decreases without bound (that is, as $x \to -\infty$), $f(x) \to 0$.

- The graph is a smooth continuous increasing curve.

Now consider the graph of an exponential function for which the base is between 0 and 1. The graph of $f(x) = \left(\dfrac{1}{2}\right)^x$ is shown in **Figure 4.16.** The coordinates of some of the points on the curve are given in **Table 4.3.**

TABLE 4.3

x	$y = f(x) = \left(\dfrac{1}{2}\right)^x$	(x, y)
−3	$f(-3) = \left(\dfrac{1}{2}\right)^{-3} = 8$	$(-3, 8)$
−2	$f(-2) = \left(\dfrac{1}{2}\right)^{-2} = 4$	$(-2, 4)$
−1	$f(-1) = \left(\dfrac{1}{2}\right)^{-1} = 2$	$(-1, 2)$
0	$f(0) = \left(\dfrac{1}{2}\right)^0 = 1$	$(0, 1)$
1	$f(1) = \left(\dfrac{1}{2}\right)^1 = \dfrac{1}{2}$	$\left(1, \dfrac{1}{2}\right)$
2	$f(2) = \left(\dfrac{1}{2}\right)^2 = \dfrac{1}{4}$	$\left(2, \dfrac{1}{4}\right)$

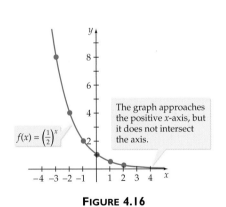

FIGURE 4.16

Note the following properties of the graph of $f(x) = \left(\dfrac{1}{2}\right)^x$ in **Figure 4.16.**

- The y-intercept is $(0, 1)$.

- The graph passes through $\left(1, \dfrac{1}{2}\right)$.

- As x increases without bound, the y-values decrease toward 0. That is, as $x \to \infty$, $f(x) \to 0$.

- The graph is a smooth continuous decreasing curve.

The basic properties of exponential functions are provided in the following summary.

P   **Properties of $f(x) = b^x$**

For positive real numbers b, $b \neq 1$, the exponential function defined by $f(x) = b^x$ has the following properties:

1. The function f is a one-to-one function. It has the set of real numbers as its domain and the set of positive real numbers as its range.

2. The graph of f is a smooth continuous curve with a y-intercept of $(0, 1)$, and the graph passes through $(1, b)$.

3. If $b > 1$, f is an increasing function and the graph of f is asymptotic to the negative x-axis. [As $x \to \infty$, $f(x) \to \infty$, and as $x \to -\infty$, $f(x) \to 0$.] See **Figure 4.17a.**

4. If $0 < b < 1$, f is a decreasing function and the graph of f is asymptotic to the positive x-axis. [As $x \to -\infty$, $f(x) \to \infty$, and as $x \to \infty$, $f(x) \to 0$.] See **Figure 4.17b.**

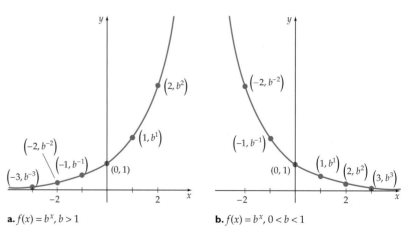

a. $f(x) = b^x$, $b > 1$ **b.** $f(x) = b^x$, $0 < b < 1$

P   **FIGURE 4.17**

? QUESTION What is the x-intercept of the graph of $f(x) = \left(\dfrac{1}{3}\right)^x$?

? ANSWER The graph does not have an x-intercept. As x increases, the graph approaches the x-axis, but it does not intersect the x-axis.

Alternative to Example 2
Exercise 24, page 377.

EXAMPLE 2   **Graph an Exponential Function**

Graph $g(x) = \left(\dfrac{3}{4}\right)^x$.

Solution

Because the base $\dfrac{3}{4}$ is less than 1, we know that the graph of g is a decreasing function that is asymptotic to the positive x-axis. The y-intercept of the graph is the point $(0, 1)$, and the graph also passes through $\left(1, \dfrac{3}{4}\right)$.

Plot a few additional points (see **Table 4.4**), and then draw a smooth curve through the points as in **Figure 4.18**.

TABLE 4.4

x	$y = g(x) = \left(\dfrac{3}{4}\right)^x$	(x, y)
−3	$\left(\dfrac{3}{4}\right)^{-3} = \dfrac{64}{27}$	$\left(-3, \dfrac{64}{27}\right)$
−2	$\left(\dfrac{3}{4}\right)^{-2} = \dfrac{16}{9}$	$\left(-2, \dfrac{16}{9}\right)$
−1	$\left(\dfrac{3}{4}\right)^{-1} = \dfrac{4}{3}$	$\left(-1, \dfrac{4}{3}\right)$
2	$\left(\dfrac{3}{4}\right)^{2} = \dfrac{9}{16}$	$\left(2, \dfrac{9}{16}\right)$
3	$\left(\dfrac{3}{4}\right)^{3} = \dfrac{27}{64}$	$\left(3, \dfrac{27}{64}\right)$

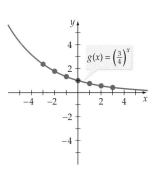

FIGURE 4.18

▶ **TRY EXERCISE 22, PAGE 377**

Consider the functions $F(x) = 2^x - 3$ and $G(x) = 2^{x-3}$. You can construct the graphs of these functions by plotting points; however, it is easier to construct their graphs by using translations of the graph of $f(x) = 2^x$, as shown in Example 3.

Alternative to Example 3
Exercise 26, page 377.

EXAMPLE 3   **Use a Translation to Produce a Graph**

a. Explain how to use the graph of $f(x) = 2^x$ to produce the graph of $F(x) = 2^x - 3$.

b. Explain how to use the graph of $f(x) = 2^x$ to produce the graph of $G(x) = 2^{x-3}$.

Solution

a. $F(x) = 2^x - 3 = f(x) - 3$. The graph of F is a vertical translation of f down 3 units, as shown in **Figure 4.19**.

Continued ▶

b. $G(x) = 2^{x-3} = f(x - 3)$. The graph of G is a horizontal translation of f to the right 3 units, as shown in **Figure 4.20.**

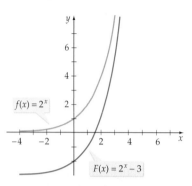

FIGURE 4.19

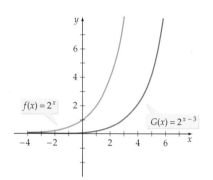

FIGURE 4.20

▶ **TRY EXERCISE 28, PAGE 377**

The graphs of some functions can be constructed by stretching, compressing, or reflecting the graph of an exponential function.

Alternative to Example 4
Exercise 32, page 377.

EXAMPLE 4   **Use Stretching or Reflecting Procedures to Produce a Graph**

a. Explain how to use the graph of $f(x) = 2^x$ to produce the graph of $M(x) = 2(2^x)$.

b. Explain how to use the graph of $f(x) = 2^x$ to produce the graph of $N(x) = 2^{-x}$.

Solution

a. $M(x) = 2(2^x) = 2f(x)$. The graph of M is a vertical stretching of f, as shown in **Figure 4.21.** If (x, y) is a point on the graph of $f(x) = 2^x$, then $(x, 2y)$ is a point on the graph of M.

b. $N(x) = 2^{-x} = f(-x)$. The graph of N is the graph of f reflected across the y-axis, as shown in **Figure 4.22.** If (x, y) is a point on the graph of $f(x) = 2^x$, then $(-x, y)$ is a point on the graph of N.

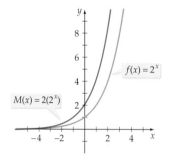

FIGURE 4.21

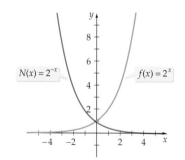

FIGURE 4.22

▶ **TRY EXERCISE 30, PAGE 377**

MATH MATTERS

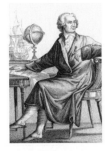

Leonhard Euler (1707–1783)

Some mathematicians consider Euler to be the greatest mathematician of all time. He certainly was the most prolific writer of mathematics of all time. He made substantial contributions in the areas of number theory, geometry, calculus, differential equations, differential geometry, topology, complex variables, and analysis, to name but a few. Euler was the first to introduce many of the mathematical notations that we use today. For instance, he introduced the symbol i for the square root of -1, the symbol π for pi, the functional notation $f(x)$, and the letter e for the base of the natural exponential function. Euler's computational skills were truly amazing. The mathematician François Arago remarked, "Euler calculated without apparent effort, as men breathe, or as eagles sustain themselves in the wind."

● THE NATURAL EXPONENTIAL FUNCTION

The irrational number π is often used in applications that involve circles. Another irrational number, denoted by the letter e, is useful in applications that involve growth or decay.

Ⓟ   **Definition of e**

The **number e** is defined as the number that

$$\left(1 + \frac{1}{n}\right)^n$$

approaches as n increases without bound.

The letter e was chosen in honor of the Swiss mathematician Leonhard Euler. He was able to compute the value of e to several decimal places by evaluating $\left(1 + \frac{1}{n}\right)^n$ for large values of n, as shown in **Table 4.5.**

TABLE 4.5

Value of n	Value of $\left(1 + \dfrac{1}{n}\right)^n$
1	2
10	2.59374246
100	2.704813829
1000	2.716923932
10,000	2.718145927
100,000	2.718268237
1,000,000	2.718280469
10,000,000	2.718281693

The value of e accurate to eight decimal places is 2.71828183.

The Natural Exponential Function

For all real numbers x, the function defined by

$$f(x) = e^x$$

is called the **natural exponential function.**

A calculator can be used to evaluate e^x for specific values of x. For instance,

$$e^2 \approx 7.389056, \quad e^{3.5} \approx 33.115452, \quad \text{and} \quad e^{-1.4} \approx 0.246597$$

On a TI-83 calculator the e^x function is located above the ⌷LN⌷ key.

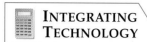

INTEGRATING
TECHNOLOGY

The graph below was
produced on a TI-83
graphing calculator by
entering e^x in the Y= menu.

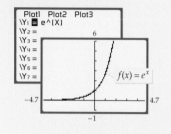

To graph $f(x) = e^x$, use a calculator to find the range values for a few domain values. The range values in **Table 4.6** have been rounded to the nearest tenth.

TABLE 4.6

x	-2	-1	0	1	2
$f(x) = e^x$	0.1	0.4	1.0	2.7	7.4

Plot the points given in **Table 4.6,** and then connect the points with a smooth curve. Because $e > 1$, we know that the graph is an increasing function. To the far left, the graph will approach the x-axis. The y-intercept is $(0, 1)$. See **Figure 4.23.** Note in **Figure 4.24** how the graph of $f(x) = e^x$ compares with the graphs of $g(x) = 2^x$ and $h(x) = 3^x$. You may have anticipated that the graph of $f(x) = e^x$ would lie between the two other graphs because e is between 2 and 3.

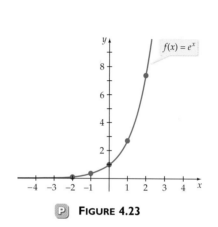

P FIGURE 4.23

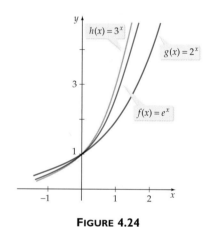

FIGURE 4.24

● APPLICATIONS OF EXPONENTIAL FUNCTIONS

Many applications can be effectively modeled by functions that involve an exponential function. For instance, in Example 5 we make use of a function that involves an exponential function to model the temperature of a cup of coffee.

Alternative to Example 5
Exercise 48, page 378.

EXAMPLE 5   **Use a Mathematical Model**

A cup of coffee is heated to 160°F and placed in a room that maintains a temperature of 70°F. The temperature T of the coffee, in degrees Fahrenheit, after t minutes is given by

$$T = 70 + 90e^{-0.0485t}$$

a.   Find the temperature of the coffee, to the nearest degree, 20 minutes after it is placed in the room.

b.   Use a graphing utility to determine when the temperature of the coffee will reach 90°F.

take note

In Example 5**b.**, we use a graphing utility to solve the equation $90 = 70 + 90e^{-0.0485t}$. Analytic methods of solving this type of equation without the use of a graphing utility will be developed in Section 4.5.

Solution

a. $T = 70 + 90e^{-0.0485t}$
  $= 70 + 90e^{-0.0485 \cdot (20)}$ • **Substitute 20 for t.**
  $\approx 70 + 34.1$
  ≈ 104.1

After 20 minutes the temperature of the coffee is about 104°F.

b.   Graph $T = 70 + 90e^{-0.0485t}$ and $T = 90$. See the following figure.

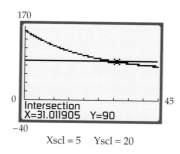

The graphs intersect at about (31.01, 90). It takes the coffee about 31 minutes to cool to 90°F.

▶ **TRY EXERCISE 44, PAGE 378**

Alternative to Example 6
Exercise 58, page 380.

EXAMPLE 6 **Use a Mathematical Model**

 The weekly revenue R, in dollars, from the sale of a product varies with time according to the function

$$R(x) = \frac{1760}{8 + 14e^{-0.03x}}$$

where x is the number of weeks that have passed since the product was put on the market. What will the weekly revenue approach as time goes by?

Solution

Method 1 Use a graphing utility to graph $R(x)$, and use the TRACE feature to see what happens to the revenue as the time increases. The following graph shows that as the weeks go by, the weekly revenue will increase and approach $220.00 per week.

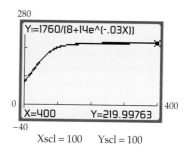

Continued ▶

Method 2   Write the revenue function in the following form.

$$R(x) = \frac{1760}{8 + \dfrac{14}{e^{0.03x}}} \qquad \bullet\ 14e^{-0.03x} = \frac{14}{e^{0.03x}}$$

As x increases without bound, $e^{0.03x}$ increases without bound, and the fraction $\dfrac{14}{e^{0.03x}}$ approaches 0. Therefore, as $x \to \infty$, $R(x) \to \dfrac{1760}{8 + 0} = 220$. Both methods indicate that as the number of weeks increases, the revenue approaches $220 per week.

▶ **TRY EXERCISE 54, PAGE 379**

  TOPICS FOR DISCUSSION

1. Explain how to use the graph of $f(x) = 2^x$ to produce the graph of $g(x) = 2^{(x-3)} + 4$.

2. At what point does the function $g(x) = e^{-x^2/2}$ take on its maximum value?

3. Without using a graphing utility, determine whether the revenue function $R(t) = 10 + e^{-0.05t}$ is an increasing function or a decreasing function.

4. Discuss the properties of the graph of $f(x) = b^x$ when $b > 1$.

5. What is the base of the natural exponential function? How is it calculated? What is its approximate value?

EXERCISE SET 4.2

—Suggested Assignment: Exercises 1–59, odd; 68–73, all.
—Answer graphs to Exercises 17–24, 35–42, and 62–63 are on page AA15.

In Exercises 1 to 8, evaluate the exponential function for the given x-values.

1. $f(x) = 3^x$; $x = 0$ and $x = 4$ $f(0) = 1$; $f(4) = 81$

▶ **2.** $f(x) = 5^x$; $x = 3$ and $x = -2$ $f(3) = 125$; $f(-2) = \dfrac{1}{25}$

3. $g(x) = 10^x$; $x = -2$ and $x = 3$ $g(-2) = \dfrac{1}{100}$; $g(3) = 1000$

4. $g(x) = 4^x$; $x = 0$ and $x = -1$ $g(0) = 1$; $g(-1) = \dfrac{1}{4}$

5. $h(x) = \left(\dfrac{3}{2}\right)^x$; $x = 2$ and $x = -3$ $h(2) = \dfrac{9}{4}$; $h(-3) = \dfrac{8}{27}$

6. $h(x) = \left(\dfrac{2}{5}\right)^x$; $x = -1$ and $x = 3$ $h(-1) = \dfrac{5}{2}$; $h(3) = \dfrac{8}{125}$

7. $j(x) = \left(\dfrac{1}{2}\right)^x$; $x = -2$ and $x = 4$ $j(-2) = 4$; $j(4) = \dfrac{1}{16}$

8. $j(x) = \left(\dfrac{1}{4}\right)^x$; $x = -1$ and $x = 5$ $j(-1) = 4$; $j(5) = \dfrac{1}{1024}$

 In Exercises 9 to 14, use a calculator to evaluate the exponential function for the given x-value. Round to the nearest hundredth.

9. $f(x) = 2^x$, $x = 3.2$ 9.19

10. $f(x) = 3^x$, $x = -1.5$ 0.19

11. $g(x) = e^x$, $x = 2.2$ 9.03

12. $g(x) = e^x$, $x = -1.3$ 0.27

13. $h(x) = 5^x$, $x = \sqrt{2}$ 9.74

14. $h(x) = 0.5^x$, $x = \pi$ 0.11

15. Examine the following four functions and the graphs labeled **a, b, c,** and **d.** For each graph, determine which function has been graphed.

$$f(x) = 5^x \qquad g(x) = 1 + 5^{-x}$$
$$h(x) = 5^{x+3} \qquad k(x) = 5^x + 3$$

a.
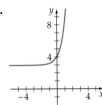

b.
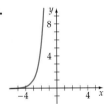

a. $k(x)$
b. $g(x)$
c. $h(x)$
d. $f(x)$

c.

d.

16. Examine the following four functions and the graphs labeled **a, b, c,** and **d.** For each graph, determine which function has been graphed.

$$f(x) = \left(\frac{1}{4}\right)^x \qquad g(x) = \left(\frac{1}{4}\right)^{-x}$$
$$h(x) = \left(\frac{1}{4}\right)^{x-2} \qquad k(x) = 3\left(\frac{1}{4}\right)^x$$

a.
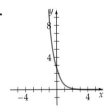

b.

a. $k(x)$
b. $f(x)$
c. $g(x)$
d. $h(x)$

c.
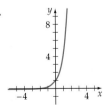

d.

In Exercises 17 to 24, sketch the graph of each function.

17. $f(x) = 3^x$

18. $f(x) = 4^x$

19. $f(x) = 10^x$

20. $f(x) = 6^x$

21. $f(x) = \left(\frac{3}{2}\right)^x$

▶ **22.** $f(x) = \left(\frac{5}{2}\right)^x$

23. $f(x) = \left(\frac{1}{3}\right)^x$

24. $f(x) = \left(\frac{2}{3}\right)^x$

In Exercises 25 to 34, explain how to use the graph of the first function f to produce the graph of the second function F.

25. $f(x) = 3^x$, $F(x) = 3^x + 2$
Shift the graph of f vertically upward 2 units.

26. $f(x) = 4^x$, $F(x) = 4^x - 3$
Shift the graph of f vertically downward 3 units.

27. $f(x) = 10^x$, $F(x) = 10^{x-2}$
Shift the graph of f horizontally to the right 2 units.

▶ **28.** $f(x) = 6^x$, $F(x) = 6^{x+5}$
Shift the graph of f horizontally to the left 5 units.

29. $f(x) = \left(\frac{3}{2}\right)^x$, $F(x) = \left(\frac{3}{2}\right)^{-x}$ Reflect the graph of f across the y-axis.

▶ **30.** $f(x) = \left(\frac{5}{2}\right)^x$, $F(x) = -\left[\left(\frac{5}{2}\right)^x\right]$ Reflect the graph of f across the x-axis.

31. $f(x) = \left(\frac{1}{3}\right)^x$, $F(x) = 2\left[\left(\frac{1}{3}\right)^x\right]$ Stretch the graph of f vertically away from the x-axis by a factor of 2.

32. $f(x) = \left(\frac{2}{3}\right)^x$, $F(x) = \frac{1}{2}\left[\left(\frac{2}{3}\right)^x\right]$ Shrink the graph of f vertically toward the x-axis by a factor of $\frac{1}{2}$.

33. $f(x) = e^x$, $F(x) = e^{-x} + 2$ Reflect the graph of f across the y-axis and then shift this graph vertically upward 2 units.

34. $f(x) = e^x$, $F(x) = e^{x-3} + 1$ Shift the graph of f horizontally 3 units to the right and then shift this graph vertically upward 1 unit.

In Exercises 35 to 42, use a graphing utility to graph each function. If the function has a horizontal asymptote, state the equation of the horizontal asymptote.

35. $f(x) = \dfrac{3^x + 3^{-x}}{2}$
no horizontal asymptote

36. $f(x) = 4 \cdot 3^{-x^2}$
horizontal asymptote: $y = 0$

37. $f(x) = \dfrac{e^x - e^{-x}}{2}$
no horizontal asymptote

38. $f(x) = \dfrac{e^x + e^{-x}}{2}$
no horizontal asymptote

39. $f(x) = -e^{(x-4)}$
horizontal asymptote: $y = 0$

40. $f(x) = 0.5e^{-x}$
horizontal asymptote: $y = 0$

41. $f(x) = \dfrac{10}{1 + 0.4e^{-0.5x}}$,
$x \geq 0$
horizontal asymptote: $y = 10$

42. $f(x) = \dfrac{10}{1 + 1.5e^{-0.5x}}$,
$x \geq 0$
horizontal asymptote: $y = 10$

43. INTERNET CONNECTIONS Data from Forrester Research suggest that the number of broadband [cable and digital subscriber line (DSL)] connections to the Internet can be modeled by $f(x) = 1.353(1.9025)^x$, where x is the number of years after January 1, 1998, and $f(x)$ is the number of connections in millions.

a. How many broadband Internet connections, to the nearest million, does this model predict will exist on January 1, 2005? 122 million connections

b. According to the model, in what year will the number of broadband connections first reach 300 million? [*Hint:* Use the intersect feature of a graphing utility to determine the x-coordinate of the point of intersection of the graphs of $f(x)$ and $y = 300$.] 2006

▶ **44.** MEDICATION IN BLOODSTREAM The function $A(t) = 200e^{-0.014t}$ gives the amount of medication, in milligrams, in a patient's bloodstream t minutes after the medication has been injected into the patient's bloodstream.

a. Find the amount of medication, to the nearest milligram, in the patient's bloodstream after 45 minutes. 107 mg

b. Use a graphing utility to determine how long it will take, to the nearest minute, for the amount of medication in the patient's bloodstream to reach 50 milligrams. 99 min

45. DEMAND FOR A PRODUCT The demand d for a specific product, in items per month, is given by

$$d(p) = 25 + 880e^{-0.18p}$$

where p is the price, in dollars, of the product.

a. What will be the monthly demand, to the nearest unit, when the price of the product is $8 and when the price is $18? 233 items per month; 59 items per month

b. What will happen to the demand as the price increases without bound? The demand will approach 25 items per month.

46. SALES The monthly income I, in dollars, from a new product is given by

$$I(t) = 24{,}000 - 22{,}000e^{-0.005t}$$

where t is the time, in months, since the product was first put on the market.

a. What was the monthly income after the 10th month and after the 100th month? $3072.95; $10,656.33

b. What will the monthly income from the product approach as the time increases without bound? $24,000

47. A PROBABILITY FUNCTION The manager of a home improvement store finds that between 10 A.M. and 11 A.M., customers enter the store at the average rate of 45 customers per hour. The following function gives the probability that a customer will arrive within t minutes of 10 A.M. (*Note:* A probability of 0.6 means there is a 60% chance that a customer will arrive during a given time period.)

$$P(t) = 1 - e^{-0.75t}$$

a. Find the probability, to the nearest hundredth, that a customer will arrive within 1 minute of 10 A.M. 0.53

b. Find the probability, to the nearest hundredth, that a customer will arrive within 3 minutes of 10 A.M. 0.89

c. Use a graph of $P(t)$ to determine how many minutes, to the nearest tenth of a minute, it takes for $P(t)$ to equal 98%. 5.2 min

d. Write a sentence that explains the meaning of the answer in part **c**. There is a 98% probability that at least one customer will arrive between 10:00 A.M. and 10:05.2 A.M.

48. A PROBABILITY FUNCTION The owner of a sporting goods store finds that between 9 A.M. and 10 A.M., customers enter the store at the average rate of 12 customers per hour. The following function gives the probability that a customer will arrive within t minutes of 9 A.M.

$$P(t) = 1 - e^{-0.2t}$$

a. Find the probability, to the nearest hundredth, that a customer will arrive within 5 minutes of 9 A.M. 0.63

b. Find the probability, to the nearest hundredth, that a customer will arrive within 15 minutes of 9 A.M. 0.95

c. Use a graph of $P(t)$ to determine how many minutes, to the nearest 0.1 minute, it takes for $P(t)$ to equal 90%. 11.5 min

d. Write a sentence that explains the meaning of the answer in part **c**. There is a 90% probability that at least one customer will arrive between 9:00 A.M. and 9:11.5 A.M.

Exercises 49 and 50 involve the factorial function x!, which is defined for whole numbers x as

$$x! = \begin{cases} 1, & \text{if } x = 0 \\ x \cdot (x-1) \cdot (x-2) \cdot \cdots \cdot 3 \cdot 2 \cdot 1, & \text{if } x \geq 1 \end{cases}$$

For example, 3! = 3 · 2 · 1 = 6 and 5! = 5 · 4 · 3 · 2 · 1 = 120.

49. QUEUING THEORY During the 30-minute period before a Broadway play begins, the members of the audience arrive at the theater at the average rate of 12 people per minute. The probability that x people will arrive during a particular minute is given by $P(x) = \dfrac{12^x e^{-12}}{x!}$. Find the probability, to the nearest 0.1%, that

a. 9 people will arrive during a given minute. 8.7%

b. 18 people will arrive during a given minute. 2.6%

50. QUEUING THEORY During the period from 2:00 P.M. to 3:00 P.M., a bank finds that an average of seven people enter the bank every minute. The probability that x people will enter the bank during a particular minute is given by $P(x) = \dfrac{7^x e^{-7}}{x!}$. Find the probability, to the nearest 0.1%, that

a. only two people will enter the bank during a given minute. 2.2%

b. 11 people will enter the bank during a given minute. 4.5%

51. E. COLI INFEC-TION *Escherichia coli (E. coli)* is a bacterium that can reproduce at an exponential rate. The *E. coli* reproduce by dividing. A small number of *E. coli* bacteria in the large intestine 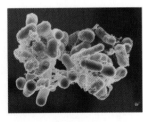 of a human can trigger a serious infection within a few hours. Consider a particular *E. coli* infection that starts with 100 *E. coli* bacteria. Each bacterium splits into two parts every half hour. Assuming none of the bacteria die, the size of the *E. coli* population after t hours is given by $P(t) = 100 \cdot 2^{2t}$, where $0 \le t \le 16$.

a. Find $P(3)$ and $P(6)$. 6400; 409,600

b. Use a graphing utility to find the time, to the nearest tenth of an hour, it takes for the *E. coli* population to number 1 billion. 11.6 h

52. RADIATION Lead shielding is used to contain radiation. The percentage of a certain radiation that can penetrate x millimeters of lead shielding is given by $I(x) = 100e^{-1.5x}$.

a. What percentage of radiation, to the nearest tenth of a percent, will penetrate a lead shield that is 1 millimeter thick? 22.3%

b. How many millimeters of lead shielding are required so that less than 0.05% of the radiation penetrates the shielding? Round to the nearest millimeter. 5 mm

53. AIDS An exponential function that approximates the number of people in the United States who have been infected with AIDS is given by $N(t) = 138{,}000(1.39)^t$, where t is the number of years after January 1, 1990.

a. According to this function, how many people had been infected with AIDS as of January 1, 1994? Round to the nearest thousand. 515,000 people

b. Use a graph to estimate during what year the number of people in the United States who had been infected with AIDS first reached 1.5 million. 1997

▶ **54.** FISH POPULATION The number of bass in a lake is given by

$$P(t) = \dfrac{3600}{1 + 7e^{-0.05t}},$$

where t is the number of months that have passed since the lake was stocked with bass.

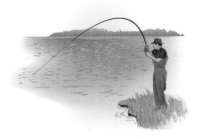

a. How many bass were in the lake immediately after it was stocked? 450 bass

b. How many bass were in the lake 1 year after the lake was stocked? ≈744 bass

c. What will happen to the bass population as t increases without bound? The bass population will increase, approaching 3600.

55. THE PAY IT FOR-WARD MODEL In the movie *Pay It Forward*, Trevor McKinney, played by Haley Joel Osment, is given a school assignment to "think of an idea to change the world—and then put it into action." In 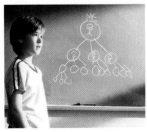 response to this assignment, Trevor develops a *pay it forward* project. In this project, anyone who benefits from another person's good deed must do a good deed for three additional people. Each of these three people is then obligated to do a good deed for another three people, and so on.

The following diagram shows the number of people who have been a beneficiary of a good deed after 1 round and after 2 rounds of this project.

Three beneficiaries after one round.

A total of 12 beneficiaries after two rounds $(3 + 9 = 12)$.

A mathematical model for the number of pay it forward beneficiaries after n rounds is given by $B(n) = \dfrac{3^{n+1} - 3}{2}$.

Use this model to determine

a. the number of beneficiaries after 5 rounds and after 10 rounds. Assume that no person is a beneficiary of more than one good deed.
363 beneficiaries; 88,572 beneficiaries

b. how many rounds are required to produce at least 2 million beneficiaries. 13 rounds

56. **INTENSITY OF LIGHT** The percent $I(x)$ of the original intensity of light striking the surface of a lake that is available x feet below the surface of the lake is given by $I(x) = 100e^{-0.95x}$.

a. What percentage of the light, to the nearest tenth of a percent, is available 2 feet below the surface of the lake? 15.0%

b. At what depth, to the nearest hundredth of a foot, is the intensity of the light one-half the intensity at the surface? 0.73 ft

57. **A TEMPERATURE MODEL** A cup of coffee is heated to 180°F and placed in a room that maintains a temperature of 65°F. The temperature of the coffee after t minutes is given by $T(t) = 65 + 115e^{-0.042t}$.

a. Find the temperature, to the nearest degree, of the coffee 10 minutes after it is placed in the room. 141°F

b. Use a graphing utility to determine when, to the nearest tenth of a minute, the temperature of the coffee will reach 100°F. after 28.3 min

58. **A TEMPERATURE MODEL** Soup that is at a temperature of 170°F is poured into a bowl in a room that maintains a constant temperature. The temperature of the soup decreases according to the model given by $T(t) = 75 + 95e^{-0.12t}$, where t is time in minutes after the soup is poured.

a. What is the temperature, to the nearest tenth of a degree, of the soup after 2 minutes? 149.7°F

b. A certain customer prefers soup at a temperature of 110°F. How many minutes, to the nearest 0.1 minute, after the soup is poured does the soup reach that temperature? 8.3 min

c. What is the temperature of the room? 75°F

59. **MUSICAL SCALES** Starting on the left side of a standard 88-key piano, the frequency, in vibrations per second, of the nth note is given by $f(n) = (27.5)2^{(n-1)/12}$.

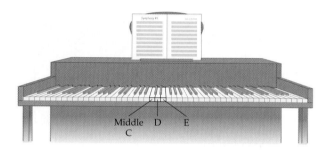

Middle C   D   E

a. Using this formula, determine the frequency, to the nearest hundredth of a vibration per second, of middle C, key number 40 on an 88-key piano.
261.63 vibrations per second

b. Is the difference in frequency between middle C (key number 40) and D (key number 42) the same as the difference in frequency between D (key number 42) and E (key number 44)? Explain. No. The function $f(n)$ is not a linear function. Therefore, the graph of $f(n)$ does not increase at a constant rate.

CONNECTING CONCEPTS

60. Verify that the hyperbolic cosine function $\cosh(x) = \dfrac{e^x + e^{-x}}{2}$ is an even function.

61. Verify that the hyperbolic sine function $\sinh(x) = \dfrac{e^x - e^{-x}}{2}$ is an odd function.

62. Graph $g(x) = 10^x$, and then sketch the graph of g reflected across the line given by $y = x$.

63. Graph $f(x) = e^x$, and then sketch the graph of f reflected across the line given by $y = x$.

In Exercises 64 to 67, determine the domain of the given function. Write the domain using interval notation.

64. $f(x) = \dfrac{e^x - e^{-x}}{e^x + e^{-x}}$ $(-\infty, \infty)$

65. $f(x) = \dfrac{e^{|x|}}{1 + e^x}$ $(-\infty, \infty)$

66. $f(x) = \sqrt{1 - e^x}$ $(-\infty, 0]$

67. $f(x) = \sqrt{e^x - e^{-x}}$ $[0, \infty)$

PREPARE FOR SECTION 4.3

68. If $2^x = 16$, determine the value of x. [4.2] 4

69. If $3^{-x} = \dfrac{1}{27}$, determine the value of x. [4.2] 3

70. If $x^4 = 625$, determine the value of x. [4.2] 5

71. Find the inverse of $f(x) = \dfrac{2x}{x + 3}$. [4.1] $f^{-1}(x) = \dfrac{3x}{2 - x}$

72. State the domain of $g(x) = \sqrt{x - 2}$. [2.2] $\{x \mid x \geq 2\}$

73. If the range of $h(x)$ is the set of all positive real numbers, then what is the domain of $h^{-1}(x)$? [4.2]
the set of all positive real numbers

PROJECTS

1.   **THE SAINT LOUIS GATEWAY ARCH** The Gateway Arch in Saint Louis was designed in the shape of an inverted **catenary,** as shown by the red curve in the drawing at the right. The Gateway Arch is one of the largest optical illusions ever created. As you look at the arch (and its basic shape defined by the catenary curve), it appears to be much taller than it is wide. However, this is not the case. The height of the catenary is given by

$$h(x) = 693.8597 - 68.7672\left(\dfrac{e^{0.0100333x} + e^{-0.0100333x}}{2}\right)$$

where x and $h(x)$ are measured in feet and $x = 0$ represents the position at ground level that is directly below the highest point of the catenary.

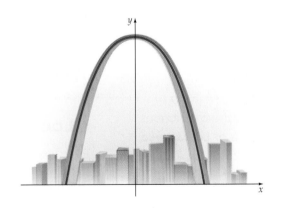

a. Use a graphing utility to graph $h(x)$.
See the *Instructor's Solutions Manual.*

b. Use your graph to find the height of the catenary for $x = 0$, 100, 200, and 299 feet. Round each result to the nearest tenth of a foot. 625.1 ft, 587.5 ft, 433.5 ft, 1.6 ft

c. What is the width of the catenary at ground level and what is the maximum height of the catenary? Round each result to the nearest tenth of a foot.
width ≈ 598.5 ft, height ≈ 625.1 ft

d. By how much does the maximum height of the catenary exceed its width at ground level? Round to the nearest tenth of a foot.   26.6 ft

2.   **AN EXPONENTIAL REWARD** According to legend, when Sissa Ben Dahir of India invented the game of chess, King Shirham was so impressed with the game that he summoned the game's inventor and offered him the reward of his choosing. The inventor pointed to the chessboard and requested, for his reward, one grain of wheat on the first square, two grains of wheat on the second square, four grains on the third square, eight grains on the fourth square, and so on for all 64 squares on the chessboard. The King considered this a very modest reward and said he would grant the inventor's wish. The following table shows how many grains of rice are on each of the first six squares and the total number of grains of wheat needed to cover squares 1 to n for $n \leq 6$.

Square number, n	Number of grains of wheat on square n	Total number of grains of wheat on squares 1 through n
1	1	1
2	2	3
3	4	7
4	8	15
5	16	31
6	32	63

a. If all 64 squares of the chessboard are piled with wheat as requested by Sissa Ben Dahir, how many grains of wheat are on the board? $2^{64} - 1 \approx 1.8446744 \times 10^{19}$

b. A grain of wheat weighs approximately 0.000008 kilogram. Find the total weight of the wheat requested by Sissa Ben Dahir.   Approximately 1.4757395×10^{14} kilograms

c. In a recent year, a total of 6.5×10^8 metric tons of wheat were produced in the world. At this level, how many years, to the nearest year, of wheat production would be required to fill the request of Sissa Ben Dahir? One metric ton equals 1000 kilograms.   227 years

LOGARITHMIC FUNCTIONS AND THEIR APPLICATIONS

SECTION 4.3

- LOGARITHMIC FUNCTIONS
- GRAPHS OF LOGARITHMIC FUNCTIONS
- DOMAINS OF LOGARITHMIC FUNCTIONS
- COMMON AND NATURAL LOGARITHMS
- APPLICATIONS OF LOGARITHMIC FUNCTIONS

● LOGARITHMIC FUNCTIONS

Every exponential function of the form $g(x) = b^x$ is a one-to-one function and therefore has an inverse function. Sometimes we can determine the inverse of a function represented by an equation by interchanging the variables of its equation and then solving for the dependent variable. If we attempt to use this procedure for $g(x) = b^x$, we obtain

$$g(x) = b^x$$
$$y = b^x$$
$$x = b^y \qquad \text{• Interchange the variables.}$$

None of our previous methods can be used to solve the equation $x = b^y$ for the exponent y. Thus we need to develop a new procedure. One method would be to merely write

$$y = \text{the power of } b \text{ that produces } x$$

Although this would work, it is not very concise. We need a compact notation to represent "y is the power of b that produces x." This more compact notation is given in the following definition.

MATH MATTERS

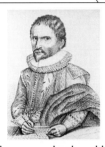

Logarithms were developed by John Napier (1550–1617) as a means of simplifying the calculations of astronomers. One of his ideas was to devise a method by which the product of two numbers could be determined by performing an addition.

Definition of a Logarithm and a Logarithmic Function

If $x > 0$ and b is a positive constant ($b \neq 1$), then

$$y = \log_b x \qquad \text{if and only if} \qquad b^y = x$$

The notation $\log_b x$ is read "the **logarithm** (or log) base b of x." The function defined by $f(x) = \log_b x$ is a **logarithmic function** with base b. This function is the inverse of the exponential function $g(x) = b^x$.

It is essential to remember that $f(x) = \log_b x$ is the inverse function of $g(x) = b^x$. Because these functions are inverses and because functions that are inverses have the property that $f(g(x)) = x$ and $g(f(x)) = x$, we have the following important relationships.

Composition of Logarithmic and Exponential Functions

Let $g(x) = b^x$ and $f(x) = \log_b x$ ($x > 0, b > 0, b \neq 1$). Then

$$g(f(x)) = b^{\log_b x} = x \qquad \text{and} \qquad f(g(x)) = \log_b b^x = x$$

As an example of these relationships, let $g(x) = 2^x$ and $f(x) = \log_2 x$. Then

$$2^{\log_2 x} = x \qquad \text{and} \qquad \log_2 2^x = x$$

The equations

$$y = \log_b x \qquad \text{and} \qquad b^y = x$$

are different ways of expressing the same concept.

Exponential Form and Logarithmic Form

The **exponential form** of $y = \log_b x$ is $b^y = x$.

The **logarithmic form** of $b^y = x$ is $y = \log_b x$.

take note

The notation $\log_b x$ replaces the phrase "the power of b that produces x." For instance, "3 is the power of 2 that produces 8" is abbreviated $3 = \log_2 8$. In your work with logarithms, remember that a logarithm is an *exponent*.

These concepts are illustrated in the next two examples.

Alternative to Example 1
Write $4 = \log_3 81$ in its exponential form.
- $3^4 = 81$

EXAMPLE 1   **Change from Logarithmic to Exponential Form**

Write each equation in its exponential form.

a. $3 = \log_2 8$ b. $2 = \log_{10}(x + 5)$ c. $\log_e x = 4$ d. $\log_b b^3 = 3$

Solution

Use the definition $y = \log_b x$ if and only if $b^y = x$.

┌─── **Logarithms are exponents.** ───┐
a. $3 = \log_2 8$ if and only if $2^3 = 8$
└──────── **Base** ────────┘

b. $2 = \log_{10}(x + 5)$ if and only if $10^2 = x + 5$.

c. $\log_e x = 4$ if and only if $e^4 = x$.

d. $\log_b b^3 = 3$ if and only if $b^3 = b^3$.

▶ **TRY EXERCISE 4, PAGE 391**

Alternative to Example 2
Write $5^4 = 625$ in its logarithmic form.
- $4 = \log_5 625$

EXAMPLE 2   **Change from Exponential to Logarithmic Form**

Write each equation in its logarithmic form.

a. $3^2 = 9$ b. $5^3 = x$ c. $a^b = c$ d. $b^{\log_b 5} = 5$

Solution

The logarithmic form of $b^y = x$ is $y = \log_b x$.

┌─── **Exponent** ───┐
a. $3^2 = 9$ if and only if $2 = \log_3 9$
└──────── **Base** ────────┘

b. $5^3 = x$ if and only if $3 = \log_5 x$.

c. $a^b = c$ if and only if $b = \log_a c$.

d. $b^{\log_b 5} = 5$ if and only if $\log_b 5 = \log_b 5$.

▶ **TRY EXERCISE 12, PAGE 391**

The definition of a logarithm and the definition of inverse functions can be used to establish many properties of logarithms. For instance:

- $\log_b b = 1$ because $b = b^1$.
- $\log_b 1 = 0$ because $1 = b^0$.
- $\log_b(b^x) = x$ because $b^x = b^x$.
- $b^{\log_b x} = x$ because $f(x) = \log_b x$ and $g(x) = b^x$ are inverse functions. Thus $g[f(x)] = x$.

We will refer to the preceding properties as the *basic logarithmic properties*.

Basic Logarithmic Properties

1. $\log_b b = 1$ **2.** $\log_b 1 = 0$ **3.** $\log_b(b^x) = x$ **4.** $b^{\log_b x} = x$

Alternative to Example 3
Evaluate each of the following.
a. $\log_2 1$ **b.** $\log_8 8$
c. $5^{\log_5 9}$ **d.** $\log_3(3^5)$
● **a.** 0 **b.** 1 **c.** 9 **d.** 5

EXAMPLE 3   Apply the Basic Logarithmic Properties

Evaluate each of the following logarithms.

a. $\log_8 1$ **b.** $\log_5 5$ **c.** $\log_2(2^4)$ **d.** $3^{\log_3 7}$

Solution

a. By Property 2, $\log_8 1 = 0$.

b. By Property 1, $\log_5 5 = 1$.

c. By Property 3, $\log_2(2^4) = 4$.

d. By Property 4, $3^{\log_3 7} = 7$.

▶ **TRY EXERCISE 28, PAGE 391**

Some logarithms can be evaluated just by remembering that a logarithm is an exponent. For instance, $\log_5 25$ equals 2 because the base 5 raised to the second power equals 25.

● $\log_{10} 100 = 2$ because $10^2 = 100$.

● $\log_4 64 = 3$ because $4^3 = 64$.

● $\log_7 \dfrac{1}{49} = -2$ because $7^{-2} = \dfrac{1}{7^2} = \dfrac{1}{49}$.

❓ **QUESTION** What is the value of $\log_5 625$?

● GRAPHS OF LOGARITHMIC FUNCTIONS

Because $f(x) = \log_b x$ is the inverse function of $g(x) = b^x$, the graph of f is a reflection of the graph of g across the line given by $y = x$. The graph of $g(x) = 2^x$ is shown in **Figure 4.25**. **Table 4.7** below shows some of the ordered pairs on the graph of g.

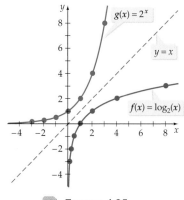
P **FIGURE 4.25**

TABLE 4.7

x	−3	−2	−1	0	1	2	3
$g(x) = 2^x$	$\dfrac{1}{8}$	$\dfrac{1}{4}$	$\dfrac{1}{2}$	1	2	4	8

❓ **ANSWER** $\log_5 625 = 4$ because $5^4 = 625$.

The graph of the inverse of g, which is $f(x) = \log_2 x$, is also shown in **Figure 4.25.** Some of the ordered pairs of f are shown in **Table 4.8.** Note that if (x, y) is a point on the graph of g, then (y, x) is a point on the graph of f. Also notice that the graph of f is a reflection of the graph of g across the line given by $y = x$.

TABLE 4.8

x	$\frac{1}{8}$	$\frac{1}{4}$	$\frac{1}{2}$	1	2	4	8
$f(x) = \log_2 x$	-3	-2	-1	0	1	2	3

The graph of a logarithmic function can be drawn by first rewriting the function in its exponential form. This procedure is illustrated in Example 4.

Alternative to Example 4
Exercise 34, page 391.

EXAMPLE 4   **Graph a Logarithmic Function**

Graph $f(x) = \log_3 x$.

Solution

To graph $f(x) = \log_3 x$, consider the equivalent exponential equation $x = 3^y$. Because this equation is solved for x, choose values of y and calculate the corresponding values of x, as shown in **Table 4.9.**

TABLE 4.9

$x = 3^y$	$\frac{1}{9}$	$\frac{1}{3}$	1	3	9
y	-2	-1	0	1	2

Now plot the ordered pairs and connect the points with a smooth curve, as shown in **Figure 4.26.**

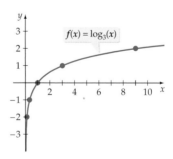

FIGURE 4.26

▶ **TRY EXERCISE 32, PAGE 391**

We can use a similar procedure to draw the graph of a logarithmic function with a fractional base. For instance, consider $y = \log_{2/3} x$. Rewriting this in expo-

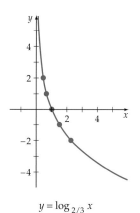

$$y = \log_{2/3} x$$

FIGURE 4.27

nential form gives us $\left(\dfrac{2}{3}\right)^y = x$. Choose values of y and calculate the corresponding x-values. See **Table 4.10.** Plot the points corresponding to the ordered pairs (x, y), and then draw a smooth curve through the points, as shown in **Figure 4.27.**

TABLE 4.10

$x = \left(\dfrac{2}{3}\right)^y$	$\left(\dfrac{2}{3}\right)^{-2} = \dfrac{9}{4}$	$\left(\dfrac{2}{3}\right)^{-1} = \dfrac{3}{2}$	$\left(\dfrac{2}{3}\right)^{0} = 1$	$\left(\dfrac{2}{3}\right)^{1} = \dfrac{2}{3}$	$\left(\dfrac{2}{3}\right)^{2} = \dfrac{4}{9}$
y	-2	-1	0	1	2

P **Properties of $f(x) = \log_b x$**

For all positive real numbers b, $b \neq 1$, the function $f(x) = \log_b x$ has the following properties:

1. The domain of f consists of the set of positive real numbers and its range consists of the set of all real numbers.

2. The graph of f has an x-intercept of $(1, 0)$ and passes through $(b, 1)$.

3. If $b > 1$, f is an increasing function and its graph is asymptotic to the negative y-axis. [As $x \to \infty$, $f(x) \to \infty$, and as $x \to 0$ from the right, $f(x) \to -\infty$.] See **Figure 4.28a.**

4. If $0 < b < 1$, f is a decreasing function and its graph is asymptotic to the positive y-axis. [As $x \to \infty$, $f(x) \to -\infty$, and as $x \to 0$ from the right, $f(x) \to \infty$.] See **Figure 4.28b.**

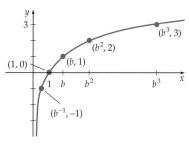

a. $f(x) = \log_b x$, $b > 1$

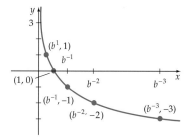

b. $f(x) = \log_b x$, $0 < b < 1$

P **FIGURE 4.28**

● **DOMAINS OF LOGARITHMIC FUNCTIONS**

The function $f(x) = \log_b x$ has as its domain the set of positive real numbers. The function $f(x) = \log_b(g(x))$ has as its domain the set of all x for which $g(x) > 0$. To determine the domain of a function such as $f(x) = \log_b(g(x))$, we must determine the values of x that make $g(x)$ positive. This process is illustrated in Example 5.

Alternative to Example 5
Exercise 44, page 391.

EXAMPLE 5   Find the Domain of a Logarithmic Function

Find the domain of each of the following logarithmic functions.

a. $f(x) = \log_6(x - 3)$ **b.** $F(x) = \log_2|x + 2|$ **c.** $R(x) = \log_5\left(\dfrac{x}{8 - x}\right)$

Solution

a. Solving $(x - 3) > 0$ for x gives us $x > 3$. The domain of f consists of all real numbers greater than 3. In interval notation the domain is $(3, \infty)$.

b. The solution set of $|x + 2| > 0$ consists of all real numbers x except $x = -2$. The domain of F consists of all real numbers $x \ne -2$. In interval notation the domain is $(-\infty, -2) \cup (-2, \infty)$.

c. Solving $\left(\dfrac{x}{8 - x}\right) > 0$ yields the set of all real numbers x between 0 and 8. The domain of R is all real numbers x such that $0 < x < 8$. In interval notation the domain is $(0, 8)$.

▶ **TRY EXERCISE 40, PAGE 391**

Some logarithmic functions can be graphed by using horizontal and/or vertical translations of a previously drawn graph.

Alternative to Example 6
Exercise 52, page 391.

EXAMPLE 6   Use Translations to Graph Logarithmic Functions

Graph: **a.** $f(x) = \log_4(x + 3)$ **b.** $f(x) = \log_4 x + 3$

Solution

a. The graph of $f(x) = \log_4(x + 3)$ can be obtained by shifting the graph of $g(x) = \log_4 x$ to the left 3 units. See **Figure 4.29**. Note that the domain of f consists of all real numbers x greater than -3 because $x + 3 > 0$ for $x > -3$. The graph of f is asymptotic to the vertical line $x = -3$.

b. The graph of $f(x) = \log_4 x + 3$ can be obtained by shifting the graph of $g(x) = \log_4 x$ upward 3 units. See **Figure 4.30**.

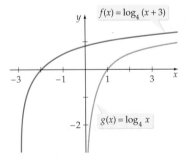

FIGURE 4.29

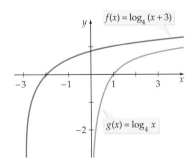

FIGURE 4.30

▶ **TRY EXERCISE 50, PAGE 391**

• COMMON AND NATURAL LOGARITHMS

Two of the most frequently used logarithmic functions are *common logarithms,* which have base 10, and *natural logarithms,* which have base e (the base of the natural exponential function).

Definition of Common and Natural Logarithms

The function defined by $f(x) = \log_{10} x$ is called the **common logarithmic function.** It is customarily written without stating the base as $f(x) = \log x$.

The function defined by $f(x) = \log_e x$ is called the **natural logarithmic function.** It is customarily written as $f(x) = \ln x$.

Most scientific or graphing calculators have a $\boxed{\text{LOG}}$ key for evaluating common logarithms and an $\boxed{\text{LN}}$ key to evaluate natural logarithms. For instance, using a graphing calculator,

$$\log 24 \approx 1.3802112 \qquad \text{and} \qquad \ln 81 \approx 4.3944492$$

The graphs of $f(x) = \log x$ and $f(x) = \ln x$ can be drawn using the same techniques we used to draw the graphs in the preceding examples. However, these graphs also can be produced with a graphing calculator by entering $\log x$ and $\ln x$ into the Y= menu. See **Figure 4.31** and **Figure 4.32.**

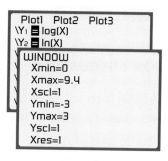

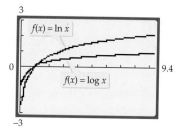

| **FIGURE 4.31** | **FIGURE 4.32** |

Observe that each graph passes through $(1, 0)$. Also note that as $x \to 0$ from the right, the functional values $f(x) \to -\infty$. Thus the y-axis is a vertical asymptote for each of the graphs. The domain of both $f(x) = \log x$ and $f(x) = \ln x$ is the set of positive real numbers. Each of these functions has a range consisting of the set of real numbers.

• APPLICATIONS OF LOGARITHMIC FUNCTIONS

Many applications can be modeled by logarithmic functions.

Alternative to Example 7
Exercise 74, page 392.

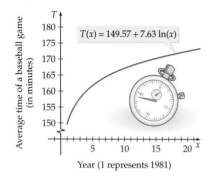

Year (1 represents 1981)

$T(x) = 149.57 + 7.63 \ln(x)$

MATH MATTERS

Although logarithms were originally developed to assist with computations, logarithmic functions have a much broader use today. They are often used in such disciplines as geology, acoustics, chemistry, physics, and economics, to name a few.

EXAMPLE 7 Average Time of a Major League Baseball Game

From 1981 to 1999, the average time of a major league baseball game tended to increase each year. If the year 1981 is represented by $x = 1$, then the function

$$T(x) = 149.57 + 7.63 \ln x$$

approximates the average time T, in minutes, of a major league baseball game for the years 1981 to 1999—that is, for $x = 1$ to $x = 19$.

a. Use the function T to determine the average time of a major league baseball game during the 1981 season and during the 1999 season.

b. By how much did the average time of a major league baseball game increase during the years 1981 to 1999?

Solution

a. The year 1981 is represented by $x = 1$ and the year 1999 by $x = 19$.

$$T(1) = 149.57 + 7.63 \ln(1) = 149.57$$

In 1981 the average time of a baseball game was about 149.57 minutes.

$$T(19) = 149.57 + 7.63 \ln(19) \approx 172.04$$

In 1999 the average time of a baseball game was about 172.04 minutes.

b. $T(19) - T(1) \approx 172.04 - 149.57 = 22.47$. During the years 1981 to 1999, the average time of a baseball game increased by about 22.47 minutes.

▶ **TRY EXERCISE 70, PAGE 392**

 TOPICS FOR DISCUSSION

1. If $m > n$, must $\log_b m > \log_b n$?

2. For what values of x is $\ln x > \log x$?

3. What is the domain of $f(x) = \log(x^2 + 1)$? Explain why the graph of f does not have a vertical asymptote.

4. The subtraction $3 - 5$ does not have an answer if we require that the answer be positive. Keep this idea in mind as you work the rest of this exercise.

   Press the $\boxed{\text{MODE}}$ key of a TI-83 graphing calculator, and choose "Real" from the menu. Now use the calculator to evaluate $\log(-2)$. What output is given by the calculator? Press the $\boxed{\text{MODE}}$ key, and choose "a + bi" from the menu. Now use the calculator to evaluate $\log(-2)$. What output is given by the calculator? Write a sentence or two that explain why the output is different for these two evaluations.

EXERCISE SET 4.3

—Suggested Assignment: Exercises 1–73, odd; 81–86, all.
—Answer graphs to Exercises 31–38, 49–56, and 59–68 are on pages AA15–AA17.

In Exercises 1 to 10, change each equation to its exponential form.

1. $\log 10 = 1$ $10^1 = 10$

2. $\log 10{,}000 = 4$ $10^4 = 10{,}000$

3. $\log_8 64 = 2$ $8^2 = 64$

▶ **4.** $\log_4 64 = 3$ $4^3 = 64$

5. $\log_7 x = 0$ $7^0 = x$

6. $\log_3 \dfrac{1}{81} = -4$ $3^{-4} = \dfrac{1}{81}$

7. $\ln x = 4$ $e^4 = x$

8. $\ln e^2 = 2$ $e^2 = e^2$

9. $\ln 1 = 0$ $e^0 = 1$

10. $\ln x = -3$ $e^{-3} = x$

In Exercises 11 to 20, change each equation to its logarithmic form. Assume $y > 0$ and $b > 0$.

11. $3^2 = 9$ $\log_3 9 = 2$

▶ **12.** $5^3 = 125$ $\log_5 125 = 3$

13. $4^{-2} = \dfrac{1}{16}$ $\log_4 \dfrac{1}{16} = -2$

14. $10^0 = 1$ $\log 1 = 0$

15. $b^x = y$ $\log_b y = x$

16. $2^x = y$ $\log_2 y = x$

17. $y = e^x$ $\ln y = x$

18. $5^1 = 5$ $\log_5 5 = 1$

19. $100 = 10^2$ $\log 100 = 2$

20. $2^{-4} = \dfrac{1}{16}$ $\log_2 \dfrac{1}{16} = -4$

In Exercises 21 to 30, evaluate each logarithm. Do not use a calculator.

21. $\log_4 16$ 2

22. $\log_{3/2} \dfrac{8}{27}$ -3

23. $\log_3 \dfrac{1}{243}$ -5

24. $\log_b 1$ 0

25. $\ln e^3$ 3

26. $\log_b b$ 1

27. $\log \dfrac{1}{100}$ -2

▶ **28.** $\log 1{,}000{,}000$ 6

29. $\log_{0.5} 16$ -4

30. $\log_{0.3} \dfrac{100}{9}$ -2

In Exercises 31 to 38, graph each function by using its exponential form.

31. $f(x) = \log_4 x$

▶ **32.** $f(x) = \log_6 x$

33. $f(x) = \log_{12} x$

34. $f(x) = \log_8 x$

35. $f(x) = \log_{1/2} x$

36. $f(x) = \log_{1/4} x$

37. $f(x) = \log_{5/2} x$

38. $f(x) = \log_{7/3} x$

In Exercises 39 to 48, find the domain of the function. Write the domains using interval notation.

39. $f(x) = \log_5(x - 3)$
$(3, \infty)$

▶ **40.** $k(x) = \log_4(5 - x)$
$(-\infty, 5)$

41. $k(x) = \log_{2/3}(11 - x)$
$(-\infty, 11)$

42. $H(x) = \log_{1/4}(x^2 + 1)$
$(-\infty, \infty)$

43. $P(x) = \ln(x^2 - 4)$
$(-\infty, -2) \cup (2, \infty)$

44. $J(x) = \ln\left(\dfrac{x - 3}{x}\right)$
$(-\infty, 0) \cup (3, \infty)$

45. $h(x) = \ln\left(\dfrac{x^2}{x - 4}\right)$
$(4, \infty)$

46. $R(x) = \ln(x^4 - x^2)$
$(-\infty, -1) \cup (1, \infty)$

47. $N(x) = \log_2(x^3 - x)$
$(-1, 0) \cup (1, \infty)$

48. $s(x) = \log_7(x^2 + 7x + 10)$
$(-\infty, -5) \cup (-2, \infty)$

In Exercises 49 to 56, use translations of the graphs in Exercises 31 to 38 to produce the graph of the given function.

49. $f(x) = \log_4(x - 3)$

▶ **50.** $f(x) = \log_6(x + 3)$

51. $f(x) = \log_{12} x + 2$

52. $f(x) = \log_8 x - 4$

53. $f(x) = 3 + \log_{1/2} x$

54. $f(x) = 2 + \log_{1/4} x$

55. $f(x) = 1 + \log_{5/2}(x - 4)$

56. $f(x) = \log_{7/3}(x - 3) - 1$

57. Examine the following four functions and the graphs labeled **a**, **b**, **c**, and **d**. Determine which graph is the graph of each function.

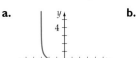

$f(x) = \log_5(x - 2) \qquad g(x) = 2 + \log_5 x$

$h(x) = \log_5(-x) \qquad k(x) = -\log_5(x + 3)$

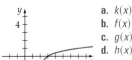

a.   b.

a. $k(x)$
b. $f(x)$
c. $g(x)$
d. $h(x)$

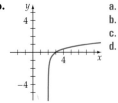

c.   d.

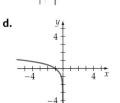

58. Examine the following four functions and the graphs labeled **a, b, c,** and **d.** Determine which graph is the graph of each function.

$$f(x) = \ln x + 3 \qquad g(x) = \ln(x - 3)$$
$$h(x) = \ln(3 - x) \qquad k(x) = -\ln(-x)$$

a.
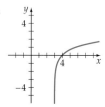

b.
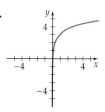

a. $k(x)$
b. $h(x)$
c. $g(x)$
d. $f(x)$

c.

d.

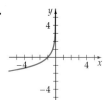

In Exercises 59 to 68, use a graphing utility to graph the function.

59. $f(x) = -2 \ln x$

60. $f(x) = -\log x$

61. $f(x) = |\ln x|$

62. $f(x) = \ln |x|$

63. $f(x) = \log \sqrt[3]{x}$

64. $f(x) = \ln \sqrt{x}$

65. $f(x) = \log(x + 10)$

66. $f(x) = \ln(x + 3)$

67. $f(x) = 3 \log |2x + 10|$

68. $f(x) = \frac{1}{2} \ln |x - 4|$

69. **MONEY MARKET RATES** The function

$$r(t) = 0.69607 + 0.60781 \ln t$$

gives the annual interest rate r, as a percent, a bank will pay on its money market accounts, where t is the term (the time the money is invested) in months.

a. What interest rate, to the nearest tenth of a percent, will the bank pay on a money market account with a term of 9 months? 2.0%

b. What is the minimum number of complete months during which a person must invest to receive an interest rate of at least 3%? 45 months

▶ **70.** **AVERAGE TYPING SPEED** The following function models the average typing speed S, in words per minute, of a student who has been typing for t months.

$$S(t) = 5 + 29 \ln(t + 1), \quad 0 \le t \le 16$$

a. What was the student's average typing speed, to the nearest word per minute, when the student first started to type? What was the student's average typing speed, to the nearest word per minute, after 3 months? 5 words/min; 45 words/min

b. Use a graph of S to determine how long, to the nearest tenth of a month, it will take the student to achieve an average typing speed of 65 words per minute. 6.9 months

71. **ADVERTISING COSTS AND SALES** The function

$$N(x) = 2750 + 180 \ln\left(\frac{x}{1000} + 1\right)$$

models the relationship between the dollar amount x spent on advertising a product and the number of units N that a company can sell.

a. Find the number of units that will be sold with advertising expenditures of $20,000, $40,000, and $60,000. 3298 units; 3418 units; 3490 units

b. How many units will be sold if the company does not pay to advertise the product? 2750 units

In anesthesiology it is necessary to accurately estimate the body surface area of a patient. One formula for estimating body surface area (*BSA*) was developed by Edith Boyd (University of Minnesota Press, 1935). Her formula for the *BSA* (in square meters) of a patient of height H (in centimeters) and weight W (in grams) is

$$BSA = 0.0003207 \cdot H^{0.3} \cdot W^{(0.7285 - 0.0188 \log W)}$$

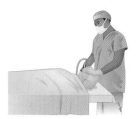

MEDICINE In Exercises 72 and 73, use Boyd's formula to estimate the body surface area of a patient with the given weight and height. Round to the nearest hundredth of a square meter.

72. $W = 110$ pounds (49,895.2 grams); $H = 5$ feet 4 inches (162.56 centimeters) 1.50 m²

73. $W = 180$ pounds (81,646.6 grams); $H = 6$ feet 1 inch (185.42 centimeters) 2.05 m²

74. **ASTRONOMY** Astronomers measure the apparent brightness of a star by a unit called the **apparent magnitude.** This unit was created in the second century B.C. when the Greek astronomer Hipparchus classified the relative brightness of several stars. In his list he assigned the number 1 to the stars that appeared to be the brightest (Sirius, Vega, and Deneb). They are first-magnitude stars. Hipparchus assigned the number 2 to all the stars in the Big Dipper. They are second-magnitude stars. The following table shows the relationship between a star's brightness relative to a first-magnitude star and the star's apparent magnitude. Notice from the table that a first-magnitude star appears in the sky to be about 2.51 times as bright as a second-magnitude star.

Brightness relative to a first-magnitude star x	Apparent magnitude $M(x)$
1	1
$\dfrac{1}{2.51}$	2
$\dfrac{1}{6.31} \approx \dfrac{1}{2.51^2}$	3
$\dfrac{1}{15.85} \approx \dfrac{1}{2.51^3}$	4
$\dfrac{1}{39.82} \approx \dfrac{1}{2.51^4}$	5
$\dfrac{1}{100} \approx \dfrac{1}{2.51^5}$	6

The following logarithmic function gives the apparent magnitude $M(x)$ of a star as a function of its brightness x.

$$M(x) = -2.51 \log x + 1, \quad 0 < x \le 1$$

a. Use $M(x)$ to find the apparent magnitude of a star that is $\dfrac{1}{10}$ as bright as a first-magnitude star. Round to the nearest hundredth. 3.51

b. Find the approximate apparent magnitude of a star that is $\dfrac{1}{400}$ as bright as a first-magnitude star. Round to the nearest hundredth. 7.53

c. Which star appears brighter: a star with an apparent magnitude of 12 or a star with an apparent magnitude of 15? apparent magnitude of 12

d. Is $M(x)$ an increasing function or a decreasing function? decreasing function

75. NUMBER OF DIGITS IN b^x An engineer has determined that the number of digits N in the expansion of b^x, where both b and x are positive integers, is $N = \text{int}(x \log b) + 1$, where $\text{int}(x \log b)$ denotes the greatest integer of $x \log b$. (*Note:* The greatest integer of the real number x is x if x is an integer and is the largest integer less than x if x is not an integer. For example, the greatest integer of 5 is 5 and the greatest integer of 7.8 is 7.)

a. Because $2^{10} = 1024$, we know that 2^{10} has four digits. Use the equation $N = \text{int}(x \log b) + 1$ to verify this result. Answers will vary.

b. Find the number of digits in 3^{200}. 96 digits

c. Find the number of digits in 7^{4005}. 3385 digits

d. The largest known prime number as of November 17, 2003 was $2^{20996011} - 1$. Find the number of digits in this prime number. (*Hint:* Because $2^{20996011}$ is not a power of 10, both $2^{20996011}$ and $2^{20996011} - 1$ have the same number of digits.) 6,320,430 digits

76. NUMBER OF DIGITS IN $9^{(9^9)}$ A science teacher has offered 10 points extra credit to any student who will write out all the digits in the expansion of $9^{(9^9)}$.

a. Use the formula from Exercise 75 to determine the number of digits in this number. 369,693,100 digits

b. Assume that you can write 1000 digits per page and that 500 pages of paper are in a ream of paper. How many reams of paper, to the nearest tenth of a ream, are required to write out the expansion of $9^{(9^9)}$? Assume that you write on only one side of each page. ≈ 739.4 reams

CONNECTING CONCEPTS

77. Use a graphing utility to graph $f(x) = \dfrac{e^x - e^{-x}}{2}$ and $g(x) = \ln\left(x + \sqrt{x^2 + 1}\right)$ on the same screen. Use a square viewing window. What appears to be the relationship between f and g? f and g are inverse functions.

78. Use a graphing utility to graph $f(x) = \dfrac{e^x + e^{-x}}{2}$, for $x \ge 0$, and $g(x) = \ln\left(x + \sqrt{x^2 - 1}\right)$, for $x \ge 1$, on the same screen. Use a square viewing window. What appears to be the relationship between f and g? f and g are inverse functions.

79. The functions $f(x) = \dfrac{e^x - e^{-x}}{e^x + e^{-x}}$ and $g(x) = \dfrac{1}{2} \ln \dfrac{1 + x}{1 - x}$ are inverse functions. The domain of f is the set of all real numbers. The domain of g is $\{x \mid -1 < x < 1\}$. Use this information to determine the range of f and the range of g. range of f: $\{y \mid -1 < y < 1\}$; range of g: all real numbers

80. Use a graph of $f(x) = \dfrac{2}{e^x + e^{-x}}$ to determine the domain and the range of f. domain: all real numbers; range: $\{y \mid 0 < y \le 1\}$

PREPARE FOR SECTION 4.4

In Exercises 81 to 86, use a calculator to compare each of the given expressions.

81. $\log 3 + \log 2$; $\log 6$ [4.2] ≈ 0.77815 for each expression

82. $\ln 8 - \ln 3$; $\ln\left(\dfrac{8}{3}\right)$ [4.2] ≈ 0.98083 for each expression

83. $3 \log 4$; $\log(4^3)$ [4.2] ≈ 1.80618 for each expression

84. $2 \ln 5$; $\ln(5^2)$ [4.2] ≈ 3.21888 for each expression

85. $\ln 5$; $\dfrac{\log 5}{\log e}$ [4.2] ≈ 1.60944 for each expression

86. $\log 8$; $\dfrac{\ln 8}{\ln 10}$ [4.2] ≈ 0.90309 for each expression

PROJECTS

1. **BENFORD'S LAW** The authors of this text know some interesting details about your finances. For instance, of the last 150 checks you have written, about 30% are for amounts that start with the number 1. Also, you have written about 3 times as many checks for amounts that start with the number 2 than you have for amounts that start with the number 7.

We are sure of these results because of a mathematical formula known as **Benford's Law.** This law was first discovered by the mathematician Simon Newcomb in 1881 and then rediscovered by the physicist Frank Benford in 1938. Benford's Law states that the probability P that the first digit of a number selected from a wide range of numbers is d is given by

$$P(d) = \log\left(1 + \frac{1}{d}\right)$$

a. Use Benford's Law to complete the table below and the bar graph at the top of the next column.

d	$P(d) = \log\left(1 + \dfrac{1}{d}\right)$
1	0.301
2	0.176
3	0.125
4	0.097
5	0.079
6	0.067
7	0.058
8	0.051
9	0.046

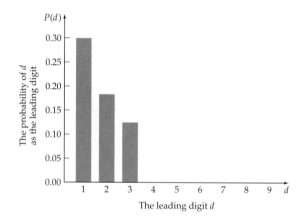

The probability of d as the leading digit — The leading digit d

Benford's Law applies to most data with a wide range. For instance, it applies to

- the populations of the cities in the U.S.
- the numbers of dollars in the savings accounts at your local bank.
- the number of miles driven during a month by each person in a state. See the *Instructor's Solution Manual.*

b. Use the table in part **a.** to find the probability that in a U.S. city selected at random, the number of telephones in that city will be a number starting with 6. about 0.067, or 6.7%

c. Use the table in part **a.** to estimate how many times as many purchases you have made for dollar amounts that start with a 1 than for dollar amounts that start with a 9. about 6.54 times as many

d. ✎ Explain why Benford's Law would not apply to the set of telephone numbers of the people living in a small city such as Le Mars, Iowa. Telephone numbers in many small towns start with the same digit.

e. Explain why Benford's Law would not apply to the set of all the ages, in years, of students at a local high school. Most high school students are teenagers.

AN APPLICATION OF BENFORD'S LAW Benford's Law has been used to identify fraudulent accountants. In most cases these accountants are unaware of Benford's Law and have replaced valid numbers with numbers selected at random. Their numbers do not conform to Benford's Law. Hence an audit is warranted.

SECTION 4.4

LOGARITHMS AND LOGARITHMIC SCALES

- **PROPERTIES OF LOGARITHMS**
- **CHANGE-OF-BASE FORMULA**
- **LOGARITHMIC SCALES**

PROPERTIES OF LOGARITHMS

In Section 4.3 we introduced the following basic properties of logarithms.

$$\log_b b = 1 \quad \text{and} \quad \log_b 1 = 0$$

Also, because exponential functions and logarithmic functions are inverses of each other, we observed the relationships

$$\log_b(b^x) = x \quad \text{and} \quad b^{\log_b x} = x$$

We can use the properties of exponents to establish the following additional logarithmic properties.

P | Properties of Logarithms

In the following properties, b, M, and N are positive real numbers ($b \neq 1$).

Product property	$\log_b(MN) = \log_b M + \log_b N$
Quotient property	$\log_b \dfrac{M}{N} = \log_b M - \log_b N$
Power property	$\log_b(M^p) = p \log_b M$
Logarithm-of-each-side property	$M = N$ implies $\log_b M = \log_b N$
One-to-one property	$\log_b M = \log_b N$ implies $M = N$

> **take note**
>
> Pay close attention to these properties. Note that
> $$\log_b(MN) \neq \log_b M \cdot \log_b N$$
> and
> $$\log_b \frac{M}{N} \neq \frac{\log_b M}{\log_b N}$$
> Also,
> $$\log_b(M + N) \neq \log_b M + \log_b N$$
> In fact, the expression $\log_b(M + N)$ cannot be expanded at all.

? QUESTION Is it true that $\ln 5 + \ln 10 = \ln 50$?

The above properties of logarithms are often used to rewrite logarithmic expressions in an equivalent form.

INSTRUCTOR NOTE
Stress the importance of the properties of logarithms. An understanding of these properties is essential to the study and use of logarithms.

? ANSWER Yes. By the product property, $\ln 5 + \ln 10 = \ln(5 \cdot 10)$.

Alternative to Example 1
Use the properties of logarithms to express

$$\log_2\left(\frac{a^3 b^2}{\sqrt{c}}\right)$$

in terms of logarithms of a, b, and c.

● $3 \log_2 a + 2 \log_2 b - \dfrac{1}{2} \log_2 c$

EXAMPLE 1   Rewrite Logarithmic Expressions

Use the properties of logarithms to express the following logarithms in terms of logarithms of x, y, and z.

a. $\log_5(xy^2)$ b. $\log_b \dfrac{2\sqrt{y}}{z^5}$

Solution

a. $\log_5(xy^2) = \log_5 x + \log_5 y^2$ • **Product property**

$\qquad\qquad = \log_5 x + 2 \log_5 y$ • **Power property**

b. $\log_b \dfrac{2\sqrt{y}}{z^5} = \log_b\left(2\sqrt{y}\right) - \log_b z^5$ • **Quotient property**

$\qquad\qquad = \log_b 2 + \log_b \sqrt{y} - \log_b z^5$ • **Product property**

$\qquad\qquad = \log_b 2 + \log_b y^{1/2} - \log_b z^5$ • **Replace $\sqrt{y}$ with $y^{1/2}$.**

$\qquad\qquad = \log_b 2 + \dfrac{1}{2} \log_b y - 5 \log_b z$ • **Power property**

▶ **TRY EXERCISE 2, PAGE 403**

The properties of logarithms are also used to rewrite expressions that involve several logarithms as a single logarithm.

Alternative to Example 2
Use the properties of logarithms to rewrite

$$5 \log_4(x - 7) - 3 \log_4 x$$

as a single logarithm with a coefficient of 1.

● $\log_4 \dfrac{(x - 7)^5}{x^3}$

EXAMPLE 2   Rewrite Logarithmic Expressions

Use the properties of logarithms to rewrite each expression as a single logarithm with a coefficient of 1.

a. $2 \log_b x + \dfrac{1}{2} \log_b(x + 4)$ b. $4 \log_3(x + 2) - 3 \log_3(x - 5)$

Solution

a. $2 \log_b x + \dfrac{1}{2} \log_b(x + 4)$

$\qquad = \log_b x^2 + \log_b(x + 4)^{1/2}$ • **Power property**

$\qquad = \log_b[x^2(x + 4)^{1/2}]$ • **Product property**

$\qquad = \log_b\left(x^2\sqrt{x + 4}\right)$

b. $4 \log_3(x + 2) - 3 \log_3(x - 5)$

$\qquad = \log_3(x + 2)^4 - \log_3(x - 5)^3$ • **Power property**

$\qquad = \log_3 \dfrac{(x + 2)^4}{(x - 5)^3}$ • **Quotient property**

▶ **TRY EXERCISE 10, PAGE 403**

● CHANGE-OF-BASE FORMULA

Recall that to determine the value of y in $\log_3 81 = y$, we are basically asking, "What power of 3 is equal to 81?" Because $3^4 = 81$, we have $\log_3 81 = 4$. Now suppose that we need to determine the value of $\log_3 50$. In this case we need to find the power of 3 that produces 50. Because $3^3 = 27$ and $3^4 = 81$, the value we are seeking is somewhere between 3 and 4. The following procedure can be used to produce an estimate of $\log_3 50$.

The exponential form of $\log_3 50 = y$ is $3^y = 50$. Applying logarithmic properties gives us

$$3^y = 50$$

$$\ln 3^y = \ln 50 \qquad \bullet \text{ Logarithm-of-each-side property}$$

$$y \ln 3 = \ln 50 \qquad \bullet \text{ Power property}$$

$$y = \frac{\ln 50}{\ln 3} \approx 3.56088 \qquad \bullet \text{ Solve for } y.$$

Thus $\log_3 50 \approx 3.56088$. In the above procedure we could just as well have used logarithms of any base and arrived at the same value. Thus any logarithm can be expressed in terms of logarithms of any base we wish. This general result is summarized in the following formula.

(P) Change-of-Base Formula

If x, a, and b are positive real numbers with $a \neq 1$ and $b \neq 1$, then

$$\log_b x = \frac{\log_a x}{\log_a b}$$

Because most calculators use only common logarithms ($a = 10$) or natural logarithms ($a = e$), the change-of-base formula is used most often in the following form.

If x and b are positive real numbers and $b \neq 1$, then

$$\log_b x = \frac{\log x}{\log b} = \frac{\ln x}{\ln b}$$

Alternative to Example 3

Evaluate $\log_8 75$. Round to the nearest ten thousandth.

⊙ **2.0763**

---

take note

If common logarithms had been used for the calculation in Example 3a., the final result would be the same.

$$\log_3 18 = \frac{\log 18}{\log 3} \approx 2.63093$$

EXAMPLE 3 **Use the Change-of-Base Formula**

Evaluate each logarithm. Round to the nearest hundred thousandth.

a. $\log_3 18$ **b.** $\log_{12} 400$

Solution

To approximate these logarithms, we may use the change-of-base formula with $a = 10$ or $a = e$. For this example we choose to use the change-of-base formula with $a = e$. That is, we will evaluate these logarithms by using the $\boxed{\text{LN}}$ key on a scientific or graphing calculator.

a. $\log_3 18 = \frac{\ln 18}{\ln 3} \approx 2.63093$ **b.** $\log_{12} 400 = \frac{\ln 400}{\ln 12} \approx 2.41114$

▶ **TRY EXERCISE 16, PAGE 404**

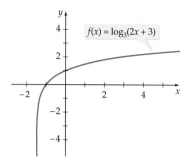

FIGURE 4.33

Alternative to Example 4
Exercise 26, page 404.

The change-of-base formula and a graphing calculator can be used to graph logarithmic functions that have a base other than 10 or e. For instance, to graph $f(x) = \log_3(2x + 3)$, we rewrite the function in terms of base 10 or base e. Using base 10 logarithms, we have $f(x) = \log_3(2x + 3) = \dfrac{\log(2x + 3)}{\log 3}$. The graph is shown in **Figure 4.33**.

EXAMPLE 4   Use the Change-of-Base Formula to Graph a Logarithmic Function

Graph $f(x) = \log_2|x - 3|$.

Solution

Rewrite f using the change-of-base formula. We will use the natural logarithm function; however, the common logarithm function could be used instead.

$$f(x) = \log_2|x - 3| = \frac{\ln|x - 3|}{\ln 2}$$

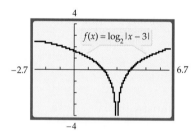

• Enter $\dfrac{\ln|x - 3|}{\ln 2}$ into Y1. Note that the domain of $f(x) = \log_2|x - 3|$ is all real numbers except 3, because $|x - 3| = 0$ when $x = 3$ and $|x - 3|$ is positive for all other values of x.

▶ **TRY EXERCISE 24, PAGE 404**

● **LOGARITHMIC SCALES**

Logarithmic functions are often used to scale very large (or very small) numbers into numbers that are easier to comprehend. For instance, the *Richter scale* magnitude of an earthquake uses a logarithmic function to convert the intensity of the earthquake's shock waves I into a number M, which for most earthquakes is in the range of 0 to 10. The intensity I of an earthquake is often given in terms of the constant I_0, where I_0 is the intensity of the smallest earthquake (called a **zero-level earthquake**) that can be measured on a seismograph near the earthquake's epicenter. The following formula is used to compute the Richter scale magnitude of an earthquake.

MATH MATTERS

The Richter scale was created by the seismologist Charles F. Richter in 1935. Notice that a tenfold increase in the intensity level of an earthquake only increases the Richter scale magnitude of the earthquake by 1.

The Richter Scale Magnitude of an Earthquake

An earthquake with an intensity of I has a **Richter scale magnitude** of

$$M = \log\left(\frac{I}{I_0}\right)$$

where I_0 is the measure of the intensity of a zero-level earthquake.

Alternative to Example 5
Find the Richter scale magnitude of an
earthquake with intensity $I = 8,250,000I_0$
● **6.9**

---

take note

Notice in Example 5 that we
didn't need to know the value of I_0
to determine the Richter scale
magnitude of the quake.

EXAMPLE 5 Determine the Magnitude of an Earthquake

  Find the Richter scale magnitude (to the nearest 0.1) of the
1999 Joshua Tree, California earthquake that had an intensity
of $I = 12,589,254I_0$.

Solution

$$M = \log\left(\frac{I}{I_0}\right) = \log\left(\frac{12,589,254I_0}{I_0}\right) = \log(12,589,254) \approx 7.1$$

The 1999 Joshua Tree earthquake had a Richter scale magnitude of 7.1.

▶ **TRY EXERCISE 56, PAGE 405**

If you know the Richter scale magnitude of an earthquake, you can determine
the intensity of the earthquake.

Alternative to Example 6
Find the intensity of an earthquake
measuring 9.2 on the Richter scale.
● $\approx 1,584,893,000I_0$

EXAMPLE 6 Determine the Intensity of an Earthquake

 Find the intensity of the 1999 Taiwan earthquake, which measured 7.6
on the Richter scale.

Solution

$$\log\left(\frac{I}{I_0}\right) = 7.6$$

$$\frac{I}{I_0} = 10^{7.6}$$ • **Write in exponential form.**

$$I = 10^{7.6}I_0$$ • **Solve for I.**

$$I \approx 39,810,717I_0$$

The 1999 Taiwan earthquake had an intensity that was approximately
39,811,000 times the intensity of a zero-level earthquake.

▶ **TRY EXERCISE 58, PAGE 405**

In Example 7 we make use of the Richter scale magnitudes of two earthquakes
to compare the intensities of the earthquakes.

Alternative to Example 7
How many times more intense is an
earthquake with a Richter scale magnitude
of 8.5 than a 6.8-magnitude quake?
● ≈ 50 times

EXAMPLE 7 Compare Earthquakes

The 1960 Chile earthquake had a Richter scale magnitude of 9.5. The
1989 San Francisco earthquake had a Richter scale magnitude of 7.1.
Compare the intensities of the earthquakes.

Continued ▶

take note

The results of Example 7 show that if an earthquake has a Richter scale magnitude of M_1 and a smaller earthquake has a Richter scale magnitude of M_2, then the larger earthquake is $10^{M_1 - M_2}$ times as intense as the smaller earthquake.

Solution

Let I_1 be the intensity of the Chilean earthquake and I_2 the intensity of the San Francisco earthquake. Then

$$\log\left(\frac{I_1}{I_0}\right) = 9.5 \qquad \text{and} \qquad \log\left(\frac{I_2}{I_0}\right) = 7.1$$

$$\frac{I_1}{I_0} = 10^{9.5} \qquad\qquad\qquad \frac{I_2}{I_0} = 10^{7.1}$$

$$I_1 = 10^{9.5} I_0 \qquad\qquad\qquad I_2 = 10^{7.1} I_0$$

To compare the intensities of the earthquakes, we compute the ratio I_1/I_2.

$$\frac{I_1}{I_2} = \frac{10^{9.5} I_0}{10^{7.1} I_0} = \frac{10^{9.5}}{10^{7.1}} = 10^{9.5-7.1} = 10^{2.4} \approx 251$$

The earthquake in Chile was approximately 251 times as intense as the San Francisco earthquake.

▶ **TRY EXERCISE 60, PAGE 405**

Seismologists generally determine the Richter scale magnitude of an earthquake by examining a *seismogram*. See **Figure 4.34.**

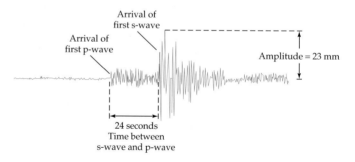

FIGURE 4.34

The magnitude of an earthquake cannot be determined just by examining the amplitude of a seismogram because this amplitude decreases as the distance between the epicenter of the earthquake and the observation station increases. To account for the distance between the epicenter and the observation station, a seismologist examines a seismogram for both small waves called **p-waves** and larger waves called **s-waves**. The Richter scale magnitude M of the earthquake is a function of both the amplitude A of the s-waves and the difference in time t between the occurrence of the s-waves and the p-waves. In the 1950s, Charles Richter developed the following formula to determine the magnitude of an earthquake from the data in a seismogram.

Amplitude-Time-Difference Formula

The Richter scale magnitude M of an earthquake is given by

$$M = \log A + 3 \log 8t - 2.92$$

where A is the amplitude, in millimeters, of the s-waves on a seismogram and t is the difference in time, in seconds, between the s-waves and the p-waves.

Alternative to Example 8
Determine the Richter scale magnitude of an earthquake that produced a seismogram in which the amplitude of the s-waves is $A = 11$ millimeters, and the time difference between the s-waves and the p-waves is $t = 28$ seconds.

● ≈**5.2**

take note

The Richter scale magnitude is usually rounded to the nearest tenth.

EXAMPLE 8   **Determine the Magnitude of an Earthquake from Its Seismogram**

Find the Richter scale magnitude of the earthquake that produced the seismogram in **Figure 4.34**.

Solution

$$M = \log A + 3 \log 8t - 2.92$$
$$= \log 23 + 3 \log[8 \cdot 24] - 2.92 \qquad \text{• Substitute 23 for } A \text{ and 24 for } t.$$
$$\approx 1.36173 + 6.84990 - 2.92$$
$$\approx 5.3$$

The earthquake had a magnitude of about 5.3 on the Richter scale.

▶ **TRY EXERCISE 64, PAGE 405**

Logarithmic scales are also used in chemistry. One example concerns the pH of a liquid, which is a measure of the liquid's **acidity** or **alkalinity.** (You may have tested the pH of a swimming pool or an aquarium.) Pure water, which is considered neutral, has a pH of 7.0. The pH scale ranges from 0 to 14, with 0 corresponding to the most acidic solutions and 14 to the most alkaline. Lemon juice has a pH of about 2, whereas household ammonia measures about 11.

Specifically, the pH of a solution is a function of the hydronium-ion concentration of the solution. Because the hydronium-ion concentration of a solution can be very small (with values such as 0.00000001), pH uses a logarithmic scale.

take note

One mole is equivalent to 6.022×10^{23} ions.

The pH of a Solution

The **pH of a solution** with a hydronium-ion concentration of H^+ moles per liter is given by

$$pH = -\log[H^+]$$

Alternative to Example 9
Find the pH of a solution with
$H^+ = 5.77 \times 10^{-6}$ mole per liter.
● ≈ 5.2

EXAMPLE 9   **Find the pH of a Solution**

Find the pH of each liquid. Round to the nearest tenth.

a. Orange juice with $H^+ = 2.8 \times 10^{-4}$ mole per liter

b. Milk with $H^+ = 3.97 \times 10^{-7}$ mole per liter

c. Rainwater with $H^+ = 6.31 \times 10^{-5}$ mole per liter

d. A baking soda solution with $H^+ = 3.98 \times 10^{-9}$ mole per liter

Solution

a. $pH = -\log[H^+] = -\log(2.8 \times 10^{-4}) \approx 3.6$
The orange juice has a pH of 3.6.

b. $pH = -\log[H^+] = -\log(3.97 \times 10^{-7}) \approx 6.4$
The milk has a pH of 6.4.

c. $pH = -\log[H^+] = -\log(6.31 \times 10^{-5}) \approx 4.2$
The rainwater has a pH of 4.2.

d. $pH = -\log[H^+] = -\log(3.98 \times 10^{-9}) \approx 8.4$
The baking soda solution has a pH of 8.4.

▶ **TRY EXERCISE 48, PAGE 404**

MATH MATTERS

The pH scale was created by the
Danish biochemist Søren Sørensen
in 1909 to measure the acidity of
water used in the brewing of beer.
pH is an abbreviation for *pondus
hydrogenii*, which translates as
"potential hydrogen."

Figure 4.35 illustrates the pH scale, along with the corresponding hydronium-ion concentrations. A solution on the left half of the scale, with a pH of less
than 7, is an **acid**, and a solution on the right half of the scale is an **alkaline solution** or a **base**. Because the scale is logarithmic, a solution with a pH of 5 is 10
times more acidic than a solution with a pH of 6. From Example 9 we see that
the orange juice, rainwater, and milk are acids, whereas the baking soda solution
is a base.

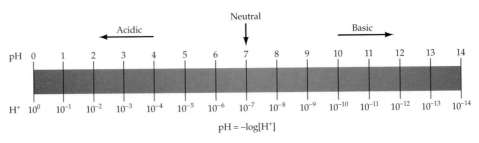

FIGURE 4.35

Alternative to Example 10

Find the hydronium-ion concentration of a cleaning solution with a pH of 3.4.

● $3.98 \times 10^{-4}\,\text{mol}/\text{L}$

EXAMPLE 10   **Find the Hydronium-Ion Concentration**

A sample of blood has a pH of 7.3. Find the hydronium-ion concentration of the blood.

Solution

$$\text{pH} = -\log[\text{H}^+]$$
$$7.3 = -\log[\text{H}^+] \qquad \bullet \text{ Substitute 7.3 for pH.}$$
$$-7.3 = \log[\text{H}^+] \qquad \bullet \text{ Multiply both sides by } -1.$$
$$10^{-7.3} = \text{H}^+ \qquad \bullet \text{ Change to exponential form.}$$
$$5.0 \times 10^{-8} \approx \text{H}^+$$

The hydronium-ion concentration of the blood is about 5.0×10^{-8} mole per liter.

▶ **TRY EXERCISE 50, PAGE 405**

TOPICS FOR DISCUSSION

1. The function $f(x) = \log_b x$ is defined only for $x > 0$. Explain why this condition is imposed.

2. If p and q are positive numbers, explain why $\ln(p + q)$ isn't normally equal to $\ln p + \ln q$.

3. If $f(x) = \log_b x$ and $f(c) = f(d)$, can we conclude that $c = d$?

4. Give examples of situations in which it is advantageous to use logarithmic scales.

EXERCISE SET 4.4

—Suggested Assignment: Exercises 1–29, odd; 31–40, all; 45–57, odd; 60 and 66–71, all.
—Answer graphs to Exercises 23–30 are on page AA17.

In Exercises 1 to 8, write the given logarithm in terms of logarithms of x, y, and z.

1. $\log_b(xyz)$

$\log_b x + \log_b y + \log_b z$

▶ **2.** $\ln \dfrac{z^3}{\sqrt{xy}}$

$3 \ln z - \dfrac{1}{2} \ln x - \dfrac{1}{2} \ln y$

3. $\ln \dfrac{x}{z^4}$ $\ln x - 4 \ln z$

4. $\log_5 \dfrac{xy^2}{z^4}$

$\log_5 x + 2 \log_5 y - 4 \log_5 z$

5. $\log_2 \dfrac{\sqrt{x}}{y^3}$ $\dfrac{1}{2} \log_2 x - 3 \log_2 y$

6. $\log_b\left(x\sqrt[3]{y}\right)$

$\log_b x + \dfrac{1}{3} \log_b y$

7. $\log_7 \dfrac{\sqrt{xz}}{y^2}$

$\dfrac{1}{2} \log_7 x + \dfrac{1}{2} \log_7 z - 2 \log_7 y$

8. $\ln \sqrt[3]{x^2 \sqrt{y}}$

$\dfrac{2}{3} \ln x + \dfrac{1}{6} \ln y$

In Exercises 9 to 14, write each logarithmic expression as a single logarithm with a coefficient of 1. Simplify when possible.

9. $\log(x + 5) + 2 \log x$ $\log[x^2(x + 5)]$

▶ **10.** $3 \log_2 t - \dfrac{1}{3} \log_2 u + 4 \log_2 v$ $\log_2 \dfrac{t^3 v^4}{\sqrt[3]{u}}$

11. $\ln(x^2 - y^2) - \ln(x - y)$ $\ln(x + y)$

12. $\dfrac{1}{2} \log_8(x + 5) - 3 \log_8 y$ $\log_8 \dfrac{\sqrt{x + 5}}{y^3}$

13. $3 \log x + \dfrac{1}{3} \log y + \log(x + 1)$ $\log\left[x^3 \cdot \sqrt[3]{y}\,(x + 1)\right]$

14. $\ln(xz) - \ln\left(x\sqrt{y}\right) + 2 \ln \dfrac{y}{z}$ $\ln \dfrac{y^{3/2}}{z}$

In Exercises 15 to 22, use the change-of-base formula to approximate the logarithm accurate to the nearest ten thousandth.

15. $\log_7 20$ 1.5395

▶ **16.** $\log_5 37$ 2.2436

17. $\log_{11} 8$ 0.8672

18. $\log_{50} 22$ 0.7901

19. $\log_6 \dfrac{1}{3}$ -0.6131

20. $\log_3 \dfrac{7}{8}$ -0.1215

21. $\log_9 \sqrt{17}$ 0.6447

22. $\log_4 \sqrt{7}$ 0.7018

In Exercises 23 to 30, use a graphing utility and the change-of-base formula to graph the logarithmic function.

23. $f(x) = \log_4 x$

▶ **24.** $g(x) = \log_8(5 - x)$

25. $g(x) = \log_8(x - 3)$

26. $t(x) = \log_9(5 - x)$

27. $h(x) = \log_3(x - 3)^2$

28. $J(x) = \log_{12}(-x)$

29. $F(x) = -\log_5|x - 2|$

30. $n(x) = \log_2\sqrt{x - 8}$

In Exercises 31 to 40, determine if the statement is true or false for all $x > 0$, $y > 0$. If it is false, write an example that disproves the statement.

31. $\log_b(x + y) = \log_b x + \log_b y$ False; $\log 10 + \log 10 = 2$ but $\log(10 + 10) = \log 20 \neq 2$.

32. $\log_b(xy) = \log_b x \cdot \log_b y$ False; $\log(10 \cdot 10) = 2$ but $\log 10 \cdot \log 10 = 1$.

33. $\log_b(xy) = \log_b x + \log_b y$ True

34. $\log_b x \cdot \log_b y = \log_b x + \log_b y$ False; $\log 10 \cdot \log 10 = 1$ but $\log 10 + \log 10 = 2$.

35. $\log_b x - \log_b y = \log_b(x - y)$, $x > y$ False; $\log 100 - \log 10 = 1$ but $\log(100 - 10) = \log 90 \neq 1$.

36. $\log_b \dfrac{x}{y} = \dfrac{\log_b x}{\log_b y}$ False; $\log \dfrac{100}{10} = \log 10 = 1$ but $\dfrac{\log 100}{\log 10} = \dfrac{2}{1} = 2$.

37. $\dfrac{\log_b x}{\log_b y} = \log_b x - \log_b y$ False; $\dfrac{\log 100}{\log 10} = \dfrac{2}{1} = 2$ but $\log 100 - \log 10 = 1$.

38. $\log_b(x^n) = n \log_b x$ True

39. $(\log_b x)^n = n \log_b x$ False; $(\log 10)^2 = 1$ but $2 \log 10 = 2$.

40. $\log_b \sqrt{x} = \dfrac{1}{2} \log_b x$ True

41. Evaluate the following *without* using a calculator.
$$\log_3 5 \cdot \log_5 7 \cdot \log_7 9 \quad 2$$

42. Evaluate the following *without* using a calculator.
$$\log_5 20 \cdot \log_{20} 60 \cdot \log_{60} 100 \cdot \log_{100} 125 \quad 3$$

43. Which is larger, 500^{501} or 506^{500}? These numbers are too large for most calculators to handle. (They each have 1353 digits!) (*Hint:* Let $x = 500^{501}$ and $y = 506^{500}$ and then compare $\ln x$ with $\ln y$.) 500^{501}

44. Which number is smaller, $\dfrac{1}{50^{300}}$ or $\dfrac{1}{151^{233}}$? $\dfrac{1}{50^{300}}$

45. **ANIMATED MAPS** A software company that creates interactive maps for Web sites has designed an animated zooming feature so that when a user selects the zoom-in option, the map appears to expand on a location. This is accomplished by displaying several intermediate maps to give the illusion of motion. The company has determined that zooming in on a location is more informative and pleasing to observe when the scale of each step of the animation is determined using the equation
$$S_n = S_0 \cdot 10^{\frac{n}{N}(\log S_f - \log S_0)}$$
where S_n represents the scale of the current step n ($n = 0$ corresponds to the initial scale), S_0 is the starting scale of the map, S_f is the final scale, and N is the number of steps in the animation following the initial scale. (If the initial scale of the map is $1:200$, then $S_0 = 200$.) Determine the scales to be used at each intermediate step if a map is to start with a scale of $1:1,000,000$ and proceed through five intermediate steps to end with a scale of $1:500,000$. $1:870,551$; $1:757,858$; $1:659,754$; $1:574,349$; $1:500,000$

46. **ANIMATED MAPS** Use the equation in Exercise 45 to determine the scales for each stage of an animated map zoom that goes from a scale of $1:250,000$ to a scale of $1:100,000$ in four steps (following the initial scale). $1:198,818$; $1:158,114$; $1:125,743$; $1:100,000$

47. **pH** Milk of magnesia has a hydronium-ion concentration of about 3.97×10^{-11} mole per liter. Determine the pH of milk of magnesia and state whether it is an acid or a base.   10.4; base

▶ **48.** **pH** Vinegar has a hydronium-ion concentration of 1.26×10^{-3} mole per liter. Determine the pH of vinegar and state whether it is an acid or a base.   2.9; acid

49. **HYDRONIUM-ION CONCENTRATION** A morphine solution has a pH of 9.5. Determine the hydronium-ion concentration of the morphine solution. 3.16×10^{-10} mol/L

▶ **50.** **HYDRONIUM-ION CONCENTRATION** A rainstorm in New York City produced rainwater with a pH of 5.6. Determine the hydronium-ion concentration of the rainwater. 2.51×10^{-6} mol/L

51. **DECIBEL LEVEL** The range of sound intensities that the human ear can detect is so large that a special decibel scale (named after Alexander Graham Bell) is used to measure and compare sound intensities. The **decibel level** dB of a sound is given by

$$dB(I) = 10 \log \left(\frac{I}{I_0} \right)$$

where I_0 is the intensity of sound that is barely audible to the human ear. Find the decibel level for the following sounds. Round to the nearest tenth of a decibel.

Sound	Intensity	
a. Automobile traffic	$I = 1.58 \times 10^8 \cdot I_0$	82.0 dB
b. Quiet conversation	$I = 10,800 \cdot I_0$	40.3 dB
c. Fender guitar	$I = 3.16 \times 10^{11} \cdot I_0$	115.0 dB
d. Jet engine	$I = 1.58 \times 10^{15} \cdot I_0$	152.0 dB

52. **COMPARISON OF SOUND INTENSITIES** A team in Arizona installed a 48,000-watt sound system in a Ford Bronco that it claims can output 175-decibel sound. The human pain threshold for sound is 125 decibels. How many times more intense is the sound from the Bronco than the human pain threshold? 100,000 times more intense

53. **COMPARISON OF SOUND INTENSITIES** How many times more intense is a sound that measures 120 decibels than a sound that measures 110 decibels? 10 times more intense

54. **DECIBEL LEVEL** If the intensity of a sound is doubled, what is the increase in the decibel level? (*Hint:* Find $dB(2I) - dB(I)$.) ≈ 3.0103 dB

55. **EARTHQUAKE MAGNITUDE** What is the Richter scale magnitude of an earthquake with an intensity of $I = 100,000I_0$? 5

▶ **56.** **EARTHQUAKE MAGNITUDE** The Colombia earthquake of 1906 had an intensity of $I = 398,107,000I_0$. What did it measure on the Richter scale? 8.6

57. **EARTHQUAKE INTENSITY** The Coalinga, California, earthquake of 1983 had a Richter scale magnitude of 6.5. Find the intensity of this earthquake. $10^{6.5}I_0$ or about $3,162,277.7I_0$

▶ **58.** **EARTHQUAKE INTENSITY** The earthquake that occurred just south of Concepción, Chile, in 1960 had a Richter scale magnitude of 9.5. Find the intensity of this earthquake. $3,162,277,660I_0$

59. **COMPARISON OF EARTHQUAKES** Compare the intensity of an earthquake that measures 5.0 on the Richter scale to the intensity of an earthquake that measures 3.0 on the Richter scale by finding the ratio of the larger intensity to the smaller intensity. 100 to 1

▶ **60.** **COMPARISON OF EARTHQUAKES** How many times more intense was the 1960 earthquake in Chile, which measured 9.5 on the Richter scale, than the San Francisco earthquake of 1906, which measured 8.3 on the Richter scale? $10^{1.2} \approx 15.8$ times as intense

61. **COMPARISON OF EARTHQUAKES** On March 2, 1933, an earthquake of magnitude 8.9 on the Richter scale struck Japan. In October 1989, an earthquake of magnitude 7.1 on the Richter scale struck San Francisco, California. Compare the intensity of the larger earthquake to the intensity of the smaller earthquake by finding the ratio of the larger intensity to the smaller intensity. $10^{1.8}$ to 1 or about 63 to 1

62. **COMPARISON OF EARTHQUAKES** An earthquake that occurred in China in 1978 measured 8.2 on the Richter scale. In 1988, an earthquake in California measured 6.9 on the Richter scale. Compare the intensity of the larger earthquake to the intensity of the smaller earthquake by finding the ratio of the larger intensity to the smaller intensity. $10^{1.3}$ to 1 or about 20 to 1

63. **EARTHQUAKE MAGNITUDE** Find the Richter scale magnitude of the earthquake that produced the seismogram in the following figure. 5.5

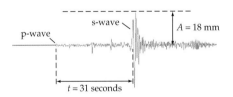

64. **EARTHQUAKE MAGNITUDE** Find the Richter scale magnitude of the earthquake that produced the seismogram in the following figure. 4.9

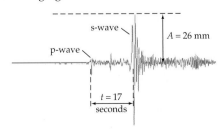

CONNECTING CONCEPTS

65. NOMOGRAMS AND LOGARITHMIC SCALES A **nomogram** is a diagram used to determine a numerical result by drawing a line across numerical scales. The following nomogram, used by Richter, determines the magnitude of an earthquake from its seismogram. To use the nomogram, mark the amplitude of a seismogram on the amplitude scale and mark the time between the s-wave and the p-wave on the S-P scale. Draw a line between these marks. The Richter scale magnitude of the earthquake that produced the seismogram is shown by the intersection of the line and the center scale. The example below shows that an earthquake with a seismogram amplitude of 23 millimeters and an S-P time of 24 seconds has a Richter scale magnitude of about 5.

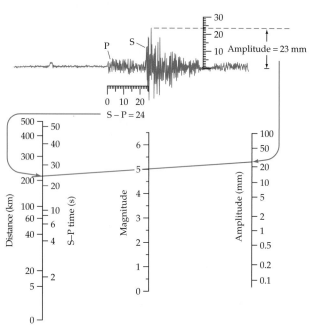

Richter's earthquake nomogram

The amplitude and the S-P time are shown on logarithmic scales. On the amplitude scale, the distance from 1 to 10 is the same as the distance from 10 to 100, because $\log 100 - \log 10 = \log 10 - \log 1$.

Use the nomogram at the left to determine the Richter scale magnitude of an earthquake with a seismogram

a. amplitude of 50 millimeters and S-P time of 40 seconds. $M \approx 6$

b. amplitude of 1 millimeter and S-P time of 30 seconds. $M \approx 4$

c. How do the results in parts **a.** and **b.** compare with the Richter scale magnitude produced by using the amplitude-time-difference formula?
The results are close to the magnitudes produced by using the amplitude-time-difference formula.

PREPARE FOR SECTION 4.5

66. Use the definition of a logarithm to write the exponential equation $3^6 = 729$ in logarithmic form. [4.2] $\log_3 729 = 6$

67. Use the definition of a logarithm to write the logarithmic equation $\log_5 625 = 4$ in exponential form. [4.2] $5^4 = 625$

68. Use the definition of a logarithm to write the exponential equation $a^{x+2} = b$ in logarithmic form. [4.2] $\log_a b = x + 2$

69. Solve for x: $4a = 7bx + 2cx$. [1.2] $x = \dfrac{4a}{7b + 2c}$

70. Solve for x: $165 = \dfrac{300}{1 + 12x}$. [1.4] $x = \dfrac{3}{44}$

71. Solve for x: $A = \dfrac{100 + x}{100 - x}$. [1.4] $x = \dfrac{100(A - 1)}{A + 1}$

PROJECTS

1. **LOGARITHMIC SCALES** Sometimes **logarithmic scales** are used to better view a collection of data that span a wide range of values. For instance, consider the table below, which lists the approximate masses of various marine creatures in grams. Next we have attempted to plot the masses on a number line.

Animal	Mass (g)
Rotifer	0.000000006
Dwarf goby	0.30
Lobster	15,900
Leatherback turtle	851,000
Giant squid	1,820,000
Whale shark	4,700,000
Blue whale	120,000,000

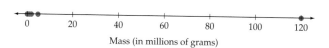

Mass (in millions of grams)

As you can see, we had to use such a large span of numbers that the data for most of the animals are bunched up at the left. Visually, this number line isn't very helpful for any comparisons.

a. Make a new number line, this time plotting the logarithm (base 10) of each of the masses.
See the *Instructor's Solution Manual.*

b. Which number line is more helpful to compare the masses of the different animals?
the logarithmic number line

c. If the data points for two animals on the logarithmic number line are 1 unit apart, how do the animals' masses compare? What if the points are 2 units apart?
One mass is 10 times heavier; one mass is 100 times heavier.

2. **LOGARITHMIC SCALES** The distances of the planets in our solar system from the sun are given in the table at the top of the next column.

a. Draw a number line with an appropriate scale to plot the distances.
See the *Instructor's Solution Manual.*

b. Draw a second number line, this time plotting the logarithm (base 10) of each distance.
See the *Instructor's Solution Manual.*

c. Which number line do you find more helpful to compare the different distances? Answers will vary.

d. If two distances are 3 units apart on the logarithmic number line, how do the distances of the corresponding planets compare? The distance of one planet is 1000 times greater than that of the other.

Planet	Distance (million km)
Mercury	58
Venus	108
Earth	150
Mars	228
Jupiter	778
Saturn	1427
Uranus	2871
Neptune	4497
Pluto	5913

3. **BIOLOGIC DIVERSITY** To discuss the variety of species that live in a certain environment, a biologist needs a precise definition of *diversity*. Let $p_1, p_2, \ldots, p_n$ be the proportions of n species that live in an environment. The biologic diversity D of this system is

$$D = -(p_1 \log_2 p_1 + p_2 \log_2 p_2 + \cdots + p_n \log_2 p_n)$$

Suppose that an ecosystem has exactly five different varieties of grass: rye (R), bermuda (B), blue (L), fescue (F), and St. Augustine (A).

a. Calculate the diversity of this ecosystem if the proportions of these grasses are as shown in Table 4.1. Round to the nearest hundredth. 2.32

Table 4.1

R	B	L	F	A
$\dfrac{1}{5}$	$\dfrac{1}{5}$	$\dfrac{1}{5}$	$\dfrac{1}{5}$	$\dfrac{1}{5}$

b. Because bermuda and St. Augustine are virulent grasses, after a time the proportions will be as shown in Table 4.2. Calculate the diversity of this system. Does this system have more or less diversity than the system given in Table 4.1? 2.06; less

Table 4.2

R	B	L	F	A
$\dfrac{1}{8}$	$\dfrac{3}{8}$	$\dfrac{1}{16}$	$\dfrac{1}{8}$	$\dfrac{5}{16}$

c. After an even longer time period, the bermuda and St. Augustine grasses completely overrun the environment and the proportions are as shown in Table 4.3. Calculate the diversity of this system. (*Note:* Although the equation is not technically correct, for purposes of the diversity definition, we may say that $0 \log_2 0 = 0$. By using very small values of p_i, we can demonstrate that this definition makes sense.) Does this system have more or less diversity than the system given in Table 4.2?

0.81; less

d. Finally, the St. Augustine grasses overrun the bermuda grasses and the proportions are as shown in Table 4.4. Calculate the diversity of this system. Write a sentence that explains the meaning of the value you obtained.

0; With only one variety of grass, the system has no diversity.

Table 4.3

R	B	L	F	A
0	$\dfrac{1}{4}$	0	0	$\dfrac{3}{4}$

Table 4.4

R	B	L	F	A
0	0	0	0	1

EXPONENTIAL AND LOGARITHMIC EQUATIONS

SECTION 4.5

- **SOLVE EXPONENTIAL EQUATIONS**
- **SOLVE LOGARITHMIC EQUATIONS**
- **APPLICATION**

• SOLVE EXPONENTIAL EQUATIONS

If a variable appears in an exponent of a term of an equation, such as $2^{x+1} = 32$, then the equation is called an **exponential equation**. Example 1 uses the following equality-of-exponents theorem to solve $2^{x+1} = 32$.

> **Equality of Exponents Theorem**
>
> If $b^x = b^y$, then $x = y$, provided that $b > 0$ and $b \neq 1$.

Alternative to Example 1

Use the Equality of Exponents Theorem to solve $3^{x-2} = 81$.

- $x = 6$

EXAMPLE 1   Solve an Exponential Equation

Use the Equality of Exponents Theorem to solve $2^{x+1} = 32$.

Solution

$$2^{x+1} = 32$$
$$2^{x+1} = 2^5 \qquad \text{• Write each side as a power of 2.}$$
$$x + 1 = 5 \qquad \text{• Equate the exponents.}$$
$$x = 4$$

Check: Let $x = 4$, then $2^{x+1} = 2^{4+1}$
$$= 2^5$$
$$= 32$$

▶ **TRY EXERCISE 2, PAGE 415**

A graphing utility can also be used to find solutions of an equation of the form $f(x) = g(x)$. Either of the following two methods can be employed.

Ⓟ Using a Graphing Utility to Find the Solutions of $f(x) = g(x)$

Intersection Method   Graph $y_1 = f(x)$ and $y_2 = g(x)$ on the same screen. The solutions of $f(x) = g(x)$ are the x-coordinates of the points of intersection of the graphs.

Intercept Method   The solutions of $f(x) = g(x)$ are the x-coordinates of the x-intercepts of the graph of $y = f(x) - g(x)$.

Figures 4.36 and **4.37** illustrate the graphical methods for solving $2^{x+1} = 32$.

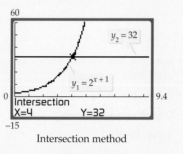

Intersection method

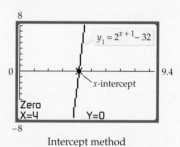

Intercept method

FIGURE 4.36   **FIGURE 4.37**

In Example 1 we were able to write both sides of the equation as a power of the same base. If you find it difficult to write both sides of an exponential equation in terms of the same base, then try the procedure of taking the logarithm of each side of the equation. This procedure is used in Example 2.

EXAMPLE 2   **Solve an Exponential Equation**

Solve: $5^x = 40$ *Alternative to Example 2*
Exercise 12, page 415.

Algebraic Solution

$$5^x = 40$$
$$\log(5^x) = \log 40 \qquad \bullet \text{ Take the logarithm of each side.}$$
$$x \log 5 = \log 40 \qquad \bullet \text{ Power property}$$
$$x = \frac{\log 40}{\log 5} \qquad \bullet \text{ Exact solution}$$
$$x \approx 2.3 \qquad \bullet \text{ Decimal approximation}$$

To the nearest tenth, the solution is 2.3.

Visualize the Solution

Intersection Method   The solution of $5^x = 40$ is the x-coordinate of the point of intersection of $y = 5^x$ and $y = 40$ (see **Figure 4.38**).

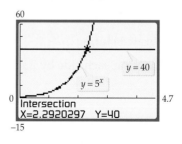

FIGURE 4.38

▶ **TRY EXERCISE 10, PAGE 415**

An alternative approach to solving the equation in Example 2 is to rewrite the exponential equation in logarithmic form: $5^x = 40$ is equivalent to the logarithmic equation $\log_5 40 = x$. Using the change-of-base formula, we find that $x = \log_5 40 = \dfrac{\log 40}{\log 5}$. In the following example, however, we must take logarithms of both sides to reach a solution.

EXAMPLE 3   **Solve an Exponential Equation**

Solve: $3^{2x-1} = 5^{x+2}$ ***Alternative to Example 3***
Exercise 20, page 415.

Algebraic Solution

$$3^{2x-1} = 5^{x+2}$$

$$\ln 3^{2x-1} = \ln 5^{x+2}$$ • Take the natural logarithm of each side.

$$(2x - 1)\ln 3 = (x + 2)\ln 5$$ • Power property

$$2x \ln 3 - \ln 3 = x \ln 5 + 2 \ln 5$$ • Distributive property

$$2x \ln 3 - x \ln 5 = 2 \ln 5 + \ln 3$$ • Solve for x.

$$x(2 \ln 3 - \ln 5) = 2 \ln 5 + \ln 3$$

$$x = \frac{2 \ln 5 + \ln 3}{2 \ln 3 - \ln 5}$$ • Exact solution

$$x \approx 7.3$$ • Decimal approximation

To the nearest tenth, the solution is 7.3.

Visualize the Solution

Intercept Method   The solution of $3^{2x-1} = 5^{x+2}$ is the x-coordinate of the x-intercept of $y = 3^{2x-1} - 5^{x+2}$ (see **Figure 4.39**).

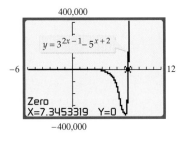

FIGURE 4.39

▶ **TRY EXERCISE 18, PAGE 415**

In Example 4 we solve an exponential equation that has two solutions.

EXAMPLE 4   **Solve an Exponential Equation Involving $b^x + b^{-x}$**

Solve: $\dfrac{2^x + 2^{-x}}{2} = 3$ ***Alternative to Example 4***
Exercise 42, page 415.

Algebraic Solution

Multiplying each side by 2 produces

$$2^x + 2^{-x} = 6$$

$$2^{2x} + 2^0 = 6(2^x)$$ • Multiply each side by 2^x to clear negative exponents.

$$(2^x)^2 - 6(2^x) + 1 = 0$$ • Write in quadratic form.

$$(u)^2 - 6(u) + 1 = 0$$ • Substitute u for 2^x.

Visualize the Solution

Intersection Method   The solutions of $\dfrac{2^x + 2^{-x}}{2} = 3$ are the x-coordinates of the points of intersection of

By the quadratic formula,

$$u = \frac{6 \pm \sqrt{36 - 4}}{2} = \frac{6 \pm 4\sqrt{2}}{2} = 3 \pm 2\sqrt{2}$$

$$2^x = 3 \pm 2\sqrt{2}$$ • Replace u with 2^x.

$$\log 2^x = \log(3 \pm 2\sqrt{2})$$ • Take the common logarithm of each side.

• Power property

$$x \log 2 = \log(3 \pm 2\sqrt{2})$$

$$x = \frac{\log(3 \pm 2\sqrt{2})}{\log 2} \approx \pm 2.54$$

The approximate solutions are -2.54 and 2.54.

▶ **TRY EXERCISE 40, PAGE 415**

$y = \dfrac{2^x + 2^{-x}}{2}$ and $y = 3$ (see **Figure 4.40**).

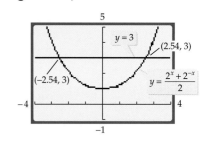

FIGURE 4.40

● SOLVE LOGARITHMIC EQUATIONS

Equations that involve logarithms are called **logarithmic equations**. The properties of logarithms, along with the definition of a logarithm, are often used to find the solutions of a logarithmic equation.

Alternative to Example 5
Solve: $\log(9x + 1) = 3$
● $x = 111$

EXAMPLE 5   **Solve a Logarithmic Equation**

Solve: $\log(3x - 5) = 2$

Solution

$$\log(3x - 5) = 2$$

$$3x - 5 = 10^2$$ • Definition of a logarithm

$$3x = 105$$ • Solve for x.

$$x = 35$$

Check: $\log[3(35) - 5] = \log 100 = 2$

▶ **TRY EXERCISE 22, PAGE 415**

❓ **QUESTION** Can a negative number be a solution of a logarithmic equation?

❓ **ANSWER** Yes. For instance, -10 is a solution of $\log(-x) = 1$.

Alternative to Example 6
Solve: $\log x + \log(x + 15) = 2$
○ $x = 5$

EXAMPLE 6   **Solve a Logarithmic Equation**

Solve: $\log 2x - \log(x - 3) = 1$

Solution

$$\log 2x - \log(x - 3) = 1$$

$$\log \frac{2x}{x - 3} = 1 \qquad \bullet \text{ Quotient property}$$

$$\frac{2x}{x - 3} = 10^1 \qquad \bullet \text{ Definition of logarithm}$$

$$2x = 10x - 30 \qquad \bullet \text{ Solve for } x.$$

$$-8x = -30$$

$$x = \frac{15}{4}$$

Check the solution by substituting $\dfrac{15}{4}$ into the original equation.

▶ **TRY EXERCISE 26, PAGE 415**

In Example 7 we make use of the one-to-one property of logarithms to find the solution of a logarithmic equation. This example illustrates that the process of solving a logarithmic equation by using logarithmic properties may introduce an extraneous solution.

EXAMPLE 7   **Solve a Logarithmic Equation**

Solve: $\ln(3x + 8) = \ln(2x + 2) + \ln(x - 2)$

Alternative to Example 7
Exercise 30, page 415.

Algebraic Solution

$$\ln(3x + 8) = \ln(2x + 2) + \ln(x - 2)$$

$$\ln(3x + 8) = \ln[(2x + 2)(x - 2)] \qquad \bullet \text{ Product property}$$

$$\ln(3x + 8) = \ln(2x^2 - 2x - 4)$$

$$3x + 8 = 2x^2 - 2x - 4 \qquad \bullet \text{ One-to-one property of logarithms}$$

$$0 = 2x^2 - 5x - 12$$

$$0 = (2x + 3)(x - 4) \qquad \bullet \text{ Solve for } x.$$

$$x = -\frac{3}{2} \quad \text{or} \quad x = 4$$

Thus $-\dfrac{3}{2}$ and 4 are possible solutions. A check will show that 4 is a solution, but $-\dfrac{3}{2}$ is not a solution.

▶ **TRY EXERCISE 36, PAGE 415**

Visualize the Solution

The graph of $y = \ln(3x + 8) - \ln(2x + 2) - \ln(x - 2)$ has only one x-intercept (see **Figure 4.41**). Thus there is only one real solution.

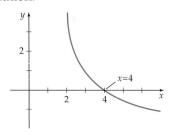

$$y = \ln(3x + 8) - \ln(2x + 2) - \ln(x - 2)$$

FIGURE 4.41

? QUESTION Why does $x = -\dfrac{3}{2}$ not check in Example 7?

● **APPLICATION**

Alternative to Example 8
Use the formula

$$t = 2.43 \ln \frac{150 + v}{150 - v}$$

for $0 \le v \le 150$, where t is the time in seconds required for a dropped object to reach a velocity v (in feet per second), to find the velocity of an object that has been falling for 10 seconds. Round your answer to the nearest tenth.

● **145.2 feet per second**

EXAMPLE 8   **Velocity of a Sky Diver Experiencing Air Resistance**

During the free-fall portion of a jump, the time t in seconds required for a sky diver to reach a velocity v in feet per second is given by

$$t = -\frac{175}{32} \ln\left(1 - \frac{v}{175}\right)$$

a. Determine the velocity of the diver after 5 seconds.

b. The graph of the above function has a vertical asymptote at $v = 175$. Explain the meaning of the vertical asymptote in the context of this example.

Solution

a. Substitute 5 for t and solve for v.

$$t = -\frac{175}{32} \ln\left(1 - \frac{v}{175}\right)$$

$$5 = -\frac{175}{32} \ln\left(1 - \frac{v}{175}\right) \qquad \text{• Replace } t \text{ with 5.}$$

$$\left(-\frac{32}{175}\right)5 = \ln\left(1 - \frac{v}{175}\right) \qquad \text{• Solve for } v.$$

$$-\frac{32}{35} = \ln\left(1 - \frac{v}{175}\right)$$

$$e^{-32/35} = 1 - \frac{v}{175} \qquad \text{• Write in exponential form.}$$

$$e^{-32/35} - 1 = -\frac{v}{175}$$

$$v = 175(1 - e^{-32/35})$$

$$v \approx 104.86$$

Continued ▶

take note

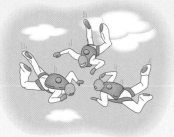

If air resistance is not considered, then the time in seconds required for a sky diver to reach a given velocity (in feet per second) is

$t = \dfrac{v}{32}$. The function in Example 8

is a more realistic model of the time required to reach a given velocity during the free-fall of a sky diver who is experiencing air resistance.

? ANSWER If $x = -\dfrac{3}{2}$, the original equation becomes $\ln\left(\dfrac{7}{2}\right) = \ln(-1) + \ln\left(-\dfrac{7}{2}\right)$.

This cannot be true, because the function $f(x) = \ln x$ is not defined for negative values of x.

After 5 seconds the velocity of the sky diver will be about 104.9 feet per second. See **Figure 4.42.**

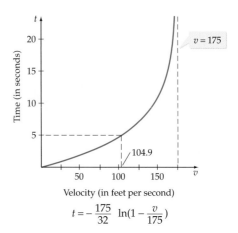

$$t = -\frac{175}{32}\ln\left(1 - \frac{v}{175}\right)$$

FIGURE 4.42

b. The vertical asymptote $v = 175$ indicates that the sky diver will not attain a velocity greater than 175 feet per second. In **Figure 4.42,** note that as $v \to 175$ from the left, $t \to \infty$.

▶ **TRY EXERCISE 68, PAGE 417**

 TOPICS FOR DISCUSSION

1. Discuss how to solve the equation $a = \log_b x$ for x.

2. What is the domain of $y = \log_4(2x - 5)$? Explain why this means that the equation $\log_4(x - 3) = \log_4(2x - 5)$ has no real number solution.

3. -8 is not a solution of the equation $\log_2 x + \log_2(x + 6) = 4$. Discuss at which step in the following solution the extraneous solution -8 was introduced.

$$\log_2 x + \log_2(x + 6) = 4$$
$$\log_2 x(x + 6) = 4$$
$$x(x + 6) = 2^4$$
$$x^2 + 6x = 16$$
$$x^2 + 6x - 16 = 0$$
$$(x + 8)(x - 2) = 0$$
$$x = -8 \quad \text{or} \quad x = 2$$

EXERCISE SET 4.5

—Suggested Assignment: Exercises 1–73, every other odd; 81–86, all.

In Exercises 1 to 46, solve for x algebraically.

1. $2^x = 64$ 6

▶ 2. $3^x = 243$ 5

3. $49^x = \dfrac{1}{343}$ $-\dfrac{3}{2}$

4. $9^x = \dfrac{1}{243}$ $-\dfrac{5}{2}$

5. $2^{5x+3} = \dfrac{1}{8}$ $-\dfrac{6}{5}$

6. $3^{4x-7} = \dfrac{1}{9}$ $\dfrac{5}{4}$

7. $\left(\dfrac{2}{5}\right)^x = \dfrac{8}{125}$ 3

8. $\left(\dfrac{2}{5}\right)^x = \dfrac{25}{4}$ -2

9. $5^x = 70$ $\dfrac{\log 70}{\log 5}$

▶ 10. $6^x = 50$ $\dfrac{\ln 50}{\ln 6}$

11. $3^{-x} = 120$ $-\dfrac{\log 120}{\log 3}$

12. $7^{-x} = 63$ $-\dfrac{\ln 63}{\ln 7}$

13. $10^{2x+3} = 315$ $\dfrac{\log 315 - 3}{2}$

14. $10^{6-x} = 550$ $6 - \log 550$

15. $e^x = 10$ $\ln 10$

16. $e^{x+1} = 20$ $\ln 20 - 1$

17. $2^{1-x} = 3^{x+1}$ $\dfrac{\ln 2 - \ln 3}{\ln 6}$

▶ 18. $3^{x-2} = 4^{2x+1}$ $\dfrac{\ln 4 + 2\ln 3}{\ln 3 - 2\ln 4}$

19. $2^{2x-3} = 5^{-x-1}$ $\dfrac{3\log 2 - \log 5}{2\log 2 + \log 5}$

20. $5^{3x} = 3^{x+4}$ $\dfrac{4\ln 3}{3\ln 5 - \ln 3}$

21. $\log(4x - 18) = 1$ 7

▶ 22. $\log(x^2 + 19) = 2$ $-9, 9$

23. $\ln(x^2 - 12) = \ln x$ 4

24. $\log(2x^2 + 3x) = \log(10x + 30)$ $-\dfrac{5}{2}, 6$

25. $\log_2 x + \log_2(x - 4) = 2$ $2 + 2\sqrt{2}$

▶ 26. $\log_3 x + \log_3(x + 6) = 3$ 3

27. $\log(5x - 1) = 2 + \log(x - 2)$ $\dfrac{199}{95}$

28. $1 + \log(3x - 1) = \log(2x + 1)$ $\dfrac{11}{28}$

29. $\ln(1 - x) + \ln(3 - x) = \ln 8$ -1

30. $\log(4 - x) = \log(x + 8) + \log(2x + 13)$ -5

31. $\log\sqrt{x^3 - 17} = \dfrac{1}{2}$ 3

32. $\log(x^3) = (\log x)^2$ $1, 1000$

33. $\log(\log x) = 1$ 10^{10}

34. $\ln(\ln x) = 2$ e^{e^2}

35. $\ln(e^{3x}) = 6$ 2

▶ 36. $\ln x = \dfrac{1}{2}\ln\left(2x + \dfrac{5}{2}\right) + \dfrac{1}{2}\ln 2$ 5

37. $e^{\ln(x-1)} = 4$ 5

38. $10^{\log(2x+7)} = 8$ $\dfrac{1}{2}$

39. $\dfrac{10^x - 10^{-x}}{2} = 20$ $\log(20 + \sqrt{401})$

▶ 40. $\dfrac{10^x + 10^{-x}}{2} = 8$ $\log(8 \pm 3\sqrt{7})$

41. $\dfrac{10^x + 10^{-x}}{10^x - 10^{-x}} = 5$ $\dfrac{1}{2}\log\left(\dfrac{3}{2}\right)$

42. $\dfrac{10^x - 10^{-x}}{10^x + 10^{-x}} = \dfrac{1}{2}$ $\dfrac{\log 3}{2}$

43. $\dfrac{e^x + e^{-x}}{2} = 15$ $\ln(15 \pm 4\sqrt{14})$

44. $\dfrac{e^x - e^{-x}}{2} = 15$ $\ln(15 + \sqrt{226})$

45. $\dfrac{1}{e^x - e^{-x}} = 4$ $\ln(1 + \sqrt{65}) - \ln 8$

46. $\dfrac{e^x + e^{-x}}{e^x - e^{-x}} = 3$ $\dfrac{\ln 2}{2}$

In Exercises 47 to 56, use a graphing utility to approximate the solutions of the equation to the nearest hundredth.

47. $2^{-x+3} = x + 1$ 1.61

48. $3^{x-2} = -2x - 1$ -0.53

49. $e^{3-2x} - 2x = 1$ 0.96

50. $2e^{x+2} + 3x = 2$ -1.05

51. $3\log_2(x - 1) = -x + 3$ 2.20

52. $2\log_3(2 - 3x) = 2x - 1$ 0.38

53. $\ln(2x + 4) + \dfrac{1}{2}x = -3$ -1.93

54. $2\ln(3 - x) + 3x = 4$ 0.81, 2.91

55. $2^{x+1} = x^2 - 1$ -1.34

56. $\ln x = -x^2 + 4$ 1.84

57. POPULATION GROWTH The population P of a city grows exponentially according to the function

$$P(t) = 8500(1.1)^t, \quad 0 \le t \le 8$$

where t is measured in years.

a. Find the population at time $t = 0$ and also at time $t = 2$. 8500, 10,285

b. When, to the nearest year, will the population reach 15,000? in 6 years

58. PHYSICAL FITNESS After a race, a runner's pulse rate R in beats per minute decreases according to the function

$$R(t) = 145e^{-0.092t}, \quad 0 \le t \le 15$$

where t is measured in minutes.

a. Find the runner's pulse rate at the end of the race and also 1 minute after the end of the race.
$R(0) = 145$, $R(1) \approx 132$

b. How long, to the nearest minute, after the end of the race will the runner's pulse rate be 80 beats per minute? 6 min

59. RATE OF COOLING A can of soda at 79°F is placed in a refrigerator that maintains a constant temperature of 36°F. The temperature T of the soda t minutes after it is placed in the refrigerator is given by

$$T(t) = 36 + 43e^{-0.058t}$$

a. Find the temperature, to the nearest degree, of the soda 10 minutes after it is placed in the refrigerator. 60°F

b. When, to the nearest minute, will the temperature of the soda be 45°F? 27 min

60. MEDICINE During surgery, a patient's circulatory system requires at least 50 milligrams of an anesthetic. The amount of anesthetic present t hours after 80 milligrams of anesthetic is administered is given by

$$T(t) = 80(0.727)^t$$

a. How much, to the nearest milligram, of the anesthetic is present in the patient's circulatory system 30 minutes after the anesthetic is administered? 68 mg

b. How long, to the nearest minute, can the operation last if the patient does not receive additional anesthetic? 88 min

61. PSYCHOLOGY Industrial psychologists study employee training programs to assess the effectiveness of the instruction. In one study, the percent score P on a test for a person who had completed t hours of training was given by

$$P = \frac{100}{1 + 30e^{-0.088t}}$$

a. Use a graphing utility to graph the equation for $t \geq 0$. Answer on page AA17.

b. Use the graph to estimate (to the nearest hour) the number of hours of training necessary to achieve a 70% score on the test. 48 h

c. From the graph, determine the horizontal asymptote. $P = 100$

d. Write a sentence that explains the meaning of the horizontal asymptote. As the number of hours of training increases, the test scores approach 100%.

62. PSYCHOLOGY An industrial psychologist has determined that the average percent score for an employee on a test of the employee's knowledge of the company's product is given by

$$P = \frac{100}{1 + 40e^{-0.1t}}$$

where t is the number of weeks on the job and P is the percent score.

a. Use a graphing utility to graph the equation for $t \geq 0$. Answer on page AA17.

b. Use the graph to estimate (to the nearest week) the number of weeks of employment that are necessary for the average employee to earn a 70% score on the test. 45 weeks

c. Determine the horizontal asymptote of the graph. $P = 100$

d. Write a sentence that explains the meaning of the horizontal asymptote. The more experience a person has, the closer the person's score is to 100%.

63. ECOLOGY A herd of bison was placed in a wildlife preserve that can support a maximum of 1000 bison. A population model for the bison is given by

$$B = \frac{1000}{1 + 30e^{-0.127t}}$$

where B is the number of bison in the preserve and t is time in years, with the year 1999 represented by $t = 0$.

a. Use a graphing utility to graph the equation for $t \geq 0$. Answer on page AA17.

b. Use the graph to estimate (to the nearest year) the number of years before the bison population reaches 500. in 27 years, or the year 2026

c. Determine the horizontal asymptote of the graph. $B = 1000$

d. Write a sentence that explains the meaning of the horizontal asymptote. As the number of years increases, the bison population approaches but never reaches or exceeds 1000.

64. POPULATION GROWTH A yeast culture grows according to the equation

$$Y = \frac{50,000}{1 + 250e^{-0.305t}}$$

where Y is the number of yeast and t is time in hours.

a. Use a graphing utility to graph the equation for $t \geq 0$. Answer on page AA18.

b. Use the graph to estimate (to the nearest hour) the number of hours before the yeast population reaches 35,000. 21 h

c. From the graph, estimate the horizontal asymptote. $Y = 50,000$

d. Write a sentence that explains the meaning of the horizontal asymptote. The number of yeast approaches but never reaches or exceeds 50,000.

65. CONSUMPTION OF NATURAL RESOURCES A model for how long our coal resources will last is given by

$$T = \frac{\ln(300r + 1)}{\ln(r + 1)}$$

where r is the percent increase in consumption from current levels of use and T is the time (in years) before the resource is depleted.

a. Use a graphing utility to graph this equation. Answer on page AA18.

b. If our consumption of coal increases by 3% per year, in how many years will we deplete our coal resources? 78 yrs

c. What percent increase in consumption of coal will deplete the resource in 100 years? Round to the nearest tenth of a percent. 1.9%

66. **CONSUMPTION OF NATURAL RESOURCES** A model for how long our aluminum resources will last is given by

$$T = \frac{\ln(20{,}500r + 1)}{\ln(r + 1)}$$

where r is the percent increase in consumption from current levels of use and T is the time (in years) before the resource is depleted.

a. Use a graphing utility to graph this equation. Answer on page AA18.

b. If our consumption of aluminum increases by 5% per year, in how many years (to the nearest year) will we deplete our aluminum resources? 142 yrs

c. What percent increase in consumption of aluminum will deplete the resource in 100 years? Round to the nearest tenth of a percent. 7.6%

67. **VELOCITY OF A MEDICAL CARE PACKAGE** A medical care package is air lifted and dropped to a disaster area. During the free-fall portion of the drop, the time, in seconds, required for the package to obtain a velocity of v feet per second is given by the function

$$t = 2.43 \ln \frac{150 + v}{150 - v}, \quad 0 \le v < 150$$

a. Determine the velocity of the package 5 seconds after it is dropped. Round to the nearest foot per second. 116 ft/s

b. Determine the vertical asymptote of the function. $v = 150$

c. Write a sentence that explains the meaning of the vertical asymptote in the context of this application. The velocity of the package approaches, but never reaches or exceeds 150 feet per second.

▶ **68.** **EFFECTS OF AIR RESISTANCE ON VELOCITY** If we assume that air resistance is proportional to the square of the velocity, then the time t in seconds required for an object to reach a velocity v in feet per second is given by

$$t = \frac{9}{24} \ln \frac{24 + v}{24 - v}, \quad 0 \le v < 24$$

a. Determine the velocity, to the nearest hundredth foot per second of the object after 1.5 seconds. 23.14 ft/s

b. Determine the vertical asymptote for the graph of this function. $v = 24$

c. Write a sentence that describes the meaning of the vertical asymptote in the context of this problem. The velocity of the object cannot reach or exceed 24 feet per second.

69. **TERMINAL VELOCITY WITH AIR RESISTANCE** The velocity v of an object t seconds after it has been dropped from a height above the surface of the earth is given by the equation $v = 32t$ feet per second, assuming no air resistance. If we assume that air resistance is proportional to the square of the velocity, then the velocity after t seconds is given by

$$v = 100 \left(\frac{e^{0.64t} - 1}{e^{0.64t} + 1} \right)$$

a. In how many seconds will the velocity be 50 feet per second? 1.72 s

b. Determine the horizontal asymptote for the graph of this function. $v = 100$

c. Write a sentence that describes the meaning of the horizontal asymptote in the context of this problem. The object cannot fall faster than 100 ft/s.

70. **TERMINAL VELOCITY WITH AIR RESISTANCE** If we assume that air resistance is proportional to the square of the velocity, then the velocity v in feet per second of an object t seconds after it has been dropped is given by

$$v = 50 \left(\frac{e^{1.6t} - 1}{e^{1.6t} + 1} \right)$$

(See Exercise 69. The reason for the difference in the equations is that the proportionality constants are different.)

a. In how many seconds will the velocity be 20 feet per second? 0.53 s

b. Determine the horizontal asymptote for the graph of this function. $v = 50$

c. Write a sentence that describes the meaning of the horizontal asymptote in the context of this problem. The velocity of the object cannot reach or exceed 50 ft/s.

71. **EFFECTS OF AIR RESISTANCE ON DISTANCE** The distance s, in feet, that the object in Exercise 69 will fall in t seconds is given by

$$s = \frac{100^2}{32} \ln \left(\frac{e^{0.32t} + e^{-0.32t}}{2} \right)$$

a. Use a graphing utility to graph this equation for $t \ge 0$. Answer on page AA18.

b. How long does it take for the object to fall 100 feet? Round to the nearest tenth of a second. 2.6 s

72. **EFFECTS OF AIR RESISTANCE ON DISTANCE** The distance s, in feet, that the object in Exercise 70 will fall in t seconds is given by

$$s = \frac{50^2}{40} \ln\left(\frac{e^{0.8t} + e^{-0.8t}}{2}\right)$$

a. Use a graphing utility to graph this equation for $t \geq 0$. Answer on page AA18.

b. How long does it take for the object to fall 100 feet? Round to the nearest tenth of a second. 2.9 s

73. **RETIREMENT PLANNING** The retirement account for a graphic designer contains $250,000 on January 1, 2002, and earns interest at a rate of 0.5% per month. On February 1, 2002, the designer withdraws $2000 and plans to continue these withdrawals as retirement income each month. The value V of the account after x months is

$$V = 400{,}000 - 150{,}000(1.005)^x$$

If the designer wishes to leave $100,000 to a scholarship foundation, what is the maximum number of withdrawals (to the nearest month) the designer can make from this account and still have $100,000 to donate? 138

74. **HANGING CABLE** The height h, in feet, of any point P on the cable shown is given by

$$h(x) = 10(e^{x/20} + e^{-x/20}), \quad -15 \leq x \leq 15$$

where $|x|$ is the horizontal distance in feet between P and the y-axis.

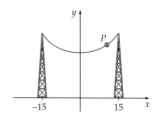

a. What is the lowest height of the cable? 20 ft

b. What is the height of the cable 10 feet to the right of the y-axis? Round to the nearest tenth of a foot. 22.6 ft

c. How far to the right of the y-axis is the cable 24 feet in height? Round to the nearest tenth of a foot. 12.4 ft

---

CONNECTING CONCEPTS

75. The following argument seems to indicate that $0.125 > 0.25$. Find the first incorrect statement in the argument.

$$3 > 2$$
$$3(\log 0.5) > 2(\log 0.5)$$
$$\log 0.5^3 > \log 0.5^2$$
$$0.5^3 > 0.5^2$$
$$0.125 > 0.25$$

The second step; because $\log 0.5 < 0$, the inequality sign must be reversed.

76. The following argument seems to indicate that $4 = 6$. Find the first incorrect statement in the argument.

$$4 = \log_2 16$$
$$4 = \log_2(8 + 8)$$
$$4 = \log_2 8 + \log_2 8$$
$$4 = 3 + 3$$
$$4 = 6$$

The third step. $\log_2(8 + 8)$ does not equal $\log_2 8 + \log_2 8$.

77. A common mistake that students make is to write $\log(x + y)$ as $\log x + \log y$. For what values of x and y does $\log(x + y) = \log x + \log y$? (*Hint:* Solve for x in terms of y.) $x = \dfrac{y}{y - 1}$

78. Let $f(x) = 2 \ln x$ and $g(x) = \ln x^2$. Does $f(x) = g(x)$ for all real numbers x? No

79. Explain why the functions $F(x) = 1.4^x$ and $G(x) = e^{0.336x}$ represent essentially the same function. $e^{0.336} \approx 1.4$

80. Find the constant k that will make $f(t) = 2.2^t$ and $g(t) = e^{-kt}$ represent essentially the same function. $k = -\ln 2.2 \approx -0.788$

PREPARE FOR SECTION 4.6

81. Evaluate $A = 1000\left(1 + \dfrac{0.1}{12}\right)^{12t}$ for $t = 2$. Round to the nearest hundredth. [4.2] 1220.39

82. Evaluate $A = 600\left(1 + \dfrac{0.04}{4}\right)^{4t}$ for $t = 8$. Round to the nearest hundredth. [4.2] 824.96

83. Solve $0.5 = e^{14k}$ for k. Round to the nearest ten-thousandth. [4.5] −0.0495

84. Solve $0.85 = 0.5^{t/5730}$ for t. Round to the nearest ten. [4.5] 1340

85. Solve $6 = \dfrac{70}{5 + 9e^{-k \cdot 12}}$ for k. Round to the nearest thousandth. [4.5] 0.025

86. Solve $2,000,000 = \dfrac{3^{n+1} - 3}{2}$ for n. Round to the nearest tenth. [4.5] 12.8

PROJECTS

1.   **NAVIGATING** The pilot of a boat is trying to cross a river to a point O two miles due west of the boat's starting position by always pointing the nose of the boat toward O. Suppose the speed of the current is w miles per hour and the speed of the boat is v miles per hour. If point O is the origin and the boat's starting position is $(2, 0)$ (see the diagram at the right), then the equation of the boat's path is given by

$$y = \left(\frac{x}{2}\right)^{1-(w/v)} - \left(\frac{x}{2}\right)^{1+(w/v)}$$

a. If the speed of the current and the speed of the boat are the same, can the pilot reach point O by always having the nose of the boat pointed toward O? If not, at what point will the pilot arrive? Explain your answer.

b. If the speed of the current is greater than the speed of the boat, can the pilot reach point O by always pointing the nose of the boat toward O? If not, where will the pilot arrive? Explain.

c. If the speed of the current is less than the speed of the boat, can the pilot reach point O by always pointing the nose of the boat toward O? If not, where will the pilot arrive? Explain.

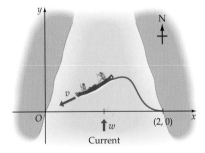

EXPONENTIAL GROWTH AND DECAY

In many applications, a quantity N grows or decays according to the function $N(t) = N_0 e^{kt}$. In this function, N is a function of time t, and N_0 is the value of N at time $t = 0$. If k is a *positive* constant, then $N(t) = N_0 e^{kt}$ is called an **exponential growth function**. If k is a *negative* constant, then $N(t) = N_0 e^{kt}$ is called an **exponential decay function**. The following examples illustrate how growth and decay functions arise naturally in the investigation of certain phenomena.

Interest is money paid for the use of money. The interest I is called **simple interest** if it is a fixed percent r, per time period t, of the amount of money invested. The amount of money invested is called the **principal** P. Simple interest is computed using the formula $I = Prt$. For example, if $1000 is invested at 12% for 3 years, the simple interest is

$$I = Prt = \$1000(0.12)(3) = \$360$$

The balance after t years is $A = P + I = P + Prt$. In the previous example, the $1000 invested for 3 years produced $360 interest. Thus the balance after 3 years is $1000 + $360 = $1360.

● COMPOUND INTEREST

In many financial transactions, interest is added to the principal at regular intervals so that interest is paid on interest as well as on the principal. Interest earned in this manner is called **compound interest.** For example, if $1000 is invested at 12% annual interest compounded annually for 3 years, then the total interest after 3 years is

First-year interest	$1000(0.12) = $120.00
Second-year interest	$1120(0.12) = $134.40
Third-year interest	$1254.40(0.12) ≈ $150.53
	$404.93 • Total interest

This method of computing the balance can be tedious and time-consuming. A *compound interest formula* that can be used to determine the balance due after t years of compounding can be developed as follows.

Note that if P dollars is invested at an interest rate of r per year, then the balance after one year is $A_1 = P + Pr = P(1 + r)$, where Pr represents the interest earned for the year. Observe that A_1 is the product of the original principal P and $(1 + r)$. If the amount A_1 is reinvested for another year, then the balance after the second year is

$$A_2 = (A_1)(1 + r) = P(1 + r)(1 + r) = P(1 + r)^2$$

Successive reinvestments lead to the results shown in **Table 4.11.** The equation $A_t = P(1 + r)^t$ is valid if r is the annual interest rate paid during each of the t years.

TABLE 4.11

Number of Years	Balance
3	$A_3 = P(1 + r)^3$
4	$A_4 = P(1 + r)^4$
⋮	⋮
t	$A_t = P(1 + r)^t$

If r is an annual interest rate and n is the number of compounding periods per year, then the interest rate each period is r/n and the number of compounding periods after t years is nt. Thus the compound interest formula is expressed as follows:

The Compound Interest Formula

A principal P invested at an annual interest rate r, expressed as a decimal and compounded n times per year for t years, produces the balance

$$A = P\left(1 + \frac{r}{n}\right)^{nt}$$

Alternative to Example 1
Exercise 2, page 430.

EXAMPLE 1   **Solve a Compound Interest Application**

Find the balance if $1000 is invested at an annual interest rate of 10% for 2 years compounded

a.   annually   b.   monthly   c.   daily

Solution

a.   Use the compound interest formula with $P = 1000$, $r = 0.1$, $t = 2$, and $n = 1$.

$$A = \$1000\left(1 + \frac{0.1}{1}\right)^{1 \cdot 2} = \$1000(1.1)^2 = \$1210.00$$

b.   Because there are 12 months in a year, use $n = 12$.

$$A = \$1000\left(1 + \frac{0.1}{12}\right)^{12 \cdot 2} \approx \$1000(1.008333333)^{24} \approx \$1220.39$$

c.   Because there are 365 days in a year, use $n = 365$.

$$A = \$1000\left(1 + \frac{0.1}{365}\right)^{365 \cdot 2} \approx \$1000(1.000273973)^{730} \approx \$1221.37$$

▶ **TRY EXERCISE 4, PAGE 430**

To **compound continuously** means to increase the number of compounding periods without bound.

To derive a continuous compounding interest formula, substitute $\frac{1}{m}$ for $\frac{r}{n}$ in the compound interest formula

$$A = P\left(1 + \frac{r}{n}\right)^{nt} \tag{1}$$

to produce

$$A = P\left(1 + \frac{1}{m}\right)^{nt} \tag{2}$$

This substitution is motivated by the desire to express $\left(1 + \dfrac{r}{n}\right)^n$ as $\left[\left(1 + \dfrac{1}{m}\right)^m\right]^r$, which approaches e^r as m gets larger without bound.

Solving the equation $\dfrac{1}{m} = \dfrac{r}{n}$ for n yields $n = mr$, so the exponent nt can be written as mrt. Therefore Equation (2) can be expressed as

$$A = P\left(1 + \frac{1}{m}\right)^{mrt} = P\left[\left(1 + \frac{1}{m}\right)^m\right]^{rt} \tag{3}$$

By the definition of e, we know that as m increases without bound,

$$\left(1 + \frac{1}{m}\right)^m \qquad \text{approaches} \qquad e$$

Thus, using continuous compounding, Equation (3) simplifies to $A = Pe^{rt}$.

Alternative to Example 2
Find the balance after 10 years on $5000 invested at an annual rate of 5% compounded continuously.
● **$8243.61**

Ⓟ **Continuous Compounding Interest Formula**

If an account with principal P and annual interest rate r is compounded continuously for t years, then the balance is $A = Pe^{rt}$.

EXAMPLE 2 **Solve a Continuous Compound Interest Application**

Find the balance after 4 years on $800 invested at an annual rate of 6% compounded continuously.

Algebraic Solution

Use the continuous compounding formula with $P = 800$, $r = 0.06$, and $t = 4$.

$$\begin{aligned}
A &= Pe^{rt} \\
&= 800e^{0.06(4)} \\
&= 800e^{0.24} \\
&\approx 800(1.27124915) \\
&\approx 1017.00 \qquad \text{• To the nearest cent}
\end{aligned}$$

The balance after 4 years will be $1017.00.

Visualize the Solution

Figure 4.43, a graph of $A = 800e^{0.06t}$, shows that the balance is about $1017.00 when $t = 4$.

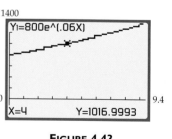

FIGURE 4.43

▶ **TRY EXERCISE 6, PAGE 430**

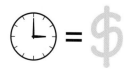

You have probably heard it said that time is money. In fact, many investors ask the question "How long will it take to double my money?" The following example answers this question for two different investments.

Alternative to Example 3
Find the time required for money invested at an annual rate of 8% to triple in value if the investment is compounded monthly.
● ≈**13.78 years**

EXAMPLE 3 Double Your Money

Find the time required for money invested at an annual rate of 6% to double in value if the investment is compounded

a. semiannually

b. continuously

Solution

a. Use $A = P\left(1 + \dfrac{r}{n}\right)^{nt}$ with $r = 0.06$, $n = 2$, and the balance A equal to twice the principal ($A = 2P$).

$$2P = P\left(1 + \frac{0.06}{2}\right)^{2t}$$

$$2 = \left(1 + \frac{0.06}{2}\right)^{2t} \qquad \text{• Divide each side by } P.$$

$$\ln 2 = \ln\left(1 + \frac{0.06}{2}\right)^{2t} \qquad \text{• Take the natural logarithm of each side.}$$

$$\ln 2 = 2t \ln\left(1 + \frac{0.06}{2}\right) \qquad \text{• Apply the power property.}$$

$$2t = \frac{\ln 2}{\ln\left(1 + \dfrac{0.06}{2}\right)} \qquad \text{• Solve for } t.$$

$$t = \frac{1}{2} \cdot \frac{\ln 2}{\ln\left(1 + \dfrac{0.06}{2}\right)}$$

$$t \approx 11.72$$

If the investment is compounded semiannually, it will double in value in about 11.72 years.

b. Use $A = Pe^{rt}$ with $r = 0.06$ and $A = 2P$.

$$2P = Pe^{0.06t}$$

$$2 = e^{0.06t} \qquad \text{• Divide each side by } P.$$

$$\ln 2 = 0.06t \qquad \text{• Write in logarithm form.}$$

$$t = \frac{\ln 2}{0.06} \qquad \text{• Solve for } t.$$

$$t \approx 11.55$$

If the investment is compounded continuously, it will double in value in about 11.55 years.

▶ **TRY EXERCISE 10, PAGE 430**

● EXPONENTIAL GROWTH

Given any two points on the graph of $N(t) = N_0e^{kt}$, you can use the given data to solve for the constants N_0 and k.

Alternative to Example 4
Exercise 16, page 430.

EXAMPLE 4	Find the Exponential Growth Function That Models Given Data

a. Find the exponential growth function for a town whose population was 16,400 in 1990 and 20,200 in 2000.

b. Use the function from part **a.** to predict, to the nearest 100, the population of the town in 2005.

Solution

a. We need to determine N_0 and k in $N(t) = N_0e^{kt}$. If we represent the year 1990 by $t = 0$, then our given data are $N(0) = 16,400$ and $N(10) = 20,200$. Because N_0 is defined to be $N(0)$, we know that $N_0 = 16,400$. To determine k, substitute $t = 10$ and $N_0 = 16,400$ into $N(t) = N_0e^{kt}$ to produce

$$N(10) = 16,400e^{k \cdot 10}$$

$$20,200 = 16,400e^{10k} \qquad \text{• Substitute 20,200 for } N(10).$$

$$\frac{20,200}{16,400} = e^{10k} \qquad \text{• Solve for } e^{10k}.$$

$$\ln \frac{20,200}{16,400} = 10k \qquad \text{• Write in logarithmic form.}$$

$$\frac{1}{10} \ln \frac{20,200}{16,400} = k \qquad \text{• Solve for } k.$$

$$0.0208 \approx k$$

The exponential growth function is $N(t) \approx 16,400e^{0.0208t}$.

b. The year 1990 was represented by $t = 0$, so we will use $t = 15$ to represent the year 2005.

$$N(t) \approx 16,400e^{0.0208t}$$

$$N(15) \approx 16,400e^{0.0208 \cdot 15}$$

$$\approx 22,400 \quad \text{(nearest 100)}$$

The exponential growth function yields 22,400 as the approximate population of the town in 2005.

---

take note

Because $e^{0.0208} \approx 1.021$, the growth equation can also be written as

$$N(t) \approx 16,400(1.021)^t$$

In this form we see that the population is growing by 2.1% $(1.021 - 1 = 0.021 = 2.1\%)$ per year.

▶ **TRY EXERCISE 18, PAGE 431**

● EXPONENTIAL DECAY

Many radioactive materials *decrease* in mass exponentially over time. This decrease, called radioactive decay, is measured in terms of **half-life,** which is defined as the time required for the disintegration of half the atoms in a sample of a radioactive substance. **Table 4.12** shows the half-lives of selected radioactive isotopes.

Table 4.12

Isotope	Half-Life
Carbon (^{14}C)	5730 years
Radium (^{226}Ra)	1660 years
Polonium (^{210}Po)	138 days
Phosphorus (^{32}P)	14 days
Polonium (^{214}Po)	1/10,000th of a second

Alternative to Example 5
Exercise 22, page 431.

EXAMPLE 5 **Find the Exponential Decay Function That Models Given Data**

Find the exponential decay function for the amount of phosphorus (^{32}P) that remains in a sample after t days.

Solution

When $t = 0$, $N(0) = N_0e^{k(0)} = N_0$. Thus $N(0) = N_0$. Also, because the phosphorus has a half-life of 14 days (from **Table 4.12**), $N(14) = 0.5N_0$. To find k, substitute $t = 14$ into $N(t) = N_0e^{kt}$ and solve for k.

$$N(14) = N_0 \cdot e^{k \cdot 14}$$
$$0.5N_0 = N_0e^{14k} \qquad \text{• Substitute } 0.5N_0 \text{ for } N(14).$$
$$0.5 = e^{14k} \qquad \text{• Divide each side by } N_0.$$
$$\ln 0.5 = 14k \qquad \text{• Write in logarithmic form.}$$
$$\frac{1}{14}\ln 0.5 = k \qquad \text{• Solve for } k.$$
$$-0.0495 \approx k$$

The exponential decay function is $N(t) = N_0e^{-0.0495t}$.

take note

Because $e^{-0.0495} \approx (0.5)^{1/14}$, the decay function $N(t) = N_0e^{-0.0495t}$ can also be written as $N(t) = N_0(0.5)^{t/14}$. In this form it is easy to see that if t is increased by 14, then N will decrease by a factor of 0.5.

▶ **TRY EXERCISE 20, PAGE 431**

EXAMPLE 6   **Application to Air Resistance**

Assuming that air resistance is proportional to the velocity of a falling object, the velocity (in feet per second) of the object t seconds after it has been dropped is given by $v = 82(1 - e^{-0.39t})$.

Alternative to Example 6
Exercise 28, page 431.

a. Determine when the velocity will be 70 feet per second.

b. Write a sentence that explains the meaning of the horizontal asymptote, which is $v = 82$, in the context of this example.

Algebraic Solution

a.
$$v = 82(1 - e^{-0.39t})$$
$$70 = 82(1 - e^{-0.39t})$$ • Replace v by 70.

$$\frac{70}{82} = 1 - e^{-0.39t}$$ • Divide each side by 82.

$$e^{-0.39t} = 1 - \frac{70}{82}$$ • Solve for $e^{-0.39t}$.

$$-0.39t = \ln\frac{6}{41}$$ • Write in logarithmic form.

$$t = \frac{\ln(6/41)}{-0.39} \approx 4.9277246$$ • Solve for t.

The time is approximately 4.9 seconds.

b. The horizontal asymptote $v = 82$ means that as time increases, the velocity of the object will approach but never reach or exceed 82 feet per second.

► **TRY EXERCISE 32, PAGE 432**

Visualize the Solution

a. A graph of $y = 82(1 - e^{-0.39x})$ and $y = 70$ shows that the x-coordinate of the point of intersection is about 4.9.

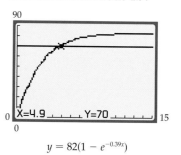

$$y = 82(1 - e^{-0.39x})$$

FIGURE 4.44

Note: The x value shown is rounded to the nearest tenth.

● **CARBON DATING**

The bone tissue in all living animals contains both carbon-12, which is nonradioactive, and carbon-14, which is radioactive with a half-life of approximately 5730 years. See **Figure 4.45**. As long as the animal is alive, the ratio of carbon-14 to carbon-12 remains constant. When the animal dies ($t = 0$), the carbon-14 begins to decay. Thus a bone that has a smaller ratio of carbon-14 to carbon-12 is older than a bone that has a larger ratio. The percent of carbon-14 present at time t is

$$P(t) = 0.5^{t/5730}$$

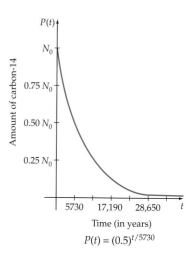

$$P(t) = (0.5)^{t/5730}$$

FIGURE 4.45

Alternative to Example 7
How long ago did an animal die if one of its bones now contains 99% of its original amount of carbon-14? Round to the nearest year.
● **83 years**

MATH MATTERS

The chemist Willard Frank Libby developed the carbon-14 dating technique in 1947. In 1960 he was awarded the Nobel Prize in chemistry for this achievement.

EXAMPLE 7   Application to Archeology

Find the age of a bone if it now has 85% of the carbon-14 it had when $t = 0$.

Solution

Let t be the time at which $P(t) = 0.85$.

$$0.85 = 0.5^{t/5730}$$

$$\ln 0.85 = \ln 0.5^{t/5730} \qquad \bullet \text{ Take the natural logarithm of each side.}$$

$$\ln 0.85 = \frac{t}{5730} \ln 0.5 \qquad \bullet \text{ Power property}$$

$$5730\left(\frac{\ln 0.85}{\ln 0.5}\right) = t \qquad \bullet \text{ Solve for } t.$$

$$1340 \approx t$$

The bone is about 1340 years old.

▶ TRY EXERCISE 24, PAGE 431

● THE LOGISTIC MODEL

The population growth function $P(t) = P_0 e^{kt}$ is called the **Malthusian growth model.** It was developed by Robert Malthus (1766–1834) in *An Essay on the Principle of Population Growth,* which was published in 1798. The Malthusian growth model is an unrestricted growth model that does not consider any limited resources that eventually will curb population growth.

The **logistic model** is a restricted growth model that takes into consideration the effects of limited resources. The logistic model was developed by Pierre Verhulst in 1836.

The Logistic Model (A Restricted Growth Model)

The magnitude of a population at time $t \geq 0$ is given by

$$P(t) = \frac{c}{1 + ae^{-bt}}$$

where c is the **carrying capacity** (the maximum population that can be supported by available resources as $t \to \infty$) and b is a positive constant called the **growth rate constant.**

The **initial population** is $P_0 = P(0)$. The constant a is related to the initial population P_0 and the carrying capacity c by the formula

$$a = \frac{c - P_0}{P_0}$$

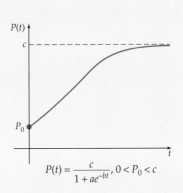

$$P(t) = \frac{c}{1 + ae^{-bt}}, 0 < P_0 < c$$

In the following example we determine a logistic growth model for a coyote population.

Alternative to Example 8
Exercise 50, page 433.

EXAMPLE 8 Find and Use a Logistic Model

At the beginning of 2002, the coyote population in a wilderness area was estimated at 200. By the beginning of 2004, the coyote population had increased to 250. A park ranger estimates that the carrying capacity of the wilderness area is 500 coyotes.

a. Use the given data to determine the growth rate constant for the logistic model of this coyote population.

b. Use the logistic model determined in part **a.** to predict the year in which the coyote population will first reach 400.

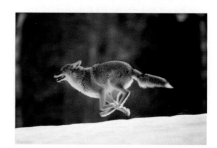

Solution

a. If we represent the beginning of the year 2002 by $t = 0$, then the beginning of the year 2004 will be represented by $t = 2$. In the logistic model, make the following substitutions: $P(2) = 250$, $c = 500$, and

$$a = \frac{c - P_0}{P_0} = \frac{500 - 200}{200} = 1.5.$$

$$P(t) = \frac{c}{1 + ae^{-bt}}$$

$$P(2) = \frac{500}{1 + 1.5e^{-b \cdot 2}}$$ • **Substitute the given values.**

$$250 = \frac{500}{1 + 1.5e^{-b \cdot 2}}$$

$$250(1 + 1.5e^{-b \cdot 2}) = 500$$ • **Solve for the growth rate constant b.**

$$1 + 1.5e^{-b \cdot 2} = \frac{500}{250}$$

$$1.5e^{-b \cdot 2} = 2 - 1$$

$$e^{-b \cdot 2} = \frac{1}{1.5}$$

$$-2b = \ln\left(\frac{1}{1.5}\right)$$

$$b = -\frac{1}{2}\ln\left(\frac{1}{1.5}\right)$$

$$b \approx 0.20273255$$

Using $a = 1.5$, $b = 0.20273255$, and $c = 500$ gives us the following logistic model.

$$P(t) = \frac{500}{1 + 1.5e^{-0.20273255t}}$$

b. To determine during what year the logistic model predicts the coyote population will first reach 400, replace $P(t)$ with 400 and solve for t.

$$400 = \frac{500}{1 + 1.5e^{-0.20273255t}}$$

$$400(1 + 1.5e^{-0.20273255t}) = 500$$

$$1 + 1.5e^{-0.20273255t} = \frac{500}{400}$$

$$1.5e^{-0.20273255t} = 1.25 - 1$$

$$e^{-0.20273255t} = \frac{0.25}{1.5}$$

$$-0.20273255t = \ln\left(\frac{0.25}{1.5}\right) \qquad \text{• Write in logarithmic form.}$$

$$t = \frac{1}{-0.20273255}\ln\left(\frac{0.25}{1.5}\right) \qquad \text{• Solve for } t.$$

$$\approx 8.8$$

According to the logistic model, the coyote population will reach 400 about 8.8 years after the beginning of 2002, which is during the year 2010. The graph of the logistic model is shown in **Figure 4.46.** Note that $P(8.8) \approx 400$ and that as $t \to \infty$, $P(t) \to 500$.

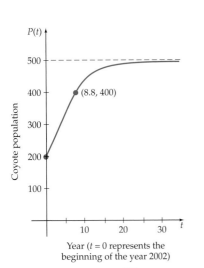

Year ($t = 0$ represents the beginning of the year 2002)

$$P(t) = \frac{500}{1 + 1.5e^{-0.20273255t}}$$

FIGURE 4.46

 TRY EXERCISE 48, PAGE 433

TOPICS FOR DISCUSSION

1. Explain the difference between compound interest and simple interest.

2. What is an exponential growth model? Give an example of an application for which the exponential growth model might be appropriate.

3. What is an exponential decay model? Give an example of an application for which the exponential decay model might be appropriate.

4. Consider the exponential model $P(t) = P_0e^{kt}$ and the logistic model $P(t) = \dfrac{c}{1 + ae^{-bt}}$. Explain the similarities and differences between the two models.

EXERCISE SET 4.6

—Suggested Assignment: Exercises 1–57, every other odd; 59–64, all.

1. COMPOUND INTEREST If $8000 is invested at an annual interest rate of 5% and compounded annually, find the balance after

   a. 4 years   **b.** 7 years
     $9724.05 $11,256.80

2. COMPOUND INTEREST If $22,000 is invested at an annual interest rate of 4.5% and compounded annually, find the balance after

   a. 2 years   **b.** 10 years
     $24,024.55 $34,165.33

3. COMPOUND INTEREST If $38,000 is invested at an annual interest rate of 6.5% for 4 years, find the balance if the interest is compounded

   a. annually   **b.** daily   **c.** hourly
     $48,885.72 $49,282.20 $49,283.30

▶ **4. COMPOUND INTEREST** If $12,500 is invested at an annual interest rate of 8% for 10 years, find the balance if the interest is compounded

   a. annually   **b.** daily   **c.** hourly
     $26,986.56 $27,816.82 $27,819.16

5. COMPOUND INTEREST Find the balance if $15,000 is invested at an annual rate of 10% for 5 years, compounded continuously. $24,730.82

▶ **6. COMPOUND INTEREST** Find the balance if $32,000 is invested at an annual rate of 8% for 3 years, compounded continuously. $40,679.97

7. COMPOUND INTEREST How long will it take $4000 to double if it is invested in a certificate of deposit that pays 7.84% annual interest compounded continuously? Round to the nearest tenth of a year. 8.8 yrs

8. COMPOUND INTEREST How long will it take $25,000 to double if it is invested in a savings account that pays 5.88% annual interest compounded continuously? Round to the nearest tenth of a year. 11.8 yrs

9. CONTINUOUS COMPOUNDING INTEREST Use the Continuous Compounding Interest Formula to derive an expression for the time it will take money to triple when invested at an annual interest rate of r compounded continuously. $t = \dfrac{\ln 3}{r}$

▶ **10. CONTINUOUS COMPOUNDING INTEREST** How long will it take $1000 to triple if it is invested at an annual interest rate of 5.5% compounded continuously? Round to the nearest year. 20 yrs

11. CONTINUOUS COMPOUNDING INTEREST How long will it take $6000 to triple if it is invested in a savings account that pays 7.6% annual interest compounded continuously? Round to the nearest year. 14 yrs

12. CONTINUOUS COMPOUNDING INTEREST How long will it take $10,000 to triple if it is invested in a savings account that pays 5.5% annual interest compounded continuously? Round to the nearest year. 20 yrs

13. POPULATION GROWTH The number of bacteria $N(t)$ present in a culture at time t hours is given by

$$N(t) = 2200(2)^t$$

Find the number of bacteria present when

   a. $t = 0$ hours   **b.** $t = 3$ hours
     2200 bacteria   17,600 bacteria

14. POPULATION GROWTH The population of a town grows exponentially according to the function

$$f(t) = 12,400(1.14)^t$$

for $0 \le t \le 5$ years. Find, to the nearest hundred, the population of the town when t is

   a. 3 years   **b.** 4.25 years
     18,400   21,600

15. POPULATION GROWTH A town had a population of 22,600 in 1990 and a population of 24,200 in 1995.

   a. Find the exponential growth function for the town. Use $t = 0$ to represent the year 1990. $N(t) \approx 22,600 e^{0.01368t}$

   b. Use the growth function to predict the population of the town in 2005. Round to the nearest hundred. 27,700

16. POPULATION GROWTH A town had a population of 53,700 in 1996 and a population of 58,100 in 2000.

   a. Find the exponential growth function for the town. Use $t = 0$ to represent the year 1996. $N(t) \approx 53,700 e^{0.01969t}$

   b. Use the growth function to predict the population of the town in 2008. Round to the nearest hundred. 68,000

17. POPULATION GROWTH The growth of the population of Los Angeles, California, for the years 1992 through 1996 can be approximated by the equation

$$P = 10,130(1.005)^t$$

where $t = 0$ corresponds to January 1, 1992 and P is in thousands.

   a. Assuming this growth rate continues, what will be the population of Los Angeles on January 1 in the year 2004? 10,755,000

b. In what year will the population of Los Angeles first exceed 13,000,000? 2042

▶ **18.** 🌐 **POPULATION GROWTH** The growth of the population of Mexico City, Mexico, for the years 1991 through 1998 can be approximated by the equation

$$P = 20,899(1.027)^t$$

where $t = 0$ corresponds to 1991 and P is in thousands.

a. Assuming this growth rate continues, what will be the population of Mexico City in the year 2003? 28,772,000

b. Assuming this growth rate continues, in what year will the population of Mexico City first exceed 35,000,000? 2010

19. MEDICINE Sodium-24 is a radioactive isotope of sodium that is used to study circulatory dysfunction. Assuming that 4 micrograms of sodium-24 is injected into a person, the amount A in micrograms remaining in that person after t hours is given by the equation $A = 4e^{-0.046t}$.

a. Graph this equation.
Answer on page AA18.

b. What amount of sodium-24 remains after 5 hours? 3.18 micrograms

c. What is the half-life of sodium-24? ≈15.07 h

d. In how many hours will the amount of sodium-24 be 1 microgram? ≈30.14 h

▶ **20.** 🌐 **RADIOACTIVE DECAY** Polonium (^{210}Po) has a half-life of 138 days. Find the decay function for the amount of polonium (^{210}Po) that remains in a sample after t days.
$N(t) \approx N_0 e^{-0.005023t}$

21. 🌐 **GEOLOGY** Geologists have determined that Crater Lake in Oregon was formed by a volcanic eruption. Chemical analysis of a wood chip that is assumed to be from a tree that died during the eruption has shown that it contains approximately 45% of its original carbon-14. Determine how long ago the volcanic eruption occurred. Use 5730 years as the half-life of carbon-14. ≈6601 years ago

22. 🌐 **RADIOACTIVE DECAY** Use $N(t) = N_0(0.5)^{t/138}$, where t is measured in days, to estimate the percentage of polonium (^{210}Po) that remains in a sample after 2 years. Round to the nearest hundredth of a percent. 2.56%

23. 🌐 **ARCHEOLOGY** The Rhind papyrus, named after A. Henry Rhind, contains most of what we know today of ancient Egyptian mathematics. A chemical analysis of a sample from the papyrus has shown that it contains approximately 75% of its original carbon-14. What is the age of the Rhind papyrus? Use 5730 years as the half-life of carbon-14. ≈2378 years old

▶ **24. ARCHEOLOGY** Determine the age of a bone if it now contains 65% of its original amount of carbon-14. Round to the nearest 100 years. 3600 yrs

25. PHYSICS Newton's Law of Cooling states that if an object at temperature T_0 is placed into an environment at constant temperature A, then the temperature of the object, $T(t)$ (in degrees Fahrenheit), after t minutes is given by $T(t) = A + (T_0 - A)e^{-kt}$, where k is a constant that depends on the object.

a. Determine the constant k (to the nearest thousandth) for a canned soda drink that takes 5 minutes to cool from 75°F to 65°F after being placed in a refrigerator that maintains a constant temperature of 34°F. 0.056

b. What will be the temperature (to the nearest degree) of the soda drink after 30 minutes? 42°F

c. When (to the nearest minute) will the temperature of the soda drink be 36°F? after 54 min

26. PSYCHOLOGY According to a software company, the users of its typing tutorial can expect to type $N(t)$ words per minute after t hours of practice with the product, according to the function $N(t) = 100(1.04 - 0.99^t)$.

a. How many words per minute can a student expect to type after 2 hours of practice? 6 wpm

b. How many words per minute can a student expect to type after 40 hours of practice? 37 wpm

c. According to the function N, how many hours (to the nearest hour) of practice will be required before a student can expect to type 60 words per minute? 82 h

27. PSYCHOLOGY In the city of Whispering Palms, which has a population of 80,000 people, the number of people $P(t)$ exposed to a rumor in t hours is given by the function $P(t) = 80,000(1 - e^{-0.0005t})$.

a. Find the number of hours until 10% of the population have heard the rumor. 211 h

b. Find the number of hours until 50% of the population have heard the rumor. 1386 h

28. LAW A lawyer has determined that the number of people $P(t)$ in a city of 1,200,000 people who have been exposed to a news item after t days is given by the function

$$P(t) = 1,200,000(1 - e^{-0.03t})$$

a. How many days after a major crime has been reported have 40% of the population heard of the crime? 17 days

b. A defense lawyer knows it will be very difficult to pick an unbiased jury after 80% of the population have heard of the crime. After how many days will 80% of the population have heard of the crime? 54 days

29. DEPRECIATION An automobile depreciates according to the function $V(t) = V_0(1 - r)^t$, where $V(t)$ is the value in dollars after t years, V_0 is the original value, and r is the yearly depreciation rate. A car has a yearly depreciation rate of 20%. Determine, to the nearest 0.1 year, in how many years the car will depreciate to half its original value. 3.1 yrs

30. PHYSICS The current $I(t)$ (measured in amperes) of a circuit is given by the function $I(t) = 6(1 - e^{-2.5t})$, where t is the number of seconds after the switch is closed.

a. Find the current when $t = 0$. 0 amps

b. Find the current when $t = 0.5$. ≈4.28 amps

c. Solve the equation for t.
$$t = -\frac{2}{5}\ln\left(1 - \frac{I(t)}{6}\right)$$

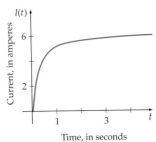

Time, in seconds

31. AIR RESISTANCE Assuming that air resistance is proportional to velocity, the velocity v, in feet per second, of a falling object after t seconds is given by $v = 32(1 - e^{-t})$.

a. Graph this equation for $t \geq 0$.
Answer on page AA18.

b. Determine algebraically, to the nearest 0.01 second, when the velocity is 20 feet per second. 0.98 s

c. Determine the horizontal asymptote of the graph of v.
$v = 32$

d. ✎ Write a sentence that explains the meaning of the horizontal asymptote in the context of this application. As time increases, the velocity approaches but never reaches or exceeds 32 feet per second.

▶ **32. AIR RESISTANCE** Assuming that air resistance is proportional to velocity, the velocity v, in feet per second, of a falling object after t seconds is given by $v = 64(1 - e^{-t/2})$.

a. Graph this equation for $t \geq 0$.
Answer on page AA18.

b. Determine algebraically, to the nearest 0.1 second, when the velocity is 50 feet per second. 3.0 s

c. Determine the horizontal asymptote of the graph of v.
$v = 64$

d. ✎ Write a sentence that explains the meaning of the horizontal asymptote in the context of this application. As time increases, the object's velocity approaches but never reaches or exceeds 64 feet per second.

33. 🖩 The distance s (in feet) that the object in Exercise 31 will fall in t seconds is given by $s = 32t + 32(e^{-t} - 1)$.

a. Use a graphing utility to graph this equation for $t \geq 0$.
Answer on page AA18.

b. Determine, to the nearest 0.1 second, the time it takes the object to fall 50 feet. 2.5 s

c. Calculate the slope of the secant line through $(1, s(1))$ and $(2, s(2))$.
≈24.56 ft/s

d. ✎ Write a sentence that explains the meaning of the slope of the secant line you calculated in **c.**
The average speed of the object was approximately 24.56 feet per second during the period from $t = 1$ to $t = 2$ seconds.

34. 🖩 The distance s (in feet) that the object in Exercise 32 will fall in t seconds is given by $s = 64t + 128(e^{-t/2} - 1)$.

a. Use a graphing utility to graph this equation for $t \geq 0$.
Answer on page AA18.

b. Determine, to the nearest 0.1 second, the time it takes the object to fall 50 feet. 2.1 s

c. Calculate the slope of the secant line through $(1, s(1))$ and $(2, s(2))$.
≈33.5 ft/s

d. ✎ Write a sentence that explains the meaning of the slope of the secant line you calculated in **c.**
The average speed of the object was approximately 33.5 feet per second during the period from $t = 1$ to $t = 2$ seconds.

In Exercises 35 to 40, determine the following constants for the given logistic growth model.
a. The carrying capacity
b. The growth rate constant
c. The initial population P_0

35. $P(t) = \dfrac{1900}{1 + 8.5e^{-0.16t}}$
   a. 1900 **b.** 0.16 **c.** 200

36. $P(t) = \dfrac{32,550}{1 + 0.75e^{-0.08t}}$
   a. 32,550 **b.** 0.08 **c.** 18,600

37. $P(t) = \dfrac{157,500}{1 + 2.5e^{-0.04t}}$
   a. 157,500 **b.** 0.04 **c.** 45,000

38. $P(t) = \dfrac{51}{1 + 1.04e^{-0.03t}}$
   a. 51 **b.** 0.03 **c.** 25

39. $P(t) = \dfrac{2400}{1 + 7e^{-0.12t}}$
   a. 2400 **b.** 0.12 **c.** 300

40. $P(t) = \dfrac{320}{1 + 15e^{-0.12t}}$
   a. 320 **b.** 0.12 **c.** 20

In Exercises 41 to 44, use algebraic procedures to find the logistic growth model for the data.

41. $P_0 = 400$, $P(2) = 780$, and the carrying capacity is 5500.
$$P(t) \approx \frac{5500}{1 + 12.75e^{-0.37263t}}$$

42. $P_0 = 6200$, $P(8) = 7100$, and the carrying capacity is 9500.
$$P(t) \approx \frac{9500}{1 + 0.53226e^{-0.05675t}}$$

43. $P_0 = 18$, $P(3) = 30$, and the carrying capacity is 100.
$$P(t) \approx \frac{100}{1 + 4.55556e^{-0.22302t}}$$

44. $P_0 = 3200$, $P(22) \approx 5565$, and the growth rate constant is 0.056.
$$P(t) \approx \frac{8000}{1 + 1.5e^{-0.056t}}$$

45. **REVENUE** The annual revenue R, in dollars, of a new company can be closely modeled by the logistic growth function

$$R(t) = \frac{625,000}{1 + 3.1e^{-0.045t}}$$

where the *natural* number t is the time, in years, since the company was founded.

a. According to the model, what will be the company's annual revenue for its first year and its second year ($t = 1$ and $t = 2$) of operation? Round to the nearest $1000.
$158,000, $163,000

b. According to the model, what will the company's annual revenue approach in the long-term future?
$625,000

46. **NEW CAR SALES** The number of cars A sold annually by an automobile dealership can be closely modeled by the logistic growth function

$$A(t) = \frac{1650}{1 + 2.4e^{-0.055t}}$$

where the *natural* number t is the time, in years, since the dealership was founded.

a. According to the model, what number of cars will the dealership sell during its first year and its second year ($t = 1$ and $t = 2$) of operation? Round to the nearest unit. 504 cars, 524 cars

b. According to the model, what will the dealership's annual car sales approach in the long-term future?
1650 cars

47. **POPULATION GROWTH** The population of wolves in a preserve satisfies a logistic growth model in which $P_0 = 312$ in the year 2002, $c = 1600$, and $P(6) = 416$.

a. Determine the logistic growth model for this population, where t is the number of years after 2002.
$$P(t) \approx \frac{1600}{1 + 4.12821e^{-0.06198t}}$$

b. Use the logistic growth model from part **a.** to predict the size of the wolf population in 2012. about 497 wolves

▶ **48.** **POPULATION GROWTH** The population of ground-hogs on a ranch satisfies a logistic growth model in which $P_0 = 240$ in the year 2001, $c = 3400$, and $P(1) = 310$.
$$P(t) \approx \frac{3400}{1 + 13.16667e^{-0.27833t}}$$

a. Determine the logistic growth model for this population, where t is the number of years after 2001.

b. Use the logistic growth model from part **a.** to predict the size of the groundhog population in 2008.
about 1182 groundhogs

49. **POPULATION GROWTH** The population of squirrels in a nature preserve satisfies a logistic growth model in which $P_0 = 1500$ in the year 2001. The carrying capacity of the preserve is estimated at 8500 squirrels and $P(2) = 1900$.
$$P(t) \approx \frac{8500}{1 + 4.66667e^{-0.14761t}}$$

a. Determine the logistic growth model for this population, where t is the number of years after 2001.

b. Use the logistic growth model from part **a.** to predict the year in which the squirrel population will first exceed 4000. 2010

50. **POPULATION GROWTH** The population of walruses on an island satisfies a logistic growth model in which $P_0 = 800$ in the year 2000. The carrying capacity of the island is estimated at 5500 walruses, and $P(1) = 900$.

a. Determine the logistic growth model for this population, where t is the number of years after 2000.
$$P(t) \approx \frac{5500}{1 + 5.875e^{-0.13929t}}$$

b. Use the logistic growth model from part **a.** to predict the year in which the walrus population will first exceed 2000. 2008

51. **LEARNING THEORY** The logistic model is also used in learning theory. Suppose that historical records from employee training at a company show that the percent score on a product information test is given by

$$P = \frac{100}{1 + 25e^{-0.095t}}$$

where t is the number of hours of training. What is the number of hours (to the nearest hour) of training needed before a new employee will answer 75% of the questions correctly? 45 h

52. **LEARNING THEORY** A company provides training in the assembly of a computer circuit to new employees. Past experience has shown that the number of correctly assembled circuits per week can be modeled by

$$N = \frac{250}{1 + 249e^{-0.503t}}$$

where t is the number of weeks of training. What is the number of weeks (to the nearest week) of training needed before a new employee will correctly make 140 circuits? 11 weeks

CONNECTING CONCEPTS

53. **MEDICATION LEVEL** A patient is given three dosages of aspirin. Each dosage contains 1 gram of aspirin. The second and third dosages are each taken 3 hours after the previous dosage is administered. The half-life of the aspirin is 2 hours. The amount of aspirin, A, in the patient's body t hours after the first dosage is administered is

$$A(t) = \begin{cases} 0.5^{t/2} & 0 \le t < 3 \\ 0.5^{t/2} + 0.5^{(t-3)/2} & 3 \le t < 6 \\ 0.5^{t/2} + 0.5^{(t-3)/2} + 0.5^{(t-6)/2} & t \ge 6 \end{cases}$$

Find, to the nearest hundredth of a gram, the amount of aspirin in the patient's body when

a. $t = 1$ **b.** $t = 4$ **c.** $t = 9$
   0.71 g   0.96 g   0.52 g

54. **MEDICATION LEVEL** Use a graphing calculator and the dosage formula in Exercise 53 to determine when, to the nearest tenth of an hour, the amount of aspirin in the patient's body first reaches 0.25 gram. 11.1 h

Exercises 55 to 57 make use of the factorial function, which is defined as follows. For whole numbers n, the number $n!$ (which is read "n factorial") is given by

$$n! = \begin{cases} n(n-1)(n-2)\cdots 1, & \text{if } n \ge 1 \\ 1, & \text{if } n = 0 \end{cases}$$

Thus, $0! = 1$ and $4! = 4 \cdot 3 \cdot 2 \cdot 1 = 24$.

55. **QUEUEING THEORY** A study shows that the number of people who arrive at a bank teller's window averages 4.1 people every 10 minutes. The probability P that exactly x people will arrive at the teller's window in a given 10-minute period is

$$P(x) = \frac{4.1^x e^{-4.1}}{x!}$$

Find, to the nearest 0.1%, the probability that in a given 10-minute period, exactly

a. 0 people arrive at the window. 1.7%

b. 2 people arrive at the window. 13.9%

c. 3 people arrive at the window. 19.0%

d. 4 people arrive at the window. 19.5%

e. 9 people arrive at the window. 1.5%

As $x \to \infty$, what does P approach? 0

56. **STIRLING'S FORMULA** *Stirling's Formula* (after James Stirling, 1692–1770),

$$n! \approx \left(\frac{n}{e}\right)^n \sqrt{2\pi n}$$

is often used to approximate very large factorials. Use Stirling's Formula to approximate 10!, and then compute the ratio of Stirling's approximation of 10! divided by the actual value of 10!, which is 3,628,800. $\approx$3,598,696; $\approx$0.9917

57. **RUBIK'S CUBE** The Rubik's cube shown here was invented by Erno Rubik in 1975. The small outer cubes are held together in such a way that they can be rotated around three axes. The total number of positions in which the Rubik's cube can be arranged is

$$\frac{3^8 2^{12} 8! \, 12!}{2 \cdot 3 \cdot 2}$$

If you can arrange a Rubik's cube into a new arrangement every second, how many centuries would it take to place the cube into each of its arrangements? Assume that there are 365 days in a year. 13,715,120,270 centuries

58. **OIL SPILLS** Crude oil leaks from a tank at a rate that depends on the amount of oil that remains in the tank. Because $\frac{1}{8}$ of the oil in the tank leaks out every 2 hours, the volume of oil $V(t)$ in the tank after t hours is given by $V(t) = V_0(0.875)^{t/2}$, where $V_0 = 350,000$ gallons is the number of gallons in the tank at the time the tank started to leak ($t = 0$).

a. How many gallons does the tank hold after 3 hours? 286,471 gal

b. How many gallons does the tank hold after 5 hours? 250,662 gal

c. How long, to the nearest hour, will it take until 90% of the oil has leaked from the tank? 34 h

PREPARE FOR SECTION 4.7

59. Determine whether $N(t) = 4 - \ln t$ is an increasing or a decreasing function. [4.3] decreasing

60. Determine whether $P(t) = 1 - 2(1.05^t)$ is an increasing or a decreasing function. [4.2] decreasing

61. Evaluate $P(t) = \dfrac{108}{1 + 2e^{-0.1t}}$ for $t = 0$. [4.2] 36

62. Evaluate $N(t) = 840e^{1.05t}$ for $t = 0$. [4.2] 840

63. Solve $10 = \dfrac{20}{1 + 2.2e^{-0.05t}}$ for t. Round to the nearest tenth. [4.5] 15.8

64. Determine the horizontal asymptote of the graph of $P(t) = \dfrac{55}{1 + 3e^{-0.08t}}$. [4.2] $P = 55$

PROJECTS

A DECLINING LOGISTIC MODEL If $P_0 > c$ (which implies that $-1 < a < 0$), then the logistic function $P(t) = \dfrac{c}{1 + ae^{-bt}}$ decreases as t increases. Biologists often use this type of logistic function to model populations that decrease over time. See the following figure.

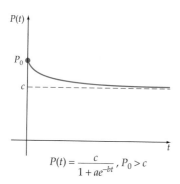

$$P(t) = \frac{c}{1 + ae^{-bt}},\ P_0 > c$$

1. **A DECLINING FISH POPULATION** A biologist finds that the fish population in a small lake can be closely modeled by the logistic function

$$P(t) = \frac{1000}{1 + (-0.3333)e^{-0.05t}}$$

where t is the time, in years, since the lake was first stocked with fish.

a. What was the fish population when the lake was first stocked with fish? 1500 fish

b. According to the logistic model, what will the fish population approach in the long-term future? 1000 fish

2. **A DECLINING DEER POPULATION** The deer population in a reserve is given by the logistic function

$$P(t) = \frac{1800}{1 + (-0.25)e^{-0.07t}}$$

where t is the time, in years, since July 1, 2001.

a. What was the deer population on July 1, 2001? What was the deer population on July 1, 2003? 2400 deer; ≈2300 deer

b. According to the logistic model, what will the deer population approach in the long-term future? 1800 deer

3. **MODELING WORLD RECORD TIMES IN THE MEN'S MILE RACE** In the early 1950s, many people speculated that no runner would ever run a mile race in under 4 minutes. During the period from 1913 to 1945, the world record in the mile event had been reduced from 4.14.4 (4 minutes, 14.4 seconds) to 4.01.4, but no one seemed capable of running a sub-four-minute mile. Then, in 1954, Roger Bannister broke through the four-minute barrier by running a mile in 3.59.6. In 1999, the current record of 3.43.13 was established. It is fun to think about future record times in the mile race. Will they ever go below 3 minutes, 30 seconds? Below 3 minutes, 20 seconds? What about a sub-three-minute mile?

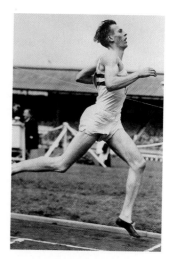

A declining logistic function that closely models the world record times *WR*, in seconds, in the men's mile run from 1913 ($t = 0$) to 1999 ($t = 86$) is given by

$$WR(t) = \frac{199.13}{1 + (-0.21726)e^{-0.0079889t}}$$

a. Use the above logistic model to predict the world record time for the men's mile run in the year 2020 and the year 2050. 3 min, 39.41 s; 3 min, 34.75 s

b. According to the logistic function, what time will the world record in the men's mile event approach but never break through? 3 min, 19.13 s

MODELING DATA WITH EXPONENTIAL AND LOGARITHMIC FUNCTIONS

SECTION 4.7

- **ANALYZE SCATTER PLOTS**
- **APPLICATIONS**
- **USE REGRESSION TO FIND A LOGISTIC GROWTH MODEL**

● **ANALYZE SCATTER PLOTS**

In Section 2.7 we used linear and quadratic functions to model several data sets. However, in some applications, data can be modeled more closely by using exponential or logarithmic functions. For instance, **Figure 4.47** illustrates some scatter plots that can be effectively modeled by exponential and logarithmic functions.

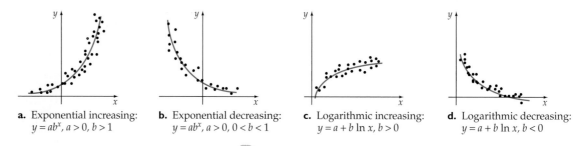

a. Exponential increasing: $y = ab^x$, $a > 0$, $b > 1$
b. Exponential decreasing: $y = ab^x$, $a > 0$, $0 < b < 1$
c. Logarithmic increasing: $y = a + b \ln x$, $b > 0$
d. Logarithmic decreasing: $y = a + b \ln x$, $b < 0$

P **FIGURE 4.47**
Exponential and Logarithmic Models

The terms *concave upward* and *concave downward* are often used to describe a graph. For instance, **Figures 4.48a** and **4.48b** show the graphs of two increasing functions that join the points P and Q. The graphs of f and g differ in that they bend in different directions. We can distinguish between these two types of "bending" by examining the positions of *tangent lines* to the graphs. In **Figures 4.48c** and **4.48d,** tangent lines (in red) have been drawn to the graphs of f and g. The graph of f lies above its tangent lines and the graph of g lies below its tangent lines. The function f is said to be concave upward, and g is concave downward.

a.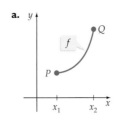

b.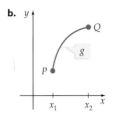

c. *f* is concave upward.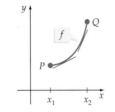

d. *g* is concave downward.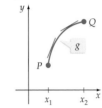

FIGURE 4.48

P **Definition of Concavity**

If the graph of *f* lies above all of its tangents on an interval $[x_1, x_2]$, then *f* is **concave upward** on $[x_1, x_2]$.

If the graph of *f* lies below all of its tangents on an interval $[x_1, x_2]$, then *f* is **concave downward** on $[x_1, x_2]$.

An examination of the graphs in **Figure 4.47** shows that the graphs of all exponential functions of the form $y = ab^x, a > 0, b > 0, b \neq 1$ are concave upward. The graphs of increasing logarithmic functions are concave downward, and the graphs of decreasing logarithmic functions are concave upward.

In Example 1 we analyze scatter plots by determining whether the shape of the scatter plot can best be approximated by an increasing or a decreasing function, and by a function that is concave upward or concave downward.

? QUESTION Is the graph of $y = 5 - 2 \ln x$ concave upward or concave downward?

? ANSWER The equation $y = 5 - 2 \ln x$ has the form $y = a + b \ln x$, with $a > 0$ and $b < 0$. The graph of $y = 5 - 2 \ln x$ is concave upward because the *b*-value, -2, is less than zero. See **Figure 4.47d.**

Alternative to Example 1
Exercise 6, page 444.

See Section 2.7 if you need to review the steps needed to create a scatter plot on a TI-83 calculator.

EXAMPLE 1 **Analyze Scatter Plots**

For each of the following data sets, determine whether the most suitable model of the data would be an increasing exponential function or an increasing logarithmic function.

$$A = \{(1, 0.6), (2, 0.7), (2.8, 0.8), (4, 1.3), (6, 1.5),$$
$$(6.5, 1.6), (8, 2.1), (11.2, 4.1), (12, 4.6), (15, 8.2)\}$$
$$B = \{(1.5, 2.8), (2, 3.5), (4.1, 5.1), (5, 5.5), (5.5, 5.7), (7, 6.1),$$
$$(7.2, 6.4), (8, 6.6), (9, 6.9), (11.6, 7.4), (12.3, 7.5), (14.7, 7.9)\}$$

Solution

For each set construct a scatter plot of the data. See **Figure 4.49.**

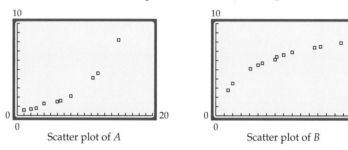

Scatter plot of A Scatter plot of B

FIGURE 4.49

The scatter plot of A suggests that A is an increasing function that is concave upward. Thus A can be effectively modeled by an increasing exponential function.

The scatter plot of B suggests that B is an increasing function that is concave downward. Thus B can be effectively modeled by an increasing logarithmic function.

▶ **TRY EXERCISE 4, PAGE 444**

● APPLICATIONS

The methods used to model data using exponential or logarithmic functions are similar to the methods used in Section 2.7 to model data using linear or quadratic functions. Here is a summary of the modeling process.

The Modeling Process

Use a graphing utility to:

1. **Construct a** *scatter plot* **of the data** to determine which type of function will effectively model the data.

2. **Find the** *regression equation* of the modeling function and the correlation coefficient for the regression.

3. **Examine the** *correlation coefficient* **and** *view a graph* that displays both the modeling function and the scatter plot to determine how well your function fits the data.

In the following example we use the modeling process to find an exponential function that closely models the value of a diamond as a function of its weight.

Alternative to Example 2
Exercise 34, page 447.

EXAMPLE 2   Model an Application with an Exponential Function

A diamond merchant has determined the values of several white diamonds that have different weights (measured in carats), but are *similar in quality.* See **Table 4.13.**

TABLE 4.13

0.50 ct	0.75 ct	1.00 ct	1.25 ct	1.50 ct	1.75 ct	2.00 ct	3.00 ct	4.00 ct
$4,600	$5,000	$5,800	$6,200	$6,700	$7,300	$7,900	$10,700	$14,500

Find a function that models the values of the diamonds as a function of their weights and use the function to predict the value of a 3.5-carat diamond of similar quality.

Solution

1. **Construct a scatter plot of the data.**

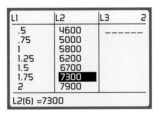
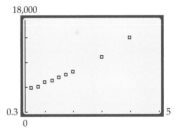

FIGURE 4.50

From the scatter plot in **Figure 4.50** it appears that the data can be closely modeled by an exponential function of the form $y = ab^x$, $a > 0$ and $b > 1$.

2. **Find the regression equation.** The calculator display in **Figure 4.51** shows that the exponential regression equation is $y \approx 4067.6(1.3816)^x$, where x is the carat weight of the diamond and y is the value of the diamond.

```
ExpReg
y=a*b^x
a=4067.641145
b=1.381644186
r²=.994881215
r=.9974373238
```

FIGURE 4.51
ExpReg display (DiagnosticOn)

Continued ▶

take note

The value of a diamond is generally determined by its color, cut, clarity, and carat weight. These characteristics of a diamond are known as the four c's. In Example 2 we have assumed that the color, cut, and clarity of all the diamonds are similar. This assumption enables us to model the value of each diamond as a function of just its carat weight.

INTEGRATING TECHNOLOGY

Most graphing utilities have built-in routines that can be used to determine the exponential or logarithmic regression function that best models a set of data. On a TI-83, the ExpReg instruction is used to find the exponential regression function and the LnReg instruction is used to find the logarithmic regression function. The TI-83 does not show the value of the regression coefficient *r* unless the DiagnosticOn command has been entered. The DiagnosticOn command is in the CATALOG menu.

MATH MATTERS

The Hope Diamond, shown below, is the world's largest deep blue diamond. It has a weight of 45.52 carats. We should not expect the function $y \approx 4067.6 \times 1.3816^x$ in Example 2 to yield an accurate value of the Hope Diamond because the Hope Diamond is not the same type of diamond as the diamonds in **Table 4.13** and its weight is much larger than the weights of the diamonds in **Table 4.13**.

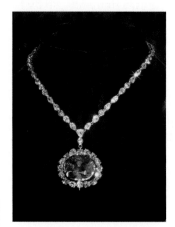

The Hope Diamond is on display at the Smithsonian Museum of Natural History in Washington, D.C.

Alternative to Example 3
Exercise 20, page 444.

3. **Examine the correlation coefficient.** The correlation coefficient $r \approx 0.9974$ is close to 1. This indicates that the exponential regression function $y \approx 4067.6(1.3816)^x$ provides a good fit for the data. The graph in **Figure 4.52** also shows that the exponential regression function provides a good model for the data.

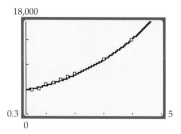

FIGURE 4.52

To estimate the value of a 3.5-carat diamond, replace x in the exponential regression function with 3.5.

$$y \approx 4067.6(1.3816)^{3.5} \approx \$12,610$$

According to the exponential regression function, the value of a 3.5-carat diamond of similar quality is about $12,610.

▶ **TRY EXERCISE 22, PAGE 445**

In the next example we consider a data set that can be effectively modeled by more than one type of function.

EXAMPLE 3 **Choosing the Best Model**

  Table 4.14 shows the winning times in the women's Olympic 100-meter freestyle event for the years 1968 to 2000.

TABLE 4.14 **Women's Olympic 100-Meter Freestyle, 1968 to 2000**

Year	Time (in seconds)	Year	Time (in seconds)
1968	60.0	1988	54.93
1972	58.59	1992	54.64
1976	55.65	1996	54.50
1980	54.79	2000	53.83
1984	55.92		

Source: Time Almanac 2002.

a. Determine whether the data in **Table 4.14** can best be modeled by an exponential function or a logarithmic function.

b. Use the function you chose in part **a.** to predict the winning time in the women's Olympic 100-meter freestyle event for the year 2008.

Solution

a. Construct a scatter plot of the data. In this example we have represented the year 1968 by $x = 68$, the year 2000 by $x = 100$, and the winning time by y.

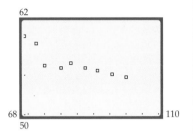

FIGURE 4.53

From the scatter plot in **Figure 4.53,** it appears that the data can be effectively modeled by a decreasing exponential function and also by a decreasing logarithmic function. Use a graphing utility to determine both an exponential regression function and a logarithmic regression function for the data. **Figure 4.54** shows the exponential regression function, and **Figure 4.55** shows the logarithmic regression function.

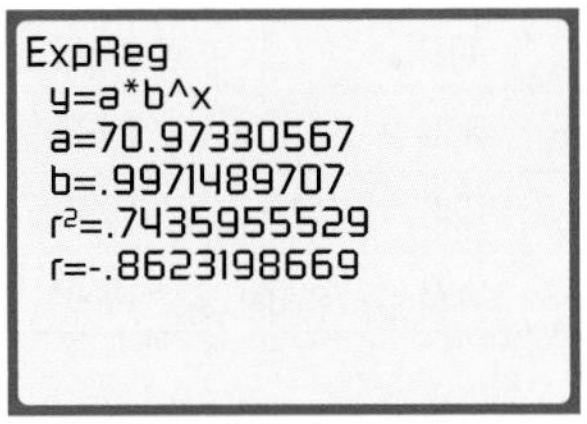

```
ExpReg
y=a*b^x
a=70.97330567
b=.9971489707
r²=.7435955529
r=-.8623198669
```

FIGURE 4.54

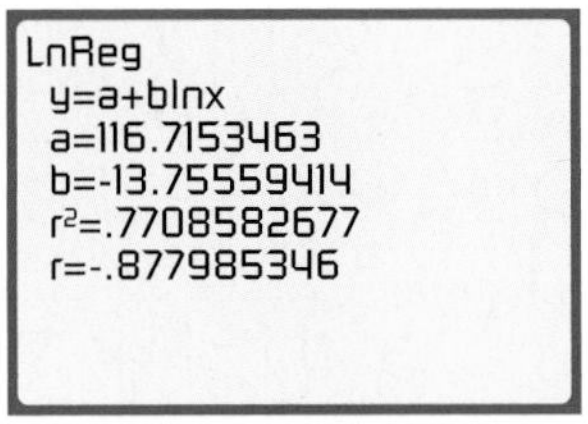

```
LnReg
y=a+blnx
a=116.7153463
b=-13.75559414
r²=.7708582677
r=-.877985346
```

FIGURE 4.55

In this example the regression coefficients are both negative. In such cases, the regression function that has a correlation coefficient closer to -1 provides the better fit for the given data. Thus the logarithmic model provides a slightly better fit for the data in this example. The logarithmic regression function is $y \approx 116.72 - 13.756 \ln x$. The graph of $y \approx 116.72 - 13.756 \ln x$, along with a scatter plot of the data, is shown in **Figure 4.56.**

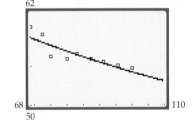

FIGURE 4.56

b. To predict the winning time for the women's Olympic 100-meter freestyle event in the year 2008, replace x in the logarithmic regression function with 108.

$$y \approx 116.72 - 13.756 \ln(108) \approx 52.31$$

According to the logarithmic regression function, the winning time for the women's Olympic 100-meter freestyle event in the year 2008 will be about 52.31 seconds.

▶ **TRY EXERCISE 24, PAGE 445**

● USE REGRESSION TO FIND A LOGISTIC GROWTH MODEL

If a scatter plot of a set of data suggests that the data can be effectively modeled by a logistic growth model, then you can use the logistic regression feature of a graphing utility to find the logistic growth model that provides the best fit for the data. This process is illustrated in Example 4.

Alternative to Example 4
Exercise 36, page 448.

EXAMPLE 4   Use Logistic Regression to Find a Logistic Growth Model

 Table 4.15 shows the population of deer in an animal preserve for the years 1990 to 2004.

TABLE 4.15   Deer Population at the Wild West Animal Preserve

Year	Population	Year	Population	Year	Population
1990	320	1995	1150	2000	2620
1991	410	1996	1410	2001	2940
1992	560	1997	1760	2002	3100
1993	730	1998	2040	2003	3300
1994	940	1999	2310	2004	3460

Use a graphing utility to find a logistic regression model that approximates the deer population as a function of the year. Use the model to predict the deer population in the year 2010.

Solution

1. **Construct a scatter plot of the data.** Enter the data into a graphing utility, and then use the utility to display a scatter plot of the data. In this example we represent the year 1990 by $x = 0$, the year 2004 by $x = 14$, and the deer population by y.

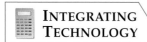 **INTEGRATING TECHNOLOGY**

On a TI-83 graphing calculator, the logistic growth model is given in the form

$$y = \frac{c}{1 + ae^{-bx}}$$

Think of the variable x as the time t and the variable y as $P(t)$.

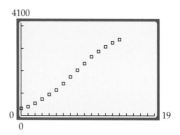

FIGURE 4.57

Figure 4.57 shows that the data can be closely approximated by a logistic growth model.

2. **Find the regression function.** Use a graphing utility to perform a logistic regression on the data. On a TI-83 graphing calculator, select B: Logistic, which is in the STAT CALC menu. The logistic regression function for the data is $y \approx \dfrac{3965.3}{1 + 11.445e^{-0.31152x}}$. See **Figure 4.58.**

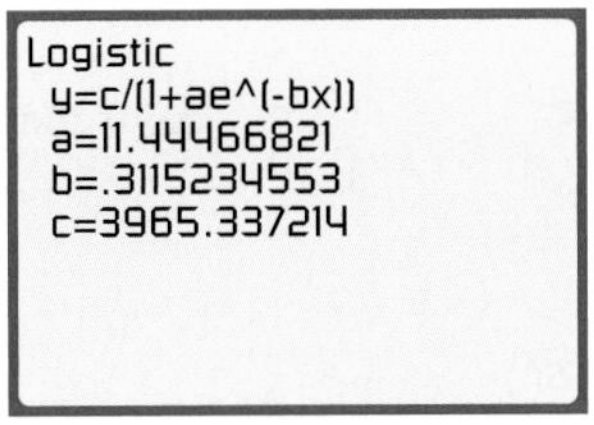

```
Logistic
y=c/(1+ae^(-bx))
a=11.44466821
b=.3115234553
c=3965.337214
```

4100

0 ⌐ 19
 0

FIGURE 4.58 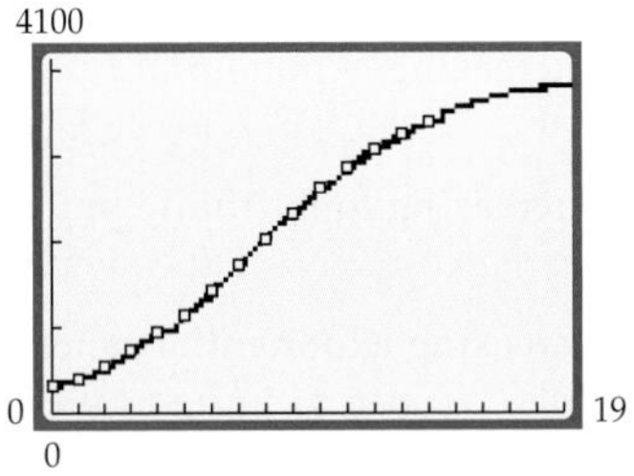   **FIGURE 4.59**

3. **Examine the fit.** A TI-83 calculator does not give a correlation coefficient for a logistic regression. However, Figure 4.59 shows that the graph of $y \approx \dfrac{3965.3}{1 + 11.445e^{-0.31152x}}$ provides a good fit for the data. The logistic model predicts that in the year 2010 ($x = 20$), the deer population will be about 3878.

$$y \approx \frac{3965.3}{1 + 11.445e^{-0.31152(20)}} \approx 3878$$

▶ TRY EXERCISE 26, PAGE 446

TOPICS FOR DISCUSSION

1. A student tries to determine the exponential regression equation for the following data.

x	1	2	3	4	5
y	8	2	0	−1.5	−2

The student's calculator displays an ERROR message. Explain why the calculator was unable to determine the exponential regression equation for the data.

2. Consider the logarithmic model $h(x) = 6 - 2 \ln x$.

   a. Is h an increasing or a decreasing function?

   b. Is h concave up or concave down on the interval $(0, \infty)$?

   c. Find, if possible, $h(0)$ and $h(e)$.

   d. Does h have a horizontal asymptote? Explain.

EXERCISE SET 4.7

—*Suggested Assignment: Exercises 1–39, odd.*
—*Answer graphs for Exercises 1–6 are on pages AA18–AA19.*

In Exercises 1 to 6, use a scatter plot of the given data to determine which of the following types of functions might provide a suitable model of the data:

- an increasing exponential function
  $y = ab^x$, $a > 0$, $b > 1$ (See **Figure 4.47a.**)

- an increasing logarithmic function
  $y = a + b \ln x$, $b > 0$ (See **Figure 4.47c.**)

- a decreasing exponential function
  $y = ab^x$, $a > 0$, $0 < b < 1$ (See **Figure 4.47b.**)

- a decreasing logarithmic function
  $y = a + b \ln x$, $b < 0$ (See **Figure 4.47d.**)

(*Note:* Some data sets can be closely modeled by more than one type of function.)

1. $\{(1, 3), (1.5, 4), (2, 6), (3, 13), (3.5, 19), (4, 27)\}$
increasing exponential function

2. $\{(1.0, 1.12), (2.1, 0.87), (3.2, 0.68), (3.5, 0.63), (4.4, 0.52)\}$
decreasing exponential function; decreasing logarithmic function

3. $\{(1, 2.4), (2, 1.1), (3, 0.5), (4, 0.2), (5, 0.1)\}$
decreasing exponential function; decreasing logarithmic function

▶ **4.** $\{(5, 2.3), (7, 3.9), (9, 4.5), (12, 5.0), (16, 5.4), (21, 5.8), (26, 6.1)\}$
increasing logarithmic function

5. $\{(1, 2.5), (1.5, 1.7), (2, 0.7), (3, -0.5), (3.5, -1.3), (4, -1.5)\}$
decreasing logarithmic function

6. $\{(1, 3), (1.5, 3.8), (2, 4.4), (3, 5.2), (4, 5.8), (6, 6.6)\}$
increasing logarithmic function

In Exercises 7 to 10, use a graphing utility to find the exponential regression function for the data. State the correlation coefficient r. Round a, b, and r to the nearest hundred thousandth.

7. $\{(10, 6.8), (12, 6.9), (14, 15.0), (16, 16.1), (18, 50.0), (19, 20.0)\}$ $y \approx 0.99628(1.20052)^x$; $r \approx 0.85705$

8. $\{(2.6, 16.2), (3.8, 48.8), (5.1, 160.1), (6.5, 590.2), (7, 911.2)\}$
$y \approx 1.48874(2.50469)^x$; $r \approx 0.99999$

9. $\{(0, 1.83), (1, 0.92), (2, 0.51), (3, 0.25), (4, 0.13), (5, 0.07)\}$
$y \approx 1.81505(0.51979)^x$; $r \approx -0.99978$

10. $\{(4.5, 1.92), (6.0, 1.48), (7.5, 1.14), (10.2, 0.71), (12.3, 0.49)\}$
$y \approx 4.23016(0.83937)^x$; $r \approx -0.99999$

In Exercises 11 to 14, use a graphing utility to find the logarithmic regression function for the data. State the correlation coefficient r. Round a, b, and r to the nearest hundred thousandth.

11. $\{(5, 2.7), (6, 2.5), (7.2, 2.2), (9.3, 1.9), (11.4, 1.6), (14.2, 1.3)\}$
$y \approx 4.89060 - 1.35073 \ln x$; $r \approx -0.99921$

12. $\{(11, 15.75), (14, 15.52), (17, 15.34), (20, 15.18), (23, 15.05)\}$
$y \approx 18.02743 - 0.94970 \ln x$; $r \approx -0.99997$

13. $\{(3, 16.0), (4, 16.5), (5, 16.9), (7, 17.5), (8, 17.7), (9.8, 18.1)\}$
$y \approx 14.05858 + 1.76393 \ln x$; $r \approx 0.99983$

14. $\{(8, 67.1), (10, 67.8), (12, 68.4), (14, 69.0), (16, 69.4)\}$
$y \approx 60.08692 + 3.36076 \ln x$; $r \approx 0.99932$

In Exercises 15 to 18, use a graphing utility to find the logistic regression function for the data. Round the constants a, b, and c to the nearest hundred thousandth.

15. $\{(0, 81), (2, 87), (6, 98), (10, 110), (15, 125)\}$ $y \approx \dfrac{235.58598}{1 + 1.90188e^{-0.05101x}}$

16. $\{(0, 175), (5, 195), (10, 217), (20, 264), (35, 341)\}$ $y \approx \dfrac{710.56899}{1 + 3.06263e^{-0.02968x}}$

17. $\{(0, 955), (10, 1266), (20, 1543), (30, 1752)\}$ $y \approx \dfrac{2098.68307}{1 + 1.19794e^{-0.06004x}}$

18. $\{(0, 1588), (5, 2598), (10, 3638), (25, 5172)\}$ $y \approx \dfrac{5398.79784}{1 + 2.40005e^{-0.16010x}}$

19. **INTEREST RATES ON AUTO LOANS** The following table shows the annual interest rates for new car loans in 2002 based on the length (term) of the loan.

Term *t*, in months	12	24	36	48
Annual interest rate, *r*	5.72%	5.97%	6.23%	6.50%

a. Find an exponential model for the data in the table and use the model to predict the interest rate *r*, to the nearest 0.01%, on an auto loan with a term of 60 months. Round *a*, *b*, and *r* to the nearest hundred thousandth.
$y \approx 5.48184(1.00356)^x$; 6.78%

b. According to your model in part **a.**, what is the term of a loan with a 7.00% interest rate? Round to the nearest month. 69 months

20. **GENERATION OF GARBAGE** According to the U.S. Environmental Protection Agency, the amount of garbage generated per person has been increasing over the last few decades. The following table shows the per capita garbage, in pounds per day, generated in the United States.

Year, *t*	1960	1970	1980	1990	2000
Pounds per day, *p*	2.66	3.27	3.61	4.00	4.30

Represent the year 1960 by $t = 60$.

a. Use a graphing utility to find a linear model and a logarithmic model for the data. Use *t* as the independent variable (domain) and *p* as the dependent variable (range). LinReg: $p \approx 0.0401t + 0.36$, LnReg: $p \approx -10.23519 + 3.161541 \ln t$

b. Examine the correlation coefficients of the two regression models to determine which model provides a better fit for the data. Linear model: $r \approx 0.99096$; logarithmic model: $r \approx 0.99738$. The logarithmic model provides a slightly better fit.

c. Use the model you selected in part **b.** to predict the amount of garbage that will be generated per capita per day in 2005. Round to the nearest hundredth of a pound. 4.48 lb per capita per day

21. **HYPOTHERMIA** The following table shows the time T, in hours, before a scuba diver wearing a 3-millimeter-thick wet suit reaches hypothermia (95°F) for various water temperatures F, in degrees Fahrenheit.

Water temperature, °F	Time T, hours
41	1.1
46	1.4
50	1.8
59	3.7

a. Find an exponential regression model for the data. Round the constants a and b to the nearest hundred thousandth. $T \approx 0.06273(1.07078)^F$

b. Use the model from part **a.** to estimate the time it takes for the diver to reach hypothermia in water that has a temperature of 65°F. Round to the nearest tenth of an hour. 5.3 h

22. **ATMOSPHERIC PRESSURE** The following table shows the earth's atmospheric pressure P (in newtons per square centimeter) at an altitude of a kilometers. Find a suitable function that models the atmospheric pressure as a function of the altitude. Use the function to estimate the atmospheric pressure at an altitude of 24 kilometers. Round to the nearest tenth of a newton per square centimeter. $P \approx 10.147(0.89104)^a$; 0.6 newton/cm²

Altitude a, kilometers	Pressure P, newtons/cm²
0	10.3
2	8.0
4	6.4
6	5.1
8	4.0
10	3.2
12	2.5
14	2.0
16	1.6
18	1.3

23. **HYPOTHERMIA** The following table shows the time T, in hours, before a scuba diver wearing a 4-millimeter-thick wet suit reaches hypothermia (95°F) for various water temperatures F, in degrees Fahrenheit.

Water temperature, °F	Time T, hours
41	1.5
46	1.9
50	2.4
59	5.2

a. Find an exponential regression model for the data. Round the constants a and b to the nearest hundred thousandth. $T \approx 0.07881(1.07259)^F$

b. Use the model from part **a.** to estimate the time it takes for the diver to reach hypothermia in water that has a temperature of 65°F. Round to the nearest tenth of an hour. How much greater is this result compared with the answer to Exercise 21**b.**? 7.5 h; 2.2 h

24. **400-METER RACE** The following table lists the progression of world record times in the men's 400-meter race for the years from 1948 to 2002.

World Record Times in the Men's 400-Meter Race, 1948 to 2002

Year	Time, in seconds	Year	Time, in seconds
1948	45.9	1964	44.9
1950	45.8	1967	44.5
1955	45.4	1968	44.1
1956	45.2	1968	43.86
1960	44.9	1988	43.29
1960	44.9	1999	43.18
1963	44.9		

Source: Track and Field Statistics, http://trackfield.brinkster.net/Main.asp.

a. Determine whether the data can best be modeled by a decreasing exponential function or a decreasing logarithmic function. Let $x = 48$ represent the year 1948. a decreasing logarithmic function

b. Use the function you chose in part **a.** to predict the world record time in the men's 400-meter race for the year 2008. Round to the nearest hundredth of a second. 42.52 s

25. INTERNET VIRUSES The CERT Coordination Center (CERT/CC) is an organization that, among other activities, monitors the number of Internet virus incidents. The data in the table below were compiled from CERT/CC and show the number of virus incidents for various years.

Year	Number of incidents
1996	2573
1997	2134
1998	3734
1999	9859
2000	21,756
2001	52,658
2002	82,094

a. Find an exponential regression model for these data. Use $t = 0$ to correspond to 1996. Round each constant to the nearest thousandth. $N(t) \approx 1500.093(1.940)^t$

b. Use the model to predict the year in which the number of incidents will first exceed one million. 2005

▶ **26.** POPULATION OF HAWAII The following table shows the population of the state of Hawaii for selected years from 1950 to 2002.

Population of the State of Hawaii

Year	Population	Year	Population
1950	499,000	1985	1,039,698
1955	529,000	1990	1,113,491
1960	642,000	1995	1,196,854
1965	704,000	2000	1,212,670
1970	762,920	2001	1,227,024
1975	875,052	2002	1,244,898
1980	967,710		

Source: economagic.com, http://www.economagic.com/em-cgi/data.exe/beapi/a15300.

a. Use the logistic regression feature of a graphing utility to find a logistic growth model that approximates the population of the state of Hawaii as a function of the year. Use $t = 0$ to represent the year 1950. $P(t) \approx \dfrac{1,541,897}{1 + 2.24580e^{-0.043411t}}$

b. Use the model from part **a.** to predict the population of the state of Hawaii for the year 2010. Round to the nearest ten thousand. 1,320,000

c. What is the carrying capacity of the model? Round to the nearest thousand. 1,542,000

27. OPTOMETRY The *near point p* of a person is the closest distance at which the person can see an object distinctly. As one grows older, one's near point increases. The table below shows data for the average near point of various people with normal eyesight.

Age y, years	Near point p (cm)
15	11
20	13
25	15
30	17
35	20
40	23
50	26

a. Find an exponential regression model for these data. Round each constant to the nearest thousandth. $p \approx 7.862(1.026)^y$

b. What near point does this equation predict for a person 60 years old? Round to the nearest centimeter. 36 cm

28. CHEMISTRY The amount of oxygen x, in milliliters per liter, that can be absorbed by water at a certain temperature T, in degrees Fahrenheit, is given in the following table.

Temperature, °F	Oxygen absorbed, ml/L
32	10.5
38	8.4
46	7.6
52	7.1
58	6.8
64	6.5

a. Find a logarithmic regression equation for these data. Round each constant to the nearest thousandth. $T \approx 28.502 - 5.372 \ln x$

b. Using your model, how much oxygen, to the nearest tenth of a milliliter per liter, can be absorbed in water that is 50°F? 7.5 ml/L

29. THE HENDERSON-HASSELBACH FUNCTION The scientists Henderson and Hasselbach determined that the pH of blood is a function of the ratio q of the amounts of bicarbonate and carbonic acid in the blood.

a. Use a graphing utility and the data in the following table to determine a linear model and a logarithmic model for the data. Use q as the independent variable (domain) and pH as the dependent variable (range). State the correlation coefficient for each model. Round a and b to 5 decimal places and r to 6 decimal places. Which model provides the better fit for the data? LinReg: pH $\approx 0.01353q + 7.02852$, $r \approx 0.956627$; LnReg: pH $\approx 6.10251 + 0.43369 \ln q$, $r \approx 0.999998$

q	7.9	12.6	31.6	50.1	79.4
pH	7.0	7.2	7.6	7.8	8.0

The logarithmic model provides a better fit.

b. Use the model you chose in part **a.** to find the q-value associated with a pH of 8.2. Round to the nearest tenth. 126.0

30. WORLD POPULATION The following table lists the years in which the world's population first reached 3, 4, 5, and 6 billion.

World Population Milestones

Year	Population
1960	3 billion
1974	4 billion
1987	5 billion
1999	6 billion

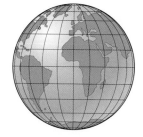

Source: Time Almanac 2002, p. 708.

a. Find an exponential model for the data in the table. Let $x = 0$ represent the year 1960. $y \approx 3.05401(1.0179)^x$

b. Use the model to predict the year in which the world's population will first reach 7 billion. 2006

31. PANDA POPULATION One estimate gives the world panda population as 3200 in 1980 and 590 in 2000.

a. Find an exponential model for the data and use the model to predict the year in which the panda population p will be reduced to 200. (Let $t = 0$ represent the year 1980.) $p \approx 3200(0.91894)^t$; 2012

b. Because the exponential model in part **a.** fits the data perfectly, does this mean that the model will accurately predict future panda populations? Explain.
No. The model fits the data perfectly because there are only two data points.

32. OLYMPIC RECORDS The following table shows the Olympic gold medal distances for the women's high jump from 1968 to 2000.

Women's Olympic High Jump, 1968 to 2000

Year	Distance	Year	Distance
1968	5 ft 11$\frac{3}{4}$ in.	1988	6 ft 8 in.
1972	6 ft 3$\frac{5}{8}$ in.	1992	6 ft 7$\frac{1}{2}$ in.
1976	6 ft 4 in.	1996	6 ft 8$\frac{3}{4}$ in.
1980	6 ft 5$\frac{1}{2}$ in.	2000	6 ft 7 in.
1984	6 ft 7$\frac{1}{2}$ in.		

Source: Time Almanac 2002.

Represent the year 1968 by 68.

a. Use a graphing utility to determine a linear model and a logarithmic model for the data, with the distance measured in inches. State the correlation coefficient r for each model. LinReg: $y \approx 0.22448x + 58.87986$, $r \approx 0.86012$; LnReg: $y \approx -7.07160 + 19.17358 \ln x$, $r \approx 0.88386$

b. Use the correlation coefficient for each of the models in part **a.** to determine which model provides the better fit for the data. The logarithmic model provides the better fit.

c. Use the model you selected in part **b.** to predict the women's Olympic gold medal high jump distance in 2012. Round to the nearest tenth of an inch.
83.4 in. (6 ft 11.4 in.)

33. NUMBER OF AUTOMOBILES In 1900, the number of automobiles in the United States was around 8000. By 2000, the number of automobiles in the United States had reached 200 million.

a. Find an exponential model for the data and use the model to predict the number of automobiles, to the nearest 100,000, in the United States in 2010. Use $t = 0$ to represent the year 1900.
ExpReg: $a \approx 8000(1.10657)^t$; 550,500,000 automobiles

b. According to the model, in what year will the number of automobiles in the United States first reach 300 million? 2004

34. TEMPERATURE OF COFFEE A cup of coffee is placed in a room that maintains a constant temperature of 70°F. The following table shows both the coffee temperature T after t minutes and the difference between the coffee temperature and the room temperature after t minutes.

Time t (minutes)	0	5	10	15	20	25
Coffee temp. T (°F)	165°	140°	121°	107°	97°	89°
$T - 70°$	95°	70°	51°	37°	27°	19°

a. Use a graphing utility to find an exponential model for the difference $T - 70°$ as a function of t.
$T - 70° \approx 96.16777(0.93787)^t$

b. Use the model to predict how long it will take (to the nearest minute) for the coffee to cool to 80°F. 35 min

35. **OLYMPIC DISTANCES** The following table shows the winning Olympic distances for the men's shot put for the years 1948 to 2000.

Men's Olympic Shot Put, 1948 to 2000

Year	Distance	Year	Distance
1948	56 ft 2 in.	1976	69 ft $\frac{3}{4}$ in.
1952	57 ft $1\frac{1}{2}$ in.	1980	70 ft $\frac{1}{2}$ in.
1956	60 ft 11 in.	1984	69 ft 9 in.
1960	64 ft $6\frac{3}{4}$ in.	1988	73 ft $8\frac{3}{4}$ in.
1964	66 ft $8\frac{1}{4}$ in.	1992	71 ft $2\frac{1}{2}$ in.
1968	67 ft $4\frac{3}{4}$ in.	1996	70 ft $11\frac{1}{4}$ in.
1972	69 ft 6 in.	2000	69 ft $10\frac{1}{4}$ in.

Source: Time Almanac 2002

Represent the year 1948 by $t = 48$.

a. Use the regression features of a graphing utility to determine a logistic growth model and a logarithmic model for the data.
Answer on page AA19.

b. Use graphs of the models in part a. to determine which model provides the better fit for the data.
logistic growth model

c. Use the model you selected in part b. to predict the men's shot put distance for the year 2008. Round to the nearest hundredth of a foot. 71.65 ft

36. **WORLD POPULATION** The following table lists the years in which the world's population first reached 3, 4, 5, and 6 billion.

World Population Milestones

Year	Population
1960	3 billion
1974	4 billion
1987	5 billion
1999	6 billion

Source: Time Almanac 2002, p. 708.

a. Find a logistic growth model, $P(t)$, for the data in the table. Let t represent the number of years after 1960 ($t = 0$ represents the year 1960).
$$P(t) \approx \frac{11.26828}{1 + 2.74965e^{-0.02924t}}$$

b. According to the logistic growth model, what will the world's population approach as $t \to \infty$? Round to the nearest billion. 11 billion people

37. **DESALINATION** The following table shows the amount of fresh water w (in cubic yards) produced from saltwater after t hours of a desalination process.

t	1	2.5	3.5	4.0	5.1	6.5
w	18.2	46.6	57.4	61.5	68.7	76.2

a. Use a graphing utility to find a linear model and a logarithmic model for the data. LinReg: $w \approx 10.17227t + 16.45111$, $r \approx 0.95601$; LnReg: $w \approx 18.26750 + 31.03499 \ln t$, $r \approx 0.99996$

b. Examine the correlation coefficients of the two regression models to determine which model provides the better fit for the data. State the correlation coefficient r for each model. The logarithmic model provides a better fit.

c. Use the model you selected in part b. to predict the amount of fresh water that will be produced after 10 hours of the desalination process. Round to the nearest tenth of a cubic yard. 89.7 yd³

38. A CORRELATION COEFFICIENT OF 1 A scientist uses a graphing utility to model the data set $\{(2, 5), (4, 6)\}$ with a logarithmic function. The following display shows the results.

What is the significance of the fact that the correlation coefficient for the regression equation is $r = 1$?
The graph of the logarithmic regression equation passes through both data points.

```
LnReg
 y=a+blnx
 a=4
 b=1.442695041
 r²=1
 r=1
```

CONNECTING CONCEPTS

39. **DUPLICATE DATA POINTS** An engineer needs to model the data in set A with an exponential function.

$$A = \{(2, 5), (3, 10), (4, 17), (4, 17), (5, 28)\}$$

Because the ordered pair $(4, 17)$ is listed twice, the engineer decides to eliminate one of these ordered pairs and model the data in set B.

$$B = \{(2, 5), (3, 10), (4, 17), (5, 28)\}$$

Determine whether A and B both have the same exponential regression function.
A and B have different exponential regression functions.

40. **DOMAIN ERROR** A scientist needs to model the data in set A.

$$A = \{(0, 1.2), (1, 2.3), (2, 2.8), (3, 3.1), (4, 3.3), (5, 3.4)\}$$

The scientist views a scatter plot of the data and decides to model the data with a logarithmic function of the form $y = a + b \ln x$.

a. When the scientist attempts to use a graphing calculator to determine the logarithmic regression equation, the calculator displays the message

"ERR:DOMAIN"

Explain why the calculator was unable to determine the logarithmic regression equation for the data.
The x-coordinate of the first ordered pair is 0, and 0 is not in the domain of y = ln x.

b. Explain what the scientist could do so that the data in set A could be modeled by a logarithmic function of the form $y = a + b \ln x$.
Answer on page AA19.

41. **POWER FUNCTIONS** A function that can be written in the form $y = ax^b$ is said to be a **power function.** Some data sets can best be modeled by a power function.

On a TI-83, the PwrReg instruction is used to produce a power regression function for a set of data.

a. Use a graphing utility to find an exponential regression function and a power regression function for the following data. State the correlation coefficient r for each model. ExpReg: $y \approx 1.81120(1.61740)^x$, $r \approx 0.96793$; PwrReg: $y \approx 2.09385(x)^{1.40246}$, $r \approx 0.99999$

x	1	2	3	4	5	6
y	2.1	5.5	9.8	14.6	20.1	25.8

b. Which of the two regression functions provides the better fit for the data?
The power regression function provides the better fit.

42. **PERIOD OF A PENDULUM** The following table shows the time t (in seconds) of the period of a pendulum (the time it takes the pendulum to complete a swing to the left and back) of length l (in feet).

a. Use a graphing utility to determine the equation of the best model for the data. Your model must be a power function or an exponential function.
the power function $t \approx 1.11088(l^{0.50113})$

Length l	1	2	3	4	6	8
Time t	1.11	1.57	1.92	2.25	2.72	3.14

b. According to the model you chose in part **a.**, what is the length of a pendulum, to the nearest tenth of a foot, that has a period of 12 seconds? 115.4 ft

PROJECTS

I. **A MODELING PROJECT** The purpose of this Project is for you to find data that can be modeled by an exponential or a logarithmic function. Choose data from a *real-life* situation that you find interesting. Search for the data in a magazine, a newspaper, an almanac, or on the Internet. If you wish, you can collect your data by performing an experiment.
Responses will vary.

a. List the source of your data. Include the date, page number, and any other specifics about the source. If your data were collected by performing an experiment, then provide all the details of the experiment.

b. Explain what you have chosen as your variables. Which variable is the dependent variable and which variable is the independent variable?

c. Use the three-step modeling process to find a regression equation that models the data.

d. Graph the regression equation on the scatter plot of the data. What is the correlation coefficient for the model? Do you think that your regression equation accurately models your data? Explain.

e. Use the regression equation to predict the value of

- the dependent variable for a specific value of the independent variable.

- the independent variable for a specific value of the dependent variable.

f. Write a few comments about what you have learned from this Project.

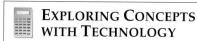

EXPLORING CONCEPTS WITH TECHNOLOGY

TABLE 4.16

T	V
90	700
100	500
110	350
120	250
130	190
140	150
150	120

Using a Semilog Graph to Model Exponential Decay

Consider the data in **Table 4.16,** which shows the viscosity V of SAE 40 motor oil at various temperatures T. The graph of these data is shown below, along with a curve that passes through the points. The graph in **Figure 4.60** appears to have the shape of an exponential decay model.

One way to determine whether the graph in **Figure 4.60** is the graph of an exponential function is to plot the data on *semilog* graph paper. On this graph paper, the horizontal axis remains the same, but the vertical axis uses a logarithmic scale.

The data in **Table 4.16** are graphed again in **Figure 4.61,** but this time the vertical axis is a natural logarithm axis. This graph is approximately a straight line.

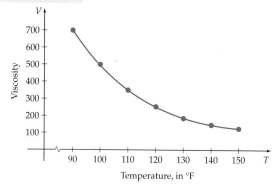

FIGURE 4.60   **FIGURE 4.61**

The slope of the line in **Figure 4.61,** to the nearest ten-thousandth, is

$$m = \frac{\ln 500 - \ln 120}{100 - 150} \approx -0.0285$$

Using this slope and the point-slope formula with V replaced by $\ln V$, we have

$$\ln V - \ln 120 = -0.0285(T - 150)$$
$$\ln V \approx -0.0285T + 9.062 \tag{1}$$

Equation (1) is the equation of the line on a semilog coordinate grid.

Now solve Equation (1) for V.

$$e^{\ln V} = e^{-0.0285T + 9.062}$$
$$V = e^{-0.0285T}e^{9.062}$$
$$V \approx 8621e^{-0.0285T} \tag{2}$$

TABLE 4.17

t	A
1	91.77
4	70.92
8	50.30
15	27.57
20	17.95
30	7.60

Equation (2) is a model of the data in the rectangular coordinate system shown in **Figure 4.60.**

1. A chemist wishes to determine the decay characteristics of iodine-131. A 100-mg sample of iodine-131 is observed over a 30-day period. **Table 4.17** shows the amount A (in milligrams) of iodine-131 remaining after t days.

    a. Graph the ordered pairs (t, A) on semilog paper. (*Note:* Semilog paper comes in different varieties. Our calculations are based on semilog paper that has a natural logarithm scale on the vertical axis.)

b. Use the points (4, 4.3) and (15, 3.3) to approximate the slope of the line that passes through the points.

c. Using the slope calculated in part **b.** and the point (4, 4.3), determine the equation of the line.

d. Solve the equation you derived in part **c.** for A.

e. Graph the equation you derived in part **d.** in a rectangular coordinate system.

f. What is the half-life of iodine-131?

2. The live birth rates B per thousand births in the United States are given in **Table 4.18** for the years 1986 through 1990 ($t = 0$ corresponds to 1986).

a. Graph the ordered pairs $(t, \ln B)$. (You will need to adjust the scale so that you can discriminate between plotted points. A suggestion is given in **Figure 4.62.**)

b. Use the points (1, 2.754) and (3, 2.785) to approximate the slope of the line that passes through the points.

c. Using the slope calculated in part **b.** and the point (1, 2.754), determine the equation of the line.

d. Solve the equation you derived in part **c.** for B.

e. Graph the equation you derived in part **d.** in a rectangular coordinate system.

f. If the birth rate continues as predicted by your model, in what year will the birth rate be 17.5 per thousand?

The difference in graphing strategies between Exercise 1 and Exercise 2 is that in Exercise 1, semilog paper was used. When a point is graphed on this coordinate paper, the y-coordinate is $\ln y$. In Exercise 2, graphing a point $(x, \ln y)$ in a rectangular coordinate system has the same effect as graphing (x, y) in a semilog coordinate system.

TABLE 4.18

t	B
0	15.5
1	15.7
2	15.9
3	16.2
4	16.7

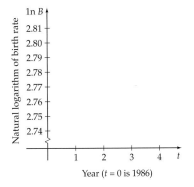

FIGURE 4.62

CHAPTER 4 SUMMARY

4.1 Inverse Functions

- If f is a one-to-one function with domain X and range Y, and g is a function with domain Y and range X, then g is the inverse function of f if and only if $(f \circ g)(x) = x$ for all x in the domain of g and $(g \circ f)(x) = x$ for all x in the domain of f.

- A function f has an inverse function if and only if it is a one-to-one function. The graph of a function f and the graph of the inverse function f^{-1} are symmetric with respect to the line given by $y = x$.

4.2 Exponential Functions and Their Applications

- For all positive real numbers b, $b \neq 1$, the exponential function defined by $f(x) = b^x$ has the following properties:

  1. f has the set of real numbers as its domain.

  2. f has the set of positive real numbers as its range.

  3. f has a graph with a y-intercept of $(0, 1)$.

  4. f has a graph asymptotic to the x-axis.

  5. f is a one-to-one function.

6. f is an increasing function if $b > 1$.

7. f is a decreasing function if $0 < b < 1$.

- As n increases without bound, $(1 + 1/n)^n$ approaches an irrational number denoted by e. The value of e accurate to eight decimal places is 2.71828183.

- The function defined by $f(x) = e^x$ is called the natural exponential function.

4.3 Logarithmic Functions and Their Applications

- *Definition of a Logarithm* If $x > 0$ and b is a positive constant ($b \neq 1$), then

$$y = \log_b x \quad \text{if and only if} \quad b^y = x$$

- For all positive real numbers b, $b \neq 1$, the function defined by $f(x) = \log_b x$ has the following properties:

  1. f has the set of positive real numbers as its domain.

  2. f has the set of real numbers as its range.

  3. f has a graph with an x-intercept of $(1, 0)$.

  4. f has a graph asymptotic to the y-axis.

  5. f is a one-to-one function.

  6. f is an increasing function if $b > 1$.

  7. f is a decreasing function if $0 < b < 1$.

- The exponential form of $y = \log_b x$ is $b^y = x$.

- The logarithmic form of $b^y = x$ is $y = \log_b x$.

- *Basic Logarithmic Properties*

  1. $\log_b b = 1$ **2.** $\log_b 1 = 0$ **3.** $\log_b (b^p) = p$

- The function $f(x) = \log_{10} x$ is the common logarithmic function. It is customarily written as $f(x) = \log x$.

- The function $f(x) = \log_e x$ is the natural logarithmic function. It is customarily written as $f(x) = \ln x$.

4.4 Logarithms and Logarithmic Scales

- If b, M, and N are positive real numbers ($b \neq 1$), and p is any real number, then

$\log_b(MN) = \log_b M + \log_b N$

$\log_b \dfrac{M}{N} = \log_b M - \log_b N$

$\log_b(M^p) = p \log_b M$

$\log_b M = \log_b N \quad \text{implies} \quad M = N$

$M = N \quad \text{implies} \quad \log_b M = \log_b N$

$b^{\log_b p} = p \quad \text{(for } p > 0\text{)}$

- *Change-of-Base Formula* If x, a, and b are positive real numbers with $a \neq 1$ and $b \neq 1$, then

$$\log_b x = \frac{\log_a x}{\log_a b}$$

- An earthquake with an intensity of I has a Richter scale magnitude of $M = \log\left(\dfrac{I}{I_0}\right)$, where I_0 is the measure of the intensity of a zero-level earthquake.

- The pH of a solution with a hydronium-ion concentration of H^+ mole per liter is given by $pH = -\log[H^+]$.

4.5 Exponential and Logarithmic Equations

- *Equality of Exponents Theorem* If b is a positive real number ($b \neq 1$) such that $b^x = b^y$, then $x = y$.

- Exponential equations of the form $b^x = b^y$ can be solved by using the Equality of Exponents Theorem.

- Exponential equations of the form $b^x = c$ can be solved by taking either the common logarithm or the natural logarithm of each side of the equation.

- Logarithmic equations can often be solved by using the properties of logarithms and the definition of a logarithm.

4.6 Exponential Growth and Decay

- The function defined by $N(t) = N_0 e^{kt}$ is called an exponential growth function if k is a positive constant, and it is called an exponential decay function if k is a negative constant.

- *The Compound Interest Formula* A principal P invested at an annual interest rate r, expressed as a decimal and compounded n times per year for t years, produces the balance

$$A = P\left(1 + \frac{r}{n}\right)^{nt}$$

- *Continuous Compounding Interest Formula* If an account with principal P and annual interest rate r is compounded continuously for t years, then the balance is $A = Pe^{rt}$.

- *The Logistic Model* The magnitude of a population at time t is given by

$$P(t) = \frac{c}{1 + ae^{-bt}}$$

where $P_0 = P(0)$ is the population at time $t = 0$, c is the carrying capacity of the population, and b is a constant called the growth rate constant.

4.7 Modeling Data with Exponential and Logarithmic Functions

• If the graph of f lies above all of its tangents on $[x_1, x_2]$, then f is concave upward on $[x_1, x_2]$.

• If the graph of f lies below all of its tangents on $[x_1, x_2]$, then f is concave downward on $[x_1, x_2]$.

• *The Modeling Process* Use a graphing utility to

1. construct a scatter plot of the data to determine which type of function will best model the data.

2. find the regression equation of the modeling function and the correlation coefficient for the regression.

3. examine the correlation coefficient and view a graph that displays both the function and the scatter plot to determine how well the function fits the data.

CHAPTER 4 TRUE/FALSE EXERCISES

In Exercises I to 16, answer true or false. If the statement is false, give an example or state a reason to demonstrate that the statement is false.

1. Every function has an inverse function.
  False. $f(x) = x^2$ does not have an inverse function.

2. If $(f \circ g)(a) = a$ and $(g \circ f)(a) = a$ for some constant a, then f and g are inverse functions. False. Let $f(x) = 2x$, $g(x) = 3x$. Then $f(g(0)) = 0$ and $g(f(0)) = 0$, but f and g are not inverse functions.

3. If $7^x = 40$, then $\log_7 40 = x$. True

4. If $\log_4 x = 3.1$, then $4^{3.1} = x$. True

5. If $f(x) = \log x$ and $g(x) = 10^x$, then $f[g(x)] = x$ for all real numbers x. True

6. If $f(x) = \log x$ and $g(x) = 10^x$, then $g[f(x)] = x$ for all real numbers x. False; f is not defined for negative values of x, and thus $g(f(x))$ is undefined for negative values of x.

7. The exponential function $h(x) = b^x$ is an increasing function.
  False; $h(x)$ is not an increasing function for $0 < b < 1$.

8. The logarithmic function $j(x) = \log_b x$ is an increasing function.
  False; $j(x)$ is not an increasing function for $0 < b < 1$.

9. The exponential function $h(x) = b^x$ is a one-to-one function. True

10. The logarithmic function $j(x) = \log_b x$ is a one-to-one function. True

11. The graph of $f(x) = \dfrac{2^x + 2^{-x}}{2}$ is symmetric with respect to the y-axis. True

12. The graph of $f(x) = \dfrac{2^x - 2^{-x}}{2}$ is symmetric with respect to the origin. True

13. If $x > 0$ and $y > 0$, then $\log(x + y) = \log x + \log y$.
  False; $\log x + \log y = \log(xy)$.

14. If $x > 0$, then $\log x^2 = 2 \log x$. True

15. If M and N are positive real numbers, then

$$\ln \frac{M}{N} = \ln M - \ln N \quad \text{True}$$

16. For all $p > 0$, $e^{\ln p} = p$. True

CHAPTER 4 REVIEW EXERCISES

—Answer graphs to Exercises 5–8 and 21–32 are on page AA19.

In Exercises 1 to 4, determine whether the given functions are inverses.

1. $F(x) = 2x - 5$ $G(x) = \dfrac{x + 5}{2}$ Yes [4.1]

2. $h(x) = \sqrt{x}$ $k(x) = x^2, \quad x \ge 0$ Yes [4.1]

3. $l(x) = \dfrac{x + 3}{x}$ $m(x) = \dfrac{3}{x - 1}$ Yes [4.1]

4. $p(x) = \dfrac{x - 5}{2x}$ $q(x) = \dfrac{2x}{x - 5}$ No [4.1]

In Exercises 5 to 8, find the inverse of the function. Sketch the graph of the function and its inverse on the same set of coordinate axes.

5. $f(x) = 3x - 4$
$f^{-1}(x) = \dfrac{x + 4}{3}$ [4.1]

6. $g(x) = -2x + 3$
$g^{-1}(x) = -\dfrac{1}{2}x + \dfrac{3}{2}$ [4.1]

7. $h(x) = -\dfrac{1}{2}x - 2$
$h^{-1}(x) = -2x - 4$ [4.1]

8. $k(x) = \dfrac{1}{x}$
$k^{-1}(x) = k(x) = \dfrac{1}{x}$ [4.1]

In Exercises 9 to 20, solve each equation. Do not use a calculator.

9. $\log_5 25 = x$
2 [4.3]

10. $\log_3 81 = x$
4 [4.3]

11. $\ln e^3 = x$
3 [4.3]

12. $\ln e^{\pi} = x$
π [4.3]

13. $3^{2x+7} = 27$
-2 [4.5]

14. $5^{x-4} = 625$
8 [4.5]

15. $2^x = \dfrac{1}{8}$
-3 [4.5]

16. $27(3^x) = 3^{-1}$
-4 [4.5]

17. $\log x^2 = 6$
± 1000 [4.5]

18. $\dfrac{1}{2}\log |x| = 5$
$\pm 10^{10}$ [4.5]

19. $10^{\log 2x} = 14$
7 [4.5]

20. $e^{\ln x^2} = 64$
± 8 [4.5]

In Exercises 21 to 30, sketch the graph of each function.

21. $f(x) = (2.5)^x$

22. $f(x) = \left(\dfrac{1}{4}\right)^x$

23. $f(x) = 3^{|x|}$

24. $f(x) = 4^{-|x|}$

25. $f(x) = 2^x - 3$

26. $f(x) = 2^{(x-3)}$

27. $f(x) = \dfrac{1}{3}\log x$

28. $f(x) = 3 \log x^{1/3}$

29. $f(x) = -\dfrac{1}{2}\ln x$

30. $f(x) = -\ln |x|$

In Exercises 31 and 32, use a graphing utility to graph each function.

31. $f(x) = \dfrac{4^x + 4^{-x}}{2}$

32. $f(x) = \dfrac{3^x - 3^{-x}}{2}$

In Exercises 33 to 36, change each logarithmic equation to its exponential form.

33. $\log_4 64 = 3$
$4^3 = 64$ [4.3]

34. $\log_{1/2} 8 = -3$
$\left(\dfrac{1}{2}\right)^{-3} = 8$ [4.3]

35. $\log_{\sqrt{2}} 4 = 4$
$\left(\sqrt{2}\right)^4 = 4$ [4.3]

36. $\ln 1 = 0$
$e^0 = 1$ [4.3]

In Exercises 37 to 40, change each exponential equation to its logarithmic form.

37. $5^3 = 125$
$\log_5 125 = 3$ [4.3]

38. $2^{10} = 1024$
$\log_2 1024 = 10$ [4.3]

39. $10^0 = 1$
$\log_{10} 1 = 0$ [4.3]

40. $8^{1/2} = 2\sqrt{2}$
$\log_8 2\sqrt{2} = \dfrac{1}{2}$ [4.3]

In Exercises 41 to 44, write the given logarithm in terms of logarithms of x, y, and z.

41. $\log_b \dfrac{x^2 y^3}{z}$
$2\log_b x + 3\log_b y - \log_b z$ [4.4]

42. $\log_b \dfrac{\sqrt{x}}{y^2 z}$
$\dfrac{1}{2}\log_b x - 2\log_b y - \log_b z$ [4.4]

43. $\ln xy^3$
$\ln x + 3\ln y$ [4.4]

44. $\ln \dfrac{\sqrt{xy}}{z^4}$
$\dfrac{1}{2}\ln x + \dfrac{1}{2}\ln y - 4\ln z$ [4.4]

In Exercises 45 to 48, write each logarithmic expression as a single logarithm with a coefficient of 1.

45. $2\log x + \dfrac{1}{3}\log (x + 1)$
$\log\left(x^2 \sqrt[3]{x + 1}\right)$ [4.4]

46. $5\log x - 2\log (x + 5)$
$\log \dfrac{x^5}{(x + 5)^2}$ [4.4]

47. $\dfrac{1}{2}\ln 2xy - 3\ln z$
$\ln \dfrac{\sqrt{2xy}}{z^3}$ [4.4]

48. $\ln x - (\ln y - \ln z)$
$\ln \dfrac{xz}{y}$ [4.4]

In Exercises 49 to 52, use the change-of-base formula and a calculator to approximate each logarithm accurate to six significant digits.

49. $\log_5 101$
2.86754 [4.4]

50. $\log_3 40$
3.35776 [4.4]

51. $\log_4 0.85$
-0.117233 [4.4]

52. $\log_8 0.3$
-0.578989 [4.4]

In Exercises 53 to 68, solve each equation for x. Give exact answers. Do not use a calculator.

53. $4^x = 30$
$\dfrac{\ln 30}{\ln 4}$ [4.5]

54. $5^{x+1} = 41$
$\dfrac{\log 41}{\log 5} - 1$ [4.5]

55. $\ln 3x - \ln(x - 1) = \ln 4$
4 [4.5]

56. $\ln 3x + \ln 2 = 1$
$\dfrac{1}{6}e$ [4.5]

57. $e^{\ln(x+2)} = 6$
4 [4.5]

58. $10^{\log(2x+1)} = 31$
15 [4.5]

59. $\dfrac{4^x + 4^{-x}}{4^x - 4^{-x}} = 2$ $\quad \dfrac{\ln 3}{2 \ln 4}$ [4.5]

60. $\dfrac{5^x + 5^{-x}}{2} = 8$ $\quad \dfrac{\ln(8 \pm 3\sqrt{7})}{\ln 5}$ [4.5]

61. $\log(\log x) = 3$
10^{1000} [4.5]

62. $\ln(\ln x) = 2$
$e^{(e^2)}$ [4.5]

63. $\log \sqrt{x-5} = 3$
1,000,005 [4.5]

64. $\log x + \log(x - 15) = 1$
$\dfrac{15 + \sqrt{265}}{2}$ [4.5]

65. $\log_4(\log_3 x) = 1$
81 [4.5]

66. $\log_7(\log_5 x^2) = 0$
$\pm\sqrt{5}$ [4.5]

67. $\log_5 x^3 = \log_5 16x$
4 [4.5]

68. $25 = 16^{\log_4 x}$
5 [4.5]

69. **EARTHQUAKE MAGNITUDE** Determine, to the nearest 0.1, the Richter scale magnitude of an earthquake with an intensity of $I = 51{,}782{,}000 I_0$. 7.7 [4.4]

70. **EARTHQUAKE MAGNITUDE** A seismogram has an amplitude of 18 millimeters and a time delay of 21 seconds. Find, to the nearest tenth, the Richter scale magnitude of the earthquake that produced the seismogram. 5.0 [4.4]

71. **COMPARISON OF EARTHQUAKES** An earthquake had a Richter scale magnitude of 7.2. Its aftershock had a Richter scale magnitude of 3.7. Compare the intensity of the earthquake to the intensity of the aftershock by finding, to the nearest unit, the ratio of the larger intensity to the smaller intensity. 3162 to 1 [4.4]

72. **COMPARISON OF EARTHQUAKES** An earthquake has an intensity 600 times the intensity of a second earthquake. Find, to the nearest tenth, the difference between the Richter scale magnitudes of the earthquakes. 2.8 [4.4]

73. **CHEMISTRY** Find the pH of tomatoes that have a hydronium-ion concentration of 6.28×10^{-5}. Round to the nearest tenth. 4.2 [4.4]

74. **CHEMISTRY** Find the hydronium-ion concentration of rainwater that has a pH of 5.4. $\approx 3.98 \times 10^{-6}$ [4.4]

75. **COMPOUND INTEREST** Find the balance when $16,000 is invested at an annual rate of 8% for 3 years if the interest is compounded

a. monthly
$20,323.79

b. continuously
$20,339.99 [4.6]

76. **COMPOUND INTEREST** Find the balance when $19,000 is invested at an annual rate of 6% for 5 years if the interest is compounded

a. daily
$25,646.69

b. continuously
$25,647.32 [4.6]

77. **DEPRECIATION** The scrap value S of a product with an expected life span of n years is given by $S(n) = P(1 - r)^n$, where P is the original purchase price of the product and r is the annual rate of depreciation. A taxicab is purchased

for $12,400 and is expected to last 3 years. What is its scrap value if it depreciates at a rate of 29% per year?
$4,438.10 [4.6]

78. **MEDICINE** A skin wound heals according to the function given by $N(t) = N_0 e^{-0.12t}$, where N is the number of square centimeters of unhealed skin t days after the injury, and N_0 is the number of square centimeters covered by the original wound.

a. What percentage of the wound will be healed after 10 days? 69.9%

b. How many days, to the nearest day, will it take for 50% of the wound to heal? 6 days

c. How long, to the nearest day, will it take for 90% of the wound to heal? 19 days [4.6]

In Exercises 79 to 82, find the exponential growth/decay function $N(t) = N_0 e^{kt}$ that satisfies the given conditions.

79. $N(0) = 1, N(2) = 5$
$N(t) \approx e^{0.8047t}$ [4.6]

80. $N(0) = 2, N(3) = 11$
$N(t) \approx 2e^{0.5682t}$ [4.6]

81. $N(1) = 4, N(5) = 5$
$N(t) \approx 3.783 e^{0.0558t}$ [4.6]

82. $N(-1) = 2, N(0) = 1$
$N(t) \approx e^{-0.6931t}$ [4.6]

83. **POPULATION GROWTH**

a. Find the exponential growth function for a city whose population was 25,200 in 2002 and 26,800 in 2003. Use $t = 0$ to represent the year 2002. $P(t) \approx 25{,}200 e^{0.06155789t}$

b. Use the growth function to predict, to the nearest hundred, the population of the city in 2009. 38,800 [4.6]

84. **CARBON DATING** Determine, to the nearest ten years, the age of a bone if it now contains 96% of its original amount of carbon-14. The half-life of carbon-14 is 5730 years.
340 yrs [4.6]

85. **ACTIVE MILITARY DUTY PERSONNEL** The following table shows the number of U.S. military personnel on active duty for each year from 1991 to 2000. (*Source: Time Almanac 2003* with *Information Please.*)

Active Military Duty Personnel, 1991–2000

1991	1,985,555	1996	1,471,722
1992	1,807,177	1997	1,438,562
1993	1,705,103	1998	1,406,830
1994	1,610,490	1999	1,385,703
1995	1,518,224	2000	1,384,338

a. Use a graphing utility to find a linear model, an exponential model, and a logarithmic model for the number of active-duty personnel, P, as a function of the year. Represent the year 1991 by $t = 91$.

85. a. linear: $P \approx -63{,}121t + 7{,}599{,}401$, $r \approx -0.93813$; exponential: $P \approx 64{,}717{,}271(0.96174359)^t$, $r \approx -0.95227$; logarithmic: $P \approx 29{,}163{,}839 - 6{,}052{,}741 \ln t$, $r \approx -0.94256$

b. Examine the correlation coefficients of the three regression models to determine which model provides the best fit.
The exponential equation provides the best fit for the data.

c. Use the model you selected in part **b.** to predict, to the nearest 10,000, the number of active duty military personnel for the year 2006. 1,040,000 [4.7]

86. 📟 🥧 **MORTALITY RATE** The following table shows the infant mortality rate in the United States for selected years from 1960 to 2000. (*Source: The World Almanac 2003.*)

U.S. Infant Mortality Rate, 1960–2000 (per 1000 live births)

Year	Rate
1960	26.0
1970	20.0
1980	12.6
1990	9.2
1995	7.6
1999	7.1
2000	6.9

86. a. linear: $R \approx -0.475297t + 53.1037$, $r \approx -0.98118$
exponential: $R \approx 207.544(0.966206)^t$, $r \approx -0.99660$
logarithmic: $R \approx 181.202 - 38.0586 \ln t$, $r \approx -0.99073$

a. Use a graphing utility to find a linear model, an exponential model, and a logarithmic model for the infant mortality rate, R, as a function of the year. Represent the year 1960 by $t = 60$.
See answer below.

b. Examine the correlation coefficients of the three regression models to determine which model provides the best fit.
The exponential equation provides the best fit for the data.

c. Use the model you selected in part **b.** to predict, to the nearest 0.1, the infant mortality rate in 2008.
5.1 per 1000 live births [4.7]

87. LOGISTIC GROWTH The population of coyotes in a national park satisfies the logistic model with $P_0 = 210$ in 1992, $c = 1400$, and $P(3) = 360$ (the population in 1995).

a. Determine the logistic model. $P(t) \approx \dfrac{1400}{1 + \frac{17}{3}e^{-0.22458t}}$

b. Use the model to predict, to the nearest 10, the coyote population in 2005. 1070 [4.6]

88. Consider the logistic function

$$P(t) = \frac{128}{1 + 5e^{-0.27t}}$$

a. Find P_0. $21\frac{1}{3}$

b. What does $P(t)$ approach as $t \to \infty$? $P(t) \to 128$ [4.6]

CHAPTER 4 TEST

1. Find the inverse of $f(x) = 2x - 3$. Graph f and f^{-1} on the same coordinate axes. $f^{-1}(x) = \frac{1}{2}x + \frac{3}{2}$ Answer graph on page AA19. [4.1]

2. Find the inverse of $f(x) = \dfrac{x}{4x - 8}$. State the domain and the range of f^{-1}. $f^{-1}(x) = \dfrac{8x}{4x - 1}$; Domain f^{-1}: all real numbers except $\frac{1}{4}$; Range f^{-1}: all real numbers except 2 [4.1]

3. a. Write $\log_b(5x - 3) = c$ in exponential form.
$b^c = 5x - 3$

b. Write $3^{x/2} = y$ in logarithmic form. $\log_3 y = \dfrac{x}{2}$ [4.3]

4. Write $\log_b \dfrac{z^2}{y^3\sqrt{x}}$ in terms of logarithms of x, y, and z.
$2\log_b z - 3\log_b y - \frac{1}{2}\log_b x$ [4.4]

5. Write $\log(2x + 3) - 3\log(x - 2)$ as a single logarithm with a coefficient of 1.
$\log \dfrac{2x + 3}{(x - 2)^3}$ [4.4]

6. Use the change-of-base formula and a calculator to approximate $\log_4 12$. Round your result to the nearest ten thousandth. 1.7925 [4.4]

7. Graph: $f(x) = 3^{-x/2}$
Answer on page AA19. [4.2]

8. Graph: $f(x) = -\ln(x + 1)$
Answer on page AA19. [4.3]

9. Solve: $5^x = 22$. Round your solution to the nearest ten thousandth. 1.9206 [4.5]

10. Find the *exact* solution of $4^{5-x} = 7^x$. $\dfrac{5\ln 4}{\ln 28}$ [4.5]

11. Solve: $\log(x + 99) - \log(3x - 2) = 2$ 1 [4.5]

12. Solve: $\ln(2 - x) + \ln(5 - x) = \ln(37 - x)$ -3 [4.5]

13. Find the balance on $20,000 invested at an annual interest rate of 7.8% for 5 years:

a. compounded monthly. $29,502.36

b. compounded continuously. $29,539.62 [4.6]

14. Find the time required for money invested at an annual rate of 4% to double in value if the investment is compounded monthly. Round to the nearest hundredth of a year. 17.36 yrs [4.6]

15. a. What, to the nearest tenth, will an earthquake measure on the Richter scale if it has an intensity of $I = 42,304,000I_0$? 7.6

b. Compare the intensity of an earthquake that measures 6.3 on the Richter scale to the intensity of an earthquake that measures 4.5 on the Richter scale by finding the ratio of the larger intensity to the smaller intensity. Round to the nearest whole number. 63 to 1 [4.4]

16. a. Find the exponential growth function for a city whose population was 34,600 in 1996 and 39,800 in 1999. Use $t = 0$ to represent the year 1996. $P(t) \approx 34,600e^{(0.04667108)t}$

b. Use the growth function to predict the population of the city in 2006. Round to the nearest thousand. 55,000 [4.6]

17. Determine, to the nearest ten years, the age of a bone if it now contains 92% of its original amount of carbon-14. The half-life of carbon-14 is 5730 years. 690 yrs [4.6]

18. a. Use a graphing utility to find the exponential regression function for the following data.

{(2.5, 16), (3.7, 48), (5.0, 155), (6.5, 571), (6.9, 896)}
$y \approx 1.67199(2.47188)^x$

b. Use the function to predict, to the nearest whole number, the y-value associated with $x = 7.8$. 1945 [4.7]

19. The following table shows the interest rates paid by a bank on certificates of deposit (CDs) of different terms in May of 2003.

CD term, t years	0.5	1.0	2.0	5.0
Rate	1.38%	1.66%	2.01%	3.20%

a. Find the *logarithmic regression function* for the data and use the function to predict, to the nearest 0.01%, the interest rate on a CD invested for 3.5 years. $R(t) \approx 1.74830 + 0.78089 \ln x$; 2.73%

b. According to your function, for how long (to the nearest 0.1 year) would you need to invest to receive a 2.5% interest rate? 2.6 yrs [4.7]

20. The population of raccoons in a state park satisfies a logistic growth model with $P_0 = 160$ in 1999 and $P(1) = 190$. A park ranger has estimated the carrying capacity of the park to be 1100 raccoons. Use these data to

a. find the logistic growth model for the raccoon population. $P(t) \approx \dfrac{1100}{1 + 5.875e^{-0.20429t}}$

b. predict the raccoon population in 2006. $\approx$457 raccoons [4.6]

CUMULATIVE REVIEW EXERCISES

1. Solve $|x - 4| \le 2$. Write the solution set using interval notation. [2, 6] [1.1]

2. Solve $\dfrac{x}{2x - 6} \ge 1$. Write the solution set using set-builder notation. $\{x \mid 3 < x \le 6\}$ [1.5]

3. Find, to the nearest tenth, the distance between the points (5, 2) and (11, 7). 7.8 [2.1]

4. The height, in feet, of a ball released with an initial upward velocity of 44 feet per second and at an initial height of 8 feet is given by $h(t) = -16t^2 + 44t + 8$, where t is the time in seconds after the ball is released. Find the maximum height the ball will reach. 38.25 ft [2.4]

5. Given $f(x) = 2x + 1$ and $g(x) = x^2 - 5$, find $(g \circ f)$. $4x^2 + 4x - 4$ [2.6]

6. Find the inverse of $f(x) = 3x - 5$. $f^{-1}(x) = \dfrac{1}{3}x + \dfrac{5}{3}$ [4.1]

7. The load that a horizontal beam can safely support varies jointly as the width and the square of the depth of the beam. It has been determined that a beam with a width of 4 inches and a depth of 8 inches can safely support a load of 1500 pounds. How many pounds can a beam of the same material and the same length safely support if it has a width of 6 inches and a depth of 10 inches? Round to the nearest hundred pounds. 3500 lb [1.6]

8. Use Descartes' Rule of Signs to determine the number of possible real zeros of $P(x) = x^4 - 3x^3 + x^2 - x - 6$.
3 or 1 positive real zeros; 1 negative real zero [3.3]

9. Find the zeros of $P(x) = x^4 - 5x^3 + x^2 + 15x - 12$.
$1, 4, -\sqrt{3}, \sqrt{3}$ [3.3]

10. Find a polynomial function of lowest degree that has 2, $1 - i$, and $1 + i$ as zeros. $P(x) = x^3 - 4x^2 + 6x - 4$ [3.4]

11. Find the equations of the vertical and horizontal asymptotes of the graph of $r(x) = \dfrac{3x - 5}{x - 4}$.
vertical asymptote: $x = 4$, horizontal asymptote: $y = 3$ [3.5]

12. Determine the domain and the range of the rational function $R(x) = \dfrac{4}{x^2 + 1}$.
domain: all real numbers; range: $\{y \mid 0 < y \le 4\}$ [3.5]

13. State whether $f(x) = 0.4^x$ is an increasing function or a decreasing function. decreasing function [4.2]

14. Write $\log_4 x = y$ in exponential form. $4^y = x$ [4.3]

15. Write $5^3 = 125$ in logarithmic form. $\log_5 125 = 3$ [4.3]

16. Find, to the nearest tenth, the Richter scale magnitude of an earthquake with an intensity of $I = 11{,}650{,}600I_0$.
7.1 [4.4]

17. Solve $2e^x = 15$. Round to the nearest ten thousandth.
2.0149 [4.5]

18. Find the age of a bone if it now has 94% of the carbon-14 it had at time $t = 0$. Round to the nearest ten years.
510 years old [4.6]

19. The following table shows the progression of the world record distances for the men's javelin throw for the years 1986 to 1996. (*Source:* http://www.athletix. org/Statistics/stats.html)

World Record Progression in the Men's Javelin Throw

Year	Distance (in meters)
1986	85.74
1987	87.66
1990	89.10
1992	91.46
1993	95.54
1993	95.66
1996	98.48

a. Use a graphing utility to determine a logarithmic model for the data. Use $x = 1$ to represent the year 1986 and $x = 11$ to represent the year 1996.
$y \approx 84.41319 + 4.88166 \ln x$

b. Use the model from part **a.** to predict the men's world record javelin throw distance for 2006. Round to the nearest hundredth of a meter. 99.28 m [4.7]

20. The wolf population in a national park satisfies a logistic growth model with $P_0 = 160$ in 1998 and $P(3) = 205$ (the population in 2001). It has been determined that the maximum population the park can support is 450 wolves.

a. Determine the logistic growth model for the data.
$P(x) \approx \dfrac{450}{1 + 1.8125e^{-0.13882x}}$

b. Use the model to predict, to the nearest 10, the wolf population in 2008. 310 wolves [4.7]

TOPICS IN ANALYTIC GEOMETRY

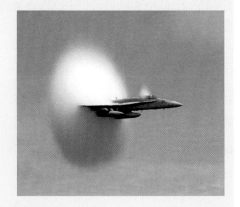

Sonic Booms

When the speed of a boat exceeds the speed at which waves can propagate through the water, a wake is created. In a similar way, when a plane travels at speeds that exceed the speed of sound, a "sound wake" is created. This sound wake results in a sonic boom.

The sound wake is in the form of a cone with the plane at the vertex. When the wave-cone intersects flat land, a hyperbola is formed. People standing along the hyperbola hear the sonic boom at the same time. Hyperbolas are one of the topics of this chapter. See **Exercise 55 on page 497.**

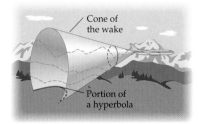

The photo at the left, by George Standsbery, shows a B1-B Lancer as it accelerates through the speed of sound. The white cloud is condensation from the shock wave created when the plane exceeded the speed of sound. In what may seem like a totally unrelated phenomenon, the sound produced when a bullwhip is snapped occurs for exactly the same reason as a sonic boom: The tip of the whip exceeds the speed of sound, thereby producing the characteristic popping sound.

Proof by Contradiction

In a detective television show, a suspect might be asked, "Where were you Friday night?", to which the suspect replies, "I was in New York." However, several eyewitnesses agree that they saw the suspect in California on that Friday night. Their testimony *contradicts* what the suspect claimed to be a factual statement.

A similar strategy is used by mathematicians to prove some theorems. The mathematician assumes that the theorem is false and then shows that the assumption contradicts a statement that is known to be true. This method of proof is called a *proof by contradiction*. To illustrate this method, consider the following theorem.

The $\sqrt{3}$ is an irrational number.

To prove this theorem, we begin by assuming that $\sqrt{3}$ is not an irrational number—that is, it is a rational number. This is the opposite of what we want to prove. If $\sqrt{3}$ is a rational number, then $\sqrt{3}$ can be represented as the ratio of two integers. That is, $\sqrt{3} = \dfrac{a}{b}$, where a and b are integers with no common factors and $b \neq 0$. From this assumption, we have

$$\sqrt{3} = \frac{a}{b}$$

$$3 = \frac{a^2}{b^2} \qquad \text{• Square both sides of the equation.}$$

$$3b^2 = a^2 \qquad \text{• Multiply each side by } b^2.$$

The last equation implies that a^2 is divisible by 3. Because 3 is prime, a is divisible by 3. Thus $a = 3k$ for some integer k and $a^2 = (3k)^2 = 9k^2$.

Replacing a^2 by $9k^2$, we have

$$3b^2 = 9k^2$$

$$b^2 = 3k^2 \qquad \text{• Divide each side by 3.}$$

The equation $b^2 = 3k^2$ implies that b is divisible by 3. Thus we have shown that both a and b are divisible by 3. This, however, contradicts our statement that a and b have no common factors. This contradiction means that our assumption that $\sqrt{3}$ can be represented as the quotient of integers is not possible, and therefore, $\sqrt{3}$ must be an irrational number.

PARABOLAS

MATH MATTERS

Appollonius (262–200 B.C.) wrote an eight-volume treatise entitled *On Conic Sections* in which he derived the formulas for all the conic sections. He was the first to use the words *parabola, ellipse,* and *hyperbola.*

take note

If the intersection of a plane and a cone is a point, a line, or two intersecting lines, then the intersection is called a *degenerate conic section.*

The graph of a parabola, a circle, an ellipse, or a hyperbola can be formed by the intersection of a plane and a cone. Hence these figures are referred to as conic sections. See **Figure 5.1.**

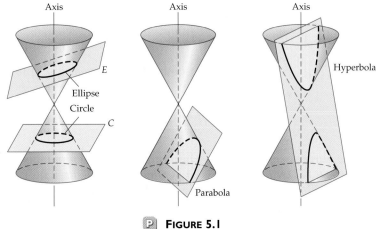

Ⓟ **FIGURE 5.1**
Cones intersected by planes

A plane perpendicular to the axis of the cone intersects the cone in a circle (plane *C*). The plane *E*, tilted so that it is not perpendicular to the axis, intersects the cone in an ellipse. When the plane is parallel to a line on the surface of the cone, the plane intersects the cone in a parabola. When the plane intersects both portions of the cone, a hyperbola is formed.

● PARABOLAS WITH VERTEX AT (0, 0)

Besides the geometric description of a conic section just given, a conic section can be defined as a set of points. This method uses some specified conditions about the curve to determine which points in a coordinate system are points of the graph. For example, a parabola can be defined by the following set of points.

Definition of a Parabola

A **parabola** is the set of points in the plane that are equidistant from a fixed line (the **directrix**) and a fixed point (the **focus**) not on the directrix.

The line that passes through the focus and is perpendicular to the directrix is called the **axis of symmetry** of the parabola. The midpoint of the line segment between the focus and directrix on the axis of symmetry is the **vertex** of the parabola, as shown in **Figure 5.2.**

Using this definition of a parabola, we can determine an equation of a parabola. Suppose that the coordinates of the vertex of a parabola are $V(0, 0)$ and

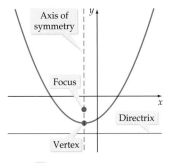

Ⓟ **FIGURE 5.2**

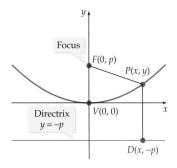

FIGURE 5.3

To review **AXIS OF SYMMETRY**, see p. 214.

take note

The tests for y-axis and x-axis symmetry can be used to verify these statements and provide connections to earlier topics on symmetry.

the axis of symmetry is the y-axis. The equation of the directrix is $y = -p, p > 0$. The focus lies on the axis of symmetry and is the same distance from the vertex as the vertex is from the directrix. Thus the coordinates of the focus are $F(0, p)$, as shown in **Figure 5.3**.

Let $P(x, y)$ be any point P on the parabola. Then, using the distance formula and the fact that the distance between any point P on the parabola and the focus is equal to the distance from the point P to the directrix, we can write the equation

$$d(P, F) = d(P, D)$$

By the distance formula,

$$\sqrt{(x - 0)^2 + (y - p)^2} = y + p$$

Now, squaring each side and simplifying, we get

$$\left(\sqrt{(x - 0)^2 + (y - p)^2}\right)^2 = (y + p)^2$$
$$x^2 + y^2 - 2py + p^2 = y^2 + 2py + p^2$$
$$x^2 = 4py$$

This is an equation of a parabola with vertex at the origin and the y-axis as its axis of symmetry. The equation of a parabola with vertex at the origin and the x-axis as its axis of symmetry is derived in a similar manner.

Standard Forms of the Equation of a Parabola with Vertex at the Origin

Axis of Symmetry Is the y-Axis

The standard form of the equation of a parabola with vertex $(0, 0)$ and the y-axis as its axis of symmetry is $x^2 = 4py$. The focus is $(0, p)$, and the equation of the directrix is $y = -p$.

Axis of Symmetry Is the x-Axis

The standard form of the equation of a parabola with vertex $(0, 0)$ and the x-axis as its axis of symmetry is $y^2 = 4px$. The focus is $(p, 0)$ and the equation of the directrix is $x = -p$.

In the equation $x^2 = 4py$, $x^2 \geq 0$. Therefore, $4py \geq 0$. Thus if $p > 0$, then $y \geq 0$, and the parabola opens up. If $p < 0$, then $y \leq 0$, and the parabola opens down. A similar analysis shows that for $y^2 = 4px$, the parabola opens to the right when $p > 0$ and opens to the left when $p < 0$.

❓ **QUESTION** Does the graph of $y^2 = -4x$ open up, down, to the left, or to the right?

Alternative to Example 1
Find the focus and directrix of the parabola given by the equation $x = 4y^2$.

● The focus is $\left(\dfrac{1}{16}, 0\right)$. The directrix is $x = -\dfrac{1}{16}$.

EXAMPLE 1   **Find the Focus and Directrix of a Parabola**

Find the focus and directrix of the parabola given by the equation

$$y = -\frac{1}{2}x^2.$$

❓ **ANSWER** To the left.

Solution

Because the x term is squared, the standard form of the equation is $x^2 = 4py$.

$$y = -\frac{1}{2}x^2$$

$$x^2 = -2y \qquad \bullet \text{ Write the given equation}$$
$$\text{in standard form.}$$

Comparing this equation with $x^2 = 4py$ gives

$$4p = -2$$

$$p = -\frac{1}{2}$$

Because p is negative, the parabola opens down, and the focus is below the vertex $(0, 0)$, as shown in **Figure 5.4.** The coordinates of the focus are $\left(0, -\frac{1}{2}\right)$. The equation of the directrix is $y = \frac{1}{2}$.

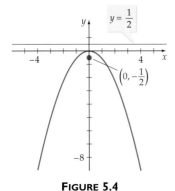

FIGURE 5.4

▶ **TRY EXERCISE 4, PAGE 468**

Alternative to Example 2
Find the equation of the parabola in standard form with vertex at the origin and focus at $(0, -4)$.
● $x^2 = -16y$

EXAMPLE 2 **Find the Equation of a Parabola in Standard Form**

Find the equation of the parabola in standard form with vertex at the origin and focus at $(-2, 0)$.

Solution

Because the vertex is $(0, 0)$ and the focus is at $(-2, 0)$, $p = -2$. The graph of the parabola opens toward the focus, so in this case the parabola opens to the left. The equation of the parabola in standard form that opens to the left is $y^2 = 4px$. Substitute -2 for p in this equation and simplify.

$$y^2 = 4(-2)x = -8x$$

The equation of the parabola is $y^2 = -8x$.

▶ **TRY EXERCISE 28, PAGE 468**

INTEGRATING TECHNOLOGY

The graph of $y^2 = -8x$ is shown in **Figure 5.5.** Note that the graph is not the graph of a function. To graph $y^2 = -8x$ with a graphing utility, we first solve for y to produce $y = \pm\sqrt{-8x}$. From this equation we can see that for any $x < 0$, there are two values of y. For example, when $x = -2$,

$$y = \pm\sqrt{(-8)(-2)} = \pm\sqrt{16} = \pm 4$$

The graph of $y^2 = -8x$ in **Figure 5.5** was drawn by graphing both $y_1 = \sqrt{-8x}$ and $y_2 = -\sqrt{-8x}$ in the same window.

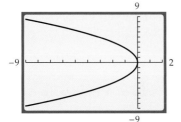

FIGURE 5.5

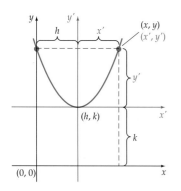

FIGURE 5.6

PARABOLAS WITH VERTEX AT (h, k)

The equation of a parabola with a vertical or horizontal axis of symmetry and with the vertex at a point (h, k) can be found by using the translations discussed previously. Consider a coordinate system with coordinate axes labeled x' and y' placed so that its origin is at (h, k) of the xy-coordinate system.

The relationship between an ordered pair in the $x'y'$-coordinate system and in the xy-coordinate system is given by the transformation equations

$$x' = x - h$$
$$y' = y - k \tag{1}$$

Now consider a parabola with vertex at (h, k), as shown in **Figure 5.6.** Create a new coordinate system with axes labeled x' and y' and with its origin at (h, k). The equation of a parabola in the $x'y'$-coordinate system is

$$(x')^2 = 4py' \tag{2}$$

Using the transformation Equations (1), we can substitute the expressions for x' and y' into Equation (2). The standard form of the equation of the parabola with vertex (h, k) and a vertical axis of symmetry is

$$(x - h)^2 = 4p(y - k)$$

Similarly, we can derive the standard form of the equation of the parabola with vertex (h, k) and a horizontal axis of symmetry.

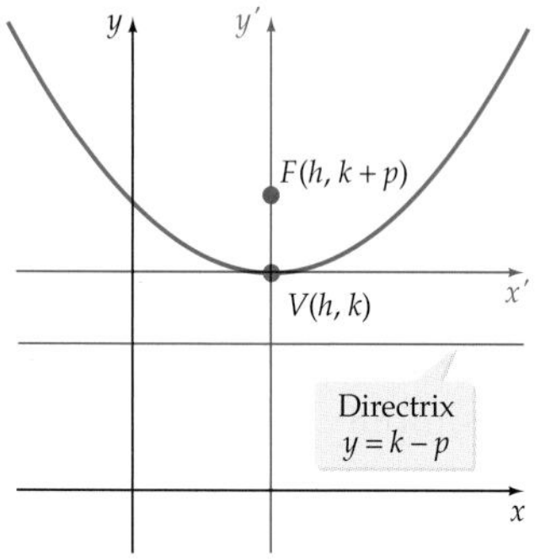

FIGURE 5.7

Standard Forms of the Equation of a Parabola with Vertex at (h, k)

Vertical Axis of Symmetry

The standard form of the equation of the parabola with vertex $V(h, k)$ and a vertical axis of symmetry is

$$(x - h)^2 = 4p(y - k)$$

The focus is $(h, k + p)$, and the equation of the directrix is $y = k - p$. See **Figure 5.7.**

Horizontal Axis of Symmetry

The standard form of the equation of the parabola with vertex (h, k) and a horizontal axis of symmetry is

$$(y - k)^2 = 4p(x - h)$$

The focus is $(h + p, k)$, and the equation of the directrix is $x = h - p$.

Alternative to Example 3
Find the equation of the directrix and the coordinates of the vertex and focus of the parabola given by the equation $12x + y^2 - 8y + 40 = 0$.
● **The equation of the directrix is $x = 1$. The coordinates of the vertex are $(-2, 4)$. The coordinates of the focus are $(-5, 4)$.**

EXAMPLE 3   **Find the Focus and Directrix of a Parabola**

Find the equation of the directrix and the coordinates of the vertex and focus of the parabola given by the equation $3x + 2y^2 + 8y - 4 = 0$.

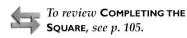

To review **COMPLETING THE SQUARE**, *see p. 105.*

Solution

Rewrite the equation so that the y terms are on one side of the equation, and then complete the square on y.

$$3x + 2y^2 + 8y - 4 = 0$$
$$2y^2 + 8y = -3x + 4$$
$$2(y^2 + 4y) = -3x + 4$$
$$2(y^2 + 4y + 4) = -3x + 4 + 8 \qquad \bullet \text{ Complete the square. Note that } 2 \cdot 4 = 8 \text{ is added to each side.}$$
$$2(y + 2)^2 = -3(x - 4) \qquad \bullet \text{ Simplify and then factor.}$$
$$(y + 2)^2 = -\frac{3}{2}(x - 4) \qquad \bullet \text{ Write the equation in standard form.}$$

Comparing this equation to $(y - k)^2 = 4p(x - h)$, we have a parabola that opens to the left with vertex $(4, -2)$ and $4p = -\frac{3}{2}$. Thus $p = -\frac{3}{8}$.

The coordinates of the focus are

$$\left(4 + \left(-\frac{3}{8}\right), -2\right) = \left(\frac{29}{8}, -2\right)$$

The equation of the directrix is

$$x = 4 - \left(-\frac{3}{8}\right) = \frac{35}{8}$$

Choosing some values for y and finding the corresponding values for x, we plot a few points. Because the line $y = -2$ is the axis of symmetry, for each point on one side of the axis of symmetry there is a corresponding point on the other side. Two points are $(-2, 1)$ and $(-2, -5)$. See **Figure 5.8.**

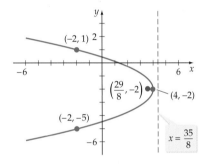

FIGURE 5.8

▶ **TRY EXERCISE 20, PAGE 468**

EXAMPLE 4   **Find the Equation in Standard Form of a Parabola**

Find the equation in standard form of the parabola with directrix $x = -1$ and focus $(3, 2)$.

Solution

The vertex is the midpoint of the line segment joining the focus $(3, 2)$ and the point $(-1, 2)$ on the directrix.

$$(h, k) = \left(\frac{-1 + 3}{2}, \frac{2 + 2}{2}\right) = (1, 2)$$

The standard form of the equation is $(y - k)^2 = 4p(x - h)$. The distance from the vertex to the focus is 2. Thus $4p = 4(2) = 8$, and the equation of the parabola in standard form is $(y - 2)^2 = 8(x - 1)$. See **Figure 5.9.**

Alternative to Example 4
Find the equation in standard form of the parabola with directrix $y = 3$ and focus $(1, -5)$.
● $(x - 1)^2 = -16(y + 1)$

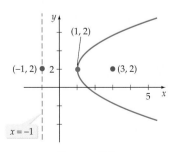

FIGURE 5.9

▶ **TRY EXERCISE 30, PAGE 468**

● APPLICATIONS

A principle of physics states that when light is reflected from a point P on a surface, the angle of incidence (that of the incoming ray) equals the angle of reflection (that of the outgoing ray). See **Figure 5.10.** This principle applied to parabolas has some useful consequences.

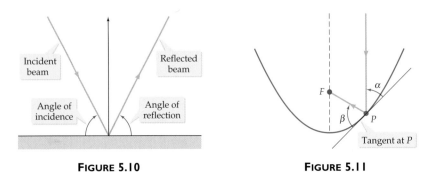

FIGURE 5.10   **FIGURE 5.11**

Optical Property of a Parabola

The line tangent to a parabola at a point P makes equal angles with the line through P and parallel to the axis of symmetry and the line through P and the focus of the parabola (see **Figure 5.11**).

A cross section of the reflecting mirror of a telescope has the shape of a parabola. The incoming parallel rays of light are reflected from the surface of the mirror and to the focus. See **Figure 5.12.**

Flashlights and car headlights also make use of this property. The light bulb is positioned at the focus of the parabolic reflector, which causes the reflected light to be reflected outward in parallel rays. See **Figure 5.13.**

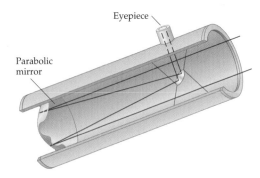

FIGURE 5.12

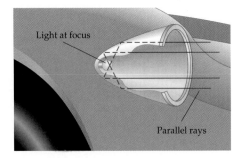

FIGURE 5.13

Alternative to Example 5

A flashlight reflector has the shape of a paraboloid. If the flashlight lens is 4 inches in diameter and the reflector is 2 inches deep, determine the location of the focus of the flashlight reflector.

● **The focus of the flashlight reflector is on the axis of symmetry of the flashlight reflector and is $\frac{1}{2}$ inch from the vertex of the reflector.**

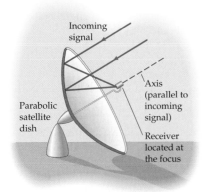

FIGURE 5.14

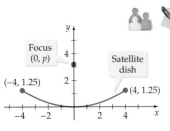

FIGURE 5.15

EXAMPLE 5 **Find the Focus of a Satellite Dish**

A satellite dish has the shape of a paraboloid. The signals that it receives are reflected to a receiver that is located at the focus of the paraboloid. If the dish is 8 feet across at its opening and 1.25 feet deep at its center, determine the location of its focus.

Solution

Figure 5.14 shows that a cross section of the paraboloid along its axis of symmetry is a parabola. **Figure 5.15** shows this cross section placed in a rectangular coordinate system with the vertex of the parabola at $(0, 0)$ and the axis of symmetry of the parabola on the y-axis. The parabola has an equation of the form

$$4py = x^2$$

Because the parabola contains the point $(4, 1.25)$, this equation is satisfied by the substitutions $x = 4$ and $y = 1.25$. Thus we have

$$4p(1.25) = 4^2$$
$$5p = 16$$
$$p = \frac{16}{5}$$

The focus of the satellite dish is on the axis of symmetry of the dish, and it is $3\frac{1}{5}$ feet above the vertex of the dish. See **Figure 5.15.**

▶ **TRY EXERCISE 38, PAGE 468**

TOPICS FOR DISCUSSION

1. Do the graphs of the parabola given by $y = x^2$ and the vertical line given by $x = 10,000$ intersect? Explain.

2. A student claims that the focus of the parabola given by $y = 8x^2$ is at $(0, 2)$ because $4p = 8$ implies that $p = 2$. Explain the error in the student's reasoning.

3. "The vertex of a parabola is always halfway between its focus and its directrix." Do you agree? Explain.

4. A tutor claims that the graph of $(x - h)^2 = 4p(y - k)$ has a y-intercept of $\left(0, \dfrac{h^2}{4p} + k\right)$. Explain why the tutor is correct.

EXERCISE SET 5.1

—*Suggested Assignment: Exercises 1–51, every other odd; 58–63.*
—*Answer graphs to Exercises 1–26 are on pages AA20–AA21.*

In Exercises 1 to 26, find the vertex, focus, and directrix of the parabola given by each equation. Sketch the graph.

1. $x^2 = -4y$

2. $2y^2 = x$

3. $y^2 = \dfrac{1}{3}x$

▶ **4.** $x^2 = -\dfrac{1}{4}y$

5. $(x - 2)^2 = 8(y + 3)$

6. $(y + 1)^2 = 6(x - 1)$

7. $(y + 4)^2 = -4(x - 2)$

8. $(x - 3)^2 = -(y + 2)$

9. $(y - 1)^2 = 2x + 8$

10. $(x + 2)^2 = 3y - 6$

11. $(2x - 4)^2 = 8y - 16$

12. $(3x + 6)^2 = 18y - 36$

13. $x^2 + 8x - y + 6 = 0$

14. $x^2 - 6x + y + 10 = 0$

15. $x + y^2 - 3y + 4 = 0$

16. $x - y^2 - 4y + 9 = 0$

17. $2x - y^2 - 6y + 1 = 0$

18. $3x + y^2 + 8y + 4 = 0$

19. $x^2 + 3x + 3y - 1 = 0$

▶ **20.** $x^2 + 5x - 4y - 1 = 0$

21. $2x^2 - 8x - 4y + 3 = 0$

22. $6x - 3y^2 - 12y + 4 = 0$

23. $2x + 4y^2 + 8y - 5 = 0$

24. $4x^2 - 12x + 12y + 7 = 0$

25. $3x^2 - 6x - 9y + 4 = 0$

26. $2x - 3y^2 + 9y + 5 = 0$

27. Find the equation in standard form of the parabola with vertex at the origin and focus $(0, -4)$. $x^2 = -16y$

▶ **28.** Find the equation in standard form of the parabola with vertex at the origin and focus $(5, 0)$. $y^2 = 20x$

29. Find the equation in standard form of the parabola with vertex at $(-1, 2)$ and focus $(-1, 3)$. $(x + 1)^2 = 4(y - 2)$

▶ **30.** Find the equation in standard form of the parabola with vertex at $(2, -3)$ and focus $(0, -3)$. $(y + 3)^2 = -8(x - 2)$

31. Find the equation in standard form of the parabola with focus $(3, -3)$ and directrix $y = -5$. $(x - 3)^2 = 4(y + 4)$

32. Find the equation in standard form of the parabola with focus $(-2, 4)$ and directrix $x = 4$. $(y - 4)^2 = -12(x - 1)$

33. Find the equation in standard form of the parabola that has vertex $(-4, 1)$, has its axis of symmetry parallel to the y-axis, and passes through the point $(-2, 2)$. $(x + 4)^2 = 4(y - 1)$

34. Find the equation in standard form of the parabola that has vertex $(3, -5)$, has its axis of symmetry parallel to the x-axis, and passes through the point $(4, 3)$. $(y + 5)^2 = 64(x - 3)$

35. **STRUCTURAL DEFECTS** Ultrasound is used as a nondestructive method of determining whether a support beam for a structure has an internal fracture. In one scanning procedure, if the resulting image is a parabola, engineers know that there is a structural defect. Suppose that a scan produced an image whose equation is

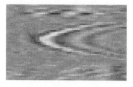

$$x = -0.325y^2 + 13y + 120$$

Determine the vertex and focus of the graph of this parabola. vertex: $(250, 20)$; focus: $\left(\dfrac{3240}{13}, 20\right)$

36. **FOUNTAIN DESIGN** A fountain in a shopping mall has two parabolic arcs of water intersecting as shown below. If the equation of one parabola is $y = -0.25x^2 + 2x$ and the equation of the second parabola is $y = -0.25x^2 + 4.5x - 16.25$, how high above the base of the fountain do the parabolas intersect? All dimensions are in feet. 2.4375 ft

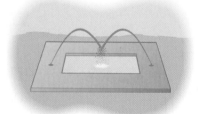

37. **SATELLITE DISH** A satellite dish has the shape of a paraboloid. The signals that it receives are reflected to a receiver that is located at the focus of the paraboloid. If the dish is 8 feet across at its opening and 1 foot deep at its vertex, determine the location (distance above the vertex of the dish) of its focus. on axis 4 ft above vertex

▶ **38.** **RADIO TELESCOPES** The antenna of a radio telescope is a paraboloid measuring 81 feet across with a depth of 16 feet. Determine, to the nearest 0.1 of a foot, the distance from the vertex to the focus of this antenna. 25.6 ft

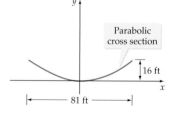

Parabolic cross section

16 ft

81 ft

39. CAPTURING THE SOUND During televised football games, a parabolic microphone is used to capture sounds. The shield of the microphone is a paraboloid with a diameter of 18.75 inches and a depth of 3.66 inches. To pick up the sounds, a microphone is placed at the focus of the paraboloid. How far (to the nearest 0.1 of an inch) from the vertex of the paraboloid should the microphone be placed? 6.0 in.

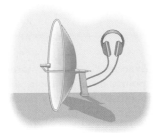

40. 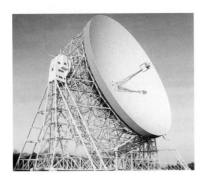 **THE LOVELL TELESCOPE** The Lovell Telescope is a radio telescope located at the Jodrell Bank Observatory in Cheshire, England. The dish of the telescope has the shape of a paraboloid with a diameter of 250 feet and a focal length of 75 feet.

a. Find an equation of a cross section of the paraboloid that passes through the vertex of the paraboloid. Assume that the dish has its vertex at $(0, 0)$ and a vertical axis of symmetry. $y = \dfrac{1}{300}x^2$

b. Find the depth of the dish. Round to the nearest foot. 52 ft

41. 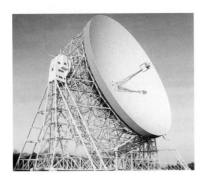 The surface area of a paraboloid with radius r and depth d is given by $S = \dfrac{\pi r}{6d^2}[(r^2 + 4d^2)^{3/2} - r^3]$.

Approximate (to the nearest 100 square feet) the surface area of:

a. The radio telescope in Exercise 38. 5900 ft²

b. The Lovell Telescope (see Exercise 40). 56,800 ft²

42. THE HALE TELESCOPE The parabolic mirror in the Hale telescope at the Palomar Observatory in southern Califor-

nia has a diameter of 200 inches, and it has a concave depth of 3.75375 inches. Determine the location of its focus (to the nearest inch). 666 in. above the vertex

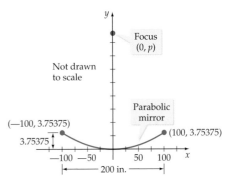

Mirror in the Hale Telescope

43. THE LICK TELESCOPE The parabolic mirror in the Lick telescope at the Lick Observatory on Mount Hamilton has a diameter of 120 inches, and it has a focal length of 600 inches. In the construction of the mirror, workers grind the mirror as shown in the following diagram. Determine the dimension a, which is the concave depth of the mirror. $a = 1.5$ in.

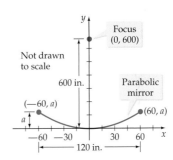

Mirror in the Lick Telescope

44. HEADLIGHT DESIGN A light source is to be placed on the axis of symmetry of the parabolic reflector shown in the figure below. How far to the right of the vertex point should the light source be located if the designer wishes the reflected light rays to form a beam of parallel rays? 0.375 in. to the right of the vertex

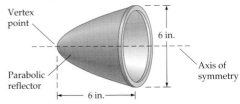

In Exercises 45 to 48, graph each equation, and find the coordinates of the points of intersection of the two graphs to the nearest ten-thousandth.

45. $y = 2x^2 - x - 1$
$y = x$ $(-0.3660, -0.3660)$ and
$(1.3660, 1.3660)$

46. $y = x^2 + 2x - 4$
$y = x - 1$ $(-2.3028, -3.3028)$ and
$(1.3028, 0.3028)$

47. $y = 2x^2 - 1$
$y = x^2 + x + 3$
$(-1.5616, 3.8769)$ and
$(2.5616, 12.1231)$

48. $y = 2x^2 - x - 1$
$y = x^2 - 4$ no solution

CONNECTING CONCEPTS

In Exercises 49 to 51, use the following definition of latus rectum: The line segment that has endpoints on a parabola, passes through the focus of the parabola, and is perpendicular to the axis of symmetry is called the *latus rectum* of the parabola.

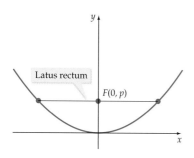

49. Find the length of the latus rectum for the parabola $x^2 = 4y$. 4

50. Find the length of the latus rectum for the parabola $y^2 = -8x$. 8

51. Find the length of the latus rectum for any parabola in terms of $|p|$, the distance from the vertex of the parabola to the focus. $4|p|$

The result of Exercise 51 can be stated as the following theorem: **Two points on a parabola will be $2|p|$ units on each side of the axis of symmetry on the line through the focus and perpendicular to that axis.**

52. Use the theorem to sketch a graph of the parabola given by the equation $(x - 3)^2 = 2(y + 1)$.
Answer on page AA21.

53. Use the theorem to sketch a graph of the parabola given by the equation $(y + 4)^2 = -(x - 1)$.
Answer on page AA21.

54. By using the definition of a parabola, find the equation in standard form of the parabola with $V(0, 0)$, $F(-c, 0)$, and directrix $x = c$. $y^2 = -4cx$

55. Sketch a graph of $4(y - 2) = x|x| - 1$.
Answer on page AA21.

56. Find the equation of the directrix of the parabola with vertex at the origin and focus at the point $(1, 1)$. $y = -x - 2$

57. Find the equation of the parabola with vertex at the origin and focus at the point $(1, 1)$. (*Hint:* You will need the answer to Exercise 56 and the definition of a parabola.)
$x^2 + y^2 - 8x - 8y - 2xy = 0$

PREPARE FOR SECTION 5.2

58. Find the midpoint and the length of the line segment between $P_1(5, 1)$ and $P_2(-1, 5)$. [2.1] midpoint: (2, 3); length: $2\sqrt{13}$

59. Solve: $x^2 + 6x - 16 = 0$ [1.3] $-8, 2$

60. Solve: $x^2 - 2x = 2$ [1.3] $1 \pm \sqrt{3}$

61. Complete the square of $x^2 - 8x$ and write the result as the square of a binomial. [1.3] $x^2 - 8x + 16 = (x - 4)^2$

62. Solve $(x - 2)^2 + y^2 = 4$ for y. [1.3] $y = \pm\sqrt{4 - (x - 2)^2}$

63. Graph: $(x - 2)^2 + (y + 3)^2 = 16$ [2.1]
Answer on page AA21.

PROJECTS

I. PARABOLAS AND TANGENTS Calculus procedures can be used to show that the equation of a tangent line to the parabola $4py = x^2$ at the point (x_0, y_0) is given by

$$y - y_0 = \left(\frac{1}{2p}x_0\right)(x - x_0)$$

Use this equation to verify each of the following statements.

a. If two tangent lines to a parabola intersect at right angles, then the point of intersection of the tangent lines is on the directrix of the parabola.

b. If two tangent lines to a parabola intersect at right angles, then the focus of the parabola is located on the line segment that connects the two points of tangency.

c. The tangent line to the parabola $4py = x^2$ at the point (x_0, y_0) intersects the y-axis at the point $(0, -y_0)$.

SECTION 5.2

ELLIPSES

- **ELLIPSES WITH CENTER AT $(0, 0)$**
- **ELLIPSES WITH CENTER AT (h, k)**
- **ECCENTRICITY OF AN ELLIPSE**
- **APPLICATIONS**
- **ACOUSTIC PROPERTY OF AN ELLIPSE**

An ellipse is another of the conic sections formed when a plane intersects a right circular cone. If β is the angle at which the plane intersects the axis of the cone and α is the angle shown in **Figure 5.16,** an ellipse is formed when $\alpha < \beta < 90°$. If $\beta = 90°$, then a circle is formed.

take note

If the plane intersects the cone at the vertex of the cone so that the resulting figure is a point, the point is a degenerate ellipse. See the accompanying figure.

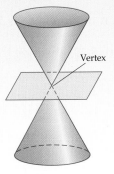

Degenerate ellipse

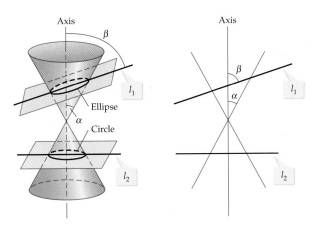

FIGURE 5.16

As was the case for a parabola, there is a definition for an ellipse in terms of a certain set of points in the plane.

Definition of an Ellipse

An **ellipse** is the set of all points in the plane, the sum of whose distances from two fixed points (**foci**) is a positive constant.

INSTRUCTOR NOTE
Remind students that the plural of *focus* is *foci*. The plural of *axis* is *axes*. The plural of *vertex* is *vertices*.

We can use this definition to draw an ellipse, equipped only with a piece of string and two tacks (see **Figure 5.17**). Tack the ends of the string to the foci, and trace a curve with a pencil held tight against the string. The resulting curve is an ellipse. The positive constant mentioned in the definition of an ellipse is the length of the string.

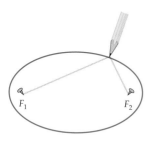

FIGURE 5.17

• ELLIPSES WITH CENTER AT (0, 0)

The graph of an ellipse has two axes of symmetry (see **Figure 5.18**). The longer axis is called the **major axis.** The foci of the ellipse are on the major axis. The shorter axis is called the **minor axis.** It is customary to denote the length of the major axis as $2a$ and the length of the minor axis as $2b$. The **semiaxes** are one-half the axes in length. Thus the length of the semimajor axis is denoted by a and the length of the semiminor axis by b. The **center** of the ellipse is the midpoint of the major axis. The endpoints of the major axis are the **vertices** (plural of *vertex*) of the ellipse.

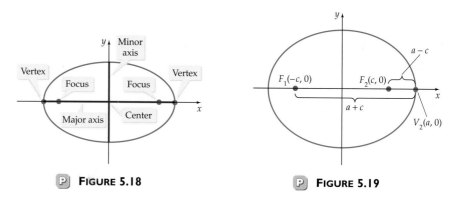

P **FIGURE 5.18**   P **FIGURE 5.19**

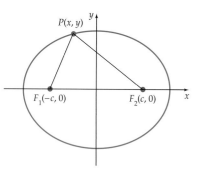

FIGURE 5.20

Consider the point $V_2(a, 0)$, which is one vertex of an ellipse, and the points $F_2(c, 0)$ and $F_1(-c, 0)$, which are the foci of the ellipse shown in **Figure 5.19**. The distance from V_2 to F_1 is $a + c$. Similarly, the distance from V_2 to F_2 is $a - c$. From the definition of an ellipse, the sum of the distances from any point on the ellipse to the foci is a positive constant. By adding the expressions $a + c$ and $a - c$, we have

$$(a + c) + (a - c) = 2a$$

Thus the positive constant referred to in the definition of an ellipse is $2a$, the length of the major axis.

Now let $P(x, y)$ be any point on the ellipse (see **Figure 5.20**). By using the definition of an ellipse, we have

$$d(P, F_1) + d(P, F_2) = 2a$$
$$\sqrt{(x + c)^2 + y^2} + \sqrt{(x - c)^2 + y^2} = 2a$$

Subtract the second radical from each side of the equation, and then square each side.

$$\left[\sqrt{(x + c)^2 + y^2}\right]^2 = \left[2a - \sqrt{(x - c)^2 + y^2}\right]^2$$
$$(x + c)^2 + y^2 = 4a^2 - 4a\sqrt{(x - c)^2 + y^2} + (x - c)^2 + y^2$$

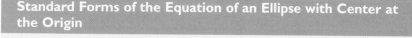

$$4cx - 4a^2 = -4a\sqrt{(x-c)^2 + y^2}$$

$$\left[-cx + a^2\right]^2 = \left[a\sqrt{(x-c)^2 + y^2}\right]^2$$ • Divide by -4, and then square each side.

$$c^2x^2 - 2cxa^2 + a^4 = a^2x^2 - 2cxa^2 + a^2c^2 + a^2y^2$$

$$-a^2x^2 + c^2x^2 - a^2y^2 = -a^4 + a^2c^2$$ • Rewrite with x and y terms on the left side.

$$-(a^2 - c^2)x^2 - a^2y^2 = -a^2(a^2 - c^2)$$ • Factor and let $b^2 = a^2 - c^2$.

$$-b^2x^2 - a^2y^2 = -a^2b^2$$ • Divide each side by $-a^2b^2$.

$$\frac{x^2}{a^2} + \frac{y^2}{b^2} = 1$$ • An equation of an ellipse with center at $(0, 0)$

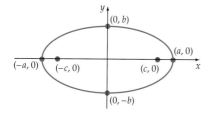

a. Major axis on x-axis

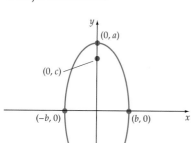

b. Major axis on y-axis

FIGURE 5.21

Standard Forms of the Equation of an Ellipse with Center at the Origin

Major Axis on the x-Axis

The standard form of the equation of an ellipse with the center at the origin and major axis on the x-axis (see **Figure 5.21a**) is given by

$$\frac{x^2}{a^2} + \frac{y^2}{b^2} = 1, \quad a > b$$

The length of the major axis is $2a$. The length of the minor axis is $2b$. The coordinates of the vertices are $(a, 0)$ and $(-a, 0)$, and the coordinates of the foci are $(c, 0)$ and $(-c, 0)$, where $c^2 = a^2 - b^2$.

Major Axis on the y-Axis

The standard form of the equation of an ellipse with the center at the origin and major axis on the y-axis (see **Figure 5.21b**) is given by

$$\frac{x^2}{b^2} + \frac{y^2}{a^2} = 1, \quad a > b$$

The length of the major axis is $2a$. The length of the minor axis is $2b$. The coordinates of the vertices are $(0, a)$ and $(0, -a)$, and the coordinates of the foci are $(0, c)$ and $(0, -c)$, where $c^2 = a^2 - b^2$.

❓ **QUESTION** For the graph of $\dfrac{x^2}{16} + \dfrac{y^2}{25} = 1$, is the major axis on the x-axis or the y-axis?

❓ **ANSWER** Because $25 > 16$, the major axis is on the y-axis.

Alternative to Example 1

Find the vertices and foci of the ellipse given by the equation $\dfrac{x^2}{64} + \dfrac{y^2}{4} = 1$.

Sketch the graph.

● The vertices are $(-8, 0)$ and $(8, 0)$. The foci are $\left(-2\sqrt{15}, 0\right)$ and $\left(2\sqrt{15}, 0\right)$.

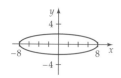

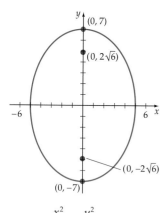

$$\frac{x^2}{25} + \frac{y^2}{49} = 1$$

FIGURE 5.22

EXAMPLE 1   Find the Vertices and Foci of an Ellipse

Find the vertices and foci of the ellipse given by the equation $\dfrac{x^2}{25} + \dfrac{y^2}{49} = 1$.

Sketch the graph.

Solution

Because the y^2 term has the larger denominator, the major axis is on the y-axis.

$$a^2 = 49 \qquad b^2 = 25 \qquad c^2 = a^2 - b^2$$
$$a = 7 \qquad b = 5 \qquad = 49 - 25 = 24$$
$$c = \sqrt{24} = 2\sqrt{6}$$

The vertices are $(0, 7)$ and $(0, -7)$. The foci are $\left(0, 2\sqrt{6}\right)$ and $\left(0, -2\sqrt{6}\right)$. See **Figure 5.22.**

▶ **TRY EXERCISE 20, PAGE 481**

An ellipse with foci $(3, 0)$ and $(-3, 0)$ and major axis of length 10 is shown in **Figure 5.23.** To find the equation of the ellipse in standard form, we must find a^2 and b^2. Because the foci are on the major axis, the major axis is on the x-axis. The length of the major axis is $2a$. Thus $2a = 10$. Solving for a, we have $a = 5$ and $a^2 = 25$.

Because the foci are $(3, 0)$ and $(-3, 0)$ and the center of the ellipse is the midpoint between the two foci, the distance from the center of the ellipse to a focus is 3. Therefore, $c = 3$. To find b^2, use the equation

$$c^2 = a^2 - b^2$$
$$9 = 25 - b^2$$
$$b^2 = 16$$

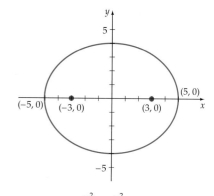

$$\frac{x^2}{25} + \frac{y^2}{16} = 1$$

FIGURE 5.23

The equation of the ellipse in standard form is $\dfrac{x^2}{25} + \dfrac{y^2}{16} = 1$.

● ELLIPSES WITH CENTER AT (h, k)

The equation of an ellipse with center (h, k) and with horizontal or vertical major axis can be found by using a translation of coordinates. On a coordinate system with axes labeled x' and y', the standard form of the equation of an ellipse with center at the origin of the $x'y'$-coordinate system is

$$\frac{(x')^2}{a^2} + \frac{(y')^2}{b^2} = 1$$

Now place the origin of the $x'y'$-coordinate system at (h, k) in an xy-coordinate system. See **Figure 5.24.**

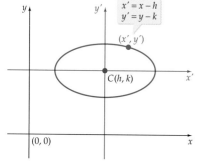

FIGURE 5.24

The relationship between an ordered pair in the $x'y'$-coordinate system and one in the xy-coordinate system is given by the transformation equations

$$x' = x - h$$
$$y' = y - k$$

Substitute the expressions for x' and y' into the equation of an ellipse. The equation of the ellipse with center at (h, k) is

$$\frac{(x - h)^2}{a^2} + \frac{(y - k)^2}{b^2} = 1$$

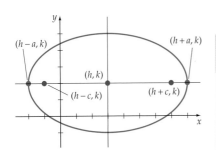

a. Major axis parallel to x-axis

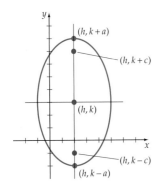

b. Major axis parallel to y-axis

FIGURE 5.25

Standard Forms of the Equation of an Ellipse with Center at (h, k)

Major Axis Parallel to the x-Axis

The standard form of the equation of an ellipse with the center at (h, k) and major axis parallel to the x-axis (see **Figure 5.25a**) is given by

$$\frac{(x - h)^2}{a^2} + \frac{(y - k)^2}{b^2} = 1, \quad a > b$$

The length of the major axis is $2a$. The length of the minor axis is $2b$. The coordinates of the vertices are $(h + a, k)$ and $(h - a, k)$, and the coordinates of the foci are $(h + c, k)$ and $(h - c, k)$, where $c^2 = a^2 - b^2$.

Major Axis Parallel to the y-Axis

The standard form of the equation of an ellipse with the center at (h, k) and major axis parallel to the y-axis (see **Figure 5.25b**) is given by

$$\frac{(x - h)^2}{b^2} + \frac{(y - k)^2}{a^2} = 1, \quad a > b$$

The length of the major axis is $2a$. The length of the minor axis is $2b$. The coordinates of the vertices are $(h, k + a)$ and $(h, k - a)$, and the coordinates of the foci are $(h, k + c)$ and $(h, k - c)$, where $c^2 = a^2 - b^2$.

Alternative to Example 2
Find the vertices and foci of the ellipse
$36x^2 + 25y^2 + 288x - 150y - 99 = 0$.
● **The vertices are $(-4, 9)$ and $(-4, -3)$. The foci are $\left(-4, 3 - \sqrt{11}\right)$ and $\left(-4, 3 + \sqrt{11}\right)$.**

EXAMPLE 2   Find the Vertices and Foci of an Ellipse

Find the vertices and foci of the ellipse $4x^2 + 9y^2 - 8x + 36y + 4 = 0$. Sketch the graph.

Solution

Write the equation of the ellipse in standard form by completing the square.

$$4x^2 + 9y^2 - 8x + 36y + 4 = 0$$

$$4x^2 - 8x + 9y^2 + 36y = -4 \qquad \text{• Rearrange terms.}$$

$$4(x^2 - 2x) + 9(y^2 + 4y) = -4 \qquad \text{• Factor.}$$

$$4(x^2 - 2x + 1) + 9(y^2 + 4y + 4) = -4 + 4 + 36 \qquad \text{• Complete the square.}$$

$$4(x - 1)^2 + 9(y + 2)^2 = 36 \qquad \text{• Factor.}$$

$$\frac{(x - 1)^2}{9} + \frac{(y + 2)^2}{4} = 1 \qquad \text{• Divide by 36.}$$

Continued ▶

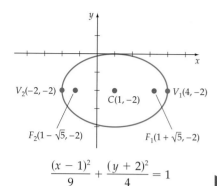

$$\frac{(x-1)^2}{9} + \frac{(y+2)^2}{4} = 1$$

FIGURE 5.26

From the equation of the ellipse in standard form, the coordinates of the center of the ellipse are $(1, -2)$. Because the larger denominator is 9, the major axis is parallel to the x-axis and $a^2 = 9$. Thus $a = 3$. The vertices are $(4, -2)$ and $(-2, -2)$.

To find the coordinates of the foci, we find c.

$$c^2 = a^2 - b^2 = 9 - 4 = 5$$
$$c = \sqrt{5}$$

The foci are $\left(1 + \sqrt{5}, -2\right)$ and $\left(1 - \sqrt{5}, -2\right)$. See **Figure 5.26**.

▶ **TRY EXERCISE 26, PAGE 481**

INTEGRATING TECHNOLOGY

A graphing utility can be used to graph an ellipse. For instance, consider the equation $4x^2 + 9y^2 - 8x + 36y + 4 = 0$ from Example 2. Rewrite the equation as

$$9y^2 + 36y + (4x^2 - 8x + 4) = 0$$

In this form, the equation is a quadratic equation in terms of the variable y with

$$A = 9, B = 36, \text{ and } C = 4x^2 - 8x + 4$$

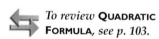

To review **QUADRATIC FORMULA**, *see p. 103.*

Apply the quadratic formula to produce

$$y = \frac{-36 \pm \sqrt{1296 - 36(4x^2 - 8x + 4)}}{18}$$

The graph of $Y1 = \dfrac{-36 + \sqrt{1296 - 36(4x^2 - 8x + 4)}}{18}$ is the part of the ellipse on or above the line $y = -2$ (see **Figure 5.27**).

The graph of $Y2 = \dfrac{-36 - \sqrt{1296 - 36(4x^2 - 8x + 4)}}{18}$ is the part of the ellipse on or below the line $y = -2$, as shown in **Figure 5.27.**

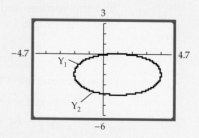

FIGURE 5.27

One advantage of this graphing procedure is that it does not require us to write the given equation in standard form. A disadvantage of the graphing procedure is that it does not indicate where the foci of the ellipse are located.

Alternative to Example 3
Find the standard form of the equation of the ellipse with center at (3, 4), foci $F_1(0, 4)$ and $F_2(6, 4)$, and minor axis of length 8.

● $\dfrac{(x-3)^2}{25} + \dfrac{(y-4)^2}{16} = 1$

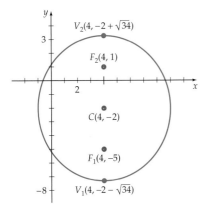

FIGURE 5.28

EXAMPLE 3   Find the Equation of an Ellipse

Find the standard form of the equation of the ellipse with center at $(4, -2)$, foci $F_2(4, 1)$ and $F_1(4, -5)$, and minor axis of length 10, as shown in **Figure 5.28**.

Solution

Because the foci are on the major axis, the major axis is parallel to the y-axis. The distance from the center of the ellipse to a focus is c. The distance between the center $(4, -2)$ and the focus $(4, 1)$ is 3. Therefore, $c = 3$.

The length of the minor axis is $2b$. Thus $2b = 10$ and $b = 5$.

To find a^2, use the equation $c^2 = a^2 - b^2$.

$$9 = a^2 - 25$$
$$a^2 = 34$$

Thus the equation in standard form is

$$\frac{(x-4)^2}{25} + \frac{(y+2)^2}{34} = 1$$

▶ **TRY EXERCISE 42, PAGE 481**

● **ECCENTRICITY OF AN ELLIPSE**

INSTRUCTOR NOTE

Eccentric literally means "out of the center." Eccentricity is a measure of how much an ellipse is *not* like a set of points the same distance from the center. The higher the eccentricity, the more unlike a circle the ellipse is and therefore the longer and thinner it is.

The graph of an ellipse can be very long and thin, or it can be much like a circle. The **eccentricity** of an ellipse is a measure of its "roundness."

Eccentricity (e) of an Ellipse

The eccentricity e of an ellipse is the ratio of c to a, where c is the distance from the center to a focus and a is one-half the length of the major axis. (See **Figure 5.29**.) That is,

$$e = \frac{c}{a}$$

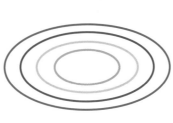

Eccentricity = 0.87

FIGURE 5.29

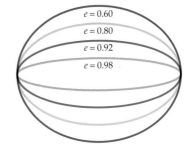

FIGURE 5.30

Because $c < a$, for an ellipse, $0 < e < 1$. When $e \approx 0$, the graph is almost a circle. When $e \approx 1$, the graph is long and thin. See **Figure 5.30**.

Alternative to Example 4
Find the eccentricity of the ellipse given by $4x^2 + 8y^2 = 12$.
● **The eccentricity of the ellipse is** $\dfrac{\sqrt{2}}{2}$, **or approximately 0.707.**

EXAMPLE 4 **Find the Eccentricity of an Ellipse**

Find the eccentricity of the ellipse given by $8x^2 + 9y^2 = 18$.

Solution

First, write the equation of the ellipse in standard form. Divide each side of the equation by 18.

$$\frac{8x^2}{18} + \frac{9y^2}{18} = 1$$

$$\frac{4x^2}{9} + \frac{y^2}{2} = 1$$

$$\frac{x^2}{9/4} + \frac{y^2}{2} = 1 \qquad \cdot \frac{4}{9} = \frac{1}{9/4}$$

The last step is necessary because the standard form of the equation has coefficients of 1 in the numerator. Thus

$$a^2 = \frac{9}{4} \qquad \text{and} \qquad a = \frac{3}{2}$$

Use the equation $c^2 = a^2 - b^2$ to find c.

$$c^2 = \frac{9}{4} - 2 = \frac{1}{4} \qquad \text{and} \qquad c = \sqrt{\frac{1}{4}} = \frac{1}{2}$$

Now find the eccentricity.

$$e = \frac{c}{a} = \frac{1/2}{3/2} = \frac{1}{3}$$

The eccentricity of the ellipse is $\dfrac{1}{3}$.

▶ **TRY EXERCISE 48, PAGE 481**

INSTRUCTOR NOTE
The literal translation of the word *perihelion* is "near sun." The perihelion is the point nearest the sun. *Aphelion* means "from sun" and refers to the point farthest from the sun.

TABLE 5.1

Planet	Eccentricity
Mercury	0.206
Venus	0.007
Earth	0.017
Mars	0.093
Jupiter	0.049
Saturn	0.051
Uranus	0.046
Neptune	0.005
Pluto	0.250

● **APPLICATIONS**

The planets travel around the sun in elliptical orbits. The sun is located at a focus of the orbit. The eccentricities of the orbits for the planets in our solar system are given in **Table 5.1.**

❓ **QUESTION** Which planet has the most nearly circular orbit?

The terms *perihelion* and *aphelion* are used to denote the position of a planet in its orbit around the sun. The perihelion is the point nearest the sun; the aphelion is the point farthest from the sun. See **Figure 5.31.** The length of the semimajor axis of a planet's elliptical orbit is called the *mean distance* of the planet from the sun.

❓ **ANSWER** Neptune has the smallest eccentricity, so it is the planet with the most nearly circular orbit.

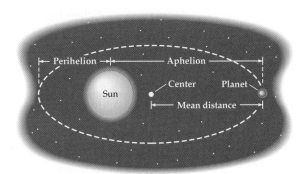

FIGURE 5.31

Alternative to Example 5
Mars has a mean distance of 141.3 million miles and a perihelion distance of 115.8 million miles. Find an equation for the orbit of Mars.

● **An equation for the orbit of Mars is**
$$\frac{x^2}{141.3^2} + \frac{y^2}{139.0^2} = 1.$$

EXAMPLE 5   **Determine an Equation for the Orbit of Earth**

 Earth has a mean distance of 93 million miles and a perihelion distance of 91.5 million miles. Find an equation for Earth's orbit.

Solution

A mean distance of 93 million miles implies that the length of the semimajor axis of the orbit is $a = 93$ million miles. Earth's aphelion distance is the length of the major axis less the length of the perihelion distance. Thus

$$\text{Aphelion distance} = 2(93) - 91.5 = 94.5 \text{ million miles}$$

The distance c from the sun to the center of Earth's orbit is

$$c = \text{aphelion distance} - 93 = 94.5 - 93 = 1.5 \text{ million miles}$$

The length b of the semiminor axis of the orbit is

$$b = \sqrt{a^2 - c^2} = \sqrt{93^2 - 1.5^2} = \sqrt{8646.75}$$

An equation of Earth's orbit is

$$\frac{x^2}{93^2} + \frac{y^2}{8646.75} = 1$$

▶ **TRY EXERCISE 56, PAGE 482**

● **ACOUSTIC PROPERTY OF AN ELLIPSE**

Sound waves, although different from light waves, have a similar reflective property. When sound is reflected from a point P on a surface, the angle of incidence equals the angle of reflection. Applying this principle to a room with an elliptical ceiling results in what are called whispering galleries. These galleries are based on the following theorem.

The Reflective Property of an Ellipse

The lines from the foci to a point on an ellipse make equal angles with the tangent line at that point. See **Figure 5.32.**

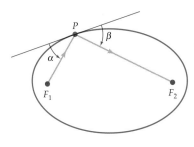

$\alpha = \beta$

FIGURE 5.32

The Statuary Hall in the Capital Building in Washington, D.C., is a whispering gallery. Two people standing at the foci of the elliptical ceiling can whisper and yet hear each other even though they are a considerable distance apart. The whisper from one person is reflected to the person standing at the other focus.

Alternative to Example 6

A room 100 feet long is constructed to be a whispering gallery. The room has an elliptical ceiling. If the maximum height of the ceiling is 24 feet, determine where the foci are located.

● **The foci are located approximately 43.9 feet from the center of the room, or about 6.1 feet from the walls, along the major axis of the elliptical ceiling.**

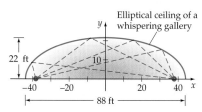

Elliptical ceiling of a whispering gallery

FIGURE 5.33

> **EXAMPLE 6**   Locate the Foci of a Whispering Gallery

A room 88 feet long is constructed to be a whispering gallery. The room has an elliptical ceiling, as shown in **Figure 5.33.** If the maximum height of the ceiling is 22 feet, determine where the foci are located.

Solution

The length a of the semimajor axis of the elliptical ceiling is 44 feet. The height b of the semiminor axis is 22 feet. Thus

$$c^2 = a^2 - b^2$$
$$c^2 = 44^2 - 22^2$$
$$c = \sqrt{44^2 - 22^2} \approx 38.1 \text{ feet}$$

The foci are located about 38.1 feet from the center of the elliptical ceiling along its major axis.

▶ **TRY EXERCISE 58, PAGE 482**

  TOPICS FOR DISCUSSION

1. In every ellipse, the length of the semimajor axis a is greater than the length of the semiminor axis b and greater than the distance c from a focus to the center of the ellipse. Do you agree? Explain.

2. How many vertices does an ellipse have?

3. Every ellipse has two y-intercepts. Do you agree? Explain.

4. Explain why the eccentricity of every ellipse is a number between 0 and 1.

EXERCISE SET 5.2

—Suggested Assignment: Exercises 1–73, every other odd; 81, 83–88.
—Answer graphs to Exercises 1–32 and 64–69 are on pages AA21–AA24.

In Exercises 1 to 32, find the center, vertices, and foci of the ellipse given by each equation. Sketch the graph.

1. $\dfrac{x^2}{16} + \dfrac{y^2}{25} = 1$

2. $\dfrac{x^2}{49} + \dfrac{y^2}{36} = 1$

3. $\dfrac{x^2}{9} + \dfrac{y^2}{4} = 1$

4. $\dfrac{x^2}{64} + \dfrac{y^2}{25} = 1$

5. $\dfrac{x^2}{7} + \dfrac{y^2}{9} = 1$

6. $\dfrac{x^2}{5} + \dfrac{y^2}{4} = 1$

7. $\dfrac{4x^2}{9} + \dfrac{y^2}{16} = 1$

8. $\dfrac{x^2}{9} + \dfrac{9y^2}{16} = 1$

9. $\dfrac{(x-3)^2}{25} + \dfrac{(y+2)^2}{16} = 1$

10. $\dfrac{(x+3)^2}{9} + \dfrac{(y+1)^2}{16} = 1$

11. $\dfrac{(x+2)^2}{9} + \dfrac{y^2}{25} = 1$

12. $\dfrac{x^2}{25} + \dfrac{(y-2)^2}{81} = 1$

13. $\dfrac{(x-1)^2}{21} + \dfrac{(y-3)^2}{4} = 1$ **14.** $\dfrac{(x+5)^2}{9} + \dfrac{(y-3)^2}{7} = 1$

15. $\dfrac{9(x-1)^2}{16} + \dfrac{(y+1)^2}{9} = 1$ **16.** $\dfrac{(x+6)^2}{25} + \dfrac{25y^2}{144} = 1$

17. $3x^2 + 4y^2 = 12$ **18.** $5x^2 + 4y^2 = 20$

19. $25x^2 + 16y^2 = 400$ ▶ **20.** $25x^2 + 12y^2 = 300$

21. $64x^2 + 25y^2 = 400$ **22.** $9x^2 + 64y^2 = 144$

23. $4x^2 + y^2 - 24x - 8y + 48 = 0$ **42.** $\dfrac{(x+4)^2}{256/7} + \dfrac{(y-1)^2}{16} = 1$

24. $x^2 + 9y^2 + 6x - 36y + 36 = 0$ **43.** $\dfrac{(x-5)^2}{16} + \dfrac{(y-1)^2}{25} = 1$

25. $5x^2 + 9y^2 - 20x + 54y + 56 = 0$ **44.** $\dfrac{(x+1)^2}{36} + \dfrac{(y+1)^2}{20} = 1$

▶ **26.** $9x^2 + 16y^2 + 36x - 16y - 104 = 0$

27. $16x^2 + 9y^2 - 64x - 80 = 0$

28. $16x^2 + 9y^2 + 36y - 108 = 0$

29. $25x^2 + 16y^2 + 50x - 32y - 359 = 0$

30. $16x^2 + 9y^2 - 64x - 54y + 1 = 0$

31. $8x^2 + 25y^2 - 48x + 50y + 47 = 0$

32. $4x^2 + 9y^2 + 24x + 18y + 44 = 0$

In Exercises 33 to 44, find the equation in standard form of each ellipse, given the information provided.

33. Center $(0,0)$, major axis of length 10, foci at $(4,0)$ and $(-4,0)$ $\dfrac{x^2}{25} + \dfrac{y^2}{9} = 1$

34. Center $(0,0)$, minor axis of length 6, foci at $(0,4)$ and $(0,-4)$ $\dfrac{x^2}{9} + \dfrac{y^2}{25} = 1$

35. Vertices $(6,0)$, $(-6,0)$; ellipse passes through $(0,-4)$ and $(0,4)$ $\dfrac{x^2}{36} + \dfrac{y^2}{16} = 1$

36. Vertices $(7,0)$, $(-7,0)$; ellipse passes through $(0,5)$ and $(0,-5)$ $\dfrac{x^2}{49} + \dfrac{y^2}{25} = 1$

37. Major axis of length 12 on the x-axis, center at $(0,0)$; ellipse passes through $(2,-3)$ $\dfrac{x^2}{36} + \dfrac{y^2}{81/8} = 1$

38. Major axis of length 8, center at $(0,0)$; ellipse passes through $(-2,2)$ $\dfrac{x^2}{16} + \dfrac{y^2}{16/3} = 1$ or $\dfrac{x^2}{16/3} + \dfrac{y^2}{16} = 1$

39. Center $(-2,4)$, vertices $(-6,4)$ and $(2,4)$, foci at $(-5,4)$ and $(1,4)$ $\dfrac{(x+2)^2}{16} + \dfrac{(y-4)^2}{7} = 1$

40. Center $(0,3)$, minor axis of length 4, foci at $(0,0)$ and $(0,6)$ $\dfrac{x^2}{4} + \dfrac{(y-3)^2}{13} = 1$ **41.** $\dfrac{(x-2)^2}{25/24} + \dfrac{(y-4)^2}{25} = 1$

41. Center $(2,4)$, major axis parallel to the y-axis and of length 10; ellipse passes through the point $(3,3)$

▶ **42.** Center $(-4,1)$, minor axis parallel to the y-axis and of length 8; ellipse passes through the point $(0,4)$

43. Vertices $(5,6)$ and $(5,-4)$, foci at $(5,4)$ and $(5,-2)$

44. Vertices $(-7,-1)$ and $(5,-1)$, foci at $(-5,-1)$ and $(3,-1)$

In Exercises 45 to 52, use the eccentricity of each ellipse to find its equation in standard form.

45. Eccentricity $\dfrac{2}{5}$, major axis on the x-axis and of length 10, center at $(0,0)$ $\dfrac{x^2}{25} + \dfrac{y^2}{21} = 1$

46. Eccentricity $\dfrac{3}{4}$, foci at $(9,0)$ and $(-9,0)$ $\dfrac{x^2}{144} + \dfrac{y^2}{63} = 1$

47. Foci at $(0,-4)$ and $(0,4)$, eccentricity $\dfrac{2}{3}$ $\dfrac{x^2}{20} + \dfrac{y^2}{36} = 1$

▶ **48.** Foci at $(0,-3)$ and $(0,3)$, eccentricity $\dfrac{1}{4}$ $\dfrac{x^2}{135} + \dfrac{y^2}{144} = 1$

49. Eccentricity $\dfrac{2}{5}$, foci at $(-1,3)$ and $(3,3)$ $\dfrac{(x-1)^2}{25} + \dfrac{(y-3)^2}{21} = 1$

50. Eccentricity $\dfrac{1}{4}$, foci at $(-2,4)$ and $(-2,-2)$ $\dfrac{(x+2)^2}{135} + \dfrac{(y-1)^2}{144} = 1$

51. Eccentricity $\dfrac{2}{3}$, major axis of length 24 on the y-axis, center at $(0,0)$ $\dfrac{x^2}{80} + \dfrac{y^2}{144} = 1$

52. Eccentricity $\dfrac{3}{5}$, major axis of length 15 on the x-axis, center at $(0,0)$ $\dfrac{x^2}{225/4} + \dfrac{y^2}{36} = 1$

53. **MEDICINES** A *lithotripter* is an instrument used to remove a kidney stone in a patient without having to do surgery. A high-frequency sound wave is emitted from a source that is located at the focus of an ellipse. The patient is placed so that the kidney stone is located at the other focus of the ellipse. If the equation of the ellipse is

$$\frac{(x-11)^2}{484} + \frac{y^2}{64} = 1 \ (x \text{ and } y \text{ are measured in centimeters}),$$

where, to the nearest centimeter, should the patient's kidney stone be placed so that the reflected sound hits the kidney stone?   **41 cm from the emitter**

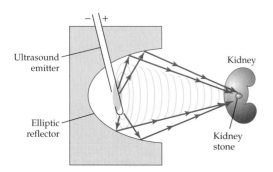

54. CONSTRUCTION A circular vent pipe is placed on a roof that has a slope of $\frac{4}{5}$, as shown in the figure at the right.

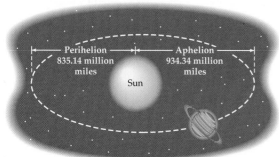

   a. Use the slope to find the value of h.   **3.6 in.**

   b. The intersection of the vent pipe and the roof is an ellipse. To the nearest thousandth of an inch, what are the lengths of the major and minor axes?   **5.76 in., 4.50 in.**

   c. Find an equation of the ellipse that should be cut from the roof so that the pipe will fit. $\dfrac{x^2}{8.3025} + \dfrac{y^2}{5.0625} = 1$

55. THE ORBIT OF SATURN The distance from Saturn to the sun at Saturn's aphelion is 934.34 million miles, and the distance from Saturn to the sun at its perihelion is 835.14 million miles. Find an equation for the orbit of Saturn. $\dfrac{x^2}{884.74^2} + \dfrac{y^2}{883.35^2} = 1$

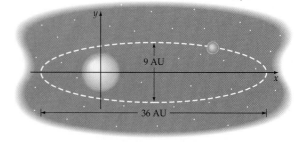

56. $\dfrac{x^2}{67.08^2} + \dfrac{y^2}{67.078^2} = 1$

▶ **56. THE ORBIT OF VENUS** Venus has a mean distance from the sun of 67.08 million miles, and the distance

from Venus to the sun at its aphelion is 67.58 million miles. Find an equation for the orbit of Venus.

57. WHISPERING GALLERY An architect wishes to design a large room that will be a whispering gallery. See Example 6. The ceiling of the room has a cross section that is an ellipse, as shown in the following figure.

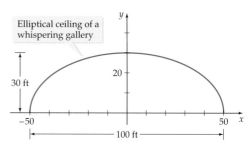

How far to the right and to the left of center are the foci located?   **40 ft**

▶ **58. WHISPERING GALLERY** An architect wishes to design a large room 100 feet long that will be a whispering gallery. The ceiling of the room has a cross section that is an ellipse, as shown in the following figure.

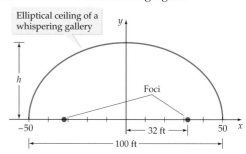

If the foci are to be located 32 feet to the right and to the left of center, find the height h of the elliptical ceiling (to the nearest 0.1 foot). $b \approx 38.4$ ft

59. HALLEY'S COMET Find the equation of the path of Halley's comet in astronomical units by letting the sun (one focus) be at the origin and letting the other focus be on the positive x-axis. The length of the major axis of the orbit of Halley's comet is approximately 36 astronomical units (36 AU), and the length of the minor axis is 9 AU (1 AU = 92,960,000 miles). $\dfrac{(x - 9\sqrt{15}/2)^2}{324} + \dfrac{y^2}{81/4} = 1$

60. ELLIPTICAL RECEIVERS Some satellite receivers are made in an elliptical shape that enables the receiver to pick up signals from two satellites. The receiver shown below has a major axis of 24 inches and a minor axis of 18 inches.

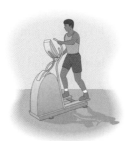

Determine, to the nearest 0.1 inch, the coordinates in the xy-plane of the foci of the ellipse. (*Note:* Because the receiver has only a slight curvature, we can estimate the location of the foci by assuming the receiver is flat.) $(-7.9, 0), (7.9, 0)$

In Exercises 61 and 62, use the following formula for the perimeter p of an ellipse with semimajor axis a and semiminor axis b.

$$p \approx \pi \sqrt{2(a^2 + b^2)}$$

61. ELLIPTICAL EXERCISE EQUIPMENT Many exercise clubs have installed elliptical trainers. These machines are similar to step machines except that the motion of the feet follows an elliptical path. On one elliptical trainer, the path of a person's foot is elliptical with a major axis of 16 inches and a minor axis of 10 inches. How many revolutions must the left foot make to complete a distance of 1 mile on this elliptical trainer? 1512

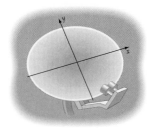

62. **ORBIT OF MARS** Mars travels around the sun in an elliptical orbit. The orbit has a major axis of 3.04 AU and a minor axis of 2.99 AU. (1 AU is 1 astronomical unit, or approximately 92,960,000 miles, the average distance of Earth from the sun.) Estimate, to the nearest million miles, the perimeter of the orbit of Mars. $881,000,000$ mi

63. **THE COLOSSEUM** The base of the Colosseum in Rome has an elliptical shape.

a. Find an equation in standard form for the base of the Colosseum, which has a major axis of 615 feet and a minor axis of 510 feet. $\dfrac{x^2}{307.5^2} + \dfrac{y^2}{255^2} = 1$

b. The area of an ellipse with a semimajor axis of length a and a semiminor axis of length b is given by $A = \pi ab$. Find, to the nearest 100 square feet, the area of the base of the Colosseum. $246,300$ ft²

In Exercises 64 to 69, use the quadratic formula to solve for y in terms of x. Then use a graphing utility to graph each equation.

64. $16x^2 + 9y^2 - 64x - 80 = 0$

65. $16x^2 + 9y^2 + 36y - 108 = 0$

66. $25x^2 + 16y^2 + 50x - 32y - 359 = 0$

67. $16x^2 + 9y^2 - 64x - 54y + 1 = 0$

68. $8x^2 + 25y^2 - 48x + 50y + 47 = 0$

69. $4x^2 + 9y^2 + 24x + 18y + 44 = 0$

74. $\dfrac{(x + 1)^2}{7} + \dfrac{(y - 4)^2}{16} = 1$

CONNECTING CONCEPTS

70. Explain why the graph of $4x^2 + 9y - 16x - 2 = 0$ is or is not an ellipse. Sketch the graph of this equation. Answer on page AA24.

In Exercises 71 to 74, find the equation in standard form of each ellipse by using the definition of an ellipse.

71. Find the equation of the ellipse with foci at $(-3, 0)$ and $(3, 0)$ that passes through the point $\left(3, \dfrac{9}{2}\right)$. $\dfrac{x^2}{36} + \dfrac{y^2}{27} = 1$

72. Find the equation of the ellipse with foci at $(0, 4)$ and $(0, -4)$ that passes through the point $\left(\dfrac{9}{5}, 4\right)$. $\dfrac{x^2}{9} + \dfrac{y^2}{25} = 1$

73. Find the equation of the ellipse with foci at $(-1, 2)$ and $(3, 2)$ that passes through the point $(3, 5)$. $\dfrac{(x - 1)^2}{16} + \dfrac{(y - 2)^2}{12} = 1$

74. Find the equation of the ellipse with foci at $(-1, 1)$ and $(-1, 7)$ that passes through the point $\left(\dfrac{3}{4}, 1\right)$. See answer above.

In Exercises 75 and 76, find the latus rectum of the given ellipse. A line segment with endpoints on the ellipse that is perpendicular to the major axis and passes through a focus is a *latus rectum* of the ellipse.

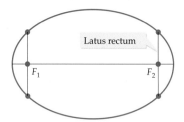

Latus rectum

75. Find the length of a latus rectum of the ellipse given by

$$\frac{(x-1)^2}{9} + \frac{(y+1)^2}{16} = 1 \quad \frac{9}{2}$$

76. Find the length of a latus rectum of the ellipse given by

$$9x^2 + 16y^2 - 36x + 96y + 36 = 0 \quad \frac{9}{2}$$

77. Show that for any ellipse, the length of a latus rectum is $\frac{2b^2}{a}$.

78. Use the definition of an ellipse to find the equation of an ellipse with center at $(0, 0)$ and foci at $(0, c)$ and $(0, -c)$.

$$1 = \frac{x^2}{b^2} + \frac{y^2}{a^2}$$

Recall that a parabola has a directrix that is a line perpendicular to the axis of symmetry. An ellipse has two directrices, both of which are perpendicular to the major axis and outside the ellipse. For an ellipse with center at the origin and whose major axis is the *x*-axis, the equations of the directrices are $x = \frac{a^2}{c}$ and $x = -\frac{a^2}{c}$.

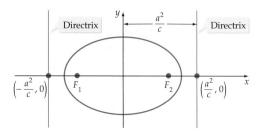

79. Find the directrices of the ellipse in Exercise 3. $x = \pm\frac{9\sqrt{5}}{5}$

80. Find the directrices of the ellipse in Exercise 4.

$$x = \frac{64\sqrt{39}}{39} \text{ and } x = -\frac{64\sqrt{39}}{39}$$

81. Let $P(x, y)$ be a point on the ellipse $\frac{x^2}{12} + \frac{y^2}{8} = 1$. Show that the distance from the point P to the focus $(2, 0)$ divided by the distance from the point P to the directrix $x = 6$ equals the eccentricity. (*Hint:* Solve the equation of the ellipse for y^2. Substitute this value for y^2 after applying the distance formula.)

82. Generalize the results of Exercise 81. That is, show that if $P(x, y)$ is a point on the ellipse $\frac{x^2}{a^2} + \frac{y^2}{b^2} = 1$, where $F(c, 0)$ is a focus and $x = \frac{a^2}{c}$ is a directrix, then the following equation is true: $e = \frac{d(P, F)}{d(P, D)}$. (*Hint:* Solve the equation of the ellipse for y^2. Substitute this value for y^2 after applying the distance formula.)

--- **PREPARE FOR SECTION 5.3** ---

83. Find the midpoint and the length of the line segment between $P_1(4, -3)$ and $P_2(-2, 1)$. [2.1] midpoint: $(1, -1)$; length: $2\sqrt{13}$

84. Solve: $(x - 1)(x + 3) = 5$ [1.3] $-4, 2$

85. Simplify: $\frac{4}{\sqrt{8}}$ [P.2] $\sqrt{2}$

86. Complete the square of $4x^2 + 24x$ and write the result as the square of a binomial. [1.3] $4(x^2 + 6x + 9) = 4(x + 3)^2$

87. Solve $\frac{x^2}{4} - \frac{y^2}{9} = 1$ for y. [1.3] $y = \pm\frac{3}{2}\sqrt{x^2 - 4}$

88. Graph: $\frac{(x-2)^2}{16} + \frac{(y+3)^2}{9} = 1$ [5.2]

Answer on page AA24.

PROJECTS

1. 📟 **I. M. Pei's Oval** The poet and architect I. M. Pei suggested that the oval with the most appeal to the eye is given by the equation

$$\left(\frac{x}{a}\right)^{3/2} + \left(\frac{y}{b}\right)^{3/2} = 1$$

Use a graphing utility to graph this equation with $a = 5$ and $b = 3$. Then compare your graph with the graph of

$$\left(\frac{x}{5}\right)^{2} + \left(\frac{y}{3}\right)^{2} = 1$$

2. 📝 **Kepler's Laws** The German astronomer Johannes Kepler (1571–1630) derived three laws that describe how the planets orbit the sun. Write an essay that includes biographical information about Kepler and a statement of Kepler's Laws. In addition, use Kepler's Laws to answer the following questions.

a. Where is a planet located in its orbit around the sun when it achieves its greatest velocity?

b. What is the period of Mars if it has a mean distance from the sun of 1.52 astronomical units? (*Hint:* Use Earth as a reference with a period of 1 year and a mean distance from the sun of 1 astronomical unit.)

3. 📝 **Neptune** The position of the planet Neptune was discovered by using celestial mechanics and mathematics. Write an essay that tells how, when, and by whom Neptune was discovered.

4. 📟 **Graph the Colosseum** Some of the Colosseum scenes in the movie *Gladiator* (Universal Studios, 2000) were computer-generated.

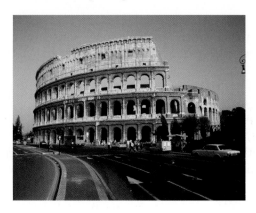

a. You can create a simple but accurate scale image of the exterior of the Colosseum by using a computer and the mathematics software program *Maple*. Open a new *Maple* worksheet and enter the following two commands.

with(plots);
plots[implicitplot3d]((x^2)/(307.5^2)+(y^2)/(255^2)=
1, x= –310..310, y= –260..260, z=0..157,
scaling=CONSTRAINED, style=PATCHNOGRID,
axes=FRAMED);

Execute each of the commands by placing the cursor in a command and pressing the ENTER key. After execution of the second command a three-dimensional graph will appear. Click and drag on the graph to rotate the image.

b. A graphing calculator can also be used to generate a simple "graph" of the exterior of the Colosseum. Here is a procedure for the TI-83 graphing calculator.

Enter the following in the WINDOW menu.

Xmin=–4.7 Xmax=4.7 Xscl=1 Ymin=–4
Ymax=9 Yscl=1

Enter the following formulas in the Y= menu.

$Y_1 = \sqrt{(9 - X^2)}$ $Y_2 = Y_1 + 4$ $Y_3 = -Y_1$ $Y_4 = Y_3 + 4$

Press: QUIT (2nd MODE)

Enter: Shade(Y₃,Y₄) and press ENTER.
     Note: "Shade(" is in the DRAW menu.

📝 Explain why this "Colosseum graph" appears to be constructed with ellipses even though the functions entered in the Y= menu are the equations of semicircles.

SECTION 5.3   HYPERBOLAS

The hyperbola is a conic section formed when a plane intersects a right circular cone at a certain angle. If β is the angle at which the plane intersects the axis of the cone and α is the angle shown in **Figure 5.34,** a hyperbola is formed when $0° < \beta < \alpha$ or when the plane is parallel to the axis of the cone.

As with the other conic sections, there is a definition of a hyperbola in terms of a certain set of points in the plane.

> **take note**
>
> If the plane intersects the cone along the axis of the cone, the resulting curve is two intersecting straight lines. This is the *degenerate* form of a hyperbola. See the accompanying figure.

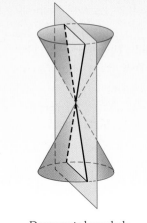

Degenerate hyperbola

FIGURE 5.34

Definition of a Hyperbola

A **hyperbola** is the set of all points in the plane, the difference between whose distances from two fixed points (foci) is a positive constant.

This definition differs from that of an ellipse in that the ellipse was defined in terms of the *sum* of two distances, whereas the hyperbola is defined in terms of the *difference* of two distances.

● HYPERBOLAS WITH CENTER AT (0, 0)

The **transverse axis** of a hyperbola is the line segment joining the intercepts (see **Figure 5.35**). The midpoint of the transverse axis is called the **center** of the hyperbola. The **conjugate axis** passes through the center of the hyperbola and is perpendicular to the transverse axis.

The length of the transverse axis is customarily represented as $2a$, and the distance between the two foci is represented as $2c$. The length of the conjugate axis is represented as $2b$.

The **vertices** of a hyperbola are the points where the hyperbola intersects the transverse axis.

To determine the positive constant stated in the definition of a hyperbola, consider the point $V_1(a, 0)$, which is one vertex of a hyperbola, and the points $F_1(c, 0)$ and $F_2(-c, 0)$, which are the foci of the hyperbola (see **Figure 5.36**). The difference between the distance from $V_1(a, 0)$ to $F_1(c, 0)$, $c - a$, and the distance from $V_1(a, 0)$ to $F_2(-c, 0)$, $c + a$, must be a constant. By subtracting these distances, we find

$$|(c - a) - (c + a)| = |-2a| = 2a$$

Thus the constant is $2a$ and is the length of the transverse axis. The absolute value is used to ensure that the distance is a positive number.

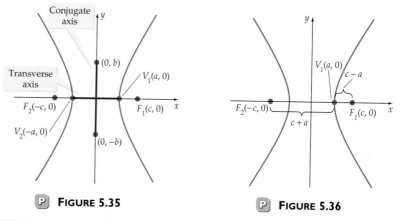

P **FIGURE 5.35**   **P** **FIGURE 5.36**

Standard Forms of the Equation of a Hyperbola with Center at the Origin

Transverse Axis on the x-Axis

The standard form of the equation of a hyperbola with the center at the origin and transverse axis on the x-axis (see **Figure 5.37a**) is given by

$$\frac{x^2}{a^2} - \frac{y^2}{b^2} = 1$$

The coordinates of the vertices are $(a, 0)$ and $(-a, 0)$, and the coordinates of the foci are $(c, 0)$ and $(-c, 0)$, where $c^2 = a^2 + b^2$.

Transverse Axis on the y-Axis

The standard form of the equation of a hyperbola with the center at the origin and transverse axis on the y-axis (see **Figure 5.37b**) is given by

$$\frac{y^2}{a^2} - \frac{x^2}{b^2} = 1$$

The coordinates of the vertices are $(0, a)$ and $(0, -a)$, and the coordinates of the foci are $(0, c)$ and $(0, -c)$, where $c^2 = a^2 + b^2$.

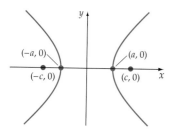

a. Transverse axis on the x-axis

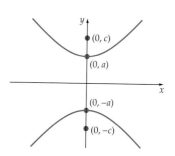

b. Transverse axis on the y-axis

FIGURE 5.37

❓ **QUESTION** For the graph of $\dfrac{y^2}{9} - \dfrac{x^2}{4} = 1$, is the transverse axis on the x-axis or the y-axis?

❓ **ANSWER** Because the y-term is positive, the transverse axis is on the y-axis.

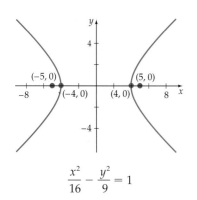

$$\frac{x^2}{16} - \frac{y^2}{9} = 1$$

FIGURE 5.38

By looking at the equations, it is possible to determine the location of the transverse axis by finding which term in the equation is positive. When the x^2 term is positive, the transverse axis is on the x-axis. When the y^2 term is positive, the transverse axis is on the y-axis.

Consider the hyperbola given by the equation $\frac{x^2}{16} - \frac{y^2}{9} = 1$. Because the x^2 term is positive, the transverse axis is on the x-axis, $a^2 = 16$, and thus $a = 4$. The vertices are $(4, 0)$ and $(-4, 0)$. To find the foci, we determine c.

$$c^2 = a^2 + b^2 = 16 + 9 = 25$$
$$c = \sqrt{25} = 5$$

The foci are $(5, 0)$ and $(-5, 0)$. The graph is shown in **Figure 5.38**.

Each hyperbola has two asymptotes that pass through the center of the hyperbola. The asymptotes of the hyperbola are a useful guide to sketching the graph of the hyperbola.

Asymptotes of a Hyperbola with Center at the Origin

The **asymptotes** of the hyperbola defined by $\frac{x^2}{a^2} - \frac{y^2}{b^2} = 1$ are given by the equations $y = \frac{b}{a}x$ and $y = -\frac{b}{a}x$ (see **Figure 5.39a**).

The asymptotes of the hyperbola defined by $\frac{y^2}{a^2} - \frac{x^2}{b^2} = 1$ are given by the equations $y = \frac{a}{b}x$ and $y = -\frac{a}{b}x$ (see **Figure 5.39b**).

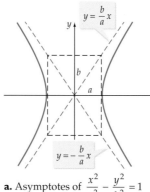

a. Asymptotes of $\frac{x^2}{a^2} - \frac{y^2}{b^2} = 1$

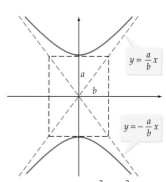

b. Asymptotes of $\frac{y^2}{a^2} - \frac{x^2}{b^2} = 1$

FIGURE 5.39

One method for remembering the equations of the asymptotes is to write the equation of a hyperbola in standard form but to replace 1 by 0 and then solve for y.

$$\frac{x^2}{a^2} - \frac{y^2}{b^2} = 0 \quad \text{so} \quad y^2 = \frac{b^2}{a^2}x^2, \text{ or } y = \pm\frac{b}{a}x$$

$$\frac{y^2}{a^2} - \frac{x^2}{b^2} = 0 \quad \text{so} \quad y^2 = \frac{a^2}{b^2}x^2, \text{ or } y = \pm\frac{a}{b}x$$

Alternative to Example 1
Find the vertices, foci, and asymptotes of
the hyperbola given by the equation
$\frac{x^2}{9} - \frac{y^2}{16} = 1$. Sketch the graph.

● **The vertices are $(-3, 0)$ and $(3, 0)$.
The foci are $(-5, 0)$ and $(5, 0)$. The
asymptotes are $y = -\frac{4}{3}x$ and
$y = \frac{4}{3}x$.**

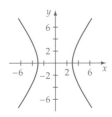

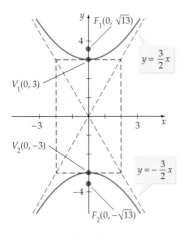

$$\frac{y^2}{9} - \frac{x^2}{4} = 1$$

FIGURE 5.40

EXAMPLE 1   Find the Vertices, Foci, and Asymptotes of a Hyperbola

Find the vertices, foci, and asymptotes of the hyperbola given by the equation $\frac{y^2}{9} - \frac{x^2}{4} = 1$. Sketch the graph.

Solution

Because the y^2 term is positive, the transverse axis is on the y-axis. We know $a^2 = 9$; thus $a = 3$. The vertices are $V_1(0, 3)$ and $V_2(0, -3)$.

$$c^2 = a^2 + b^2 = 9 + 4$$
$$c = \sqrt{13}$$

The foci are $F_1(0, \sqrt{13})$ and $F_2(0, -\sqrt{13})$.

Because $a = 3$ and $b = 2$ ($b^2 = 4$), the equations of the asymptotes are

$$y = \frac{3}{2}x \text{ and } y = -\frac{3}{2}x.$$

To sketch the graph, we draw a rectangle that has its center at the origin and has dimensions equal to the lengths of the transverse and conjugate axes. The asymptotes are extensions of the diagonals of the rectangle. See **Figure 5.40.**

▶ **TRY EXERCISE 4, PAGE 495**

● HYPERBOLAS WITH CENTER AT (h, k)

Using a translation of coordinates similar to that used for ellipses, we can write the equation of a hyperbola with its center at the point (h, k). Given coordinate axes labeled x' and y', an equation of a hyperbola with center at the origin is

$$\frac{(x')^2}{a^2} - \frac{(y')^2}{b^2} = 1 \qquad (1)$$

Now place the origin of this coordinate system at the point (h, k) of the xy-coordinate system, as shown in **Figure 5.41.** The relationship between an ordered pair in the $x'y'$-coordinate system and one in the xy-coordinate system is given by the transformation equations

$$x' = x - h$$
$$y' = y - k$$

Substitute the expressions for x' and y' into Equation (1). The equation of the hyperbola with center at (h, k) is

$$\frac{(x - h)^2}{a^2} - \frac{(y - k)^2}{b^2} = 1$$

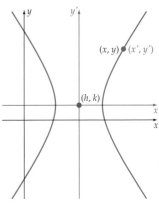

FIGURE 5.41

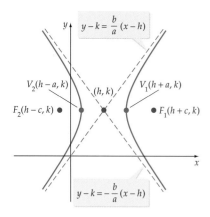

a. Transverse axis parallel to the x-axis

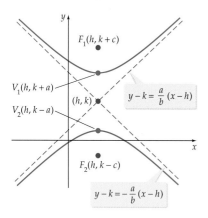

b. Transverse axis parallel to the y-axis

FIGURE 5.42

Standard Forms of the Equation of a Hyperbola with Center at (h, k)

Transverse Axis Parallel to the x-Axis

The standard form of the equation of a hyperbola with center at (h, k) and transverse axis parallel to the x-axis (see **Figure 5.42a**) is given by

$$\frac{(x - h)^2}{a^2} - \frac{(y - k)^2}{b^2} = 1$$

The coordinates of the vertices are $V_1(h + a, k)$ and $V_2(h - a, k)$. The coordinates of the foci are $F_1(h + c, k)$ and $F_2(h - c, k)$, where $c^2 = a^2 + b^2$.

The equations of the asymptotes are $y - k = \pm \dfrac{b}{a}(x - h)$.

Transverse Axis Parallel to the y-Axis

The standard form of the equation of a hyperbola with center at (h, k) and transverse axis parallel to the y-axis (see **Figure 5.42b**) is given by

$$\frac{(y - k)^2}{a^2} - \frac{(x - h)^2}{b^2} = 1$$

The coordinates of the vertices are $V_1(h, k + a)$ and $V_2(h, k - a)$. The coordinates of the foci are $F_1(h, k + c)$ and $F_2(h, k - c)$, where $c^2 = a^2 + b^2$.

The equations of the asymptotes are $y - k = \pm \dfrac{a}{b}(x - h)$.

EXAMPLE 2   **Find the Vertices, Foci, and Asymptotes of a Hyperbola**

Find the vertices, foci, and asymptotes of the hyperbola given by the equation $4x^2 - 9y^2 - 16x + 54y - 29 = 0$. Sketch the graph.

Solution

Write the equation of the hyperbola in standard form by completing the square.

$$4x^2 - 9y^2 - 16x + 54y - 29 = 0$$
$$4x^2 - 16x - 9y^2 + 54y = 29 \qquad \text{• Rearrange terms.}$$
$$4(x^2 - 4x) - 9(y^2 - 6y) = 29 \qquad \text{• Factor.}$$
$$4(x^2 - 4x + 4) - 9(y^2 - 6y + 9) = 29 + 16 - 81 \qquad \text{• Complete the square.}$$
$$4(x - 2)^2 - 9(y - 3)^2 = -36 \qquad \text{• Factor.}$$
$$\frac{(y - 3)^2}{4} - \frac{(x - 2)^2}{9} = 1 \qquad \text{• Divide by } -36.$$

The coordinates of the center are $(2, 3)$. Because the term containing $(y - 3)^2$ is positive, the transverse axis is parallel to the y-axis. We know $a^2 = 4$; thus

---

Alternative to Example 2

Find the center, vertices, foci, and asymptotes of the hyperbola given by the equation $x^2 - y^2 - 4x - 4y + 4 = 0$. Sketch the graph.

● The center is $(2, -2)$. The vertices are $(2, -4)$ and $(2, 0)$. The foci are $\left(2, -2 - 2\sqrt{2}\right)$ and $\left(2, -2 + 2\sqrt{2}\right)$. The asymptotes are $y = x - 4$ and $y = -x$.

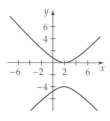

Note: The standard form of the hyperbola is $\dfrac{(y + 2)^2}{4} - \dfrac{(x - 2)^2}{4} = 1$.

$a = 2$. The vertices are $(2, 5)$ and $(2, 1)$. See **Figure 5.43.**

$$c^2 = a^2 + b^2 = 4 + 9$$
$$c = \sqrt{13}$$

The foci are $\left(2, 3 + \sqrt{13}\right)$ and $\left(2, 3 - \sqrt{13}\right)$. We know $b^2 = 9$; thus $b = 3$. The equations of the asymptotes are $y - 3 = \pm\left(\dfrac{2}{3}\right)(x - 2)$, which simplifies to

$$y = \frac{2}{3}x + \frac{5}{3} \qquad \text{and} \qquad y = -\frac{2}{3}x + \frac{13}{3}$$

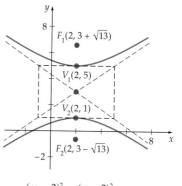

$$\frac{(y - 3)^2}{4} - \frac{(x - 2)^2}{9} = 1$$

FIGURE 5.43

▶ **TRY EXERCISE 26, PAGE 496**

INTEGRATING TECHNOLOGY

A graphing utility can be used to graph a hyperbola. For instance, consider the equation $4x^2 - 9y^2 - 16x + 54y - 29 = 0$ from Example 2. Rewrite the equation as

$$-9y^2 + 54y + (4x^2 - 16x - 29) = 0$$

In this form, the equation is a quadratic equation in terms of the variable y with

$$A = -9, B = 54, \text{ and } C = 4x^2 - 16x - 29$$

Apply the quadratic formula to produce

$$y = \frac{-54 \pm \sqrt{2916 + 36(4x^2 - 16x - 29)}}{-18}$$

The graph of $Y1 = \dfrac{-54 + \sqrt{2916 + 36(4x^2 - 16x - 29)}}{-18}$ is the upper branch of the hyperbola (see **Figure 5.44**).

The graph of $Y2 = \dfrac{-54 - \sqrt{2916 + 36(4x^2 - 16x - 29)}}{-18}$ is the lower branch of the hyperbola, as shown in **Figure 5.44.**

One advantage of this graphing procedure is that it does not require us to write the given equation in standard form. A disadvantage of the graphing procedure is that it does not indicate where the foci of the hyperbola are located.

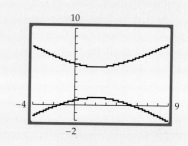

FIGURE 5.44

● ECCENTRICITY OF A HYPERBOLA

The graph of a hyperbola can be very wide or very narrow. The **eccentricity** of a hyperbola is a measure of its "wideness."

Eccentricity (e) of a Hyperbola
The eccentricity e of a hyperbola is the ratio of c to a, where c is the distance from the center to a focus and a is the length of the semitransverse axis. $$e = \frac{c}{a}$$

For a hyperbola, $c > a$ and therefore $e > 1$. As the eccentricity of the hyperbola increases, the graph becomes wider and wider, as shown in **Figure 5.45.**

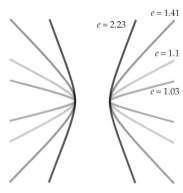

FIGURE 5.45

Alternative to Example 3
Find the standard form of the equation of

the hyperbola that has eccentricity $\frac{5}{2}$,

center at the origin, and a focus at (0, 10).

● $\dfrac{y^2}{16} - \dfrac{x^2}{84} = 1$

EXAMPLE 3   **Find the Equation of a Hyperbola Given Its Eccentricity**

Find the standard form of the equation of the hyperbola that has eccentricity $\frac{3}{2}$, center at the origin, and a focus $(6, 0)$.

Solution

Because the focus is located at $(6, 0)$ and the center is at the origin, $c = 6$. An extension of the transverse axis contains the foci, so the transverse axis is on the x-axis.

$$e = \frac{3}{2} = \frac{c}{a}$$

$$\frac{3}{2} = \frac{6}{a} \qquad \text{• Substitute 6 for } c.$$

$$a = 4 \qquad \text{• Solve for } a.$$

To find b^2, use the equation $c^2 = a^2 + b^2$ and the values for c and a.

$$c^2 = a^2 + b^2$$
$$36 = 16 + b^2$$
$$b^2 = 20$$

The equation of the hyperbola is $\dfrac{x^2}{16} - \dfrac{y^2}{20} = 1$. See **Figure 5.46.**

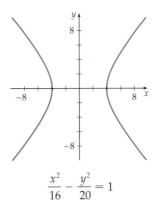

$$\frac{x^2}{16} - \frac{y^2}{20} = 1$$

FIGURE 5.46

▶ **TRY EXERCISE 48, PAGE 496**

MATH MATTERS

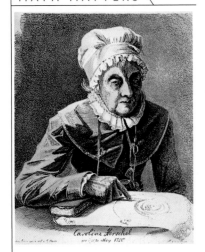

Caroline Herschel

Caroline Herschel (1750–1848) became interested in mathematics and astronomy after her brother William discovered the planet Uranus. She was the first woman to receive credit for the discovery of a comet. In fact, between 1786 and 1797 she discovered eight comets. In 1828 she completed a catalog of over 2000 nebulae for which the Royal Astronomical Society of England presented her with its prestigious gold medal.

● **APPLICATIONS**

Orbits of Comets   In Section 5.2 we noted that the orbits of the planets are elliptical. Some comets have elliptical orbits also, the most notable being Halley's comet, whose eccentricity is 0.97.

Other comets have hyperbolic orbits with the sun at a focus. These comets pass by the sun only once. The velocity of a comet determines whether its orbit is elliptical or hyperbolic. See **Figure 5.47.**

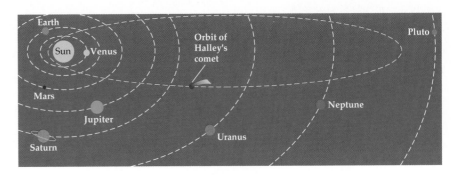

FIGURE 5.47

Hyperbolas as an Aid to Navigation   Consider two radio transmitters, T_1 and T_2, placed some distance apart. A ship with electronic equipment measures the difference between the times it takes signals from the transmitters to reach the ship.

Because the difference between the times is proportional to the difference between the distances of the ship from the transmitters, the ship must be located on the hyperbola with foci at the two transmitters.

Using a third transmitter, T_3, we can find a second hyperbola with foci T_2 and T_3. The ship lies on the intersection of the two hyperbolas, as shown in **Figure 5.48.**

Alternative to Example 4
Two radio transmitters, T_1 and T_2, are positioned along a straight coastline, 600 miles apart. A ship's LORAN receives a radio signal from transmitter T_1 2000 microseconds before it receives a simultaneous signal from transmitter T_2. Find an equation of a hyperbola (with foci located at T_1 and T_2) on which the ship lies. (Assume that the radio signals travel at 0.186 mile per microsecond.)

○ $\dfrac{x^2}{(186)^2} - \dfrac{y^2}{(235.4)^2} = 1$

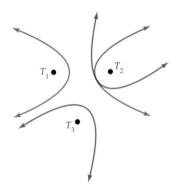

FIGURE 5.48

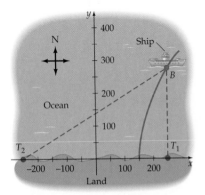

FIGURE 5.49

EXAMPLE 4 Determine the Position of a Ship

Two radio transmitters are positioned along a coastline, 500 miles apart. See **Figure 5.49.** Using a LORAN (LOng RAnge Navigation) system, a ship determines that a radio signal from transmitter T_1 reaches the ship 1600 microseconds before it receives a simultaneous signal from transmitter T_2.

a. Find an equation of a hyperbola (with foci located at T_1 and T_2) on which the ship lies. See **Figure 5.49.** (Assume the radio signals travel at 0.186 mile per microsecond.)

b. If the ship is directly north of transmitter T_1, determine how far (to the nearest mile) the ship is from the transmitter.

Solution

a. The ship lies on a hyperbola at point B, with foci at T_1 and T_2. The difference of the distances $d(T_2, B)$ and $d(T_1, B)$ is given by

$$\text{Distance} = \text{rate} \times \text{time}$$
$$= 0.186 \text{ mile/microsecond} \times 1600 \text{ microseconds}$$
$$= 297.6 \text{ mile}$$

Thus the ship is located on a hyperbola with transverse axis of 297.6 miles and semitransverse axis $a = 148.8$ miles. **Figure 5.49** shows that the foci are located at $(250, 0)$ and $(-250, 0)$. Thus $c = 250$ miles, and

$$b = \sqrt{c^2 - a^2} = \sqrt{250^2 - 148.8^2} \approx 200.9 \text{ miles}$$

The ship is located on the hyperbola given by

$$\frac{x^2}{148.8^2} - \frac{y^2}{200.9^2} = 1$$

b. If the ship is directly north of T_1, then $x = 250$, and the distance from the ship to the transmitter T_1 is y, where

$$-\frac{y^2}{200.9^2} = 1 - \frac{250^2}{148.8^2}$$
$$y = \frac{200.9}{148.8} \sqrt{250^2 - 148.8^2} \approx 271 \text{ miles}$$

The ship is about 271 miles north of transmitter T_1.

▶ **TRY EXERCISE 54, PAGE 497**

Hyperbolas also have a reflective property that makes them useful in many applications.

Reflective Property of a Hyperbola

A ray of light directed toward one focus of a hyperbolic mirror is reflected toward the other focus. See **Figures 5.50** and **5.51.**

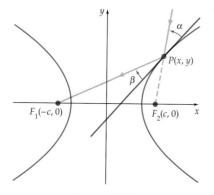

FIGURE 5.50

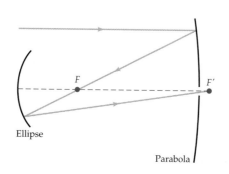

Ellipse

Parabola

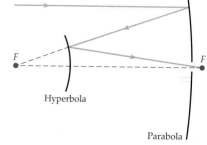

Hyperbola

Parabola

FIGURE 5.51

TOPICS FOR DISCUSSION

1. In every hyperbola, the distance c from a focus to the center of the hyperbola is greater than the length of the semitransverse axis a. Do you agree? Explain.

2. How many vertices does a hyperbola have?

3. Explain why the eccentricity of every hyperbola is a number greater than 1.

4. Is the conjugate axis of a hyperbola perpendicular to the transverse axis of the hyperbola?

EXERCISE SET 5.3

—*Suggested Assignment: Exercises 1–65, every other odd; 71, 75–80.*
—*Answer graphs to Exercises 1–26, 27–32 and 57–64 are on pages AA24–AA27.*

In Exercises 1 to 26, find the center, vertices, foci, and asymptotes for the hyperbola given by each equation. Graph each equation.

1. $\dfrac{x^2}{16} - \dfrac{y^2}{25} = 1$

2. $\dfrac{x^2}{16} - \dfrac{y^2}{9} = 1$

3. $\dfrac{y^2}{4} - \dfrac{x^2}{25} = 1$

▶ **4.** $\dfrac{y^2}{25} - \dfrac{x^2}{36} = 1$

5. $\dfrac{x^2}{7} - \dfrac{y^2}{9} = 1$

6. $\dfrac{x^2}{5} - \dfrac{y^2}{4} = 1$

7. $\dfrac{4x^2}{9} - \dfrac{y^2}{16} = 1$

8. $\dfrac{x^2}{9} - \dfrac{9y^2}{16} = 1$

9. $\dfrac{(x-3)^2}{16} - \dfrac{(y+4)^2}{9} = 1$

10. $\dfrac{(x+3)^2}{25} - \dfrac{y^2}{4} = 1$

11. $\dfrac{(y+2)^2}{4} - \dfrac{(x-1)^2}{16} = 1$

12. $\dfrac{(y-2)^2}{36} - \dfrac{(x+1)^2}{49} = 1$

13. $\dfrac{(x+2)^2}{9} - \dfrac{y^2}{25} = 1$

14. $\dfrac{x^2}{25} - \dfrac{(y-2)^2}{81} = 1$

15. $\dfrac{9(x-1)^2}{16} - \dfrac{(y+1)^2}{9} = 1$

16. $\dfrac{(x+6)^2}{25} - \dfrac{25y^2}{144} = 1$

17. $x^2 - y^2 = 9$

18. $4x^2 - y^2 = 16$

19. $16y^2 - 9x^2 = 144$

20. $9y^2 - 25x^2 = 225$

21. $9y^2 - 36x^2 = 4$

22. $16x^2 - 25y^2 = 9$

23. $x^2 - y^2 - 6x + 8y - 3 = 0$

24. $4x^2 - 25y^2 + 16x + 50y - 109 = 0$

25. $9x^2 - 4y^2 + 36x - 8y + 68 = 0$

▶ **26.** $16x^2 - 9y^2 - 32x - 54y + 79 = 0$

In Exercises 27 to 32, use the quadratic formula to solve for y in terms of x. Then use a graphing utility to graph each equation.

27. $4x^2 - y^2 + 32x + 6y + 39 = 0$

28. $x^2 - 16y^2 + 8x - 64y + 16 = 0$

29. $9x^2 - 16y^2 - 36x - 64y + 116 = 0$

30. $2x^2 - 9y^2 + 12x - 18y + 18 = 0$

31. $4x^2 - 9y^2 + 8x - 18y - 6 = 0$

32. $2x^2 - 9y^2 - 8x + 36y - 46 = 0$

In Exercises 33 to 46, find the equation in standard form of the hyperbola that satisfies the stated conditions.

33. Vertices $(3, 0)$ and $(-3, 0)$, foci $(4, 0)$ and $(-4, 0)$
$$\text{33. } \frac{x^2}{9} - \frac{y^2}{7} = 1$$

34. Vertices $(0, 2)$ and $(0, -2)$, foci $(0, 3)$ and $(0, -3)$
$$\text{34. } \frac{y^2}{4} - \frac{x^2}{5} = 1$$

35. Foci $(0, 5)$ and $(0, -5)$, asymptotes $y = 2x$ and $y = -2x$
$$\text{35. } \frac{y^2}{20} - \frac{x^2}{5} = 1$$

36. Foci $(4, 0)$ and $(-4, 0)$, asymptotes $y = x$ and $y = -x$
$$\text{36. } \frac{x^2}{8} - \frac{y^2}{8} = 1$$

37. Vertices $(0, 3)$ and $(0, -3)$, passing through $(2, 4)$
$$\text{37. } \frac{y^2}{9} - \frac{x^2}{36/7} = 1$$

38. Vertices $(5, 0)$ and $(-5, 0)$, passing through $(-1, 3)$
$$\frac{1}{25} - \frac{9}{b^2} = 1, b^2 = -\frac{225}{24} \quad \text{However, } b^2 \text{ must be positive. Therefore, no such hyperbola exists.}$$

39. Asymptotes $y = \frac{1}{2}x$ and $y = -\frac{1}{2}x$, vertices $(0, 4)$ and $(0, -4)$ $\frac{y^2}{16} - \frac{x^2}{64} = 1$

40. Asymptotes $y = \frac{2}{3}x$ and $y = -\frac{2}{3}x$, vertices $(6, 0)$ and $(-6, 0)$ $\frac{x^2}{36} - \frac{y^2}{16} = 1$

41. Vertices $(6, 3)$ and $(2, 3)$, foci $(7, 3)$ and $(1, 3)$ $\frac{(x-4)^2}{4} - \frac{(y-3)^2}{5} = 1$

42. Vertices $(-1, 5)$ and $(-1, -1)$, foci $(-1, 7)$ and $(-1, -3)$
$$\frac{(y-2)^2}{9} - \frac{(x+1)^2}{16} = 1$$

43. Foci $(1, -2)$ and $(7, -2)$, slope of an asymptote $\frac{5}{4}$
$$\frac{(x-4)^2}{144/41} - \frac{(y+2)^2}{225/41} = 1$$

44. Foci $(-3, -6)$ and $(-3, -2)$, slope of an asymptote 1
$$\frac{(y+4)^2}{2} - \frac{(x+3)^2}{2} = 1 \quad \textbf{45. } \frac{(y-2)^2}{3} - \frac{(x-7)^2}{12} = 1$$

45. Passing through $(9, 4)$, slope of an asymptote $\frac{1}{2}$, center $(7, 2)$, transverse axis parallel to the y-axis

46. Passing through $(6, 1)$, slope of an asymptote 2, center $(3, 3)$, transverse axis parallel to the x-axis
$$\frac{(x-3)^2}{8} - \frac{(y-3)^2}{32} = 1$$

In Exercises 47 to 52, use the eccentricity to find the equation in standard form of each hyperbola.

47. Vertices $(1, 6)$ and $(1, 8)$, eccentricity 2
$$\frac{(y-7)^2}{1} - \frac{(x-1)^2}{3} = 1$$

▶ **48.** Vertices $(2, 3)$ and $(-2, 3)$, eccentricity $\frac{5}{2}$ $\frac{x^2}{4} - \frac{(y-3)^2}{21} = 1$

49. Eccentricity 2, foci $(4, 0)$ and $(-4, 0)$ $\frac{x^2}{4} - \frac{y^2}{12} = 1$

50. Eccentricity $\frac{4}{3}$, foci $(0, 6)$ and $(0, -6)$ $\frac{y^2}{81/4} - \frac{x^2}{63/4} = 1$

51. $\frac{(x-4)^2}{36/7} - \frac{(y-1)^2}{4} = 1$ and $\frac{(y-1)^2}{36/7} - \frac{(x-4)^2}{4} = 1$

51. Center $(4, 1)$, conjugate axis of length 4, eccentricity $\frac{4}{3}$ (*Hint:* There are two answers.)

52. $\frac{(x+3)^2}{3} - \frac{(y+3)^2}{9} = 1$ and $\frac{(y+3)^2}{3} - \frac{(x+3)^2}{9} = 1$

52. Center $(-3, -3)$, conjugate axis of length 6, eccentricity 2 (*Hint:* There are two answers.)

53. LORAN Two radio transmitters are positioned along the coast, 250 miles apart. A signal is sent simultaneously from each transmitter. The signal from transmitter T_2 is received by a ship's LORAN 500 microseconds after it receives the signal from T_1. The radio signals travel 0.186 mile per microsecond.

a. Find an equation of a hyperbola, with foci at T_1 and T_2, on which the ship is located. $\frac{x^2}{2162.25} - \frac{y^2}{13,462.75} = 1$

b. If the ship is 100 miles east of the y-axis, determine its distance from the coastline (to the nearest mile). 221 mi

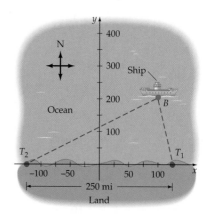

▶ **54.** **LORAN** Two radio transmitters are positioned along the coast, 300 miles apart. A signal is sent simultaneously from each transmitter. The signal from transmitter T_1 is received by a ship's LORAN 800 microseconds after it receives the signal from T_2. The radio signals travel 0.186 mile per microsecond.

a. Find an equation of a hyperbola, with foci at T_1 and T_2, on which the ship is located. $\dfrac{x^2}{74.4^2} - \dfrac{y^2}{130.25^2} = 1$

b. If the ship continues to travel so that the difference of 800 microseconds is maintained, determine the point at which the ship will reach the coastline.
74.4 mi to the left of the origin, at the point $(-74.4, 0)$

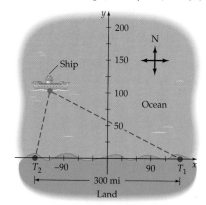

55. **SONIC BOOMS** When a plane exceeds the speed of sound, a sonic boom is produced by the wake of the sound waves. (See the chapter opener on page 459.) For a plane flying at 10,000 feet, the circular wave front can be given by

$$y^2 = x^2 + (z - 10{,}000)^2$$

where z is the height of the wave front above Earth. See the diagram below. Note that the xy-plane is Earth's surface, which is approximately flat over small distances.

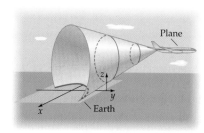

Find and name the equation formed when the wave front hits Earth. $y^2 - x^2 = 10{,}000^2$, hyperbola

56. **WATER WAVES** If two pebbles are dropped into a pond at different places $F_1(-2, 0)$ and $F_2(2, 0)$, circular waves are propagated with F_1 as the center of one set of circular waves (in green) and F_2 as the center of the other set of circular waves (in red).

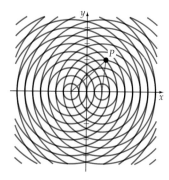

Let P be a point at which the waves intersect. In the diagram above, $|F_1P - F_2P| = 2$.

a. What curve is generated by connecting all points P for which $|F_1P - F_2P| = 2$? hyperbola

b. What is the equation of the curve in part **a.**? $x^2 - \dfrac{y^2}{3} = 1$

In Exercises 57 to 64, identify the graph of each equation as a parabola, an ellipse, or a hyperbola. Graph each equation.

57. $4x^2 + 9y^2 - 16x - 36y + 16 = 0$ ellipse

58. $2x^2 + 3y - 8x + 2 = 0$ parabola

59. $5x - 4y^2 + 24y - 11 = 0$ parabola

60. $9x^2 - 25y^2 - 18x + 50y = 0$ hyperbola

61. $x^2 + 2y - 8x = 0$ parabola

62. $9x^2 + 16y^2 + 36x - 64y - 44 = 0$ ellipse

63. $25x^2 + 9y^2 - 50x - 72y - 56 = 0$ ellipse

64. $(x - 3)^2 + (y - 4)^2 = (x + 1)^2$ parabola

CONNECTING CONCEPTS

In Exercises 65 to 68, use the definition of a hyperbola to find the equation of the hyperbola in standard form.

65. Foci $(2, 0)$ and $(-2, 0)$; passes through the point $(2, 3)$

$$\frac{x^2}{1} - \frac{y^2}{3} = 1$$

66. Foci $(0, 3)$ and $(0, -3)$; passes through the point $\left(\frac{5}{2}, 3\right)$

$$\frac{y^2}{4} - \frac{x^2}{5} = 1$$

67. Foci $(0, 4)$ and $(0, -4)$; passes through the point $\left(\frac{7}{3}, 4\right)$

$$\frac{y^2}{9} - \frac{x^2}{7} = 1$$

68. Foci $(5, 0)$ and $(-5, 0)$; passes through the point $\left(5, \frac{9}{4}\right)$

$$\frac{x^2}{16} - \frac{y^2}{9} = 1$$

Recall that an ellipse has two directrices that are lines perpendicular to the line containing the foci. A hyperbola also has two directrices; they are perpendicular to the transverse axis and outside the hyperbola. For a hyperbola with center at the origin and transverse axis on the x-axis, the equations of the directrices are $x = \dfrac{a^2}{c}$ and $x = -\dfrac{a^2}{c}$. In Exercises 69 to 72, use this information to solve each exercise.

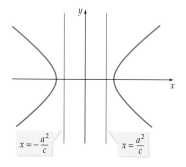

69. Find the directrices for the hyperbola in Exercise 1. $x = \pm\dfrac{16\sqrt{41}}{41}$

70. Find the directrices for the hyperbola in Exercise 2. $x = \pm\dfrac{16}{5}$

71. Let $P(x, y)$ be a point on the hyperbola $\dfrac{x^2}{9} - \dfrac{y^2}{16} = 1$. Show that the distance from the point P to the focus $(5, 0)$ divided by the distance from the point P to the directrix $x = \dfrac{9}{5}$ equals the eccentricity.

72. Generalize the results of Exercise 71. That is, show that if $P(x, y)$ is a point on the hyperbola $\dfrac{x^2}{a^2} - \dfrac{y^2}{b^2} = 1$, $F(c, 0)$ is a focus, and $x = \dfrac{a^2}{c}$ is a directrix, then the following equation is true:

$$e = \frac{d(P, F)}{d(P, D)}$$

73. Sketch a graph of $\dfrac{x|x|}{16} - \dfrac{y|y|}{9} = 1$.

Answer on page AA27.

74. Sketch a graph of $\dfrac{x|x|}{16} + \dfrac{y|y|}{9} = 1$.

Answer on page AA27.

PROJECTS

1.   **A HYPERBOLIC PARABOLOID** A *hyperbolic paraboloid* is a three-dimensional figure. Some of its cross sections are parabolas and some are hyperbolas. Make a drawing of a hyperbolic paraboloid. Explain the relationship that exists between the equations of the parabolic cross sections and the relationship that exists between the equations of the hyperbolic cross sections.

2.   **A HYPERBOLOID OF ONE SHEET** Make a sketch of a *hyperboloid of one sheet*. Explain the different cross sections of the hyperboloid of one sheet. Do some research on nuclear power plants, and explain why nuclear cooling towers are designed in the shape of hyperboloids of one sheet.

EXPLORING CONCEPTS WITH TECHNOLOGY

Using a Graphing Calculator to Illustrate a Property of Parabolas

Some graphing calculators can be used to graph a *family of curves*. For instance, on a TI-83 graphing calculator, the graph of

$$Y_1=\{-1,0,1,2,3,4\}$$

is six horizontal lines. The graphs of

$$Y_2=1+\sqrt{\{1,2,3,4\}^2 - X^2} \quad \text{and} \quad Y_3=1-\sqrt{\{1,2,3,4\}^2 - X^2}$$

form four circles. Each circle has a center at $(0, 1)$. The radii of the four circles are

$$r_1 = 1, r_2 = 2, r_3 = 3, \text{ and } r_4 = 4$$

The graph of $Y_4=\frac{1}{4}X^2$ is a parabola with focus $(0, 1)$ and directrix $y = -1$.

a.   Graph Y_1, Y_2, Y_3, and Y_4 on the same screen with

  Xmin=-4.7, Xmax=4.7, Xscl=1, Ymin=-2, Ymax=4.2, Yscl=1

b.   Locate point A, in Quadrant I, where the parabola intersects the line $y = 3$ and the circle with radius 4. How far is it from A to the focus $(0, 1)$? How far is it from A to the directrix $y = -1$?

c.   Locate point B, in Quadrant I, where the parabola intersects the line $y = 2$ and the circle with radius 3. How far is it from B to the focus $(0, 1)$? How far is it from B to the directrix $y = -1$?

d.   Explain why you should not be surprised by the results from parts **b.** and **c.**

CHAPTER 5 SUMMARY

5.1 Parabolas

• A parabola is the set of points in the plane that are equidistant from a fixed line (the directrix) and a fixed point (the focus) not on the directrix.

• The equations of a parabola with vertex at (h, k) and axis of symmetry parallel to a coordinate axis are given by

$(x - h)^2 = 4p(y - k)$; focus $(h, k + p)$; directrix $y = k - p$

$(y - k)^2 = 4p(x - h)$; focus $(h + p, k)$; directrix $x = h - p$

5.2 Ellipses

• A ellipse is the set of all points in the plane, the sum of whose distances from two fixed points (foci) is a positive constant.

• The equations of an ellipse with center at (h, k) and major axis parallel to a coordinate axis are given by

$\frac{(x - h)^2}{a^2} + \frac{(y - k)^2}{b^2} = 1$; foci $(h \pm c, k)$; vertices $(h \pm a, k)$

$\frac{(x - h)^2}{b^2} + \frac{(y - k)^2}{a^2} = 1$; foci $(h, k \pm c)$; vertices $(h, k \pm a)$

For each equation, $a > b$ and $c^2 = a^2 - b^2$.

• The eccentricity e of an ellipse is given by $e = \frac{c}{a}$.

5.3 Hyperbolas

• A hyperbola is the set of all points in the plane, the difference of whose distances from two fixed points (foci) is a positive constant.

- The equations of a hyperbola with center at (h, k) and transverse axis parallel to a coordinate axis are given by

$$\frac{(x - h)^2}{a^2} - \frac{(y - k)^2}{b^2} = 1; \text{ foci } (h \pm c, k); \text{ vertices } (h \pm a, k)$$

$$\frac{(y - k)^2}{a^2} - \frac{(x - h)^2}{b^2} = 1; \text{ foci } (h, k \pm c); \text{ vertices } (h, k \pm a)$$

For each equation, $c^2 = a^2 + b^2$.

- The eccentricity e of a hyperbola is given by $e = \dfrac{c}{a}$.

CHAPTER 5 TRUE/FALSE EXERCISES

In Exercises 1 to 9, answer true or false. If the statement is false, give a reason or an example to show that the statement is false.

1. The graph of a parabola is the same shape as that of one branch of a hyperbola. False; a parabola has no asymptotes.

2. For the two axes of an ellipse, the major axis and the minor axis, the major axis is always the longer axis. True

3. For the two axes of a hyperbola, the transverse axis and the conjugate axis, the transverse axis is always the longer axis. False; by keeping the foci fixed and varying the asymptotes, we can make the conjugate axis any size needed.

4. If two ellipses have the same foci, they have the same graph. False; $\dfrac{x^2}{25} + \dfrac{y^2}{9} = 1$ and $\dfrac{x^2}{36} + \dfrac{y^2}{20} = 1$ have the same c's but different a's.

5. A hyperbola is similar to a parabola in that both curves have asymptotes. False; parabolas have no asymptotes.

6. If a hyperbola with center at the origin and a parabola with vertex at the origin have the same focus, $(0, c)$, then the two graphs always intersect. True

7. The graphs of all the conic sections are not the graphs of functions. False; the graph of a parabola can be a function.

8. If F_1 and F_2 are the two foci of an ellipse and P is a point on the ellipse, then $d(P, F_1) + d(P, F_2) = 2a$, where a is the length of the semimajor axis of the ellipse. True

9. The eccentricity of a hyperbola is always greater than 1. True

CHAPTER 5 REVIEW EXERCISES

—Answer graphs to Exercises 1–12 are on pages AA27–AA28.

In Exercises 1 to 12, if the equation is that of an ellipse or a hyperbola, find the center, vertices, and foci. For hyperbolas, find the equations of the asymptotes. If the equation is that of a parabola, find the vertex, focus, and equation of the directrix. Graph each equation.

1. $x^2 - y^2 = 4$ [5.3]

2. $y^2 = 16x$ [5.1]

3. $x^2 + 4y^2 - 6x + 8y - 3 = 0$ [5.2]

4. $3x^2 - 4y^2 + 12x - 24y - 36 = 0$ [5.3]

5. $3x - 4y^2 + 8y + 2 = 0$ [5.1]

6. $3x + 2y^2 - 4y - 7 = 0$ [5.1]

7. $9x^2 + 4y^2 + 36x - 8y + 4 = 0$ [5.2]

8. $11x^2 - 25y^2 - 44x - 50y - 256 = 0$ [5.3]

9. $4x^2 - 9y^2 - 8x + 12y - 144 = 0$ [5.3]

10. $9x^2 + 16y^2 + 36x - 16y - 104 = 0$ [5.2]

11. $4x^2 + 28x + 32y + 81 = 0$ [5.1]

12. $x^2 - 6x - 9y + 27 = 0$ [5.1]

In Exercises 13 to 20, find the equation of the conic that satisfies the given conditions.

13. Ellipse with vertices at $(7, 3)$ and $(-3, 3)$; length of minor axis is 8. $\dfrac{(x - 2)^2}{25} + \dfrac{(y - 3)^2}{16} = 1$ [5.2]

14. Hyperbola with vertices at $(4, 1)$ and $(-2, 1)$; eccentricity is $\dfrac{4}{3}$. $\dfrac{(x-1)^2}{9} - \dfrac{(y-1)^2}{7} = 1$ [5.3]

15. Hyperbola with foci $(-5, 2)$ and $(1, 2)$; length of transverse axis is 4. $\dfrac{(x+2)^2}{4} - \dfrac{(y-2)^2}{5} = 1$ [5.3]

16. Parabola with focus $(2, -3)$ and directrix $x = 6$. $(y+3)^2 = -8(x-4)$ [5.1]

17. Parabola with vertex $(0, -2)$ and passing through the point $(3, 4)$. $x^2 = \dfrac{3(y+2)}{2}$ or $(y+2)^2 = 12x$ [5.1]

18. Ellipse with eccentricity $\dfrac{2}{3}$ and foci $(-4, -1)$ and $(0, -1)$. $\dfrac{(x+2)^2}{9} + \dfrac{(y+1)^2}{5} = 1$ [5.2]

19. Hyperbola with vertices $(\pm 6, 0)$ and asymptotes whose equations are $y = \pm\dfrac{1}{9}x$. $\dfrac{x^2}{36} - \dfrac{y^2}{4/9} = 1$ [5.3]

20. Parabola passing through the points $(1, 0)$, $(2, 1)$, and $(0, 1)$ with axis of symmetry parallel to the y-axis. $(x-1)^2 = y$ [5.1]

21. Find the equation of the parabola traced by a point $P(x, y)$ that moves in such a way that the distance between $P(x, y)$ and the line $x = 2$ equals the distance between $P(x, y)$ and the point $(-2, 3)$. $(y-3)^2 = -8x$ [5.1]

22. Find the equation of the parabola traced by a point $P(x, y)$ that moves in such a way that the distance between $P(x, y)$ and the line $y = 1$ equals the distance between $P(x, y)$ and the point $(-1, 2)$. $(x+1)^2 = 2\left(y - \dfrac{3}{2}\right)$ [5.1]

23. Find the equation of the ellipse traced by a point $P(x, y)$ that moves in such a way that the sum of its distances to $(-3, 1)$ and $(5, 1)$ is 10. $\dfrac{(x-1)^2}{25} + \dfrac{(y-1)^2}{9} = 1$ [5.2]

24. Find the equation of the ellipse traced by a point $P(x, y)$ that moves in such a way that the sum of its distances to $(3, 5)$ and $(3, -1)$ is 8. $\dfrac{(x-3)^2}{7} + \dfrac{(y-2)^2}{16} = 1$ [5.2]

CHAPTER 5 TEST

1. Find the vertex, focus, and directrix of the parabola given by the equation $y = \dfrac{1}{8}x^2$. focus: $(0, 2)$ vertex: $(0, 0)$ directrix: $y = -2$ [5.1]

2. Find the vertex, focus, and directrix of the parabola given by the equation $x^2 + 4x - 12y + 16 = 0$. focus: $(-2, 4)$, vertex: $(-2, 1)$, directrix: $y = -2$ [5.1]

3. Find the equation in standard form of the parabola with directrix $x = 3$ and focus $(-1, -2)$. $(y+2)^2 = -8(x-1)$ [5.1]

4. Graph the parabola with focus $(0, -1)$ and directrix $y = -5$. Answer on page AA28. [5.1]

5. Find the vertices and foci of the ellipse given by the equation $\dfrac{x^2}{9} + \dfrac{y^2}{64} = 1$. vertices: $(0, 8)$, $(0, -8)$, foci: $\left(0, \sqrt{55}\right), \left(0, -\sqrt{55}\right)$ [5.2]

6. Graph: $\dfrac{x^2}{16} + \dfrac{y^2}{1} = 1$ Answer on page AA28. [5.2]

7. Find the vertices and foci of the ellipse given by the equation $25x^2 - 150x + 9y^2 + 18y + 9 = 0$. vertices: $(3, 4)$, $(3, -6)$; foci: $(3, 3)$, $(3, -5)$ [5.2]

8. Find the equation in standard form of the ellipse with center $(0, -3)$, foci $(-6, -3)$ and $(6, -3)$, and minor axis of length 6. $\dfrac{x^2}{45} + \dfrac{(y+3)^2}{9} = 1$ [5.2]

9. Find the eccentricity of the ellipse given by the equation $9x^2 + 25y^2 = 81$. $\dfrac{4}{5}$ [5.2]

10. Graph: $\dfrac{y^2}{25} - \dfrac{x^2}{16} = 1$ Answer on page AA28. [5.3]

11. Find the vertices, foci, and asymptotes of the hyperbola given by the equation $\dfrac{x^2}{36} - \dfrac{y^2}{64} = 1$. vertices: $(6, 0)$, $(-6, 0)$, foci: $(-10, 0)$, $(10, 0)$, asymptotes: $y = \pm\dfrac{4x}{3}$ [5.3]

12. Graph: $16y^2 + 32y - 4x^2 - 24x = 84$ Answer on page AA28. [5.3]

13. Find the vertices and foci of the hyperbola given by the equation $\dfrac{(y-4)^2}{36} - \dfrac{(x+5)^2}{9} = 1$. vertices: $(-5, 10)$, $(-5, -2)$; foci: $\left(-5, 4 + 3\sqrt{5}\right), \left(-5, 4 - 3\sqrt{5}\right)$ [5.3]

14. Find the equation in standard form of the hyperbola with vertices at $(-2, -3)$ and $(-6, -3)$ and foci $(-4 + \sqrt{34}, -3)$ and $(-4 - \sqrt{34}, -3)$. $\dfrac{(x+4)^2}{4} - \dfrac{(y+3)^2}{30} = 1$ [5.3]

15. Find the equation in standard form of the parabola with focus $(-2, 4)$ and directrix $x = 6$. $(y-4)^2 = -16(x-2)$ [5.1]

CUMULATIVE REVIEW EXERCISES

1. Solve: $x^4 - 2x^2 - 8 = 0$ $\pm 2, \pm i\sqrt{2}$ [1.4]

2. Simplify: $\dfrac{2}{x - 1} - \dfrac{3}{x + 2} \cdot \dfrac{-x + 7}{(x - 1)(x + 2)}$ [P.5]

3. Given $f(x) = 1 - x^2$, write the difference quotient $\dfrac{f(2 + h) - f(2)}{h}$ in simplest form. $-4 - h$ [2.6]

4. Let $f(x) = 3x + 2$ and $g(x) = 2 - x^2$. Find $(f \circ g)(-3)$. -19 [2.6]

5. How many complex number solutions are there to the equation $x^6 + 2x^4 - 3x^3 - x^2 + 5x - 7 = 0$? 6 [3.4]

6. Find the equation of the line that passes through the points $P_1(1, -4)$ and $P_2(-3, 2)$. $y = -\dfrac{3}{2}x - \dfrac{5}{2}$ [2.3]

7. Find the equations of the asymptotes of the graph of $f(x) = \dfrac{2x - 4}{x + 3}$. $x = -3, y = 2$ [3.5]

8. Find the length of the line segment connecting $P_1(4, -5)$ and $P_2(-1, -3)$. $\sqrt{29}$ [2.1]

9. Graph: $f(x) = 2^{-x+1}$
Answer on page AA28. [4.2]

10. Solve: $\log_2(x + 3) - \log_2(x) = 2$ 1 [4.5]

11. Given the graph below, sketch the graph of $y = -f(x) + 2$.
Answer on page AA28. [2.5]

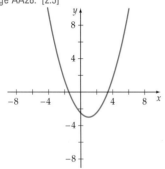

12. Find the inverse function for $f(x) = 2x - 8$. $f^{-1}(x) = \dfrac{1}{2}x + 4$ [4.1]

13. Given that 3 and $2i$ are zeros of $P(x) = x^4 + x^3 - 8x^2 + 4x - 48$, find the remaining zeros. $-4, -2i$ [3.4]

14. Let $f(x) = \dfrac{3x}{x^2 + 1}$. Is f an even function, an odd function, or neither? odd [2.5]

15. Is the graph of $x = y^3 - y$ symmetric with respect to the x-axis, the y-axis, or the origin? origin [2.5]

16. Solve: $3^x = 5$. Round to the nearest thousandth. 1.465 [4.5]

17. Solve $x^2 + 3x - 4 < 0$. Write the answer using interval notation. $(-4, 1)$ [1.5]

18. What is the domain of $G(x) = \dfrac{x}{x^2 - 4}$? all real numbers except -2 and 2 [2.2]

19. Express the area of a square in terms of a diagonal d of the square. $A(d) = \dfrac{d^2}{2}$ [2.2]

20. The temperature, in degrees Fahrenheit, of a cup of hot chocolate t seconds after hot milk is poured into the cup is given by $T(t) = 70 + 100e^{-0.25t}$. How long will it take before the temperature of the hot chocolate is $100°F$? Round to the nearest tenth. 4.8 s [4.2]

SYSTEMS OF EQUATIONS

Tax Brackets Versus a Flat Tax

A perennial issue in Congress is the equity of the income tax laws. Currently, there are six tax brackets. As a person's income increases, the percent of adjusted gross income (income after allowable deductions) that the person pays in income tax increases. In 2003, Congress passed the Tax Relief Reconciliation Act of 2003, which changed the laws relating to income taxes. An alternative proposal before Congress that year was to replace these brackets with one bracket so that all taxpayers paid 20% of their income as tax. This type of tax structure is called a *flat tax* and is used in some states and countries. The flat-tax proposal was not passed by Congress.

The graph below shows the amount of tax a single person would pay using tax brackets and a flat tax. (Only the first three tax brackets are shown.)

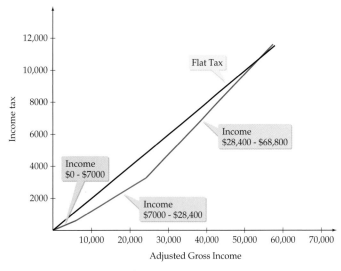

Source: www.irs.gov

The x-coordinate of the point at which the graphs intersect is the income at which a taxpayer pays the same amount of tax whether brackets are used or a flat tax is used. The coordinates of that point can be found by solving a system of equations. See **Exercise 59 on page 515.**

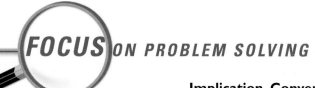

Implication, Converse, and Contrapositive

In the movie *Star Wars,* Episode IV, *A New Hope,* Obi-Wan Kenobi says, "If you strike me down, I shall become more powerful than you can possibly imagine." The sentence uttered by Obi-Wan is called an *implication.* Statements such as these can be symbolized by *if p, then q* or *if p, q.* The statement *p* is called the *antecedent,* and *q* is called the *consequent.* For Obi-Wan Kenobi, we have

> *p:* You strike me down.
>
> *q:* I shall become more powerful than you can possibly imagine.

In mathematics, many theorems are stated as implications. For instance, consider the following theorem.

Theorem   If a number ends in 0, then the number is divisible by 5.

The antecedent is "a number ends in 0"; the consequent is "the number is divisible by 5."

Interchanging the order of the antecedent and the consequent results in the **converse** of the implication. For the theorem above, we have

Converse   If a number is divisible by 5, then the number ends in 0.

This is *not* a true statement because 15 is divisible by 5 but 15 does not end in 0. In this case, interchanging the antecedent and consequent turned a true statement into a false statement. This demonstrates that the converse of a theorem is not always true.

Although the converse of a theorem *may* not be a true statement, the **contrapositive** of a theorem is always a true statement. The contrapositive is formed by interchanging the antecedent and the consequent (as we did for the converse) and then negating each statement. For the theorem above, we have

Contrapositive   If a number is *not* divisible by 5, then the number does *not* end in 0.

Some theorems are stated in the form "*p* if and only if *q.*" These are very powerful theorems because both the implication and its converse are true. Here is an example.

> A linear system of two equations in two variables has a unique solution if and only if the graphs of the equations are not parallel.

In this case, we have the implication, "If a linear system of equations in two variables has a unique solution, the graphs of the equations are not parallel"— a true statement. The converse of the implication is "If the graphs of the two equations of a linear system of equations in two variables are not parallel, the system has a unique solution"—also a true statement.

SYSTEMS OF LINEAR EQUATIONS IN TWO VARIABLES

- **SUBSTITUTION METHOD FOR SOLVING A SYSTEM OF LINEAR EQUATIONS**
- **ELIMINATION METHOD FOR SOLVING A SYSTEM OF EQUATIONS**
- **APPLICATIONS OF SYSTEMS OF EQUATIONS**

Recall that an equation of the form $Ax + By = C$ is a linear equation in two variables. A solution of a linear equation in two variables is an ordered pair (x, y) that makes the equation a true statement. For example, $(-2, 3)$ is a solution of the equation

$$2x + 3y = 5 \qquad \text{since} \qquad 2(-2) + 3(3) = 5$$

The graph of a linear equation in two variables, a straight line, is the set of points whose ordered pairs satisfy the equation. **Figure 6.1** is the graph of $2x + 3y = 5$.

A **system of equations** is two or more equations considered together. The following system of equations is a **linear system of equations** in two variables.

$$\begin{cases} 2x + 3y = 4 \\ 3x - 2y = -7 \end{cases}$$

A **solution** of a system of equations in two variables is an ordered pair that is a solution of both equations.

In **Figure 6.2**, the graphs of the two equations in the system of equations above intersect at the point $(-1, 2)$. Because that point lies on both lines, $(-1, 2)$ is a solution of both equations and thus is a solution of the system of equations. The point $(5, -2)$ is a solution of the first equation but not the second equation. Therefore, $(5, -2)$ is not a solution of the system of equations.

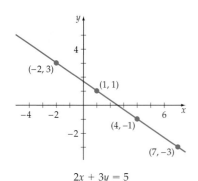

$2x + 3y = 5$

FIGURE 6.1

❓ **QUESTION** Is $(3, -4)$ a solution of $\begin{cases} 2x - 3y = 18 \\ x + 4y = -13 \end{cases}$?

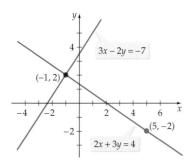

FIGURE 6.2

The graphs of two linear equations in two variables can intersect at a single point, be the same line, or be parallel. When the graphs intersect at a single point or are the same line, the system is called a **consistent** system of equations. The system is called an **independent** system of equations when the lines intersect at exactly one point. The system is called a **dependent** system of equations when the equations represent the same line. In this case, the system has an infinite number of solutions. When the graphs of the two equations are parallel lines, the system is called **inconsistent** and has no solution. See **Figure 6.3.**

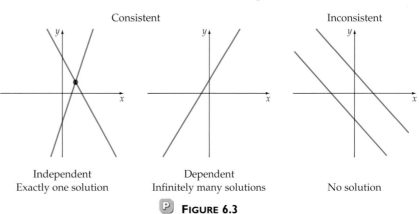

Consistent

Inconsistent

Independent
Exactly one solution

Dependent
Infinitely many solutions

No solution

Ⓟ **FIGURE 6.3**

❓ **ANSWER** Yes.

• SUBSTITUTION METHOD FOR SOLVING A SYSTEM OF LINEAR EQUATIONS

The **substitution method** is one procedure for solving a system of equations. This method is illustrated in Example 1.

EXAMPLE 1 Solve a System of Equations by the Substitution Method

Solve: $\begin{cases} 3x - 5y = 7 & (1) \\ y = 2x & (2) \end{cases}$

Alternative to Example 1

Solve: $\begin{cases} 5x + 2y = -4 & (1) \\ y = -3x & (2) \end{cases}$

• **(4, −12)**

Algebraic Solution

The solutions of $y = 2x$ are the ordered pairs $(x, 2x)$. For the system of equations to have a solution, ordered pairs of the form $(x, 2x)$ also must be solutions of $3x - 5y = 7$. To determine whether the ordered pairs $(x, 2x)$ are solutions of Equation (1), substitute $(x, 2x)$ into Equation (1) and solve for x. Think of this as *substituting* $2x$ for y.

$$3x - 5y = 7 \qquad \text{• Equation (1)}$$
$$3x - 5(2x) = 7 \qquad \text{• Substitute 2x for y.}$$
$$3x - 10x = 7$$
$$-7x = 7$$
$$x = -1$$

$$y = 2x \qquad \text{• Equation (2)}$$
$$= 2(-1) = -2 \qquad \text{• Substitute −1 for x in Equation 2.}$$

The only ordered-pair solution of the system of equations is $(-1, -2)$. When a system of equations has a unique solution, the system of equations is independent.

Visualize the Solution

Graphing $3x - 5y = 7$ and $y = 2x$ shows that the ordered pair $(-1, -2)$ belongs to both lines. Therefore, $(-1, -2)$ is a solution of the system of equations. See **Figure 6.4.**

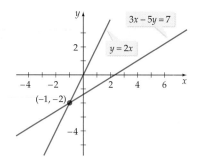

FIGURE 6.4

An independent system of equations

▶ **TRY EXERCISE 6, PAGE 513**

EXAMPLE 2 Identify an Inconsistent System of Equations

Solve: $\begin{cases} x + 3y = 6 & (1) \\ 2x + 6y = -18 & (2) \end{cases}$

Alternative to Example 2

Solve: $\begin{cases} 3x + 2y = -4 & (1) \\ 9x + 6y = -8 & (2) \end{cases}$

• **This system is inconsistent and has no solution.**

Algebraic Solution

Solve Equation (1) for y:

$$x + 3y = 6$$
$$y = -\frac{1}{3}x + 2$$

The solutions of $y = -\frac{1}{3}x + 2$ are the ordered pairs $\left(x, -\frac{1}{3}x + 2\right)$. For the system of equations to have a solution, ordered pairs of this form must also be solutions of $2x + 6y = -18$. To determine whether the

Visualize the Solution

Solving Equations (1) and (2) for y gives $y = -\frac{1}{3}x + 2$ and $y = -\frac{1}{3}x - 3$. Note that these two equations have the same slope, $-\frac{1}{3}$, and different y-intercepts.

ordered pairs $\left(x, -\dfrac{1}{3}x + 2\right)$ are solutions of Equation (2), substitute

$\left(x, -\dfrac{1}{3}x + 2\right)$ into Equation (2) and solve for x.

$$2x + 6y = -18 \qquad \text{• Equation (2)}$$
$$2x + 6\left(-\dfrac{1}{3}x + 2\right) = -18 \qquad \text{• Substitute } -\dfrac{1}{3}x + 2 \text{ for } y.$$
$$2x - 2x + 12 = -18$$
$$12 = -18 \qquad \text{• A false statement}$$

The false statement $12 = -18$ means that no ordered pair that is a solution of Equation (1) is also a solution of Equation (2). The equations have no ordered pairs in common and thus the system of equations has no solution. This is an inconsistent system of equations.

Therefore, the graphs of the two lines are parallel and never intersect. See **Figure 6.5.**

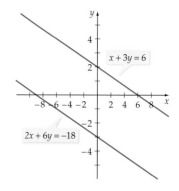

FIGURE 6.5

An inconsistent system of equations

▶ **TRY EXERCISE 18, PAGE 514**

EXAMPLE 3   **Identify a Dependent System of Equations**

Solve: $\begin{cases} 8x - 4y = 16 & (1) \\ 2x - y = 4 & (2) \end{cases}$

Alternative to Example 3

Solve: $\begin{cases} 10x - 5y = 8 & (1) \\ 30x - 15y = 24 & (2) \end{cases}$

⊙ $\left(c, 2c - \dfrac{8}{5}\right)$

Algebraic Solution

Solve Equation (2) for y:

$$2x - y = 4$$
$$y = 2x - 4$$

The solutions of $y = 2x - 4$ are the ordered pairs $(x, 2x - 4)$. For the system of equations to have a solution, ordered pairs of the form $(x, 2x - 4)$ also must be solutions of $8x - 4y = 16$. To determine whether the ordered pairs $(x, 2x - 4)$ are solutions of Equation (1), substitute $(x, 2x - 4)$ into Equation (1) and solve for x.

$$8x - 4y = 16 \qquad \text{• Equation (1)}$$
$$8x - 4(2x - 4) = 16 \qquad \text{• Substitute } 2x - 4 \text{ for } y.$$
$$8x - 8x + 16 = 16$$
$$16 = 16 \qquad \text{• A true statement}$$

The true statement $16 = 16$ means that the ordered pairs $(x, 2x - 4)$ that are solutions of Equation (2) are also solutions of Equation (1). Because x can be replaced by any real number c, the solution of the system of equations is the set of ordered pairs $(c, 2c - 4)$. This is a dependent system of equations.

Visualize the Solution

Solving Equations (1) and (2) for y gives $y = 2x - 4$ and $y = 2x - 4$. Note that these two equations have the same slope, 2, and the same y-intercept, $(0, -4)$. Therefore, the graphs of the two lines are exactly the same. One graph intersects the second graph infinitely often. See **Figure 6.6.**

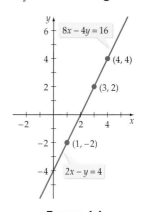

FIGURE 6.6

▶ **TRY EXERCISE 20, PAGE 514**

Some of the specific ordered-pair solutions in Example 3 can be found by choosing various values for c. The table below shows the ordered pairs that result from choosing c as 1, 3, and 4. The ordered pairs $(1, -2)$, $(3, 2)$, and $(4, 4)$ are specific solutions of the system of equations. These points are on the graphs of Equation (1) and Equation (2), as shown in **Figure 6.6.**

c	$(c, 2c - 4)$	(x, y)
1	$(1, 2(1) - 4)$	$(1, -2)$
3	$(3, 2(3) - 4)$	$(3, 2)$
4	$(4, 2(4) - 4)$	$(4, 4)$

Before leaving Example 3, note that there is more than one way to represent the ordered-pair solutions. To illustrate this point, solve Equation (2) for x.

$$2x - y = 4 \qquad \bullet \text{ Equation (2)}$$

$$x = \frac{1}{2}y + 2 \qquad \bullet \text{ Solve for } x.$$

Because y can be replaced by any real number b, there are an infinite number of ordered pairs $\left(\frac{1}{2}b + 2, b\right)$ that are solutions of the system of equations. Choosing b as -2, 2, and 4 gives the same ordered pairs: $(1, -2)$, $(3, 2)$, and $(4, 4)$. There is always more than one way to describe the ordered pairs when writing the solution of a dependent system of equations. For Example 3, either the ordered pairs $(c, 2c - 4)$ or the ordered pairs $\left(\frac{1}{2}b + 2, b\right)$ would generate all the solutions of the system of equations.

take note

When a system of equations is dependent, there is more than one way to write the solutions of the solution set. The solution to Example 3 is the set of ordered pairs

$$(c, 2c - 4) \text{ or } \left(\frac{1}{2}b + 2, b\right)$$

However, there are infinitely more ways in which the ordered pairs could be expressed. For instance, let $b = 2w$. Then

$$\frac{1}{2}b + 2 = \frac{1}{2}(2w) + 2 = w + 2$$

The ordered-pair solutions, written in terms of w, are $(w + 2, 2w)$.

● ELIMINATION METHOD FOR SOLVING A SYSTEM OF EQUATIONS

Two systems of equations are **equivalent** if each system has exactly the same solutions. The systems

$$\begin{cases} 3x + 5y = 9 \\ 2x - 3y = -13 \end{cases} \quad \text{and} \quad \begin{cases} x = -2 \\ y = 3 \end{cases}$$

are equivalent systems of equations. Each system has the solution $(-2, 3)$, as shown in **Figure 6.7.**

A second technique for solving a system of equations is similar to the strategy for solving first-degree equations in one variable. The system of equations is replaced by a series of equivalent systems until the solution is obvious.

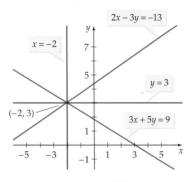

FIGURE 6.7

Operations That Produce Equivalent Systems of Equations

1. Interchange any two equations.

2. Replace an equation with a nonzero multiple of that equation.

3. Replace an equation with the sum of that equation and a nonzero constant multiple of another equation in the system.

Because the order in which the equations are written does not affect the system of equations, interchanging the equations does not affect its solution. The second operation restates the property that says that multiplying each side of an equation by the same nonzero constant does not change the solutions of the equation.

The third operation can be illustrated as follows. Consider the system of equations

$$\begin{cases} 3x + 2y = 10 & (1) \\ 2x - 3y = -2 & (2) \end{cases}$$

Multiply each side of Equation (2) by 2. (Any nonzero number would work.) Add the resulting equation to Equation (1).

$$
\begin{array}{ll}
3x + 2y = 10 & \text{• Equation (1)} \\
\underline{4x - 6y = -4} & \text{• 2 times Equation (2)} \\
7x - 4y = 6 \quad (3) & \text{• Add the equations.}
\end{array}
$$

Replace Equation (1) with the new Equation (3) to produce the following equivalent system of equations.

$$\begin{cases} 7x - 4y = 6 & (3) \\ 2x - 3y = -2 & (2) \end{cases}$$

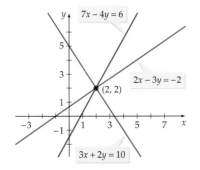

The third property states that the resulting system of equations has the same solutions as the original system and is therefore equivalent to the original system of equations. **Figure 6.8** shows the graph of $7x - 4y = 6$. Note that the line passes through the same point at which the lines of the original system of equations intersect, the point $(2, 2)$.

FIGURE 6.8

EXAMPLE 4   Solve a System of Equations by the Elimination Method

Solve: $\begin{cases} 3x - 4y = 10 & (1) \\ 2x + 5y = -1 & (2) \end{cases}$

Alternative to Example 4

Solve: $\begin{cases} 8x + 5y = 9 & (1) \\ 3x - 2y = -16 & (2) \end{cases}$

● $(-2, 5)$

Algebraic Solution

Use the operations that produce equivalent equations to eliminate a variable from one of the equations. We will eliminate x from Equation (2) by multiplying each equation by a different constant so as to have a new system of equations in which the coefficients of x are additive inverses.

$$
\begin{array}{ll}
6x - 8y = 20 & \text{• 2 times Equation (1)} \\
\underline{-6x - 15y = 3} & \text{• -3 times Equation (2)} \\
 -23y = 23 & \text{• Add the equations.} \\
 y = -1 & \text{• Solve for y.}
\end{array}
$$

Solve Equation (1) for x by substituting -1 for y.

$$3x - 4(-1) = 10$$
$$3x = 6$$
$$x = 2$$

The solution of the system of equations is $(2, -1)$.

Visualize the Solution

Graphing $3x - 4y = 10$ and $2x + 5y = -1$ shows that $(2, -1)$ belongs to both lines. Therefore, $(2, -1)$ is a solution of the system of equations. See **Figure 6.9**.

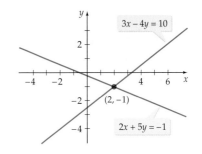

FIGURE 6.9

▶ **TRY EXERCISE 24, PAGE 514**

The method just described is called the **elimination method** for solving a system of equations, because it involves *eliminating* a variable from one of the equations.

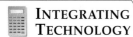
INTEGRATING TECHNOLOGY

You can use a graphing calculator to solve a system of equations in two variables. First, algebraically solve each equation for y.

Solve for y.

$$3x - 4y = 10 \quad \rightarrow \quad y = 0.75x - 2.5$$
$$2x + 5y = -1 \quad \rightarrow \quad y = -0.4x - 0.2$$

Now graph the equations. Enter **0.75X-2.5** into Y_1 and **-0.4X-0.2** into Y_2 and graph the two equations in the standard viewing window. The sequence of steps shown in **Figure 6.10** can be used to find the point of intersection with a TI-83 calculator.

Press [2nd] CALC.
Select 5: intersect.
Press [ENTER].

The "First curve?" shown on the bottom of the screen means to select the first of the two graphs that intersect. Just press [ENTER].

The "Second curve?" shown on the bottom of the screen means to select the second of the two graphs that intersect. Just press [ENTER].

```
CALCULATE
1: value
2: zero
3: minimum
4: maximum
5: intersect
6: dy/dx
7: ∫f(x)dx
```

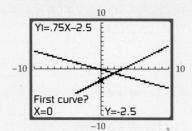

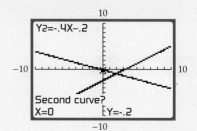

"Guess?" is shown on the bottom of the screen. Move the cursor until it is approximately on the point of intersection. Press [ENTER].

The coordinates of the point of intersection $(2, -1)$ are shown at the bottom of the screen.

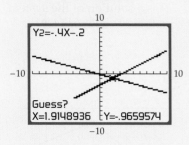

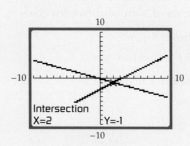

FIGURE 6.10

For the system of equations in Example 4, the intersection of the two graphs occurs at a point in the standard viewing window. If the point of intersection does not appear on the screen, you must adjust the viewing window so that the point of intersection is visible.

Alternative to Example 5

Solve: $\begin{cases} 2x + 6y = 4 & (1) \\ 5x + 15y = 10 & (2) \end{cases}$

• **Answers may vary but might include**

$\left(c, -\dfrac{1}{3}c + \dfrac{2}{3} \right)$ or $(-3b + 2, b)$.

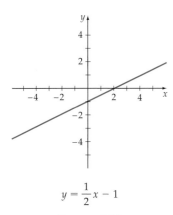

$y = \dfrac{1}{2}x - 1$

FIGURE 6.11

---

take note

Referring again to Example 5 and solving Equation (1) for x, we have x = 2y + 2. Because y can be any real number b, the ordered-pair solutions of the system of equations can also be written as (2b + 2, b).

EXAMPLE 5   Solve a Dependent System of Equations

Solve: $\begin{cases} x - 2y = 2 & (1) \\ 3x - 6y = 6 & (2) \end{cases}$

Solution

Eliminate x by multiplying Equation (2) by $-\dfrac{1}{3}$ and then adding the result to Equation (1).

$$x - 2y = 2 \qquad \text{• Equation (1)}$$
$$\underline{-x + 2y = -2} \qquad \text{• } -\dfrac{1}{3} \text{ times Equation (2)}$$
$$0 = 0 \qquad \text{• Add the two equations.}$$

Replace Equation (2) by $0 = 0$.

$$\begin{cases} x - 2y = 2 \\ 0 = 0 \end{cases} \qquad \text{• This is an equivalent system of equations.}$$

Because the equation $0 = 0$ is an identity, an ordered pair that is a solution of Equation (1) is also a solution of $0 = 0$. Thus the solutions are the solutions of $x - 2y = 2$. Solving for y, we find that $y = \dfrac{1}{2}x - 1$.

Because x can be replaced by any real number c, the solutions of the system of equations are the ordered pairs $\left(c, \dfrac{1}{2}c - 1 \right)$. See **Figure 6.11**.

▶ **TRY EXERCISE 28, PAGE 514**

If one equation of the system of equations is replaced by a false equation, the system of equations has no solution. For example, the system of equations

$$\begin{cases} x + y = 4 \\ 0 = 5 \end{cases}$$

has no solution because the second equation is false for any choice of x and y.

• APPLICATIONS OF SYSTEMS OF EQUATIONS

Consider the situation of a Corvette car dealership. If the dealership were willing to sell a Corvette for $10, there would be many consumers willing to buy a Corvette. The problem with this plan is that the dealership would soon be out of business. On the other hand, if the dealership tried to sell each Corvette for $1 million, the dealership would not sell any cars and would still go out of business. Between $10 and $1 million, there is a price at which a dealership can sell Corvettes (and stay in business) and at which consumers are willing to pay that price. This price is referred to as the **equilibrium price**.

Economists refer to these types of problems as **supply-demand problems**. Businesses are willing to *supply* a product at a certain price and there is consumer *demand* for the product at that price. To find the equilibrium point, a system of equations is created. One equation of the system is the demand model of the business. The second equation is the supply model of the consumer.

Alternative to Example 6
The number x of laptop computers a manufacturer is willing to sell at price p, in dollars, is given by $x = \dfrac{9}{5}p - 1530$. The number of laptop computers a computer store is willing to purchase at price p is given by $x = -\dfrac{3}{10}p + 780$. Find the equilibrium price.
● **$1100**

EXAMPLE 6   Solve a Supply-Demand Problem

Suppose that the number of bushels x of apples a farmer is willing to sell is given by $x = 100p - 25$, where p is the price, in dollars, per bushel of apples. The number of bushels x of apples a grocer is willing to purchase is given by $x = -150p + 655$, where p is the price per bushel of apples. Find the equilibrium price.

Solution

Using the supply and demand equations, we have the system of equations

$$\begin{cases} x = 100p - 25 \\ x = -150p + 655 \end{cases}$$

Solve the system of equations by substitution.

$$-150p + 655 = 100p - 25$$
$$-250p + 655 = -25 \qquad \text{• Subtract } 100p \text{ from each side.}$$
$$-250p = -680 \qquad \text{• Subtract } 655 \text{ from each side.}$$
$$p = 2.72 \qquad \text{• Divide by } -250.$$

The equilibrium price is $2.72 per bushel.

▶ **TRY EXERCISE 42, PAGE 514**

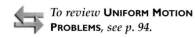
To review **UNIFORM MOTION PROBLEMS**, *see p. 94.*

As the application problems we studied earlier in the text become more complicated, a system of equations may be the method for solving these problems. The next example involves the distance-rate-time equation $d = rt$.

Alternative to Example 7
A plane flying with the wind traveled 700 miles in 2 hours. Flying against the wind, the plane traveled only 660 miles in 2 hours. Find the rate of the plane in calm air and the rate of the wind.
● **The rate of the plane in calm air is 340 mph. The rate of the wind is 10 mph.**

EXAMPLE 7   Solve an Application to River Currents

A rowing team rowing with the current traveled 18 miles in 2 hours. Against the current, the team rowed 10 miles in 2 hours. Find the rate of the boat in calm water and the rate of the current.

Solution

Let r_1 represent the rate of the boat in calm water, and let r_2 represent the rate of the current.

The rate of the boat *with the current* is $r_1 + r_2$.

The rate of the boat *against the current* is $r_1 - r_2$.

Because the rowing team traveled 18 miles in 2 hours with the current, we use the equation $d = rt$.

$$d = r \cdot t$$
$$18 = (r_1 + r_2) \cdot 2 \qquad \bullet\ d = 18, t = 2$$
$$9 = r_1 + r_2 \qquad\qquad \bullet\ \textbf{Divide each side by 2.}$$

Because the team rowed 10 miles in 2 hours against the current, we write

$$10 = (r_1 - r_2) \cdot 2 \qquad \bullet\ d = 10, t = 2$$
$$5 = r_1 - r_2 \qquad\qquad \bullet\ \textbf{Divide each side by 2.}$$

Thus we have a system of two linear equations in the variables r_1 and r_2.

$$\begin{cases} 9 = r_1 + r_2 \\ 5 = r_1 - r_2 \end{cases}$$

Solving the system by using the elimination method, we find that r_1 is 7 mph and r_2 is 2 mph. Thus the rate of the boat in calm water is 7 mph and the rate of the current is 2 mph. You should verify these solutions.

▶ **TRY EXERCISE 46, PAGE 514**

TOPICS FOR DISCUSSION

1. Explain how to use the substitution method to solve a system of equations.

2. Explain how to use the elimination method to solve a system of equations.

3. Give an example of a system of equations in two variables that is

   a. independent   b. dependent   c. inconsistent

4. If a linear system of equations in two variables has no solution, what does that mean about the graphs of the equations of the system?

5. If $A = \{(x, y) \mid x + y = 5\}$ and $B = \{(x, y) \mid x - y = 3\}$, explain the meaning of $A \cap B$.

EXERCISE SET 6.1   —*Suggested Assignment: Exercises 1–61, every other odd; 63, 65, 72–77.*

In Exercises 1 to 20, solve each system of equations by the substitution method.

1. $\begin{cases} 2x - 3y = 16 \\ x = 2 \end{cases}$ $(2, -4)$

2. $\begin{cases} 3x - 2y = -11 \\ y = 1 \end{cases}$ $(-3, 1)$

3. $\begin{cases} 3x + 4y = 18 \\ y = -2x + 3 \end{cases}$ $\left(-\dfrac{6}{5}, \dfrac{27}{5}\right)$

4. $\begin{cases} 5x - 4y = -22 \\ y = 5x - 2 \end{cases}$ $(2, 8)$

5. $\begin{cases} -2x + 3y = 6 \\ x = 2y - 5 \end{cases}$ $(3, 4)$

▶ **6.** $\begin{cases} 8x + 3y = -7 \\ x = 3y + 15 \end{cases}$ $\left(\dfrac{8}{9}, -\dfrac{127}{27}\right)$

7. $\begin{cases} 6x + 5y = 1 \\ x - 3y = 4 \end{cases}$ $(1, -1)$

8. $\begin{cases} -3x + 7y = 14 \\ 2x - y = -13 \end{cases}$ $(-7, -1)$

9. $\begin{cases} 7x + 6y = -3 \\ y = \dfrac{2}{3}x - 6 \end{cases}$ $(3, -4)$

10. $\begin{cases} 9x - 4y = 3 \\ x = \dfrac{4}{3}y + 3 \end{cases}$ $(-1, -3)$

11. $\begin{cases} y = 4x - 3 \\ y = 3x - 1 \end{cases}$ $(2, 5)$

12. $\begin{cases} y = 5x + 1 \\ y = 4x - 2 \end{cases}$ $(-3, -14)$

13. $\begin{cases} y = 5x + 4 \\ x = -3y - 4 \end{cases}$ $(-1, -1)$ **14.** $\begin{cases} y = -2x - 6 \\ x = -2y - 2 \end{cases}$ $\left(-\dfrac{10}{3}, \dfrac{2}{3}\right)$

15. $\begin{cases} 3x - 4y = 2 \\ 4x + 3y = 14 \end{cases}$ $\left(\dfrac{62}{25}, \dfrac{34}{25}\right)$ **16.** $\begin{cases} 6x + 7y = -4 \\ 2x + 5y = 4 \end{cases}$ $(-3, 2)$

17. $\begin{cases} 3x - 3y = 5 \\ 4x - 4y = 9 \end{cases}$ no solution   ▶ **18.** $\begin{cases} 3x - 4y = 8 \\ 6x - 8y = 9 \end{cases}$ no solution

19. $\begin{cases} 4x + 3y = 6 \\ \\ y = -\dfrac{4}{3}x + 2 \end{cases}$ $\left(c, -\dfrac{4}{3}c + 2\right)$ ▶ **20.** $\begin{cases} 5x + 2y = 2 \\ \\ y = -\dfrac{5}{2}x + 1 \end{cases}$ $\left(c, -\dfrac{5}{2}c + 1\right)$

In Exercises 21 to 40, solve each system of equations by the elimination method.

21. $\begin{cases} 3x - y = 10 \\ 4x + 3y = -4 \end{cases}$ $(2, -4)$ **22.** $\begin{cases} 3x + 4y = -5 \\ x - 5y = -8 \end{cases}$ $(-3, 1)$

23. $\begin{cases} 4x + 7y = 21 \\ 5x - 4y = -12 \end{cases}$ $(0, 3)$ ▶ **24.** $\begin{cases} 3x - 8y = -6 \\ -5x + 4y = 10 \end{cases}$ $(-2, 0)$

25. $\begin{cases} 5x - 3y = 0 \\ 10x - 6y = 0 \end{cases}$ $\left(\dfrac{3}{5}c, c\right)$ **26.** $\begin{cases} 3x + 2y = 0 \\ 2x + 3y = 0 \end{cases}$ $(0, 0)$

27. $\begin{cases} 6x + 6y = 1 \\ 4x + 9y = 4 \end{cases}$ $\left(-\dfrac{1}{2}, \dfrac{2}{3}\right)$ ▶ **28.** $\begin{cases} 4x + 5y = 2 \\ 8x - 15y = 9 \end{cases}$ $\left(\dfrac{3}{4}, -\dfrac{1}{5}\right)$

29. $\begin{cases} 3x + 6y = 11 \\ 2x + 4y = 9 \end{cases}$ no solution   **30.** $\begin{cases} 4x - 2y = 9 \\ 2x - y = 3 \end{cases}$ no solution

31. $\begin{cases} \dfrac{5}{6}x - \dfrac{1}{3}y = -6 \\ \\ \dfrac{1}{6}x + \dfrac{2}{3}y = 1 \end{cases}$ $(-6, 3)$ **32.** $\begin{cases} \dfrac{3}{4}x + \dfrac{2}{5}y = 1 \\ \\ \dfrac{1}{2}x - \dfrac{3}{5}y = -1 \end{cases}$ $\left(\dfrac{4}{13}, \dfrac{25}{13}\right)$

33. $\begin{cases} \dfrac{3}{4}x + \dfrac{1}{3}y = 1 \\ \\ \dfrac{1}{2}x + \dfrac{2}{3}y = 0 \end{cases}$ $\left(2, -\dfrac{3}{2}\right)$ **34.** $\begin{cases} \dfrac{3}{5}x - \dfrac{2}{3}y = 7 \\ \\ \dfrac{2}{5}x - \dfrac{5}{6}y = 7 \end{cases}$ $(5, -6)$

35. $\begin{cases} 2\sqrt{3}x - 3y = 3 \\ 3\sqrt{3}x + 2y = 24 \end{cases}$ $(2\sqrt{3}, 3)$ **36.** $\begin{cases} 4x - 3\sqrt{5}y = -19 \\ 3x + 4\sqrt{5}y = 17 \end{cases}$ $(-1, \sqrt{5})$

37. $\begin{cases} 3\pi x - 4y = 6 \\ 2\pi x + 3y = 5 \end{cases}$ $\left(\dfrac{38}{17\pi}, \dfrac{3}{17}\right)$ **38.** $\begin{cases} 2x - 5\pi y = 3 \\ 3x + 4\pi y = 2 \end{cases}$ $\left(\dfrac{22}{23}, -\dfrac{5}{23\pi}\right)$

39. $\begin{cases} 3\sqrt{2}x - 4\sqrt{3}y = -6 \\ 2\sqrt{2}x + 3\sqrt{3}y = 13 \end{cases}$ $(\sqrt{2}, \sqrt{3})$

40. $\begin{cases} 2\sqrt{2}x + 3\sqrt{5}y = 7 \\ 3\sqrt{2}x - \sqrt{5}y = -17 \end{cases}$ $(-2\sqrt{2}, \sqrt{5})$

In Exercises 41 to 61, solve by using a system of equations.

41. SUPPLY/DEMAND The number x of MP3 players a manufacturer is willing to sell is given by $x = 20p - 2000$, where p is the price, in dollars, per MP3 player. The number x of MP3 players a store is willing to purchase is given by $x = -4p + 1000$, where p is the price per MP3 player. Find the equilibrium price. $125

▶ **42. SUPPLY/DEMAND** The number x of digital cameras a manufacturer is willing to sell is given by $x = 25p - 500$, where p is the price, in dollars, per digital camera. The number x of digital cameras a store is willing to purchase is given by $x = -7p + 1100$, where p is the price per digital camera. Find the equilibrium price. $50

43. RATE OF WIND Flying with the wind, a plane traveled 450 miles in 3 hours. Flying against the wind, the plane traveled the same distance in 5 hours. Find the rate of the plane in calm air and the rate of the wind.
plane: 120 mph, wind: 30 mph

44. RATE OF WIND A plane flew 800 miles in 4 hours while flying with the wind. Against the wind, it took the plane 5 hours to travel 800 miles. Find the rate of the plane in calm air and the rate of the wind. plane = 180 mph
wind = 20 mph

45. RATE OF CURRENT A motorboat traveled a distance of 120 miles in 4 hours while traveling with the current. Against the current, the same trip took 6 hours. Find the rate of the boat in calm water and the rate of the current.
boat: 25 mph, current: 5 mph

▶ **46. RATE OF CURRENT** A canoeist can row 12 miles with the current in 2 hours. Rowing against the current, it takes the canoeist 4 hours to travel the same distance. Find the rate of the canoeist in calm water and the rate of the current.
canoeist: 4.5 mph; current: 1.5 mph

47. METALLURGY A metallurgist made two purchases. The first purchase, which cost $1080, included 30 kilograms of an iron alloy and 45 kilograms of a lead alloy. The second purchase, at the same prices, cost $372 and included 15 kilograms of the iron alloy and 12 kilograms of the lead alloy. Find the cost per kilogram of the iron and lead alloys. $12/kg for iron, $16/kg for lead

48. CHEMISTRY For $14.10, a chemist purchased 10 liters of hydrochloric acid and 15 liters of silver nitrate. A second purchase, at the same prices, cost $18.16 and included 12 liters of hydrochloric acid and 20 liters of silver nitrate. Find the cost per liter of each of the two chemicals.
hydrochloric acid: $0.48/1; silver nitrate: $0.62/1

49. CHEMISTRY A goldsmith has two gold alloys. The first alloy is 40% gold; the second alloy is 60% gold. How many grams of each should be mixed to produce 20 grams of an alloy that is 52% gold?
8 g of 40% gold, 12 g of 60% gold

50. CHEMISTRY One acetic acid solution is 70% water and another is 30% water. How many liters of each solution should be mixed to produce 20 liters of a solution that is 40% water? 70% solution: 5 l; 30% solution: 15 l

51. GEOMETRY A right triangle in the first quadrant is bounded by the lines $y = 0$, $y = \frac{1}{2}x$, and $y = -2x + 6$. Find its area. $\frac{9}{5}$ square units

52. GEOMETRY The lines whose equations are $2x + 3y = 1$, $3x - 4y = 10$, and $4x + ky = 5$ all intersect at the same point. What is the value of k? 3

53. NUMBER THEORY Adding a three-digit number 5Z7 to 256 gives XY3. If XY3 is divisible by 3, then what is the largest possible value of Z? 8

54. NUMBER THEORY Find the value of k if $2x + 5 = 6x + k = 4x - 7$. -19

55. NUMBER THEORY A *Pythagorean triple* is three positive integers a, b, and c for which $a^2 + b^2 = c^2$. Given $a = 42$, find all the values of b and c such that a, b, and c form a Pythagorean triple. (*Suggestion:* If $a = 42$, then $1764 + b^2 = c^2$ or $1764 = c^2 - b^2 = (c - b)(c + b)$. Because $(c - b)(c + b) = 1764$, $c - b$ and $b + c$ must be factors of 1764. For instance, one possibility is $2 = c - b$ and $882 = c + b$. Solving this system of equations yields one set of Pythagorean triples. Now repeat for other possible factors of 1764. Remember that answers must be positive integers.)
42, 56, 70; 42, 40, 58; 42, 144, 150; 42, 440, 442

56. NUMBER THEORY Given $a = 30$, find all the values of b and c such that a, b, and c form a Pythagorean triple. (See the preceding exercise.)
30, 16, 34; 30, 40, 50; 30, 72, 78; 30, 224, 226

57. MARKETING A marketing company asked 100 people whether they liked a new skin cream and lip balm. The company found that 80% of the people who liked the new skin cream also liked the new lip balm and that 50% of the people who did not like the skin cream liked the new lip

balm. If 77 people liked the lip balm, how many people liked the skin cream? 90 people

58. FIRE SCIENCE An analysis of 200 scores on a firefighter qualifying exam found that 75% of those who passed the basic fire science exam also passed the exam on containing chemical fires. Of those who did not pass the basic fire science exam, 25% passed the exam on containing chemical fires. If 120 people passed the exam on containing chemical fires, how many people passed the basic fire science exam? 140 people

59. INCOME TAX The chapter opener on page 503 shows the graph of the income tax a taxpayer pays for various income levels for both a flat tax and variable tax brackets. Given that the equation of the line in red is $T = 0.25I - 3190$ for $28,400 < I \le 68,800$, find and interpret the point at which the flat tax graph crosses the variable tax bracket graph. (*Suggestion:* Use the fact that flat tax is 20% of adjusted gross income to find the equation of the line in black. Now solve a system of equations.)
See answer below.

60. INCOME TAX The chapter opener on page 503 shows the graph of the income tax a taxpayer pays for various income levels for both a flat tax and variable tax brackets. The equation of the line segment in green is $T = 0.10I$ for $0 \le I \le 7000$; the equation of the line segment in blue is $T = 0.15I - 350$ for $7000 < I \le 28,400$; the equation of the line segment in red is $T = 0.25I - 3190$ for $28,400 < I \le 68,800$. If the flat-tax proposal for each taxpayer is reduced to 14%, does the line representing the flat-tax proposal intersect the green, blue, or red line segment? What is the point of intersection? red; (29,000, 4060)

61. INVESTMENT A broker invests $25,000 of a client's money in two different bond funds. The annual rate of return on one bond fund is 6%, and the annual rate of return on the second bond fund is 6.5%. The investor receives a total annual interest payment from the two bond funds of $1555. Find the amount invested in each fund.
$14,000 at 6%, $11,000 at 6.5%

59. (63,800, 12,760). This point indicates that a person with an adjusted gross income of $63,800 would pay the same tax using either tax method.

CONNECTING CONCEPTS

In Exercises 62 to 71, solve for x and y. Use the fact that if $z_1 = a_1 + b_1i$ and $z_2 = a_2 + b_2i$ are two complex numbers, then $z_1 = z_2$ if and only if $a_1 = a_2$ and $b_1 = b_2$.

62. $(2 + i)x + (3 - i)y = 7$ $x = \frac{7}{5}, y = \frac{7}{5}$

63. $(3 + 2i)x + (4 - 3i)y = 2 - 16i$ $x = -\frac{58}{17}, y = \frac{52}{17}$

64. $(4 - 3i)x + (5 + 2i)y = 11 + 9i$ $x = -1, y = 3$

65. $(2 + 6i)x + (4 - 5i)y = -8 - 7i$ $x = -2, y = -1$

66. $(-3 - i)x - (4 + 2i)y = 1 - i$ $x = -3, y = 2$

67. $(5 - 2i)x + (-3 - 4i)y = 12 - 35i$ $x = \frac{153}{26}, y = \frac{151}{26}$

68. $\begin{cases} 2x + 5y = 11 + 3i \\ 3x + y = 10 - 2i \end{cases}$
$x = 3 - i, y = 1 + i$

69. $\begin{cases} 4x + 3y = 11 + 6i \\ 3x - 5y = 1 + 19i \end{cases}$
$x = 2 + 3i, y = 1 - 2i$

70. $\begin{cases} 2x + 3y = 11 + 5i \\ 3x - 3y = 9 - 15i \end{cases}$
$x = 4 - 2i, y = 1 + 3i$

71. $\begin{cases} 5x - 4y = 15 - 41i \\ 3x + 5y = 9 + 5i \end{cases}$
$x = 3 - 5i, y = 4i$

PREPARE FOR SECTION 6.2
---

72. Solve $2x - 5y = 15$ for y. [1.1] $y = \dfrac{2}{5}x - 3$

73. If $x = 2c + 1$, $y = -c + 3$, and $z = 2x + 5y - 4$, write z in terms of c. [P.1] $z = -c + 13$

74. Solve: $\begin{cases} 5x - 2y = 10 \\ 2y = 8 \end{cases}$ [6.1] $\left(\dfrac{18}{5}, 4\right)$

75. Solve: $\begin{cases} 3x - y = 11 \\ 2x + 3y = -11 \end{cases}$ [6.1] $(2, -5)$

76. Solve: $\begin{cases} y = 3x - 4 \\ y = 4x - 2 \end{cases}$ [6.1] $(-2, -10)$

77. Solve: $\begin{cases} 4x + y = 9 \\ -8x - 2y = -18 \end{cases}$ [6.1] $(c, -4c + 9)$

PROJECTS

I. INDEPENDENT AND DEPENDENT CONDITIONS Consider the following problem: "Maria and Michael drove from Los Angeles to New York in 60 hours. How long did Maria drive?" It is difficult to answer this question. She may have driven all 60 hours while Michael relaxed, or she may have relaxed while Michael drove all 60 hours. The difficulty is that there are two unknowns (how long each drove) and only one condition (the total driving time) relating the unknowns. If we added another condition, such as Michael drove 25 hours, then we could determine how long Maria drove, 35 hours. In most cases, an application problem will have a single answer only when there are as many *independent* conditions as there are variables. Conditions are independent if knowing one does *not* enable you to know the other.

Here is an example of conditions that are not independent. "The perimeter of a rectangle is 50 meters. The sum of the width and length is 25 meters." To see that these conditions are dependent, write the perimeter equation and divide each side by 2.

$$2w + 2l = 50$$
$$w + l = 25 \qquad \bullet \textbf{ Divide each side by 2.}$$

Note that the resulting equation is the second condition: the sum of the width and length is 25. Thus, knowing the first condition enables us to determine the second condition. The conditions are not independent, so there is no one solution to this problem.

For each of the following problems, determine whether the conditions are independent or dependent. For those problems that have independent conditions, find the solution (if possible). For those problems for which the conditions are dependent, find two solutions.

a. The sum of two numbers is 30. The difference between the two numbers is 10. Find the numbers.

b. The area of a square is 25 square meters. Find the length of each side.

c. The area of a rectangle is 25 square meters. Find the length of each side.

d. Emily spent $1000 for carpeting and tile. Carpeting cost $20 per square yard and tile cost $30 per square yard. How many square yards of each did she purchase?

e. The sum of two numbers is 20. Twice the smaller number is 10 minus twice the larger number. Find the two numbers.

f. Make up a word problem for which there are two independent conditions. Solve the problem.

g. Make up a word problem for which there are two dependent conditions. Find at least two solutions.

SYSTEMS OF LINEAR EQUATIONS IN MORE THAN TWO VARIABLES

● SYSTEMS OF EQUATIONS IN THREE VARIABLES

An equation of the form $Ax + By + Cz = D$, with A, B, and C not all zero, is a linear equation in three variables. A solution of an equation in three variables is an **ordered triple** (x, y, z).

The ordered triple $(2, -1, -3)$ is one of the solutions of the equation $2x - 3y + z = 4$. The ordered triple $(3, 1, 1)$ is another solution. In fact, an infinite number of ordered triples are solutions of the equation.

Graphing an equation in three variables requires a third coordinate axis perpendicular to the xy-plane. This third axis is commonly called the **z-axis.** The result is a three-dimensional coordinate system called the xyz-coordinate system (**Figure 6.12**). To help visualize a three-dimensional coordinate system, think of a corner of a room: the floor is the xy-plane, one wall is the yz-plane, and the other wall is the xz-plane.

Graphing an ordered triple requires three moves, the first along the x-axis, the second along the y-axis, and the third along the z-axis. **Figure 6.13** is the graph of the points $(-5, -4, 3)$ and $(4, 5, -2)$.

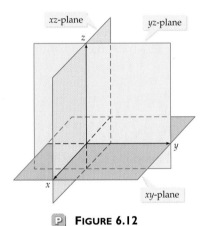

FIGURE 6.12

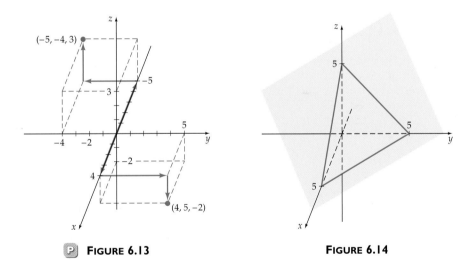

FIGURE 6.13   **FIGURE 6.14**

The graph of a linear equation in three variables is a plane. That is, if all the solutions of a linear equation in three variables were plotted in an xyz-coordinate system, the graph would look like a large, flat piece of paper with infinite extent. **Figure 6.14** is a portion of the graph of $x + y + z = 5$.

There are different ways in which three planes can be oriented in an xyz-coordinate system. **Figure 6.15** illustrates several ways.

For a linear system of equations in three variables to have a solution, the graphs of the planes must intersect at a single point, they must intersect along a common line, or all equations must have a graph that is the same plane. In **Figure 6.15,** the graphs in (a), (b), and (c) represent systems of equations that

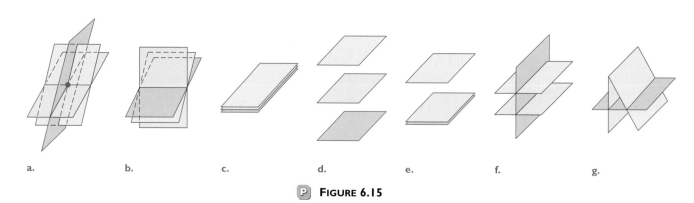

a.   b.   c.   d.   e.   f.   g.

P **FIGURE 6.15**

have a solution. The system of equations represented in **Figure 6.15a** is a consistent system of equations. **Figures 6.15b** and **6.15c** are graphs of a dependent system of equations. The remaining graphs are examples of inconsistent systems of equations.

A system of equations in more than two variables can be solved by using the substitution method or the elimination method. To illustrate the substitution method, consider the system of equations

$$\begin{cases} x - 2y + z = 7 & (1) \\ 2x + y - z = 0 & (2) \\ 3x + 2y - 2z = -2 & (3) \end{cases}$$

Solve Equation (1) for x and substitute the result into Equations (2) and (3).

$$x = 2y - z + 7 \quad (4)$$

$2(2y - z + 7) + y - z = 0$ • **Substitute $2y - z + 7$ for x in Equation (2).**

$4y - 2z + 14 + y - z = 0$ • **Simplify.**

$$5y - 3z = -14 \quad (5)$$

$3(2y - z + 7) + 2y - 2z = -2$ • **Substitute $2y - z + 7$ for x in Equation (3).**

$6y - 3z + 21 + 2y - 2z = -2$ • **Simplify.**

$$8y - 5z = -23 \quad (6)$$

Now solve the system of equations formed from Equations (5) and (6).

$$\begin{cases} 5y - 3z = -14 & \text{multiply by 8} \rightarrow \quad 40y - 24z = -112 \\ 8y - 5z = -23 & \text{multiply by } -5 \rightarrow \quad -40y + 25z = 115 \end{cases}$$
$$z = 3$$

INSTRUCTOR NOTE

If three-dimensional graphing software is available, a graph of the three planes

$x - 2y + z = 7$
$2x + y - z = 0$
$3x + 2y - 2z = -2$

can be drawn and the point of intersection $(2, -1, 3)$ indicated.

Substitute 3 for z into Equation (5) and solve for y.

$$5y - 3z = -14 \quad \text{• Equation (5)}$$
$$5y - 3(3) = -14$$
$$5y - 9 = -14$$
$$5y = -5$$
$$y = -1$$

Substitute -1 for y and 3 for z into Equation (4) and solve for x.

$$x = 2y - z + 7 = 2(-1) - (3) + 7 = 2$$

The ordered-triple solution is $(2, -1, 3)$. The graphs of the three planes intersect at a single point.

● TRIANGULAR FORM

There are many approaches one can take to determine the solution of a system of equations by the elimination method. For consistency, we will always follow a plan that produces an equivalent system of equations in **triangular form.** Three examples of systems of equations in triangular form are

$$\begin{cases} 2x - 3y + z = -4 \\ \quad\quad 2y + 3z = 9 \\ \quad\quad\quad\quad -2z = -2 \end{cases} \quad \begin{cases} w + 3x - 2y + 3z = 0 \\ \quad\quad 2x - y + 4z = 8 \\ \quad\quad\quad\quad -3y - 2z = -1 \\ \quad\quad\quad\quad\quad\quad 3z = 9 \end{cases} \quad \begin{cases} 3x - 4y + z = 1 \\ \quad\quad 3y + 2z = 3 \end{cases}$$

Once a system of equations is written in triangular form, the solution can be found by *back substitution*—that is, by solving the last equation of the system and substituting *back* into the previous equation. This process is continued until the value of each variable has been found.

As an example of solving a system of equations by back substitution, consider the following system of equations in triangular form.

$$\begin{cases} 2x - 4y + z = -3 & (1) \\ \quad\quad 3y - 2z = 9 & (2) \\ \quad\quad\quad\quad 3z = -9 & (3) \end{cases}$$

Solve Equation (3) for z. Substitute the value of z into Equation (2) and solve for y.

$$3z = -9 \quad \text{• Equation (3)} \quad\quad\quad 3y - 2z = 9 \quad \text{• Equation (2)}$$
$$z = -3 \quad\quad\quad\quad\quad\quad\quad\quad\quad 3y - 2(-3) = 9 \quad \text{• z = -3}$$
$$\quad\quad\quad\quad\quad\quad\quad\quad\quad\quad\quad\quad 3y = 3$$
$$\quad\quad\quad\quad\quad\quad\quad\quad\quad\quad\quad\quad y = 1$$

Replace z by -3 and y by 1 in Equation (1) and then solve for x.

$$2x - 4y + z = -3 \quad \text{• Equation (1)}$$
$$2x - 4(1) + (-3) = -3$$
$$2x - 7 = -3$$
$$x = 2$$

The solution is the ordered triple $(2, 1, -3)$.

? **QUESTION**   What is the solution of $\begin{cases} x + 2y + z = 2 \\ \quad\quad y - z = 3? \\ \quad\quad\quad\quad z = 2 \end{cases}$

? **ANSWER** $(-10, 5, 2)$

Alternative to Example 1

Solve: $\begin{cases} x - 2y - z = -5 & (1) \\ 3x + y + z = 9 & (2) \\ 2x - y - z = 1 & (3) \end{cases}$

⊙ **(2, 4, −1)**

INSTRUCTOR NOTE

We often find the solution of a system of equations by producing an equivalent system of equations in triangular form. This will help prepare students for row reduction of matrices in the next chapter. It may be helpful to point out to students that this method is not always the quickest way to the solution. However, the method always works.

> **EXAMPLE 1**   Solve an Independent System of Equations

Solve: $\begin{cases} x + 2y - z = 1 & (1) \\ 2x - y + z = 6 & (2) \\ 2x - y - z = 0 & (3) \end{cases}$

Solution

Eliminate x from Equation (2) by multiplying Equation (1) by -2 and then adding it to Equation (2). Replace Equation (2) by the new equation.

$$\begin{array}{rl} -2x - 4y + 2z = -2 & \quad \bullet \ -2 \text{ times Equation (1)} \\ \underline{2x - y + z = 6} & \quad \bullet \ \text{Equation (2)} \\ -5y + 3z = 4 & \quad \bullet \ \text{Add the equations.} \end{array}$$

$\begin{cases} x + 2y - z = 1 & (1) \\ -5y + 3z = 4 & (4) \quad \bullet \ \text{Replace Equation (2).} \\ 2x - y - z = 0 & (3) \end{cases}$

Eliminate x from Equation (3) by multiplying Equation (1) by -2 and adding it to Equation (3). Replace Equation (3) by the new equation.

$$\begin{array}{rl} -2x - 4y + 2z = -2 & \quad \bullet \ -2 \text{ times Equation (1)} \\ \underline{2x - y - z = 0} & \quad \bullet \ \text{Equation (3)} \\ -5y + z = -2 & \quad \bullet \ \text{Add the equations.} \end{array}$$

$\begin{cases} x + 2y - z = 1 & (1) \\ -5y + 3z = 4 & (4) \\ -5y + z = -2 & (5) \quad \bullet \ \text{Replace Equation (3).} \end{cases}$

Eliminate y from Equation (5) by multiplying Equation (4) by -1 and then adding it to Equation (5). Replace Equation (5) by the new equation.

$$\begin{array}{rl} 5y - 3z = -4 & \quad \bullet \ -1 \text{ times Equation (4)} \\ \underline{-5y + z = -2} & \quad \bullet \ \text{Equation (5)} \\ -2z = -6 & \quad \bullet \ \text{Add the equations.} \end{array}$$

$\begin{cases} x + 2y - z = 1 & (1) \\ -5y + 3z = 4 & (4) \\ -2z = -6 & (6) \quad \bullet \ \text{Replace Equation (5).} \end{cases}$

The system of equations is now in triangular form. Solve the system of equations by back substitution.

Solve Equation (6) for z. Substitute the value into Equation (4) and then solve for y.

$$\begin{array}{ll} -2z = -6 \quad \bullet \ \text{Equation (6)} & \qquad -5y + 3z = 4 \quad \bullet \ \text{Equation (4)} \\ z = 3 & \qquad -5y + 3(3) = 4 \quad \bullet \ \text{Replace z by 3.} \\ & \qquad -5y = -5 \quad \bullet \ \text{Solve for y.} \\ & \qquad y = 1 \end{array}$$

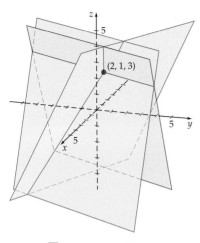

(P) **FIGURE 6.16**

Alternative to Example 2

$$\text{Solve: } \begin{cases} 4x - 2y + 5z = 11 & (1) \\ -2x + 3y - z = -2 & (2) \\ 2x + y + 4z = 9 & (3) \end{cases}$$

○ There is more than one correct way to write the answer. One way is
$$\left(-\frac{13}{8}c + \frac{29}{8}, -\frac{3}{4}c + \frac{7}{4}, c \right).$$

Replace z by 3 and y by 1 in Equation (1) and solve for x.

$$\begin{aligned} x + 2y - z &= 1 & &\bullet \textbf{ Equation (1)} \\ x + 2(1) - 3 &= 1 & &\bullet \textbf{ Replace y by 1; replace z by 3.} \\ x &= 2 \end{aligned}$$

The system of equations is consistent. The solution is the ordered triple $(2, 1, 3)$. See **Figure 6.16.**

▶ **TRY EXERCISE 12, PAGE 528**

EXAMPLE 2   **Solve a Dependent System of Equations**

$$\text{Solve: } \begin{cases} 2x - y - z = -1 & (1) \\ -x + 3y - z = -3 & (2) \\ -5x + 5y + z = -1 & (3) \end{cases}$$

Solution

Eliminate x from Equation (2) by multiplying Equation (2) by 2 and then adding it to Equation (1). Replace Equation (2) by the new equation.

$$\begin{aligned} 2x - y - z &= -1 & &\bullet \textbf{ Equation (1)} \\ -2x + 6y - 2z &= -6 & &\bullet \textbf{ 2 times Equation (2)} \\ \hline 5y - 3z &= -7 & &\bullet \textbf{ Add the equations.} \end{aligned}$$

$$\begin{cases} 2x - y - z = -1 & (1) \\ 5y - 3z = -7 & (4) & \bullet \textbf{ Replace Equation (2).} \\ -5x + 5y + z = -1 & (3) \end{cases}$$

Eliminate x from Equation (3) by multiplying Equation (1) by 5 and multiplying Equation (3) by 2. Then add. Replace Equation (3) by the new equation.

$$\begin{aligned} 10x - 5y - 5z &= -5 & &\bullet \textbf{ 5 times Equation (1)} \\ -10x + 10y + 2z &= -2 & &\bullet \textbf{ 2 times Equation (3)} \\ \hline 5y - 3z &= -7 & &\bullet \textbf{ Add the equations.} \end{aligned}$$

$$\begin{cases} 2x - y - z = -1 & (1) \\ 5y - 3z = -7 & (4) \\ 5y - 3z = -7 & (5) & \bullet \textbf{ Replace Equation (3).} \end{cases}$$

Eliminate y from Equation (5) by multiplying Equation (4) by -1 and then adding it to Equation (5). Replace Equation (5) by the new equation.

$$\begin{aligned} -5y + 3z &= 7 & &\bullet \textbf{ -1 times Equation (4)} \\ 5y - 3z &= -7 & &\bullet \textbf{ Equation (5)} \\ \hline 0 &= 0 & &\bullet \textbf{ Add the equations.} \end{aligned}$$

$$\begin{cases} 2x - y - z = -1 & (1) \\ 5y - 3z = -7 & (4) \\ 0 = 0 & (6) & \bullet \textbf{ Replace Equation (5).} \end{cases}$$

Continued ▶

Because any ordered triple (x, y, z) is a solution of Equation (6), the solutions of the system of equations will be the ordered triples that are solutions of Equations (1) and (4).

Solve Equation (4) for y.

$$5y - 3z = -7$$
$$5y = 3z - 7$$
$$y = \frac{3}{5}z - \frac{7}{5}$$

Substitute $\frac{3}{5}z - \frac{7}{5}$ for y in Equation (1) and solve for x.

$$2x - y - z = -1 \qquad \text{• Equation (1)}$$
$$2x - \left(\frac{3}{5}z - \frac{7}{5}\right) - z = -1 \qquad \text{• Replace } y \text{ by } \frac{3}{5}z - \frac{7}{5}.$$
$$2x - \frac{8}{5}z + \frac{7}{5} = -1 \qquad \text{• Simplify and solve for } x.$$
$$2x = \frac{8}{5}z - \frac{12}{5}$$
$$x = \frac{4}{5}z - \frac{6}{5}$$

By choosing any real number c for z, we have $y = \frac{3}{5}c - \frac{7}{5}$ and $x = \frac{4}{5}c - \frac{6}{5}$. For any real number c, the ordered-triple solutions of the system of equations are $\left(\frac{4}{5}c - \frac{6}{5}, \frac{3}{5}c - \frac{7}{5}, c\right)$. The solid red line shown in **Figure 6.17** is a graph of the solutions.

The three planes intersect along this line.

P **FIGURE 6.17**

▶ **TRY EXERCISE 16, PAGE 528**

TRY EXERCISE 16, PAGE 528

---

take note

Although the ordered triples

$$\left(\frac{4}{5}c - \frac{6}{5}, \frac{3}{5}c - \frac{7}{5}, c\right)$$

and

$$\left(a, \frac{3}{4}a - \frac{1}{2}, \frac{5}{4}a + \frac{3}{2}\right)$$

appear to be different, they represent exactly the same set of ordered triples. For instance, choosing $c = -1$, we have $(-2, -2, -1)$. Choosing $a = -2$ results in the same ordered triple, $(-2, -2, -1)$.

As in the case of a dependent system of equations in two variables, there is more than one way to represent the solutions of a dependent system of equations in three variables. For instance, from Example 2, let $a = \frac{4}{5}c - \frac{6}{5}$, the x-coordinate of the ordered triple $\left(\frac{4}{5}c - \frac{6}{5}, \frac{3}{5}c - \frac{7}{5}, c\right)$, and solve for c.

$$a = \frac{4}{5}c - \frac{6}{5} \quad \rightarrow \quad c = \frac{5}{4}a + \frac{3}{2}$$

Substitute this value of c into each component of the ordered triple.

$$\left(\frac{4}{5}\left(\frac{5}{4}a + \frac{3}{2}\right) - \frac{6}{5}, \frac{3}{5}\left(\frac{5}{4}a + \frac{3}{2}\right) - \frac{7}{5}, \frac{5}{4}a + \frac{3}{2}\right) = \left(a, \frac{3}{4}a - \frac{1}{2}, \frac{5}{4}a + \frac{3}{2}\right)$$

Thus the solutions of the system of equations can also be written as

$$\left(a, \frac{3}{4}a - \frac{1}{2}, \frac{5}{4}a + \frac{3}{2}\right)$$

Alternative to Example 3

Solve: $\begin{cases} x - y - z = 6 & (1) \\ x - 3y + 2z = 2 & (2) \\ -x + 5y - 5z = 3 & (3) \end{cases}$

● This system is inconsistent and has no solution.

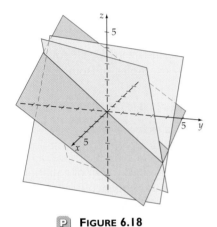

Ⓟ **FIGURE 6.18**

EXAMPLE 3 Identify an Inconsistent System of Equations

Solve: $\begin{cases} x + 2y + 3z = 4 & (1) \\ 2x - y - z = 3 & (2) \\ 3x + y + 2z = 5 & (3) \end{cases}$

Solution

Eliminate x from Equation (2) by multiplying Equation (1) by -2 and then adding it to Equation (2). Replace Equation (2). Eliminate x from Equation (3) by multiplying Equation (1) by -3 and adding it to Equation (3). Replace Equation (3). The equivalent system is

$$\begin{cases} x + 2y + 3z = 4 & (1) \\ -5y - 7z = -5 & (4) \\ -5y - 7z = -7 & (5) \end{cases}$$

Eliminate y from Equation (5) by multiplying Equation (4) by -1 and adding it to Equation (5). Replace Equation (5). The equivalent system is

$$\begin{cases} x + 2y + 3z = 4 & (1) \\ -5y - 7z = -5 & (4) \\ 0 = -2 & (6) \end{cases}$$

This system of equations contains a false equation. The system is inconsistent and has no solution. There is no point on all three planes, as shown in **Figure 6.18**.

▶ **TRY EXERCISE 18, PAGE 528**

● NONSQUARE SYSTEMS OF EQUATIONS

The linear systems of equations that we have solved so far contain the same number of variables as equations. These are *square systems of equations*. If there are fewer equations than variables—a *nonsquare system of equations*—the system has either no solution or an infinite number of solutions.

Alternative to Example 4

Solve: $\begin{cases} x + 2y - 3z = 5 & (1) \\ 3x + 7y - 10z = 13 & (2) \end{cases}$

● $(c + 9, c - 2, c)$

EXAMPLE 4 Solve a Nonsquare System of Equations

Solve: $\begin{cases} x - 2y + 2z = 3 & (1) \\ 2x - y - 2z = 15 & (2) \end{cases}$

Solution

Eliminate x from Equation (2) by multiplying Equation (1) by -2 and adding it to Equation (2). Replace Equation (2).

$$\begin{cases} x - 2y + 2z = 3 & (1) \\ 3y - 6z = 9 & (3) \end{cases}$$

Solve Equation (3) for y.

$$3y - 6z = 9$$
$$y = 2z + 3$$

Continued ▶

Substitute $2z + 3$ for y into Equation (1) and solve for x.

$$x - 2y + 2z = 3$$
$$x - 2(2z + 3) + 2z = 3 \qquad \bullet\, y = 2z + 3$$
$$x = 2z + 9$$

For each value of z selected, there correspond values for x and y. If z is any real number c, then the solutions of the system are the ordered triples $(2c + 9, 2c + 3, c)$.

▶ **TRY EXERCISE 20, PAGE 528**

● HOMOGENEOUS SYSTEMS OF EQUATIONS

A linear system of equations for which the constant term is zero for all equations is called a **homogeneous system of equations.** Two examples of homogeneous systems of equations are

$$\begin{cases} 3x + 4y = 0 \\ 2x + 3y = 0 \end{cases} \qquad \begin{cases} 2x - 3y + 5z = 0 \\ 3x + 2y + z = 0 \\ x - 4y + 5z = 0 \end{cases}$$

The solution $(0, 0)$ is always a solution of a homogeneous system of equations in two variables, and $(0, 0, 0)$ is always a solution of a homogeneous system of equations in three variables. This solution is called the **trivial solution.**

Sometimes a homogeneous system of equations may have solutions other than the trivial solution. For example, $(1, -1, -1)$ is a solution of the homogeneous system of three equations in three variables above.

If a homogeneous system of equations has a unique solution, the graphs intersect only at the origin. Solutions of a homogeneous system of equations can be found by using the substitution method or the elimination method.

Alternative to Example 5

Solve: $\begin{cases} x - 4y + 2z = 0 & (1) \\ -x + 7y - 4z = 0 & (2) \\ 2x - 17y + 10z = 0 & (3) \end{cases}$

● $\left(\dfrac{2}{3}c, \dfrac{2}{3}c, c\right)$

EXAMPLE 5   **Solve a Homogeneous System of Equations**

Solve: $\begin{cases} x + 2y - 3z = 0 & (1) \\ 2x - y + z = 0 & (2) \\ 3x + y - 2z = 0 & (3) \end{cases}$

Solution

Eliminate x from Equations (2) and (3) and replace these equations by the new equations.

$$\begin{cases} x + 2y - 3z = 0 & (1) \\ -5y + 7z = 0 & (4) \\ -5y + 7z = 0 & (5) \end{cases}$$

Eliminate y from Equation (5). Replace Equation (5).

$$\begin{cases} x + 2y - 3z = 0 & (1) \\ -5y + 7z = 0 & (4) \\ 0 = 0 & (6) \end{cases}$$

Because Equation (6) is an identity, the solutions of the system are the solutions of Equations (1) and (4).

Solve Equation (4) for y.

$$y = \frac{7}{5}z$$

Substitute the expression for y into Equation (1) and solve for x.

$$x + 2y - 3z = 0 \qquad \bullet \text{ Equation (1)}$$

$$x + 2\left(\frac{7}{5}z\right) - 3z = 0 \qquad \bullet \, y = \frac{7}{5}z$$

$$x = \frac{1}{5}z$$

Letting z be any real number c, we find that the solutions of the system are $\left(\frac{1}{5}c, \frac{7}{5}c, c\right)$.

▶ **TRY EXERCISE 32, PAGE 528**

● **APPLICATIONS**

One application of a system of equations is "curve fitting." Given a set of points in the plane, try to find an equation whose graph passes through those points, or "fits" those points.

Alternative to Example 6
Find an equation of the form
$y = ax^2 + bx + c$ whose graph passes
through the points whose coordinates are
$(1, 2)$, $(2, 15)$, and $(-2, -1)$.
● $y = 3x^2 + 4x - 5$

EXAMPLE 6   Solve an Application of a System of Equations to Curve Fitting

Find an equation of the form $y = ax^2 + bx + c$ whose graph passes through the points whose coordinates are $(1, 4)$, $(-1, 6)$, and $(2, 9)$.

Solution

Substitute each of the given ordered pairs into the equation $y = ax^2 + bx + c$. Write the resulting system of equations.

$$\begin{cases} 4 = a(1)^2 + b(1) + c \\ 6 = a(-1)^2 + b(-1) + c \\ 9 = a(2)^2 + b(2) + c \end{cases} \quad \text{or} \quad \begin{cases} a + b + c = 4 & (1) \\ a - b + c = 6 & (2) \\ 4a + 2b + c = 9 & (3) \end{cases}$$

Solve the resulting system of equations for a, b, and c.

Eliminate a from Equation (2) by multiplying Equation (1) by -1 and then adding it to Equation (2). Now eliminate a from Equation (3) by multiplying Equation (1) by -4 and adding it to Equation (3). The result is

$$\begin{cases} a + b + c = 4 \\ -2b = 2 \\ -2b - 3c = -7 \end{cases}$$

Continued ▶

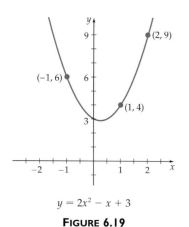

$$y = 2x^2 - x + 3$$

FIGURE 6.19

Alternative to Example 7
Exercise 40, page 528.

Although this system of equations is not in triangular form, we can solve the second equation for b and use this value to find a and c.

Solving by substitution, we obtain $a = 2$, $b = -1$, $c = 3$. The equation of the form $y = ax^2 + bx + c$ whose graph passes through $(1, 4)$, $(-1, 6)$, and $(2, 9)$ is $y = 2x^2 - x + 3$. See **Figure 6.19.**

▶ **TRY EXERCISE 36, PAGE 528**

Traffic engineers use systems of equations to study the flow of traffic. The analysis of traffic flow is based on the principle that the numbers of cars that enter and leave an intersection must be equal.

EXAMPLE 7   Traffic Flow

Suppose the traffic flow for some one-way streets can be modeled by the diagram below, where the numbers and the variables represent the numbers of cars entering or leaving an intersection per hour.

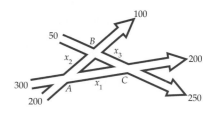

If the street connecting intersections A and C has an estimated traffic flow of between 100 and 200 cars per hour, what is the estimated traffic flow between A and B (which is x_2) and between B and C (which is x_3)?

Solution

Let x_1, x_2, and x_3 represent the numbers of cars per hour that are traveling on AC, AB, and BC, respectively. Now consider intersection A. There are $300 + 200 = 500$ cars per hour entering A and $x_1 + x_2$ cars leaving A. Therefore, $x_1 + x_2 = 500$. For intersection B, we have $50 + x_2$ cars per hour entering the intersection and $100 + x_3$ cars leaving the intersection. Thus $50 + x_2 = 100 + x_3$, or $x_2 - x_3 = 50$. Applying the same reasoning to C, we have $x_1 + x_3 = 450$. These equations result in the system of equations

$$\begin{cases} x_1 + x_2 = 500 & (1) \\ x_2 - x_3 = 50 & (2) \\ x_1 + x_3 = 450 & (3) \end{cases}$$

Subtracting Equation (2) from Equation (1) gives

$$\begin{array}{ll} x_1 + x_2 = 500 & (1) \\ \underline{x_2 - x_3 = 50} & (2) \\ x_1 + x_3 = 450 & (4) \end{array}$$

Subtracting Equation (4) from Equation (3) gives

$$x_1 + x_3 = 450 \qquad (3)$$
$$\underline{x_1 + x_3 = 450} \qquad (4)$$
$$0 = 0$$

This indicates that the system of equations is dependent. Because we are given that between 100 and 200 cars per hour flow between A and C (the value of x_1), we will solve each equation in terms of x_1. From Equation (1) we have $x_2 = -x_1 + 500$ and from Equation (3) we have $x_3 = -x_1 + 450$. Because $100 \le x_1 \le 200$, we have, by substituting for x_1, $300 \le x_2 \le 400$ and $250 \le x_3 \le 350$.

▶ **TRY EXERCISE 42, PAGE 529**

TOPICS FOR DISCUSSION

1. Can a system of equations contain more equations than variables? If not, explain why not. If so, give an example.

2. If a linear system of three equations in three variables is dependent, what does that mean about the graphs of the equations of the system?

3. If a linear system of three equations in three variables is inconsistent, what does that mean about the graphs of the equations of the system?

4. The equation of a circle centered at the origin with radius 5 is given by $x^2 + y^2 = 25$. Discuss the shape of $x^2 + y^2 + z^2 = 25$ in an xyz-coordinate system.

5. Consider the plane P given by $2x + 4y - 3z = 12$. The *trace* of the graph of P is obtained by letting one of the variables equal zero. For instance, the trace in the xy-plane is the graph of $2x + 4y = 12$ that is obtained by letting $z = 0$. Determine the traces of P in the xz- and yz-planes, and discuss how the traces can be used to visualize the graph of P.

EXERCISE SET 6.2   —*Suggested Assignment: Exercises 1–29, every other odd; 35–47, odd; 58–63.*

In Exercises 1 to 24, solve each system of equations.

1.
$$\begin{cases} 2x - y + z = 8 \\ 2y - 3z = -11 \\ 3y + 2z = 3 \end{cases}$$
$(2, -1, 3)$

2.
$$\begin{cases} 3x + y + 2z = -4 \\ -3y - 2z = -5 \\ 2y + 5z = -4 \end{cases}$$
$(-1, 3, -2)$

3.
$$\begin{cases} x + 3y - 2z = 8 \\ 2x - y + z = 1 \\ 3x + 2y - 3z = 15 \end{cases}$$
$(2, 0, -3)$

4.
$$\begin{cases} x - 2y + 3z = 5 \\ 3x - 3y + z = 9 \\ 5x + y - 3z = 3 \end{cases}$$
$(1, -2, 0)$

5.
$$\begin{cases} 3x + 4y - z = -7 \\ x - 5y + 2z = 19 \\ 5x + y - 2z = 5 \end{cases}$$
$(2, -3, 1)$

6.
$$\begin{cases} 2x - 3y - 2z = 12 \\ x + 4y + z = -9 \\ 4x + 2y - 3z = 6 \end{cases}$$
$(1, -2, -2)$

7.
$$\begin{cases} 2x - 5y + 3z = -18 \\ 3x + 2y - z = -12 \\ x - 3y - 4z = -4 \end{cases}$$
$(-5, 1, -1)$

8.
$$\begin{cases} 4x - y + 2z = -1 \\ 2x + 3y - 3z = -13 \\ x + 5y + z = 7 \end{cases}$$
$(-2, 1, 4)$

9. $\begin{cases} x + 2y - 3z = -7 \\ 2x - y + 4z = 11 \\ 4x + 3y - 4z = -3 \end{cases}$
$(3, -5, 0)$

10. $\begin{cases} x - 3y + 2z = -11 \\ 3x + y + 4z = 4 \\ 5x - 5y + 8z = -18 \end{cases}$
$\left(\dfrac{1 - 14c}{10}, \dfrac{37 + 2c}{10}, c \right)$

11. $\begin{cases} 2x - 5y + 2z = -4 \\ 3x + 2y + 3z = 13 \\ 5x - 3y - 4z = -18 \end{cases}$
$(0, 2, 3)$

▶ 12. $\begin{cases} 3x + 2y - 5z = 6 \\ 5x - 4y + 3z = -12 \\ 4x + 5y - 2z = 15 \end{cases}$
$(0, 3, 0)$

13. $\begin{cases} 2x + y - z = -2 \\ 3x + 2y + 3z = 21 \\ 7x + 4y + z = 17 \end{cases}$
$(5c - 25, 48 - 9c, c)$

14. $\begin{cases} 3x + y + 2z = 2 \\ 4x - 2y + z = -4 \\ 11x - 3y + 4z = -6 \end{cases}$
$\left(-\dfrac{c}{2}, \dfrac{4 - c}{2}, c \right)$

15. $\begin{cases} 3x - 2y + 3z = 11 \\ 2x + 3y + z = 3 \\ 5x + 14y - z = 1 \end{cases}$
$(3, -1, 0)$

▶ 16. $\begin{cases} 2x + 3y + 2z = 14 \\ x - 3y + 4z = 4 \\ -x + 12y - 6z = 2 \end{cases}$
$\left(6, \dfrac{2}{3}, 0 \right)$

17. $\begin{cases} 2x - 3y + 6z = 3 \\ x + 2y - 4z = 5 \\ 3x + 4y - 8z = 7 \end{cases}$
no solution

▶ 18. $\begin{cases} 2x + 3y - 6z = 4 \\ 3x - 2y - 9z = -7 \\ 2x + 5y - 6z = 8 \end{cases}$
$(3c - 1, 2, c)$

19. $\begin{cases} 2x - 3y + 5z = 14 \\ x + 4y - 3z = -2 \end{cases}$
$\left(\dfrac{50 - 11c}{11}, \dfrac{11c - 18}{11}, c \right)$

▶ 20. $\begin{cases} x - 3y + 4z = 9 \\ 3x - 8y - 2z = 4 \end{cases}$
$(38c - 60, 14c - 23, c)$

21. $\begin{cases} 6x - 9y + 6z = 7 \\ 4x - 6y + 4z = 9 \end{cases}$
no solution

22. $\begin{cases} 4x - 2y + 6z = 5 \\ 2x - y + 3z = 2 \end{cases}$
no solution

23. $\begin{cases} 5x + 3y + 2z = 10 \\ 3x - 4y - 4z = -5 \end{cases}$
$\left(\dfrac{25 + 4c}{29}, \dfrac{55 - 26c}{29}, c \right)$

24. $\begin{cases} 3x - 4y - 7z = -5 \\ 2x + 3y - 5z = 2 \end{cases}$
$\left(\dfrac{41c - 7}{17}, \dfrac{16 + c}{17}, c \right)$

In Exercises 25 to 32, solve each homogeneous system of equations.

25. $\begin{cases} x + 3y - 4z = 0 \\ 2x + 7y + z = 0 \\ 3x - 5y - 2z = 0 \end{cases}$ $(0, 0, 0)$

26. $\begin{cases} x - 2y + 3z = 0 \\ 3x - 7y - 4z = 0 \\ 4x - 4y + z = 0 \end{cases}$ $(0, 0, 0)$

27. $\begin{cases} 2x - 3y + z = 0 \\ 2x + 4y - 3z = 0 \\ 6x - 2y - z = 0 \end{cases}$
$\left(\dfrac{5c}{14}, \dfrac{4c}{7}, c \right)$

28. $\begin{cases} 5x - 4y - 3z = 0 \\ 2x + y + 2z = 0 \\ x - 6y - 7z = 0 \end{cases}$
$\left(-\dfrac{5}{13}c, -\dfrac{16}{13}c, c \right)$

29. $\begin{cases} 3x - 5y + 3z = 0 \\ 2x - 3y + 4z = 0 \\ 7x - 11y + 11z = 0 \end{cases}$
$(-11c, -6c, c)$

30. $\begin{cases} 5x - 2y - 3z = 0 \\ 3x - y - 4z = 0 \\ 4x - y - 9z = 0 \end{cases}$
$(5c, 11c, c)$

31. $\begin{cases} 4x - 7y - 2z = 0 \\ 2x + 4y + 3z = 0 \\ 3x - 2y - 5z = 0 \end{cases}$
$(0, 0, 0)$

▶ 32. $\begin{cases} 5x + 2y + 3z = 0 \\ 3x + y - 2z = 0 \\ 4x - 7y + 5z = 0 \end{cases}$
$(0, 0, 0)$

In Exercises 33 to 44, solve each exercise by solving a system of equations.

33. CURVE FITTING Find an equation of the form $y = ax^2 + bx + c$ whose graph passes through the points $(2, 3), (-2, 7),$ and $(1, -2)$. $y = 2x^2 - x - 3$

34. CURVE FITTING Find an equation of the form $y = ax^2 + bx + c$ whose graph passes through the points $(1, -2), (3, -4),$ and $(2, -2)$. $y = -x^2 + 3x - 4$

35. CURVE FITTING Find the equation of the circle whose graph passes through the points $(5, 3), (-1, -5),$ and $(-2, 2)$. (*Hint:* Use the equation $x^2 + y^2 + ax + by + c = 0$.)
$x^2 + y^2 - 4x + 2y - 20 = 0$

▶ 36. CURVE FITTING Find the equation of the circle whose graph passes through the points $(0, 6), (1, 5),$ and $(-7, -1)$. (*Hint:* See Exercise 35.)
$x^2 + y^2 + 6x - 4y - 12 = 0$

37. CURVE FITTING Find the center and radius of the circle whose graph passes through the points $(-2, 10), (-12, -14),$ and $(5, 3)$. (*Hint:* See Exercise 35.)
center $(-7, -2)$, radius 13

38. CURVE FITTING Find the center and radius of the circle whose graph passes through the points $(2, 5), (-4, -3),$ and $(3, 4)$. (*Hint:* See Exercise 35.)
center $(-1, 1)$, radius 5

39. TRAFFIC FLOW Suppose that the traffic flow for some one-way streets can be modeled by the diagram below, where each number or variable represents the number of cars entering or leaving an intersection per hour.

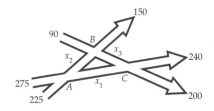

What is the minimum number of cars that can travel between A and C? 500 cars per hour

40. TRAFFIC FLOW A *roundabout* is a type of intersection that accommodates traffic flow in one direction, around a circular island. The graphic model on the following page shows the numbers of cars per hour that are entering or leaving a roundabout.

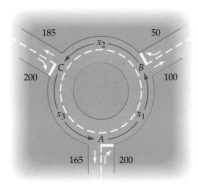

If the portion of the roundabout between A and B has an estimated traffic flow of from 60 to 80 cars per hour, what is the estimated traffic flow between C and A and between B and C? *CA:* 25 to 45 cars per hour, *BC:* 10 to 30 cars per hour

41. TRAFFIC FLOW Suppose that the traffic flow for some one-way streets can be modeled by the diagram below, where each number or variable represents the number of cars entering or leaving an intersection per hour.

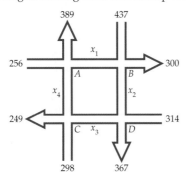

If the street connecting intersections A and B has an estimated traffic flow of from 125 to 175 cars per hour, what is the estimated traffic flow between C and A, D and C, and B and D? *CA:* 258 to 308, *DC:* 209 to 259, *BD:* 262 to 312

▶ **42. TRAFFIC FLOW** A *roundabout* is a type of intersection that accommodates traffic flow in one direction, around a circular island. The graphic model below shows the numbers of cars per hour that are entering and leaving a roundabout.

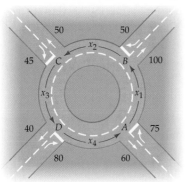

What is the minimum number of cars per hour that can travel between B and C? 5 cars per hour

43. ART A sculptor is creating a windchime consisting of three chimes that will be suspended from a rod 13 inches long. The weights, in ounces, of the chimes are shown in the diagram. For the rod to remain horizontal, the chimes must be positioned so that $w_1d_1 + w_2d_2 = w_3d_3$. If the sculptor wants d_2 to be one-third of d_1, find the position of each chime so that the windchime will balance. $d_1 = 9$ in., $d_2 = 3$ in., $d_3 = 4$ in.

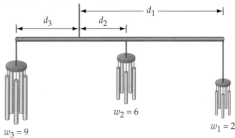

44. ART A designer wants to create a mobile of colored blocks as shown in the diagram below. The weight, in ounces, of each of the blocks is shown next to the block.

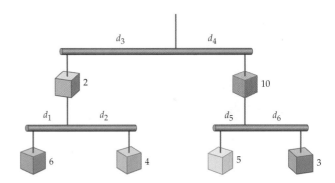

Given that $d_3 + d_4 = 20$ inches, $d_1 + d_2 = 10$ inches, and $d_5 + d_6 = 8$ inches, find the values of d_1 through d_6 so that each bar is horizontal. (A bar is horizontal when the value of weight times distance on each side of a vertical support is equal. For instance, for the above diagram, $6d_1$ must equal $4d_2$. Because there are six variables, the resulting system of equations must contain six equations.) $d_1 = 4$ in., $d_2 = 6$ in., $d_3 = 12$ in., $d_4 = 8$ in., $d_5 = 3$ in., $d_6 = 5$ in.

CONNECTING CONCEPTS

In Exercises 45 to 50, solve each system of equations.

45. $\begin{cases} 2x + y - 3z + 2w = -1 \\ 2y - 5z - 3w = 9 \\ 3y - 8z + w = -4 \\ 2y - 2z + 3w = -3 \end{cases}$ $(3, 5, 2, -3)$

46. $\begin{cases} 3x - y + 2z - 3w = 5 \\ 2y - 5z + 2w = -7 \\ 4y - 9z + w = -19 \\ 3y + z - 2w = -12 \end{cases}$ $(2, -3, 1, 2)$

47. $\begin{cases} x - 3y + 2z - w = 2 \\ 2x - 5y - 3z + 2w = 21 \\ 3x - 8y - 2z - 3w = 12 \\ -2x + 8y + z + 2w = -13 \end{cases}$ $(1, -2, -1, 3)$

48. $\begin{cases} x - 2y + 3z + 2w = 8 \\ 3x - 7y - 2z + 3w = 18 \\ 2x - 5y + 2z - w = 19 \\ 4x - 8y + 3z + 2w = 29 \end{cases}$ $(3, -2, 1, -1)$

49. $\begin{cases} x + 2y - 2z + 3w = 2 \\ 2x + 5y + 2z + 4w = 9 \\ 4x + 9y - 2z + 10w = 13 \\ -x - y + 8z - 5w = 3 \end{cases}$ $(14a - 7b - 8, -6a + 2b + 5, a, b)$

50. $\begin{cases} x - 2y + 3z - 2w = -1 \\ 3x - 7y - 2z - 3w = -19 \\ 2x - 5y + 2z - w = -11 \\ -x + 3y - 2z - w = 3 \end{cases}$ no solution

In Exercises 51 and 52, use the system of equations

$$\begin{cases} x - 3y - 2z = A^2 \\ 2x - 5y + Az = 9 \\ 2x - 8y + z = 18 \end{cases}$$

51. Find all values of A for which the system has no solution. $A = -\dfrac{13}{2}$

52. Find all values of A for which the system has a unique solution. $2A + 13 \neq 0$ or $A \neq -\dfrac{13}{2}$

In Exercises 53 to 55, use the system of equations

$$\begin{cases} x + 2y + z = A^2 \\ -2x - 3y + Az = 1 \\ 7x + 12y + A^2z = 4A^2 - 3 \end{cases}$$

53. Find all values of A for which the system has a unique solution. $A \neq -3, A \neq 1$

54. Find all values of A for which the system has an infinite number of solutions. $A = 1$

55. Find all values of A for which the system has no solution. $A = -3$

56. Find an equation of the plane that contains the points $(2, 1, 1)$, $(-1, 2, 12)$, and $(3, 2, 0)$. (*Hint:* The equation of a plane can be written as $z = ax + by + c$.) $z = -3x + 2y + 5$

57. Find an equation of the plane that contains the points $(1, -1, 5)$, $(2, -2, 9)$, and $(-3, -1, -1)$. (*Hint:* The equation of a plane can be written as $z = ax + by + c$.) $3x - 5y - 2z = -2$

PREPARE FOR SECTION 6.3

58. Solve $x^2 + 2x - 2 = 0$ for x. [1.3] $-1 \pm \sqrt{3}$

59. Solve: $\begin{cases} x + 4y = -11 \\ 3x - 2y = 9 \end{cases}$ [6.1] $(1, -3)$

60. Name the graph of $(y + 3)^2 = 8x$. [5.1] parabola

61. Name the graph of $\dfrac{(x - 2)^2}{4} - \dfrac{(y + 3)^2}{9} = 1$. [5.3] hyperbola

62. How many times do the graphs of $y = 2x - 1$ and $x^2 + y^2 = 4$ intersect? [2.1/2.2] 2

63. How many times do the graphs of $\dfrac{x^2}{4} + \dfrac{y^2}{9} = 1$ and $\dfrac{x^2}{9} + \dfrac{y^2}{4} = 1$ intersect? [5.2] 4

PROJECTS

1. ✎ **CONCEPT OF DIMENSION** In this chapter we graphed first-degree equations in three variables. If we were to attempt to graph an equation in four variables, we would need a fourth axis perpendicular to the three axes of an *xyz*-coordinate system. It seems impossible to imagine a fourth dimension, but incorporating it is really a quite practical matter in mathematics. In fact, there are some systems that require an infinite-dimensional coordinate system. To gain some insight into the concept of dimension, read the book *Flatland* by Edwin A. Abbott, and then write an essay explaining what this book has to do with dimension.

2. ✎ **ABILITIES OF A FOUR-DIMENSIONAL HUMAN** There have been a number of attempts to describe the abilities of a four-dimensional human in a three-dimensional world. Read some of these accounts, and then write an essay on some of the actions a four-dimensional person could perform. Answer the following question in your essay. Can a four-dimensional person remove the money from a locked safe without first opening the safe?

| SECTION **6.3** | # NONLINEAR SYSTEMS OF EQUATIONS |

● SOLVING NONLINEAR SYSTEMS OF EQUATIONS

● SOLVING NONLINEAR SYSTEMS OF EQUATIONS

A **nonlinear system of equations** is one in which one or more equations of the system are not linear equations. **Figure 6.20** shows examples of nonlinear systems of equations and the corresponding graphs of the equations. Each point of intersection of the graphs is a solution of the system of equations. In the third example, the graphs do not intersect; therefore, the system of equations has no real number solution.

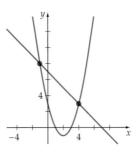

$$\begin{cases} y = x^2 - 4x + 3 \\ y = -x + 7 \end{cases}$$

2 solutions

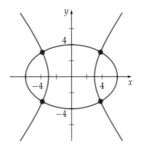

$$\begin{cases} \dfrac{x^2}{36} + \dfrac{y^2}{16} = 1 \\ \dfrac{x^2}{9} - \dfrac{y^2}{16} = 1 \end{cases}$$

4 solutions

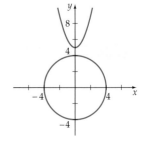

$$\begin{cases} y = x^2 + 5 \\ x^2 + y^2 = 16 \end{cases}$$

no solution

FIGURE 6.20

To solve a nonlinear system of equations, use the substitution method or the elimination method. The substitution method is usually easier for solving a nonlinear system that contains a linear equation.

? **QUESTION** What is the solution of the equation $3x - y = 5$ for y in terms of x?

EXAMPLE 1   **Solve a Nonlinear System by the Substitution Method**

Solve: $\begin{cases} y = x^2 - x - 1 & (1) \\ 3x - y = 4 & (2) \end{cases}$

Alternative to Example 1

Solve: $\begin{cases} 5x + y = 3 \\ y = x^2 - 3x - 5 \end{cases}$

● The solutions are $(-4, 23)$ and $(2, -7)$.

Algebraic Solution

We will use the substitution method. Using the equation $y = x^2 - x - 1$, substitute the expression for y into $3x - y = 4$.

$$3x - y = 4$$
$$3x - (x^2 - x - 1) = 4 \qquad \bullet\, y = x^2 - x - 1$$
$$-x^2 + 4x + 1 = 4 \qquad \bullet\, \textbf{Simplify.}$$
$$x^2 - 4x + 3 = 0 \qquad \bullet\, \textbf{Write the quadratic equation in standard form.}$$
$$(x - 3)(x - 1) = 0 \qquad \bullet\, \textbf{Solve for } x.$$
$$x - 3 = 0 \quad \text{or} \quad x - 1 = 0$$
$$x = 3 \quad \text{or} \quad x = 1$$

Substitute these values into Equation (1) and solve for y.

$$y = 3^2 - 3 - 1 = 5 \quad \text{or} \quad y = 1^2 - 1 - 1 = -1$$

The solutions are $(3, 5)$ and $(1, -1)$. See **Figure 6.21**.

Visualize the Solution

Graphing $y = x^2 - x - 1$ and $3x - y = 4$ shows that $(1, -1)$ and $(3, 5)$ belong to each graph. Therefore, these ordered pairs are solutions of the system of equations.

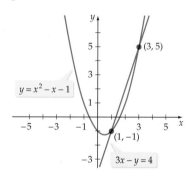

FIGURE 6.21

▶ **TRY EXERCISE 8, PAGE 536**

? **ANSWER** $y = 3x - 5$

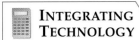

You can use a graphing calculator to solve some nonlinear systems of equations in two variables. For instance, to solve

$$\begin{cases} y = x^2 - 2x + 2 \\ y = x^3 + 2x^2 - 7x - 3 \end{cases}$$

enter X²-2X+2 into Y₁ and X^3+2X²-7X-3 into Y₂ and graph the two equations. Be sure to use a viewing window that will show all points of intersection. The sequence of steps shown in **Figure 6.22** can be used to find the points of intersection with a TI-83 calculator.

Press 2nd CALC. Select 5: intersect. Press ENTER.

```
CALCULATE
1: value
2: zero
3: minimum
4: maximum
5: intersect
6: dy/dx
7: ∫f(x)dx
```

The "First curve?" shown on the bottom of the screen means to select the first of the two graphs that intersect. Just press ENTER.

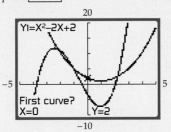

The "Second curve?" shown on the bottom of the screen means to select the second of the two graphs that intersect. Just press ENTER.

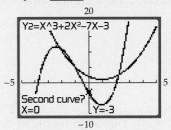

"Guess?" is shown on the bottom of the screen. Move the cursor until it is approximately at the first point of intersection. Press ENTER.

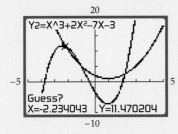

The approximate coordinates of the point of intersection, $(-2.24, 11.47)$, are shown at the bottom of the screen.

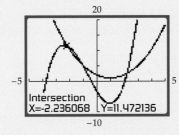

Repeat these steps two more times to find the remaining points of intersection. The graphs are shown below.

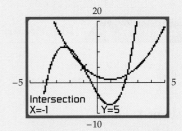

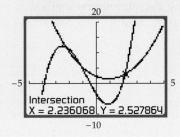

FIGURE 6.22

The coordinates of the points of intersection are $(-2.24, 11.47)$, $(-1, 5)$, and $(2.24, 2.53)$.

EXAMPLE 2 Solve a Nonlinear System by the Elimination Method

Solve: $\begin{cases} 4x^2 + 3y^2 = 48 & (1) \\ 3x^2 + 2y^2 = 35 & (2) \end{cases}$

Alternative to Example 2

Solve: $\begin{cases} 2x^2 + 3y^2 = 21 \\ x^2 + 2y^2 = 12 \end{cases}$

• $(\sqrt{6}, \sqrt{3}), (\sqrt{6}, -\sqrt{3}),$
  $(-\sqrt{6}, \sqrt{3}), (-\sqrt{6}, -\sqrt{3})$

Algebraic Solution

We will eliminate the x^2 term. Multiply Equation (1) by -3 and Equation (2) by 4. Then add the two equations.

$$-12x^2 - 9y^2 = -144$$
$$\underline{12x^2 + 8y^2 = 140}$$
$$-y^2 = -4$$
$$y^2 = 4$$
$$y = \pm 2$$

Substitute 2 for y into Equation (1) and solve for x.

$$4x^2 + 3(2)^2 = 48$$
$$4x^2 = 36$$
$$x^2 = 9$$
$$x = \pm 3$$

Because $(-2)^2 = 2^2$, replacing y by -2 yields the same values of x: $x = 3$ or $x = -3$. The solutions are $(3, 2)$, $(3, -2)$, $(-3, 2)$, and $(-3, -2)$. See **Figure 6.23.**

Visualize the Solution

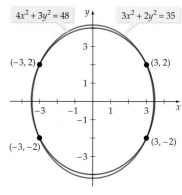

P **FIGURE 6.23**

▶ **TRY EXERCISE 16, PAGE 536**

EXAMPLE 3 Identify an Inconsistent System of Equations

Solve: $\begin{cases} 4x^2 + 9y^2 = 36 & (1) \\ x^2 - y^2 = 25 & (2) \end{cases}$

Alternative to Example 3

Solve: $\begin{cases} 9x^2 + 4y^2 = 144 & (1) \\ x^2 + y^2 = 9 & (2) \end{cases}$

• The system of equations has no real solutions.

Algebraic Solution

Using the elimination method, we will eliminate the x^2 term from each equation. Multiplying Equation (2) by -4 and then adding, we have

$$4x^2 + 9y^2 = 36$$
$$\underline{-4x^2 + 4y^2 = -100}$$
$$13y^2 = -64$$

Because the equation $13y^2 = -64$ has no real number solutions, the system of equations has no real solutions. The graphs of the equations do not intersect. See **Figure 6.24.**

Visualize the Solution

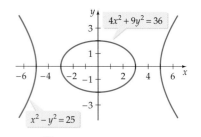

P **FIGURE 6.24**

▶ **TRY EXERCISE 20, PAGE 536**

| EXAMPLE 4 | Solve a Nonlinear System of Equations |

Solve: $\begin{cases} (x+3)^2 + (y-4)^2 = 20 \\ (x+4)^2 + (y-3)^2 = 26 \end{cases}$

Alternative to Example 4

Solve: $\begin{cases} (x-2)^2 + (y+3)^2 = 20 & (1) \\ (x-3)^2 + (y+2)^2 = 10 & (2) \end{cases}$

● (4, 1) and (6, −1)

Algebraic Solution

Expand the binomials in each equation. Then subtract the two equations and simplify.

$$x^2 + 6x + 9 + y^2 - 8y + 16 = 20 \qquad (1)$$
$$\underline{x^2 + 8x + 16 + y^2 - 6y + 9 = 26} \qquad (2)$$
$$-2x - 7 \qquad - 2y + 7 = -6$$
$$x + y = 3$$

Now solve the resulting equation for y.

$$y = -x + 3$$

Substitute $-x + 3$ for y into Equation (1) and solve for x.

$$x^2 + 6x + 9 + (-x+3)^2 - 8(-x+3) + 16 = 20$$
$$2(x^2 + 4x - 5) = 0$$
$$2(x+5)(x-1) = 0$$
$$x = -5 \quad \text{or} \quad x = 1$$

Substitute -5 and 1 for x into the equation $y = -x + 3$ and solve for y. This yields $y = 8$ or $y = 2$. The solutions of the system of equations are $(-5, 8)$ and $(1, 2)$. See **Figure 6.25**.

Visualize the Solution

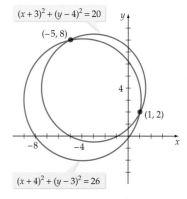

$(x+3)^2 + (y-4)^2 = 20$

$(-5, 8)$

$(1, 2)$

$(x+4)^2 + (y-3)^2 = 26$

Ⓟ **FIGURE 6.25**

▶ TRY EXERCISE 28, PAGE 536

 TOPICS FOR DISCUSSION

1. What distinguishes a system of linear equations from a system of nonlinear equations? Give an example of both types of systems of equations.

2. Is the system of equations

$$\begin{cases} xy = 1 \\ x + y = 1 \end{cases}$$

a nonlinear system of equations? Why or why not?

3. Can a nonlinear system of equations have no solution? If so, give an example. If not, explain why not.

4. Create a nonlinear system of equations in two variables that has at least $(2, -3)$ as a solution, contains one nonlinear equation, and contains one linear equation.

EXERCISE SET 6.3

—Suggested Assignment: Exercises 1–33, every other odd; 35, 37, 39, 45, 51, 54–59.

In Exercises 1 to 32, solve the system of equations.

1. $\begin{cases} y = x^2 - x \\ y = 2x - 2 \end{cases}$ (1, 0), (2, 2)

2. $\begin{cases} y = x^2 + 2x - 3 \\ y = x - 1 \end{cases}$
(−2, −3) and (1, 0)

3. $\begin{cases} y = 2x^2 - 3x - 3 \\ y = x - 4 \end{cases}$
See answer at bottom of page.

4. $\begin{cases} y = -x^2 + 2x - 4 \\ y = \frac{1}{2}x + 1 \end{cases}$
no real number solutions

5. $\begin{cases} y = x^2 - 2x + 3 \\ y = x^2 - x - 2 \end{cases}$ (5, 18)

6. $\begin{cases} y = 2x^2 - x + 1 \\ y = x^2 + 2x + 5 \end{cases}$
(4, 29) and (−1, 4)

7. $\begin{cases} x + y = 10 \\ xy = 24 \end{cases}$ (4, 6), (6, 4)

▶8. $\begin{cases} x - 2y = 3 \\ xy = -1 \end{cases}$ $\left(2, -\frac{1}{2}\right)$ and (1, −1)

9. $\begin{cases} 2x - y = 1 \\ xy = 6 \end{cases}$ $\left(-\frac{3}{2}, -4\right)$, (2, 3)

10. $\begin{cases} x - 3y = 7 \\ xy = -4 \end{cases}$ $\left(3, -\frac{4}{3}\right)$ and (4, −1)

11. $\begin{cases} 3x^2 - 2y^2 = 1 \\ y = 4x - 3 \end{cases}$ $\left(\frac{19}{29}, -\frac{11}{29}\right)$, (1, 1)

12. $\begin{cases} x^2 + 3y^2 = 7 \\ x + 4y = 6 \end{cases}$ $\left(-\frac{2}{19}, \frac{29}{19}\right)$ and (2, 1)

13. $\begin{cases} y = x^3 + 4x^2 - 3x - 5 \\ y = 2x^2 - 2x - 3 \end{cases}$ (−2, 9), (1, −3), (−1, 1)

14. $\begin{cases} y = x^3 - 2x^2 + 5x + 1 \\ y = x^2 + 7x - 5 \end{cases}$
(3, 25), $\left(\sqrt{2}, -3 + 7\sqrt{2}\right)$, and $\left(-\sqrt{2}, -3 - 7\sqrt{2}\right)$

15. $\begin{cases} 2x^2 + y^2 = 9 \\ x^2 - y^2 = 3 \end{cases}$ (−2, 1), (−2, −1), (2, 1), (2, −1)

▶16. $\begin{cases} 3x^2 - 2y^2 = 19 \\ x^2 - y^2 = 5 \end{cases}$
(3, −2), (3, 2), (−3, 2), and (−3, −2)

17. $\begin{cases} x^2 - 2y^2 = 8 \\ x^2 + 3y^2 = 28 \end{cases}$
(4, 2), (−4, 2), (4, −2), (−4, −2)

18. $\begin{cases} 2x^2 + 3y^2 = 5 \\ x^2 - 3y^2 = 4 \end{cases}$
no real number solutions

19. $\begin{cases} 2x^2 + 4y^2 = 5 \\ 3x^2 + 8y^2 = 14 \end{cases}$
no real number solutions

▶20. $\begin{cases} 2x^2 + 3y^2 = 11 \\ 3x^2 + 2y^2 = 19 \end{cases}$
no real number solutions

21. $\begin{cases} x^2 - 2x + y^2 = 1 \\ 2x + y = 5 \end{cases}$ $\left(\frac{12}{5}, \frac{1}{5}\right)$, (2, 1)

22. $\begin{cases} x^2 + y^2 + 3y = 22 \\ 2x + y = -1 \end{cases}$ $\left(\frac{12}{5}, -\frac{29}{5}\right)$ and (−2, 3)

23. $\begin{cases} (x - 3)^2 + (y + 1)^2 = 5 \\ x - 3y = 7 \end{cases}$ $\left(\frac{26}{5}, -\frac{3}{5}\right)$, (1, −2)

24. $\begin{cases} (x + 2)^2 + (y - 2)^2 = 13 \\ 2x + y = 6 \end{cases}$ $\left(\frac{7}{5}, \frac{16}{5}\right)$ and (1, 4)

25. $\begin{cases} x^2 - 3x + y^2 = 4 \\ 3x + y = 11 \end{cases}$ $\left(\frac{39}{10}, -\frac{7}{10}\right)$, (3, 2)

26. $\begin{cases} x^2 + y^2 - 4y = 4 \\ 5x - 2y = 2 \end{cases}$ $\left(\frac{2}{29}, -\frac{24}{29}\right)$ and (2, 4)

27. $\begin{cases} (x - 1)^2 + (y + 2)^2 = 14 \\ (x + 2)^2 + (y - 1)^2 = 2 \end{cases}$ $\left(\frac{-3 + \sqrt{3}}{2}, \frac{1 + \sqrt{3}}{2}\right)$, $\left(\frac{-3 - \sqrt{3}}{2}, \frac{1 - \sqrt{3}}{2}\right)$

▶28. $\begin{cases} (x + 2)^2 + (y - 3)^2 = 10 \\ (x - 3)^2 + (y + 1)^2 = 13 \end{cases}$ $\left(-\frac{15}{41}, \frac{12}{41}\right)$ and (1, 2)

29. $\begin{cases} (x + 3)^2 + (y - 2)^2 = 20 \\ (x - 2)^2 + (y - 3)^2 = 2 \end{cases}$ $\left(\frac{19}{13}, \frac{22}{13}\right)$, (1, 4)

30. $\begin{cases} (x - 4)^2 + (y - 5)^2 = 8 \\ (x + 1)^2 + (y + 2)^2 = 34 \end{cases}$ $\left(\frac{102}{37}, \frac{91}{37}\right)$ and (2, 3)

31. $\begin{cases} (x - 1)^2 + (y + 1)^2 = 2 \\ (x + 2)^2 + (y - 3)^2 = 3 \end{cases}$
no real number solutions

32. $\begin{cases} (x + 1)^2 + (y - 3)^2 = 4 \\ (x - 3)^2 + (y + 2)^2 = 2 \end{cases}$
no real number solutions

33. GEOMETRY Find the perimeter of the rectangle below.
82 units

(rectangle with top side labeled $3y + 5$, left side labeled x^2, right side labeled y, bottom side labeled $18x - 22$)

34. CONSTRUCTION A painter leans a ladder against a vertical wall. The top of the ladder is 7 meters above the ground. When the bottom of the ladder is moved 1 meter farther away from the wall, the top of the ladder is 5 meters above the ground. What is the length of the ladder? Round to the nearest hundredth of a meter. 13.46 m

35. ANALYTIC GEOMETRY For what values of the radius does the line $y = 2x + 1$ intersect (at one or more points) the circle whose equation is $x^2 + y^2 = r^2$? $r \geq \sqrt{\frac{1}{5}}$ or $\frac{\sqrt{5}}{5}$

36. GEOMETRY Three rectangles have exactly the same area. The dimensions of each rectangle (as length and width) are a and b; $a - 3$ and $b + 2$; and $a + 3$ and $b - 1$. Find the area of the rectangles. 36 square units

37. SUPPLY/DEMAND The number x of picture cellphones a manufacturer is willing to sell at price p is given by $x = \frac{p^2}{5} - 20$, where p is the price, in dollars, per picture cellphone. The number x of picture cellphones a distributor

3. $\left(\frac{2 + \sqrt{2}}{2}, \frac{-6 + \sqrt{2}}{2}\right)$, $\left(\frac{2 - \sqrt{2}}{2}, \frac{-6 - \sqrt{2}}{2}\right)$

is willing to purchase is given by $x = \dfrac{17{,}710}{p + 1}$, where p is the price, in dollars, per picture cellphone. Find the equilibrium price. (See Section 6.1 for a discussion of supply-demand equations.)
$45

38. SUPPLY/DEMAND The number x of a certain type of personal digital assistant (PDA) a manufacturer is willing to sell at price p is given by $x = \dfrac{p^2}{6} - 384$, where p is the price, in dollars, per PDA. The number x of these PDAs an office supply store is willing to purchase is given by $x = \dfrac{22{,}914}{p + 1}$, where p is the price per PDA. Find the equilibrium price. (See Section 6.1 for a discussion of supply-demand equations.) $66

 In Exercises 39 to 46, approximate the real number solutions of each system of equations to the nearest ten-thousandth.

39. $\begin{cases} y = 2^x \\ y = x + 1 \end{cases}$ (0, 1), (1, 2)

40. $\begin{cases} y = \log_2 x \\ y = x - 3 \end{cases}$
(0.1375, −2.8625) and (5.4449, 2.4449)

41. $\begin{cases} y = e^{-x} \\ y = x^2 \end{cases}$ (0.7035, 0.4949)

42. $\begin{cases} y = \ln x \\ y = -x + 4 \end{cases}$
(2.9263, 1.0737)

43. $\begin{cases} y = \sqrt{x} \\ y = \dfrac{1}{x - 1} \end{cases}$ (1.7549, 1.3247)

44. $\begin{cases} y = \dfrac{6}{x + 1} \\ y = \dfrac{x}{x - 1} \end{cases}$ (2, 2) and $\left(3, \dfrac{3}{2}\right)$

45. $\begin{cases} y = |x| \\ y = 2^{-x^2} \end{cases}$
(−0.7071, 0.7071), (0.7071, 0.7071)

46. $\begin{cases} y = \dfrac{2^x + 2^{-x}}{2} \\ y = \dfrac{2^x - 2^{-x}}{2} \end{cases}$ no solution

---

CONNECTING CONCEPTS

In Exercises 47 to 52, solve the system of equations for *rational number* ordered pairs.

47. $\begin{cases} y = x^2 + 4 \\ x = y^2 - 24 \end{cases}$ (1, 5)

48. $\begin{cases} y = x^2 - 5 \\ x = y^2 - 13 \end{cases}$ (3, 4)

49. $\begin{cases} x^2 - 3xy + y^2 = 5 \\ x^2 - xy - 2y^2 = 0 \end{cases}$ (−1, 1), (1, −1)

(*Hint:* Factor the second equation. Now use the principle of zero products and the substitution principle.)

50. $\begin{cases} x^2 + 2xy - y^2 = 1 \\ x^2 + 3xy + 2y^2 = 0 \end{cases}$ no rational number solution

(*Hint:* See Exercise 49.)

51. $\begin{cases} 2x^2 - 4xy - y^2 = 6 \\ 4x^2 - 3xy - y^2 = 6 \end{cases}$ (1, −2), (−1, 2)

(*Hint:* Subtract the two equations.)

52. $\begin{cases} 3x^2 + 2xy - 5y^2 = 11 \\ x^2 + 3xy + y^2 = 11 \end{cases}$ (2, 1) and (−2, −1)

(*Hint:* Subtract the two equations.)

53. Show that the line $y = mx$ intersects the hyperbola given by the equation $\dfrac{x^2}{a^2} - \dfrac{y^2}{b^2} = 1$ if and only if $|m| < \left|\dfrac{b}{a}\right|$.

PREPARE FOR SECTION 6.4

54. Factor $x^4 + 14x^2 + 49$ over the real numbers. [P.4]
$(x^2 + 7)^2$

55. Add: $\dfrac{5}{x - 1} + \dfrac{1}{x + 2}$ [P.5] $\dfrac{6x + 9}{(x - 1)(x + 2)}$

56. Simplify: $\dfrac{7}{x} - \dfrac{6}{x - 1} + \dfrac{10}{(x - 1)^2}$ [P.5] $\dfrac{x^2 + 2x + 7}{x(x - 1)^2}$

57. Solve: $\begin{cases} 1 = A + B \\ 11 = -5A + 3B \end{cases}$ [6.1]   (−1, 2)

58. Solve: $\begin{cases} 0 = A + B \\ 3 = -2B + C \\ 16 = 7A - 2C \end{cases}$ [6.2]   (2, −2, −1)

59. Divide: $\dfrac{x^3 - 4x^2 - 19x - 35}{x^2 - 7x}$ [3.1] $x + 3 + \dfrac{2x - 35}{x^2 - 7x}$

PROJECTS

---

1. **FINDING ZEROS OF A POLYNOMIAL** One zero of $P(x) = x^3 + 2x^2 + Cx - 6$ is the sum of the other two zeros of $P(x)$. Find C and the three zeros of $P(x)$.

2. **PROVING A GEOMETRY THEOREM** Consider the triangle that is shown at the right inscribed in a circle of radius a with one side along the diameter of the circle. Prove that the triangle is a right triangle by completing the following steps.

a. Let $y = mx$, $m \geq 0$. Show that the graph of $y = mx$, $m \geq 0$, intersects the circle whose equation is $(x - a)^2 + y^2 = a^2$, $a > 0$, at $P\left(\dfrac{2a}{1 + m^2}, \dfrac{2ma}{1 + m^2}\right)$.

b. Show that the slope of the line through P and $Q(2a, 0)$ is $-\dfrac{1}{m}$.

c. What is the slope of the line between O and P?

d. Prove that line segment OP is perpendicular to line segment PQ.

e. How can you conclude from the foregoing that triangle OPQ is a right triangle?

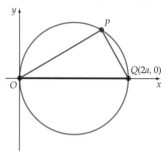

| SECTION 6.4 | **PARTIAL FRACTIONS** |

● **PARTIAL FRACTION DECOMPOSITION**

● **PARTIAL FRACTION DECOMPOSITION**

An algebraic application of systems of equations is a technique known as *partial fractions*. In Chapter P, we reviewed the problem of adding two rational expressions. For example,

$$\frac{5}{x - 1} + \frac{1}{x + 2} = \frac{6x + 9}{(x - 1)(x + 2)}$$

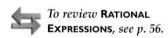

To review **RATIONAL EXPRESSIONS,** *see p. 56.*

Now we will take an opposite approach. That is, given a rational expression, we will find simpler rational expressions whose sum is the given expression. The method by which a more complicated rational expression is written as a sum of rational expressions is called **partial fraction decomposition.** This technique is based on the following theorem.

Partial Fraction Decomposition Theorem

If
$$f(x) = \frac{p(x)}{q(x)}$$

is a rational expression in which the degree of the numerator is less than the degree of the denominator, and $p(x)$ and $q(x)$ have no common factors, then $f(x)$ can be written as a partial fraction decomposition in the form

$$f(x) = f_1(x) + f_2(x) + \cdots + f_n(x)$$

where each $f_i(x)$ has one of the following forms:

$$\frac{A}{(px + q)^m} \quad \text{or} \quad \frac{Bx + C}{(ax^2 + bx + c)^m}$$

The procedure for finding a partial fraction decomposition of a rational expression depends on factorization of the denominator of the rational expression. There are four cases.

Case 1 Nonrepeated Linear Factors

The partial fraction decomposition will contain an expression of the form $\dfrac{A}{x + a}$ for each nonrepeated linear factor of the denominator. Example:

$$\frac{3x - 1}{x(3x + 4)(x - 2)} \qquad \bullet \textbf{ Each linear factor of the denominator occurs only once.}$$

Partial fraction decomposition:

$$\frac{3x - 1}{x(3x + 4)(x - 2)} = \frac{A}{x} + \frac{B}{3x + 4} + \frac{C}{x - 2}$$

Case 2 Repeated Linear Factors

The partial fraction decomposition will contain an expression of the form

$$\frac{A_1}{(x + a)} + \frac{A_2}{(x + a)^2} + \cdots + \frac{A_m}{(x + a)^m}$$

for each repeated linear factor of multiplicity m. Example:

$$\frac{4x + 5}{(x - 2)^2(2x + 1)} \qquad \bullet \textbf{ } (x - 2)^2 = (x - 2)(x - 2), \textbf{ a repeated linear factor.}$$

Partial fraction decomposition:

$$\frac{4x + 5}{(x - 2)^2(2x + 1)} = \frac{A_1}{x - 2} + \frac{A_2}{(x - 2)^2} + \frac{B}{2x + 1}$$

Case 3 Nonrepeated Quadratic Factors

The partial fraction decomposition will contain an expression of the form

$$\frac{Ax + B}{ax^2 + bx + c}$$

for each quadratic factor irreducible over the real numbers. Example:

$$\frac{x - 4}{(x^2 + x + 1)(x - 4)} \qquad \bullet \textbf{ } x^2 + x + 1 \textbf{ is irreducible over the real numbers.}$$

Partial fraction decomposition:

$$\frac{x - 4}{(x^2 + x + 1)(x - 4)} = \frac{Ax + B}{x^2 + x + 1} + \frac{C}{x - 4}$$

Case 4 Repeated Quadratic Factors

The partial fraction decomposition will contain an expression of the form

$$\frac{A_1x + B_1}{ax^2 + bx + c} + \frac{A_2x + B_2}{(ax^2 + bx + c)^2} + \cdots + \frac{A_mx + B_m}{(ax^2 + bx + c)^m}$$

for each quadratic factor irreducible over the real numbers. Example:

$$\frac{2x}{(x-2)(x^2+4)^2}$$ • $(x^2+4)^2$ is a repeated quadratic factor.

Partial fraction decomposition:

$$\frac{2x}{(x-2)(x^2+4)^2}=\frac{A_1x+B_1}{x^2+4}+\frac{A_2x+B_2}{(x^2+4)^2}+\frac{C}{x-2}$$

❓ QUESTION Which of the four cases of a partial fraction decomposition apply to $\dfrac{x+2}{(x-2)(x^2+4)}$?

There are various methods for finding the constants of a partial fraction decomposition. One such method is based on a property of polynomials.

Equality of Polynomials

If the two polynomials $p(x)=a_nx^n+a_{n-1}x^{n-1}+\cdots+a_1x+a_0$ and $r(x)=b_nx^n+b_{n-1}x^{n-1}+\cdots+b_1x+b_0$ are of degree n, then $p(x)=r(x)$ if and only if $a_0=b_0, a_1=b_1, a_2=b_2,\ldots, a_n=b_n$.

Alternative to Example 1
Find a partial fraction decomposition of $\dfrac{x-5}{x^2-1}$.

○ $\dfrac{3}{x+1}-\dfrac{2}{x-1}$

INSTRUCTOR NOTE
Another way to approach solving for A and B is to evaluate the left and right sides of

$x+11=A(x-5)+B(x+3)$

at "convenient" values of x—that is, the values of x for which $x+3=0$ or $x-5=0$.

Find a Partial Fraction Decomposition
EXAMPLE 1   **Case 1: Nonrepeated Linear Factors**

Find a partial fraction decomposition of $\dfrac{x+11}{x^2-2x-15}$.

Solution

First factor the denominator.

$$x^2-2x-15=(x+3)(x-5)$$

The factors are nonrepeated linear factors. Therefore, the partial fraction decomposition will have the form

$$\frac{x+11}{(x+3)(x-5)}=\frac{A}{x+3}+\frac{B}{x-5} \tag{1}$$

To solve for A and B, multiply each side of the equation by the least common multiple of the denominators, $(x+3)(x-5)$.

$$x+11=A(x-5)+B(x+3)$$
$$x+11=(A+B)x+(-5A+3B)$$ • Combine like terms.

❓ ANSWER Cases 1 and 4.

Using the Equality of Polynomials Theorem, equate coefficients of like powers. The result will be the system of equations

$$\begin{cases} 1 = A + B \\ 11 = -5A + 3B \end{cases}$$

• Recall that $x = 1 \cdot x$.

Solving the system of equations for A and B, we have $A = -1$ and $B = 2$. Substituting -1 for A and 2 for B into the form of the partial fraction decomposition (1), we obtain

$$\frac{x + 11}{(x + 3)(x - 5)} = \frac{-1}{x + 3} + \frac{2}{x - 5}$$

You should add the two expressions to verify the equality.

▶ **TRY EXERCISE 14, PAGE 544**

Alternative to Example 2

Find a partial fraction decomposition of $\dfrac{-7x + 27}{x(x - 3)^2}$.

⊙ $\dfrac{3}{x} - \dfrac{3}{x - 3} + \dfrac{2}{(x - 3)^2}$

EXAMPLE 2

Find the Partial Fraction Decomposition Case 2: Repeated Linear Factors

Find a partial fraction decomposition of $\dfrac{x^2 + 2x + 7}{x(x - 1)^2}$.

Solution

The denominator has one nonrepeated factor and one repeated factor. The partial fraction decomposition will have the form

$$\frac{x^2 + 2x + 7}{x(x - 1)^2} = \frac{A}{x} + \frac{B}{x - 1} + \frac{C}{(x - 1)^2}$$

Multiplying each side by the LCD $x(x - 1)^2$, we have

$$x^2 + 2x + 7 = A(x - 1)^2 + B(x - 1)x + Cx$$

Expanding the right side and combining like terms gives

$$x^2 + 2x + 7 = (A + B)x^2 + (-2A - B + C)x + A$$

Using the Equality of Polynomials Theorem, equate coefficients of like powers. This will result in the system of equations

$$\begin{cases} 1 = A + B \\ 2 = -2A - B + C \\ 7 = A \end{cases}$$

The solution is $A = 7$, $B = -6$, and $C = 10$. Thus the partial fraction decomposition is

$$\frac{x^2 + 2x + 7}{x(x - 1)^2} = \frac{7}{x} + \frac{-6}{x - 1} + \frac{10}{(x - 1)^2}$$

▶ **TRY EXERCISE 22, PAGE 544**

Alternative to Example 3
Find a partial fraction decomposition of
$\dfrac{3x^2 + 6x - 21}{(x - 5)(x^2 + 3)}$.

● $\dfrac{3}{x - 5} + \dfrac{6}{(x^2 + 3)}$

INSTRUCTOR NOTE

Example 3 can be solved in a manner that is similar to the method discussed in the instructor note accompanying Example 1. Substitute $i\sqrt{7}$ for x in

$$3x + 16 = A(x^2 + 7)$$
$$+ (Bx + C)(x - 2)$$

and solve for B and C by equating complex numbers. This may be a good challenge problem for some students.

EXAMPLE 3   **Find the Partial Fraction Decomposition**
Case 3: Nonrepeated Quadratic Factor

Find the partial fraction decomposition of $\dfrac{3x + 16}{(x - 2)(x^2 + 7)}$.

Solution

Because $(x - 2)$ is a nonrepeated linear factor and $x^2 + 7$ is an irreducible quadratic over the real numbers, the partial fraction decomposition will have the form

$$\frac{3x + 16}{(x - 2)(x^2 + 7)} = \frac{A}{x - 2} + \frac{Bx + C}{x^2 + 7}$$

Multiplying each side by the LCD $(x - 2)(x^2 + 7)$ yields

$$3x + 16 = A(x^2 + 7) + (Bx + C)(x - 2)$$

Expanding the right side and combining like terms, we have

$$3x + 16 = (A + B)x^2 + (-2B + C)x + (7A - 2C)$$

Using the Equality of Polynomials Theorem, equate coefficients of like powers. This will result in the system of equations

$$\begin{cases} 0 = A + B \\ 3 = \quad -2B + C \\ 16 = 7A \quad\quad - 2C \end{cases}$$

• Think of $3x + 16$ as $0x^2 + 3x + 16$.

The solution is $A = 2$, $B = -2$, and $C = -1$. Thus the partial fraction decomposition is

$$\frac{3x + 16}{(x - 2)(x^2 + 7)} = \frac{2}{x - 2} + \frac{-2x - 1}{x^2 + 7}$$

▶ **TRY EXERCISE 24, PAGE 544**

Alternative to Example 4
Find a partial fraction decomposition of
$\dfrac{2x^3 - x^2 - 6x - 7}{(x^2 - x - 3)^2}$.

● $\dfrac{2x + 1}{x^2 - x - 3} + \dfrac{x - 4}{(x^2 - x - 3)^2}$

EXAMPLE 4   **Find a Partial Fraction Decomposition**
Case 4: Repeated Quadratic Factors

Find the partial fraction decomposition of $\dfrac{4x^3 + 5x^2 + 7x - 1}{(x^2 + x + 1)^2}$.

Solution

The quadratic factor $(x^2 + x + 1)$ is irreducible over the real numbers and is a repeated factor. The partial fraction decomposition will be of the form

$$\frac{4x^3 + 5x^2 + 7x - 1}{(x^2 + x + 1)^2} = \frac{Ax + B}{x^2 + x + 1} + \frac{Cx + D}{(x^2 + x + 1)^2}$$

Multiplying each side by the LCD $(x^2 + x + 1)^2$ and collecting like terms, we obtain

$$4x^3 + 5x^2 + 7x - 1 = (Ax + B)(x^2 + x + 1) + Cx + D$$
$$= Ax^3 + Ax^2 + Ax + Bx^2 + Bx + B + Cx + D$$
$$= Ax^3 + (A + B)x^2 + (A + B + C)x + (B + D)$$

Equating coefficients of like powers gives the system of equations

$$\begin{cases} 4 = A \\ 5 = A + B \\ 7 = A + B + C \\ -1 = B + D \end{cases}$$

Solving this system, we have $A = 4$, $B = 1$, $C = 2$, and $D = -2$. Thus the partial fraction decomposition is

$$\frac{4x^3 + 5x^2 + 7x - 1}{(x^2 + x + 1)^2} = \frac{4x + 1}{x^2 + x + 1} + \frac{2x - 2}{(x^2 + x + 1)^2}$$

▶ **TRY EXERCISE 30, PAGE 545**

The Partial Fraction Decomposition Theorem requires that the degree of the numerator be less than the degree of the denominator. If this is *not* the case, use long division to first write the rational expression as a polynomial plus a remainder over the denominator.

Alternative to Example 5
Find a partial fraction decomposition of
$\dfrac{2x^3 - 11x^2 + 8x + 9}{x^2 - 3x}$.

● $2x - 5 - \dfrac{3}{x} - \dfrac{4}{x - 3}$

EXAMPLE 5

Find a Partial Fraction Decomposition When the Degree of the Numerator Exceeds the Degree of the Denominator

Find the partial fraction decomposition of $F(x) = \dfrac{x^3 - 4x^2 - 19x - 35}{x^2 - 7x}$.

Solution

Because the degree of the denominator is less than the degree of the numerator, use long division first to obtain

$$F(x) = x + 3 + \frac{2x - 35}{x^2 - 7x}$$

The partial fraction decomposition of $\dfrac{2x - 35}{x^2 - 7x}$ will have the form

$$\frac{2x - 35}{x^2 - 7x} = \frac{2x - 35}{x(x - 7)} = \frac{A}{x} + \frac{B}{x - 7}$$

Multiplying each side by $x(x - 7)$ and combining like terms, we have

$$2x - 35 = (A + B)x + (-7A)$$

Equating coefficients of like powers yields

$$\begin{cases} 2 = A + B \\ -35 = -7A \end{cases}$$

The solution of this system is $A = 5$ and $B = -3$. The partial fraction decomposition is

$$\frac{x^3 - 4x^2 - 19x - 35}{x^2 - 7x} = x + 3 + \frac{5}{x} + \frac{-3}{x - 7}$$

▶ **TRY EXERCISE 34, PAGE 545**

TOPICS FOR DISCUSSION

1. What is the purpose of a partial fraction decomposition?

2. Discuss how the factors of the denominator of a rational expression dictate how a partial fraction decomposition is determined.

3. Discuss the Equality of Polynomials Theorem and how it is used in a partial fraction decomposition.

4. For the rational expression $\dfrac{3x - 1}{x^3 - 2x^2 - x + 2}$, what is the first step you perform to find a partial fraction decomposition? What equation or equations do you solve to find the partial fraction decomposition?

EXERCISE SET 6.4   *—Suggested Assignment: Exercises 1–37, every other odd; 45–50.*

In Exercises 1 to 10, determine the constants A, B, C, and D.

1. $\dfrac{x + 15}{x(x - 5)} = \dfrac{A}{x} + \dfrac{B}{x - 5}$ $A = -3, B = 4$

2. $\dfrac{5x - 6}{x(x + 3)} = \dfrac{A}{x} + \dfrac{B}{x + 3}$ $A = -2, B = 7$

3. $\dfrac{1}{(2x + 3)(x - 1)} = \dfrac{A}{2x + 3} + \dfrac{B}{x - 1}$ $A = -\dfrac{2}{5}, B = \dfrac{1}{5}$

4. $\dfrac{6x - 5}{(x + 4)(3x + 2)} = \dfrac{A}{x + 4} + \dfrac{B}{3x + 2}$ $A = \dfrac{29}{10}, B = -\dfrac{27}{10}$

5. $\dfrac{x + 9}{x(x - 3)^2} = \dfrac{A}{x} + \dfrac{B}{x - 3} + \dfrac{C}{(x - 3)^2}$ $A = 1, B = -1, C = 4$

6. $\dfrac{2x - 7}{(x + 1)(x - 2)^2} = \dfrac{A}{x + 1} + \dfrac{B}{x - 2} + \dfrac{C}{(x - 2)^2}$
$A = -1, B = 1, C = -1$

7. $\dfrac{4x^2 + 3}{(x - 1)(x^2 + x + 5)} = \dfrac{A}{x - 1} + \dfrac{Bx + C}{x^2 + x + 5}$
$A = 1, B = 3, C = 2$

8. $\dfrac{x^2 + x + 3}{(x^2 + 7)(x - 3)} = \dfrac{Ax + B}{x^2 + 7} + \dfrac{C}{x - 3}$ $A = \dfrac{1}{16}, B = \dfrac{19}{16}, C = \dfrac{15}{16}$

9. $\dfrac{x^3 + 2x}{(x^2 + 1)^2} = \dfrac{Ax + B}{x^2 + 1} + \dfrac{Cx + D}{(x^2 + 1)^2}$ $A = 1, B = 0, C = 1, D = 0$

10. $\dfrac{3x^3 + x^2 - x - 5}{(x^2 + 2x + 5)^2} = \dfrac{Ax + B}{x^2 + 2x + 5} + \dfrac{Cx + D}{(x^2 + 2x + 5)^2}$
$A = 3, B = -5, C = -6, D = 20$

In Exercises 11 to 36, find the partial fraction decomposition of the given rational expression.

11. $\dfrac{8x + 12}{x(x + 4)}$ $\dfrac{3}{x} + \dfrac{5}{x + 4}$

12. $\dfrac{x - 14}{x(x - 7)}$ $\dfrac{2}{x} + \dfrac{-1}{x - 7}$

13. $\dfrac{3x + 50}{x^2 - 7x - 18}$ $\dfrac{7}{x - 9} + \dfrac{-4}{x + 2}$

▶14. $\dfrac{7x + 44}{x^2 + 10x + 24}$ $\dfrac{8}{x + 4} + \dfrac{-1}{x + 6}$

15. $\dfrac{16x + 34}{4x^2 + 16x + 15}$ $\dfrac{5}{2x + 3} + \dfrac{3}{2x + 5}$

16. $\dfrac{-15x + 37}{9x^2 - 12x - 5}$ $\dfrac{-7}{3x + 1} + \dfrac{2}{3x - 5}$

17. $\dfrac{x - 5}{(3x + 5)(x - 2)}$ $\dfrac{20}{11(3x + 5)} + \dfrac{-3}{11(x - 2)}$

18. $\dfrac{1}{(x + 7)(2x - 5)}$ $\dfrac{-1}{19(x + 7)} + \dfrac{2}{19(2x - 5)}$

19. $\dfrac{x^3 + 3x^2 - 4x - 8}{x^2 - 4}$ $x + 3 + \dfrac{1}{x - 2} + \dfrac{-1}{x + 2}$

20. $\dfrac{x^3 - 13x - 9}{x^2 - x - 12}$ $x + 1 + \dfrac{3}{7(x - 4)} + \dfrac{-3}{7(x + 3)}$

21. $\dfrac{3x^2 + 49}{x(x + 7)^2}$ $\dfrac{1}{x} + \dfrac{2}{x + 7} + \dfrac{-28}{(x + 7)^2}$

▶22. $\dfrac{x - 18}{x(x - 3)^2}$ $\dfrac{-2}{x} + \dfrac{2}{x - 3} + \dfrac{-5}{(x - 3)^2}$

23. $\dfrac{5x^2 - 7x + 2}{x^3 - 3x^2 + x}$ $\dfrac{2}{x} + \dfrac{3x - 1}{x^2 - 3x + 1}$

▶24. $\dfrac{9x^2 - 3x + 49}{x^3 - x^2 + 10x - 10}$ $\dfrac{5}{x - 1} + \dfrac{4x + 1}{x^2 + 10}$

25. $\dfrac{2x^3 + 9x^2 + 26x + 41}{(x + 3)^2(x^2 + 1)}$

$\dfrac{2}{x + 3} + \dfrac{-1}{(x + 3)^2} + \dfrac{4}{x^2 + 1}$

26. $\dfrac{12x^3 - 37x^2 + 48x - 36}{(x - 2)^2(x^2 + 4)}$

$\dfrac{5}{x - 2} + \dfrac{1}{(x - 2)^2} + \dfrac{7x}{x^2 + 4}$

27. $\dfrac{3x - 7}{(x - 4)^2}$

$\dfrac{3}{x - 4} + \dfrac{5}{(x - 4)^2}$

28. $\dfrac{5x - 53}{(x - 11)^2}$

$\dfrac{5}{x - 11} + \dfrac{2}{(x - 11)^2}$

29. $\dfrac{3x^3 - x^2 + 34x - 10}{(x^2 + 10)^2}$

$\dfrac{3x - 1}{x^2 + 10} + \dfrac{4x}{(x^2 + 10)^2}$

▶ **30.** $\dfrac{2x^3 + 9x + 1}{x^4 + 14x^2 + 49}$

$\dfrac{2x}{x^2 + 7} + \dfrac{-5x + 1}{(x^2 + 7)^2}$

31. $\dfrac{1}{k^2 - x^2}$, where k is a constant

$\dfrac{1}{2k(k - x)} + \dfrac{1}{2k(k + x)}$

32. $\dfrac{1}{x(k + mx)}$, where k and m are constants $\dfrac{1}{kx} + \dfrac{-m}{k(k + mx)}$

33. $\dfrac{x^3 - x^2 - x - 1}{x^2 - x}$

$x + \dfrac{1}{x} + \dfrac{-2}{x - 1}$

34. $\dfrac{2x^3 + 5x^2 + 3x - 8}{2x^2 + 3x - 2}$

$x + 1 + \dfrac{-2}{2x - 1} + \dfrac{2}{x + 2}$

35. $\dfrac{2x^3 - 4x^2 + 5}{x^2 - x - 1}$

$2x - 2 + \dfrac{3}{x^2 - x - 1}$

36. $\dfrac{x^4 - 2x^3 - 2x^2 - x + 3}{x^2(x - 3)}$

$x + 1 + \dfrac{-1}{x^2} + \dfrac{1}{x - 3}$

—Answers to Exercises 37–44 are on page AA28.

CONNECTING CONCEPTS

In Exercises 37 to 42, find the partial fraction decomposition of the given rational expression.

37. $\dfrac{x^2 - 1}{(x - 1)(x + 2)(x - 3)}$

38. $\dfrac{x^2 + x}{x^2(x - 4)}$

39. $\dfrac{-x^4 - 4x^2 + 3x - 6}{x^4(x - 2)}$

40. $\dfrac{3x^2 - 2x - 1}{(x^2 - 1)^2}$

41. $\dfrac{2x^2 + 3x - 1}{x^3 - 1}$

42. $\dfrac{x^3 - 2x^2 + x - 2}{x^4 - x^3 + x - 1}$

44. Use the result of Exercise 43 to find the partial fraction decomposition of

a. $\dfrac{1}{(x^2 + 4)(x^2 + 1)}$

b. $\dfrac{1}{(x^2 + 1)(x^2 + 9)}$

c. $\dfrac{1}{(x^2 + x + 1)(x^2 + x + 2)}$

d. $\dfrac{1}{(x^2 + 2x + 4)(x^2 + 2x + 9)}$

There is a shortcut for finding some partial fraction decompositions of quadratic polynomials that do not factor over the real numbers. Exercises 43 and 44 give one method and some examples.

43. Show that for real numbers a and b with $a \neq b$,

$$\dfrac{1}{(b - a)[\,p(x) + a\,]} + \dfrac{1}{(a - b)[\,p(x) + b\,]} = \dfrac{1}{[\,p(x) + a\,][\,p(x) + b\,]}$$

—Answer graphs to Exercises 45–50 are on page AA28.

PREPARE FOR SECTION 6.5

45. Graph: $y = -2x + 3$ [2.3]

46. Graph: $y = -x^2 + 3x + 4$ [2.4]

47. Graph: $y = |x| + 1$ [2.2]

48. Graph: $\dfrac{x^2}{4} - \dfrac{y^2}{9} = 1$ [5.3]

49. Graph: $\dfrac{x^2}{16} + \dfrac{y^2}{25} = 1$ [5.2]

50. Graph: $(y + 2)^2 = 4x$ [5.1]

PROJECTS

1. Computer algebra systems (CAS) such as *Mathematica* and *Derive* provide computer assistance for partial fraction decompositions. The command in *Mathematica* is **Apart** and the command in *Derive* is **Expand**. Here is an example of using each of these programs to find the partial fraction decomposition of $\dfrac{x^3 - 4x^2 - 19x - 35}{x^2 - 7x}$.

Derive

Start up the *Derive* program. The menu bar on the bottom of the screen should begin with **Author**. If it does not, press the ESC key until it does. Now type

A((x^3–4x^2–19x–35)/(x^2–7x)) ENTER E ENTER

The **A** allows you to input the expression into the computer. The **E** after the first ENTER is the command **Expand**, which performs the partial fraction decomposition. The result is displayed as

$$\frac{3}{7 - x} + x + \frac{5}{x} + 3.$$

Mathematica

Start up the *Mathematica* program. Now type

Apart[(x^3–4x^2–19x–35)/(x^2–7x)] ENTER

The brackets, [and], are not interchangeable with parentheses, (and). The result is displayed as

$$3 - \frac{3}{-7 + x} + \frac{5}{x} + x.$$

Use a CAS program to find partial fraction decompositions for some of the exercises in this section. Include a printout of your work.

INEQUALITIES IN TWO VARIABLES AND SYSTEMS OF INEQUALITIES

- GRAPH AN INEQUALITY
- SYSTEMS OF INEQUALITIES IN TWO VARIABLES
- NONLINEAR SYSTEMS OF INEQUALITIES

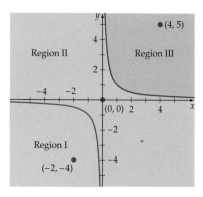

$xy \geq 1$

P **FIGURE 6.26**

• GRAPH AN INEQUALITY

Two examples of inequalities in two variables are

$$2x + 3y > 6 \quad \text{and} \quad xy \leq 1$$

A solution of an inequality in two variables is an ordered pair (x, y) that satisfies the inequality. For example, $(-2, 4)$ is a solution of the first inequality because $2(-2) + 3(4) > 6$. The ordered pair $(2, 1)$ is not a solution of the second inequality because $(2)(1) \not\leq 1$.

The **solution set of an inequality** in two variables is the set of all ordered pairs that satisfy the inequality. The **graph** of an inequality is the graph of the solution set.

To sketch the graph of an inequality, first replace the inequality symbol by an equality sign and sketch the graph of the equation. Use a dashed graph for < or > to indicate that the curve is not part of the solution set. Use a solid graph for ≤ or ≥ to show that the graph *is* part of the solution set.

It is important to test an ordered pair in each region of the plane defined by the graph. If the ordered pair satisfies the inequality, shade that entire region. Do this for each region into which the graph divides the plane. For example, consider the inequality $xy \geq 1$. **Figure 6.26** shows the three regions of the plane defined by this inequality. Because the inequality is ≥, a solid graph is used.

Choose an ordered pair in each of the three regions and determine whether that ordered pair satisfies the inequality. In Region I, choose a point, say $(-2, -4)$. Because $(-2)(-4) \geq 1$, Region I is part of the solution set. In Region II, choose a point, say $(0, 0)$. Because $0 \cdot 0 \not\geq 1$, Region II is not part of the solution set. In Region III, choose $(4, 5)$. Because $4 \cdot 5 \geq 1$, Region III is part of the solution set.

You may choose the coordinates of any point not on the graph of the equation as a test ordered pair; $(0, 0)$ is usually a good choice.

❓ QUESTION Is $(0, 0)$ a solution of $y \geq x^2 + 2x - 3$?

EXAMPLE 1 **Graph a Linear Inequality**

Graph: $3x + 4y > 12$

Solution

Graph the line $3x + 4y = 12$ using a dashed line.

$$\text{Test the ordered pair } (0, 0): \quad 3(0) + 4(0) = 0 \not> 12$$

Because $(0, 0)$ does not satisfy the inequality, do not shade this region.

$$\text{Test the ordered pair } (2, 3): \quad 3(2) + 4(3) = 18 > 12$$

Because $(2, 3)$ satisfies the inequality, the half-plane that includes $(2, 3)$ is the solution set. See **Figure 6.27**.

▶ **TRY EXERCISE 6, PAGE 551**

In general, the solution set of a *linear inequality in two variables* will be one of the regions of the plane separated by a line. Each region is called a **half-plane.**

EXAMPLE 2 **Graph a Nonlinear Inequality**

Graph: $y \leq x^2 + 2x - 3$

Solution

Graph the parabola $y = x^2 + 2x - 3$ using a solid curve.

$$\text{Test the ordered pair } (0, 0): \quad 0 \not\leq 0^2 + 2(0) - 3$$

Because $(0, 0)$ does not satisfy the inequality, do not shade this region.

$$\text{Test the ordered pair } (3, 2): \quad 2 \leq (3)^2 + 2(3) - 3$$

Because $(3, 2)$ satisfies the inequality, shade this region of the plane. See **Figure 6.28**.

▶ **TRY EXERCISE 12, PAGE 551**

Alternative to Example 1
Graph: $2x - 3y < 6$

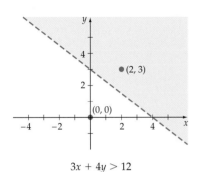

$3x + 4y > 12$

FIGURE 6.27

Alternative to Example 2
Graph: $y \geq x^2 - 4x - 5$

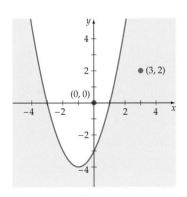

$y \leq x^2 + 2x - 3$

FIGURE 6.28

❓ ANSWER Yes.

Alternative to Example 3
Graph $y < |x - 1|$.

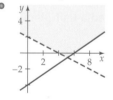

$$y \geq |x| + 1$$

FIGURE 6.29

EXAMPLE 3 Graph an Absolute Value Inequality

Graph: $y \geq |x| + 1$

Solution

Graph the equation $y = |x| + 1$ using a solid graph.

$$\text{Test the ordered pair } (0, 0): \quad 0 \not\geq |0| + 1$$

Because $0 \not\geq 1$, $(0, 0)$ does not belong to the solution set. Do not shade the portion of the plane that contains $(0, 0)$.

$$\text{Test the ordered pair } (0, 4): \quad 4 \geq |0| + 1$$

Because $(0, 4)$ satisfies the inequality, shade this region. See **Figure 6.29**.

▶ **TRY EXERCISE 20, PAGE 551**

● **SYSTEMS OF INEQUALITIES IN TWO VARIABLES**

The **solution set of a system of inequalities** is the intersection of the solution sets of the individual inequalities. To graph the solution set of a system of inequalities, first graph the solution set of each inequality. The solution set of the system of inequalities is the region of the plane represented by the intersection of the shaded regions.

Alternative to Example 4
Graph the solution set of the system of inequalities.

$$\begin{cases} x + 2y > 4 \\ 2x - 3y \leq 12 \end{cases}$$

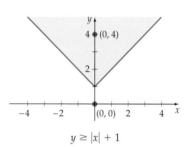

EXAMPLE 4 Graph a System of Linear Inequalities

Graph the solution set of the system of inequalities.

$$\begin{cases} 3x - 2y > 6 \\ 2x - 5y \leq 10 \end{cases}$$

Solution

Graph the line $3x - 2y = 6$ using a dashed line. Test the ordered pair $(0, 0)$. Because $3(0) - 2(0) \not> 6$, $(0, 0)$ does not belong to the solution set. Do not shade the region that contains $(0, 0)$. Instead, shade the region below and to the right of the graph of $3x - 2y = 6$, because any ordered pair from this region satisfies $3x - 2y > 6$.

Graph the line $2x - 5y = 10$ using a solid line. Test the ordered pair $(0, 0)$. Because $2(0) - 5(0) \leq 10$, shade the region that contains $(0, 0)$.

The solution set is the region of the plane represented by the intersection of the solution sets of the individual inequalities. See **Figure 6.30**.

▶ **TRY EXERCISE 28, PAGE 551**

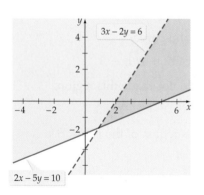

FIGURE 6.30

Alternative to Example 5
Graph the solution set of the system of inequalities.

$$\begin{cases} x^2 + 4y^2 > 4 \\ x + y \le 1 \end{cases}$$

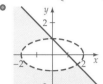

● **NONLINEAR SYSTEMS OF INEQUALITIES**

EXAMPLE 5   Graph a Nonlinear System of Inequalities

Graph the solution set of the system of inequalities.

$$\begin{cases} x^2 - y^2 \le 9 \\ 2x + 3y > 12 \end{cases}$$

Solution

Graph the hyperbola $x^2 - y^2 = 9$ by using a solid graph. Test the ordered pair $(0, 0)$. Because $0^2 - 0^2 \le 9$, shade the region containing the origin. By choosing points in the other regions, you should show that those regions are not part of the solution set.

Graph the line $2x + 3y = 12$ by using a dashed graph. Test the ordered pair $(0, 0)$. Because $2(0) + 3(0) \not> 12$, do not shade the half-plane below the line. Testing the ordered pair $(4, 4)$ will show that we need to shade the half-plane above the line $2x + 3y = 12$.

The solution set is the region of the plane represented by the intersection of the solution sets of the individual inequalities. This intersection is shown by the dark color in **Figure 6.31**.

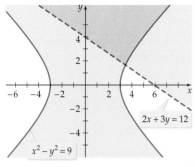

$2x + 3y = 12$

$x^2 - y^2 = 9$

Ⓟ **FIGURE 6.31**

▶ **TRY EXERCISE 38, PAGE 551**

Alternative to Example 6
Graph the solution set of the system of inequalities.

$$\begin{cases} x^2 + y^2 > 25 \\ x^2 + 4y^2 \le 16 \end{cases}$$

● **The system has no solution.**

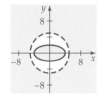

EXAMPLE 6   Identify a System of Inequalities with No Solution

Graph the solution set of the system of inequalities

$$\begin{cases} x^2 + y^2 \le 16 \\ x^2 - y^2 \ge 36 \end{cases}$$

Solution

Graph the circle $x^2 + y^2 = 16$ by using a solid graph. Test the ordered pair $(0, 0)$. Because $0^2 + 0^2 \le 16$, shade the inside of the circle.

Graph the hyperbola $x^2 - y^2 = 36$ by using a solid graph. Use ordered pairs from each of the regions defined by the hyperbola to determine that the solution of $x^2 - y^2 > 36$ consists of the region to the right of the right branch of the hyperbola and the region to the left of the left branch.

Because the solution sets of the inequalities do not intersect, the system has no solution. The solution set is the empty set. See **Figure 6.32.**

$x^2 + y^2 = 16$

$x^2 - y^2 = 36$

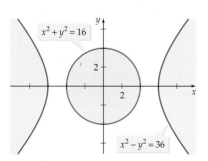

Ⓟ **FIGURE 6.32**

▶ **TRY EXERCISE 42, PAGE 551**

Alternative to Example 7
Graph the solution set of the system of inequalities.

$$\begin{cases} x + 3y \leq 6 \\ 3x - 4y \leq 12 \\ x \geq -3, y \geq -1 \end{cases}$$

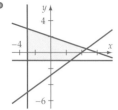

INSTRUCTOR NOTE
This example is in preparation for linear programming, which is covered in the next section.

EXAMPLE 7 **Graph a System of Four Inequalities**

Graph the solution set of the system of inequalities.

$$\begin{cases} 2x - 3y \leq 2 \\ 3x + 4y \geq 12 \\ x \geq -1, y \geq 2 \end{cases}$$

Solution

First graph the inequalities $x \geq -1$ and $y \geq 2$. Because $x \geq -1$ and $y \geq 2$, the solution set for this system will be on or above the line $y = 2$ and on or to the right of the line $x = -1$. See **Figure 6.33.**

Graph the solution set of $2x - 3y = 2$ by using a solid graph. Because $2(0) - 3(0) \leq 2$, shade the region above the line.

Graph the solution set of $3x + 4y = 12$ by using a solid graph. Test an ordered pair, say $(3, 3)$, to determine that we need to shade above the line $3x + 4y = 12$.

The solution set of the system of inequalities is the region where the graphs of the solution sets of all four inequalities intersect. This intersection is indicated by the dark color in **Figure 6.34.**

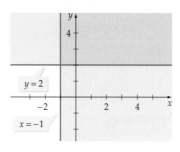

FIGURE 6.33

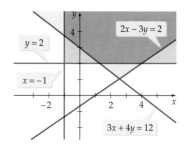

FIGURE 6.34

 TRY EXERCISE 44, PAGE 552

TOPICS FOR DISCUSSION

1. Does the graph of a linear inequality in two variables represent the graph of a function? Why or why not?

2. What is a half-plane?

3. Is it possible for a system of inequalities to have no solution? If so, give an example. If not, explain why not.

4. Let $A = \{(x, y)|x + y > 5\}$ and let $B = \{(x, y)|x - y < 3\}$. What is the significance of $A > B$?

5. Suppose a company makes two types of frying pans: regular and nonstick. Each week the company plans on making at least twice as many nonstick pans as regular. Production facilities are such that the company can make a maxi-

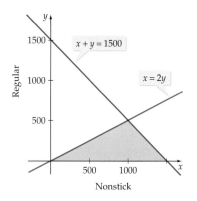

Regular

Nonstick

$x + y = 1500$

$x = 2y$

mum of 1500 pans per week. Letting x represent the number of nonstick pans and y represent the number of regular pans, the system of inequalities

$$\begin{cases} x \geq 2y \\ x + y \leq 1500 \\ x \geq 0, y \geq 0 \end{cases}$$

represents this situation. The graph of the solution set is shown in the accompanying figure. Explain the meaning of the solution set (shown shaded) in the context of this problem.

EXERCISE SET 6.5

—Suggested Assignment: Exercises 1–45, every other odd; 47, 51, 53, 57, 59–64.
—Answer graphs to Exercises 1–24, 25–48, 49–58 and 59–62 are on pages AA29–AA30.

In Exercises 1 to 24, sketch the graph of each inequality.

1. $y \leq -2$

2. $x + y > -2$

3. $y \geq 2x + 3$

4. $y < -2x + 1$

5. $2x - 3y < 6$

▶ 6. $3x + 4y \leq 4$

7. $4x + 3y \leq 12$

8. $5x - 2y < 8$

9. $y < x^2$

10. $x > y^2$

11. $y \geq x^2 - 2x - 3$

▶ 12. $y < 2x^2 - x - 3$

13. $(x - 2)^2 + (y - 1)^2 < 16$

14. $(x + 2)^2 + (y - 3)^2 > 25$

15. $\dfrac{(x - 3)^2}{9} - \dfrac{(y + 1)^2}{16} > 1$

16. $\dfrac{(x + 1)^2}{25} - \dfrac{(y - 3)^2}{16} \leq 1$

17. $4x^2 + 9y^2 - 8x + 18y \geq 23$

18. $25x^2 - 16y^2 - 100x - 64y < 64$

19. $y \geq |2x - 4|$

▶ 20. $y < |x|$

21. $y < 2^{x-1}$

22. $y > \log_3 x$

23. $y \leq \log_2 (x - 1)$

24. $y > 3^x + 1$

In Exercises 25 to 48, sketch the graph of the solution set of each system of inequalities.

25. $\begin{cases} 1 \leq x < 3 \\ -2 < y \leq 4 \end{cases}$

26. $\begin{cases} -2 < x < 4 \\ y \geq -1 \end{cases}$

27. $\begin{cases} 3x + 2y \geq 1 \\ x + 2y < -1 \end{cases}$

▶ 28. $\begin{cases} 2x - 5y < -6 \\ 3x + y < 8 \end{cases}$

29. $\begin{cases} 2x - y \geq -4 \\ 4x - 2y \leq -17 \end{cases}$

30. $\begin{cases} 4x + 2y > 5 \\ 6x + 3y > 10 \end{cases}$

31. $\begin{cases} 4x - 3y < 14 \\ 2x + 5y \leq -6 \end{cases}$

32. $\begin{cases} 3x + 5y \geq -8 \\ 2x - 3y \geq 1 \end{cases}$

33. $\begin{cases} y < 2x + 3 \\ y > 2x - 2 \end{cases}$

34. $\begin{cases} y > 3x + 1 \\ y < 3x - 2 \end{cases}$ no solution

35. $\begin{cases} y < 2x - 1 \\ y \geq x^2 + 3x - 7 \end{cases}$

36. $\begin{cases} y \leq 2x + 7 \\ y > x^2 + 3x + 1 \end{cases}$

37. $\begin{cases} x^2 + y^2 \leq 49 \\ 9x^2 + 4y^2 \geq 36 \end{cases}$

▶ 38. $\begin{cases} y < 2x - 1 \\ y > x^2 - 2x + 2 \end{cases}$

39. $\begin{cases} (x - 1)^2 + (y + 1)^2 \leq 16 \\ (x - 1)^2 + (y + 1)^2 \geq 4 \end{cases}$

40. $\begin{cases} (x + 2)^2 + (y - 3)^2 > 25 \\ (x + 2)^2 + (y - 3)^2 < 16 \end{cases}$ no solution

41. $\begin{cases} \dfrac{(x - 4)^2}{16} - \dfrac{(y + 2)^2}{9} > 1 \\ \dfrac{(x - 4)^2}{25} + \dfrac{(y + 2)^2}{9} < 1 \end{cases}$

▶ 42. $\begin{cases} \dfrac{(x + 1)^2}{36} + \dfrac{(y - 2)^2}{25} < 1 \\ \dfrac{(x + 1)^2}{25} + \dfrac{(y - 2)^2}{36} < 1 \end{cases}$

43. $\begin{cases} 2x - 3y \geq -5 \\ x + 2y \leq 7 \\ x \geq -1, y \geq 0 \end{cases}$ ▶ **44.** $\begin{cases} 5x + y \leq 9 \\ 2x + 3y \leq 14 \\ x \geq -2, y \geq 2 \end{cases}$ **47.** $\begin{cases} 3x + 4y \leq 12 \\ 2x + 5y \leq 10 \\ x \geq 0, y \geq 0 \end{cases}$ **48.** $\begin{cases} 5x + 3y \leq 15 \\ x + 4y \leq 8 \\ x \geq 0, y \geq 0 \end{cases}$

45. $\begin{cases} 3x + 2y \geq 14 \\ x + 3y \geq 14 \\ x \leq 10, y \leq 8 \end{cases}$ **46.** $\begin{cases} 4x + y \geq 13 \\ 3x + 2y \geq 16 \\ x \leq 15, y \leq 12 \end{cases}$

CONNECTING CONCEPTS

In Exercises 49 to 58, sketch the graph of the inequality.

49. $|y| \geq |x|$

50. $|y| \leq |x - 1|$

51. $|x + y| \leq 1$

52. $|x - y| > 1$

53. $|x| + |y| \leq 1$

54. $|x| - |y| > 1$

55. $y > [\![x]\!]$, where $[\![x]\!]$ is the greatest integer function

56. $y > x - [\![x]\!]$, where $[\![x]\!]$ is the greatest integer function

57. Sketch the graphs of $xy > 1$ and $y > \dfrac{1}{x}$. Note that the two graphs are not the same, yet the second inequality can be derived from the first by dividing each side by x. Explain.

58. Sketch the graph of $\dfrac{x}{y} < 1$ and the graph of $x < y$. Note that the two graphs are not the same, yet the second inequality can be derived from the first by multiplying each side by y. Explain.

PREPARE FOR SECTION 6.6

59. Graph: $2x + 3y \leq 12$ [6.5]

60. Graph the solution set of $\begin{cases} 3x + y \geq 6 \\ x + 3y \geq 6 \end{cases}$. [6.5]

61. Graph the solution set of $\begin{cases} x + y \geq 1 \\ 2x - y \leq 5 \\ x \geq 0, y \geq 0 \end{cases}$. [6.5]

62. Graph the solution set of $\begin{cases} 2x - y \leq 0 \\ 0 \leq x \leq 10 \\ 0 \leq y \leq 10 \end{cases}$. [6.5]

63. Solve: $\begin{cases} 3x + y = 6 \\ x + y = 4 \end{cases}$ [6.1] $(1, 3)$

64. Solve: $\begin{cases} 300x + 100y = 900 \\ 400x + 300y = 2200 \end{cases}$ [6.1] $(1, 6)$

PROJECTS

1. **A PARALLELOGRAM COORDINATE SYSTEM** The xy-coordinate system described in this chapter consisted of two coordinate lines that intersected at right angles. It is not necessary that coordinate lines intersect at right angles for a coordinate system to exist. Draw two coordinate axes that intersect at 0 but for which the angle between the two axes is 45°. You now have a *parallelogram* coordinate system rather than a *rectangular* coordinate system. Explain the last sentence. Now experiment in this system. For example, is the graph of $3x + 4y = 12$ a straight line in the *parallelogram* coordinate system? In a parallelogram coordinate system, is the graph of $y = x^2$ a parabola?

LINEAR PROGRAMMING

● INTRODUCTION TO LINEAR PROGRAMMING

Consider a business analyst who is trying to maximize the profit from the production of a product or an engineer who is trying to minimize the amount of energy an electrical circuit needs to operate. Generally, problems that seek to maximize or minimize a situation are called **optimization problems.** One strategy for solving certain of these problems was developed in the 1940s and is called **linear programming.**

A linear programming problem involves a **linear objective function,** which is the function that must be maximized or minimized. This objective function is subject to some **constraints,** which are inequalities or equations that restrict the values of the variables. To illustrate these concepts, suppose a manufacturer produces two types of computer monitors: monochrome and color. Past sales experience shows that at least twice as many monochrome monitors are sold as color monitors. Suppose further that the manufacturing plant is capable of producing 12 monitors per day. Let x represent the number of monochrome monitors produced, and let y represent the number of color monitors produced. Then

$$\begin{cases} x \geq 2y \\ x + y \leq 12 \end{cases} \qquad \bullet \textbf{These are the constraints.}$$

These two inequalities place a constraint, or restriction, on the manufacturer. For example, the manufacturer cannot produce five color monitors, because that would require producing at least ten monochrome monitors, and $5 + 10 \neq 12$.

Suppose a profit of \$50 is earned on each monochrome monitor sold and \$75 is earned on each color monitor sold. Then the manufacturer's profit P, in dollars, is given by the equation

$$P = 50x + 75y \qquad \bullet \textbf{Objective function}$$

The equation $P = 50x + 75y$ defines the objective function. The goal of this linear programming problem is to determine how many of each monitor should be produced to maximize the manufacturer's profit and at the same time satisfy the constraints.

Because the manufacturer cannot produce fewer than zero units of either monitor, there are two other implied constraints, $x \geq 0$ and $y \geq 0$. Our linear programming problem now looks like

Objective function: $\quad P = 50x + 75y$

Constraints: $\quad \begin{cases} x - 2y \geq 0 \\ x + y \leq 12 \\ x \geq 0, y \geq 0 \end{cases}$

To solve this problem, graph the solution set of the constraints. The solution set of the constraints is called the **set of feasible solutions.** Ordered pairs in this set are used to evaluate the objective function to determine which ordered pair

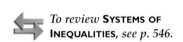

To review **SYSTEMS OF INEQUALITIES,** *see p. 546.*

---

take note

The set of feasible solutions includes ordered pairs with whole number coordinates as well as fractional coordinates. For instance, the ordered pair $\left(5, 2\frac{1}{2}\right)$ is in the set of feasible solutions. During one day, the company could produce 5 monochrome monitors and $2\frac{1}{2}$ color monitors.

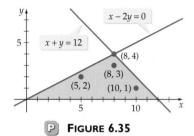

P **FIGURE 6.35**

maximizes the profit. For example, (5, 2), (8, 3), and (10, 1) are three ordered pairs in the set. See **Figure 6.35.** For these ordered pairs, the profit would be

$$P = 50(5) + 75(2) = 400 \qquad \bullet\, x = 5, y = 2$$
$$P = 50(8) + 75(3) = 625 \qquad \bullet\, x = 8, y = 3$$
$$P = 50(10) + 75(1) = 575 \qquad \bullet\, x = 10, y = 1$$

It would be impossible to check every ordered pair in the set of feasible solutions to find which maximizes profit. Fortunately, we can find that ordered pair by solving the objective function $P = 50x + 75y$ for y.

$$y = -\frac{2}{3}x + \frac{P}{75}$$

In this form, the objective function is a linear equation whose graph has slope $-\frac{2}{3}$ and y-intercept $\frac{P}{75}$. If P is as large as possible (P a maximum), then the y-intercept will be as large as possible. Thus the maximum profit will occur on the line that has a slope of $-\frac{2}{3}$, has the largest possible y-intercept, and intersects the set of feasible solutions.

From **Figure 6.36,** the largest possible y-intercept occurs when the line passes through the point with coordinates (8, 4). At this point, the profit is

$$P = 50(8) + 75(4) = 700$$

The manufacturer will maximize profit by producing eight monochrome monitors and four color monitors each day. The profit will be $700 per day.

In general, the goal of any linear programming problem is to maximize or minimize the objective function, subject to the constraints. Minimization problems occur, for example, when a manufacturer wants to minimize the cost of operations.

Suppose that a cost minimization problem results in the following objective function and constraints.

$$\text{Objective function:} \quad C = 3x + 4y$$

$$\text{Constraints:} \quad \begin{cases} x + y \geq 1 \\ 2x - y \leq 5 \\ x + 2y \leq 10 \\ x \geq 0, y \geq 0 \end{cases}$$

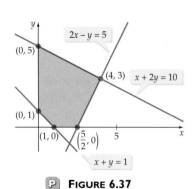

P **FIGURE 6.36**

Figure 6.37 is the graph of the solution set of the constraints. The task is to find the ordered pair that satisfies all the constraints and that will give the smallest value of C. We again could solve the objective function for y and, because we want to minimize C, find the smallest y-intercept. However, a theorem from linear programming simplifies our task even more. The proof of this theorem, omitted here, is based on the techniques we used to solve our examples.

P **FIGURE 6.37**

Fundamental Linear Programming Theorem

If an objective function has an optimal solution, then that solution will be at a vertex of the set of feasible solutions.

Following is a list of the values of C at the vertices. The minimum value of the objective function occurs at the point whose coordinates are $(1, 0)$.

$$(x, y) \qquad C = 3x + 4y$$
$$(1, 0) \qquad C = 3(1) + 4(0) = 3 \qquad \bullet \text{ Minimum}$$
$$\left(\frac{5}{2}, 0\right) \quad C = 3\left(\frac{5}{2}\right) + 4(0) = 7.5$$
$$(4, 3) \qquad C = 3(4) + 4(3) = 24 \qquad \bullet \text{ Maximum}$$
$$(0, 5) \qquad C = 3(0) + 4(5) = 20$$
$$(0, 1) \qquad C = 3(0) + 4(1) = 4$$

The maximum value of the objective function can also be determined from the list. It occurs at $(4, 3)$.

It is important to realize that the maximum or minimum value of an objective function depends on the objective function and on the set of feasible solutions. For example, using the same set of feasible solutions as in **Figure 6.37** but changing the objective function to $C = 2x + 5y$ changes the maximum value of C to 25 at the ordered pair $(0, 5)$. You should verify this result by making a list similar to the one shown above.

> **? QUESTION** What is the minimum value of the objective function $C = 2x + 5y$ for the set of feasible solutions in **Figure 6.37?**

● SOLVING OPTIMIZATION PROBLEMS

Alternative to Example 1
Maximize the objective function
$P = 3x + 5y$ with the constraints
$$\begin{cases} x + y \le 5 \\ 2x + y \ge 6 \\ x \ge 0, y \ge 0 \end{cases}$$
● The maximum value of the objective function is 25 at **(0, 5)**.

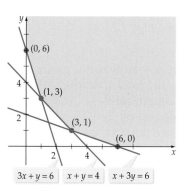

$3x + y = 6$ | $x + y = 4$ | $x + 3y = 6$

P **FIGURE 6.38**

EXAMPLE 1   **Solve a Minimization Problem**

Minimize the objective function $C = 4x + 7y$ with the constraints

$$\begin{cases} 3x + y \ge 6 \\ x + y \ge 4 \\ x + 3y \ge 6 \\ x \ge 0, y \ge 0 \end{cases}$$

Solution

Determine the set of feasible solutions by graphing the solution set of the inequalities. See **Figure 6.38.** Note that in this instance the set of feasible solutions is an unbounded set.

Find the vertices of the region by solving the following systems of equations. These systems are formed by the equations of the lines that intersect to form a vertex of the set of feasible solutions.

$$\begin{cases} 3x + y = 6 \\ x + y = 4 \end{cases} \qquad \begin{cases} x + 3y = 6 \\ x + y = 4 \end{cases}$$

The solutions of the two systems are $(1, 3)$ and $(3, 1)$, respectively. The points $(0, 6)$ and $(6, 0)$ are the vertices on the y- and x-axes.

Continued ▶

? ANSWER 2

Evaluate the objective function at each of the four vertices of the set of feasible solutions.

$$(x, y) \quad C = 4x + 7y$$
$$(0, 6) \quad C = 4(0) + 7(6) = 42$$
$$(1, 3) \quad C = 4(1) + 7(3) = 25$$
$$(3, 1) \quad C = 4(3) + 7(1) = 19 \qquad \bullet \textbf{ Minimum}$$
$$(6, 0) \quad C = 4(6) + 7(0) = 24$$

The minimum value of the objective function is 19 at $(3, 1)$.

▶ **TRY EXERCISE 12, PAGE 559**

Linear programming can be used to determine the best allocation of the resources available to a company. In fact, the word *programming* refers to a "program to allocate resources."

Alternative to Example 2

A dietician formulates a special diet using two food groups, *A* and *B*. Each ounce of food group *A* contains 10 units of iron, 4 units of calcium, 4 units of vitamin C, and 2 units of cholesterol. Each ounce of food group *B* contains 2 units of iron, 7 units of calcium, 2 units of vitamin C, and 5 units of cholesterol. If the minimum daily requirements are 16 units of iron, 36 units of calcium, and 16 units of vitamin C, find the amount of each food group that should be used to minimize the cholesterol intake. What is the minimum amount of cholesterol?

⊙ **The minimum amount of cholesterol is 18 units. It occurs when 9 ounces of food group *A* and none of group *B* are used.**

EXAMPLE 2   **Solve an Applied Minimization Problem**

A manufacturer of animal food makes two grain mixtures, G_1 and G_2. Each kilogram of G_1 contains 300 grams of vitamins, 400 grams of protein, and 100 grams of carbohydrate. Each kilogram of G_2 contains 100 grams of vitamins, 300 grams of protein, and 200 grams of carbohydrate. Minimum nutritional guidelines require that a feed mixture made from these grains contain at least 900 grams of vitamins, 2200 grams of protein, and 800 grams of carbohydrate. G_1 costs \$2.00 per kilogram to produce, and G_2 costs \$1.25 per kilogram to produce. Find the number of kilograms of each grain mixture that should be produced to minimize cost.

Solution

Let

$$x = \text{the number of kilograms of } G_1$$
$$y = \text{the number of kilograms of } G_2$$

The objective function is the cost function $C = 2x + 1.25y$.

Because x kilograms of G_1 contain $300x$ grams of vitamins and y kilograms of G_2 contain $100y$ grams of vitamins, the total amount of vitamins contained in x kilograms of G_1 and y kilograms of G_2 is $300x + 100y$. At least 900 grams of vitamins are necessary, so $300x + 100y \geq 900$. Following similar reasoning, we have the constraints

$$\begin{cases} 300x + 100y \geq 900 \\ 400x + 300y \geq 2200 \\ 100x + 200y \geq 800 \\ x \geq 0, y \geq 0 \end{cases}$$

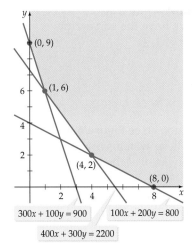

P FIGURE 6.39

Two of the vertices of the set of feasible solutions (see **Figure 6.39**) can be found by solving two systems of equations. These systems are formed by the equations of the lines that intersect to form a vertex of the set of feasible solutions.

$$\begin{cases} 300x + 100y = 900 \\ 400x + 300y = 2200 \end{cases}$$ • The vertex is (1, 6).

$$\begin{cases} 100x + 200y = 800 \\ 400x + 300y = 2200 \end{cases}$$ • The vertex is (4, 2).

The vertices on the x- and y-axes are the x- and y-intercepts (8, 0) and (0, 9). Substitute the coordinates of the vertices into the objective function.

(x, y) $C = 2x + 1.25y$

$(0, 9)$ $C = 2(0) + 1.25(9) = 11.25$

$(1, 6)$ $C = 2(1) + 1.25(6) = 9.50$ • Minimum

$(4, 2)$ $C = 2(4) + 1.25(2) = 10.50$

$(8, 0)$ $C = 2(8) + 1.25(0) = 16.00$

The minimum value of the objective function is $9.50. It occurs when the company produces a feed mixture that contains 1 kilogram of G_1 and 6 kilograms of G_2.

▶ TRY EXERCISE 22, PAGE 560

Alternative to Example 3
A tent manufacturer makes two types of tents, a two-person tent and a family tent. Each two-person tent requires 2 hours in the cutting room and 2 hours in the assembly room. Each family tent requires 2 hours in the cutting room and 4 hours in the assembly room. The total number of hours available in the cutting room is 50. There are 80 hours available in the assembly room. The regional manager requires that the number of two-person tents manufactured be not more than four times the number of family tents that are manufactured. The profit for the two-person tent is $34, and the profit for the family tent is $49. Assuming that all the tents produced can be sold, how many of each should be manufactured to maximize profit? What is the maximum profit?
● **The maximum profit of $1075 can be attained when 10 two-person tents and 15 family tents are manufactured and sold.**

EXAMPLE 3 **Solve an Applied Maximization Problem**

A chemical firm produces two types of industrial solvents, S_1 and S_2. Each solvent is a mixture of three chemicals. Each kiloliter of S_1 requires 12 liters of chemical 1, 9 liters of chemical 2, and 30 liters of chemical 3. Each kiloliter of S_2 requires 24 liters of chemical 1, 5 liters of chemical 2, and 30 liters of chemical 3. The profit per kiloliter of S_1 is $100, and the profit per kiloliter of S_2 is $85. The inventory of the company shows 480 liters of chemical 1, 180 liters of chemical 2, and 720 liters of chemical 3. Assuming the company can sell all the solvent it makes, find the number of kiloliters of each solvent the company should make to maximize profit.

Solution

Let

$x =$ the number of kiloliters of S_1

$y =$ the number of kiloliters of S_2

The objective function is the profit function $P = 100x + 85y$.
    Because x kiloliters of S_1 require $12x$ liters of chemical 1, and y kiloliters of S_2 require $24y$ liters of chemical 1, the total amount of chemical 1 needed

Continued ▶

is $12x + 24y$. There are 480 liters of chemical 1 in inventory, so $12x + 24y \leq 480$. Following similar reasoning, we have the constraints

$$\begin{cases} 12x + 24y \leq 480 \\ 9x + 5y \leq 180 \\ 30x + 30y \leq 720 \\ x \geq 0, y \geq 0 \end{cases}$$

Two of the vertices of the set of feasible solutions (see **Figure 6.40**) can be found by solving two systems of equations. These systems are formed by the equations of the lines that intersect to form a vertex of the set of feasible solutions.

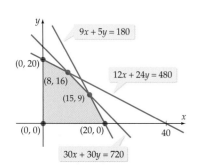

$9x + 5y = 180$

$(0, 20)$

$(8, 16)$

$12x + 24y = 480$

$(15, 9)$

$(0, 0)$ $(20, 0)$ 40

$30x + 30y = 720$

 FIGURE 6.40

$$\begin{cases} 12x + 24y = 480 \\ 30x + 30y = 720 \end{cases}$$ • **The vertex is (8, 16).**

$$\begin{cases} 9x + 5y = 180 \\ 30x + 30y = 720 \end{cases}$$ • **The vertex is (15, 9).**

The vertices on the x- and y-axes are the x- and y-intercepts $(20, 0)$ and $(0, 20)$.

Substitute the coordinates of the vertices into the objective function.

$$\begin{array}{ll} (x, y) & P = 100x + 85y \\ (0, 20) & P = 100(0) + 85(20) = 1700 \\ (8, 16) & P = 100(8) + 85(16) = 2160 \\ (15, 9) & P = 100(15) + 85(9) = 2265 \qquad \text{• Maximum} \\ (20, 0) & P = 100(20) + 85(0) = 2000 \end{array}$$

The maximum value of the objective function is \$2265 when the company produces 15 kiloliters of S_1 and 9 kiloliters of S_2.

▶ **TRY EXERCISE 24, PAGE 560**

TOPICS FOR DISCUSSION

1. What is an optimization problem? Give an example of a situation in which optimization may be the goal.

2. What is a constraint for a linear programming problem? Explain what type of condition might be a constraint for the situation you gave in Exercise 1.

3. What is the objective function for a linear programming problem? Explain what the objective function might be for the situation you gave in Exercise 1.

4. What is the set of feasible solutions for a linear programming problem?

5. If a linear programming problem has an optimal solution, where in the set of feasible solutions must that optimal solution occur?

EXERCISE SET 6.6   —*Suggested Assignment: Exercises 1–23, odd.*

In Exercises 1 to 20, solve the linear programming problem. Assume $x \geq 0$ and $y \geq 0$.

1. Minimize $C = 4x + 2y$ with the constraints
The minimum is 16 at
$(0, 8)$.
$$\begin{cases} x + y \geq 7 \\ 4x + 3y \geq 24 \\ x \leq 10, y \leq 10 \end{cases}$$

2. Minimize $C = 5x + 4y$ with the constraints
The minimum is 32 at
$(0, 8)$.
$$\begin{cases} 3x + 4y \geq 32 \\ x + 4y \geq 24 \\ x \leq 12, y \leq 15 \end{cases}$$

3. Maximize $C = 6x + 7y$ with the constraints
The maximum is 71 at
$(6, 5)$.
$$\begin{cases} x + 2y \leq 16 \\ 5x + 3y \leq 45 \end{cases}$$

4. Maximize $C = 6x + 5y$ with the constraints
The maximum is 53 at
$(3, 7)$.
$$\begin{cases} 2x + 3y \leq 27 \\ 7x + 3y \leq 42 \end{cases}$$

5. Minimize $C = 5x + 6y$ with the constraints
The minimum is 20 at
$\left(0, \dfrac{10}{3}\right)$.
$$\begin{cases} 4x - 3y \leq 2 \\ 2x + 3y \geq 10 \end{cases}$$

6. Maximize $C = 4x + 5y$ with the constraints
The maximum is 70 at
$(5, 10)$.
$$\begin{cases} 2x - y \leq 0 \\ 0 \leq y \leq 10 \\ 0 \leq x \leq 10 \end{cases}$$

7. Maximize $C = x + 6y$ with the constraints
The maximum is 72 at
$(0, 12)$.
$$\begin{cases} 5x + 8y \leq 120 \\ 7x + 16y \leq 192 \end{cases}$$

8. Minimize $C = 4x + 5y$ with the constraints
The minimum is 75 at
$(0, 15)$.
$$\begin{cases} x + 3y \geq 30 \\ 3x + 4y \geq 60 \end{cases}$$

9. Minimize $C = 4x + y$ with the constraints
The minimum is 32 at
$(0, 32)$.
$$\begin{cases} 3x + 5y \geq 120 \\ x + y \geq 32 \end{cases}$$

10. Maximize $C = 7x + 2y$ with the constraints
The maximum is 280
at $(40, 0)$.
$$\begin{cases} x + 3y \leq 108 \\ 7x + 4y \leq 280 \end{cases}$$

11. Maximize $C = 2x + 7y$ with the constraints
The maximum is 56 at
$(0, 8)$.
$$\begin{cases} x + y \leq 10 \\ x + 2y \leq 16 \\ 2x + y \leq 16 \end{cases}$$

▶ **12.** Minimize $C = 4x + 3y$ with the constraints
The minimum is 20 at
$(2, 4)$.
$$\begin{cases} 2x + y \geq 8 \\ 2x + 3y \geq 16 \\ x + 3y \geq 11 \\ x \leq 20, y \leq 20 \end{cases}$$

13. Minimize $C = 3x + 2y$ with the constraints
The minimum is 18 at
$(2, 6)$.
$$\begin{cases} 3x + y \geq 12 \\ 2x + 7y \geq 21 \\ x + y \geq 8 \end{cases}$$

14. Maximize $C = 2x + 6y$ with the constraints
The maximum is 54 at
$(0, 9)$.
$$\begin{cases} x + y \leq 12 \\ 3x + 4y \leq 40 \\ x + 2y \leq 18 \end{cases}$$

15. Maximize $C = 3x + 4y$ with the constraints
The maximum is 25 at
$(3, 4)$.
$$\begin{cases} 2x + y \leq 10 \\ 2x + 3y \leq 18 \\ x - y \leq 2 \end{cases}$$

16. Minimize $C = 3x + 7y$ with the constraints
The minimum is 36 at
$(12, 0)$.
$$\begin{cases} x + y \geq 9 \\ 3x + 4y \geq 32 \\ x + 2y \geq 12 \end{cases}$$

17. Minimize $C = 3x + 2y$ with the constraints
The minimum is 12 at
$(2, 3)$.
$$\begin{cases} x + 2y \geq 8 \\ 3x + y \geq 9 \\ x + 4y \geq 12 \end{cases}$$

18. Maximize $C = 4x + 5y$ with the constraints
The maximum is 325
at $(50, 25)$.
$$\begin{cases} 3x + 4y \leq 250 \\ x + y \leq 75 \\ 2x + 3y \leq 180 \end{cases}$$

19. Maximize $C = 6x + 7y$ with the constraints
The maximum is 3400
at $(100, 400)$.
$$\begin{cases} x + 2y \leq 900 \\ x + y \leq 500 \\ 3x + 2y \leq 1200 \end{cases}$$

20. Minimize $C = 11x + 16y$ with the constraints
The minimum is 465 at (35, 5).
$$\begin{cases} x + 2y \geq 45 \\ x + y \geq 40 \\ 2x + y \geq 45 \end{cases}$$

21. MAXIMIZE PROFIT A farmer is planning to raise wheat and barley. Each acre of wheat yields a profit of $50, and each acre of barley yields a profit of $70. To sow the crop, two machines, a tractor and a tiller, are rented. The tractor is available for 200 hours, and the tiller is available for 100 hours. Sowing an acre of barley requires 3 hours of tractor time and 2 hours of tilling. Sowing an acre of wheat requires 4 hours of tractor time and 1 hour of tilling. How many acres of each crop should be planted to maximize the farmer's profit?
20 acres of wheat and 40 acres of barley

▶ **22. MINIMIZE COST** An ice cream supplier has two machines that produce vanilla and chocolate ice cream. To meet one of its contractual obligations, the company must produce at least 60 gallons of vanilla ice cream and 100 gallons of chocolate ice cream per day. One machine makes 4 gallons of vanilla and 5 gallons of chocolate ice cream per hour. The second machine makes 3 gallons of vanilla and 10 gallons of chocolate ice cream per hour. It costs $28 per hour to run machine 1 and $25 per hour to run machine 2. How many hours should each machine be operated to fulfill the contract at the least expense?
machine 1 for 12 h and machine 2 for 4 h

23. MAXIMIZE PROFIT A manufacturer makes two types of golf clubs: a starter model and a professional model. The starter model requires 4 hours in the assembly room and 1 hour in the finishing room. The professional model requires 6 hours in the assembly room and 1 hour in the finishing room. The total number of hours available in the assembly room is 108. There are 24 hours available in the finishing room. The profit for each starter model is $35, and the profit for each professional model is $55. Assuming all the sets produced can be sold, find how many of each set should be manufactured to maximize profit.
0 starter sets and 18 pro sets

▶ **24. MAXIMIZE PROFIT** A company makes two types of telephone answering machines: the standard model and the deluxe model. Each machine passes through three processes: P_1, P_2, and P_3. One standard answering machine requires 1 hour in P_1, 1 hour in P_2, and 2 hours in P_3. One deluxe answering machine requires 3 hours in P_1, 1 hour in P_2, and 1 hour in P_3. Because of employee work schedules, P_1 is available for 24 hours, P_2 is available for 10 hours, and P_3 is available for 16 hours. If the profit is $25 for each standard model and $35 for each deluxe model, how many units of each type should the company produce to maximize profit?
3 standard models and 7 deluxe models

CONNECTING CONCEPTS

25. MINIMIZE COST A dietitian formulates a special diet from two food groups: A and B. Each ounce of food group A contains 3 units of vitamin A, 1 unit of vitamin C, and 1 unit of vitamin D. Each ounce of food group B contains 1 unit of vitamin A, 1 unit of vitamin C, and 3 units of vitamin D. Each ounce of food group A costs 40 cents, and each ounce of food group B costs 10 cents. The dietary constraints are such that at least 24 units of vitamin A, 16 units of vitamin C, and 30 units of vitamin D are required. Find the amount of each food group that should be used to minimize the cost. What is the minimum cost? 24 oz of group B and 0 oz of group A yields a minimum cost of $2.40.

26. MAXIMIZE PROFIT Among the many products it produces, an oil refinery makes two specialized petroleum distillates: Pymex A and Pymex B. Each distillate passes through three stages: S_1, S_2, and S_3. Each liter of Pymex A requires 1 hour in S_1, 3 hours in S_2, and 3 hours in S_3. Each liter of Pymex B requires 1 hour in S_1, 4 hours in S_2, and 2 hours in S_3. There are 10 hours available for S_1,

36 hours available for S_2, and 27 hours available for S_3. The profit per liter of Pymex A is $12, and the profit per liter of Pymex B is $9. How many liters of each distillate should be produced to maximize profit? What is the maximum profit? 7 l of Pymex A and 3 l of Pymex B. The maximum profit is $111.

27. MAXIMIZE PROFIT An engine reconditioning company works on 4- and 6-cylinder engines. Each 4-cylinder engine requires 1 hour for cleaning, 5 hours for overhauling, and 3 hours for testing. Each 6-cylinder engine requires 1 hour for cleaning, 10 hours for overhauling, and 2 hours for testing. The cleaning station is available for at most 9 hours. The overhauling equipment is available for at most 80 hours, and the testing equipment is available for at most 24 hours. For each reconditioned 4-cylinder engine, the company makes a profit of $150. A reconditioned 6-cylinder engine yields a profit of $250. The company can sell all the reconditioned engines it produces. How many of each type should be produced to maximize profit? What is the maximum profit? Two 4-cylinder engines and seven 6-cylinder engines yields a maximum profit of $2050.

28. MINIMIZE COST A producer of animal feed makes two food products: F_1 and F_2. The products contain three major ingredients: M_1, M_2, and M_3. Each ton of F_1 requires 200 pounds of M_1, 100 pounds of M_2, and 100 pounds of M_3. Each ton of F_2 requires 100 pounds of M_1, 200 pounds of M_2, and 400 pounds of M_3. There are at least 5000 pounds of M_1 available, at least 7000 pounds of M_2 available, and at least 10,000 pounds of M_3 available. Each ton of F_1 costs \$450 to make, and each ton of F_2 costs \$300 to make. How many tons of each food product should the feed producer make to minimize cost? What is the minimum cost? To achieve minimum cost, produce 10 lb of F_1 and 30 lb of F_2. The minimum cost is \$13,500.

PROJECTS

1. 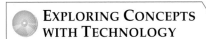 HISTORY OF LINEAR PROGRAMMING Linear programming has been used successfully to solve a wide range of problems in fields as diverse as providing health care and hardening nuclear silos. Write an essay on linear programming and some of the applications of this procedure in solving practical problems. Include in your essay the contributions of George Danzig, Narendra Karmarkar, and L. G. Khachian.

EXPLORING CONCEPTS WITH TECHNOLOGY

Ill-Conditioned Systems of Equations

Solving systems of equations algebraically as we did in this chapter is not practical for systems of equations that contain a large number of variables. In those cases, a computer solution is the only hope. Computer solutions are not without some problems, however.

Consider the system of equations

$$\begin{cases} 0.24567x + 0.49133y = 0.73700 \\ 0.84312x + 1.68623y = 2.52935 \end{cases}$$

It is easy to verify that the solution of this system of equations is $(1, 1)$. However, change the constant 0.73700 to 0.73701 (add 0.00001) and the constant 2.52935 to 2.52936 (add 0.00001), and the solution is now $(3, 0)$. Thus a very small change in the constant terms produces a dramatic change in the solution. A system of equations of this sort is said to be *ill-conditioned*.

These types of systems are important because computers generally cannot store numbers beyond a certain number of significant digits. Your calculator, for example, probably allows you to enter no more than 10 significant digits. If an exact number cannot be entered, then an approximation to that number is necessary. When a computer is solving an equation or a system of equations, the hope is that approximations of the coefficients it uses will give reasonable approximations to the solutions. For ill-conditioned systems of equations, this is not always true.

In the system of equations above, small changes in the constant terms caused a large change in the solution. It is possible that small changes in the coefficients of the variables will also cause large changes in the solution.

In the two systems of equations that follow, examine the effects of approximating the fractional coefficients on the solutions. Try approximating each fraction to the nearest hundredth, to the nearest thousandth, to the nearest ten-thousandth, and then to the limits of your calculator. The exact solution of the first system of equations is $(27, -192, 210)$. The exact solution of the second system of equations is $(-64, 900, -2520, 1820)$.

$$\begin{cases} x + \dfrac{1}{2}y + \dfrac{1}{3}z = 1 \\[2mm] \dfrac{1}{2}x + \dfrac{1}{3}y + \dfrac{1}{4}z = 2 \\[2mm] \dfrac{1}{3}x + \dfrac{1}{4}y + \dfrac{1}{5}z = 3 \end{cases} \qquad \begin{cases} x + \dfrac{1}{2}y + \dfrac{1}{3}z + \dfrac{1}{4}w = 1 \\[2mm] \dfrac{1}{2}x + \dfrac{1}{3}y + \dfrac{1}{4}z + \dfrac{1}{5}w = 2 \\[2mm] \dfrac{1}{3}x + \dfrac{1}{4}y + \dfrac{1}{5}z + \dfrac{1}{6}w = 3 \\[2mm] \dfrac{1}{4}x + \dfrac{1}{5}y + \dfrac{1}{6}z + \dfrac{1}{7}w = 4 \end{cases}$$

Note how the solutions change as the approximations change and thus how important it is to know whether a system of equations is ill-conditioned. For systems that are not ill-conditioned, approximations of the coefficients yield reasonable approximations of the solution. For ill-conditioned systems of equations, this is not always true.

CHAPTER 6 SUMMARY

6.1 Systems of Linear Equations in Two Variables

• A system of equations is two or more equations considered together. A solution of a system of equations in two variables is an ordered pair that satisfies each equation of the system. Equivalent systems of equations have the same solution set.

• A system of equations is consistent if it has one or more solutions. A system of linear equations is independent if it has exactly one solution. A system is dependent if it has infinitely many solutions. An inconsistent system of equations has no solution.

• **Operations That Produce Equivalent Systems of Equations**

  1. Interchange any two equations.
  2. Replace an equation with a nonzero multiple of that equation.
  3. Replace an equation with the sum of that equation and a nonzero constant multiple of another equation in the system.

6.2 Systems of Linear Equations in More Than Two Variables

• An equation of the form $ax + by + cz = d$, with a, b, and c not all zero, is a linear equation in three variables. A solution of a system of equations in three variables is an ordered triple that satisfies each equation of the system.

• The graph of a linear equation in three variables is a plane.

• A linear system of equations for which the constant term is zero for all equations of the system is called a homogeneous system of equations.

6.3 Nonlinear Systems of Equations

• A nonlinear system of equations is a system in which one or more equations of the system are nonlinear.

6.4 Partial Fractions

• A rational expression can be written as the sum of terms whose denominators are factors of the denominator of the rational expression. This is called a partial fraction decomposition.

6.5 Inequalities in Two Variables and Systems of Inequalities

- The graph of an inequality in two variables frequently separates the plane into two or more regions.

- The solution set of a system of inequalities is the intersection of the solution sets of the individual inequalities.

6.6 Linear Programming

- A linear programming problem consists of a linear objective function and a number of constraints, which are inequalities or equations that restrict the values of the variables.

- The Fundamental Linear Programming Theorem states that if an objective function has an optimal solution, then that solution will be at a vertex of the set of feasible solutions.

CHAPTER 6 TRUE/FALSE EXERCISES

In Exercises 1 to 10, answer true or false. If the statement is false, give an example or state a reason to show that the statement is false.

1. A system of equations will always have a solution as long as the number of equations is equal to the number of variables. False; $\begin{cases} x + y = 1 \\ x + y = 2 \end{cases}$ has no solution.

2. A system of two different quadratic equations can have at most four solutions. True

3. A homogeneous system of equations is one in which all the variables have the same exponent. False; a homogeneous system is one in which the constant term in each equation is zero.

4. In an xyz-coordinate system, the graph of the set of points formed by the intersection of two different planes is a straight line. True

5. It is possible to find a partial fraction decomposition of a rational expression if the degree of the numerator is greater than the degree of the denominator. True

6. Two systems of equations with the same solution set have the same equations in their respective systems. False; $\begin{cases} x + y = 2 \\ x + 2y = 3 \end{cases}$

7. The systems of equations
$$\begin{cases} x = 0 \\ y = 0 \end{cases} \text{ and } \begin{cases} y = x \\ y = -x \end{cases}$$
are equivalent systems of equations. True

and $\begin{cases} 2x + 3y = 5 \\ 2x - 2y = 0 \end{cases}$ are two systems with the same solution but no common equations.

8. For a linear programming problem, one or more constraints are used to define the set of feasible solutions. True

9. A system of three linear equations in three variables for which two of the planes are parallel and the third plane intersects the first two is a dependent system of equations. False; it is inconsistent.

10. The inequality $xy < 1$ and the inequality $y < \dfrac{1}{x}$ are equivalent inequalities. False; $(-1, 1)$ satisfies the first inequality but not the second, and $(-2, -1)$ satisfies the second but not the first.

CHAPTER 6 REVIEW EXERCISES

—Answer graphs to Exercises 37–48 and 49–60 are on pages AA30–AA31.

In Exercises 1 to 30, solve each system of equations.

1. $\begin{cases} 2x - 4y = -3 \\ 3x + 8y = -12 \end{cases} \left(-\dfrac{18}{7}, -\dfrac{15}{28}\right)$ [6.1]

2. $\begin{cases} 4x - 3y = 15 \\ 2x + 5y = -12 \end{cases} \left(\dfrac{3}{2}, -3\right)$ [6.1]

3. $\begin{cases} 3x - 4y = -5 \\ y = \dfrac{2}{3}x + 1 \end{cases}$ $(-3, -1)$ [6.1]

4. $\begin{cases} 7x + 2y = -14 \\ y = -\dfrac{5}{2}x - 3 \end{cases}$ $(-4, 7)$ [6.1]

5. $\begin{cases} y = 2x - 5 \\ x = 4y - 1 \end{cases}$ $(3, 1)$ [6.1]

6. $\begin{cases} y = 3x + 4 \\ x = 4y - 5 \end{cases}$ $(-1, 1)$ [6.1]

7. $\begin{cases} 6x + 9y = 15 \\ 10x + 15y = 25 \end{cases} \left(\dfrac{5 - 3c}{2}, c\right)$ [6.1]

8. $\begin{cases} 4x - 8y = 9 \\ 2x - 4y = 5 \end{cases}$ no solution [6.1]

9. $\begin{cases} 2x - 3y + z = -9 \\ 2x + 5y - 2z = 18 \\ 4x - y + 3z = -4 \end{cases} \left(\dfrac{1}{2}, 3, -1\right)$ [6.2]

10. $\begin{cases} x - 3y + 5z = 1 \\ 2x + 3y - 5z = 15 \\ 3x + 6y + 5z = 15 \end{cases} \left(\dfrac{16}{3}, \dfrac{10}{27}, -\dfrac{29}{45}\right)$ [6.2]

11. $\begin{cases} x + 3y - 5z = -12 \\ 3x - 2y + z = 7 \\ 5x + 4y - 9z = -17 \end{cases} \left(\dfrac{7c - 3}{11}, \dfrac{16c - 43}{11}, c\right)$ [6.2]

12. $\begin{cases} 2x - y + 2z = 5 \\ x + 3y - 3z = 2 \\ 5x - 9y + 8z = 13 \end{cases} \left(\dfrac{74}{31}, -\dfrac{1}{31}, \dfrac{3}{31}\right)$ [6.2]

13. $\left(2, \dfrac{3c+2}{2}, c\right)$ [6.2]

13. $\begin{cases} 3x + 4y - 6z = 10 \\ 2x + 2y - 3z = 6 \\ x - 6y + 9z = -4 \end{cases}$

14. $\begin{cases} x - 6y + 4z = 6 \\ 4x + 3y - 4z = 1 \\ 5x - 9y + 8z = 13 \end{cases}$

14. $\left(1, -\dfrac{2}{3}, \dfrac{1}{4}\right)$ [6.2]

15. $\begin{cases} 2x + 3y - 2z = 0 \\ 3x - y - 4z = 0 \\ 5x + 13y - 4z = 0 \end{cases}$

16. $\begin{cases} 3x - 5y + z = 0 \\ x + 4y - 3z = 0 \\ 2x + y - 2z = 0 \end{cases}$

15. $\left(\dfrac{14c}{11}, -\dfrac{2c}{11}, c\right)$ (0, 0, 0) [6.2]

17. $\begin{cases} x - 2y + z = 1 \\ 3x + 2y - 3z = 1 \end{cases}$ [6.2]

18. $\begin{cases} 2x - 3y + z = 1 \\ 4x + 2y + 3z = 21 \end{cases}$

See answer at bottom of page.   See answer at bottom of page.

19. $\begin{cases} y = x^2 - 2x - 3 \\ y = 2x - 7 \end{cases}$ (2, −3) [6.3]

20. $\begin{cases} y = 2x^2 + x \\ y = 2x + 1 \end{cases}$ $\left(-\dfrac{1}{2}, 0\right)$ and (1, 3) [6.3]

21. $\begin{cases} y = 3x^2 - x + 1 \\ y = x^2 + 2x - 1 \end{cases}$ no real solution [6.3]

22. $\begin{cases} y = 4x^2 - 2x - 3 \\ y = 2x^2 + 3x - 6 \end{cases}$ $\left(\dfrac{3}{2}, 3\right)$ and (1, −1) [6.3]

23. $\begin{cases} (x + 1)^2 + (y - 2)^2 = 4 \\ 2x + y = 4 \end{cases}$ $\left(\dfrac{1}{5}, \dfrac{18}{5}\right)$, (1, 2) [6.3]

24. $\begin{cases} (x - 1)^2 + (y + 1)^2 = 5 \\ y = 2x - 3 \end{cases}$ (0, −3) and (2, 1) [6.3]

25. $\begin{cases} (x - 2)^2 + (y + 2)^2 = 4 \\ (x + 2)^2 + (y + 1)^2 = 17 \end{cases}$ (2, 0), $\left(\dfrac{18}{17}, -\dfrac{64}{17}\right)$ [6.3]

26. $\begin{cases} (x + 1)^2 + (y - 2)^2 = 1 \\ (x - 2)^2 + (y + 2)^2 = 20 \end{cases}$ (0, 2) and $\left(-\dfrac{32}{25}, \dfrac{26}{25}\right)$ [6.3]

27. $\begin{cases} x^2 - 3xy + y^2 = -1 \\ 3x^2 - 5xy - 2y^2 = 0 \end{cases}$ (2, 1), (−2, −1) [6.3]

28. $\begin{cases} 2x^2 + 2xy - y^2 = -1 \\ 6x^2 + xy - y^2 = 0 \end{cases}$ (1, 3), (−1, −3), $\left(\dfrac{\sqrt{6}}{6}, -\dfrac{\sqrt{6}}{3}\right)$, and $\left(-\dfrac{\sqrt{6}}{6}, \dfrac{\sqrt{6}}{3}\right)$ [6.3]

29. $\begin{cases} 2x^2 - 5xy + 2y^2 = 56 \\ 14x^2 - 3xy - 2y^2 = 56 \end{cases}$ (2, −3), (−2, 3) [6.3]

30. $\begin{cases} 2x^2 + 7xy + 6y^2 = 1 \\ 6x^2 + 7xy + 2y^2 = 1 \end{cases}$ $\left(\dfrac{\sqrt{15}}{15}, \dfrac{\sqrt{15}}{15}\right)$, $\left(-\dfrac{\sqrt{15}}{15}, -\dfrac{\sqrt{15}}{15}\right)$, (1, −1), (−1, 1) [6.3]

In Exercises 31 to 36, find the partial fraction decomposition.

31. $\dfrac{7x - 5}{x^2 - x - 2}$ $\dfrac{3}{x-2} + \dfrac{4}{x+1}$ [6.4]

32. $\dfrac{x + 1}{(x - 1)^2}$ $\dfrac{1}{x-1} + \dfrac{2}{(x-1)^2}$ [6.4]

33. $\dfrac{2x - 2}{(x^2 + 1)(x + 2)}$ $\dfrac{6x - 2}{5(x^2 + 1)} + \dfrac{-6}{5(x + 2)}$ [6.4]

34. $\dfrac{5x^2 - 10x + 9}{(x - 2)^2(x + 1)}$ $\dfrac{-6}{3(x - 2)} + \dfrac{8}{(x - 2)^2} + \dfrac{8}{3(x + 1)}$ [6.4]

35. $\dfrac{11x^2 - x - 2}{x^3 - x^2}$ $\dfrac{2}{x} + \dfrac{4}{x - 1} + \dfrac{5}{x + 1}$ [6.4]

36. $\dfrac{x^4 + x^3 + 4x^2 + x + 3}{(x^2 + 1)^2}$ $1 + \dfrac{x + 2}{x^2 + 1}$ [6.4]

In Exercises 37 to 48, graph the solution set of each inequality.

37. $4x - 5y < 20$ [6.5]

38. $2x + 7y \geq -14$ [6.5]

39. $y \geq 2x^2 - x - 1$ [6.5]

40. $y < x^2 - 5x - 6$ [6.5]

41. $(x - 2)^2 + (y - 1)^2 > 4$ [6.5]

42. $(x + 3)^2 + (y + 1)^2 \leq 9$ [6.5]

43. $\dfrac{(x - 3)^2}{16} - \dfrac{(y + 2)^2}{25} \leq 1$ [6.5]

44. $\dfrac{(x + 1)^2}{9} - \dfrac{(y - 3)^2}{4} < -1$ [6.5]

45. $(2x - y + 1)(x - 2y - 2) > 0$ [6.5]

46. $(2x - 3y - 6)(x + 2y - 4) < 0$ [6.5]

47. $x^2 y^2 < 1$ [6.5]

48. $xy \geq 0$ [6.5]

In Exercises 49 to 60, graph the solution set of each system of inequalities.

49. $\begin{cases} 2x - 5y < 9 \\ 3x + 4y \geq 2 \end{cases}$ [6.5]

50. $\begin{cases} 3x + y > 7 \\ 2x + 5y < 9 \end{cases}$ [6.5]

51. $\begin{cases} 2x + 3y > 6 \\ 2x - y > -2 \\ x \leq 4 \end{cases}$ [6.5]

52. $\begin{cases} 2x + 5y > 10 \\ x - y > -2 \\ x \leq 4 \end{cases}$ [6.5]

53. $\begin{cases} 2x + 3y \leq 18 \\ x + y \leq 7 \\ x \geq 0, y \geq 0 \end{cases}$ [6.5]

54. $\begin{cases} 3x + 5y \geq 25 \\ 2x + 3y \geq 16 \\ x \geq 0, y \geq 0 \end{cases}$ [6.5]

55. $\begin{cases} 3x + y \geq 6 \\ x + 4y \geq 14 \\ 2x + 3y \geq 16 \\ x \geq 0, y \geq 0 \end{cases}$ [6.5]

56. $\begin{cases} 3x + 2y \geq 14 \\ x + y \geq 6 \\ 11x + 4y \leq 48 \\ x \geq 0, y \geq 0 \end{cases}$ [6.5]

57. $\begin{cases} y < x^2 - x - 2 \\ y \geq 2x - 4 \end{cases}$ [6.5]

58. $\begin{cases} y > 2x^2 + x - 1 \\ y > x + 3 \end{cases}$ [6.5]

59. $\begin{cases} x^2 + y^2 - 2x + 4y > 4 \\ y < 2x^2 - 1 \end{cases}$ [6.5]

17. $\left(\dfrac{c+1}{2}, \dfrac{3c-1}{4}, c\right)$ [6.2]

60. $\begin{cases} x^2 - y^2 - 4x - 2y < -4 \\ x^2 + y^2 - 4x + 4y > 8 \end{cases}$ [6.5]

18. $\left(\dfrac{65 - 11c}{16}, \dfrac{19 - c}{8}, c\right)$ [6.2]

In Exercises 61 to 66, solve the linear programming problem. In each problem, assume $x \geq 0$ and $y \geq 0$.

61. Objective function: $P = 2x + 2y$
Constraints: $\begin{cases} x + 2y \leq 14 \\ 5x + 2y \leq 30 \end{cases}$
Maximize the objective function.
The maximum is 18 at (4, 5). [6.6]

62. Objective function: $P = 4x + 5y$
Constraints: $\begin{cases} 2x + 3y \leq 24 \\ 4x + 3y \leq 36 \end{cases}$
Maximize the objective function.
The maximum is 44 at (6, 4). [6.6]

63. Objective function: $P = 4x + y$
Constraints: $\begin{cases} 5x + 2y \geq 16 \\ x + 2y \geq 8 \\ x \leq 20, y \leq 20 \end{cases}$
Minimize the objective function.
The minimum is 8 at (0, 8). [6.6]

64. Objective function: $P = 2x + 7y$
Constraints: $\begin{cases} 4x + 3y \geq 24 \\ 4x + 7y \geq 40 \\ x \leq 10, y \leq 10 \end{cases}$
Minimize the objective function.
The minimum is 20 at (10, 0). [6.6]

65. Objective function: $P = 6x + 3y$
Constraints: $\begin{cases} 5x + 2y \geq 20 \\ x + y \geq 7 \\ x + 2y \geq 10 \\ x \leq 15, y \leq 15 \end{cases}$
Minimize the objective function.
The minimum is 27 at (2, 5). [6.6]

66. Objective function: $P = 5x + 4y$
Constraints: $\begin{cases} x + y \leq 10 \\ 2x + y \leq 13 \\ 3x + y \leq 18 \end{cases}$
Maximize the objective function.
The maximum is 43 at (3, 7). [6.6]

In Exercises 67 to 73, solve each exercise by solving a system of equations.

67. Find an equation of the form $y = ax^2 + bx + c$ whose graph passes through the points $(1, 0)$, $(-1, 5)$, and $(2, 3)$. $y = \dfrac{11}{6}x^2 - \dfrac{5}{2}x + \dfrac{2}{3}$ [6.2]

68. Find an equation of the circle that passes through the points $(4, 2)$, $(0, 1)$, and $(3, -1)$. $x^2 + y^2 - \dfrac{47}{11}x - \dfrac{21}{11}y + \dfrac{10}{11} = 0$ [6.2]

69. Find an equation of the plane that passes through the points $(2, 1, 2)$, $(3, 1, 0)$, and $(-2, -3, -2)$. Use the equation $z = ax + by + c$. $z = -2x + 3y + 3$ [6.2]

70. How many liters of a 20% acid solution should be mixed with 10 liters of a 10% acid solution so that the resulting solution is a 16% acid solution? $x = 15$ l [6.1]

71. Flying with the wind, a small plane traveled 855 miles in 5 hours. Flying against the wind, the same plane traveled 575 miles in the same time. Find the rate of the wind and the rate of the plane in calm air.
wind: 28 mph, plane: 143 mph [6.1]

72. A collection of 10 coins has a value of $1.25. The collection consists of only nickels, dimes, and quarters. How many of each coin are in the collection? (*Hint:* There is more than one solution.) 4 nickels, 3 dimes, 3 quarters; 1 nickel, 7 dimes, 2 quarters [6.2]

73. Consider the ordered triple (a, b, c). Find all real number values for a, b, and c so that the product of any two numbers equals the remaining number.
$(0, 0, 0), (1, 1, 1), (1, -1, -1), (-1, -1, 1), (-1, 1, -1)$ [6.2]

CHAPTER 6 TEST

—Answer graphs to Exercises 9–16 are on page AA31.

In Exercises 1 to 8, solve each system of equations. If a system of equations is inconsistent, so state.

1. $\begin{cases} 3x + 2y = -5 \\ 2x - 5y = -16 \end{cases}$ $(-3, 2)$ [6.1]

2. $\begin{cases} x - \dfrac{1}{2}y = 3 \\ 2x - y = 6 \end{cases}$ $\left(\dfrac{6 + c}{2}, c\right)$ [6.1]

3. $\begin{cases} x + 3y - z = 8 \\ 2x - 7y + 2z = 1 \\ 4x - y + 3z = 13 \end{cases}$ $\left(\dfrac{173}{39}, \dfrac{29}{39}, -\dfrac{4}{3}\right)$ [6.2]

4. $\begin{cases} 3x - 2y + z = 2 \\ x + 2y - 2z = 1 \\ 4x - z = 3 \end{cases}$ $\left(\dfrac{c + 3}{4}, \dfrac{7c + 1}{8}, c\right)$ [6.2]

5. $\begin{cases} 2x - 3y + z = -1 \\ x + 5y - 2z = 5 \end{cases}$ $\left(\dfrac{c + 10}{13}, \dfrac{5c + 11}{13}, c\right)$ [6.2]

6. $\begin{cases} 4x + 2y + z = 0 \\ x - 3y - 2z = 0 \\ 3x + 5y + 3z = 0 \end{cases}$ $\left(\dfrac{c}{14}, -\dfrac{9c}{14}, c\right)$ [6.2]

7. $\begin{cases} y = x + 3 \\ y = x^2 + x - 1 \end{cases}$ $(2, 5), (-2, 1)$ [6.3]

8. $\begin{cases} y = x^2 - x - 3 \\ y = 2x^2 + 2x - 1 \end{cases}$ $(-2, 3), (-1, -1)$ [6.3]

In Exercises 9 to 12, graph each inequality.

9. $3x - 4y > 8$ [6.5]

10. $y \le x^2 - 2x - 3$ [6.5]

11. $x^2 + 4y^2 \ge 16$ [6.5]

12. $x + y^2 < 0$ [6.5]

In Exercises 13 to 16, graph each system of inequalities. If the solution set is empty, so state.

13. $\begin{cases} 2x - 5y \le 16 \\ x + 3y \ge -3 \end{cases}$ [6.5]

14. $\begin{cases} x^2 + y^2 > 9 \\ x^2 + y^2 < 4 \end{cases}$
No graph; the solution set is the empty set. [6.5]

15. $\begin{cases} x + y \ge 8 \\ 2x + y \ge 11 \\ x \ge 0, y \ge 0 \end{cases}$ [6.5]

16. $\begin{cases} 2x + 3y \le 12 \\ x + y \le 5 \\ 3x + 2y \le 11 \\ x \ge 0, y \ge 0 \end{cases}$ [6.5]

In Exercises 17 and 18, find the partial fraction decomposition.

17. $\dfrac{3x - 5}{x^2 - 3x - 4}$ $\dfrac{7}{5(x - 4)} + \dfrac{8}{5(x + 1)}$ [6.4]

18. $\dfrac{2x + 1}{x(x^2 + 1)}$ $\dfrac{1}{x} + \dfrac{-x + 2}{x^2 + 1}$ [6.4]

19. A farmer has 160 acres available on which to plant oats and barley. It costs \$15 per acre for oat seed and \$13 per acre for barley seed. The labor cost is \$15 per acre for oats and \$20 per acre for barley. The farmer has \$2200 available to purchase seed and has set aside \$2600 for labor. The profit per acre for oats is \$120, and the profit per acre for barley is \$150. How many acres of oats should the farmer plant to maximize profit? $\dfrac{680}{7}$ acres of oats and $\dfrac{400}{7}$ acres of barley [6.6]

20. Find an equation of the circle that passes through the points $(3, 5)$, $(-3, -3)$, and $(4, 4)$. (*Hint:* Use $x^2 + y^2 + ax + by + c = 0$.) $x^2 + y^2 - 2y - 24 = 0$ [6.2]

CUMULATIVE REVIEW EXERCISES

1. Find the slope of the line that passes through the points $\left(-\dfrac{1}{2}, 2\right)$ and $\left(4, -\dfrac{1}{3}\right)$. $-\dfrac{14}{27}$ [2.3]

2. Find the range of $f(x) = -x^2 + 2x - 4$. $\{y \mid y \le -3\}$ [2.4]

3. Evaluate $3x^4 - 4x^3 + 2x^2 - x + 1$ for $x = -2$. 91 [P.1]

4. Write $\log_6(x - 5) + 3\log_6(2x)$ as a single logarithm with a coefficient of 1. $\log_6[8x^3(x - 5)]$ [4.4]

5. Find the equation in standard form of the parabola that has vertex $(4, 2)$, has axis of symmetry parallel to the y-axis, and passes through the point $(-1, 1)$. $(x - 4)^2 = -25(y - 2)$ [5.1]

6. Solve $\dfrac{1}{F} = \dfrac{1}{d_0} + \dfrac{1}{d_1}$ for d_0. $d_0 = \dfrac{Fd_1}{d_1 - F}$ [1.2]

7. Find the equation of the line that passes through $P_1(-4, 2)$ and $P_2(2, -1)$. $y = -\dfrac{1}{2}x$ [2.2]

8. Let $f(x) = \dfrac{x^2 - 1}{x^4}$. Is f an even function, an odd function, or neither? even [2.5]

9. Solve: $\log x - \log(2x - 3) = 2$ $\dfrac{300}{199}$ [4.5]

10. Find the equation in standard form of the hyperbola with vertices $(2, 2)$ and $(10, 2)$ and eccentricity 3. $\dfrac{(x - 6)^2}{16} - \dfrac{(y - 2)^2}{128} = 1$ [5.3]

11. Given $g(x) = \dfrac{x - 2}{x}$, find $g\left(-\dfrac{1}{2}\right)$. 5 [2.2]

12. Given $f(x) = x^2 - 1$ and $g(x) = x^2 - 4x - 2$, find $(f \cdot g)(-2)$. 30 [2.6]

13. Evaluate: $\log_{0.25} 0.015625$ 3 [4.3]

14. Find a quadratic regression model for the data $\{(1, 1), (2, 3), (3, 10), (4, 17), (5, 26)\}$. $y = x^2 + 0.4x - 0.8$ [2.7]

15. Find the polynomial of lowest degree that has zeros of -2, $3i$, and $-3i$. $x^3 + 2x^2 + 9x + 18$ [3.4]

16. Find the inverse function of $Q(r) = \dfrac{2}{1 - r}$. $Q^{-1}(r) = \dfrac{r - 2}{r}$ [4.1]

17. Find the slant asymptote of the graph of $H(x) = \dfrac{2x^3 - x^2 - 2}{x^2 - x - 1}$. $y = 2x + 1$ [3.5]

18. Given that $f(x) = 2^x$ and $g(x) = 3^{2x}$, find $g[f(1)]$. 81 [4.2]

19. Sketch the graph of $F(x) = \dfrac{2^x - 2^{-x}}{3}$.
Answer on page AA32. [4.2]

20. How long will it take \$2000 to double if it is invested at an annual interest rate of 6.5% compounded continuously? Round to the nearest year. 11 years [4.6]

MATRICES

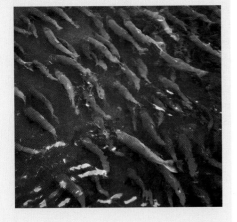

Matrices and Ecology

A *matrix* is a rectangular array of numbers such as the example below. This particular matrix is called a *Leslie* matrix and is used to model an ecological environment.

$$\begin{bmatrix} 0 & 7 & 28 & 84 \\ 0.1 & 0 & 0 & 0 \\ 0 & 0.4 & 0 & 0 \\ 0 & 0 & 0.6 & 0 \end{bmatrix}$$

To see how this matrix might be used, suppose that a biologist is studying a certain type of fish and is considering four stages of life: egg, yearling, 2-year-old, and 3-year-old. Then the numbers in the first row represent the number of eggs laid for each fish in that group. For instance, a 2-year-old fish lays 28 eggs.

The remaining numbers represent the survival rates for each stage. The 0.6 in the last row means that 60% of 2-year-old fish live to be 3 years old.

Various operations, such as addition and multiplication, can be applied to matrices. By applying these procedures, a biologist can predict the survival rates of succeeding generations of fish. If, for instance, a survey of the environment shows that today there are 600 eggs, 200 yearlings, 100 2-year-olds, and 25 3-year-olds, then the matrix product (you will study matrix multiplication in this chapter)

$$\begin{bmatrix} 0 & 7 & 28 & 84 \\ 0.1 & 0 & 0 & 0 \\ 0 & 0.4 & 0 & 0 \\ 0 & 0 & 0.6 & 0 \end{bmatrix}\begin{bmatrix} 600 \\ 200 \\ 100 \\ 25 \end{bmatrix} = \begin{bmatrix} 6300 \\ 60 \\ 80 \\ 60 \end{bmatrix}$$

tells the biologist that 1 year from now, there will be 6300 new eggs, 60 yearlings, 80 2-year-olds, and 60 3-year-olds. Subsequent products would enable the biologist to predict the number of fish in each stage for future years.

In addition to this application, there are applications of matrices to economics, physics, chemistry, and a host of other disciplines. To read about another application, see **Exercise 56, page 599.**

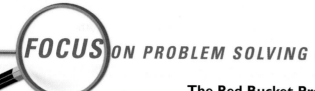

The Red Bucket Procedure

A chemistry laboratory has two buckets of sand that are available to put out any accidental fire that might occur. One bucket is red, and the other is blue.

One day a fire started as a student was working on an experiment. The student quickly put out the fire by pouring the sand from the red bucket onto the flames. Later, the *empty* red bucket was put back on the shelf alongside the blue bucket. Several weeks later another fire broke out. How would you put out this second fire? Most people would use the sand in the blue bucket to put out the second fire; however, another approach would be to pour the sand from the blue bucket into the red bucket, knowing from previous experience that sand from the red bucket can be used to put out a fire. This approach may seem a bit silly, but mathematicians *often* use this procedure of solving a problem by putting the problem in a form for which there is a known solution process.

Keep this red bucket story in mind as you study how to solve a system of equations using the Gaussian elimination method in Section 7.1. The goal of the Gaussian elimination method is to write the system in an equivalent form for which we have a known solution process. That is, to "put the problem in a red bucket."

GAUSSIAN ELIMINATION METHOD

● INTRODUCTION TO MATRICES

A **matrix** is a rectangular array of numbers. Each number in a matrix is called an **element** of the matrix. The matrix below, with three rows and four columns, is called a 3×4 (read "3 by 4") matrix.

$$\begin{bmatrix} 2 & 5 & -2 & 5 \\ -3 & 6 & 4 & 0 \\ 1 & 3 & 7 & 2 \end{bmatrix}$$

A matrix of m rows and n columns is said to be of **order** $m \times n$ or **dimension** $m \times n$. A **square matrix of order** n is a matrix with n rows and n columns. The matrix above has order 3×4. We will use the notation a_{ij} to refer to the element of a matrix in the ith row and jth column. For the matrix given above, $a_{23} = 4$, $a_{31} = 1$, and $a_{13} = -2$.

The elements $a_{11}, a_{22}, a_{23}, \ldots, a_{mm}$ form the **main diagonal** of a matrix. The elements 2, 6, and 7 form the main diagonal of the matrix shown above.

A matrix can be created from a system of linear equations. Consider the system of linear equations

$$\begin{cases} 2x - 3y + z = 2 \\ x \qquad - 3z = 4 \\ 4x - y + 4z = 3 \end{cases}$$

Using only the coefficients and constants of this system, we can write the 3×4 matrix

$$\begin{bmatrix} 2 & -3 & 1 & | & 2 \\ 1 & 0 & -3 & | & 4 \\ 4 & -1 & 4 & | & 3 \end{bmatrix}$$

This matrix is called the **augmented matrix** of the system of equations. The matrix formed by the coefficients of the system is the **coefficient matrix.** The matrix formed from the constants is the **constant matrix** for the system. The coefficient matrix and constant matrix for the given system are

Coefficient matrix: $\begin{bmatrix} 2 & -3 & 1 \\ 1 & 0 & -3 \\ 4 & -1 & 4 \end{bmatrix}$ Constant matrix: $\begin{bmatrix} 2 \\ 4 \\ 3 \end{bmatrix}$

We can write a system of equations from an augmented matrix.

Augmented matrix: $\begin{bmatrix} 2 & -1 & 4 & | & 3 \\ 1 & 1 & 0 & | & 2 \\ 3 & -2 & -1 & | & 2 \end{bmatrix}$ $\xrightarrow{\text{System:}}$ $\begin{cases} 2x - y + 4z = 3 \\ x + y \qquad = 2 \\ 3x - 2y - z = 2 \end{cases}$

In certain cases, an augmented matrix represents a system of equations that we can solve by back substitution. Consider the following augmented matrix and the equivalent system of equations.

MATH MATTERS

The word *matrix* has the Latin word *mater* as its root. The mathematician James Sylvester (1814–1897) coined the term to indicate a place from which something else originates. Sylvester, born in London, spent the last part of his life at Johns Hopkins University, where he was influential in establishing graduate study in mathematics.

---

take note

When a term is missing from one of the equations of the system (as in the second equation), the coefficient of that term is 0, and a 0 is entered in the matrix. A vertical bar that separates the coefficients of the variables from the constants is frequently drawn in the matrix.

$$\begin{bmatrix} 1 & -3 & 4 & | & 5 \\ 0 & 1 & 2 & | & -4 \\ 0 & 0 & 1 & | & -1 \end{bmatrix} \quad \xrightarrow{\text{equivalent system}} \quad \begin{cases} x - 3y + 4z = 5 \\ y + 2z = -4 \\ z = -1 \end{cases}$$

Solving this system by using back substitution, we find that the solution is $(3, -2, -1)$. The matrix above is in *row echelon form*.

Row Echelon Form

A matrix is in **row echelon form** if all the following conditions are satisfied.

1. The first nonzero number in any row is a 1.

2. Rows are arranged so that the column containing the first nonzero number in any row is to the left of the column containing the first nonzero number of the next row.

3. All rows consisting entirely of zeros appear at the bottom of the matrix.

Following are three examples of matrices in row echelon form.

$$\begin{bmatrix} 1 & -3 & 4 & 2 \\ 0 & 1 & -2 & -1 \\ 0 & 0 & 0 & 0 \end{bmatrix} \qquad \begin{bmatrix} 1 & 2 & -1 & 3 \\ 0 & 1 & 2 & -1 \end{bmatrix} \qquad \begin{bmatrix} 1 & -1 & 3 & 2 \\ 0 & 1 & 2 & 5 \\ 0 & 0 & 1 & -2 \end{bmatrix}$$

❓ **QUESTION** Is the augmented matrix $\begin{bmatrix} 1 & -2 & 3 & | & 2 \\ 0 & 0 & 1 & | & 4 \\ 0 & 1 & -1 & | & 3 \end{bmatrix}$ in row echelon form?

● ELEMENTARY ROW OPERATIONS

We can write an augmented matrix in row echelon form by using **elementary row operations**. These operations are a rewording, in matrix terminology, of the operations that produce equivalent equations.

INTEGRATING TECHNOLOGY

Many graphing calculators have the elementary row operations as built-in functions. See the Project on page 581 for more details.

Elementary Row Operations

Given the augmented matrix for a system of linear equations, each of the following elementary row operations produces a matrix of an equivalent system of equations.

1. Interchanging any two rows

2. Multiplying all the elements in a row by the same nonzero number

3. Replacing a row by the sum of that row and a nonzero multiple of any other row

---

❓ **ANSWER** No. The matrix does not satisfy condition (2) of row echelon form.

It is convenient to specify each operation symbolically as follows:

1. Interchanging the ith and jth rows: $R_i \longleftrightarrow R_j$

2. Multiplying the ith row by k, a nonzero constant: kR_i

3. Replacing the jth row by the sum of that row and a nonzero multiple of the ith row: $kR_i + R_j$

To demonstrate these operations, we will use the 3×3 matrix

$$\begin{bmatrix} 2 & 1 & -2 \\ 3 & -2 & 2 \\ 1 & -2 & 3 \end{bmatrix}$$

$$\begin{bmatrix} 2 & 1 & -2 \\ 3 & -2 & 2 \\ 1 & -2 & 3 \end{bmatrix} \xrightarrow{R_1 \longleftrightarrow R_3} \begin{bmatrix} 1 & -2 & 3 \\ 3 & -2 & 2 \\ 2 & 1 & -2 \end{bmatrix}$$

- Interchange row 1 and row 3.

$$\begin{bmatrix} 2 & 1 & -2 \\ 3 & -2 & 2 \\ 1 & -2 & 3 \end{bmatrix} \xrightarrow{-3R_2} \begin{bmatrix} 2 & 1 & -2 \\ -9 & 6 & -6 \\ 1 & -2 & 3 \end{bmatrix}$$

- Multiply row 2 by -3.

$$\begin{bmatrix} 2 & 1 & -2 \\ 3 & -2 & 2 \\ 1 & -2 & 3 \end{bmatrix} \xrightarrow{-2R_3 + R_1} \begin{bmatrix} 0 & 5 & -8 \\ 3 & -2 & 2 \\ 1 & -2 & 3 \end{bmatrix}$$

- Multiply row 3 by -2 and add to row 1. Replace row 1 by the sum.

In Example 1 we use elementary row operations to write a matrix in row echelon form. As we carry out this procedure, to conserve space, we will occasionally perform more than one elementary row operation in one step. For instance, the notation

$$\begin{array}{c} 3R_1 + R_2 \\ -5R_1 + R_3 \\ \longrightarrow \end{array}$$

means that two elementary row operations were performed. First, multiply row 1 by 3 and add it to row 2. Replace row 2. Second, multiply row 1 by -5 and add it to row 3. Replace row 3.

Alternative to Example 1

Write the matrix $\begin{bmatrix} 3 & -6 & 12 \\ 2 & 1 & -3 \end{bmatrix}$ in row echelon form.

● $\begin{bmatrix} 1 & -2 & 4 \\ 0 & 1 & -\frac{11}{5} \end{bmatrix}$

EXAMPLE 1   **Write a Matrix in Row Echelon Form**

Write the matrix $\begin{bmatrix} -3 & 13 & -1 & -7 \\ 1 & -5 & 2 & 0 \\ 5 & -20 & -2 & 5 \end{bmatrix}$ in row echelon form.

Solution

Follow the procedure to write a matrix in row echelon form. Change a_{11} to 1.

$$\begin{bmatrix} -3 & 13 & -1 & -7 \\ 1 & -5 & 2 & 0 \\ 5 & -20 & -2 & 5 \end{bmatrix} \xrightarrow{R_1 \longleftrightarrow R_2} \begin{bmatrix} 1 & -5 & 2 & 0 \\ -3 & 13 & -1 & -7 \\ 5 & -20 & -2 & 5 \end{bmatrix}$$

Continued ▶

take note

The sequence of steps used to place a matrix in row echelon form is not unique. For instance, in Example 1 we could have started by multiplying row 1 by $-\dfrac{1}{3}$. The sequence of steps you use may result in a row echelon form that is different from the one we show. See the Integrating Technology following Example 1.

INSTRUCTOR NOTE

The algorithm a calculator uses to express a matrix in row echelon form starts by moving the row whose first element has the greatest absolute value to row 1. This reduces rounding errors as the calculation proceeds. Note that the first row of the row echelon form of the matrix in the Integrating Technology below is 1, -4, -0.4, and 1. This is achieved by interchanging row 1 and row 3, and then multiplying the new row 1 by $\dfrac{1}{5}$.

Change the remaining elements in the first column to 0.

$$\begin{bmatrix} 1 & -5 & 2 & 0 \\ -3 & 13 & -1 & -7 \\ 5 & -20 & -2 & 5 \end{bmatrix} \xrightarrow[\;-5R_1 + R_3\;]{3R_1 + R_2} \begin{bmatrix} 1 & -5 & 2 & 19 \\ 0 & -2 & 5 & -7 \\ 0 & 5 & -12 & 5 \end{bmatrix}$$

Change a_{22} to 1.

$$\begin{bmatrix} 1 & -5 & 2 & 0 \\ 0 & -2 & 5 & -7 \\ 0 & 5 & -12 & 5 \end{bmatrix} \xrightarrow{-\frac{1}{2}R_2} \begin{bmatrix} 1 & -5 & 2 & 0 \\ 0 & 1 & -\frac{5}{2} & \frac{7}{2} \\ 0 & 5 & -12 & 5 \end{bmatrix}$$

Change the remaining elements under a_{22} to 0.

$$\begin{bmatrix} 1 & -5 & 2 & 0 \\ 0 & 1 & -\frac{5}{2} & \frac{7}{2} \\ 0 & 5 & -12 & 5 \end{bmatrix} \xrightarrow{-5R_2 + R_3} \begin{bmatrix} 1 & -5 & 2 & 0 \\ 0 & 1 & -\frac{5}{2} & \frac{7}{2} \\ 0 & 0 & \frac{1}{2} & -\frac{25}{2} \end{bmatrix}$$

Change a_{33} to 1.

$$\begin{bmatrix} 1 & -5 & 2 & 0 \\ 0 & 1 & -\frac{5}{2} & \frac{7}{2} \\ 0 & 0 & \frac{1}{2} & -\frac{25}{2} \end{bmatrix} \xrightarrow{2R_3} \begin{bmatrix} 1 & -5 & 2 & 0 \\ 0 & 1 & -\frac{5}{2} & \frac{7}{2} \\ 0 & 0 & 1 & -25 \end{bmatrix}$$

A row echelon form for the matrix is $\begin{bmatrix} 1 & -5 & 2 & 0 \\ 0 & 1 & -\frac{5}{2} & \frac{7}{2} \\ 0 & 0 & 1 & -25 \end{bmatrix}$.

▶ **TRY EXERCISE 6, PAGE 579**

INTEGRATING TECHNOLOGY

A graphing calculator can be used to find a row echelon form for a matrix. The screens below, from a TI-83 Plus calculator, show a row echelon form for the matrix in Example 1. The abbreviation **ref(** stands for *row echelon form*. If you need assistance with keystrokes, please see the website for this text at college.hmco.com.

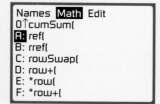

Note that the row echelon form produced by the calculator is different from the one we produced. The two forms are equivalent and either can be used for any calculation for which a row echelon form of the matrix is required.

• GAUSSIAN ELIMINATION METHOD

The **Gaussian elimination method** is an algorithm[1] that uses elementary row operations to solve a system of linear equations. The goal of this method is to rewrite an augmented matrix in row echelon form.

We will now demonstrate how to solve a system of two equations in two variables by the Gaussian elimination method. Consider the system of equations

$$\begin{cases} 2x + 5y = -1 \\ 3x - 2y = 8 \end{cases} \quad (1)$$

The augmented matrix for this system is

$$\left[\begin{array}{cc|c} 2 & 5 & -1 \\ 3 & -2 & 8 \end{array}\right]$$

The goal of the Gaussian elimination method is to rewrite the augmented matrix in row echelon form by using elementary row operations. The row operations are chosen so that first, there is a 1 as a_{11}; second, there is a 0 as a_{21}; and third, there is a 1 as a_{22}.

Begin by multiplying row 1 by $\dfrac{1}{2}$. The result is a 1 as a_{11}.

$$\left[\begin{array}{cc|c} 2 & 5 & -1 \\ 3 & -2 & 8 \end{array}\right] \xrightarrow{\ \frac{1}{2}R_1\ } \left[\begin{array}{cc|c} 1 & \frac{5}{2} & -\frac{1}{2} \\ 3 & -2 & 8 \end{array}\right]$$

Now multiply row 1 by -3 and add the result to row 2. Replace row 2. The result is a 0 as a_{21}.

$$\left[\begin{array}{cc|c} 1 & \frac{5}{2} & -\frac{1}{2} \\ 3 & -2 & 8 \end{array}\right] \xrightarrow{\ -3R_1 + R_2\ } \left[\begin{array}{cc|c} 1 & \frac{5}{2} & -\frac{1}{2} \\ 0 & -\frac{19}{2} & \frac{19}{2} \end{array}\right]$$

Now multiply row 2 by $-\dfrac{2}{19}$. The result is a 1 as a_{22}. The matrix is now in row echelon form.

$$\left[\begin{array}{cc|c} 1 & \frac{5}{2} & -\frac{1}{2} \\ 0 & -\frac{19}{2} & \frac{19}{2} \end{array}\right] \xrightarrow{\ -\frac{2}{19}R_2\ } \left[\begin{array}{cc|c} 1 & \frac{5}{2} & -\frac{1}{2} \\ 0 & 1 & -1 \end{array}\right]$$

The system of equations written from the echelon form of the matrix is

$$\begin{cases} x + \dfrac{5}{2}y = -\dfrac{1}{2} \\ \phantom{x + \dfrac{5}{2}}y = -1 \end{cases} \quad (2)$$

To solve by back substitution, replace y in the first equation by -1 and solve for x.

$$x + \left(\frac{5}{2}\right)(-1) = -\frac{1}{2}$$

$$x = 2$$

The solution of system (1) is $(2, -1)$.

[1] An algorithm is a procedure used in calculations. The word is derived from *Al-Khwarizmi*, the name of the author of an Arabic algebra book written around A.D. 825.

🖩 **INTEGRATING TECHNOLOGY**

The row echelon form shown at the bottom of page 572 is in decimal form. A form with fractions can be found by using the ▶ **Frac** command.

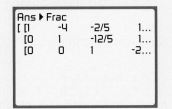

```
Ans ▶ Frac
[ [1    -4    -2/5    1...
  [0     1   -12/5    1...
  [0     0      1    -2...
```

MATH MATTERS

The Gaussian elimination method is the procedure used in some computer programs to solve a system of equations.

Alternative to Example 2
Solve by using the Gaussian elimination method.

$$\begin{cases} 2w + 3x + 4y + z = 13 \\ 3w + 2x + 5y + 2z = 19 \\ 3w + x - 4y + 6z = -27 \\ w + x + y + z = 2 \end{cases}$$

● $(3, -2, 4, -3)$

EXAMPLE 2 Solve a System of Equations by the Gaussian Elimination Method

Solve by using the Gaussian elimination method.

$$\begin{cases} 3t - 8u + 8v + 7w = 41 \\ t - 2u + 2v + w = 9 \\ 2t - 2u + 6v - 4w = -1 \\ 2t - 2u + 3v - 3w = 3 \end{cases}$$

Solution

Write the augmented matrix and then use elementary row operations to rewrite the matrix in row echelon form.

$$\left[\begin{array}{cccc|c} 3 & -8 & 8 & 7 & 41 \\ 1 & -2 & 2 & 1 & 9 \\ 2 & -2 & 6 & -4 & -1 \\ 2 & -2 & 3 & -3 & 3 \end{array}\right] \xrightarrow{R_1 \longleftrightarrow R_2} \left[\begin{array}{cccc|c} 1 & -2 & 2 & 1 & 9 \\ 3 & -8 & 8 & 7 & 41 \\ 2 & -2 & 6 & -4 & -1 \\ 2 & -2 & 3 & -3 & 3 \end{array}\right]$$

$$\begin{array}{c} -3R_1 + R_2 \\ -2R_1 + R_3 \\ -2R_1 + R_4 \\ \longrightarrow \end{array} \left[\begin{array}{cccc|c} 1 & -2 & 2 & 1 & 9 \\ 0 & -2 & 2 & 4 & 14 \\ 0 & 2 & 2 & -6 & -19 \\ 0 & 2 & -1 & -5 & -15 \end{array}\right] \xrightarrow{-\frac{1}{2}R_2} \left[\begin{array}{cccc|c} 1 & -2 & 2 & 1 & 9 \\ 0 & 1 & -1 & -2 & -7 \\ 0 & 2 & 2 & -6 & -19 \\ 0 & 2 & -1 & -5 & -15 \end{array}\right]$$

$$\begin{array}{c} -2R_2 + R_3 \\ -2R_2 + R_4 \\ \longrightarrow \end{array} \left[\begin{array}{cccc|c} 1 & -2 & 2 & 1 & 9 \\ 0 & 1 & -1 & -2 & -7 \\ 0 & 0 & 4 & -2 & -5 \\ 0 & 0 & 1 & -1 & -1 \end{array}\right] \xrightarrow{R_4 \longleftrightarrow R_3} \left[\begin{array}{cccc|c} 1 & -2 & 2 & 1 & 9 \\ 0 & 1 & -1 & -2 & -7 \\ 0 & 0 & 1 & -1 & -1 \\ 0 & 0 & 4 & -2 & -5 \end{array}\right]$$

$$\xrightarrow{-4R_3 + R_4} \left[\begin{array}{cccc|c} 1 & -2 & 2 & 1 & 9 \\ 0 & 1 & -1 & -2 & -7 \\ 0 & 0 & 1 & -1 & -1 \\ 0 & 0 & 0 & 2 & -1 \end{array}\right] \xrightarrow{\frac{1}{2}R_4} \left[\begin{array}{cccc|c} 1 & -2 & 2 & 1 & 9 \\ 0 & 1 & -1 & -2 & -7 \\ 0 & 0 & 1 & -1 & -1 \\ 0 & 0 & 0 & 1 & -\frac{1}{2} \end{array}\right]$$

The last matrix is in row echelon form. The system of equations written from the matrix is

$$\begin{cases} t - 2u + 2v + w = 9 \\ u - v - 2w = -7 \\ v - w = -1 \\ w = -\dfrac{1}{2} \end{cases}$$

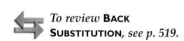

To review **BACK SUBSTITUTION**, *see p. 519.*

Solve by back substitution. The solution is $\left(-\dfrac{13}{2}, -\dfrac{19}{2}, -\dfrac{3}{2}, -\dfrac{1}{2}\right)$.

▶ **TRY EXERCISE 14, PAGE 579**

Alternative to Example 3
Solve by using the Gaussian elimination method.

$$\begin{cases} x + 4y + 2z = -3 \\ 4x + 5y + 4z = -4 \\ 10x + 7y + 8z = -6 \end{cases}$$

● $\left(-\dfrac{6}{11}c - \dfrac{1}{11}, -\dfrac{4}{11}c - \dfrac{8}{11}, c\right)$

EXAMPLE 3   **Solve a Dependent System of Equations**

Solve using the Gaussian elimination method.

$$\begin{cases} x - 3y + 4z = 1 \\ 2x - 5y + 3z = 6 \\ x - 2y - z = 5 \end{cases}$$

Solution

Write the augmented matrix and then use elementary row operations to rewrite the matrix in row echelon form.

$$\begin{bmatrix} 1 & -3 & 4 & | & 1 \\ 2 & -5 & 3 & | & 6 \\ 1 & -2 & -1 & | & 5 \end{bmatrix} \xrightarrow[\;-R_1 + R_3\;]{-2R_1 + R_2} \begin{bmatrix} 1 & -3 & 4 & | & 1 \\ 0 & 1 & -5 & | & 4 \\ 0 & 1 & -5 & | & 4 \end{bmatrix}$$

$$\xrightarrow{\;-R_2 + R_3\;} \begin{bmatrix} 1 & -3 & 4 & | & 1 \\ 0 & 1 & -5 & | & 4 \\ 0 & 0 & 0 & | & 0 \end{bmatrix}$$

$$\begin{cases} x - 3y + 4z = 1 \\ y - 5z = 4 \end{cases}$$ • **Equivalent system**

Any solution of the system of equations is a solution of $y - 5z = 4$. Solving this equation for y, we have $y = 5z + 4$.

$$x - 3y + 4z = 1$$
$$x - 3(5z + 4) + 4z = 1 \qquad \text{• } y = 5z + 4$$
$$x = 11z + 13 \qquad \text{• Solve for } x.$$

Both x and y are expressed in terms of z. Let z be any real number c. The solutions of the system of equations are $(11c + 13, 5c + 4, c)$.

▶ **TRY EXERCISE 18, PAGE 579**

Alternative to Example 4
Solve by using the Gaussian elimination method.

$$\begin{cases} x - 3y + 2z = 6 \\ 4x - y + 3z = 10 \\ 7x + y + 4z = -2 \end{cases}$$

● **The system of equations has no solution.**

EXAMPLE 4   **Identify an Inconsistent System of Equations**

Solve using the Gaussian elimination method.

$$\begin{cases} x - 3y + z = 5 \\ 3x - 7y + 2z = 12 \\ 2x - 4y + z = 3 \end{cases}$$

Continued ▶

Solution

Write the augmented matrix and then use elementary row operations to rewrite the matrix in row echelon form.

$$\begin{bmatrix} 1 & -3 & 1 & | & 5 \\ 3 & -7 & 2 & | & 12 \\ 2 & -4 & 1 & | & 3 \end{bmatrix} \xrightarrow[\substack{-3R_1 + R_2 \\ -2R_1 + R_3}]{} \begin{bmatrix} 1 & -3 & 1 & | & 5 \\ 0 & 2 & -1 & | & -3 \\ 0 & 2 & -1 & | & -7 \end{bmatrix}$$

$$\xrightarrow[\frac{1}{2}R_2]{} \begin{bmatrix} 1 & -3 & 1 & | & 5 \\ 0 & 1 & -\frac{1}{2} & | & -\frac{3}{2} \\ 0 & 2 & -1 & | & -7 \end{bmatrix} \xrightarrow[-2R_2 + R_3]{} \begin{bmatrix} 1 & -3 & 1 & | & 5 \\ 0 & 1 & -\frac{1}{2} & | & -\frac{3}{2} \\ 0 & 0 & 0 & | & -4 \end{bmatrix}$$

$$\begin{cases} x - 3y + z = 5 \\ \quad\quad y - \frac{1}{2}z = -\frac{3}{2} \\ \quad\quad\quad\quad 0z = -4 \end{cases} \quad \bullet \text{ Equivalent system}$$

Because the equation $0z = -4$ has no solution, the system of equations has no solution.

▶ **TRY EXERCISE 20, PAGE 579**

Alternative to Example 5
Solve by using the Gaussian elimination method.

$$\begin{cases} t + u - v - w = 4 \\ t - u + v - w = 0 \\ 2t + u + 2v + w = 15 \end{cases}$$

● $(c + 2, -c + 5, -c + 3, c)$

---

take note

When there are fewer equations than variables (as in Example 5), the system of equations has either no solution or an infinite number of solutions. See the Project on page 581.

EXAMPLE 5 **Solve a Nonsquare System of Equations**

Solve the system of equations using the Gaussian elimination method.

$$\begin{cases} x_1 - 2x_2 - 3x_3 - 2x_4 = 1 \\ 2x_1 - 3x_2 - 4x_3 - 2x_4 = 3 \\ x_1 + x_2 + x_3 - 7x_4 = -7 \end{cases}$$

Solution

Write the augmented matrix and then use elementary row operations to rewrite the matrix in row echelon form.

$$\begin{bmatrix} 1 & -2 & -3 & -2 & | & 1 \\ 2 & -3 & -4 & -2 & | & 3 \\ 1 & 1 & 1 & -7 & | & -7 \end{bmatrix} \xrightarrow[\substack{-2R_1 + R_2 \\ -1R_1 + R_3}]{} \begin{bmatrix} 1 & -2 & -3 & -2 & | & 1 \\ 0 & 1 & 2 & 2 & | & 1 \\ 0 & 3 & 4 & -5 & | & -8 \end{bmatrix}$$

$$\xrightarrow[\substack{-3R_2 + R_3 \\ -\frac{1}{2}R_3}]{} \begin{bmatrix} 1 & -2 & -3 & -2 & | & 1 \\ 0 & 1 & 2 & 2 & | & 1 \\ 0 & 0 & 1 & \frac{11}{2} & | & \frac{11}{2} \end{bmatrix}$$

$$\begin{cases} x_1 - 2x_2 - 3x_3 - 2x_4 = 1 \\ \quad\quad x_2 + 2x_3 + 2x_4 = 1 \\ \quad\quad\quad\quad x_3 + \frac{11}{2}x_4 = \frac{11}{2} \end{cases} \quad \bullet \text{ Equivalent system}$$

Now express each of the variables in terms of x_4. Solve the third equation for x_3.

$$x_3 = -\frac{11}{2}x_4 + \frac{11}{2}$$

Substitute this value into the second equation and solve for x_2.

$$x_2 + 2\left(-\frac{11}{2}x_4 + \frac{11}{2}\right) + 2x_4 = 1$$

$$x_2 = 9x_4 - 10 \qquad \text{• Simplify.}$$

Substitute the values for x_2 and x_3 into the first equation and solve for x_1.

$$x_1 - 2(9x_4 - 10) - 3\left(-\frac{11}{2}x_4 + \frac{11}{2}\right) - 2x_4 = 1$$

$$x_1 = \frac{7}{2}x_4 - \frac{5}{2} \qquad \text{• Simplify.}$$

If x_4 is any real number c, the solution is of the form

$$\left(\frac{7}{2}c - \frac{5}{2}, 9c - 10, -\frac{11}{2}c + \frac{11}{2}, c\right)$$

▶ **TRY EXERCISE 36, PAGE 579**

● **APPLICATIONS: INTERPOLATING POLYNOMIALS**

One application of the Gaussian elimination method of solving a system of equations is in finding *interpolating polynomials*.

Interpolating Polynomial

Let (x_0, y_0), (x_1, y_1), $(x_2, y_2), \ldots, (x_n, y_n)$ be the coordinates of a set of points for which all the x_i are distinct. Then the **interpolating polynomial** is a unique polynomial of degree at most n whose graph passes through the given points.

EXAMPLE 6 **Find an Interpolating Polynomial**

Find the interpolating polynomial that passes through the points whose coordinates are $(-2, 13)$, $(1, -2)$, and $(2, 1)$.

Solution

Because there are three given points, the degree of the interpolating polynomial will be at most 2. The form of the polynomial will be $p(x) = a_2x^2 + a_1x + a_0$. Use this polynomial to create a system of equations.

$$p(x) = a_2x^2 + a_1x + a_0$$
$$p(-2) = a_2(-2)^2 + a_1(-2) + a_0 = 4a_2 - 2a_1 + a_0 = 13 \qquad \text{• } x = -2, \; p(-2) = 13$$

$$p(1) = a_2(1)^2 + a_1(1) + a_0 = a_2 + a_1 + a_0 = -2 \qquad \text{• } x = 1, \; p(1) = -2$$
$$p(2) = a_2(2)^2 + a_1(2) + a_0 = 4a_2 + 2a_1 + a_0 = 1 \qquad \text{• } x = 2, \; p(2) = 1$$

Continued ▶

take note

Because the subscript on the first ordered pair is zero, there are $n + 1$ points. The degree of the interpolating polynomial, however, is n. Thus, if there were three ordered pairs, the degree of the interpolating polynomial would be at most 2. If there were seven ordered pairs, the degree of the interpolating polynomial would be at most 6.

Alternative to Example 6
Find the interpolating polynomial that passes through the points $(-3, 28)$, $(-1, 6)$, and $(2, 3)$.
● $p(x) = 2x^2 - 3x + 1$

The system of equations and the associated augmented matrix are

$$\begin{cases} 4a_2 - 2a_1 + a_0 = 13 \\ a_2 + a_1 + a_0 = -2 \\ 4a_2 + 2a_1 + a_0 = 1 \end{cases} \qquad \begin{bmatrix} 4 & -2 & 1 & | & 13 \\ 1 & 1 & 1 & | & -2 \\ 4 & 2 & 1 & | & 1 \end{bmatrix}$$

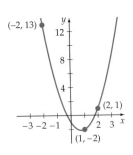

$(-2, 13)$

$(2, 1)$

$(1, -2)$

$p(x) = 2x^2 - 3x + 1$

FIGURE 7.1

The augmented matrix in row echelon form and the resulting system of equations are

$$\begin{bmatrix} 1 & -0.5 & 0.25 & | & 3.25 \\ 0 & 1 & 0 & | & -3 \\ 0 & 0 & 1 & | & -1 \end{bmatrix} \qquad \begin{cases} a_2 - 0.5a_1 + 0.25a_0 = 3.25 \\ a_1 = -3 \\ a_0 = -1 \end{cases}$$

Solving the system of equations by back substitution yields $a_0 = -1$, $a_1 = -3$, and $a_2 = 2$. The interpolating polynomial is $p(x) = 2x^2 - 3x - 1$. See **Figure 7.1**.

 TRY EXERCISE 44, PAGE 580

TOPICS FOR DISCUSSION

1. What is a matrix? What is the order of a matrix?

2. Explain how the augmented matrix differs from the coefficient matrix for a system of equations.

3. Give examples of matrices that are in row echelon form and of matrices that are not in row echelon form.

4. What are the elementary row operations? Give examples of each one.

5. After elementary row operations have been correctly performed on an augmented matrix, the result is $\begin{bmatrix} 1 & -2 & 3 & 0 \\ 0 & 1 & 2 & -1 \\ 0 & 0 & 0 & 3 \end{bmatrix}$. Does this result indicate that the system of equations has a unique solution, an infinite number of solutions, or no solution?

EXERCISE SET 7.1

—Suggested Assignment: Exercises 1–49, every other odd; 51, 55, 60–65.
—Answers to Exercises 1–12 are on page AA32.

In Exercises 1 to 4, write the augmented matrix, the coefficient matrix, and the constant matrix.

1. $\begin{cases} 2x - 3y + z = 1 \\ 3x - 2y + 3z = 0 \\ x + 5z = 4 \end{cases}$

2. $\begin{cases} -3y + 2z = 3 \\ 2x - y = -1 \\ 3x - 2y + 3z = 4 \end{cases}$

3. $\begin{cases} 2x - 3y - 4z + w = 2 \\ 2y + z = 2 \\ x - y + 2z = 4 \\ 3x - 3y - 2z = 1 \end{cases}$

4. $\begin{cases} x - y + 2z + 3w = -2 \\ 2x + z - 2w = 1 \\ 3x - 2w = 3 \\ -x + 3y - z = 3 \end{cases}$

In Exercises 5 to 12, use elementary row operations to write each matrix in row echelon form.

5. $\begin{bmatrix} 2 & -1 & 3 & -2 \\ 1 & -1 & 2 & 2 \\ 3 & 2 & -1 & 3 \end{bmatrix}$ ▶ 6. $\begin{bmatrix} 1 & 2 & 4 & 1 \\ 2 & 2 & 7 & 3 \\ 3 & 6 & 8 & -1 \end{bmatrix}$

7. $\begin{bmatrix} 4 & -5 & -1 & 2 \\ 3 & -4 & 1 & -2 \\ 1 & -2 & -1 & 3 \end{bmatrix}$ 8. $\begin{bmatrix} -2 & 1 & -1 & 3 \\ 2 & 2 & 4 & 6 \\ 3 & 1 & -1 & 2 \end{bmatrix}$

9. $\begin{bmatrix} 1 & -2 & 3 & -4 \\ 3 & -6 & 10 & -14 \\ 5 & -8 & 19 & -21 \\ 2 & -4 & 7 & -10 \end{bmatrix}$ 10. $\begin{bmatrix} 2 & -1 & 3 & 2 \\ 1 & 2 & -1 & 3 \\ 3 & 5 & -2 & 2 \\ 4 & 3 & 1 & 8 \end{bmatrix}$

11. $\begin{bmatrix} 1 & -3 & 4 & 2 & 1 \\ 2 & -3 & 5 & -2 & -1 \\ -1 & 2 & -3 & 1 & 3 \end{bmatrix}$

12. $\begin{bmatrix} 2 & -1 & 3 & 2 & 2 \\ 1 & -2 & 2 & 1 & -1 \\ 3 & -5 & -1 & -2 & 3 \end{bmatrix}$

In Exercises 13 to 38, solve each system of equations by the Gaussian elimination method.

13. $\begin{cases} x + 2y - 2z = -2 \\ 5x + 9y - 4z = -3 \\ 3x + 4y - 5z = -3 \end{cases}$
$(2, -1, 1)$

▶ 14. $\begin{cases} x - 3y + z = 8 \\ 2x - 5y - 3z = 2 \\ x + 4y + z = 1 \end{cases}$ $\left(\dfrac{12}{5}, -1, \dfrac{13}{5}\right)$

15. $\begin{cases} 3x + 7y - 7z = -4 \\ x + 2y - 3z = 0 \\ 5x + 6y + z = -8 \end{cases}$
$(1, -2, -1)$

16. $\begin{cases} 2x - 3y + 2z = 13 \\ 3x - 4y - 3z = 1 \\ 3x + y - z = 2 \end{cases}$
$(2, -1, 3)$

17. $\begin{cases} x + 2y - 2z = 3 \\ 5x + 8y - 6z = 14 \\ 3x + 4y - 2z = 8 \end{cases}$
Answer on bottom of page.

▶ 18. $\begin{cases} 3x - 5y + 2z = 4 \\ x - 3y + 2z = 4 \\ 5x - 11y + 6z = 12 \end{cases}$
$(c - 2, c - 2, c)$

19. $\begin{cases} 3x + 2y - z = 1 \\ 2x + 3y - z = 1 \\ x - y + 2z = 3 \end{cases}$
Answer on bottom of page.

▶ 20. $\begin{cases} 2x + 5y + 2z = -1 \\ x + 2y - 3z = 5 \\ 5x + 12y + z = 10 \end{cases}$
no solution

21. $\begin{cases} x - 3y + 2z = 0 \\ 2x - 5y - 2z = 0 \\ 4x - 11y + 2z = 0 \end{cases}$
$(16c, 6c, c)$

22. $\begin{cases} x + y - 2z = 0 \\ 3x + 4y - z = 0 \\ 5x + 6y - 5z = 0 \end{cases}$
$(7c, -5c, c)$

23. $\begin{cases} 2x + y - 3z = 4 \\ 3x + 2y + z = 2 \end{cases}$
$(7c + 6, -11c - 8, c)$

24. $\begin{cases} 3x - 6y + 2z = 2 \\ 2x + 5y - 3z = 2 \end{cases}$
Answer on bottom of page.

25. $\begin{cases} 2x + 2y - 4z = 4 \\ 2x + 3y - 5z = 4 \\ 4x + 5y - 9z = 8 \end{cases}$
$(c + 2, c, c)$

26. $\begin{cases} 3x - 10y + 2z = 34 \\ x - 4y + z = 13 \\ 5x - 2y + 7z = 31 \end{cases}$
$(4, -2, 1)$

27. $\begin{cases} x + 3y + 4z = 11 \\ 2x + 3y + 2z = 7 \\ 4x + 9y + 10z = 20 \\ 3x - 2y + z = 1 \end{cases}$
no solution

28. $\begin{cases} x - 4y + 3z = 4 \\ 3x - 10y + 3z = 4 \\ 5x - 18y + 9z = 10 \\ 2x + 2y - 3z = -11 \end{cases}$
no solution

29. $\begin{cases} t + 2u - 3v + w = -7 \\ 3t + 5u - 8v + 5w = -8 \\ 2t + 3u - 7v + 3w = -11 \\ 4t + 8u - 10v + 7w = -10 \end{cases}$ $(2, -2, 3, 4)$

30. $\begin{cases} t + 4u + 2v - 3w = 11 \\ 2t + 10u + 3v - 5w = 17 \\ 4t + 16u + 7v - 9w = 34 \\ t + 4u + v - w = 4 \end{cases}$ $\left(2, -\dfrac{1}{2}, 1, -3\right)$

31. $\begin{cases} 2t - u + 3v + 2w = 2 \\ t - u + 2v + w = 2 \\ 3t - 2v - 3w = 13 \\ 2t + 2u - 2w = 6 \end{cases}$ $\left(\dfrac{21}{10}, -\dfrac{8}{5}, \dfrac{2}{5}, -\dfrac{5}{2}\right)$

32. $\begin{cases} 4t + 7u - 10v + 3w = -29 \\ 3t + 5u - 7v + 2w = -20 \\ t + 2u - 3v + w = -9 \\ 2t - u + 2v - 4w = 15 \end{cases}$ $\left(\dfrac{3}{2}c + 4, -2c - 5, -\dfrac{1}{2}c + 1, c\right)$

33. $\begin{cases} 3t + 10u + 7v - 6w = 7 \\ 2t + 8u + 6v - 5w = 5 \\ t + 4u + 2v - 3w = 2 \\ 4t + 14u + 9v - 8w = 8 \end{cases}$ $\left(3, -\dfrac{3}{2}, 1, -1\right)$

34. $\begin{cases} t - 3u + 2v + 4w = 13 \\ 3t - 8u + 4v + 13w = 35 \\ 2t - 7u + 8v + 5w = 28 \\ 4t - 11u + 6v + 17w = 56 \end{cases}$ no solution

35. $\begin{cases} t - u + 2v - 3w = 9 \\ 4t + 11v - 10w = 46 \\ 3t - u + 8v - 6w = 27 \end{cases}$ $\left(\dfrac{27c}{2} + 39, \dfrac{5c}{2} + 10, -4c - 10, c\right)$

▶ 36. $\begin{cases} t - u + 3v - 5w = 10 \\ 2t - 3u + 4v + w = 7 \\ 3t + u - 2v - 2w = 6 \end{cases}$ $(c + 3, 5c + 5, 3c + 4, c)$

37. $\begin{cases} 3t - 4u + v = 2 \\ t + u - 2v + 3w = 1 \end{cases}$ $\left(c_1 - \dfrac{12c_2}{7} + \dfrac{6}{7}, c_1 - \dfrac{9c_2}{7} + \dfrac{1}{7}, c_1, c_2\right)$

38. $\begin{cases} 2t + 3v - 4w = 2 \\ t + 2u - 4v + w = -3 \end{cases}$ $\left(-\dfrac{3}{2}c_1 + 2c_2 + 1, \dfrac{11}{4}c_1 - \dfrac{3}{2}c_2 - 2, c_1, c_2\right)$

17. $\left(2 - 2c, 2c + \dfrac{1}{2}, c\right)$

19. $\left(\dfrac{1}{2}, \dfrac{1}{2}, \dfrac{3}{2}\right)$

24. $\left(\dfrac{8}{27}c + \dfrac{22}{27}, \dfrac{13}{27}c + \dfrac{2}{27}, c\right)$

Some graphing calculators and computer programs contain a program that will assist you in solving a system of linear equations by rewriting the system in row echelon form. Try one of these programs for Exercises 39 to 50.

39. INTERPOLATING POLYNOMIAL Find a polynomial that passes through the points whose coordinates are $(-2, -7)$ and $(1, -1)$. $p(x) = 2x - 3$

40. INTERPOLATING POLYNOMIAL Find a polynomial that passes through the points whose coordinates are $(-3, -8)$ and $(1, 4)$. $p(x) = 3x + 1$

41. INTERPOLATING POLYNOMIAL Find a polynomial that passes through the points whose coordinates are $(-1, 6)$, $(1, 2)$, and $(2, 3)$. $p(x) = x^2 - 2x + 3$

42. INTERPOLATING POLYNOMIAL Find a polynomial that passes through the points whose coordinates are $(-2, -3)$, $(0, -1)$, and $(3, 17)$. $p(x) = x^2 + 3x - 1$

43. INTERPOLATING POLYNOMIAL Find a polynomial that passes through the points whose coordinates are $(-2, -12)$, $(0, 2)$, $(1, 0)$, and $(3, 8)$. $p(x) = x^3 - 2x^2 - x + 2$

▶ **44. INTERPOLATING POLYNOMIAL** Find a polynomial that passes through the points whose coordinates are $(-1, -5)$, $(0, 0)$, $(1, 1)$, and $(2, 4)$. $p(x) = x^3 - 2x^2 + 2x$

45. INTERPOLATING POLYNOMIAL Find a polynomial that passes through the points whose coordinates are $(-1, 3)$, $(1, 7)$, and $(2, 9)$. This exercise illustrates that the degree of the polynomial is at most one less than the number of points. $p(x) = 2x + 5$

46. INTERPOLATING POLYNOMIAL Find a polynomial that passes through the points whose coordinates are $(-2, 7)$, $(1, -2)$, and $(2, -5)$. This exercise illustrates that the degree of the polynomial is at most one less than the number of points. $p(x) = -3x + 1$

Following a procedure similar to that for finding an interpolating polynomial, we can find various equations of graphs that pass through given points.

47. EQUATION OF A PLANE Find an equation of the plane that passes through the points $(-1, 0, -4)$, $(2, 1, 5)$, and $(-1, 1, -1)$. *Suggestion:* The equation of a plane can be written as $z = ax + by + c$. $z = 2x + 3y - 2$

48. EQUATION OF A PLANE Find an equation of the plane that passes through the points $(1, 2, -3)$, $(-2, 0, -7)$, and $(0, 1, -4)$. *Suggestion:* The equation of a plane can be written as $z = ax + by + c$. $z = 2x - y - 3$

49. EQUATION OF A CIRCLE Find an equation of the circle that passes through the points $(2, 6)$, $(-4, -2)$, and $(3, -1)$. *Suggestion:* The equation of a circle can be written as $x^2 + y^2 + ax + by = c$. $x^2 + y^2 + 2x - 4y - 20 = 0$

50. EQUATION OF A CIRCLE Find an equation of the circle that passes through the points $(2, 1)$, $(0, -7)$, and $(5, -2)$. *Suggestion:* The equation of a circle can be written as $x^2 + y^2 + ax + by = c$. $x^2 + y^2 - 2x + 6y - 7 = 0$

51. $\begin{cases} x_1 + 2x_2 - x_3 + 2x_4 + 3x_5 = 11 \\ x_1 - x_2 + 2x_3 - x_4 + 2x_5 = 0 \\ 2x_1 + x_2 - x_3 + 2x_4 - x_5 = 4 \\ 3x_1 + 2x_2 - x_3 + x_4 - 2x_5 = 2 \\ 2x_1 + x_2 - x_3 - 2x_4 + x_5 = 4 \end{cases}$ $(1, 0, -2, 1, 2)$

52. $\begin{cases} x_1 - 2x_2 + 2x_3 - 3x_4 + 2x_5 = 5 \\ x_1 - 3x_2 - x_3 + 2x_4 - x_5 = -4 \\ 3x_1 + x_2 - 2x_3 + x_4 + 3x_5 = 9 \\ 2x_1 - x_2 + 3x_3 - x_4 - 2x_5 = 2 \\ -x_1 + 2x_2 - 2x_3 + 3x_4 - x_5 = -4 \end{cases}$ $(2, 1, 0, -1, 1)$

53. $\begin{cases} x_1 + 2x_2 - 3x_3 - x_4 + 2x_5 = -10 \\ -x_1 - 3x_2 + x_3 + x_4 - x_5 = 4 \\ 2x_1 + 3x_2 - 5x_3 + 2x_4 + 3x_5 = -20 \\ 3x_1 + 4x_2 - 7x_3 + 3x_4 - 2x_5 = -16 \\ 2x_1 + x_2 - 6x_3 + 4x_4 - 3x_5 = -12 \end{cases}$

54. $\begin{cases} x_1 - 2x_2 + 2x_3 - 3x_4 + x_5 = 5 \\ 2x_1 - 3x_2 + 4x_3 - 5x_4 - x_5 = 13 \\ x_1 + x_2 - 2x_3 + 2x_4 + 2x_5 = -11 \\ 3x_1 - 2x_2 + 2x_3 - 2x_4 - 2x_5 = 7 \\ 4x_1 - 4x_2 + 4x_3 - 5x_4 - x_5 = 12 \end{cases}$

$\left(-\dfrac{3}{2}, -2, 4c + \dfrac{35}{4}, 3c + 5, c\right)$

53. $\left(\dfrac{77c + 151}{3}, \dfrac{-25c - 50}{3}, \dfrac{14c + 34}{3}, -3c - 7, c\right)$

─── **CONNECTING CONCEPTS** ───

In Exercises 55 to 57, use the system of equations

$$\begin{cases} x + 3y - a^2z = a^2 \\ 2x + 3y + az = 2 \\ 3x + 4y + 2z = 3 \end{cases}$$

55. Find all values of a for which the system of equations has a unique solution.
all values of a except $a = 1$ and $a = -6$

56. Find all values of a for which the system of equations has infinitely many solutions. $a = 1$

57. Find all values of a for which the system of equations has no solution. $a = -6$

─── **PREPARE FOR SECTION 7.2** ───

58. What is the additive inverse of a nonzero real number c? [P.1] $-c$

59. What is the multiplicative identity for the real numbers? [P.1] 1

60. Are the matrices $\begin{bmatrix} 2 & 3 \\ 5 & 7 \end{bmatrix}$ and $\begin{bmatrix} 2 & 3 & 0 \\ 5 & 7 & 0 \end{bmatrix}$ equal? [7.1] No

61. Solve $\begin{bmatrix} a & 2 \\ 3 & b \end{bmatrix} = \begin{bmatrix} 5 & 2 \\ 3 & -1 \end{bmatrix}$ for a and b. [7.1] $a = 5, b = -1$

62. What is the order of the matrix $\begin{bmatrix} 2x + 3y \\ x - 4y \\ 3x + y \end{bmatrix}$? [7.1] 3×1

63. What system of equations is represented by the matrix equation at the right? [7.1]
$\begin{bmatrix} 3x - 5y \\ 2x + 7y \end{bmatrix} = \begin{bmatrix} 16 \\ -10 \end{bmatrix}$
$$\begin{cases} 3x - 5y = 16 \\ 2x + 7y = -10 \end{cases}$$

─── **PROJECTS** ───

1. **ROW ECHELON FORM BY USING A GRAPHING CAL-CULATOR** Many graphing calculators have the elementary row operations as built-in functions. Complete this project using one of these calculators.

a. Enter into your calculator the augmented matrix for
$$\begin{cases} 2x - 3y + z = 4 \\ x + 2y - 2z = -2 \\ 3x + y - 3z = 4 \end{cases}$$

b. Complete the following steps to write the augmented matrix in row echelon form. *Suggestion:* Suppose that you enter the augmented matrix as A. If you perform an elementary row operation on A, the new matrix will be displayed. However, matrix A has *not* been changed. The new matrix must be saved as another matrix, say B. Now perform the elementary row operations on B and save the result in B. When you have finished, the original matrix will still be in A and the row echelon form of matrix A will be in B.

1. $R_1 \leftrightarrow R_2$ 2. $-2R_1 + R_2 \rightarrow R_2$ 3. $-3R_1 + R_3 \rightarrow R_3$

4. $-\dfrac{1}{7}R_2$ 5. $5R_2 + R_3 \rightarrow R_3$ 6. $-\dfrac{7}{4}R_3$

2. For more on interpolating polynomials, see our website at **http://college.hmco.com**.

SECTION 7.2 **THE ALGEBRA OF MATRICES**

● **ADDITION AND SUBTRACTION OF MATRICES**

Besides being convenient for solving systems of equations, matrices are useful tools to model problems in business and science. One very prevalent application of matrices is to spreadsheet programs.

The typical method used in spreadsheets is to number the rows 1, 2, 3, ... and to identify the columns as A, B, C, ... The partial spreadsheet below shows how a consumer's car loan is being repaid over a 5-year period. The elements in column A represent the loan amount, in dollars, at the beginning of a year; column B represents the amount owed after a year; and column C represents the amount of interest paid during the year.

$$
\begin{array}{c}
 \\
1 \\
2 \\
3 \\
4 \\
5
\end{array}
\begin{array}{ccc}
\text{A} & \text{B} & \text{C} \\
\left[\begin{array}{ccc}
10{,}000.00 & 8{,}305.60 & 738.77 \\
8{,}305.60 & 6{,}470.56 & 598.13 \\
6{,}470.56 & 4{,}483.22 & 445.82 \\
4{,}483.22 & 2{,}330.93 & 280.88 \\
2{,}330.93 & 0.00 & 102.24
\end{array}\right]
\end{array}
$$

For instance, the element in 3C means that the consumer paid $445.82 in interest during the third year of the loan.

? QUESTION What is the meaning of the element in 3A?

Matrices are effective for situations in which there are a number of items to be classified. For instance, suppose a music store has sales for January as shown in the matrix below.

$$
\begin{array}{c}
 \\
\text{CDs} \\
\text{DVDs} \\
\text{Videos}
\end{array}
\begin{array}{ccccc}
\text{Rock} & \text{R\&B} & \text{Rap} & \text{Classical} & \text{Other} \\
\left[\begin{array}{ccccc}
455 & 135 & 65 & 87 & 236 \\
252 & 68 & 32 & 40 & 101 \\
36 & 4 & 5 & 2 & 28
\end{array}\right]
\end{array}
$$

This matrix indicates, for instance, that the music store sold 40 classical DVDs in January.

Now consider a similar matrix for February.

$$
\begin{array}{c}
 \\
\text{CDs} \\
\text{DVDs} \\
\text{Videos}
\end{array}
\begin{array}{ccccc}
\text{Rock} & \text{R\&B} & \text{Rap} & \text{Classical} & \text{Other} \\
\left[\begin{array}{ccccc}
402 & 128 & 68 & 101 & 255 \\
259 & 35 & 28 & 51 & 115 \\
28 & 7 & 3 & 5 & 33
\end{array}\right]
\end{array}
$$

? ANSWER At the beginning of the third year of the loan, the consumer owed $6,470.56.

Looking at this matrix and the one for January reveals that the number of R&B DVDs sold for the two months is $68 + 35 = 103$. By adding the elements in corresponding cells, we obtain the total sales for the two months. In matrix notation, this would be shown as

$$\begin{bmatrix} 455 & 135 & 65 & 87 & 236 \\ 252 & 68 & 32 & 40 & 101 \\ 36 & 4 & 5 & 2 & 28 \end{bmatrix} + \begin{bmatrix} 402 & 128 & 68 & 101 & 255 \\ 259 & 35 & 28 & 51 & 115 \\ 28 & 7 & 3 & 5 & 33 \end{bmatrix} = \begin{bmatrix} 857 & 263 & 133 & 188 & 491 \\ 511 & 103 & 60 & 91 & 216 \\ 64 & 11 & 8 & 7 & 61 \end{bmatrix}$$

In the matrix that represents the sum, 857 (in row 1, column 1) indicates that a total of 857 rock music CDs were sold in January and February. Similarly, a total of 91 (row 2, column 4) classical DVDs were sold for the two months.

This example suggests that the addition of two matrices should be performed by adding the corresponding elements. Before we actually state this definition, we first introduce some notation and a definition of equality.

Throughout this book a matrix will be indicated by using a capital letter or by surrounding a lower-case letter with brackets. For instance, a matrix can be denoted as

$$A \quad \text{or} \quad [a_{ij}]$$

An important concept involving matrices is the principle of equality.

take note

The brackets around $[a_{ij}]$ indicate a matrix. If we write a_{ij} (no brackets), it refers to the element in the ith row and jth column.

Definition of Equality of Two Matrices

Two matrices $A = [a_{ij}]$ and $B = [b_{ij}]$ are equal if and only if

$$a_{ij} = b_{ij}$$

for every i and j.

For example, if $A = \begin{bmatrix} a & -2 & b \\ 3 & c & 1 \end{bmatrix}$ and $B = \begin{bmatrix} 3 & x & -4 \\ 3 & -1 & y \end{bmatrix}$, then $A = B$ if and only if $a = 3$, $x = -2$, $b = -4$, $c = -1$, and $y = 1$.

❷ QUESTION If two matrices A and B are equal, do they have the same order?

Definition of Addition of Matrices

If A and B are matrices of order $m \times n$, then the sum of the matrices is the $m \times n$ matrix given by

$$A + B = [a_{ij} + b_{ij}]$$

❷ ANSWER Yes. If they were of different order, there would be an element in one matrix for which there was no corresponding element in the second matrix.

Here is an example. Let $A = \begin{bmatrix} 2 & -2 & 3 \\ 1 & 3 & -4 \end{bmatrix}$ and $B = \begin{bmatrix} 5 & -2 & 6 \\ -2 & 3 & 5 \end{bmatrix}$. Then

$$A + B = \begin{bmatrix} 2 & -2 & 3 \\ 1 & 3 & -4 \end{bmatrix} + \begin{bmatrix} 5 & -2 & 6 \\ -2 & 3 & 5 \end{bmatrix} = \begin{bmatrix} 2+5 & (-2)+(-2) & 3+6 \\ 1+(-2) & 3+3 & (-4)+5 \end{bmatrix}$$

$$= \begin{bmatrix} 7 & -4 & 9 \\ -1 & 6 & 1 \end{bmatrix}$$

Now let $C = \begin{bmatrix} 2 & -3 \\ 4 & 1 \end{bmatrix}$ and $D = \begin{bmatrix} 3 & 2 & 0 \\ 1 & -5 & 3 \end{bmatrix}$. Here $C + D$ is not defined because the matrices do not have the same order.

To define the subtraction of two matrices, we first define the additive inverse of a matrix.

Additive Inverse of a Matrix

Given the matrix $A = [a_{ij}]$, the additive inverse of A is $-A = [-a_{ij}]$.

For example, if $A = \begin{bmatrix} -2 & 3 & -1 \\ 0 & -1 & 4 \end{bmatrix}$, then the additive inverse of A is

$$-A = -\begin{bmatrix} -2 & 3 & -1 \\ 0 & -1 & 4 \end{bmatrix} = \begin{bmatrix} 2 & -3 & 1 \\ 0 & 1 & -4 \end{bmatrix}$$

Subtraction of two matrices is defined in terms of the additive inverse of a matrix.

Definition of Subtraction of Matrices

Given two matrices A and B of order $m \times n$, then $A - B$ is the sum of A and the additive inverse of B.

$$A - B = A + (-B)$$

As an example, let $A = \begin{bmatrix} 2 & -3 \\ -1 & 2 \\ 2 & 4 \end{bmatrix}$ and $B = \begin{bmatrix} -1 & 2 \\ -4 & 1 \\ 3 & -2 \end{bmatrix}$. Then

$$A - B = \begin{bmatrix} 2 & -3 \\ -1 & 2 \\ 2 & 4 \end{bmatrix} - \begin{bmatrix} -1 & 2 \\ -4 & 1 \\ 3 & -2 \end{bmatrix} = \begin{bmatrix} 2 & -3 \\ -1 & 2 \\ 2 & 4 \end{bmatrix} + \begin{bmatrix} 1 & -2 \\ 4 & -1 \\ -3 & 2 \end{bmatrix} = \begin{bmatrix} 3 & -5 \\ 3 & 1 \\ -1 & 6 \end{bmatrix}$$

Of special importance is the *zero matrix*, which is the matrix that consists of all zeros. The zero matrix is the additive identity for matrices.

Definition of the Zero Matrix

The $m \times n$ **zero matrix**, denoted by O, is the matrix whose elements are all zeros.

Three examples of zero matrices are

$$\begin{bmatrix} 0 & 0 & 0 \\ 0 & 0 & 0 \end{bmatrix} \qquad \begin{bmatrix} 0 & 0 & 0 & 0 \\ 0 & 0 & 0 & 0 \\ 0 & 0 & 0 & 0 \end{bmatrix} \qquad \begin{bmatrix} 0 & 0 \\ 0 & 0 \end{bmatrix}$$

Properties of Matrix Addition

Given matrices A, B, C and the zero matrix O, each of order $m \times n$, then the following properties hold.

Commutative	$A + B = B + A$
Associative	$A + (B + C) = (A + B) + C$
Additive inverse	$A + (-A) = O$
Additive identity	$A + O = O + A = A$

● SCALAR MULTIPLICATION

Two types of products involve matrices. The first product we will discuss is the product of a real number and a matrix. Consider the matrix below, which shows the hourly wages for various job classifications in a construction firm before a 6% pay increase.

$$\begin{array}{c} \\ \text{Apprentice} \\ \text{Journeyman} \end{array} \begin{array}{cccc} \text{Carpenter} & \text{Welder} & \text{Plumber} & \text{Electrician} \end{array}$$

$$\begin{array}{c} \text{Apprentice} \\ \text{Journeyman} \end{array} \begin{bmatrix} 12.75 & 15.86 & 14.76 & 16.87 \\ 15.60 & 18.07 & 16.89 & 19.05 \end{bmatrix}$$

After the pay increase, the pay in each job category will increase by 6%. This can be shown in matrix form as

$$1.06 \begin{bmatrix} 12.75 & 15.86 & 14.76 & 16.87 \\ 15.60 & 18.07 & 16.89 & 19.05 \end{bmatrix} = \begin{bmatrix} 1.06 \cdot 12.75 & 1.06 \cdot 15.86 & 1.06 \cdot 14.76 & 1.06 \cdot 16.87 \\ 1.06 \cdot 15.60 & 1.06 \cdot 18.07 & 1.06 \cdot 16.89 & 1.06 \cdot 19.05 \end{bmatrix}$$

$$\approx \begin{bmatrix} 13.52 & 16.81 & 15.65 & 17.88 \\ 16.54 & 19.15 & 17.90 & 20.19 \end{bmatrix}$$

The element in row 1, column 4 indicates that an apprentice electrician will earn $17.88 per hour after the pay increase.

This example suggests that to multiply a matrix by a constant, we multiply each entry in the matrix by the constant.

Definition of the Product of a Real Number and a Matrix

Given the $m \times n$ matrix $A = [a_{ij}]$ and the real number c, then $cA = [ca_{ij}]$.

INSTRUCTOR NOTE
It may help some students to see that scalar multiplication of a matrix is similar to the concept that $3x = x + x + x$.

Finding the product of a real number and a matrix is called **scalar multiplication.** As an example of this definition, consider the matrix

$$A = \begin{bmatrix} 2 & -3 & 1 \\ 3 & 1 & -2 \\ 1 & -1 & 4 \end{bmatrix}$$

and the constant $c = -2$. Then

$$-2A = -2\begin{bmatrix} 2 & -3 & 1 \\ 3 & 1 & -2 \\ 1 & -1 & 4 \end{bmatrix} = \begin{bmatrix} -2(2) & -2(-3) & -2(1) \\ -2(3) & -2(1) & -2(-2) \\ -2(1) & -2(-1) & -2(4) \end{bmatrix} = \begin{bmatrix} -4 & 6 & -2 \\ -6 & -2 & 4 \\ -2 & 2 & -8 \end{bmatrix}$$

This definition is also used to factor a constant from a matrix.

$$\begin{bmatrix} \frac{3}{2} & -\frac{5}{4} & \frac{1}{4} \\ \frac{3}{4} & \frac{1}{2} & \frac{5}{2} \end{bmatrix} = \frac{1}{4}\begin{bmatrix} 6 & -5 & 1 \\ 3 & 2 & 10 \end{bmatrix}$$

Properties of Scalar Multiplication

Given real numbers a, b, and c and matrices $A = [a_{ij}]$ and $B = [b_{ij}]$ each of order $m \times n$, then

$$(b + c)A = bA + cA$$
$$c(A + B) = cA + cB$$
$$a(bA) = (ab)A$$

Alternative to Example 1
Given $A = \begin{bmatrix} 1 & -2 \\ 2 & -3 \end{bmatrix}$ and $B = \begin{bmatrix} 3 & 2 \\ 1 & 4 \end{bmatrix}$,
find $3A - 2B$.
$\bullet \begin{bmatrix} -3 & -10 \\ 4 & -17 \end{bmatrix}$

EXAMPLE 1   **Find the Sum of Two Scalar Products**

Given $A = \begin{bmatrix} -2 & 3 \\ 4 & -2 \\ 0 & 4 \end{bmatrix}$ and $B = \begin{bmatrix} 8 & -2 \\ -3 & 2 \\ -4 & 7 \end{bmatrix}$, find $2A + 5B$.

Solution

$$2A + 5B = 2\begin{bmatrix} -2 & 3 \\ 4 & -2 \\ 0 & 4 \end{bmatrix} + 5\begin{bmatrix} 8 & -2 \\ -3 & 2 \\ -4 & 7 \end{bmatrix}$$

$$= \begin{bmatrix} -4 & 6 \\ 8 & -4 \\ 0 & 8 \end{bmatrix} + \begin{bmatrix} 40 & -10 \\ -15 & 10 \\ -20 & 35 \end{bmatrix} = \begin{bmatrix} 36 & -4 \\ -7 & 6 \\ -20 & 43 \end{bmatrix}$$

▶ **TRY EXERCISE 6, PAGE 595**

• MATRIX MULTIPLICATION

Now we turn to the product of two matrices. The concept behind matrix multiplication can be illustrated with the following example. Suppose that the cost per gallon of gasoline to the owner of a gas station on a certain day is given by the table below.

Grade of gasoline	Regular	Unleaded	Super
Cost per gallon in dollars	0.87	0.98	1.20

The number of gallons of gasoline purchased by the owner on that day is given in the following table.

Grade of gasoline	Number of gallons purchased
Regular	1650
Unleaded	2456
Super unleaded	1877

The total cost of the gasoline purchased by the owner was

$$\text{Total} = 0.87(1650) + 0.98(2456) + 1.20(1877) = 6094.78$$

The total cost of the gasoline was $6094.78.

take note

A row matrix is a matrix with just one row. A column matrix has one column.

In matrix terms, the cost per gallon of gasoline can be written as the 1×3 *row matrix* $[0.87 \quad 0.98 \quad 1.20]$. The number of gallons purchased can be written as the 3×1 *column matrix* $\begin{bmatrix} 1650 \\ 2456 \\ 1877 \end{bmatrix}$. The product of the row matrix and the column matrix is

$$[0.87 \quad 0.98 \quad 1.20] \begin{bmatrix} 1650 \\ 2456 \\ 1877 \end{bmatrix} = 0.87(1650) + 0.98(2456) + 1.20(1877) = 6094.78$$

In general, if A is a row matrix of order $1 \times n$ and B is a column matrix of order $n \times 1$, then the product of A and B, written AB, is

$$AB = [a_1 \quad a_2 \quad a_3 \cdots a_n] \begin{bmatrix} b_1 \\ b_2 \\ b_3 \\ \vdots \\ b_n \end{bmatrix} = a_1b_1 + a_2b_2 + a_3b_3 + \cdots + a_nb_n$$

take note

The number of elements in the row matrix must equal the number of elements in the column matrix. If this is not the case, the product AB is not defined. For instance, if $A = [2 \quad 1 \quad 5]$ and $B = \begin{bmatrix} 3 \\ 1 \end{bmatrix}$, then AB is not defined.

For example, if $A = [2 \quad 3 \quad 5]$ and $B = \begin{bmatrix} 1 \\ 4 \\ -6 \end{bmatrix}$, then

$$AB = [2 \quad 3 \quad 5] \begin{bmatrix} 1 \\ 4 \\ -6 \end{bmatrix} = 2(1) + 3(4) + 5(-6) = -16$$

Now suppose that the gas station owner has two stations, S_1 and S_2. The table below shows the numbers of gallons of gasoline that are purchased every week for the two stations.

Grade of gasoline	Gallons for S_1	Gallons for S_2
Regular	2500	2600
Unleaded	3200	3400
Super	2800	2700

Because gasoline prices fluctuate, the cost per gallon to the owner will change from week to week. The table below shows the cost per gallon for each of the three grades for three consecutive weeks.

Grade	Regular	Unleaded	Super
Week 1	0.98	1.08	1.21
Week 2	0.95	1.07	1.18
Week 3	0.97	1.06	1.19

In terms of matrices, let the cost per gallon be denoted by C and the number of gallons purchased by N. Then

$$C = \begin{bmatrix} 0.98 & 1.08 & 1.21 \\ 0.95 & 1.07 & 1.18 \\ 0.97 & 1.06 & 1.19 \end{bmatrix} \quad \text{and} \quad N = \begin{bmatrix} 2500 & 2600 \\ 3200 & 3400 \\ 2800 & 2700 \end{bmatrix}$$

Let P denote the product CN. This product is calculated by extending the concept of the product of a row and a column matrix. Each row of C multiplies each column of N.

$$P = \begin{bmatrix} 0.98 & 1.08 & 1.21 \\ 0.95 & 1.07 & 1.18 \\ 0.97 & 1.06 & 1.19 \end{bmatrix} \begin{bmatrix} 2500 & 2600 \\ 3200 & 3400 \\ 2800 & 2700 \end{bmatrix}$$

$$= \begin{bmatrix} [0.98 \ 1.08 \ 1.21]\begin{bmatrix} 2500 \\ 3200 \\ 2800 \end{bmatrix} & [0.98 \ 1.08 \ 1.21]\begin{bmatrix} 2600 \\ 3400 \\ 2700 \end{bmatrix} \\ [0.95 \ 1.07 \ 1.18]\begin{bmatrix} 2500 \\ 3200 \\ 2800 \end{bmatrix} & [0.95 \ 1.07 \ 1.18]\begin{bmatrix} 2600 \\ 3400 \\ 2700 \end{bmatrix} \\ [0.97 \ 1.06 \ 1.19]\begin{bmatrix} 2500 \\ 3200 \\ 2800 \end{bmatrix} & [0.97 \ 1.06 \ 1.19]\begin{bmatrix} 2600 \\ 3400 \\ 2700 \end{bmatrix} \end{bmatrix}$$

$$= \begin{bmatrix} 0.98(2500) + 1.08(3200) + 1.21(2800) & 0.98(2600) + 1.08(3400) + 1.21(2700) \\ 0.95(2500) + 1.07(3200) + 1.18(2800) & 0.95(2600) + 1.07(3400) + 1.18(2700) \\ 0.97(2500) + 1.06(3200) + 1.19(2800) & 0.97(2600) + 1.06(3400) + 1.19(2700) \end{bmatrix}$$

$$= \begin{bmatrix} 9294 & 9487 \\ 9103 & 9294 \\ 9149 & 9339 \end{bmatrix}$$

Each entry in P is the total cost of gasoline for the three weeks for the two stations. For example, $p_{11} = 9294$ means that the cost of gasoline at station S_1 for the first week was \$9294. The entry in row 3, column 2 ($p_{32} = 9339$) represents the total cost of gasoline to station S_2 for week 3.

Using this application as a model, we now define the product of two matrices. The definition is an extension of the definition of the product of a row matrix and a column matrix.

Definition of the Product of Two Matrices

take note

This definition may appear complicated, but basically, to multiply two matrices, multiply each row of the first matrix by each column of the second matrix.

Let $A = [a_{ij}]$ be a matrix of order $m \times n$, and let $B = [b_{ij}]$ be a matrix of order $n \times p$. Then the product AB is the matrix of order $m \times p$ given by $AB = [c_{ij}]$, where each element c_{ij} is

$$c_{ij} = [a_{i1} \quad a_{i2} \quad a_{i3} \cdots a_{in}] \begin{bmatrix} b_{1j} \\ b_{2j} \\ b_{3j} \\ \vdots \\ b_{nj} \end{bmatrix} = a_{i1}b_{1j} + a_{i2}b_{2j} + a_{i3}b_{3j} + \cdots + a_{in}b_{nj}$$

For the product of two matrices to be possible, the number of columns of the first matrix must equal the number of rows of the second matrix.

$$\underset{m \times n}{A} \quad \cdot \quad \underset{n \times p}{B} \quad = \quad \underset{m \times p}{C}$$

Must be equal
Order of product matrix

The product matrix has as many rows as the first matrix and as many columns as the second matrix. For example, let

$$A = \begin{bmatrix} 2 & -3 & 0 \\ 1 & 4 & -1 \end{bmatrix} \quad \text{and} \quad B = \begin{bmatrix} 1 & 0 \\ 4 & -2 \\ 3 & 5 \end{bmatrix}$$

Then A has order 2×3 and B has order 3×2. Thus the order of AB is 2×2.

$$\begin{bmatrix} 2 & -3 & 0 \\ 1 & 4 & -1 \end{bmatrix}_{2\times3} \begin{bmatrix} 1 & 0 \\ 4 & -2 \\ 3 & 5 \end{bmatrix}_{3\times2} = \begin{bmatrix} [2 \ -3 \ 0]\begin{bmatrix}1\\4\\3\end{bmatrix} & [2 \ -3 \ 0]\begin{bmatrix}0\\-2\\5\end{bmatrix} \\ [1 \ 4 \ -1]\begin{bmatrix}1\\4\\3\end{bmatrix} & [1 \ 4 \ -1]\begin{bmatrix}0\\-2\\5\end{bmatrix} \end{bmatrix}_{2\times2}$$

$$= \begin{bmatrix} 2(1) + (-3)(4) + 0(3) & 2(0) + (-3)(-2) + 0(5) \\ 1(1) + 4(4) + (-1)(3) & 1(0) + 4(-2) + (-1)(5) \end{bmatrix}_{2\times2} = \begin{bmatrix} -10 & 6 \\ 14 & -13 \end{bmatrix}_{2\times2}$$

Alternative to Example 2
Find each product.

a. $\begin{bmatrix} 2 & 3 & -2 \\ 3 & 1 & 6 \end{bmatrix}\begin{bmatrix} -1 \\ 2 \\ 4 \end{bmatrix}$

b. $\begin{bmatrix} 1 & 0 & -1 \\ 2 & -1 & 4 \\ 2 & 4 & -2 \\ 0 & 1 & -3 \end{bmatrix}\begin{bmatrix} -1 & 2 \\ 2 & 1 \\ 4 & 3 \end{bmatrix}$

a. $\begin{bmatrix} -4 \\ 23 \end{bmatrix}$ b. $\begin{bmatrix} -5 & -1 \\ 12 & 15 \\ -2 & 2 \\ -10 & -8 \end{bmatrix}$

EXAMPLE 2   Find the Product of Two Matrices

Find each product.

a. $\begin{bmatrix} 2 & 3 \\ -3 & 1 \\ 1 & -3 \end{bmatrix}\begin{bmatrix} 1 & 2 & -2 & 3 \\ -1 & 0 & 3 & -4 \end{bmatrix}$ b. $\begin{bmatrix} 1 & -1 & 3 \\ 2 & 2 & -1 \\ 0 & -2 & 3 \end{bmatrix}\begin{bmatrix} 4 & -2 & 0 \\ -1 & 3 & 1 \\ 2 & -3 & 1 \end{bmatrix}$

Solution

a. $\begin{bmatrix} 2 & 3 \\ -3 & 1 \\ 1 & -3 \end{bmatrix}\begin{bmatrix} 1 & 2 & -2 & 3 \\ -1 & 0 & 3 & -4 \end{bmatrix}$

$= \begin{bmatrix} 2(1)+3(-1) & 2(2)+3(0) & 2(-2)+3(3) & 2(3)+3(-4) \\ (-3)(1)+1(-1) & (-3)(2)+1(0) & (-3)(-2)+1(3) & (-3)3+1(-4) \\ 1(1)+(-3)(-1) & 1(2)+(-3)(0) & 1(-2)+(-3)(3) & 1(3)+(-3)(-4) \end{bmatrix}$

$= \begin{bmatrix} -1 & 4 & 5 & -6 \\ -4 & -6 & 9 & -13 \\ 4 & 2 & -11 & 15 \end{bmatrix}$

b. $\begin{bmatrix} 1 & -1 & 3 \\ 2 & 2 & -1 \\ 0 & -2 & 3 \end{bmatrix}\begin{bmatrix} 4 & -2 & 0 \\ -1 & 3 & 1 \\ 2 & -3 & 1 \end{bmatrix}$

$= \begin{bmatrix} 4+1+6 & -2+(-3)+(-9) & 0+(-1)+3 \\ 8+(-2)+(-2) & -4+6+3 & 0+2+(-1) \\ 0+2+6 & 0+(-6)+(-9) & 0+(-2)+3 \end{bmatrix}$

$= \begin{bmatrix} 11 & -14 & 2 \\ 4 & 5 & 1 \\ 8 & -15 & 1 \end{bmatrix}$

▶ **TRY EXERCISE 16, PAGE 595**

INTEGRATING TECHNOLOGY

A graphing calculator can be used to perform matrix operations. Once the matrices are entered into the calculator, you can use regular arithmetic operations keys and the variable names of the matrices to perform many operations. The screens below, from a TI-83 Plus calculator, show the operations performed in Examples 1 and 2 in this section. For assistance with keystrokes, see your calculator manual or the website for this text at **college.hmco.com.**

Example 1

```
2[A]+5[B]
     [ [36   -4]
       [-7    6]
       [-20  43] ]
```

Example 2a

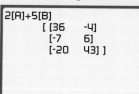

Example 2b

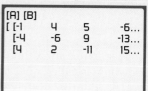

Generally, matrix multiplication is not commutative. That is, given two matrices A and B, $AB \neq BA$. In some cases, if we reverse the order of the matrices, the product will not be defined. For instance, if

$$A = \begin{bmatrix} -2 & 3 \\ 1 & 4 \end{bmatrix} \quad \text{and} \quad B = \begin{bmatrix} 5 & 6 & -3 \\ 4 & 1 & 2 \end{bmatrix}, \quad \text{then}$$

$$AB = \begin{bmatrix} -2 & 3 \\ 1 & 4 \end{bmatrix}\begin{bmatrix} 5 & 6 & -3 \\ 4 & 1 & 2 \end{bmatrix} = \begin{bmatrix} 2 & -9 & 12 \\ 21 & 10 & 5 \end{bmatrix}$$

However, BA is undefined because the number of columns of B does not equal the number of rows of A.

$$BA = \begin{bmatrix} 5 & 6 & -3 \\ 4 & 1 & 2 \end{bmatrix}_{2\times3} \begin{bmatrix} -2 & 3 \\ 1 & 4 \end{bmatrix}_{2\times2}$$

$$\text{columns} \neq \text{rows}$$

Even in cases where multiplication is defined, the products AB and BA may not be equal. For instance, if

$$A = \begin{bmatrix} 2 & -3 & 1 \\ 0 & -4 & 3 \\ 5 & 1 & 7 \end{bmatrix} \quad \text{and} \quad B = \begin{bmatrix} 4 & 6 & 1 \\ 5 & 3 & -2 \\ 1 & 0 & 5 \end{bmatrix}, \quad \text{then}$$

$$AB = \begin{bmatrix} 2 & -3 & 1 \\ 0 & -4 & 3 \\ 5 & 1 & 7 \end{bmatrix}\begin{bmatrix} 4 & 6 & 1 \\ 5 & 3 & -2 \\ 1 & 0 & 5 \end{bmatrix} = \begin{bmatrix} -6 & 3 & 13 \\ -17 & -12 & 23 \\ 32 & 33 & 38 \end{bmatrix}$$

$$BA = \begin{bmatrix} 4 & 6 & 1 \\ 5 & 3 & -2 \\ 1 & 0 & 5 \end{bmatrix}\begin{bmatrix} 2 & -3 & 1 \\ 0 & -4 & 3 \\ 5 & 1 & 7 \end{bmatrix} = \begin{bmatrix} 13 & -35 & 29 \\ 0 & -29 & 0 \\ 27 & 2 & 36 \end{bmatrix}$$

Thus, in this example, $AB \neq BA$.

Although matrix multiplication is not a commutative operation, the associative property of multiplication and the distributive property do hold for matrices.

Properties of Matrix Multiplication

Associative property   Given matrices A, B, and C of orders $m \times n$, $n \times p$, and $p \times q$, respectively, then

$$A(BC) = (AB)C$$

Distributive property   Given matrices A_1 and A_2 of order $m \times n$ and matrices B_1 and B_2 of order $n \times p$, then

$$A_1(B_1 + B_2) = A_1B_1 + A_1B_2 \qquad \text{• Left distributive property}$$
$$(A_1 + A_2)B_1 = A_1B_1 + A_2B_1 \qquad \text{• Right distributive property}$$

A square matrix that has a 1 for each element on the main diagonal and zeros elsewhere is called an *identity matrix*.

The **identity matrix** of order n, denoted I_n, is the $n \times n$ matrix

$$I_n = \begin{bmatrix} 1 & 0 & 0 & \cdots & 0 \\ 0 & 1 & 0 & \cdots & 0 \\ 0 & 0 & 1 & \cdots & 0 \\ \vdots & \vdots & \vdots & \vdots & \vdots \\ 0 & 0 & 0 & \cdots & 1 \end{bmatrix}_{n \times n}$$

The identity matrix has properties similar to those of the real number 1. For example, the product of the matrix A below and I_3 is A.

$$\begin{bmatrix} 2 & -3 & 0 \\ 4 & 7 & -5 \\ 9 & 8 & -6 \end{bmatrix} \begin{bmatrix} 1 & 0 & 0 \\ 0 & 1 & 0 \\ 0 & 0 & 1 \end{bmatrix} = \begin{bmatrix} 2 & -3 & 0 \\ 4 & 7 & -5 \\ 9 & 8 & -6 \end{bmatrix}$$

Multiplicative Identity Property for Matrices

If A is a square matrix of order n, and I_n is the identity matrix of order n, then $AI_n = I_nA = A$.

● MATRIX PRODUCTS AND SYSTEMS OF EQUATIONS

Consider the system of equations

$$\begin{cases} 2x + 3y - z = 5 \\ x - 2y + 2z = 6 \\ 4x + y - 3z = 5 \end{cases}$$

This system can be expressed as a product of matrices, as follows.

$$\begin{bmatrix} 2x + 3y - z \\ x - 2y + 2z \\ 4x + y - 3z \end{bmatrix} = \begin{bmatrix} 5 \\ 6 \\ 5 \end{bmatrix} \qquad \text{• Equality of matrices}$$

$$\begin{bmatrix} 2 & 3 & -1 \\ 1 & -2 & 2 \\ 4 & 1 & -3 \end{bmatrix} \begin{bmatrix} x \\ y \\ z \end{bmatrix} = \begin{bmatrix} 5 \\ 6 \\ 5 \end{bmatrix}$$ • **Definition of matrix multiplication**

Reversing this procedure, certain matrix products can represent systems of equations. Consider the matrix equation

$$\begin{bmatrix} 4 & 3 & -2 \\ 1 & -2 & 3 \\ 1 & 0 & 5 \end{bmatrix}_{3\times3} \begin{bmatrix} x \\ y \\ z \end{bmatrix}_{3\times1} = \begin{bmatrix} 2 \\ -1 \\ 3 \end{bmatrix}_{3\times1}$$

$$\begin{bmatrix} 4x + 3y - 2z \\ x - 2y + 3z \\ x \quad + 5z \end{bmatrix}_{3\times1} = \begin{bmatrix} 2 \\ -1 \\ 3 \end{bmatrix}_{3\times1}$$ • **Definition of matrix multiplication**

$$\begin{cases} 4x + 3y - 2z = 2 \\ x - 2y + 3z = -1 \\ x \quad + 5z = 3 \end{cases}$$ • **Equality of matrices**

Performing operations on matrices that represent a system of equations is another method of solving systems of equations. This is discussed in the next section.

Alternative to Example 3
Write the matrix equation
$$\begin{bmatrix} 3 & 1 & 2 \\ 5 & -3 & -2 \\ 0 & 4 & -1 \end{bmatrix} \begin{bmatrix} x \\ y \\ z \end{bmatrix} = \begin{bmatrix} 2 \\ 5 \\ -2 \end{bmatrix}$$ as a

system of equations.
$$\bullet \begin{cases} 3x + y + 2z = 2 \\ 5x - 3y - 2z = 5 \\ 4y - z = -2 \end{cases}$$

EXAMPLE 3 **Write a System of Equations from a Matrix Equation**

Write the matrix equation $\begin{bmatrix} 2 & 3 & 1 \\ 0 & -1 & 4 \\ 5 & -3 & 4 \end{bmatrix} \begin{bmatrix} x \\ y \\ z \end{bmatrix} = \begin{bmatrix} 0 \\ -2 \\ 8 \end{bmatrix}$ as a system of

equations.

Solution

$$\begin{bmatrix} 2 & 3 & 1 \\ 0 & -1 & 4 \\ 5 & -3 & 4 \end{bmatrix} \begin{bmatrix} x \\ y \\ z \end{bmatrix} = \begin{bmatrix} 0 \\ -2 \\ 8 \end{bmatrix}$$

$$\begin{bmatrix} 2x + 3y + z \\ -y + 4z \\ 5x - 3y + 4z \end{bmatrix} = \begin{bmatrix} 0 \\ -2 \\ 8 \end{bmatrix}$$

Using the equality of matrices, we have the system of equations

$$\begin{cases} 2x + 3y + z = 0 \\ - y + 4z = -2 \\ 5x - 3y + 4z = 8 \end{cases}$$

▶ **TRY EXERCISE 36, PAGE 596**

Matrices often can be used to solve applications in which a sequence of events repeats itself over a period of time. For instance, the following application is from the field of botany.

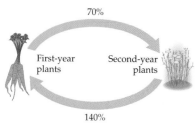

70%

First-year plants   Second-year plants

140%

Yearly transition diagram for biennial plants

FIGURE 7.2

A biennial plant matures 1 year after a seed is planted. In the second year the plant produces seeds that will become the new plants in the third year, and then the 2-year-old plant dies. Suppose that a wilderness area currently contains 500,000 of a certain biennial and that there are 225,000 plants in their first year and 275,000 in their second year. Suppose also that 70% of the 1-year-old plants survive to the second year and that each 1000 second-year plants give rise to 1400 first-year plants. See **Figure 7.2**.

With this information, a botanist can predict how many plants will be in the wilderness area after n years. The formula for the number of plants is given by

$$[225{,}000 \quad 275{,}000]\begin{bmatrix} 0 & 0.7 \\ 1.4 & 0 \end{bmatrix}^n = [\text{first-year plants} \quad \text{second-year plants}]$$

For instance, to find the number of each type of plant in 5 years, the botanist would calculate

$$[225{,}000 \quad 275{,}000]\begin{bmatrix} 0 & 0.7 \\ 1.4 & 0 \end{bmatrix}^5 = [369{,}754 \quad 151{,}263]$$

The resulting matrix indicates that after 5 years there would be 369,754 first-year plants and 151,263 second-year plants.

Alternative to Example 4
Exercise 58, page 599.

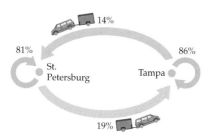

14%

81%   86%

St. Petersburg   Tampa

19%

A transition diagram for the trailer rentals

FIGURE 7.3

EXAMPLE 4   Solve an Application

A local trailer rental agency has offices in Tampa and St. Petersburg. To start with, the agency has 40% of its trailers in Tampa and the other 60% in St. Petersburg. The agency finds that each week:

- 86% of the Tampa rentals are returned to the Tampa office, and the other 14% are returned to the St. Petersburg office.

- 81% of the St. Petersburg rentals are returned to the St. Petersburg office, and the other 19% are returned to the Tampa office. See **Figure 7.3**.

The owner of the agency has determined that after n weeks the percent of the trailers that will be at the Tampa office T and the percent of the trailers that will be at the St. Petersburg office S is given by

$$[0.4 \quad 0.6]\begin{bmatrix} 0.86 & 0.14 \\ 0.19 & 0.81 \end{bmatrix}^n = [T \quad S]$$

Find the percent of the trailers that will be at the Tampa office after 3 weeks and after 8 weeks.

Solution

Using a calculator, we find

$$[0.4 \quad 0.6]\begin{bmatrix} 0.86 & 0.14 \\ 0.19 & 0.81 \end{bmatrix}^3 \approx [0.523 \quad 0.477]$$

and

$$[0.4 \quad 0.6]\begin{bmatrix} 0.86 & 0.14 \\ 0.19 & 0.81 \end{bmatrix}^8 \approx [0.569 \quad 0.431]$$

Thus, after 3 weeks, the Tampa office will have about 52.3% of the trailers, and after 8 weeks, the Tampa office will have about 56.9% of the trailers.

▶ **TRY EXERCISE 56, PAGE 599**

TOPICS FOR DISCUSSION

1. How are matrices related to spreadsheet programs?

2. Is it always possible to add two matrices? If so, explain why. If not, discuss what conditions must be met for two matrices to be added. Is matrix addition a commutative operation?

3. Is it always possible to multiply two matrices? If so, explain why. If not, discuss what conditions must be met for two matrices to be multiplied. Is matrix multiplication a commutative operation?

4. How does scalar multiplication differ from matrix multiplication?

5. Is it possible that two matrices could be added but not multiplied? Can two matrices be multiplied but not added? Discuss what types of conditions must be met for two matrices to be both added and multiplied.

EXERCISE SET 7.2

—*Suggested Assignment: Exercises 1–37, every other odd; 39–57, odd; 80–85.*
—*Answers to Exercises 1–8, 9–16, 24–32 and 59–74 are on pages AA32–AA33.*

In Exercises 1 to 8, find *a.* **$A + B$**, *b.* **$A - B$**, *c.* **$2B$**, **and** *d.* **$2A - 3B$.**

1. $A = \begin{bmatrix} 2 & -1 \\ 3 & 3 \end{bmatrix}$ $B = \begin{bmatrix} -1 & 3 \\ 2 & 1 \end{bmatrix}$

2. $A = \begin{bmatrix} 0 & -2 \\ 2 & 3 \end{bmatrix}$ $B = \begin{bmatrix} 5 & -1 \\ 3 & 0 \end{bmatrix}$

3. $A = \begin{bmatrix} 0 & -1 & 3 \\ 1 & 0 & -2 \end{bmatrix}$ $B = \begin{bmatrix} -3 & 1 & 2 \\ 2 & 5 & -3 \end{bmatrix}$

4. $A = \begin{bmatrix} 2 & -2 & 4 \\ 0 & -3 & -4 \end{bmatrix}$ $B = \begin{bmatrix} 1 & -5 & 6 \\ 4 & -2 & -3 \end{bmatrix}$

5. $A = \begin{bmatrix} -3 & 4 \\ 2 & -3 \\ -1 & 0 \end{bmatrix}$ $B = \begin{bmatrix} 4 & 1 \\ 1 & -2 \\ 3 & -4 \end{bmatrix}$

▶ 6. $A = \begin{bmatrix} 2 & -2 \\ 3 & 4 \\ 1 & 0 \end{bmatrix}$ $B = \begin{bmatrix} -1 & 8 \\ 2 & -2 \\ -4 & 3 \end{bmatrix}$

7. $A = \begin{bmatrix} -2 & 3 & -1 \\ 0 & -1 & 2 \\ -4 & 3 & 3 \end{bmatrix}$ $B = \begin{bmatrix} 1 & -2 & 0 \\ 2 & 3 & -1 \\ 3 & -1 & 2 \end{bmatrix}$

8. $A = \begin{bmatrix} 0 & 2 & 0 \\ 1 & -3 & 3 \\ 5 & 4 & -2 \end{bmatrix}$ $B = \begin{bmatrix} -1 & 2 & 4 \\ 3 & 3 & -2 \\ -4 & 4 & 3 \end{bmatrix}$

In Exercises 9 to 16, find AB and BA if possible.

9. $A = \begin{bmatrix} 2 & -3 \\ 1 & 4 \end{bmatrix}$ $B = \begin{bmatrix} -2 & 4 \\ 2 & -3 \end{bmatrix}$

10. $A = \begin{bmatrix} 3 & -2 \\ 4 & 1 \end{bmatrix}$ $B = \begin{bmatrix} -1 & -1 \\ 0 & 4 \end{bmatrix}$

11. $A = \begin{bmatrix} 3 & -1 \\ 2 & 3 \end{bmatrix}$ $B = \begin{bmatrix} 4 & 1 \\ 2 & -3 \end{bmatrix}$

12. $A = \begin{bmatrix} -3 & 2 \\ 2 & -2 \end{bmatrix}$ $B = \begin{bmatrix} 0 & 2 \\ -2 & 4 \end{bmatrix}$

13. $A = \begin{bmatrix} 2 & -1 \\ 0 & 3 \\ 1 & -2 \end{bmatrix}$ $B = \begin{bmatrix} 1 & -2 & 3 \\ 2 & 0 & 1 \end{bmatrix}$

14. $A = \begin{bmatrix} -1 & 3 \\ 2 & 1 \\ -3 & -2 \end{bmatrix}$ $B = \begin{bmatrix} 0 & -1 & 2 \\ 1 & 2 & -4 \end{bmatrix}$

15. $A = \begin{bmatrix} 2 & -1 & 3 \\ 0 & 2 & -1 \\ 0 & 0 & 2 \end{bmatrix}$ $B = \begin{bmatrix} 2 & 0 & 0 \\ 1 & -1 & 0 \\ 2 & -1 & -2 \end{bmatrix}$

▶ 16. $A = \begin{bmatrix} -1 & 2 & 0 \\ 2 & -1 & 1 \\ -2 & 2 & -1 \end{bmatrix}$ $B = \begin{bmatrix} 2 & -1 & 0 \\ 1 & 5 & -1 \\ 0 & -1 & 3 \end{bmatrix}$

In Exercises 17 to 24, find AB if possible.

17. $A = [1 \quad -2 \quad 3]$ $B = \begin{bmatrix} 1 & 0 \\ 2 & -1 \\ 1 & 2 \end{bmatrix}$ [0, 8]

18. $A = \begin{bmatrix} -2 & 3 \\ 1 & -2 \\ 0 & 2 \end{bmatrix}$ $B = \begin{bmatrix} 3 \\ -2 \end{bmatrix} \begin{bmatrix} -12 \\ 7 \\ -4 \end{bmatrix}$

19. $A = \begin{bmatrix} 2 & -1 \\ 3 & 3 \end{bmatrix}$ $B = \begin{bmatrix} 1 & -2 \\ 3 & 1 \\ 0 & -2 \end{bmatrix}$ The product is not possible.

20. $A = \begin{bmatrix} 2 & 0 & -1 \\ 3 & 4 & -3 \end{bmatrix}$ $B = \begin{bmatrix} 3 & -1 & 0 \\ 2 & 4 & 5 \end{bmatrix}$ The product is not possible.

21. $A = \begin{bmatrix} 2 & 3 \\ -4 & -6 \end{bmatrix}$ $B = \begin{bmatrix} 3 & 6 \\ -2 & -4 \end{bmatrix} \begin{bmatrix} 0 & 0 \\ 0 & 0 \end{bmatrix}$

22. $A = \begin{bmatrix} 2 & -1 & 3 \\ -1 & 2 & 1 \end{bmatrix}$ $B = \begin{bmatrix} 1 & 3 & 2 \\ 2 & -1 & 0 \\ 3 & 1 & 2 \end{bmatrix} \begin{bmatrix} 9 & 10 & 10 \\ 6 & -4 & 0 \end{bmatrix}$

23. $A = \begin{bmatrix} 1 & 2 & -2 & 3 \\ 0 & -2 & 1 & -3 \end{bmatrix}$ $B = \begin{bmatrix} -2 & 0 \\ 4 & -2 \end{bmatrix}$ The product is not possible.

24. $A = \begin{bmatrix} 2 & -2 & 4 \\ 1 & 0 & -1 \\ 2 & 1 & 3 \end{bmatrix}$ $B = \begin{bmatrix} 2 & 1 & -3 & 0 \\ 0 & -2 & 1 & -2 \\ 1 & -1 & 0 & 2 \end{bmatrix}$

In Exercises 25 to 28, given the matrices
$$A = \begin{bmatrix} -1 & 3 \\ 2 & -1 \\ 3 & 1 \end{bmatrix} \text{ and } B = \begin{bmatrix} 0 & -2 \\ 1 & 3 \\ 4 & -3 \end{bmatrix}$$
find the 3 × 2 matrix X that is a solution of the equation.

25. $3X + A = B$ **26.** $2A - 3X = 5B$

27. $2X - A = X + B$ **28.** $3X + 2B = X - 2A$

In Exercises 29 to 32, use the matrices
$$A = \begin{bmatrix} 2 & -3 \\ 1 & -1 \end{bmatrix} \text{ and } B = \begin{bmatrix} 3 & -1 & 0 \\ 2 & -2 & -1 \\ 1 & 0 & 2 \end{bmatrix}$$
If A is a square matrix, then $A^n = A \cdot A \cdot A \cdots A$, where the matrix A is repeated n times.

29. Find A^2.   **30.** Find A^3.

31. Find B^2.   **32.** Find B^3.

In Exercises 33 to 38, find the system of equations that is equivalent to the given matrix equation.

33. $\begin{cases} 3x - 8y = 11 \\ 4x + 3y = 1 \end{cases}$ **33.** $\begin{bmatrix} 3 & -8 \\ 4 & 3 \end{bmatrix} \begin{bmatrix} x \\ y \end{bmatrix} = \begin{bmatrix} 11 \\ 1 \end{bmatrix}$

34. $\begin{cases} 2x + 7y = 1 \\ 3x - 4y = 16 \end{cases}$ **34.** $\begin{bmatrix} 2 & 7 \\ 3 & -4 \end{bmatrix} \begin{bmatrix} x \\ y \end{bmatrix} = \begin{bmatrix} 1 \\ 16 \end{bmatrix}$

35. $\begin{bmatrix} 1 & -3 & -2 \\ 3 & 1 & 0 \\ 2 & -4 & 5 \end{bmatrix} \begin{bmatrix} x \\ y \\ z \end{bmatrix} = \begin{bmatrix} 6 \\ 2 \\ 1 \end{bmatrix}$ $\begin{cases} x - 3y - 2z = 6 \\ 3x + y = 2 \\ 2x - 4y + 5z = 1 \end{cases}$

▶ **36.** $\begin{bmatrix} 2 & 0 & 5 \\ 3 & -5 & 1 \\ 4 & -7 & 6 \end{bmatrix} \begin{bmatrix} x \\ y \\ z \end{bmatrix} = \begin{bmatrix} 9 \\ 7 \\ 14 \end{bmatrix}$ $\begin{cases} 2x + 5z = 9 \\ 3x - 5y + z = 7 \\ 4x - 7y + 6z = 14 \end{cases}$

37. $\begin{bmatrix} 2 & -1 & 0 & 2 \\ 4 & 1 & 2 & -3 \\ 6 & 0 & 1 & -2 \\ 5 & 2 & -1 & -4 \end{bmatrix} \begin{bmatrix} x_1 \\ x_2 \\ x_3 \\ x_4 \end{bmatrix} = \begin{bmatrix} 5 \\ 6 \\ 10 \\ 8 \end{bmatrix}$ $\begin{cases} 2x_1 - x_2 + 2x_4 = 5 \\ 4x_1 + x_2 + 2x_3 - 3x_4 = 6 \\ 6x_1 + x_3 - 2x_4 = 10 \\ 5x_1 + 2x_2 - x_3 - 4x_4 = 8 \end{cases}$

38. $\begin{bmatrix} 5 & -1 & 2 & -3 \\ 4 & 0 & 2 & 0 \\ 2 & -2 & 5 & -4 \\ 3 & 1 & -3 & 4 \end{bmatrix} \begin{bmatrix} x_1 \\ x_2 \\ x_3 \\ x_4 \end{bmatrix} = \begin{bmatrix} -2 \\ 2 \\ -1 \\ 2 \end{bmatrix}$ $\begin{cases} 5x_1 - x_2 + 2x_3 - 3x_4 = -2 \\ 4x_1 + 2x_3 = 2 \\ 2x_1 - 2x_2 + 5x_3 - 4x_4 = -1 \\ 3x_1 + x_2 - 3x_3 + 4x_4 = 2 \end{cases}$

39. LIFE SCIENCES Biologists use capture-recapture models to estimate how many animals live in a certain area. A sample of, say, fish are caught and tagged. When subsequent samples of fish are caught, a biologist can use a capture history matrix to record (with a 1) which, if any, of the fish in the original sample have been caught again. The rows of this matrix represent the particular fish (each has its own identification number), and the columns represent the number of the sample in which the fish was caught. Here is a small capture history matrix.

Samples

	1	2	3	4
Fish A	1	0	0	1
Fish B	0	1	1	1
Fish C	0	0	1	1

a. What is the dimension of this matrix? Write a sentence that explains the meaning of dimension in this case.
3 × 4. Three different fish were caught in four different samples.

b. What is the meaning of the 1 in row A, column 4?
Fish A was caught in sample 4.

c. Which fish was captured the most times?
Fish B

40. LIFE SCIENCE Biologists can use a predator-prey matrix to study the relationships among animals in an ecosystem. Each row and each column represents an animal in the system. A 1 as an element in the matrix indicates that the animal represented by that row preys on the animal represented by that column. A 0 indicates that the animal in that row does not prey on the animal in that column. A simple predator-prey matrix is shown below. The abbreviations are H = hawk, R = rabbit, S = snake, and C = coyote.

$$\begin{array}{c} \;\; \text{H R S C} \\ \begin{array}{c} H \\ R \\ S \\ C \end{array} \left[\begin{array}{cccc} 0 & 1 & 1 & 0 \\ 0 & 0 & 0 & 0 \\ 1 & 1 & 0 & 0 \\ 0 & 1 & 1 & 0 \end{array} \right] \end{array}$$

a. What is the dimension of this matrix? Write a sentence that explains the meaning of dimension in this case.
4 × 4. There are four animals in this system.

b. What is the meaning of the 0 in row R, column H?
Rabbits do not prey on hawks.

c. What is the meaning of there being all zeros in column C?
The coyote is not preyed on by any other animal in this system.

d. What is the meaning of all zeros in row R?
The rabbit does not prey on any animal in this system.

41. BUSINESS The matrix below shows the sales revenues, in millions of dollars, that a pharmaceutical company received from various divisions in different parts of the country. The abbreviations are W = western states, N = northern states, S = southern states, and E = eastern states.

$$\begin{array}{c} \text{W} \quad\;\; \text{N} \quad\;\; \text{S} \quad\;\; \text{E} \\ \begin{array}{l} \text{Patented drugs} \\ \text{Generic drugs} \\ \text{Nonprescription drugs} \end{array} \left[\begin{array}{cccc} 2.0 & 1.4 & 3.0 & 1.4 \\ 0.8 & 1.1 & 2.0 & 0.9 \\ 3.6 & 1.2 & 4.5 & 1.5 \end{array} \right] \end{array}$$

Suppose the business plan for this company indicates that it anticipates a 2% decrease in sales (because of competition) for each of its drug divisions for each region of the country. Express, to the nearest ten thousand dollars, this matrix as a scalar product and compute the anticipated sales matrix.
Answer on page AA33.

42. SALARY SCHEDULES The partial current-year salary matrix for an elementary school district is given below. Column A indicates a B.A. degree, column B a B.A. degree plus 15 graduate units, column C an M.A. degree, and column D an M.A. degree plus 30 additional graduate units. The rows give the numbers of years of teaching experience. Each entry is the annual salary in thousands of dollars.

$$\begin{array}{c} \text{A} \quad\;\;\; \text{B} \quad\;\;\; \text{C} \quad\;\;\; \text{D} \\ \textbf{Years}\;\; \begin{array}{l} \text{0 to 4} \\ \text{5 to 9} \\ \text{10 to 15} \end{array} \left[\begin{array}{cccc} 18.0 & 18.9 & 20.0 & 21.5 \\ 19.0 & 20.3 & 22.5 & 24.5 \\ 20.0 & 21.4 & 24.0 & 27.0 \end{array} \right] \end{array}$$

Express, as a matrix scalar multiplication to the nearest hundred dollars, the result of the school board's approving a 6% salary increase for all teachers in this district, and compute the scalar product.
Answer on page AA33.

43. SPORTS The matrices for the numbers of wins and losses at home, H, and away, A, are shown for the top three finishers of the 2000 American League East division baseball teams.

$$H = \begin{array}{c} \;\;\text{W} \quad\;\; \text{L} \\ \left[\begin{array}{cc} 44 & 36 \\ 42 & 39 \\ 45 & 36 \end{array} \right] \begin{array}{l} \text{New York} \\ \text{Boston} \\ \text{Toronto} \end{array} \end{array} \qquad A = \begin{array}{c} \;\;\text{W} \quad\;\; \text{L} \\ \left[\begin{array}{cc} 43 & 38 \\ 43 & 38 \\ 38 & 43 \end{array} \right] \begin{array}{l} \text{New York} \\ \text{Boston} \\ \text{Toronto} \end{array} \end{array}$$

a. Find $H + A$.
a. $\left[\begin{array}{cc} 87 & 74 \\ 85 & 77 \\ 83 & 79 \end{array} \right]$

b. Write a sentence that explains the meaning of the sum of the two matrices. The matrix represents the total number of wins and losses for each team.

c. Find $H - A$.
c. $\left[\begin{array}{cc} 1 & -2 \\ -1 & 1 \\ 7 & -7 \end{array} \right]$

d. Write a sentence that explains the meaning of the difference of the two matrices. The matrix represents the difference between performance at home and performance away.

44. BUSINESS Let A represent the number of televisions of various sizes in two stores of a company in one city, and let B represent the same situation for the company in a second city.

$$A = \begin{array}{c} \;\;\text{19-inch} \quad \text{25-inch} \quad \text{40-inch} \\ \left[\begin{array}{ccc} 23 & 35 & 49 \\ 32 & 41 & 24 \end{array} \right] \begin{array}{l} \text{Store 1} \\ \text{Store 2} \end{array} \end{array}$$

a. $\left[\begin{array}{ccc} 42 & 63 & 85 \\ 57 & 79 & 50 \end{array} \right]$

$$B = \begin{array}{c} \;\;\text{19-inch} \quad \text{25-inch} \quad \text{40-inch} \\ \left[\begin{array}{ccc} 19 & 28 & 36 \\ 25 & 38 & 26 \end{array} \right] \begin{array}{l} \text{Store 1} \\ \text{Store 2} \end{array} \end{array}$$

a. Find $A + B$.

b. The sum of A and B represents the total number of each type of television set available from both stores.

b. Write a sentence that explains the meaning of the sum of the two matrices.

45. GEOMETRIC TRANSFORMATION Consider the rectangle shown below. Each pair of x- and y-coordinates of the points shown appears as a column of a matrix of dimension 2 × 4. This is matrix A below. Matrix T is called a *translation matrix*.

$$A = \left[\begin{array}{cccc} -2 & 4 & 2 & -4 \\ 5 & 2 & -2 & 1 \end{array} \right]$$

$$T = \left[\begin{array}{cccc} 2 & 2 & 2 & 2 \\ -1 & -1 & -1 & -1 \end{array} \right]$$

a. Find $A + T$. $\left[\begin{array}{cccc} 0 & 6 & 4 & -2 \\ 4 & 1 & -3 & 0 \end{array} \right]$

b. Using the columns of $A + T$ as the x- and y-coordinates of four points, plot the points on the same coordinate grid as the original rectangle. Construct a

polygon by connecting the points in the order of the columns. What polygon have you constructed?
Answer on page AA33.

c. Write a sentence that explains the relationship between the original polygon and the new one. The new rectangle is shifted 2 units to the right and 1 unit down from the original rectangle.

46. GEOMETRIC TRANSFORMATION Use the information in Exercise 45.

a. Find $A - T$. $\begin{bmatrix} -4 & 2 & 0 & -6 \\ 6 & 3 & -1 & 2 \end{bmatrix}$

b. Using the columns of $A - T$ as the x- and y-coordinates of four points, plot the points on the same coordinate grid as the original rectangle. Construct a polygon by connecting the points in the order of the columns. What polygon have you constructed?
Answer on page AA33.

c. Write a sentence that explains the relationship between the original polygon and the new one. The new rectangle is shifted 2 units to the left and 1 unit up from the original rectangle.

47. GEOMETRIC TRANSFORMATION Consider the information in Exercise 45 and the matrix $R = \begin{bmatrix} 0 & -1 \\ 1 & 0 \end{bmatrix}$.

a. Find $R \cdot A$. $\begin{bmatrix} -5 & -2 & 2 & -1 \\ -2 & 4 & 2 & -4 \end{bmatrix}$

b. Using the columns of $R \cdot A$ as the x- and y-coordinates of four points, plot the points on the same coordinate grid as the original rectangle. Construct a polygon by connecting the points in the order of the columns. What polygon have you constructed?
Answer on page AA33.

c. Write a sentence that explains the meaning of the product of these two matrices. The second rectangle is obtained by reflecting the first about $y = x$ and then reflecting the result about $x = 0$.

48. GEOMETRIC TRANSFORMATION Consider the information in Exercise 45 and the matrix $R = \begin{bmatrix} 0 & 1 \\ 1 & 0 \end{bmatrix}$.

a. Find $R \cdot A$. $\begin{bmatrix} 5 & 2 & -2 & 1 \\ -2 & 4 & 2 & -4 \end{bmatrix}$

b. Using the columns of $R \cdot A$ as the x- and y-coordinates of four points, plot the points on the same coordinate grid as the original rectangle. Construct a polygon by connecting the points in the order of the columns. What polygon have you constructed?
Answer on page AA33.

c. Write a sentence that explains the meaning of the product of these two matrices. The new rectangle is the original rectangle reflected through the graph of $y = x$.

49. BUSINESS INVENTORY Matrix A gives the stock on hand of four products in a warehouse at the beginning of the week, and matrix B gives the stock on hand for the same

four items at the end of the week. Find and interpret $A - B$.

$$A = \begin{bmatrix} \text{Blue} & \text{Green} & \text{Red} & \\ 530 & 650 & 815 & \text{Pens} \\ 190 & 385 & 715 & \text{Pencils} \\ 485 & 600 & 610 & \text{Ink} \\ 150 & 210 & 305 & \text{Colored lead} \end{bmatrix}$$

$$B = \begin{bmatrix} \text{Blue} & \text{Green} & \text{Red} & \\ 480 & 500 & 675 & \text{Pens} \\ 175 & 215 & 345 & \text{Pencils} \\ 400 & 350 & 480 & \text{Ink} \\ 70 & 95 & 280 & \text{Colored lead} \end{bmatrix}$$

Answer on page AA33.

50. BUSINESS SERVICES Matrix A gives the numbers of employees in the divisions of a company in the west coast branch, and matrix B gives the same information for the east coast branch. Find and interpret $A + B$.

$$A = \begin{bmatrix} \text{Engineering} & \begin{array}{c}\text{Admini-}\\\text{stration}\end{array} & \begin{array}{c}\text{Data}\\\text{Processing}\end{array} & \\ 315 & 200 & 415 & \text{Division I} \\ 285 & 175 & 300 & \text{Division II} \\ 275 & 195 & 250 & \text{Division III} \end{bmatrix}$$

$$B = \begin{bmatrix} \text{Engineering} & \begin{array}{c}\text{Admini-}\\\text{stration}\end{array} & \begin{array}{c}\text{Data}\\\text{Processing}\end{array} & \\ 200 & 175 & 350 & \text{Division I} \\ 150 & 90 & 180 & \text{Division II} \\ 105 & 50 & 175 & \text{Division III} \end{bmatrix}$$

Answer on page AA33.

51. STOCK MARKET The commission rates that three companies T_1, T_2, and T_3 charge to sell one share of stock on the New York Stock Exchange (NYSE), NASDQ, and the American Stock Exchange (ASE) are shown in the matrix below.

$$C = \begin{bmatrix} \text{NYSE} & \text{NASDQ} & \text{ASE} & \\ 0.04 & 0.06 & 0.05 & T_1 \\ 0.04 & 0.04 & 0.04 & T_2 \\ 0.03 & 0.07 & 0.06 & T_3 \end{bmatrix}$$

Two customers, S_1 and S_2, own stocks that are traded on the NYSE, NASDQ, and the ASE. The numbers of shares of stocks they own for each exchange are given in the following matrix.

$$S = \begin{bmatrix} S_1 & S_2 & \\ 500 & 600 & \text{NYSE} \\ 250 & 450 & \text{NASDQ} \\ 600 & 750 & \text{ASE} \end{bmatrix} \quad \begin{bmatrix} 65 & 88.5 \\ 54 & 72 \\ 68.5 & 94.5 \end{bmatrix} ; T_2$$

Find CS. Which company should customer S_1 use to minimize commission costs?

52. YOUTH SPORTS The total unit sales matrix at three soccer games in a summer league for children is given by

$$S = \begin{array}{c} \\ \end{array} \begin{array}{cccc} \text{Soft} & \text{Hot} & & \\ \text{Drinks} & \text{Dogs} & \text{Candy} & \text{Popcorn} \end{array}$$

$$S = \begin{bmatrix} 52 & 50 & 75 & 20 \\ 45 & 48 & 80 & 20 \\ 62 & 70 & 78 & 25 \end{bmatrix} \begin{array}{l} \text{Game 1} \\ \text{Game 2} \\ \text{Game 3} \end{array}$$

The unit pricing matrix in dollars for the wholesale cost of each item and the retail price of each item is given by

$$\begin{bmatrix} 41.25 & 107.25 \\ 39.65 & 104.50 \\ 50.70 & 131.10 \end{bmatrix} \quad P = \begin{array}{c} \text{Wholesale} \quad \text{Retail} \\ \begin{bmatrix} 0.25 & 0.50 \\ 0.30 & 0.75 \\ 0.15 & 0.45 \\ 0.10 & 0.50 \end{bmatrix} \begin{array}{l} \text{Soft drinks} \\ \text{Hot dogs} \\ \text{Candy} \\ \text{Popcorn} \end{array} \end{array}$$

Use matrix multiplication to find the total cost and total revenue at each game.

53. 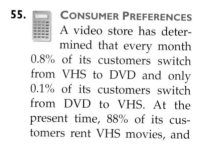 **CONSUMER PREFERENCES** A soft drink company has determined that every six months 1.1% of its customers switch from regular soda to diet soda and 0.7% of its customers switch from diet soda to regular soda. At the present time, 55% of its customers drink regular soda and 45% drink diet soda. After n 6-month periods, the percent of its customers who drink regular soda r and the percent of its customers who drink diet soda d are given by

$$[0.55 \quad 0.45] \begin{bmatrix} 0.989 & 0.011 \\ 0.007 & 0.993 \end{bmatrix}^n = [r \quad d]$$

Use a calculator and the above matrix equation to predict the percent, to the nearest 0.1%, of the customers who will be drinking diet soda

a. 1 year from now. 45.6%

b. 3 years from now. 46.7%

54. 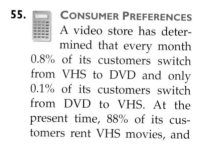 **CONSUMER PREFERENCES** Experiment with several different values of n in the matrix equation from Exercise 53 to determine how long, to the nearest year, it will be before the diet soda drinkers outnumber the regular soda drinkers. 10 yrs

55. 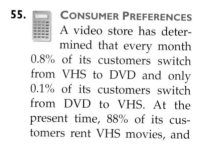 **CONSUMER PREFERENCES** A video store has determined that every month 0.8% of its customers switch from VHS to DVD and only 0.1% of its customers switch from DVD to VHS. At the present time, 88% of its customers rent VHS movies, and

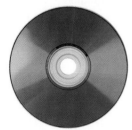

the other 12% rent DVD movies. After n months, the percent of its customers who rent VHS movies V and the percent of its customers who rent DVD movies D are given by

$$[0.88 \quad 0.12] \begin{bmatrix} 0.992 & 0.008 \\ 0.001 & 0.999 \end{bmatrix}^n = [V \quad D]$$

Use a calculator and the above matrix equation to predict the percent, to the nearest 0.1%, of the customers who will be renting DVD movies

a. 6 months from now. 16.1%

b. 18 months from now. 23.5%

▶ **56.** **CONSUMER PREFERENCES** A town has two grocery stores, A and B. Each month

● store A retains 98% of its customers and loses 2% to Store B.

● store B retains 95% of its customers and loses 5% to Store A.

To start with, store B has 75% of town's customers, and store A has the other 25%. After n months, the percent of the customers who shop at store A, denoted by a, and the percent of the customers who shop at store B, denoted by b, are given by

$$[0.25 \quad 0.75] \begin{bmatrix} 0.98 & 0.02 \\ 0.05 & 0.95 \end{bmatrix}^n = [a \quad b]$$

Find the percent, to the nearest 0.1%, of the customers who shop at store A after 5 months. 39.1%

57. CONSUMER PREFERENCES Experiment with several different values of n in the matrix equation from Exercise 56 to determine how long, to the nearest month, it will be before store A has 50% of the town's customers. 11 months

58. PLANT REPRODUCTION A biennial plant matures 1 year after a seed is planted. In the second year, the plant produces seeds that will become the new plants in the third year, and then the 2-year-old plant dies. Suppose that an animal preserve currently contains 850,000 of a certain biennial and that there are 475,000 plants in their first year and 375,000 in their second year. Suppose also that 65% of the 1-year-old plants survive to the second year and that each 1000 second-year plants give rise to 1250 first-year plants. Write a matrix product that will predict the number of plants that will be in the animal preserve in n years. Use this product to determine the number of these plants in the preserve after 4 years. Round to the nearest thousand.

$$[475{,}000 \quad 375{,}000] \begin{bmatrix} 0 & 0.65 \\ 1.25 & 0 \end{bmatrix}^n, \; 561{,}000$$

In Exercises 59 to 64, use a graphing calculator to perform the indicated operations on matrices A and B.

$$A = \begin{bmatrix} 2 & -1 & 3 & 5 & -1 \\ 2 & 0 & 2 & -1 & 1 \\ -1 & -3 & 2 & 3 & 3 \\ 5 & -4 & 1 & 0 & 3 \\ 0 & 2 & -1 & 4 & 3 \end{bmatrix}$$

$$B = \begin{bmatrix} 0 & -2 & 1 & 7 & 2 \\ -3 & 0 & 2 & 3 & 1 \\ -2 & 1 & 1 & 4 & 5 \\ 6 & 4 & -4 & 2 & -3 \\ 3 & -2 & -5 & 1 & 3 \end{bmatrix}$$

59. AB

60. BA

61. A^3

62. B^3

63. $A^2 + B^2$

64. $AB - BA$

CONNECTING CONCEPTS

The elements of a matrix can be complex numbers. In Exercises 65 to 74, let

$$A = \begin{bmatrix} 2 + 3i & 1 - 2i \\ 1 + i & 2 - i \end{bmatrix} \quad \text{and} \quad B = \begin{bmatrix} 1 - i & 2 + 3i \\ 3 + 2i & 4 - i \end{bmatrix}$$

Perform the indicated operations.

65. $3A$

66. $-2B$

67. $2iB$

68. $3iA$

69. $A + B$

70. $A - B$

71. AB

72. BA

73. A^2

74. B^2

Matrices with complex number elements play a role in the theory of the atom. The following three matrices, called Pauli spin matrices, were used by Wolfgang Pauli in his early study of the electron. Use these matrices in Exercises 75 to 77.

$$\sigma_1 = \begin{bmatrix} 0 & 1 \\ 1 & 0 \end{bmatrix} \quad \sigma_2 = \begin{bmatrix} 0 & -i \\ i & 0 \end{bmatrix} \quad \sigma_3 = \begin{bmatrix} 1 & 0 \\ 0 & -1 \end{bmatrix}$$

75. Show that $(\sigma_i)^2 = I_2$ for $i = 1, 2,$ and 3.

76. Show that $\sigma_1 \cdot \sigma_2 = i\sigma_3$.

77. Show that $\sigma_1 \cdot \sigma_2 + \sigma_2 \cdot \sigma_1 = O$.

78. Given two real numbers a and b and a matrix A of order 2×2, prove that $(a + b)A = aA + bA$.

79. Given two real numbers a and b and a matrix A of order 2×2, prove that $a(bA) = (ab)A$.

PREPARE FOR SECTION 7.3

80. What is the multiplicative inverse of $-\dfrac{2}{3}$? [P.1] $\quad -\dfrac{3}{2}$

81. Write the 3×3 multiplicative identity matrix. [7.2] $\begin{bmatrix} 1 & 0 & 0 \\ 0 & 1 & 0 \\ 0 & 0 & 1 \end{bmatrix}$

82. State the three elementary row operations for matrices. [7.1]   See Section 7.1.

83. Complete the following:

$$\begin{bmatrix} 1 & -2 & 3 \\ 2 & -1 & 4 \\ -3 & 2 & 2 \end{bmatrix} \xrightarrow[\;\; 3R_1 + R_3 \;\;]{-2R_1 + R_2} \begin{bmatrix} ? \end{bmatrix} \begin{bmatrix} 1 & -2 & 3 \\ 0 & 3 & -2 \\ 0 & -4 & 11 \end{bmatrix}$$

[7.1]

84. Solve for X: $AX = B$. Write the answer using negative exponents. [P.2/1.1] $X = A^{-1}B$

85. What system of equations is represented by the matrix equation

$$\begin{bmatrix} 2 & 3 \\ 4 & -5 \end{bmatrix} \begin{bmatrix} x \\ y \end{bmatrix} = \begin{bmatrix} 9 \\ 7 \end{bmatrix}? \text{ [7.2] } \begin{cases} 2x + 3y = 9 \\ 4x - 5y = 7 \end{cases}$$

PROJECTS

1. 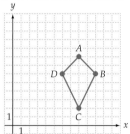 **MATRICES IN GRAPHICS ART** Matrices can be used to translate and dilate geometric figures in the plane. These concepts are important in graphics design and art. Consider the kite shown below.

a. Find the coordinates of each vertex of the kite, and prepare a matrix K of dimension 2×4 in which the columns are the x- and y-coordinates, respectively, of the vertices of the kite.

b. Find the product $\frac{1}{2}K = M$. Plot the points of M using the columns as the x- and y-coordinates, respectively, of the vertices of a new kite.

c. Find the lengths of any two line segments of the original kite and the corresponding lengths for the new

kite. Show that the **scale factor**, which is the ratio $\dfrac{\text{length of new}}{\text{length of original}}$, is $\dfrac{1}{2}$ for each pair of line segments. Observe that this is the coefficient of K in the product in part **b.**

d. Find the product $2K = N$. Plot the points of N again, using the columns as the x- and y-coordinates, respectively, of the vertices of a new kite. Show that the new kite has a scale factor of 2.

e. Consider the vertices A, B, C, and D of the original kite and the corresponding vertices A', B', C', and D' of the kite from part **c.** Show that the lines through AA', BB', CC', and DD' pass through the origin of the coordinate system. This point of intersection is called the **center of dilatation**.

2. See our website at **http://college.hmco.com** for a program that animates translation of geometric figures. *Note:* A TI-83 graphing calculator program is available to allow you to observe the effects of translation on a geometric figure. This program, TRANSLATE, can be found on our website at **http://college.hmco.com.**

| SECTION 7.3 | THE INVERSE OF A MATRIX |

- FINDING THE INVERSE OF A MATRIX
- SOLVING SYSTEMS OF EQUATIONS USING INVERSE MATRICES
- INPUT-OUTPUT ANALYSIS

● FINDING THE INVERSE OF A MATRIX

Recall that the multiplicative inverse of a nonzero real number c is $\dfrac{1}{c}$, the number whose product with c is 1. For example, the multiplicative inverse of $\dfrac{2}{3}$ is $\dfrac{3}{2}$ because $\dfrac{2}{3} \cdot \dfrac{3}{2} = 1$.

For some square matrices we can define a multiplicative inverse.

Multiplicative Inverse of a Matrix

If A is a square matrix of order n, then the **inverse** of matrix A, denoted by A^{-1}, has the property that

$$A \cdot A^{-1} = A^{-1} \cdot A = I_n$$

where I_n is the identity matrix of order n.

As we will see shortly, not all square matrices have a multiplicative inverse.

> **?** **QUESTION** Are there any real numbers that do not have a multiplicative inverse?

A procedure for finding the inverse (we will simply say *inverse* for *multiplicative inverse*) uses elementary row operations. The procedure will be illustrated by finding the inverse of a 2 × 2 matrix.

Let $A = \begin{bmatrix} 2 & 7 \\ 1 & 4 \end{bmatrix}$. To the matrix A we will merge the identity matrix I_2 to the right of A and denote this new matrix by $[A; I_2]$.

$$[A; I_2] = \begin{bmatrix} 2 & 7 & | & 1 & 0 \\ 1 & 4 & | & 0 & 1 \end{bmatrix}$$

$$A \xrightarrow{\quad\quad\quad} \uparrow \quad\quad\quad \uparrow \xrightarrow{\quad\quad} I_2$$

Now we use elementary row operations in a manner similar to that of the Gaussian elimination method. The goal is to produce

$$[I_2; A^{-1}] = \begin{bmatrix} 1 & 0 & | & b_{11} & b_{12} \\ 0 & 1 & | & b_{21} & b_{22} \end{bmatrix}$$

$$I_2 \xrightarrow{\quad\quad\quad} \uparrow \quad\quad\quad \uparrow \xrightarrow{\quad} A^{-1}$$

In this form, the inverse matrix is the matrix that is to the right of the identity matrix. That is,

$$A^{-1} = \begin{bmatrix} b_{11} & b_{12} \\ b_{21} & b_{22} \end{bmatrix}$$

To find A^{-1}, we first use a series of elementary row operations that will result in a 1 in the first row and the first column.

$$\begin{bmatrix} 2 & 7 & | & 1 & 0 \\ 1 & 4 & | & 0 & 1 \end{bmatrix} \xrightarrow{\frac{1}{2}R_1} \begin{bmatrix} 1 & \frac{7}{2} & | & \frac{1}{2} & 0 \\ 1 & 4 & | & 0 & 1 \end{bmatrix} \xrightarrow{-1R_1 + R_2} \begin{bmatrix} 1 & \frac{7}{2} & | & \frac{1}{2} & 0 \\ 0 & \frac{1}{2} & | & -\frac{1}{2} & 1 \end{bmatrix}$$

$$\xrightarrow{2R_2} \begin{bmatrix} 1 & \frac{7}{2} & | & \frac{1}{2} & 0 \\ 0 & 1 & | & -1 & 2 \end{bmatrix} \xrightarrow{-\frac{7}{2}R_2 + R_1} \begin{bmatrix} 1 & 0 & | & 4 & -7 \\ 0 & 1 & | & -1 & 2 \end{bmatrix}$$

The inverse matrix is the matrix to the right of the identity matrix. Therefore,

$$A^{-1} = \begin{bmatrix} 4 & -7 \\ -1 & 2 \end{bmatrix}$$

Each elementary row operation is chosen to advance the process of transforming the original matrix into the identity matrix.

? **ANSWER** The real number zero does not have a multiplicative inverse.

Alternative to Example 1
Find the inverse of the matrix

$$A = \begin{bmatrix} 1 & 1 & 4 \\ 2 & 3 & 6 \\ -1 & -1 & 2 \end{bmatrix}.$$

● $A^{-1} = \begin{bmatrix} 2 & -1 & -1 \\ -\dfrac{5}{3} & 1 & \dfrac{1}{3} \\ \dfrac{1}{6} & 0 & \dfrac{1}{6} \end{bmatrix}$

EXAMPLE 1   **Find the Inverse of a 3 × 3 Matrix**

Find the inverse of the matrix $A = \begin{bmatrix} 1 & -1 & 2 \\ 2 & 0 & 6 \\ 3 & -5 & 7 \end{bmatrix}$.

Solution

$$\begin{bmatrix} 1 & -1 & 2 & | & 1 & 0 & 0 \\ 2 & 0 & 6 & | & 0 & 1 & 0 \\ 3 & -5 & 7 & | & 0 & 0 & 1 \end{bmatrix}$$

- Merge the given matrix with the identity matrix I_3.

$$\begin{matrix} -2R_1 + R_2 \\ -3R_1 + R_3 \\ \longrightarrow \end{matrix} \begin{bmatrix} 1 & -1 & 2 & | & 1 & 0 & 0 \\ 0 & 2 & 2 & | & -2 & 1 & 0 \\ 0 & -2 & 1 & | & -3 & 0 & 1 \end{bmatrix}$$

- Because a_{11} is already 1, we next produce zeros in a_{21} and a_{31}.

$$\begin{matrix} \dfrac{1}{2}R_2 \\ \longrightarrow \end{matrix} \begin{bmatrix} 1 & -1 & 2 & | & 1 & 0 & 0 \\ 0 & 1 & 1 & | & -1 & \dfrac{1}{2} & 0 \\ 0 & -2 & 1 & | & -3 & 0 & 1 \end{bmatrix}$$

- Produce a 1 in a_{22}.

$$\begin{matrix} 2R_2 + R_3 \\ \longrightarrow \end{matrix} \begin{bmatrix} 1 & -1 & 2 & | & 1 & 0 & 0 \\ 0 & 1 & 1 & | & -1 & \dfrac{1}{2} & 0 \\ 0 & 0 & 3 & | & -5 & 1 & 1 \end{bmatrix}$$

- Produce a 0 in a_{32}.

$$\begin{matrix} \dfrac{1}{3}R_3 \\ \longrightarrow \end{matrix} \begin{bmatrix} 1 & -1 & 2 & | & 1 & 0 & 0 \\ 0 & 1 & 1 & | & -1 & \dfrac{1}{2} & 0 \\ 0 & 0 & 1 & | & -\dfrac{5}{3} & \dfrac{1}{3} & \dfrac{1}{3} \end{bmatrix}$$

- Produce a 1 in a_{33}.

$$\begin{matrix} -1R_3 + R_2 \\ -2R_3 + R_1 \\ \longrightarrow \end{matrix} \begin{bmatrix} 1 & -1 & 0 & | & \dfrac{13}{3} & -\dfrac{2}{3} & -\dfrac{2}{3} \\ 0 & 1 & 0 & | & \dfrac{2}{3} & \dfrac{1}{6} & -\dfrac{1}{3} \\ 0 & 0 & 1 & | & -\dfrac{5}{3} & \dfrac{1}{3} & \dfrac{1}{3} \end{bmatrix}$$

- Now work upward. Produce a 0 in a_{23} and a_{13}.

$$\begin{matrix} R_2 + R_1 \\ \longrightarrow \end{matrix} \begin{bmatrix} 1 & 0 & 0 & | & 5 & -\dfrac{1}{2} & -1 \\ 0 & 1 & 0 & | & \dfrac{2}{3} & \dfrac{1}{6} & -\dfrac{1}{3} \\ 0 & 0 & 1 & | & -\dfrac{5}{3} & \dfrac{1}{3} & \dfrac{1}{3} \end{bmatrix}$$

- Produce a 0 in a_{12}.

The inverse matrix is $A^{-1} = \begin{bmatrix} 5 & -\dfrac{1}{2} & -1 \\ \dfrac{2}{3} & \dfrac{1}{6} & -\dfrac{1}{3} \\ -\dfrac{5}{3} & \dfrac{1}{3} & \dfrac{1}{3} \end{bmatrix}$.

You should verify that this matrix satisfies the condition of an inverse matrix. That is, show that $A^{-1} \cdot A = A \cdot A^{-1} = I_3$.

▶ **TRY EXERCISE 6, PAGE 610**

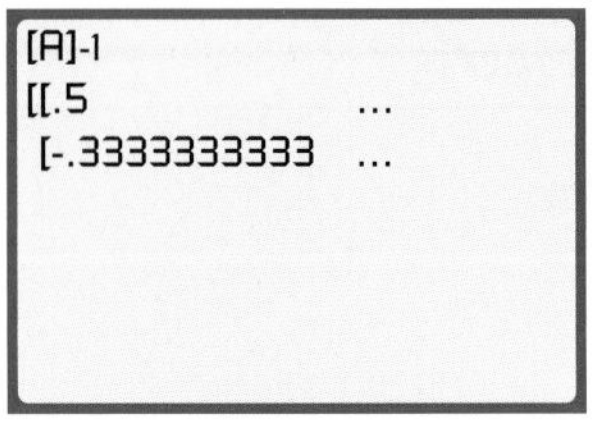

FIGURE 7.4a

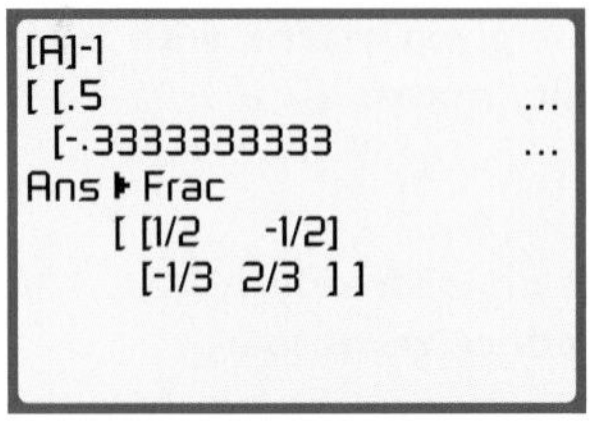

FIGURE 7.4b

> ### INTEGRATING TECHNOLOGY
>
> The inverse of a matrix can be found by using a graphing calculator. Enter and store the matrix in, say, $[A]$. To compute the inverse of A, use the $\boxed{x^{-1}}$ key. For instance, let $A = \begin{bmatrix} 4 & 3 \\ 2 & 3 \end{bmatrix}$. A typical calculator display of the inverse of A is shown in **Figure 7.4a**. Because the elements of the matrix are decimals, it is possible to see only the first column of the inverse matrix. Use the arrow keys to see the remaining columns.
>
> Another possibility for viewing the inverse of A is to use the function on your calculator that converts a decimal to a fraction. This will change the decimals to fractions, as in **Figure 7.4b**.

A **singular matrix** is a matrix that does not have a multiplicative inverse. A matrix that has a multiplicative inverse is a **nonsingular matrix.** As you apply elementary row operations to a singular matrix, there will come a point where there are all zeros in a row of the *original* matrix. When that condition exists, the original matrix does not have an inverse.

Alternative to Example 2

Show that the matrix $\begin{bmatrix} 1 & -6 & 4 \\ 3 & 4 & 2 \\ 5 & 3 & 5 \end{bmatrix}$ is a singular matrix.

● Performing the operations

$-3R_1 + R_2,\ -5R_1 + R_3,\ \dfrac{1}{22}R_2$, and

$-33R_2 + R_3$ produces the matrix

$$\left[\begin{array}{ccc|ccc} 1 & -6 & 4 & 1 & 0 & 0 \\ 0 & 1 & -\frac{5}{11} & -\frac{3}{22} & \frac{1}{22} & 0 \\ 0 & 0 & 0 & -\frac{1}{2} & -\frac{3}{2} & 1 \end{array}\right]$$

Because there are all zeros in a row of the original matrix, the original matrix does not have an inverse.

EXAMPLE 2 **Identify a Singular Matrix**

Show that the matrix $\begin{bmatrix} 1 & -1 & -1 \\ 2 & -3 & 0 \\ 1 & -2 & 1 \end{bmatrix}$ is a singular matrix.

Solution

$$\left[\begin{array}{ccc|ccc} 1 & -1 & -1 & 1 & 0 & 0 \\ 2 & -3 & 0 & 0 & 1 & 0 \\ 1 & -2 & 1 & 0 & 0 & 1 \end{array}\right] \xrightarrow[-1R_1 + R_3]{-2R_1 + R_2} \left[\begin{array}{ccc|ccc} 1 & -1 & -1 & 1 & 0 & 0 \\ 0 & -1 & 2 & -2 & 1 & 0 \\ 0 & -1 & 2 & -1 & 0 & 1 \end{array}\right]$$

$$\xrightarrow{-1 \cdot R_2} \left[\begin{array}{ccc|ccc} 1 & -1 & -1 & 1 & 0 & 0 \\ 0 & 1 & -2 & 2 & -1 & 0 \\ 0 & -1 & 2 & -1 & 0 & 1 \end{array}\right] \xrightarrow{R_2 + R_3} \left[\begin{array}{ccc|ccc} 1 & -1 & -1 & -1 & 0 & 0 \\ 0 & 1 & -2 & 2 & -1 & 0 \\ 0 & 0 & 0 & 1 & -1 & 1 \end{array}\right]$$

There are zeros in a row of the original matrix. The original matrix does not have an inverse.

▶ **TRY EXERCISE 10, PAGE 610**

● SOLVING SYSTEMS OF EQUATIONS USING INVERSE MATRICES

Systems of linear equations can be solved by finding the inverse of the coefficient matrix. Consider the following system of equations.

$$\begin{cases} 3x_1 + 4x_2 = -1 \\ 3x_1 + 5x_2 = 1 \end{cases} \quad (1)$$

Using matrix multiplication and the concept of equality of matrices, we can write this system as a matrix equation.

$$\begin{bmatrix} 3 & 4 \\ 3 & 5 \end{bmatrix}\begin{bmatrix} x_1 \\ x_2 \end{bmatrix} = \begin{bmatrix} -1 \\ 1 \end{bmatrix} \quad (2)$$

If we let

$$A = \begin{bmatrix} 3 & 4 \\ 3 & 5 \end{bmatrix} \qquad X = \begin{bmatrix} x_1 \\ x_2 \end{bmatrix} \qquad B = \begin{bmatrix} -1 \\ 1 \end{bmatrix}$$

then Equation (2) can be written as $AX = B$. The inverse of the coefficient matrix A is $A^{-1} = \begin{bmatrix} \frac{5}{3} & -\frac{4}{3} \\ -1 & 1 \end{bmatrix}$.

To solve the system of equations, multiply each side of the equation $AX = B$ by the inverse A^{-1}.

$$\begin{bmatrix} \frac{5}{3} & -\frac{4}{3} \\ -1 & 1 \end{bmatrix}\begin{bmatrix} 3 & 4 \\ 3 & 5 \end{bmatrix}\begin{bmatrix} x_1 \\ x_2 \end{bmatrix} = \begin{bmatrix} \frac{5}{3} & -\frac{4}{3} \\ -1 & 1 \end{bmatrix}\begin{bmatrix} -1 \\ 1 \end{bmatrix}$$

$$\begin{bmatrix} x_1 \\ x_2 \end{bmatrix} = \begin{bmatrix} -3 \\ 2 \end{bmatrix}$$

Thus $x_1 = -3$ and $x_2 = 2$. The solution to System (1) is $(-3, 2)$.

Alternative to Example 3
Find the solution of the system of equations by using the inverse of the coefficient matrix.

$$\begin{cases} 3x - y + 2z = 1 \\ x + y - 4z = -9 \\ 2x + 3y + 3z = 4 \end{cases}$$

● $(-1, 0, 2)$

EXAMPLE 3

Solve a System of Equations by Using the Inverse of the Coefficient Matrix

Find the solution of the system of equations by using the inverse of the coefficient matrix.

$$\begin{cases} x_1 + 7x_3 = 20 \\ 2x_1 + x_2 - x_3 = -3 \\ 7x_1 + 3x_2 + x_3 = 2 \end{cases} \quad (1)$$

Solution

Write the system as a matrix equation.

$$\begin{bmatrix} 1 & 0 & 7 \\ 2 & 1 & -1 \\ 7 & 3 & 1 \end{bmatrix}\begin{bmatrix} x_1 \\ x_2 \\ x_3 \end{bmatrix} = \begin{bmatrix} 20 \\ -3 \\ 2 \end{bmatrix} \quad (2)$$

The inverse of the coefficient matrix is $\begin{bmatrix} -\frac{4}{3} & -7 & \frac{7}{3} \\ 3 & 16 & -5 \\ \frac{1}{3} & 1 & -\frac{1}{3} \end{bmatrix}$.

Continued ▶

take note

The disadvantage of using the inverse matrix method to solve a system of equations is that this method will not work if the system is dependent or inconsistent. In addition, this method cannot distinguish between inconsistent and dependent systems. However, in some applications this method is very efficient. See the material on input-output analysis later in this section.

Multiply each side of the matrix equation (2) by the inverse.

$$\begin{bmatrix} -\frac{4}{3} & -7 & \frac{7}{3} \\ 3 & 16 & -5 \\ \frac{1}{3} & 1 & -\frac{1}{3} \end{bmatrix} \begin{bmatrix} 1 & 0 & 7 \\ 2 & 1 & -1 \\ 7 & 3 & 1 \end{bmatrix} \begin{bmatrix} x_1 \\ x_2 \\ x_3 \end{bmatrix} = \begin{bmatrix} -\frac{4}{3} & -7 & \frac{7}{3} \\ 3 & 16 & -5 \\ \frac{1}{3} & 1 & -\frac{1}{3} \end{bmatrix} \begin{bmatrix} 20 \\ -3 \\ 2 \end{bmatrix}$$

$$\begin{bmatrix} x_1 \\ x_2 \\ x_3 \end{bmatrix} = \begin{bmatrix} -1 \\ 2 \\ 3 \end{bmatrix}$$

Thus $x_1 = -1$, $x_2 = 2$, and $x_3 = 3$. The solution to System (1) is $(-1, 2, 3)$.

▶ **TRY EXERCISE 20, PAGE 610**

The temperature distribution on a metal plate can be approximated by a system of equations. The idea is based on the assumption that the temperature of a point P on the plate is the average of the temperatures of the four points shown nearest P.

Alternative to Example 4
Exercise 28, page 611.

EXAMPLE 4   **Temperature Distribution on a Metal Plate**

The edges of a metal plate are kept at a constant temperature, as shown below. Find the temperatures at x_1, x_2, x_3, and x_4.

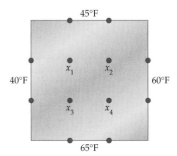

Solution

The temperature at x_1 is the average of the temperatures of the four points nearest x_1. That is,

$$x_1 = \frac{40 + 45 + x_2 + x_3}{4} = \frac{85 + x_2 + x_3}{4} \text{ or } 4x_1 - x_2 - x_3 = 85$$

Similarly, the temperatures at the remaining three points are

$$x_2 = \frac{60 + 45 + x_1 + x_4}{4} = \frac{105 + x_1 + x_4}{4} \text{ or } -x_1 + 4x_2 - x_4 = 105$$

$$x_3 = \frac{40 + 65 + x_1 + x_4}{4} = \frac{105 + x_1 + x_4}{4} \text{ or } -x_1 + 4x_3 - x_4 = 105$$

$$x_4 = \frac{60 + 65 + x_2 + x_3}{4} = \frac{125 + x_2 + x_3}{4} \text{ or } -x_2 - x_3 + 4x_4 = 125$$

The system of equations and the associated matrix equation are

$$\begin{cases} 4x_1 - x_2 - x_3 = 85 \\ -x_1 + 4x_2 - x_4 = 105 \\ -x_1 + 4x_3 - x_4 = 105 \\ -x_2 - x_3 + 4x_4 = 125 \end{cases} \qquad \begin{bmatrix} 4 & -1 & -1 & 0 \\ -1 & 4 & 0 & -1 \\ -1 & 0 & 4 & -1 \\ 0 & -1 & -1 & 4 \end{bmatrix} \begin{bmatrix} x_1 \\ x_2 \\ x_3 \\ x_4 \end{bmatrix} = \begin{bmatrix} 85 \\ 105 \\ 105 \\ 125 \end{bmatrix}$$

Solving the matrix equation by using an inverse matrix gives $\begin{bmatrix} x_1 \\ x_2 \\ x_3 \\ x_4 \end{bmatrix} = \begin{bmatrix} 47.5 \\ 52.5 \\ 52.5 \\ 57.5 \end{bmatrix}$.

The temperatures are $x_1 = 47.5°F$, $x_2 = 52.5°F$, $x_3 = 52.5°F$, and $x_4 = 57.5°F$.

▶ **TRY EXERCISE 26, PAGE 610**

● INPUT-OUTPUT ANALYSIS

The advantage of using the inverse matrix to solve a system of equations is not apparent unless it is necessary to solve repeatedly a system of equations with the same coefficient matrix but different constant matrices. *Input-output analysis* is one such application of this method.

In an economy, some of the output of an industry is used by the industry to produce its own product. For example, an electric company uses water and electricity to produce electricity, and a water company uses water and electricity to produce drinking water. **Input-output analysis** attempts to determine the necessary output of industries to satisfy each other's demands plus the demands of consumers. Wassily Leontief, a Harvard economist, was awarded the Nobel prize for his work in this field.

An **input-output matrix** is used to express the interdependence among industries in an economy. Each column of this matrix gives the dollar values of the inputs an industry needs to produce $1 worth of output.

To illustrate the concepts, we will assume an economy with only three industries: agriculture, transportation, and oil. Suppose that to produce $1 worth of agricultural products requires $.05 worth of agriculture, $.02 worth of transportation, and $.05 worth of oil. To produce $1 worth of transportation requires $.10 worth of agriculture, $.08 worth of transportation, and $.10 worth of oil. To produce $1 worth of oil requires $.10 worth of agriculture, $.15 worth of transportation, and $.13 worth of oil. The input-output matrix A is

Input requirements of

		Agriculture	Transportation	Oil
	Agriculture	0.05	0.10	0.10
from	Transportation	0.02	0.08	0.15
	Oil	0.05	0.10	0.13

Consumers (other than the industries themselves) want to purchase some of the output from these industries. The amount of output that the consumer will want is called the **final demand** on the economy. This is represented by a column matrix.

Suppose in our example that the final demand is $3 billion worth of agriculture, $1 billion worth of transportation, and $2 billion worth of oil. The final demand matrix is

$$\begin{bmatrix} 3 \\ 1 \\ 2 \end{bmatrix} = D$$

We represent the total output of each industry (in billions of dollars) as follows:

$$x = \text{total output of agriculture}$$
$$y = \text{total output of transportation}$$
$$z = \text{total output of oil}$$

The object of input-output analysis is to determine the values of x, y, and z that will satisfy the amount the consumer demands. To find these values, consider agriculture. The amount of agriculture left for the consumer (demand d) is

$$d = x - (\text{amount of agriculture used by industries}) \qquad (1)$$

To find the amount of agriculture used by the three industries in our economy, refer to the input-output matrix. Production of x billion dollars worth of agriculture takes $0.05x$ of agriculture, production of y billion dollars worth of transportation takes $0.10y$ of agriculture, and production of z billion dollars worth of oil takes $0.10z$ of agriculture. Thus

$$\text{Amount of agriculture used by industries} = 0.05x + 0.10y + 0.10z \qquad (2)$$

Combining Equations (1) and (2), we have

$$d = x - (0.05x + 0.10y + 0.10z)$$
$$3 = 0.95x - 0.10y - 0.10z \qquad \bullet \ d \text{ is \$3 billion for agriculture.}$$

We could continue this way for each of the other industries. The result would be a system of equations. Instead, however, we will use a matrix approach.

If X = total output of the three industries of the economy, then

$$X = \begin{bmatrix} x \\ y \\ z \end{bmatrix}$$

INSTRUCTOR NOTE
The system of equations for this input-output model is

$$\begin{cases} 3 = 0.95x - 0.10y - 0.10z \\ 1 = -0.02x + 0.92y - 0.15z \\ 2 = -0.05x - 0.10y + 0.87z \end{cases}$$

The product of A, the input-output matrix, and X is

$$AX = \begin{bmatrix} 0.05 & 0.10 & 0.10 \\ 0.02 & 0.08 & 0.15 \\ 0.05 & 0.10 & 0.13 \end{bmatrix}\begin{bmatrix} x \\ y \\ z \end{bmatrix}$$

This matrix represents the dollar amount of products used in production for all three industries. Thus the amount available for consumer demand is $X - AX$. As a matrix equation, we can write

$$X - AX = D$$

Solving this equation for X, we determine the output necessary to meet the needs of our industries and the consumer.

$$IX - AX = D \qquad \bullet \ I \text{ is the identity matrix. Thus } IX = X.$$
$$(I - A)X = D \qquad \bullet \ \textbf{Right distributive property}$$
$$X = (I - A)^{-1}D \qquad \bullet \ \textbf{Assuming the inverse of } (I - A) \textbf{ exists}$$

The last equation states that the solution to an input-output problem can be found by multiplying the demand matrix D by the inverse of $(I - A)$. In our example, we have

$$I - A = \begin{bmatrix} 1 & 0 & 0 \\ 0 & 1 & 0 \\ 0 & 0 & 1 \end{bmatrix} - \begin{bmatrix} 0.05 & 0.10 & 0.10 \\ 0.02 & 0.08 & 0.15 \\ 0.05 & 0.10 & 0.13 \end{bmatrix} = \begin{bmatrix} 0.95 & -0.10 & -0.10 \\ -0.02 & 0.92 & -0.15 \\ -0.05 & -0.10 & 0.87 \end{bmatrix}$$

$$(I - A)^{-1} \approx \begin{bmatrix} 1.063 & 0.131 & 0.145 \\ 0.034 & 1.112 & 0.196 \\ 0.065 & 0.135 & 1.180 \end{bmatrix}$$

The consumer demand is

$$X = (I - A)^{-1}D$$

$$X \approx \begin{bmatrix} 1.063 & 0.131 & 0.145 \\ 0.034 & 1.112 & 0.196 \\ 0.065 & 0.135 & 1.180 \end{bmatrix} \begin{bmatrix} 3 \\ 1 \\ 2 \end{bmatrix} \approx \begin{bmatrix} 3.61 \\ 1.61 \\ 2.69 \end{bmatrix}$$

This matrix indicates that $3.61 billion worth of agriculture, $1.61 billion worth of transportation, and $2.69 billion worth of oil must be produced by the industries to satisfy consumers' demands and the industries' internal requirements.

If we change the final demand matrix to,

$$D = \begin{bmatrix} 2 \\ 2 \\ 3 \end{bmatrix}$$

then the total output of the economy can be found as

$$X \approx \begin{bmatrix} 1.063 & 0.131 & 0.145 \\ 0.034 & 1.112 & 0.196 \\ 0.065 & 0.135 & 1.180 \end{bmatrix} \begin{bmatrix} 2 \\ 2 \\ 3 \end{bmatrix} \approx \begin{bmatrix} 2.82 \\ 2.88 \\ 3.94 \end{bmatrix}$$

Thus agriculture must produce output worth $2.82 billion, transportation must produce output worth $2.88 billion, and oil must produce output worth $3.94 billion to satisfy the given consumer demand and the industries' internal requirements.

TOPICS FOR DISCUSSION

1. Explain how to find the inverse of a matrix.

2. Explain the difference between a singular matrix and a nonsingular matrix.

3. Discuss the advantages and disadvantages of solving a system of equations by using an inverse matrix.

4. Do all square matrices have an inverse? If not, give an example of a square matrix that does not have an inverse.

EXERCISE SET 7.3

—*Suggested Assignment: Exercises 1, 3, 5, 9, 11, 15, 17, 19, 25–39, odd.*
—*Answers to Exercises 5–9, 11–13, and 33–36 are on page AA33.*

In Exercises 1 to 10, find the inverse of the given matrix.

1. $\begin{bmatrix} 1 & -3 \\ -2 & 5 \end{bmatrix}$ $\begin{bmatrix} -5 & -3 \\ -2 & -1 \end{bmatrix}$

2. $\begin{bmatrix} 1 & 2 \\ -2 & -3 \end{bmatrix}$ $\begin{bmatrix} -3 & -2 \\ 2 & 1 \end{bmatrix}$

3. $\begin{bmatrix} 1 & 4 \\ 2 & 10 \end{bmatrix}$ $\begin{bmatrix} 5 & -2 \\ -1 & \frac{1}{2} \end{bmatrix}$

4. $\begin{bmatrix} -2 & 3 \\ -6 & -8 \end{bmatrix}$ $\begin{bmatrix} -\frac{4}{17} & \frac{3}{34} \\ \frac{3}{17} & -\frac{1}{17} \end{bmatrix}$

5. $\begin{bmatrix} 1 & 2 & -1 \\ 2 & 5 & 1 \\ 3 & 6 & -2 \end{bmatrix}$

▶ 6. $\begin{bmatrix} 1 & 3 & -2 \\ -1 & -5 & 6 \\ 2 & 6 & -3 \end{bmatrix}$

7. $\begin{bmatrix} 1 & 2 & -1 \\ 2 & 6 & 1 \\ 3 & 6 & -4 \end{bmatrix}$

8. $\begin{bmatrix} 2 & 1 & -1 \\ 6 & 4 & -1 \\ 4 & 2 & -3 \end{bmatrix}$

9. $\begin{bmatrix} 2 & 4 & -4 \\ 1 & 3 & -4 \\ 2 & 4 & -3 \end{bmatrix}$

▶ 10. $\begin{bmatrix} 1 & -2 & 2 \\ 2 & -3 & 1 \\ 3 & -6 & 6 \end{bmatrix}$

The matrix does not have an inverse.

In Exercises 11 to 14, use a graphing calculator to find the inverse of the given matrix.

11. $\begin{bmatrix} 1 & -1 & 2 & 1 \\ 2 & -1 & 5 & 1 \\ 3 & -3 & 7 & 5 \\ -2 & 3 & -4 & -1 \end{bmatrix}$

12. $\begin{bmatrix} 1 & 1 & -1 & 2 \\ 3 & 2 & -1 & 5 \\ 2 & 2 & -1 & 5 \\ 4 & 4 & -4 & 7 \end{bmatrix}$

13. $\begin{bmatrix} 1 & -1 & 1 & 3 \\ 2 & -1 & 4 & 8 \\ 1 & 1 & 6 & 10 \\ -1 & 5 & 5 & 4 \end{bmatrix}$

14. $\begin{bmatrix} 1 & -1 & 1 & 2 \\ 2 & -1 & 6 & 6 \\ 3 & -1 & 12 & 12 \\ -2 & -1 & -14 & -10 \end{bmatrix}$

The matrix does not have an inverse.

In Exercises 15 to 24, solve each system of equations by using inverse matrix methods.

15. $\begin{cases} x + 4y = 6 \\ 2x + 7y = 11 \end{cases}$ $(2, 1)$

16. $\begin{cases} 2x + 3y = 5 \\ x + 2y = 4 \end{cases}$ $(-2, 3)$

17. $\begin{cases} x - 2y = 8 \\ 3x + 2y = -1 \end{cases}$ $\left(\frac{7}{4}, -\frac{25}{8}\right)$

18. $\begin{cases} 3x - 5y = -18 \\ 2x - 3y = -11 \end{cases}$ $(-1, 3)$

19. $\begin{cases} x + y + 2z = 4 \\ 2x + 3y + 3z = 5 \\ 3x + 3y + 7z = 14 \end{cases}$
$(1, -1, 2)$

▶ 20. $\begin{cases} x + 2y - z = 5 \\ 2x + 3y - z = 8 \\ 3x + 6y - 2z = 14 \end{cases}$
$(2, 1, -1)$

21. $\begin{cases} x + 2y + 2z = 5 \\ -2x - 5y - 2z = 8 \\ 2x + 4y + 7z = 19 \end{cases}$
$(23, -12, 3)$

22. $\begin{cases} x - y + 3z = 5 \\ 3x - y + 10z = 16 \\ 2x - 2y + 5z = 9 \end{cases}$
$(2, 0, 1)$

23. $\begin{cases} w + 2x + z = 6 \\ 2w + 5x + y + 2z = 10 \\ 2w + 4x + y + z = 8 \\ 3w + 6x + 4z = 16 \end{cases}$ $(0, 4, -6, -2)$

24. $\begin{cases} w - x + 2y = 5 \\ 2w - x + 6y + 2z = 16 \\ 3w - 2x + 9y + 4z = 28 \\ w - 2x - z = 2 \end{cases}$ $(1, -2, 1, 3)$

25. The edges of a metal plate are kept at a constant temperature, as shown below. Find the temperatures at x_1 and x_2. Round to the nearest tenth. x_1: 49.7°F, x_2: 53.7°F

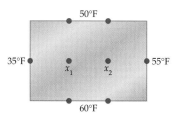

▶ 26. The edges of a metal plate are kept at a constant temperature, as shown below. Find the temperatures at x_1 and x_2. Round to the nearest tenth. x_1: 36.3°F, x_2: 40.3°F

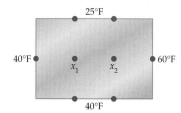

27. The edges of a metal plate are kept at a constant temperature, as shown below. Find the temperatures at x_1, x_2, x_3, and x_4.
x_1: 55°F, x_2: 57.5°F, x_3: 52.5°F, x_4: 55°F

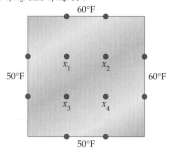

28. The edges of a metal plate are kept at a constant temperature, as shown below. Find the temperatures at x_1, x_2, x_3, and x_4. x_1: 60°F, x_2: 62.5°F, x_3: 52.5°F, x_4: 55°F

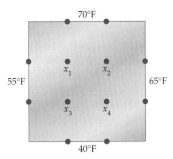

70°F

55°F x_1 x_2 65°F

x_3 x_4

40°F

In Exercises 29–32, solve each application by writing a system of equations that models the conditions and then applying inverse matrix methods.

29. BUSINESS REVENUE A vacation resort offers a helicopter tour of an island. The price for an adult ticket is $20; the price for a children's ticket is $15. The records of the tour operator show that 100 people took the tour on Saturday and 120 people took the tour on Sunday. The total receipts for Saturday were $1900, and on Sunday the receipts were $2275. Find the number of adults and the number of children who took the tour on Saturday and on Sunday. on Saturday 80 adults, 20 children; on Sunday 95 adults, 25 children

30. BUSINESS REVENUE A company sells a standard and a deluxe model tape recorder. Each standard tape recorder costs $45 to manufacture, and each deluxe model costs $60 to manufacture. The January manufacturing budget for 90 of these recorders was $4650; the February budget for 100 recorders was $5250. Find the number of each type of recorder manufactured in January and in February. In January, 50 standard models and 40 deluxe models were manufactured. In February, 50 standard models and 50 deluxe models were manufactured.

31. SOIL SCIENCE The following table shows the active chemical content of three different soil additives.

Additive	Grams per 100 Grams		
	Ammonium Nitrate	Phosphorus	Iron
1	30	10	10
2	40	15	10
3	50	5	5

A soil chemist wants to prepare two chemical samples. The first sample contains 380 grams of ammonium nitrate, 95 grams of phosphorus, and 85 grams of iron. The second sample requires 380 grams of ammonium nitrate, 110 grams of phosphorus, and 90 grams of iron. How many grams of each additive are required for sample 1, and how many grams of each additive are required for sample 2? Sample 1: 500 g of additive 1, 200 g of additive 2, 300 g of additive 3; Sample 2: 400 g of additive 1, 400 g of additive 2, 200 g of additive 3

32. NUTRITION The following table shows the carbohydrate, fat, and protein content of three food types.

Food Type	Grams per 100 Grams		
	Carbohydrate	Fat	Protein
I	13	10	13
II	4	4	3
III	1	0	10

A nutritionist must prepare two diets from these three food groups. The first diet must contain 23 grams of carbohydrate, 18 grams of fat, and 39 grams of protein. The second diet must contain 35 grams of carbohydrate, 28 grams of fat, and 42 grams of protein. How many grams of each food type are required for the first diet, and how many grams of each food type are required for the second diet? For the first diet, 100 g of Food Type I, 200 g of Food Type II, and 200 g of Food Type III are required. For the second diet, 200 g of Food Type I, 200 g of Food Type II, and 100 g of Food Type III are required.

In Exercises 33 to 36, use a graphing calculator to find the inverse of each matrix. Where necessary, round values to the nearest thousandth.

33. $\begin{bmatrix} 2 & -2 & 3 & 1 \\ 5 & 2 & -2 & 3 \\ 6 & -1 & 2 & 3 \\ 2 & 3 & -1 & 5 \end{bmatrix}$

34. $\begin{bmatrix} 3 & -1 & 0 & 1 \\ 2 & -2 & 3 & 0 \\ -1 & -3 & 5 & 3 \\ 5 & 3 & -2 & 1 \end{bmatrix}$

35. $\begin{bmatrix} -\frac{2}{7} & 4 & -\frac{1}{6} \\ -2 & \sqrt{2} & -3 \\ \sqrt{3} & 3 & -\sqrt{5} \end{bmatrix}$

36. $\begin{bmatrix} 6 & \pi & -\frac{4}{7} \\ -5 & \sqrt{7} & 2 \\ \frac{5}{6} & -\sqrt{3} & \sqrt{10} \end{bmatrix}$

37. INPUT-OUTPUT ANALYSIS A simplified economy has three industries: manufacturing, transportation, and service. The input-output matrix for this economy is

$$\begin{bmatrix} 0.20 & 0.15 & 0.10 \\ 0.10 & 0.30 & 0.25 \\ 0.20 & 0.10 & 0.10 \end{bmatrix}$$

Find the gross output needed to satisfy the consumer demand of $120 million worth of manufacturing, $60 million worth of transportation, and $55 million worth of service. $194.67 million worth of manufacturing, $157.03 million worth of transportation, $121.82 million worth of services

38. INPUT-OUTPUT ANALYSIS A four-sector economy consists of manufacturing, agriculture, service, and transportation. The input-output matrix for this economy is

$$\begin{bmatrix} 0.10 & 0.05 & 0.20 & 0.15 \\ 0.20 & 0.10 & 0.30 & 0.10 \\ 0.05 & 0.30 & 0.20 & 0.40 \\ 0.10 & 0.20 & 0.15 & 0.20 \end{bmatrix}$$

Find the gross output needed to satisfy the consumer demand of $80 million worth of manufacturing, $100 million worth of agriculture, $50 million worth of service, and $80 million worth of transportation.

39. INPUT-OUTPUT ANALYSIS A conglomerate is composed of three industries: coal, iron, and steel. To produce $1 worth of coal requires $.05 worth of coal, $.02 worth of iron, and $.10 worth of steel. To produce $1 worth of iron requires $.20 worth of coal, $.03 worth of iron, and $.12 worth of steel. To produce $1 worth of steel requires $.15 worth of coal, $.25 worth of iron, and $.05 worth of steel. How much should each industry produce to allow for a consumer demand of $30 million worth of coal, $5 million worth of iron, and $25 million worth of steel? $39.69 million worth of coal, $14.30 million worth of iron, $32.30 million worth of steel

38. $219.0 million worth of manufacturing, $294.3 million worth of agriculture, $316.7 million worth of service, $260.3 million worth of transportation

40. INPUT-OUTPUT ANALYSIS A conglomerate has three divisions: plastics, semiconductors, and computers. For each $1 worth of output, the plastics division needs $.01 worth of plastics, $.03 worth of semiconductors, and $.10 worth of computers. Each $1 worth of output from the semiconductor division requires $.08 worth from plastics, $.05 worth from semiconductors, and $.15 worth from computers. For each $1 worth of output, the computer division needs $.20 worth from plastics, $.20 worth from semiconductors, and $.10 worth from computers. The conglomerate estimates consumer demand of $100 million worth from the plastics division, $75 million worth from the semiconductor division, and $150 million worth from the computer division. At what level should each division produce to satisfy this demand? $152.63 million worth from plastics division, $126.88 million worth from semiconductor division, $204.77 million worth from computer division

CONNECTING CONCEPTS

41. Let $A = \begin{bmatrix} 2 & -3 \\ -6 & 9 \end{bmatrix}$ and $B = \begin{bmatrix} -3 & 15 \\ -2 & 10 \end{bmatrix}$. Show that $AB = O$, the 2×2 zero matrix. This illustrates that for matrices, if $AB = O$, it is not necessarily so that $A = O$ or $B = O$.

42. Show that if a matrix A has an inverse and $AB = O$, then $B = O$.

43. Let $A = \begin{bmatrix} 2 & -1 \\ -4 & 2 \end{bmatrix}$, $B = \begin{bmatrix} 3 & 4 \\ 1 & 5 \end{bmatrix}$, and $C = \begin{bmatrix} 4 & 7 \\ 3 & 11 \end{bmatrix}$. Show that $AB = AC$ but that $B \neq C$. This illustrates that the cancellation rule of real numbers may not apply to matrices.

44. (Continuation of Exercise 43.) Show that if A is a matrix that has an inverse and $AB = AC$, then $B = C$.

45. Show that if $A = \begin{bmatrix} a & b \\ c & d \end{bmatrix}$ and $ad - bc \neq 0$, then

$$A^{-1} = \frac{1}{ad - bc} \begin{bmatrix} d & -b \\ -c & a \end{bmatrix}$$

46. Use the result of Exercise 45 to show that a square matrix of order 2 has an inverse if and only if $ad - bc \neq 0$.

47. Use the result of Exercise 45 to find the inverse of each matrix.

a. $\begin{bmatrix} 2 & -3 \\ 4 & -5 \end{bmatrix}$ **b.** $\begin{bmatrix} 5 & 6 \\ 3 & 4 \end{bmatrix}$ **c.** $\begin{bmatrix} 0 & -1 \\ 4 & 4 \end{bmatrix}$

Answer on page AA33.

48. Let $A = \begin{bmatrix} 3 & -2 \\ 1 & 1 \end{bmatrix}$ and $B = \begin{bmatrix} 2 & -1 \\ 2 & 3 \end{bmatrix}$. Use Exercise 45 to show that

$$A^{-1} = \frac{1}{5} \begin{bmatrix} 1 & 2 \\ -1 & 3 \end{bmatrix} \quad \text{and} \quad B^{-1} = \frac{1}{8} \begin{bmatrix} 3 & 1 \\ -2 & 2 \end{bmatrix}$$

Now show that $(AB)^{-1} = B^{-1} \cdot A^{-1}$.
Answer on bottom of page.

49. Generalize the last result in Exercise 48. That is, show that if A and B are square matrices of order n and each has an inverse matrix, then $(AB)^{-1} = B^{-1} \cdot A^{-1}$. (*Hint:* Begin with the equation $(AB)(AB)^{-1} = I$, where I is the identity matrix. Now multiply each side of the equation by A^{-1} and then by B^{-1}.)

48. $(AB)^{-1} = B^{-1} \cdot A^{-1} = \begin{bmatrix} \dfrac{1}{20} & \dfrac{9}{40} \\ -\dfrac{1}{10} & \dfrac{1}{20} \end{bmatrix}$

─── *PREPARE FOR SECTION 7.4* ───

50. What is the order of the matrix $\begin{bmatrix} -3 & 5 \\ 0 & 1 \end{bmatrix}$? [7.1]   2

51. Evaluate $(-1)^{i+j}$ for $i = 2$ and $j = 6$. [P.2]   1

52. Evaluate $(-1)^{1+1}(-3) + (-1)^{1+2}(-2) + (-1)^{1+3}(5)$ [P.2]   4

53. If $A = \begin{bmatrix} 0 & 1 & -2 \\ 4 & -5 & 1 \\ 2 & -3 & 5 \end{bmatrix}$, what is a_{23}? [7.1]   1

54. Find $3\begin{bmatrix} -2 & 1 \\ 3 & -5 \end{bmatrix}$ [7.2] $\begin{bmatrix} -6 & 3 \\ 9 & -15 \end{bmatrix}$

55. Complete the following:

$\begin{bmatrix} 1 & 3 & -2 \\ -2 & -1 & 1 \\ 4 & 0 & 1 \end{bmatrix} \xrightarrow{\begin{array}{c} 2R_1 + R_2 \\ -4R_1 + R_3 \end{array}} \begin{bmatrix} & & ? & \end{bmatrix}$

[7.1] $\begin{bmatrix} 1 & 3 & -2 \\ 0 & 5 & -3 \\ 0 & -12 & 9 \end{bmatrix}$

─── *PROJECTS* ───

1. Cryptography is the study of the techniques of concealing the meaning of a message. The message that is to be concealed is called **plaintext**. The concealed message is called **ciphertext**. One way to change plaintext to ciphertext is to give each letter of the alphabet a numerical equivalent. Then matrices are used to scramble the numbers so that it is difficult to determine which number is associated with which letter.

a. One way to assign each letter a number is to use the ASCII coding system. Check the Internet to determine how this system assigns a number to each letter and punctuation mark.

b. Now write a short sentence, such as "THE BUCK STOPS HERE." Group the letters of the sentence into packets of, say, 3, using 0 (zero) for a space. Our sentence would look like

(THE)(0BU)(CK0)(STO)(PS0)(HER)(E.0)

Replace each letter and punctuation mark by its numerical ASCII equivalent. For our message, the first three groups would be

(84 72 69)(48 66 85)(67 75 48)...

Place these numbers in a matrix, using the set of three numbers as a column. For our example, the first three columns are

$W = \begin{bmatrix} 84 & 48 & 67 & \cdots \\ 72 & 66 & 75 & \cdots \\ 69 & 85 & 48 & \cdots \end{bmatrix}$

c. Now construct a 3×3 matrix E with integer elements that has an inverse. You can use any 3×3 matrix as long as you can find the inverse. (A graphing calculator may be useful here.)

d. Find the product $E \cdot W = M$. The numbers in the matrix M would be sent as the coded message. Do this for your message.

e. The person who receives this message would multiply the matrix M by E^{-1} to restore the message to its original form. Do this for your message.

DETERMINANTS

● DETERMINANT OF A 2 × 2 MATRIX

Associated with each square matrix A is a number called the *determinant* of A. We will denote the determinant of the matrix A by $\det(A)$ or by $|A|$. For the remainder of this chapter, we assume that all matrices are square matrices.

The Determinant of a 2 × 2 Matrix

The **determinant** of the matrix $A = [a_{ij}]$ of order 2 is

$$|A| = \begin{vmatrix} a_{11} & a_{12} \\ a_{21} & a_{22} \end{vmatrix} = a_{11}a_{22} - a_{21}a_{12}$$

Caution   Be careful not to confuse the notation for a matrix and that for a determinant. The symbol [ ] (brackets) is used for a matrix; the symbol | | (vertical bars) is used for the determinant of a matrix.

An easy way to remember the formula for the determinant of a 2 × 2 matrix is to recognize that the determinant is the difference between the products of the diagonal elements. That is,

$$\begin{vmatrix} a_{11} & a_{12} \\ a_{21} \diagdown a_{22} \end{vmatrix} = a_{11}a_{22} - a_{21}a_{12}$$

Alternative to Example 1
Find the value of the determinant of the matrix.

$$A = \begin{bmatrix} 9 & 1 \\ 8 & 2 \end{bmatrix}$$

● $|A| = 10$

EXAMPLE 1   **Find the Value of a Determinant**

Find the value of the determinant of the matrix $A = \begin{bmatrix} 5 & 3 \\ 2 & -3 \end{bmatrix}$.

Solution

$$|A| = \begin{vmatrix} 5 & 3 \\ 2 & -3 \end{vmatrix} = 5(-3) - 2(3) = -15 - 6 = -21$$

▶ **TRY EXERCISE 2, PAGE 621**

● MINORS AND COFACTORS

To define the determinant of a matrix of order greater than 2, we first need two other definitions.

The Minor of a Matrix

The **minor** M_{ij} of the element a_{ij} of a square matrix A of order $n \geq 3$ is the determinant of the matrix of order $n - 1$ obtained by deleting the ith row and the jth column of A.

Consider the matrix $A = \begin{bmatrix} 2 & -1 & 5 \\ 4 & 3 & -7 \\ 8 & -7 & 6 \end{bmatrix}$. The minor M_{23} is the determinant of the matrix A formed by deleting row 2 and column 3 from A.

$$M_{23} = \begin{vmatrix} 2 & -1 \\ 8 & -7 \end{vmatrix} \qquad \cdot \begin{vmatrix} 2 & -1 & 5 \\ 4 & 3 & -7 \\ 8 & -7 & 6 \end{vmatrix}$$

$$= 2(-7) - 8(-1) = -14 + 8 = -6$$

The minor M_{31} is the determinant of the matrix A formed by deleting row 3 and column 1 from A.

$$M_{31} = \begin{vmatrix} -1 & 5 \\ 3 & -7 \end{vmatrix} \qquad \cdot \begin{vmatrix} 2 & -1 & 5 \\ 4 & 3 & -7 \\ 8 & -7 & 6 \end{vmatrix}$$

$$= (-1)(-7) - 3(5) = 7 - 15 = -8$$

The second definition we need is that of the *cofactor* of a matrix.

INSTRUCTOR NOTE

Ask students to explain the difference between a minor and a cofactor.

Cofactor of a Matrix

The **cofactor** C_{ij} of the element a_{ij} of a square matrix A is given by $C_{ij} = (-1)^{i+j}M_{ij}$, where M_{ij} is the minor of a_{ij}.

When $i + j$ is an even integer, $(-1)^{i+j} = 1$. When $i + j$ is an odd integer, $(-1)^{i+j} = -1$. Thus

$$C_{ij} = \begin{cases} M_{ij}, & i + j \text{ is an even integer} \\ -M_{ij}, & i + j \text{ is an odd integer} \end{cases}$$

Alternative to Example 2

Given $A = \begin{bmatrix} 2 & 3 & -1 \\ 3 & 4 & 0 \\ 2 & 1 & 1 \end{bmatrix}$, find M_{12} and C_{23}.

● $M_{12} = 3$; $C_{23} = 4$

EXAMPLE 2 Find the Minor and Cofactor of a Matrix

Given $A = \begin{bmatrix} 4 & 3 & -2 \\ 5 & -2 & 4 \\ 3 & -2 & -6 \end{bmatrix}$, find M_{32} and C_{12}.

Solution

$$M_{32} = \begin{vmatrix} 4 & -2 \\ 5 & 4 \end{vmatrix} = 4(4) - 5(-2) = 16 - (-10) = 16 + 10 = 26$$

$$C_{12} = (-1)^{1+2}M_{12} = -M_{12} = -\begin{vmatrix} 5 & 4 \\ 3 & -6 \end{vmatrix} = -(-30 - 12) = 42$$

▶ **TRY EXERCISE 14, PAGE 621**

• EVALUATE A DETERMINANT USING EXPANDING BY COFACTORS

Cofactors are used to evaluate the determinant of a matrix of order 3 or greater. The technique used to evaluate a determinant by using cofactors is called *expanding by cofactors*.

Evaluating Determinants by Expanding by Cofactors

Given the square matrix A of order 3 or greater, the value of the determinant of A is the sum of the products of the elements of any row or column and their cofactors. For the rth row of A, the value of the determinant of A is

$$|A| = a_{r1}C_{r1} + a_{r2}C_{r2} + a_{r3}C_{r3} + \cdots + a_{rn}C_{rn}$$

For the cth column of A, the determinant of A is

$$|A| = a_{1c}C_{1c} + a_{2c}C_{2c} + a_{3c}C_{3c} + \cdots + a_{nc}C_{nc}$$

This theorem states that the value of a determinant can be found by expanding by cofactors of *any* row or column. The value of the determinant is the same in each case. To illustrate the method, consider the matrix $A = \begin{bmatrix} 2 & 3 & -1 \\ 4 & -2 & 3 \\ 1 & -3 & 4 \end{bmatrix}$.

Expanding the determinant of A by some row, say row 2, gives

$$|A| = \begin{vmatrix} 2 & 3 & -1 \\ 4 & -2 & 3 \\ 1 & -3 & 4 \end{vmatrix} = 4C_{21} + (-2)C_{22} + 3C_{23}$$

$$= 4(-1)^{2+1}M_{21} + (-2)(-1)^{2+2}M_{22} + 3(-1)^{2+3}M_{23}$$

$$= (-4)\begin{vmatrix} 3 & -1 \\ -3 & 4 \end{vmatrix} + (-2)\begin{vmatrix} 2 & -1 \\ 1 & 4 \end{vmatrix} + (-3)\begin{vmatrix} 2 & 3 \\ 1 & -3 \end{vmatrix}$$

$$= (-4)9 + (-2)9 + (-3)(-9) = -27$$

Expanding the determinant of A by some column, say, column 3, gives

$$|A| = \begin{vmatrix} 2 & 3 & -1 \\ 4 & -2 & 3 \\ 1 & -3 & 4 \end{vmatrix} = (-1)C_{13} + 3C_{23} + 4C_{33}$$

$$= (-1)(-1)^{1+3}M_{13} + 3(-1)^{2+3}M_{23} + 4(-1)^{3+3}M_{33}$$

$$= (-1)\begin{vmatrix} 4 & -2 \\ 1 & -3 \end{vmatrix} + (-3)\begin{vmatrix} 2 & 3 \\ 1 & -3 \end{vmatrix} + 4\begin{vmatrix} 2 & 3 \\ 4 & -2 \end{vmatrix}$$

$$= (-1)(-10) + (-3)(-9) + 4(-16) = -27$$

The value of the determinant of A is the same whether we expanded by cofactors of the elements of a row or by cofactors of the elements of a column. When evaluating a determinant, choose the most convenient row or column, which usually is the row or column containing the most zeros.

Alternative to Example 3
Evaluate the determinant of

$$A = \begin{bmatrix} -2 & 3 & 1 \\ -3 & -4 & 0 \\ 1 & 2 & 1 \end{bmatrix}$$

by expanding by cofactors.

● **15**

---

take note

Example 3 illustrates that choosing a row or column with the most zeros and then expanding about that row or column will reduce the number of calculations you must perform. For Example 3 we have $0 \cdot C_{32} = 0$, and it is not necessary to compute C_{32}.

EXAMPLE 3   **Evaluate a Determinant by Cofactors**

Evaluate the determinant of $A = \begin{bmatrix} 5 & -3 & -1 \\ -2 & 1 & -1 \\ 1 & 0 & 2 \end{bmatrix}$ by expanding by cofactors.

Solution

Because $a_{32} = 0$, expand using row 3 or column 2. Row 3 will be used here.

$$|A| = 1C_{31} + 0C_{32} + 2C_{33} = 1(-1)^{3+1}M_{31} + 0(-1)^{3+2}M_{32} + 2(-1)^{3+3}M_{33}$$

$$= 1\begin{vmatrix} -3 & -1 \\ 1 & -1 \end{vmatrix} + 0 + 2\begin{vmatrix} 5 & -3 \\ -2 & 1 \end{vmatrix} = 1[3 - (-1)] + 0 + 2[5 - 6]$$

$$= 4 - 2 = 2$$

▶ **TRY EXERCISE 20, PAGE 621**

INTEGRATING TECHNOLOGY

The determinant of a matrix can be found by using a graphing calculator. Many of these calculators use *det* as the operation that produces the value of the determinant. For

instance, if $A = \begin{bmatrix} -2 & 3 & 4 \\ 1 & 0 & -2 \\ 3 & 1 & 1 \end{bmatrix}$, then a

typical calculator display of the determinant of A is shown in **Figure 7.5.**

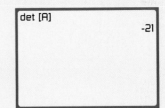

FIGURE 7.5

● **EVALUATE A DETERMINANT USING ELEMENTARY ROW OPERATIONS**

---

take note

The properties of determinants stated at the right remain true when the word *row* is replaced by *column*. In that case, we would have elementary *column* operations.

Effects of Elementary Row Operations on the Value of a Determinant of a Matrix

If A is a square matrix of order n, then the following elementary row operations produce the indicated changes in the determinant of A.

1. Interchanging any two rows of A changes the sign of $|A|$.

2. Multiplying a row of A by a constant k multiplies the determinant of A by k.

3. Adding a multiple of a row of A to another row does not change the value of the determinant of A.

MATH MATTERS

There is a vast difference between computing the determinant of a matrix by cofactors and doing so by row reduction. For instance, approximately 4×10^{12} operations are necessary to evaluate a determinant of order 15 by cofactors. At 4 million operations per second, a computer would need approximately 11 days to compute the determinant. On the other hand, approximately 2000 operations are needed to find the determinant by row reduction. Using the same computer, it would take less than 0.001 second to find the determinant.

To illustrate these properties, consider the matrix $A = \begin{bmatrix} 2 & 3 \\ 1 & -2 \end{bmatrix}$. The determinant of A is $|A| = 2(-2) - 1(3) = -7$. Now consider each of the elementary row operations.

Interchange the rows of A and evaluate the determinant.

$$\begin{vmatrix} 1 & -2 \\ 2 & 3 \end{vmatrix} = 1(3) - 2(-2) = 3 + 4 = 7 = -|A|$$

Multiply row 2 of A by -3 and evaluate the determinant.

$$\begin{vmatrix} 2 & 3 \\ -3 & 6 \end{vmatrix} = 2(6) - (-3)3 = 12 + 9 = 21 = -3|A|$$

Multiply row 1 of A by -2 and add it to row 2. Then evaluate the determinant.

$$\begin{vmatrix} 2 & 3 \\ -3 & -8 \end{vmatrix} = 2(-8) - (-3)(3) = -16 + 9 = -7 = |A|.$$

These elementary row operations are often used to rewrite a matrix in *triangular form*. A matrix is in **triangular form** if all elements below or above the main diagonal are zero. The matrices

$$A = \begin{bmatrix} 2 & -2 & 3 & 1 \\ 0 & -2 & 4 & 2 \\ 0 & 0 & 6 & 9 \\ 0 & 0 & 0 & -5 \end{bmatrix} \quad \text{and} \quad B = \begin{bmatrix} 3 & 0 & 0 & 0 \\ 2 & -3 & 0 & 0 \\ 6 & 4 & -2 & 0 \\ 8 & 3 & 4 & 2 \end{bmatrix}$$

are in triangular form.

Determinant of a Matrix in Triangular Form

Let A be a square matrix of order n in triangular form. The determinant of A is the product of the elements on the main diagonal.

$$|A| = a_{11}a_{22}a_{33} \cdots a_{nn}$$

For the matrices A and B given above,

$$|A| = 2(-2)(6)(-5) = 120$$
$$|B| = 3(-3)(-2)(2) = 36$$

Alternative to Example 4
Evaluate the determinant by rewriting it in triangular form.

$$\begin{bmatrix} 2 & 1 & -1 & 2 \\ 4 & 3 & 0 & 5 \\ -2 & -1 & 3 & -4 \\ 4 & 2 & 0 & 5 \end{bmatrix}$$

● **12**

EXAMPLE 4 Evaluate a Determinant by Elementary Row Operations

Evaluate the determinant by rewriting it in triangular form.

$$\begin{vmatrix} 2 & 1 & -1 & 3 \\ 2 & 2 & 0 & 1 \\ 4 & 5 & 4 & -3 \\ 2 & 2 & 7 & -3 \end{vmatrix}$$

Solution

Rewrite the determinant in triangular form by using elementary row operations.

$$
\begin{vmatrix} 2 & 1 & -1 & 3 \\ 2 & 2 & 0 & 1 \\ 4 & 5 & 4 & -3 \\ 2 & 2 & 7 & -3 \end{vmatrix}
\begin{matrix} -1R_1 + R_2 \\ -2R_1 + R_3 \\ -1R_1 + R_4 \\ = \end{matrix}
\begin{vmatrix} 2 & 1 & -1 & 3 \\ 0 & 1 & 1 & -2 \\ 0 & 3 & 6 & -9 \\ 0 & 1 & 8 & -6 \end{vmatrix}
$$

$$
\begin{matrix} \text{Factor 3} \\ \text{from row 3.} \\ = \end{matrix} \; 3
\begin{vmatrix} 2 & 1 & -1 & 3 \\ 0 & 1 & 1 & -2 \\ 0 & 1 & 2 & -3 \\ 0 & 1 & 8 & -6 \end{vmatrix}
\begin{matrix} -1R_2 + R_3 \\ -1R_2 + R_4 \\ = \end{matrix} \; 3
\begin{vmatrix} 2 & 1 & -1 & 3 \\ 0 & 1 & 1 & -2 \\ 0 & 0 & 1 & -1 \\ 0 & 0 & 7 & -4 \end{vmatrix}
$$

$$
\begin{matrix} -7R_3 + R_4 \\ = \end{matrix} \; 3
\begin{vmatrix} 2 & 1 & -1 & 3 \\ 0 & 1 & 1 & -2 \\ 0 & 0 & 1 & -1 \\ 0 & 0 & 0 & 3 \end{vmatrix} = 3(2)(1)(1)(3) = 18
$$

▶ **TRY EXERCISE 42, PAGE 622**

❓ **QUESTION** If I is the identity matrix of order n, what is the value of $|I|$?

In some cases it is possible to recognize when the determinant of a matrix is zero.

Conditions for a Zero Determinant

If A is a square matrix, then $|A| = 0$ when any one of the following is true.

1. A row (column) consists entirely of zeros.

2. Two rows (columns) are identical.

3. One row (column) is a constant multiple of a second row (column).

Proof To prove part 2 of this theorem, let A be the given matrix and let $D = |A|$. Now interchange the two identical rows. Then $|A| = -D$. Thus

$$D = -D$$

Zero is the only real number that is its own additive inverse, and hence $D = |A| = 0$. ◆

The proofs of the other two properties are left as exercises.
The last property of determinants that we will discuss is a product property.

❓ **ANSWER** The identity matrix is in diagonal form with 1s on the main diagonal. Thus $|I|$ is a product of 1s, or $|I| = 1$.

Product Property of Determinants

If A and B are square matrices of order n, then

$$|AB| = |A||B|$$

● CONDITION FOR A SQUARE MATRIX TO HAVE A MULTIPLICATIVE INVERSE

Recall that a singular matrix is one that does not have a multiplicative inverse. The Product Property of Determinants can be used to determine whether a matrix has an inverse.

Consider a matrix A with an inverse A^{-1}. Then, by the last theorem,

$$|A \cdot A^{-1}| = |A||A^{-1}|$$

But $A \cdot A^{-1} = I$, the identity matrix, and $|I| = 1$. Therefore,

$$1 = |A||A^{-1}|$$

From the last equation, $|A| \neq 0$. And, in particular,

$$|A^{-1}| = \frac{1}{|A|}$$

These results are summarized in the following theorem.

Existence of the Inverse of a Square Matrix

If A is a square matrix of order n, then A has a multiplicative inverse if and only if $|A| \neq 0$. Furthermore,

$$|A^{-1}| = \frac{1}{|A|}$$

We proved only part of this theorem. It remains to show that given $|A| \neq 0$, then A has an inverse. This proof can be found in most texts on linear algebra.

 ## TOPICS FOR DISCUSSION

1. Discuss the difference between a matrix and a determinant.

2. Explain the difference between the minor and the cofactor of an element of a matrix.

3. Discuss how determinants are used to discover whether a matrix has an inverse.

4. Explain how to calculate the value of a determinant by expanding by cofactors.

5. Discuss how elementary row operations are used to find the determinant of a matrix.

EXERCISE SET 7.4   —Suggested Assignment: Exercises 1–25, every other odd; 27–45, odd; 55, 61.

In Exercises 1 to 8, evaluate the determinant.

1. $\begin{vmatrix} 2 & -1 \\ 3 & 5 \end{vmatrix}$ 13   ▶ **2.** $\begin{vmatrix} 2 & 9 \\ -6 & 2 \end{vmatrix}$ 58   **3.** $\begin{vmatrix} 5 & 0 \\ 2 & -3 \end{vmatrix}$ −15

4. $\begin{vmatrix} 0 & -8 \\ 3 & 4 \end{vmatrix}$ 24   **5.** $\begin{vmatrix} 4 & 6 \\ 2 & 3 \end{vmatrix}$ 0   **6.** $\begin{vmatrix} -3 & 6 \\ 4 & -8 \end{vmatrix}$ 0

7. $\begin{vmatrix} 0 & 9 \\ 0 & -2 \end{vmatrix}$ 0   **8.** $\begin{vmatrix} -3 & 9 \\ 0 & 0 \end{vmatrix}$ 0

In Exercises 9 to 12, evaluate the indicated minor and cofactor for the determinant

$$\begin{vmatrix} 5 & -2 & -3 \\ 2 & 4 & -1 \\ 4 & -5 & 6 \end{vmatrix}$$

9. M_{11}, C_{11} 19, 19   **10.** M_{21}, C_{21} −27, 27

11. M_{32}, C_{32} 1, −1   **12.** M_{33}, C_{33} 24, 24

In Exercises 13 to 16, evaluate the indicated minor and cofactor for the determinant

$$\begin{vmatrix} 3 & -2 & 3 \\ 1 & 3 & 0 \\ 6 & -2 & 3 \end{vmatrix}$$

13. M_{22}, C_{22} −9, −9   ▶ **14.** M_{13}, C_{13} −20, −20

15. M_{31}, C_{31} −9, −9   **16.** M_{23}, C_{23} 6, −6

In Exercises 17 to 26, evaluate the determinant by expanding by cofactors.

17. $\begin{vmatrix} 2 & -3 & 1 \\ 2 & 0 & 2 \\ 3 & -2 & 4 \end{vmatrix}$ 10   **18.** $\begin{vmatrix} 3 & 1 & -2 \\ 2 & -5 & 4 \\ 3 & 2 & 1 \end{vmatrix}$ −67

19. $\begin{vmatrix} -2 & 3 & 2 \\ 1 & 2 & -3 \\ -4 & -2 & 1 \end{vmatrix}$ 53   ▶ **20.** $\begin{vmatrix} 3 & -2 & 0 \\ 2 & -3 & 2 \\ 8 & -2 & 5 \end{vmatrix}$ −45

21. $\begin{vmatrix} 2 & -3 & 10 \\ 0 & 2 & -3 \\ 0 & 0 & 5 \end{vmatrix}$ 20   **22.** $\begin{vmatrix} 6 & 0 & 0 \\ 2 & -3 & 0 \\ 7 & -8 & 2 \end{vmatrix}$ −36

23. $\begin{vmatrix} 0 & -2 & 4 \\ 1 & 0 & -7 \\ 5 & -6 & 0 \end{vmatrix}$ 46   **24.** $\begin{vmatrix} 5 & -8 & 0 \\ 2 & 0 & -7 \\ 0 & -2 & -1 \end{vmatrix}$ −86

25. $\begin{vmatrix} 4 & -3 & 3 \\ 2 & 1 & -4 \\ 6 & -2 & -1 \end{vmatrix}$ 0   **26.** $\begin{vmatrix} -2 & 3 & 9 \\ 4 & -2 & -6 \\ 0 & -8 & -24 \end{vmatrix}$ 0

In Exercises 27 to 40, without expanding, give a reason for each equality.

27. $\begin{vmatrix} 2 & -1 & 3 \\ 0 & 0 & 0 \\ 3 & 4 & 1 \end{vmatrix} = 0$ Row 2 consists of zeros, so the determinant is zero.

28. $\begin{vmatrix} 2 & 3 & 0 \\ 1 & -2 & 0 \\ 4 & 1 & 0 \end{vmatrix} = 0$ Column 3 consists entirely of zeros. Therefore, the determinant is zero.

29. $\begin{vmatrix} 1 & 4 & -1 \\ 2 & 4 & 12 \\ 3 & 1 & 4 \end{vmatrix} = 2 \begin{vmatrix} 1 & 4 & -1 \\ 1 & 2 & 6 \\ 3 & 1 & 4 \end{vmatrix}$ 2 was factored from row 2.

30. $\begin{vmatrix} 1 & -3 & 4 \\ 4 & 6 & 1 \\ 0 & -9 & 3 \end{vmatrix} = -3 \begin{vmatrix} 1 & 1 & 4 \\ 4 & -2 & 1 \\ 0 & 3 & 3 \end{vmatrix}$ −3 was factored from column 2.

31. $\begin{vmatrix} 1 & 5 & -2 \\ 2 & -1 & 4 \\ 3 & 0 & -2 \end{vmatrix} = \begin{vmatrix} 1 & 5 & -2 \\ 0 & -11 & 8 \\ 3 & 0 & -2 \end{vmatrix}$ Row 1 was multiplied by −2 and added to row 2.

32. $\begin{vmatrix} 1 & 1 & -3 \\ 2 & 2 & 5 \\ 1 & -2 & 4 \end{vmatrix} = \begin{vmatrix} 1 & 1 & -3 \\ 2 & 2 & 5 \\ 0 & -3 & 7 \end{vmatrix}$ Row 1 was multiplied by −1 and added to row 3.

33. $\begin{vmatrix} 4 & -3 & 2 \\ 6 & 2 & 1 \\ -2 & 2 & 4 \end{vmatrix} = 2 \begin{vmatrix} 2 & -3 & 2 \\ 3 & 2 & 1 \\ -1 & 2 & 4 \end{vmatrix}$ 2 was factored from column 1.

34. $\begin{vmatrix} 2 & -1 & 3 \\ 3 & 0 & 1 \\ -4 & 2 & -6 \end{vmatrix} = 0$ Row 3 is a constant multiple of row 1. $-2R_1 = R_3$. Therefore, the determinant is zero.

35. $\begin{vmatrix} 2 & -4 & 5 \\ 0 & 3 & 4 \\ 0 & 0 & -2 \end{vmatrix} = -12$ **36.** $\begin{vmatrix} 3 & 0 & 0 \\ 2 & -1 & 0 \\ 3 & 4 & 5 \end{vmatrix} = -15$

35. The matrix is in triangular form. The value of the determinant is the product of the terms on the main diagonal.

36. The matrix is in triangular form. The product of the elements on the main diagonal is −15. Therefore, the value of the determinant is −15.

37. $\begin{vmatrix} 3 & 5 & -2 \\ 2 & 1 & 0 \\ 9 & -2 & -3 \end{vmatrix} = - \begin{vmatrix} 9 & -2 & -3 \\ 2 & 1 & 0 \\ 3 & 5 & -2 \end{vmatrix}$

38. $\begin{vmatrix} 6 & 0 & -2 \\ 2 & -1 & -3 \\ 1 & 5 & -7 \end{vmatrix} = - \begin{vmatrix} 0 & 6 & -2 \\ -1 & 2 & -3 \\ 5 & 1 & -7 \end{vmatrix}$

37. Row 1 and row 3 were interchanged, so the sign of the determinant was changed.

38. Column 1 and column 2 were interchanged. Therefore, the sign of the determinant was changed.

39. $a^3 \begin{vmatrix} 1 & 1 & 1 \\ a & a & a \\ a^2 & a^2 & a^2 \end{vmatrix} = \begin{vmatrix} a & a & a \\ a^2 & a^2 & a^2 \\ a^3 & a^3 & a^3 \end{vmatrix}$ Each row of the determinant was multiplied by a.

40. $\begin{vmatrix} 1 & 1 & 1 \\ 2 & 2 & 2 \\ 3 & 3 & 3 \end{vmatrix} = 0$ Columns 1, 2, and 3 are identical. Therefore, the determinant is zero.

In Exercises 41 to 50, evaluate the determinant by first rewriting the determinant in triangular form.

41. $\begin{vmatrix} 2 & 4 & 1 \\ 1 & 2 & -1 \\ 1 & 2 & 2 \end{vmatrix} \; 0$

▶ **42.** $\begin{vmatrix} 3 & -2 & -1 \\ 1 & 2 & 4 \\ 2 & -2 & 3 \end{vmatrix} \; 38$

43. $\begin{vmatrix} 1 & 2 & -1 \\ 2 & 3 & 1 \\ 3 & 4 & 3 \end{vmatrix} \; 0$

44. $\begin{vmatrix} 1 & 2 & 5 \\ -1 & 1 & -2 \\ 3 & 1 & 10 \end{vmatrix} \; 0$

45. $\begin{vmatrix} 0 & -1 & 1 \\ 1 & 0 & -2 \\ 2 & 2 & 0 \end{vmatrix} \; 6$

46. $\begin{vmatrix} 2 & -1 & 3 \\ 1 & 1 & 1 \\ 3 & -4 & 5 \end{vmatrix} \; -1$

47. $\begin{vmatrix} 1 & 2 & -1 & 2 \\ 1 & -2 & 0 & 3 \\ 3 & 0 & 1 & 5 \\ -2 & -4 & 1 & 6 \end{vmatrix} \; -90$

48. $\begin{vmatrix} 1 & -1 & -1 & 2 \\ 0 & 2 & 4 & 6 \\ 1 & 1 & 4 & 12 \\ 1 & -1 & 0 & 8 \end{vmatrix} \; 4$

49. $\begin{vmatrix} 1 & 2 & 3 & -1 \\ 6 & 5 & 9 & 8 \\ 2 & 4 & 12 & -1 \\ 1 & 2 & 6 & -1 \end{vmatrix} \; 21$

50. $\begin{vmatrix} 1 & 2 & 0 & -2 \\ -1 & 1 & 3 & 5 \\ 2 & 1 & 4 & 0 \\ -2 & 5 & 2 & 6 \end{vmatrix} \; 0$

In Exercises 51 to 54, use a graphing calculator to find the value of the determinant of the matrix. Where necessary, round your answer to the nearest thousandth.

51. $\begin{bmatrix} 2 & -2 & 3 & 1 \\ 5 & 2 & -2 & 3 \\ 6 & -1 & 2 & 3 \\ 2 & 3 & -1 & 5 \end{bmatrix} \; 3$

52. $\begin{bmatrix} 3 & -1 & 0 & 1 \\ 2 & -2 & 3 & 0 \\ -1 & -3 & 5 & 3 \\ 5 & 3 & -2 & 1 \end{bmatrix} \; 140$

53. $\begin{bmatrix} -\frac{2}{7} & 4 & -\frac{1}{6} \\ -2 & \sqrt{2} & -3 \\ \sqrt{3} & 3 & -\sqrt{5} \end{bmatrix}$
-38.933

54. $\begin{bmatrix} 6 & \pi & -\frac{4}{7} \\ -5 & \sqrt{7} & 2 \\ \frac{5}{6} & -\sqrt{3} & \sqrt{10} \end{bmatrix}$
122.204

── **CONNECTING CONCEPTS** ──

The area of a triangle with vertices (x_1, y_1), (x_2, y_2), and (x_3, y_3) can be given as the absolute value of the determinant

$$\frac{1}{2} \begin{vmatrix} x_1 & y_1 & 1 \\ x_2 & y_2 & 1 \\ x_3 & y_3 & 1 \end{vmatrix}$$

Use this formula to find the area of each triangle whose coordinates are given in Exercises 55 to 58.

55. $(2, 3), (-1, 0), (4, 8)$ $\frac{9}{2}$ square units

56. $(-3, 4), (1, 5), (5, -2)$ 16 square units

57. $(4, 9), (8, 2), (-3, -2)$ $46\frac{1}{2}$ square units

58. $(0, 4), (-5, 7), (2, 9)$ $15\frac{1}{2}$ square units

59. Given a square matrix of order 3 in which one row is a constant multiple of a second row, show that the determinant of the matrix is zero. (*Hint:* Use an elementary row operation and part 2 of the theorem for conditions for a zero determinant.)

60. Given a square matrix of order 3 with a zero as every element in a column, show that the determinant of the matrix is zero. (*Hint:* Expand the determinant by cofactors using the column of zeros.)

64. Adding a multiple of a row to another row does not change the value of the determinant.

61. Show that the determinant $\begin{vmatrix} x & y & 1 \\ x_1 & y_1 & 1 \\ x_2 & y_2 & 1 \end{vmatrix} = 0$ is the equation of a line through the points (x_1, y_1) and (x_2, y_2).

62. Use Exercise 61 to find the equation of the line passing through the points $(2, 3)$ and $(-1, 4)$. $x + 3y = 11$

63. Use Exercise 61 to find the equation of the line passing through the points $(-3, 4)$ and $(2, -3)$. $7x + 5y = -1$

64. Show that $\begin{vmatrix} a_1 & b_1 \\ a_2 & b_2 \end{vmatrix} = \begin{vmatrix} a_1 & b_1 \\ ka_1 + a_2 & kb_1 + b_2 \end{vmatrix}$.
What property of determinants does this illustrate?
Answer on bottom of page.

65. Surveyors use a formula to find the area of a plot of land. *Surveyor's Area Formula:* If the vertices (x_1, y_1), (x_2, y_2), (x_3, y_3), ..., (x_n, y_n) of a convex polygon are listed counterclockwise around the perimeter, the area of the polygon is

$$A = \frac{1}{2}\left\{ \begin{vmatrix} x_1 & x_2 \\ y_1 & y_2 \end{vmatrix} + \begin{vmatrix} x_2 & x_3 \\ y_2 & y_3 \end{vmatrix} + \begin{vmatrix} x_3 & x_4 \\ y_3 & y_4 \end{vmatrix} + \cdots + \begin{vmatrix} x_n & x_1 \\ y_n & y_1 \end{vmatrix} \right\}$$

Use the Surveyor's Area Formula to find the area of the polygon with vertices $(8, -4)$, $(25, 5)$, $(15, 9)$, $(17, 20)$, and $(0, 10)$. 263.5 square units

——— *PREPARE FOR SECTION 7.5* ———

66. Find the determinant of the matrix $\begin{bmatrix} -5 & 2 \\ 3 & 1 \end{bmatrix}$. [7.4] −11

67. Find the determinant of the matrix $\begin{bmatrix} 3 & -1 & 6 \\ 2 & 9 & 0 \\ 1 & -2 & 3 \end{bmatrix}$. [7.4] 9

68. What is the coefficient matrix for the system of equations
$\begin{cases} 2x - 7y = 4 \\ 3x + 5y = 2 \end{cases}$? [7.1] $\begin{bmatrix} 2 & -7 \\ 3 & 5 \end{bmatrix}$

69. Find the determinant of the coefficient matrix for the system of equations $\begin{cases} x - 2y + z = 3 \\ -x + y - 2z = 1 \\ 2x + 3y - z = 4 \end{cases}$. [7.4] 10

70. Find $\dfrac{\begin{vmatrix} 3 & -1 \\ 2 & -3 \end{vmatrix}}{\begin{vmatrix} 1 & 4 \\ -2 & 5 \end{vmatrix}}$. [7.4] $-\dfrac{7}{13}$

71. Suppose that A is a matrix for which $\det(A) = 0$. Is it possible to find A^{-1}? [7.4] No.

——— *PROJECTS* ———

1. Consider the rectangle in the accompanying diagram. Construct a matrix M of dimension 2×4 in which the columns are the x- and y-coordinates, respectively, of successive vertices of the rectangle.

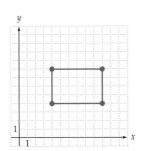

a. Consider the matrix $A = \begin{bmatrix} 2 & 1 \\ 3 & 2 \end{bmatrix}$. Find the product AM. Plot the points of AM again, using the columns as the x- and y-coordinates, respectively, of successive vertices of a new figure. Show that the area of the new figure is the same as the area of the original rectangle and that $\det(A) = 1$.

b. Proceed as in part **a.**, but use the matrix $A = \begin{bmatrix} 3 & 1 \\ 1 & 1 \end{bmatrix}$ and show that the area of the new figure is twice the area of the original rectangle. Show that $\det(A) = 2$.

c. Proceed as in part **a.**, but use the matrix $A = \begin{bmatrix} 1 & 2 \\ 0.5 & 1 \end{bmatrix}$ and show that the new figure is a line segment and that, therefore, the figure has no area. Show that $\det(A) = 0$.

d. Make a conjecture as to how the value of the determinant of A influences the area of the figure represented by AM.

e. Let $A = \begin{bmatrix} 2 & 1 \\ 5 & 2 \end{bmatrix}$ and repeat part **a.** Does your conjecture from part **d.** still hold for this matrix? If not, refine your original conjecture.

| SECTION 7.5 | **CRAMER'S RULE** |

• SOLVING A SYSTEM OF
  EQUATIONS USING
  CRAMER'S RULE

• **SOLVING A SYSTEM OF EQUATIONS USING CRAMER'S RULE**

An application of determinants is to solve a system of linear equations. Consider the system

$$\begin{cases} a_{11}x_1 + a_{12}x_2 = b_1 \\ a_{21}x_1 + a_{22}x_2 = b_2 \end{cases}$$

To eliminate x_2 from this system, we first multiply the top equation by a_{22} and the bottom equation by a_{12}. Then we subtract.

$$a_{22}a_{11}x_1 + a_{22}a_{12}x_2 = a_{22}b_1$$

$$\underline{a_{12}a_{21}x_1 + a_{12}a_{22}x_2 = a_{12}b_2}$$

$$(a_{22}a_{11} - a_{12}a_{21})x_1 \qquad = a_{22}b_1 - a_{12}b_2$$

$$x_1 = \frac{a_{22}b_1 - a_{12}b_2}{a_{22}a_{11} - a_{12}a_{21}}$$

or $\quad x_1 = \dfrac{\begin{vmatrix} b_1 & a_{12} \\ b_2 & a_{22} \end{vmatrix}}{\begin{vmatrix} a_{11} & a_{12} \\ a_{21} & a_{22} \end{vmatrix}}, \quad \begin{vmatrix} a_{11} & a_{12} \\ a_{21} & a_{22} \end{vmatrix} \neq 0$

? QUESTION Why is the condition $\begin{vmatrix} a_{11} & a_{12} \\ a_{21} & a_{22} \end{vmatrix} \neq 0$ given for the value of x_1?

We can find x_2 in a similar manner. The results are given in Cramer's Rule for a System of Two Linear Equations.

Cramer's Rule for a System of Two Linear Equations

Let $\quad \begin{cases} a_{11}x_1 + a_{12}x_2 = b_1 \\ a_{21}x_1 + a_{22}x_2 = b_2 \end{cases}$

be the system of equations for which the determinant of the coefficient matrix is not zero. The solution of the system of equations is the ordered pair whose coordinates are

$$x_1 = \frac{\begin{vmatrix} b_1 & a_{12} \\ b_2 & a_{22} \end{vmatrix}}{\begin{vmatrix} a_{11} & a_{12} \\ a_{21} & a_{22} \end{vmatrix}} \quad \text{and} \quad x_2 = \frac{\begin{vmatrix} a_{11} & b_1 \\ a_{21} & b_2 \end{vmatrix}}{\begin{vmatrix} a_{11} & a_{12} \\ a_{21} & a_{22} \end{vmatrix}}, \quad \begin{vmatrix} a_{11} & a_{12} \\ a_{21} & a_{22} \end{vmatrix} \neq 0$$

? ANSWER Division by zero is undefined.

Note that the denominator is the determinant of the coefficient matrix of the variables. The numerator of x_1 is formed by replacing column 1 of the coefficient determinant with the constants b_1 and b_2. The numerator of x_2 is formed by replacing column 2 of the coefficient determinant with the constants b_1 and b_2.

Alternative to Example 1
Solve the following system of equations using Cramer's Rule.
$$\begin{cases} 4x_1 - 5x_2 = 12 \\ 3x_1 - 4x_2 = 10 \end{cases}$$
● $(-2, -4)$

EXAMPLE I

Solve a System of Equations by Using Cramer's Rule

Solve the following system of equations using Cramer's Rule.
$$\begin{cases} 5x_1 - 3x_2 = 6 \\ 2x_1 + 4x_2 = -7 \end{cases}$$

Solution

$$x_1 = \frac{\begin{vmatrix} 6 & -3 \\ -7 & 4 \end{vmatrix}}{\begin{vmatrix} 5 & -3 \\ 2 & 4 \end{vmatrix}} = \frac{3}{26} \qquad x_2 = \frac{\begin{vmatrix} 5 & 6 \\ 2 & -7 \end{vmatrix}}{\begin{vmatrix} 5 & -3 \\ 2 & 4 \end{vmatrix}} = -\frac{47}{26}$$

The solution is $\left(\dfrac{3}{26}, -\dfrac{47}{26} \right)$.

▶ **TRY EXERCISE 4, PAGE 627**

INSTRUCTOR NOTE
For the system of equations
$$4x - 6y = 8$$
$$2x - 3y = 4$$
ask students whether
1. the system can be solved using Cramer's Rule.
   ● **No**
2. the system can be solved using the Gaussian elimination method.
   ● **Yes**

Cramer's Rule can be used for a system of three linear equations in three variables. For example, consider the system of equations
$$\begin{cases} 2x - 3y + z = 2 \\ 4x + 2z = -3 \qquad (1) \\ 3x + y - 2z = 1 \end{cases}$$

To solve this system of equations, we extend the concepts behind finding the solution for a system of two linear equations. The solution of the system has the form (x, y, z), where

$$x = \frac{D_x}{D} \qquad y = \frac{D_y}{D} \qquad z = \frac{D_z}{D}$$

The determinant D is the determinant of the coefficient matrix. The determinants D_x, D_y, and D_z are the determinants of the matrices formed by replacing the first, second, and third columns, respectively, by the constants. For System (1),

$$x = \frac{D_x}{D} \qquad y = \frac{D_y}{D} \qquad z = \frac{D_z}{D}$$

where
$$D = \begin{vmatrix} 2 & -3 & 1 \\ 4 & 0 & 2 \\ 3 & 1 & -2 \end{vmatrix} = -42 \qquad D_x = \begin{vmatrix} 2 & -3 & 1 \\ -3 & 0 & 2 \\ 1 & 1 & -2 \end{vmatrix} = 5$$

$$D_y = \begin{vmatrix} 2 & 2 & 1 \\ 4 & -3 & 2 \\ 3 & 1 & -2 \end{vmatrix} = 49 \qquad D_z = \begin{vmatrix} 2 & -3 & 2 \\ 4 & 0 & -3 \\ 3 & 1 & 1 \end{vmatrix} = 53$$

Thus

$$x = -\frac{5}{42} \qquad y = -\frac{7}{6} \qquad z = -\frac{53}{42}$$

The solution of System (1) is

$$\left(-\frac{5}{42}, -\frac{7}{6}, -\frac{53}{42}\right)$$

Cramer's Rule can be extended to a system of n linear equations in n variables.

INSTRUCTOR NOTE

Ask students what can be said about the solution of a system of equations if the determinant of the coefficient matrix is zero.

[Answer: The system does not have a unique solution. The system might have no solution or might have infinitely many solutions.]

Cramer's Rule

Let

$$\begin{cases} a_{11}x_1 + a_{12}x_2 + a_{13}x_3 + \cdots + a_{1n}x_n = b_1 \\ a_{21}x_1 + a_{22}x_2 + a_{23}x_3 + \cdots + a_{2n}x_n = b_2 \\ a_{31}x_1 + a_{32}x_2 + a_{33}x_3 + \cdots + a_{3n}x_n = b_3 \\ \quad \vdots \qquad \vdots \qquad \vdots \qquad\qquad \vdots \qquad \vdots \\ a_{n1}x_1 + a_{n2}x_2 + a_{n3}x_3 + \cdots + a_{nn}x_n = b_n \end{cases}$$

be a system of n equations in n variables. The solution of the system is given by $(x_1, x_2, x_3, \ldots, x_n)$, where

$$x_1 = \frac{D_1}{D} \qquad x_2 = \frac{D_2}{D} \qquad \cdots \qquad x_i = \frac{D_i}{D} \qquad \cdots \qquad x_n = \frac{D_n}{D}$$

and D is the determinant of the coefficient matrix, $D \neq 0$. D_i is the determinant formed by replacing the ith column of the coefficient matrix with the column of constants $b_1, b_2, b_3, \ldots, b_n$.

Because the determinant of the coefficient matrix must be nonzero for us to use Cramer's Rule, this method is not appropriate for systems of linear equations with no solution or infinitely many solutions. In fact, the only time a system of linear equations has a unique solution is when the coefficient determinant is not zero, a fact summarized in the following theorem.

Systems of Linear Equations with Unique Solutions

A system of n linear equations in n variables has a unique solution if and only if the determinant of the coefficient matrix is not zero.

Cramer's Rule is also useful when we want to determine the value of only a single variable in a system of equations.

Alternative to Example 2

Find y for the system of equations.

$$\begin{cases} 3x + 4y - 5z = 10 \\ 2x - 3y + 2z = 12 \\ 4x + 5y - 2z = 16 \end{cases}$$

● $y = -\dfrac{16}{37}$

EXAMPLE 2   Determine the Value of a Single Variable in a System of Linear Equations

Find x_3 for the system of equations

$$\begin{cases} 4x_1 \qquad + 3x_3 - 2x_4 = \quad 2 \\ 3x_1 + x_2 + 2x_3 - x_4 = \quad 4 \\ x_1 - 6x_2 - 2x_3 + 2x_4 = \quad 0 \\ 2x_1 + 2x_2 \qquad - x_4 = -1 \end{cases}$$

Solution

Find D and D_3.

$$D = \begin{vmatrix} 4 & 0 & 3 & -2 \\ 3 & 1 & 2 & -1 \\ 1 & -6 & -2 & 2 \\ 2 & 2 & 0 & -1 \end{vmatrix} = 39 \qquad D_3 = \begin{vmatrix} 4 & 0 & 2 & -2 \\ 3 & 1 & 4 & -1 \\ 1 & -6 & 0 & 2 \\ 2 & 2 & -1 & -1 \end{vmatrix} = 96$$

Thus $x_3 = \dfrac{96}{39} = \dfrac{32}{13}$.

▶ **TRY EXERCISE 24, PAGE 628**

TOPICS FOR DISCUSSION

1. Discuss the advantages and disadvantages of using Cramer's Rule to solve a system of equations.

2. Can Cramer's Rule be used to solve any system of linear equations? If not, explain when Cramer's Rule will lead to a solution and when it will not.

EXERCISE SET 7.5

—Suggested Assignment: Exercises 1–29, every other odd.
—Answers to Exercises 11–20 are on page AA34.

In Exercises 1 to 20, solve each system of equations by using Cramer's Rule.

1. $\begin{cases} 3x_1 + 4x_2 = 8 \\ 4x_1 - 5x_2 = 1 \end{cases}$ $x_1 = \dfrac{44}{31}, x_2 = \dfrac{29}{31}$

2. $\begin{cases} x_1 - 3x_2 = \quad 9 \\ 2x_1 - 4x_2 = -3 \end{cases}$ $x_1 = -\dfrac{45}{2}; x_2 = -\dfrac{21}{2}$

3. $\begin{cases} 5x_1 + 4x_2 = -1 \\ 3x_1 - 6x_2 = \quad 5 \end{cases}$ $x_1 = \dfrac{1}{3}, x_2 = -\dfrac{2}{3}$

▶ $\begin{cases} 2x_1 + 5x_2 = 9 \\ 5x_1 + 7x_2 = 8 \end{cases}$ $x_1 = -\dfrac{23}{11}, x_2 = \dfrac{29}{11}$

5. $\begin{cases} 7x_1 + 2x_2 = \quad 0 \\ 2x_1 + x_2 = -3 \end{cases}$ $x_1 = 2, x_2 = -7$

6. $\begin{cases} 3x_1 - 8x_2 = \quad 1 \\ 4x_1 + 5x_2 = -2 \end{cases}$ $x_1 = -\dfrac{11}{47}, x_2 = -\dfrac{10}{47}$

7. $\begin{cases} 3x_1 - 7x_2 = 0 \\ 2x_1 + 4x_2 = 0 \end{cases}$ $x_1 = 0, x_2 = 0$

8. $\begin{cases} 5x_1 + 4x_2 = -3 \\ 2x_1 - x_2 = \quad 0 \end{cases}$ $x_1 = -\dfrac{3}{13}, x_2 = -\dfrac{6}{13}$

9. $\begin{cases} 1.2x_1 + 0.3x_2 = \quad 2.1 \\ 0.8x_1 - 1.4x_2 = -1.6 \end{cases}$ $x_1 = 1.28125, x_2 = 1.875$

10. $\begin{cases} 3.2x_1 - 4.2x_2 = \quad 1.1 \\ 0.7x_1 + 3.2x_2 = -3.4 \end{cases}$ $x_1 \approx -0.82, x_2 \approx -0.88$

11. $\begin{cases} 3x_1 - 4x_2 + 2x_3 = \quad 1 \\ x_1 - x_2 + 2x_3 = -2 \\ 2x_1 + 2x_2 + 3x_3 = -3 \end{cases}$

12. $\begin{cases} 5x_1 - 2x_2 + 3x_3 = -2 \\ 3x_1 + x_2 - 2x_3 = \quad 3 \\ x_1 - 2x_2 + 3x_3 = -1 \end{cases}$

13. $\begin{cases} x_1 + 4x_2 - 2x_3 = \quad 0 \\ 3x_1 - 2x_2 + 3x_3 = \quad 4 \\ 2x_1 + x_2 - 3x_3 = -1 \end{cases}$

14. $\begin{cases} 4x_1 - x_2 + 2x_3 = \quad 6 \\ x_1 + 3x_2 - x_3 = -1 \\ 2x_1 + 3x_2 - 2x_3 = \quad 5 \end{cases}$

15. $\begin{cases} 2x_2 - 3x_3 = \quad 1 \\ 3x_1 - 5x_2 + x_3 = \quad 0 \\ 4x_1 + 2x_3 = -3 \end{cases}$

16. $\begin{cases} 2x_1 + 5x_2 \qquad = \quad 1 \\ x_1 \qquad - 3x_3 = -2 \\ 2x_1 - x_2 + 2x_3 = \quad 4 \end{cases}$

17. $\begin{cases} 4x_1 - 5x_2 + x_3 = -2 \\ 3x_1 + x_2 \qquad\quad = 4 \\ x_1 - x_2 + 3x_3 = 0 \end{cases}$

18. $\begin{cases} 3x_1 - x_2 + x_3 = 5 \\ x_1 \qquad + 3x_3 = -2 \\ 2x_1 + 2x_2 - 5x_3 = 0 \end{cases}$

23. Solve for x_1: $\begin{cases} x_1 - 3x_2 + 2x_3 + 4x_4 = 0 \\ 3x_1 + 5x_2 - 6x_3 + 2x_4 = -2 \\ 2x_1 - x_2 + 9x_3 + 8x_4 = 0 \\ x_1 + x_2 + x_3 - 8x_4 = -3 \end{cases}$ $x_1 = -\dfrac{121}{131}$

19. $\begin{cases} 2x_1 + 2x_2 - 3x_3 = 0 \\ x_1 - 3x_2 + 2x_3 = 0 \\ 4x_1 - x_2 + 3x_3 = 0 \end{cases}$

20. $\begin{cases} x_1 + 3x_2 \qquad\quad = -2 \\ 2x_1 - 3x_2 + x_3 = 1 \\ 4x_1 + 5x_2 - 2x_3 = 0 \end{cases}$

▶ **24.** Solve for x_3: $\begin{cases} 2x_1 + 5x_2 - 5x_3 - 3x_4 = -3 \\ x_1 + 7x_2 + 8x_3 - x_4 = 4 \\ 4x_1 \qquad + x_3 + x_4 = 3 \\ 3x_1 + 2x_2 - x_3 \qquad = 0 \end{cases}$ $x_3 = \dfrac{157}{168}$

In Exercises 21 to 26, solve for the indicated variable.

21. Solve for x_2: $\begin{cases} 2x_1 - 3x_2 + 4x_3 - x_4 = 1 \\ x_1 + 2x_2 \qquad + 2x_4 = -1 \\ 3x_1 + x_2 \qquad - 2x_4 = 2 \\ x_1 - 3x_2 + 2x_3 - x_4 = 3 \end{cases}$ $x_2 = -\dfrac{35}{19}$

25. Solve for x_4: $\begin{cases} 3x_2 - x_3 + 2x_4 = 1 \\ 5x_1 + x_2 + 3x_3 - x_4 = -4 \\ x_1 - 2x_2 \qquad + 9x_4 = 5 \\ 2x_1 \qquad + 2x_3 \qquad = 3 \end{cases}$ $x_4 = \dfrac{4}{3}$

22. Solve for x_4: $\begin{cases} 3x_1 + x_2 - 2x_3 + 3x_4 = 4 \\ 2x_1 - 3x_2 + 2x_3 \qquad = -2 \\ x_1 + x_2 - 2x_3 + 2x_4 = 3 \\ 2x_1 \qquad + 3x_3 - 2x_4 = 4 \end{cases}$ $x_4 = -17$

26. Solve for x_1: $\begin{cases} 4x_1 + x_2 \qquad - 3x_4 = 4 \\ 5x_1 + 2x_2 - 2x_3 + x_4 = 7 \\ x_1 - 3x_2 + 2x_3 - 2x_4 = -6 \\ 3x_3 + 4x_4 = -7 \end{cases}$ $x_1 = \dfrac{77}{254}$

CONNECTING CONCEPTS

27. A solution of the system of equations
$\begin{cases} 2x_1 - 3x_2 + x_3 = 9 \\ x_1 + x_2 - 2x_3 = -3 \\ 4x_1 - x_2 - 3x_3 = 3 \end{cases}$ The determinant of the coefficient matrix is zero, so Cramer's Rule cannot be used. The system of equations has infinitely many solutions.

is $(1, -2, 1)$. However, this solution cannot be found by using Cramer's Rule. Explain.

28. Verify the solution for x_2 given in Cramer's Rule for a System of Two Equations by solving the system of equations
$\begin{cases} a_{11}x_1 + a_{12}x_2 = b_1 \\ a_{21}x_1 + a_{22}x_2 = b_2 \end{cases}$ $x_2 = \dfrac{\begin{vmatrix} a_{11} & b_1 \\ a_{21} & b_2 \end{vmatrix}}{\begin{vmatrix} a_{11} & a_{12} \\ a_{21} & a_{22} \end{vmatrix}}$

for x_2 by using the elimination method.

29. For what values of k does the system of equations
$\begin{cases} kx + 3y = 7 \\ kx - 2y = 5 \end{cases}$

have a unique solution? all values of k except $k = 0$

30. For what values of k does the system of equations
$\begin{cases} kx + 4y = 5 \\ 9x - ky = 2 \end{cases}$

have a unique solution? all real values of k

31. For what values of k does the system of equations
$\begin{cases} x + 2y - 3z = 4 \\ 2x + ky - 4z = 5 \\ x - 2y + z = 6 \end{cases}$

have a unique solution? all values of k except $k = 2$

32. For what values of k does the system of equations
$\begin{cases} kx_1 + x_2 \qquad = 1 \\ x_2 - 4x_3 = 1 \\ x_1 \qquad + kx_3 = 1 \end{cases}$

have a unique solution? all values of k except $k = 2$ and $k = -2$

33. Find real values for r and s such that $ru + sv = w$, where u, v, and w are complex numbers and $u = 2 + 3i$, $v = 4 - 2i$, and $w = -6 + 15i$. $r = 3, s = -3$

34. Find real values for r and s such that $ru + sv = w$, where $u = 3 - 4i$, $v = 1 + 2i$, and $w = 4 - 22i$. $r = 3, s = -5$

PROJECTS

1. Prove Cramer's Rule for a system of three linear equations in three variables.

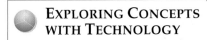

Stochastic Matrices

Matrices can be used to predict how percents of populations will change over time. Consider two neighborhood supermarkets, Super A and Super B. Each week Super A loses 5% of its customers to Super B, and each week Super B loses 8% of its customers to Super A. If this trend continues and if Super A currently has 40% of the neighborhood customers and Super B the remaining 60% of the neighborhood customers, what percent of the neighborhood customers will each have after n weeks?

We will approach this problem by examining the changes on a week-by-week basis. Because Super A loses 5% of its customers each week, it retains 95% of its customers. It has 40% of the neighborhood customers now, so after 1 week it will have 95% of its 40% share, or 38% ($0.95 \cdot 0.40$) of the customers. In that same week, it gains 8% of the customers of Super B. Because Super B has 60% of the neighborhood customers, Super A's gain is 4.8% ($0.08 \cdot 0.60$). After 1 week, Super A has 38% + 4.8% = 42.8% of the neighborhood customers. Super B has the remaining 57.2% of the customers.

The changes for the second week are calculated similarly. Super A retains 95% of its 42.8% and gains 8% of Super B's 57.2%. After week 2, Super A has

$$0.95 \cdot 0.428 + 0.08 \cdot 0.572 \approx 0.452$$

or approximately 45.2%, of the neighborhood customers. Super B has the remaining 54.8%.

We could continue in this way, but using matrices is a more convenient way to proceed. Let $T = \begin{bmatrix} 0.95 & 0.05 \\ 0.08 & 0.92 \end{bmatrix}$ where column 1 represents the percent retained by Super A and column 2 represents the percent retained by Super B. Let $X = [0.40 \quad 0.60]$ be the current market shares of Super A and Super B, respectively. Now form the product XT.

$$[0.40 \quad 0.60]\begin{bmatrix} 0.95 & 0.05 \\ 0.08 & 0.92 \end{bmatrix} = [0.428 \quad 0.572]$$

For the second week, multiply the market share after week 1 by T.

$$[0.428 \quad 0.572]\begin{bmatrix} 0.95 & 0.05 \\ 0.08 & 0.92 \end{bmatrix} \approx [0.452 \quad 0.548]$$

The last product can also be expressed as

$$\overbrace{[0.428 \quad 0.572]}$$
$$[0.452 \quad 0.548] = [0.428 \quad 0.572]\begin{bmatrix} 0.95 & 0.05 \\ 0.08 & 0.92 \end{bmatrix} = [0.40 \quad 0.60]\begin{bmatrix} 0.95 & 0.05 \\ 0.08 & 0.92 \end{bmatrix}\begin{bmatrix} 0.95 & 0.05 \\ 0.08 & 0.92 \end{bmatrix}$$
$$= [0.40 \quad 0.60]\begin{bmatrix} 0.95 & 0.05 \\ 0.08 & 0.92 \end{bmatrix}^2 = XT^2$$

Note that the exponent on T corresponds to the fact that 2 weeks have passed. In general, the market share after n weeks is XT^n. The matrix T is called a **stochastic matrix**. A stochastic matrix is characterized by the fact that each element of the matrix is nonnegative and the sum of the elements in each row is 1.

Use a calculator to calculate the market share of Super A and Super B after 20 weeks, 40 weeks, 60 weeks, and 100 weeks. What observations do you draw from your calculations? We started this problem with the assumption that Super A had 40% of the market and Super B had 60% of the market. Suppose, however, that originally Super A had 99% of the market and Super B had 1%. Does this affect the market share each will have after 100 weeks? If Super A had 1% of the market and Super B had 99% of the market, what will the market share of each be after 100 weeks?

As another example, suppose each of three department stores is vying for the business of the other two stores. In one month, Store A loses 15% of its customers to Store B and 8% of its customers to Store C. Store B loses 10% of its customers to Store A and 12% to Store C. Store C loses 5% to Store A and 9% to Store B. Assuming these three stores have 100% of the market and the trend continues, determine what market share each will have after 100 months.

CHAPTER 7 SUMMARY

7.1 Gaussian Elimination Method

• A matrix is a rectangular array of numbers. A matrix with m rows and n columns is of order $m \times n$ or dimension $m \times n$.

• For a system of equations, it is possible to form a coefficient matrix, an augmented matrix, and a constant matrix.

• A matrix is in row echelon form if all of the following conditions are satisfied:

  1. The first nonzero element in any row is a 1.

  2. Rows are arranged so that the column containing the first nonzero number is to the left of the column containing the first nonzero number of the next row.

  3. All rows consisting entirely of zeros appear at the bottom of the matrix.

• The Gaussian elimination method uses elementary row operations to solve a system of linear equations.

• **Elementary Row Operations**
  The elementary row operations for a matrix are:

  1. Interchanging two rows

  2. Multiplying all the elements in a row by the same nonzero number

  3. Replacing a row by the sum of that row and a nonzero multiple of any other row

• **Interpolating Polynomial**
  Let (x_0, y_0), (x_1, y_1), (x_2, y_2), ..., (x_n, y_n) be the coordinates of a set of points for which all the x_i are distinct. Then the interpolating polynomial is a unique polynomial of degree at most n that passes through the given points.

7.2 The Algebra of Matrices

• Two matrices $A = [a_{ij}]$ and $B = [b_{ij}]$ are equal if and only if $a_{ij} = b_{ij}$ for every i and j.

• The sum of two matrices of the same order is the matrix whose elements are the sums of the corresponding elements of the two matrices.

• The $m \times n$ zero matrix is the matrix whose elements are all zeros.

• Taking the product of a real number and a matrix is called scalar multiplication.

• In order for us to multiply two matrices, the number of columns of the first matrix must equal the number of rows of the second matrix.

• In general, matrix multiplication is not commutative.

• The multiplicative identity matrix is the matrix with 1s on the main diagonal and zeros everywhere else.

7.3 The Inverse of a Matrix

• The multiplicative inverse of a square matrix A, denoted by A^{-1}, has the property that

$$A \cdot A^{-1} = A^{-1} \cdot A = I_n$$

where I_n is the multiplicative identity matrix.

• A singular matrix is one that does not have a multiplicative inverse.

• Input-output analysis attempts to determine the necessary output of industries to satisfy each other's demands plus the demands of consumers.

7.4 Determinants

- Associated with each square matrix is a number called the determinant of the matrix.

- The minor of the element a_{ij} of a square matrix A is the determinant of the matrix obtained by deleting the ith row and the jth column of A.

- The cofactor of the element a_{ij} of a square matrix A is $(-1)^{i+j}M_{ij}$, where M_{ij} is the minor of a_{ij}.

- The value of a determinant can be found by multiplying the elements of any row or column by their respective cofactors and then adding the results. This is called expanding by cofactors.

7.5 Cramer's Rule

- Cramer's Rule is a method of solving a system of n equations in n variables by using determinants.

CHAPTER 7 TRUE/FALSE EXERCISES

In Exercises 1 to 15, answer true or false. If the statement is false, give an example to show that the statement is false.

1. If $A = \begin{bmatrix} 2 & 3 \\ 1 & 4 \end{bmatrix}$, then $A^2 = \begin{bmatrix} 4 & 9 \\ 1 & 16 \end{bmatrix}$.
   False; $A^2 = A \cdot A = \begin{bmatrix} 7 & 18 \\ 6 & 19 \end{bmatrix}$.

2. Every matrix has an additive inverse.
   True

3. Every square matrix has a multiplicative inverse.
   False; a singular matrix does not have a multiplicative inverse.

4. Let the matrices A, B, and C be square matrices of order n. If $AB = AC$, then $B = C$.
   Answer on page AA34.

5. It is possible to find the determinant of every square matrix. True

6. If A and B are square matrices of order n, then
   $$\det(A + B) = \det(A) + \det(B)$$
   Answer on page AA34.

7. Cramer's Rule can be used to solve any system of three equations in three variables. False; if the determinant of the coefficient matrix is zero, Cramer's Rule cannot be used to solve the system of equations.

8. If A and B are matrices of order n, then $AB - BA = O$.
   False; matrix multiplication is not commutative—that is, $AB \neq BA$, $AB - BA \neq 0$.

9. A nonsingular matrix has a multiplicative inverse. True

10. If A, B, and C are square matrices of order n, then the product ABC depends on which two matrices are multiplied first. That is, $(AB)C$ produces a different result from $A(BC)$. False; by the Associative Property of Matrix Multiplication, given square matrices A, B, and C of order n, $(AB)C = A(BC)$.

11. The Gaussian elimination method for solving a system of linear equations can be applied only to systems of equations that have the same number of variables as equations.
    Answer on page AA34.

12. If A is a square matrix of order n, then $\det(2A) = 2\det(A)$.
    Answer on page AA34.

13. If A and B are matrices, then the product AB is defined when the number of columns of A equals the number of rows of B. True

14. If A and B are square matrices of order n and $AB = O$ (the zero matrix), then $A = O$ or $B = O$.
    Answer on page AA34.

15. If $A = \begin{bmatrix} 3 & 6 \\ -1 & -2 \end{bmatrix}$, then $A^5 = A$. True

CHAPTER 7 REVIEW EXERCISES

—Answers to Exercises 1–18, 37–46, 48, and 61–66 are on page AA34.

In Exercises 1 to 18, perform the indicated operations. Let

$$A = \begin{bmatrix} 2 & -1 & 3 \\ 3 & 2 & -1 \end{bmatrix}, B = \begin{bmatrix} 0 & -2 \\ 4 & 2 \\ 1 & -3 \end{bmatrix}, C = \begin{bmatrix} 2 & 6 & 1 \\ 1 & 2 & -1 \\ 2 & 4 & -1 \end{bmatrix}, \text{and}$$

$$D = \begin{bmatrix} -3 & 4 & 2 \\ 4 & -2 & 5 \end{bmatrix}.$$

1. $3A$

2. $-2B$

3. $-A + D$

4. $2A - 3D$

5. AB

6. DB

7. BA

8. BD

9. C^2

10. C^3

11. BAC

12. ADB

13. $AB - BA$

14. $DB - BD$

15. $(A - D)C$

16. $AC - DC$

17. C^{-1}

18. $|C|$

In Exercises 19 to 34, solve the system of equations by using the Gaussian elimination method.

19. $\begin{cases} 2x - 3y = 7 \\ 3x - 4y = 10 \end{cases}$ $(2, -1)$ [7.1]

20. $\begin{cases} 3x + 4y = -9 \\ 2x + 3y = -7 \end{cases}$ $(1, -3)$ [7.1]

21. $\begin{cases} 4x - 5y = 12 \\ 3x + y = 9 \end{cases}$ $(3, 0)$ [7.1]

22. $\begin{cases} 2x - 5y = 10 \\ 5x + 2y = 4 \end{cases}$ $\left(\dfrac{40}{29}, -\dfrac{42}{29} \right)$ [7.1]

23. $\begin{cases} x + 2y + 3z = 5 \\ 3x + 8y + 11z = 17 \\ 2x + 6y + 7z = 12 \end{cases}$ $(3, 1, 0)$ [7.1]

24. $\begin{cases} x - y + 3z = 10 \\ 2x - y + 7z = 24 \\ 3x - 6y + 7z = 21 \end{cases}$ $(2, 1, 3)$ [7.1]

25. $\begin{cases} 2x - y - z = 4 \\ x - 2y - 2z = 5 \\ 3x - 3y - 8z = 19 \end{cases}$ $(1, 0, -2)$ [7.1]

26. $\begin{cases} 3x - 7y + 8z = 10 \\ x - 3y + 2z = 0 \\ 2x - 8y + 7z = 5 \end{cases}$ $(0, 2, 3)$ [7.1]

27. $\begin{cases} 4x - 9y + 6z = 54 \\ 3x - 8y + 8z = 49 \\ x - 3y + 2z = 17 \end{cases}$ $(3, -4, 1)$ [7.1]

28. $\begin{cases} 3x + 8y - 5z = 6 \\ 2x + 9y - z = -8 \\ x - 4y - 2z = 16 \end{cases}$ $(4, -2, -2)$ [7.1]

29. $\begin{cases} x + y + 2z = -5 \\ 2x + 3y + 5z = -13 \\ 2x + 5y + 7z = -19 \end{cases}$ $(-c - 2, -c - 3, c)$ [7.1]

30. $\begin{cases} x - 2y + 3z = 9 \\ 3x - 5y + 8z = 25 \\ x - z = 5 \end{cases}$ $(5, -2, 0)$ [7.1]

31. $\begin{cases} w + 2x - y + 2z = 1 \\ 3w + 8x + y + 4z = 1 \\ 2w + 7x + 3y + 2z = 0 \\ w + 3x - 2y + 5z = 6 \end{cases}$ $(1, -2, 2, 3)$ [7.1]

32. $\begin{cases} w - 3x - 2y + z = -1 \\ 2w - 5x + 3z = 1 \\ 3w - 7x + 3y = -18 \\ 2w - 3x - 5y - 2z = -8 \end{cases}$ $(2, 3, -1, 4)$ [7.1]

33. $\begin{cases} w + 3x + y - 4z = 3 \\ w + 4x + 3y - 6z = 5 \\ 2w + 8x + 7y - 5z = 11 \\ 2w + 5x - 6z = 4 \end{cases}$ $(-37c + 2, 16c, -7c + 1, c)$ [7.1]

34. $\begin{cases} w + 4x - 2y + 3z = 6 \\ 2w + 9x - y + 5z = 13 \\ w + 7x + 6y + 5z = 9 \\ 3w + 14x + 7z = 20 \end{cases}$ $(63c + 2, -14c + 1, 5c, c)$ [7.1]

35. INTERPOLATING POLYNOMIAL Find a polynomial that passes through the points whose coordinates are $(-1, -4)$, $(2, 8)$, and $(3, 16)$. $y = x^2 + 3x - 2$ [7.1]

36. INTERPOLATING POLYNOMIAL Find a polynomial that passes through the points whose coordinates are $(-1, 4)$, $(1, 0)$, and $(2, -5)$. $y = -x^2 - 2x + 3$ [7.1]

In Exercises 37 to 48, find the inverse, if it exists, of the given matrix.

37. $\begin{bmatrix} 2 & -2 \\ 3 & -2 \end{bmatrix}$

38. $\begin{bmatrix} 3 & 4 \\ 2 & 3 \end{bmatrix}$

39. $\begin{bmatrix} -2 & 3 \\ 2 & 4 \end{bmatrix}$

40. $\begin{bmatrix} 5 & -4 \\ 3 & 2 \end{bmatrix}$

41. $\begin{bmatrix} 1 & 2 & 1 \\ 2 & 6 & 4 \\ 3 & 8 & 6 \end{bmatrix}$

42. $\begin{bmatrix} 1 & -3 & 2 \\ 3 & -8 & 7 \\ 2 & -3 & 6 \end{bmatrix}$

43. $\begin{bmatrix} 3 & -2 & 7 \\ 2 & -1 & 5 \\ 3 & 0 & 10 \end{bmatrix}$

44. $\begin{bmatrix} 4 & 9 & -11 \\ 3 & 7 & -8 \\ 2 & 6 & -3 \end{bmatrix}$

45. $\begin{bmatrix} 1 & -1 & 2 & 3 \\ 2 & -1 & 6 & 5 \\ 3 & -1 & 9 & 6 \\ 2 & -2 & 4 & 7 \end{bmatrix}$

46. $\begin{bmatrix} 1 & 2 & -2 & 1 \\ 3 & 7 & -3 & 1 \\ 2 & 7 & 4 & 3 \\ 1 & 4 & 2 & 4 \end{bmatrix}$

47. $\begin{bmatrix} 3 & 7 & -1 & 8 \\ 2 & 5 & 0 & 5 \\ 3 & 6 & -4 & 8 \\ 2 & 4 & -4 & 4 \end{bmatrix}$ The matrix does not have an inverse. [7.3]

48. $\begin{bmatrix} 3 & 1 & 5 & -5 \\ 2 & 1 & 4 & -3 \\ 3 & 0 & 4 & -3 \\ 4 & 1 & 8 & 1 \end{bmatrix}$

In Exercises 49 to 52, solve the given system of equations for each set of constants. Use the inverse matrix method.

49. $\begin{cases} 3x + 4y = b_1 \\ 2x + 3y = b_2 \end{cases}$

  a. $b_1 = 2, b_2 = -3$
    $(18, -13)$

  b. $b_1 = -2, b_2 = 4$
    $(-22, 16)$ [7.3]

50. $\begin{cases} 2x - 5y = b_1 \\ 3x - 7y = b_2 \end{cases}$

  a. $b_1 = -3, b_2 = 4$
    $(41, 17)$

  b. $b_1 = 2, b_2 = -5$
    $(-39, -16)$ [7.3]

51. $\begin{cases} 2x + y - z = b_1 \\ 4x + 4y + z = b_2 \\ 2x + 2y - 3z = b_3 \end{cases}$

  a. $b_1 = -1, b_2 = 2, b_3 = 4$ $\left(-\dfrac{18}{7}, \dfrac{23}{7}, -\dfrac{6}{7} \right)$

  b. $b_1 = -2, b_2 = 3, b_3 = 0$ $\left(-\dfrac{31}{14}, \dfrac{20}{7}, \dfrac{3}{7} \right)$ [7.3]

52. $\begin{cases} 3x - 2y + z = b_1 \\ 3x - y + 3z = b_2 \\ 6x - 4y + z = b_3 \end{cases}$

  a. $b_1 = 0, b_2 = 3, b_3 = -2$ $\left(-\dfrac{4}{3}, -1, 2 \right)$

  b. $b_1 = 1, b_2 = 2, b_3 = -4$ $(-9, -11, 6)$ [7.3]

In Exercises 53 to 60, evaluate each determinant by using elementary row or column operations.

53. $\begin{vmatrix} 2 & 6 & 4 \\ 1 & 2 & 1 \\ 3 & 8 & 6 \end{vmatrix}$ -2 [7.4]

54. $\begin{vmatrix} 3 & 0 & 10 \\ 3 & -2 & 7 \\ 2 & -1 & 5 \end{vmatrix}$ 1 [7.4]

55. $\begin{vmatrix} 3 & -8 & 7 \\ 2 & -3 & 6 \\ 1 & -3 & 2 \end{vmatrix}$ −1 [7.4]

56. $\begin{vmatrix} 4 & 9 & -11 \\ 2 & 6 & -3 \\ 3 & 7 & -8 \end{vmatrix}$ −1 [7.4]

57. $\begin{vmatrix} 1 & -1 & 2 & 1 \\ 2 & -1 & 6 & 3 \\ 3 & -1 & 8 & 7 \\ 3 & 0 & 9 & 9 \end{vmatrix}$ 0 [7.4]

58. $\begin{vmatrix} 1 & 2 & -2 & 3 \\ 3 & 7 & -3 & 11 \\ 2 & 3 & -5 & 11 \\ 2 & 6 & 1 & 8 \end{vmatrix}$ 3 [7.4]

59. $\begin{vmatrix} 1 & 2 & -2 & 1 \\ 2 & 5 & -3 & 1 \\ 2 & 0 & -10 & 1 \\ 3 & 8 & -4 & 1 \end{vmatrix}$ 0 [7.4]

60. $\begin{vmatrix} 1 & 3 & -2 & 0 \\ 3 & 11 & -4 & 4 \\ 2 & 9 & -8 & 2 \\ 3 & 12 & -10 & 2 \end{vmatrix}$ 0 [7.4]

In Exercises 61 to 66, solve each system of equations by using Cramer's Rule.

61. $\begin{cases} 2x_1 - 3x_2 = 2 \\ 3x_1 + 5x_2 = 2 \end{cases}$

62. $\begin{cases} 3x_1 + 4x_2 = -3 \\ 5x_1 - 2x_2 = 2 \end{cases}$

63. $\begin{cases} 2x_1 + x_2 - 3x_3 = 2 \\ 3x_1 + 2x_2 + x_3 = 1 \\ x_1 - 3x_2 + 4x_3 = -2 \end{cases}$

64. $\begin{cases} 3x_1 + 2x_2 - x_3 = 0 \\ x_1 + 3x_2 - 2x_3 = 3 \\ 4x_1 - x_2 - 5x_3 = -1 \end{cases}$

65. $\begin{cases} 2x_2 + 5x_3 = 2 \\ 2x_1 - 5x_2 + x_3 = 4 \\ 4x_1 + 3x_2 = 2 \end{cases}$

66. $\begin{cases} 2x_1 - 3x_2 - 4x_3 = 2 \\ x_1 - 2x_2 + 2x_3 = -1 \\ 2x_1 + 7x_2 - x_3 = 2 \end{cases}$

In Exercises 67 and 68, use Cramer's Rule to solve for the indicated variable.

67. Solve for x_3: $\begin{cases} x_1 - 3x_2 + x_3 + 2x_4 = 3 \\ 2x_1 + 7x_2 - 3x_3 + x_4 = 2 \\ -x_1 + 4x_2 + 2x_3 - 3x_4 = -1 \\ 3x_1 + x_2 - x_3 - 2x_4 = 0 \end{cases}$ $x_3 = \dfrac{115}{126}$ [7.5]

68. Solve for x_2: $\begin{cases} 2x_1 + 3x_2 - 2x_3 + x_4 = -2 \\ x_1 - x_2 - 3x_3 + 2x_4 = 2 \\ 3x_1 + 3x_2 - 4x_3 - x_4 = 4 \\ 5x_1 - 5x_2 - x_3 + 2x_4 = 7 \end{cases}$ $x_2 = -\dfrac{289}{230}$ [7.5]

In Exercises 69 and 70, solve the input-output problem.

69. BUSINESS RESOURCE ALLOCATION An electronics conglomerate has three divisions, which produce computers, monitors, and disk drives. For each $1 worth of output, the computer division needs $.05 worth of computers, $.02 worth of monitors, and $.03 worth of disk drives. For each $1 worth of output, the monitor division needs $.06 worth of computers, $.04 worth of monitors, and $.03 worth of disk drives. For each $1 worth of output, the disk drive division requires $.08 worth of computers, $.04 worth of monitors, and $.05 worth of disk drives. Sales estimates are $30 million for the computer division, $12 million for the monitor division, and $21 million for the disk drive division. At what level should each division produce to satisfy this demand? $34.47 million computer division, $14.20 million monitor division, $23.64 million disk drive division [7.3]

70. BUSINESS RESOURCE ALLOCATION A manufacturing conglomerate has three divisions, which produce paper, lumber, and prefabricated walls. For each $1 worth of output, the lumber division needs $.07 worth of lumber, $.03 worth of paper, and $.03 worth of prefabricated walls. For each $1 worth of output, the paper division needs $.04 worth of lumber, $.07 worth of paper, and $.03 worth of prefabricated walls. For each $1 worth of output, the prefabricated walls division requires $.07 worth of lumber, $.04 worth of paper, and $.02 worth of prefabricated walls. Sales estimates are $27 million for the lumber division, $18 million for the paper division, and $10 million for the prefabricated walls division. At what level should each division produce to satisfy this demand? $30.82 million lumber division, $20.86 million paper division, $11.79 million prefabricated walls division [7.3]

CHAPTER 7 TEST —Answers for Exercises 1–2 and 6–15 are on pages AA34–AA35.

1. Write the augmented matrix, the coefficient matrix, and the constant matrix for the system of equations
$$\begin{cases} 2x + 3y - 3z = 4 \\ 3x + 2z = -1 \\ 4x - 4y + 2z = 3 \end{cases}$$

2. Write a system of equations that is equivalent to the augmented matrix $\begin{bmatrix} 3 & -2 & 5 & -1 & 9 \\ 2 & 3 & -1 & 4 & 8 \\ 1 & 0 & 3 & 2 & -1 \end{bmatrix}$.

In Exercises 3 to 5, solve the system of equations by using the Gaussian elimination method.

3. $\begin{cases} x - 2y + 3z = 10 \\ 2x - 3y + 8z = 23 \\ -x + 3y - 2z = -9 \end{cases}$ $(2, -1, 2)$ [7.1]

4. $\begin{cases} 2x + 6y - z = 1 \\ x + 3y - z = 1 \\ 3x + 10y - 2z = 1 \end{cases}$ $(3, -1, -1)$ [7.1]

5. $\begin{cases} w + 2x - 3y + 2z = 11 \\ 2w + 5x - 8y + 5z = 28 \\ -2w - 4x + 7y - z = -18 \end{cases}$ $(3c - 5, -7c + 14, 4 - 3c, c)$ [7.1]

In Exercises 6 to 18, let $A = \begin{bmatrix} -1 & 3 & 2 \\ 1 & 4 & -1 \end{bmatrix}$,

$B = \begin{bmatrix} 2 & -1 & 3 \\ 4 & -2 & -1 \\ 3 & 2 & 2 \end{bmatrix}$, and $C = \begin{bmatrix} 1 & -2 & 3 \\ 2 & -3 & 8 \\ -1 & 3 & -2 \end{bmatrix}$. Perform each possible operation. If an operation is not possible, so state.

6. $-3A$

7. $A + B$

8. $3B - 2C$

9. AB

10. $AB - A$

11. CA

12. $BC - CB$

13. A^2

14. B^2

15. C^{-1}

16. Find the minor and cofactor of b_{21} for matrix B.
$M_{21} = -8$, $C_{21} = 8$ [7.4]

17. Find the determinant of B by expanding by cofactors of row 3. 49 [7.4]

18. Find the determinant of C by using elementary row operations. -1 [7.4]

19. Find the value of z for the following system of equations by using Cramer's Rule. $-\dfrac{140}{41}$ [7.5]
$$\begin{cases} 3x + 2y - z = 12 \\ 2x - 3y + 2z = -1 \\ 5x + 6y + 3z = 4 \end{cases}$$

20. A simplified economy has three major industries: mining, manufacturing, and transportation. The input-output matrix for this economy is
$$\begin{bmatrix} 0.15 & 0.23 & 0.11 \\ 0.08 & 0.10 & 0.05 \\ 0.16 & 0.11 & 0.07 \end{bmatrix}$$
Set up, but do not solve, a matrix equation that, when solved, will determine the gross output needed to satisfy consumer demand for $50 million worth of mining, $32 million worth of manufacturing, and $8 million worth of transportation.
Answer on page AA35.

CUMULATIVE REVIEW EXERCISES

1. Find an equation in general form of the circle with center at $(-2, 4)$ and with a radius of 5.
$x^2 + y^2 + 4x - 8y - 5 = 0$ [2.1]

2. Factor: $24x^2 - 14x - 24$ $2(4x + 3)(3x - 4)$ [P.4]

3. Find the equation of the line that passes through the point $(-4, 5)$ and has a slope equal to $-\dfrac{1}{2}$. $y = -\dfrac{1}{2}x + 3$ [2.3]

4. Divide $2x^3 - 5x^2 - 13x + 30$ by $x - 3$. $2x^2 + x - 10$ [3.1]

5. Given that $h(x) = e^{-x}$ and $k(x) = 3^x$, find $h[k(0)]$. Round to the nearest ten-thousandth. 0.3679 [4.2]

6. Find the coordinates of the vertex of the parabola whose equation is $2x^2 - 4x + 3y - 1 = 0$. $(1, 1)$ [5.1]

7. Solve: $\begin{cases} 3x - 4y = 4 \\ 2x - 3y = 1 \end{cases}$ $(8, 5)$ [6.1]

8. Simplify $\dfrac{1 - i}{4 + i}$ and write the number in standard form. $\dfrac{3}{17} - \dfrac{5}{17}i$ [P.6]

9. Determine the domain of $F(x) = \sqrt{9 - x^2}$.
$\{x \mid -3 \le x \le 3\}$ [2.2]

10. Is the equation $xy - x^2 + y^2 = 0$ symmetric with respect to the origin? Yes [2.5]

11. Find all vertical asymptotes of the function $G(x) = \dfrac{x - 2}{x^2 + 4x - 5}$. $x = -5, x = 1$ [3.5]

12. Use the graph of $G(x) = |x + 2| - 3$ below to sketch the graph of $y = -G(-x)$. Answer on page AA35.

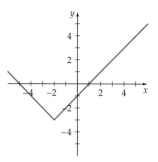

13. Solve $\dfrac{x + 2}{x + 1} > 0$. Express your answer in interval notation.
$(-\infty, -2) \cup (-1, \infty)$ [1.5]

14. Find the equation in standard form of the ellipse with center at $(3, -4)$, foci $F_1(-1, -4)$ and $F_2(7, -4)$, and major axis of length 12. $\dfrac{(x - 3)^2}{36} + \dfrac{(y + 4)^2}{20} = 1$ [5.2]

15. Solve: $\begin{cases} x - y + z = -1 \\ 2x + 3y - z = 1 \\ 3x - 2y + 3z = 12 \end{cases}$ $(-10, 15, 24)$ [6.2]

16. Find the difference quotient of $f(x) = x^2 - 3x + 2$.
$2x - 3 + h$ [2.6]

17. Solve: $125^x = \dfrac{1}{25}$. $-\dfrac{2}{3}$ [4.5]

18. Find the partial fraction decomposition of $\dfrac{x - 2}{x^2 - 5x - 6}$.
$\dfrac{4}{7(x - 6)} + \dfrac{3}{7(x + 1)}$ [6.4]

19. Solve $10^x - 10^{-x} = 2$. Round to the nearest ten-thousandth.
0.3828 [4.5]

20. A woman traveling by canoe can go downstream at 8 mph and upstream at 2 mph. If she starts paddling upstream and wishes to be away for exactly 4 hours for the round trip, how far should she travel upstream? 6.4 mi [6.1]

SEQUENCES, SERIES, AND PROBABILITY

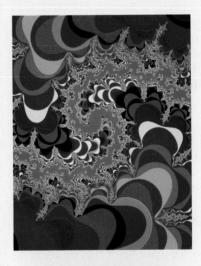

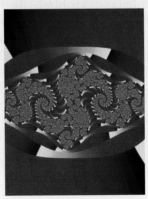

Fractals

One of the topics of this chapter is the concept of a *sequence*. The list of numbers $1, \frac{1}{2}, \frac{1}{3}, \frac{1}{4}, \frac{1}{5}, \ldots, \frac{1}{n}, \ldots$ is an example of a sequence. As the natural number n becomes very large, the numbers in the sequence become closer and closer to 0.

In addition to a sequence of numbers, we could have, for instance, a sequence of functions or a sequence of geometric figures. Although each of these sequences has important applications, we will focus here on a sequence of geometric figures.

Look at the sequence of figures below. Each succeeding figure is created by constructing right triangles using the line segments in the preceding figure as the hypotenuses.

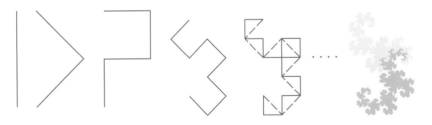

If this process is repeated over and over, the sequence of figures becomes like the last figure on the right, which is called a *fractal.* The computer-generated fractals at the left were created using a different procedure from that shown above. We will look at fractals again in **Project 1 of Section 8.3, page 662.**

VIDEO & DVD

SSG

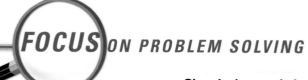

Simulation and the Monte Hall Problem

In the television game show "Let's Make a Deal," the grand prize was hidden behind one of three curtains. Behind each of the other two curtains was a less desirable prize. For instance, a box of candy might be behind one curtain and a goat behind the other.

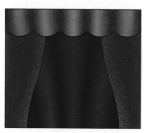 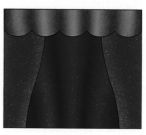 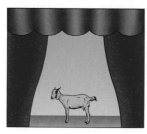

Curtain A   Curtain B   Curtain C

After a contestant chose a curtain, say, curtain *A*, the host, Monte Hall, would show the contestant one of the less desirable prizes behind one of the other two curtains. At this point the contestant could stay with her or his original choice of curtain or switch to the other unopened curtain.

Do you have a better chance of winning the grand prize by

- switching to the other closed curtain or

- staying with your original choice?

Of course there is also the possibility that it does not matter, if the chances of winning are the same with either strategy.

An analysis of the best strategy is based on calculating the probability of each alternative.

One way to decide the best strategy is to use a computer *simulation* and test each strategy. This simulation may give you some insight into a mathematical solution. One Internet site at which you can do simulations of this problem is http://www.shodor.org/interactivate/activities/monty/index.html. By selecting stay or switch and then clicking the Run Simulation button, you can see how many times you would win the grand prize by remaining with your original curtain and by switching. You may be surprised to learn that by switching, you double your chances of winning the grand prize.

An analytical solution of this problem is based on the principles of probability. For further examples of probability problems, see **Project 1 of Section 8.7, on page 694.**

INFINITE SEQUENCES AND SUMMATION NOTATION

• INFINITE SEQUENCES

The *ordered* list of numbers 2, 4, 8, 16, 32, ... is called an *infinite sequence*. The list is ordered simply because order makes a difference. The sequence 2, 8, 4, 16, 32, ... contains the same numbers but in a different order. Therefore, it is a different infinite sequence.

An infinite sequence can be thought of as a pairing between positive integers and real numbers. For example, 1, 4, 9, 16, 25, 36, ..., n^2, ... pairs a natural number with its square.

$$
\begin{array}{ccccccccc}
1 & 2 & 3 & 4 & 5 & 6 & \cdots & n & \cdots \\
\downarrow & \downarrow & \downarrow & \downarrow & \downarrow & \downarrow & & \downarrow & \\
1 & 4 & 9 & 16 & 25 & 36 & \cdots & n^2 & \cdots
\end{array}
$$

This pairing of numbers enables us to define an infinite sequence as a function whose domain is the positive integers.

Infinite Sequence

An **infinite sequence** is a function whose domain is the positive integers and whose range is a set of real numbers.

Although the positive integers do not include zero, it is occasionally convenient to include zero in the domain of an infinite sequence. Also, we will frequently use the word *sequence* instead of the phrase *infinite sequence*.

As an example of a sequence, let $f(n) = 2n - 1$. The range of this function is

$$
f(1), f(2), f(3), f(4), \ldots, \quad f(n), \quad \cdots
$$
$$
1, \quad 3, \quad 5, \quad 7, \quad \ldots, \quad 2n - 1, \quad \cdots
$$

The elements in the range of a sequence are called the **terms** of the sequence. For our example, the terms are 1, 3, 5, 7, ..., $2n - 1$, ... The **first term** of the sequence is 1, the **second term** is 3, and so on. The **nth term,** or the **general term,** is $2n - 1$.

❓ QUESTION What is the fifth term of the sequence $f(n) = 2n - 1$ given above?

Rather than use functional notation for sequences, it is customary to use a subscript notation. Thus a_n represents the nth term of a sequence. Using this notation, we would write

$$
a_n = 2n - 1
$$

Thus $a_1 = 1$, $a_2 = 3$, $a_3 = 5$, $a_4 = 7$, and so on.

❓ ANSWER $f(5) = 2(5) - 1 = 9$

Alternative to Example 1
a. Find the first three terms of the sequence.

$$a_n = \frac{n-1}{n+1}$$

◉ $0, \dfrac{1}{3}, \dfrac{1}{2}$

b. Find the fifth term of the sequence.

$$a_n = \frac{n}{2^n}$$

◉ $\dfrac{5}{32}$

INSTRUCTOR NOTE
A sequence that some students may find interesting is one by Euler for $\dfrac{2}{\pi}$. Find the fifth term of

$$a_n = \left(1 - \frac{1}{2^2}\right)\left(1 - \frac{1}{4^2}\right)\cdots\left(1 - \frac{1}{(2n)^2}\right)$$

and compare it to the calculator value of $\dfrac{2}{\pi}$. a_n approaches $\dfrac{2}{\pi}$ as n approaches infinity.

MATH MATTERS

Recursive subroutines are a part of many computer programming languages. One of the most influential people in the development of computer languages (especially COBOL) was Grace Murray Hooper. She was the first woman to receive a doctorate in mathematics from Yale University. She went on to become an admiral in the U.S. Navy.

EXAMPLE 1 **Find the Terms of a Sequence**

a. Find the first three terms of the sequence $a_n = \dfrac{1}{n(n+1)}$.

b. Find the eighth term of the sequence $a_n = \dfrac{2^n}{n^2}$.

Solution

a. $a_1 = \dfrac{1}{1(1+1)} = \dfrac{1}{2}, a_2 = \dfrac{1}{2(2+1)} = \dfrac{1}{6}, a_3 = \dfrac{1}{3(3+1)} = \dfrac{1}{12}$

b. $a_8 = \dfrac{2^8}{8^2} = \dfrac{256}{64} = 4$

▶ **TRY EXERCISE 6, PAGE 644**

An **alternating sequence** is one in which the signs of the terms *alternate* between positive and negative values. The sequence defined by $a_n = (-1)^{n+1} \cdot \dfrac{1}{n}$ is an alternating sequence.

$$a_1 = (-1)^{1+1} \cdot \frac{1}{1} = 1 \qquad a_2 = (-1)^{2+1} \cdot \frac{1}{2} = -\frac{1}{2} \qquad a_3 = (-1)^{3+1} \cdot \frac{1}{3} = \frac{1}{3}$$

The first six terms of the sequence are

$$1, -\frac{1}{2}, \frac{1}{3}, -\frac{1}{4}, \frac{1}{5}, -\frac{1}{6}$$

A **recursively defined sequence** is one in which each succeeding term of the sequence is defined by using some of the preceding terms. For example, let $a_1 = 1$, $a_2 = 1$, and $a_{n+1} = a_{n-1} + a_n$.

$$
\begin{array}{ll}
a_3 = a_1 + a_2 = 1 + 1 = 2 & \bullet \, n = 2 \\
a_4 = a_2 + a_3 = 1 + 2 = 3 & \bullet \, n = 3 \\
a_5 = a_3 + a_4 = 2 + 3 = 5 & \bullet \, n = 4 \\
a_6 = a_4 + a_5 = 3 + 5 = 8 & \bullet \, n = 5
\end{array}
$$

This recursive sequence 1, 1, 2, 3, 5, 8, ... is called the **Fibonacci sequence**, named after Leonardo Fibonacci (1180?–?1250), an Italian mathematician.

Alternative to Example 2
Let $a_1 = 2$ and $a_n = n^2 a_{n-1}$. Find a_2, a_3, and a_4.

◉ $a_2 = 8, a_3 = 72, a_4 = 1152$

EXAMPLE 2 **Find Terms of a Sequence Defined Recursively**

Let $a_1 = 1$ and $a_n = na_{n-1}$. Find a_2, a_3, and a_4.

Solution

$$a_2 = 2a_1 = 2 \cdot 1 = 2 \qquad a_3 = 3a_2 = 3 \cdot 2 = 6 \qquad a_4 = 4a_3 = 4 \cdot 6 = 24$$

▶ **TRY EXERCISE 28, PAGE 644**

● FACTORIALS

It is possible to find an nth term formula for the sequence defined recursively in Example 2 by

$$a_1 = 1 \qquad a_n = na_{n-1}$$

Consider the term a_5 of that sequence.

$$
\begin{aligned}
a_5 &= 5a_4 \\
&= 5 \cdot 4a_3 & \bullet\ a_4 = 4a_3 \\
&= 5 \cdot 4 \cdot 3a_2 & \bullet\ a_3 = 3a_2 \\
&= 5 \cdot 4 \cdot 3 \cdot 2a_1 & \bullet\ a_2 = 2a_1 \\
&= 5 \cdot 4 \cdot 3 \cdot 2 \cdot 1 & \bullet\ a_1 = 1
\end{aligned}
$$

Continuing in this manner for a_n, we have

$$
\begin{aligned}
a_n &= na_{n-1} \\
&= n(n-1)a_{n-2} \\
&= n(n-1)(n-2)a_{n-3} \\
&\ \ \vdots \\
&= n(n-1)(n-2)(n-3)\cdots 2 \cdot 1
\end{aligned}
$$

The number $n \cdot (n-1) \cdots 3 \cdot 2 \cdot 1$ is called **n factorial** and is written $n!$.

The Factorial of a Number

If n is a positive integer, then $n!$, which is read "n factorial," is

$$n! = n \cdot (n-1) \cdots 3 \cdot 2 \cdot 1$$

We also define

$$0! = 1$$

It *may* seem strange to define $0! = 1$, but we shall see later that it is a reasonable definition.

Examples of factorials include

$$5! = 5 \cdot 4 \cdot 3 \cdot 2 \cdot 1 = 120$$
$$10! = 10 \cdot 9 \cdot 8 \cdot 7 \cdot 6 \cdot 5 \cdot 4 \cdot 3 \cdot 2 \cdot 1 = 3,628,800$$

Note that we can write $12!$ as

$$12! = 12 \cdot 11! = 12 \cdot 11 \cdot 10! = 12 \cdot 11 \cdot 10 \cdot 9!$$

In general,

$$n! = n \cdot (n-1)!$$

MATH MATTERS

The factorial symbol as an exclamation point was first introduced in 1808 so that printers setting the type in a book would not have to write out, for example, $5 \cdot 4 \cdot 3 \cdot 2 \cdot 1$ but instead could write $5!$. This notation was not accepted by everyone, and alternative suggestions were made. One other notation was ⌊n. Although this angle bracket saved the printer from writing a product, it had to be constructed, whereas the exclamation point was already in the printer's tray.

Alternative to Example 3

Evaluate each factorial expression.

a. $\dfrac{12!}{10!}$

• **132**

b. $5! + 4!$

• **144**

EXAMPLE 3 Evaluate Factorial Expressions

Evaluate each factorial expression. a. $\dfrac{8!}{5!}$ b. $6! - 4!$

Solution

a. $\dfrac{8!}{5!} = \dfrac{8 \cdot 7 \cdot 6 \cdot 5!}{5!} = 8 \cdot 7 \cdot 6 = 336$

b. $6! - 4! = (6 \cdot 5 \cdot 4 \cdot 3 \cdot 2 \cdot 1) - (4 \cdot 3 \cdot 2 \cdot 1) = 720 - 24 = 696$

▶ **TRY EXERCISE 42, PAGE 644**

INSTRUCTOR NOTE

As a challenge problem, have students find the number of zeros that follow the last nonzero digit of 25!.

● PARTIAL SUMS AND SUMMATION NOTATION

Another important way of obtaining a sequence is by adding the terms of a given sequence. For example, consider the sequence whose general term is given by $a_n = \dfrac{1}{2^n}$. The terms of this sequence are

$$\frac{1}{2}, \frac{1}{4}, \frac{1}{8}, \frac{1}{16}, \frac{1}{32}, \ldots, \frac{1}{2^n}, \cdots$$

From this sequence we can generate a new sequence that is the sum of the terms of $\dfrac{1}{2^n}$.

$$S_1 = \frac{1}{2}$$

$$S_2 = \frac{1}{2} + \frac{1}{4} = \frac{3}{4}$$

$$S_3 = \frac{1}{2} + \frac{1}{4} + \frac{1}{8} = \frac{7}{8}$$

$$S_4 = \frac{1}{2} + \frac{1}{4} + \frac{1}{8} + \frac{1}{16} = \frac{15}{16}$$

MATH MATTERS

Leonhard Euler (1707–1783) found that the sequence of terms given by

$$S_n = 1 - \frac{1}{3} + \frac{1}{5} - \frac{1}{7} + \cdots + \frac{(-1)^{n-1}}{2n-1}$$

became closer and closer to $\dfrac{\pi}{4}$ as n increased. In summation notation, we would write

$$S_n = \sum_{k=1}^{n} \frac{(-1)^{k-1}}{2k-1}$$

and, in general, $S_n = \dfrac{1}{2} + \dfrac{1}{4} + \dfrac{1}{8} + \dfrac{1}{16} + \cdots + \dfrac{1}{2^n}$

The term S_n is called the **nth partial sum** of the infinite sequence, and the sequence $S_1, S_2, S_3, \ldots, S_n$ is called the **sequence of partial sums.**

A convenient notation used for partial sums is called **summation notation.** The sum of the first n terms of a sequence a_n is represented by using the Greek letter Σ (sigma).

$$\sum_{i=1}^{n} a_i = a_1 + a_2 + a_3 + \cdots + a_n$$

This sum is called a **series.** The letter i is called the **index of the summation;** n is the **upper limit** of the summation; 1 is the **lower limit** of the summation.

Alternative to Example 4
Evaluate each series.

a. $\displaystyle\sum_{i=1}^{5} \frac{i-1}{i+1}$

⊙ $\dfrac{21}{10}$

b. $\displaystyle\sum_{k=3}^{6} (-1)^k k!$

⊙ 618

EXAMPLE 4   **Evaluate Series**

Evaluate each series.   **a.** $\displaystyle\sum_{i=1}^{4} \frac{i}{i+1}$ **b.** $\displaystyle\sum_{j=2}^{5} (-1)^j j^2$

Solution

a. $\displaystyle\sum_{i=1}^{4} \frac{i}{i+1} = \frac{1}{2} + \frac{2}{3} + \frac{3}{4} + \frac{4}{5} = \frac{163}{60}$

b. $\displaystyle\sum_{j=2}^{5} (-1)^j j^2 = (-1)^2 2^2 + (-1)^3 3^2 + (-1)^4 4^2 + (-1)^5 5^2$

$$= 4 - 9 + 16 - 25 = -14$$

▶ **Try Exercise 52, page 645**

---

take note

Example 4b illustrates that it is not necessary for a summation to begin at 1. The index of the summation can be any letter.

Properties of Summation Notation

If a_n and b_n are sequences and c is a real number, then

1. $\displaystyle\sum_{i=1}^{n} (a_i \pm b_i) = \sum_{i=1}^{n} a_i \pm \sum_{i=1}^{n} b_i$

2. $\displaystyle\sum_{i=1}^{n} c a_i = c \sum_{i=1}^{n} a_i$

3. $\displaystyle\sum_{i=1}^{n} c = nc$

The proof of property (1) depends on the commutative and associative properties of real numbers.

$$\sum_{i=1}^{n} (a_i \pm b_i) = (a_1 \pm b_1) + (a_2 \pm b_2) + \cdots + (a_n \pm b_n)$$

$$= (a_1 + a_2 + \cdots + a_n) \pm (b_1 + b_2 + \cdots + b_n)$$

$$= \sum_{i=1}^{n} a_i \pm \sum_{i=1}^{n} b_i$$

Property (2) is proved by using the distributive property; this is left as an exercise.

To prove property (3), let $a_n = c$. That is, each a_n is equal to the same constant c. (This is called a **constant sequence.**) Then

$$\sum_{i=1}^{n} a_n = a_1 + a_2 + \cdots + a_n = \underbrace{c + c + \cdots + c}_{n \text{ terms}} = nc$$

TOPICS FOR DISCUSSION

1. Discuss the difference between a finite sequence and an infinite sequence. Give an example of each type.

2. Discuss the difference between a sequence and a series.

3. What is a recursive sequence? Give an example of a recursive sequence.

4. What is an alternating sequence? Give an example of an alternating sequence.

EXERCISE SET 8.1   —*Suggested Assignment: Exercises 1–65, every other odd; 74–79.*

In Exercises 1 to 24, find the first three terms and the eighth term of the sequence that has the given *n*th term.

1. $a_n = n(n - 1)$
0, 2, 6, $a_8 = 56$

2. $a_n = 2n$
2, 4, 6, $a_8 = 16$

3. $a_n = 1 - \dfrac{1}{n}$ $0, \dfrac{1}{2}, \dfrac{2}{3}, a_8 = \dfrac{7}{8}$

4. $a_n = \dfrac{n + 1}{n}$ $2, \dfrac{3}{2}, \dfrac{4}{3}, a_8 = \dfrac{9}{8}$

5. $a_n = \dfrac{(-1)^{n+1}}{n^2}$
$1, -\dfrac{1}{4}, \dfrac{1}{9}, a_8 = -\dfrac{1}{64}$

▶ **6.** $a_n = \dfrac{(-1)^{n+1}}{n(n + 1)}$ $\dfrac{1}{2}, -\dfrac{1}{6}, \dfrac{1}{12}, a_8 = -\dfrac{1}{72}$

7. $a_n = \dfrac{(-1)^{2n-1}}{3n}$
$-\dfrac{1}{3}, -\dfrac{1}{6}, -\dfrac{1}{9}, a_8 = -\dfrac{1}{24}$

8. $a_n = \dfrac{(-1)^n}{2n - 1}$ $-1, \dfrac{1}{3}, -\dfrac{1}{5}, a_8 = \dfrac{1}{15}$

9. $a_n = \left(\dfrac{2}{3}\right)^n$ $\dfrac{2}{3}, \dfrac{4}{9}, \dfrac{8}{27}, a_8 = \dfrac{256}{6561}$

10. $a_n = \left(\dfrac{-1}{2}\right)^n$ $-\dfrac{1}{2}, \dfrac{1}{4}, -\dfrac{1}{8}, a_8 = \dfrac{1}{256}$

11. $a_n = 1 + (-1)^n$
0, 2, 0, $a_8 = 2$

12. $a_n = 1 + (-0.1)^n$
0.9, 1.01, 0.999, $a_8 = 1.00000001$

13. $a_n = (1.1)^n$
1.1, 1.21, 1.331, $a_8 = 2.14358881$

14. $a_n = \dfrac{n}{n^2 + 1}$ $\dfrac{1}{2}, \dfrac{2}{5}, \dfrac{3}{10}, a_8 = \dfrac{8}{65}$

15. $a_n = \dfrac{(-1)^{n+1}}{\sqrt{n}}$
$1, -\dfrac{\sqrt{2}}{2}, \dfrac{\sqrt{3}}{3}, a_8 = -\dfrac{\sqrt{2}}{4}$

16. $a_n = \dfrac{3^{n-1}}{2^n}$ $\dfrac{1}{2}, \dfrac{3}{4}, \dfrac{9}{8}, a_8 = \dfrac{2187}{256}$

17. $a_n = n!$ 1, 2, 6, $a_8 = 40{,}320$

18. $a_n = \dfrac{n!}{(n - 1)!}$ 1, 2, 3, $a_8 = 8$

19. $a_n = \log n$ 0, 0.3010, 0.4771, $a_8 = 0.9031$

20. $a_n = \ln n$ (natural logarithm)   0, 0.6931, 1.0986, $a_8 = 2.0794$

21. a_n is the digit in the *n*th place in the decimal expansion of $\dfrac{1}{7}$.   1, 4, 2, $a_8 = 4$

22. a_n is the digit in the *n*th place in the decimal expansion of $\dfrac{1}{13}$.   0, 7, 6, $a_8 = 7$

23. $a_n = 3$ 3, 3, 3, $a_8 = 3$

24. $a_n = -2$ $-2, -2, -2, a_8 = -2$

In Exercises 25 to 34, find the first three terms of each recursively defined sequence.

25. $a_1 = 5, a_n = 2a_{n-1}$ 5, 10, 20

26. $a_1 = 2, a_n = 3a_{n-1}$ 2, 6, 18

27. $a_1 = 2, a_n = na_{n-1}$ 2, 4, 12

▶ **28.** $a_1 = 1, a_n = n^2a_{n-1}$ 1, 4, 36

29. $a_1 = 2, a_n = (a_{n-1})^2$ 2, 4, 16

30. $a_1 = 4, a_n = \dfrac{1}{a_{n-1}}$ $4, \dfrac{1}{4}, 4$

31. $a_1 = 2, a_n = 2na_{n-1}$ 2, 8, 48

32. $a_1 = 2, a_n = (-3)na_{n-1}$
2, −12, 108

33. $a_1 = 3, a_n = (a_{n-1})^{1/n}$
$3, \sqrt{3}, \sqrt[6]{3}$

34. $a_1 = 2, a_n = (a_{n-1})^n$
2, 4, 64

35. $a_1 = 1, a_2 = 3, a_n = \dfrac{1}{2}(a_{n-1} + a_{n-2})$. Find $a_3, a_4,$ and a_5.
$2, \dfrac{5}{2}, \dfrac{9}{4}$

36. $a_1 = 1, a_2 = 4, a_n = (a_{n-1})(a_{n-2})$. Find $a_3, a_4,$ and a_5.
4, 16, 64

In Exercises 37 to 44, evaluate the factorial expression.

37. $7! - 6!$
4320

38. $(4!)^2$
576

39. $\dfrac{9!}{7!}$ 72

40. $\dfrac{10!}{5!}$
30,240

41. $\dfrac{8!}{3!\,5!}$ 56

▶ **42.** $\dfrac{12!}{4!\,8!}$ 495

43. $\dfrac{100!}{99!}$ 100

44. $\dfrac{100!}{98!\,2!}$
4950

In Exercises 45 to 58, evaluate the series.

45. $\displaystyle\sum_{i=1}^{5} i$ 15

46. $\displaystyle\sum_{i=1}^{4} i^2$ 30

47. $\displaystyle\sum_{i=1}^{5} i(i - 1)$ 40

48. $\displaystyle\sum_{i=1}^{7} (2i + 1)$ 63

49. $\displaystyle\sum_{k=1}^{4} \dfrac{1}{k}$ $\dfrac{25}{12}$

50. $\displaystyle\sum_{k=1}^{6} \dfrac{1}{k(k + 1)}$ $\dfrac{6}{7}$

51. $\displaystyle\sum_{j=1}^{8} 2j$ 72

52. $\displaystyle\sum_{i=1}^{6} (2i + 1)(2i - 1)$ 358

53. $\displaystyle\sum_{i=3}^{5} (-1)^i 2^i$ -24

54. $\displaystyle\sum_{i=3}^{5} \frac{(-1)^i}{2^i}$ $-\dfrac{3}{32}$

55. $\displaystyle\sum_{n=1}^{7} \log \frac{n + 1}{n}$ 3 log 2

56. $\displaystyle\sum_{n=2}^{8} \ln \frac{n}{n + 1}$ $\ln \dfrac{2}{9} \approx -1.5041$

57. $\displaystyle\sum_{k=0}^{8} \frac{8!}{k!(8 - k)!}$ 256

58. $\displaystyle\sum_{k=0}^{7} \frac{1}{k!}$ $\dfrac{685}{252}$

60. $2 + 4 + 6 + 8 + 10 + 12 + 14$ $\displaystyle\sum_{i=1}^{7} 2i$

61. $2 - 4 + 8 - 16 + 32 - 64 + 128$ $\displaystyle\sum_{i=1}^{7} 2^i(-1)^{i+1}$

62. $1 - 8 + 27 - 64 + 125$ $\displaystyle\sum_{i=1}^{5} i^3(-1)^{i+1}$

63. $7 + 10 + 13 + 16 + 19$ $\displaystyle\sum_{i=0}^{4} (7 + 3i)$

64. $30 + 26 + 22 + 18 + 14 + 10$ $\displaystyle\sum_{i=0}^{5} (30 - 4i)$

65. $\dfrac{1}{2} + \dfrac{1}{4} + \dfrac{1}{8} + \dfrac{1}{16}$ $\displaystyle\sum_{i=1}^{4} \frac{1}{2^i}$

In Exercises 59 to 66, write the given series in summation notation.

66. $1 - \dfrac{2}{3} + \dfrac{4}{9} - \dfrac{8}{27} + \dfrac{16}{81} - \dfrac{32}{243}$ $\displaystyle\sum_{i=0}^{5} \left(-\frac{2}{3}\right)^i$

59. $\dfrac{1}{1} + \dfrac{1}{4} + \dfrac{1}{9} + \dfrac{1}{16} + \dfrac{1}{25} + \dfrac{1}{36}$ $\displaystyle\sum_{i=1}^{6} \frac{1}{i^2}$

CONNECTING CONCEPTS

67. Newton's Method Newton's approximation to the square root of a number, N, is given by the recursive sequence

$$a_1 = \frac{N}{2} \qquad a_n = \frac{1}{2}\left(a_{n-1} + \frac{N}{a_{n-1}}\right)$$

Approximate $\sqrt{7}$ by computing a_4. Compare this result with the calculator value of $\sqrt{7} \approx 2.6457513$. ≈ 2.6457520

68. Use the formula in Exercise 67 to approximate $\sqrt{10}$ by finding a_5. 3.1622777

69. Let $a_1 = N$ and $a_n = \sqrt{a_{n-1}}$. Find a_{20} when $N = 7$. (*Hint:* Enter 7 into your calculator and then press the $\boxed{\sqrt{}}$ key 19 times.) Make a conjecture as to the value of a_n as n increases without bound.
$a_{20} \approx 1.0000037$, $a_{100} \approx 1$

70. Let $a_n = i^n$, where i is the imaginary unit. Find the first eight terms of the sequence defined by a_n. Find a_{237}.
$i, -1, -i, 1, i, -1, -i, 1$; $a_{237} = i$

71. Let $a_n = \left[\dfrac{1}{2}(-1 + i\sqrt{3})\right]^n$. Find the first six terms of the sequence defined by a_n. Find a_{99}.
See answer below.

72. Stirling's Formula By using a calculator, evaluate $\sqrt{2\pi n}(n/e)^n$, where e is the base of the natural logarithms for $n = 10, 20,$ and 30. This formula is called Stirling's formula and is used as an approximation for $n!$. For $n > 20$, the error in the approximation is less than 0.1%. 3.5986956×10^6, 2.4227868×10^{18}, 2.6451710×10^{32}

73. Prove that $\displaystyle\sum_{i=1}^{n} ca_i = c\sum_{i=1}^{n} a_i$, where c is a constant.

71. $\dfrac{1}{2}(-1 + i\sqrt{3}), \dfrac{1}{2}(-1 - i\sqrt{3}), 1, \dfrac{1}{2}(-1 + i\sqrt{3}), \dfrac{1}{2}(-1 - i\sqrt{3}), 1$; $a_{99} = 1$

PREPARE FOR SECTION 8.2

74. Solve $a = b + (n - 1)d$ for d given $a = -3$, $b = 25$, and $n = 15$. [1.1] -2

75. Solve $a = b + (n - 1)d$ for d given $a = 13$, $b = 3$, and $n = 5$. [1.1] $\dfrac{5}{2}$

76. Evaluate $S = \dfrac{n[2a_1 + (n - 1)d]}{2}$ when $a_1 = 2$, $d = \dfrac{5}{4}$, and $n = 50$. [1.2] $\dfrac{6525}{4}$

77. Find the fifth term of the sequence whose nth term is $a_n = 5 + (n - 1)4$. [8.1] 21

78. Find the twentieth term of the sequence whose nth term is $a_n = 52 + (n - 1)(-3)$. [8.1] -5

79. Given the sequence $2, 5, 8, \ldots, 3n - 1, \ldots$, are the differences between successive terms equal to the same constant? [8.1] Yes

PROJECTS

I. FORMULAS FOR INFINITE SEQUENCES It is not possible to define an infinite sequence by giving a finite number of terms of the sequence. For instance, the question "What is the next term in the sequence $2, 4, 6, 8, \ldots$?" does not have a unique answer.

    a. Verify this statement by finding a formula for a_n such that the first four terms of the sequence are $2, 4, 6, 8$ and the next term is 43. *Suggestion:* The formula

$$a_n = \frac{n(n-1)(n-2)(n-3)(n-4)}{4!} + 2n$$

generates the sequence $2, 4, 6, 8, 15$ for $n = 1, 2, 3, 4, 5$.

    b. Extend the result in part **a.** by finding a formula for a_n that will give the first four terms as $2, 4, 6, 8$ and the fifth term as x, where x is any real number.

SECTION **8.2**

ARITHMETIC SEQUENCES AND SERIES

- ARITHMETIC SEQUENCES
- ARITHMETIC SERIES
- ARITHMETIC MEANS

● ARITHMETIC SEQUENCES

Note that in the sequence

$$2, 5, 8, 11, 14, \ldots, 3n - 1, \ldots$$

the difference between successive terms is always 3. Such a sequence is an *arithmetic sequence* or an *arithmetic progression*. These sequences have the following property: The difference between successive terms is the same constant. This constant is called the *common difference*. For the sequence above, the common difference is 3.

In general, an arithmetic sequence can be defined as follows:

> **Arithmetic Sequence**
>
> Let d be a real number. A sequence a_n is an **arithmetic sequence** if
> $$a_{i+1} - a_i = d \quad \text{for all } i$$
> The number d is the **common difference** for the sequence.

INSTRUCTOR NOTE

To assess students' understanding, have them do the following.

1. Consider the arithmetic sequence $2, 9, 16, \ldots, 7n - 5, \ldots$.
    a. Determine the common difference.
      ● $d = 7$
    b. Determine a_{10}.
      ● **65**
2. Determine the fifty-first term of the arithmetic sequence $3, 7, 11, 15, \ldots$.
    ● $3 + 50(4) = 203$

Further examples of arithmetic sequences include

$$3, 8, 13, 18, \ldots, 5n - 2, \ldots$$
$$11, 7, 3, -1, \ldots, -4n + 15, \ldots$$
$$1, 2, 3, 4, \ldots, n, \ldots$$

❓ QUESTION Is the sequence $2, 6, 10, 14, \ldots, 4n - 2, \ldots$ an arithmetic sequence?

❓ ANSWER Yes. The difference between any two successive terms is 4.

Consider an arithmetic sequence in which the first term is a_1 and the common difference is d. By adding the common difference to each successive term of the arithmetic sequence, we can find a formula for the nth term.

$$a_1 = a_1$$
$$a_2 = a_1 + d$$
$$a_3 = a_2 + d = a_1 + d + d = a_1 + 2d$$
$$a_4 = a_3 + d = a_1 + 2d + d = a_1 + 3d$$

Note the relationship between the term number and the coefficient of d. The coefficient is 1 less than the term number.

Formula for the nth Term of an Arithmetic Sequence

The nth term of an arithmetic sequence with common difference of d is given by
$$a_n = a_1 + (n - 1)d$$

Alternative to Example 1

a. Find the thirty-third term of the arithmetic sequence whose first three terms are 5, 0, −5.

⊙ **−155**

b. The twentieth term of an arithmetic sequence is 92 and the first term is 16. Find the twelfth term.

⊙ **60**

EXAMPLE 1   **Find the nth Term of an Arithmetic Sequence**

a. Find the twenty-fifth term of the arithmetic sequence whose first three terms are $-12, -6, 0$.

b. The fifteenth term of an arithmetic sequence is -3 and the first term is 25. Find the tenth term.

Solution

a. Find the common difference: $d = a_2 - a_1 = -6 - (-12) = 6$. Use the formula $a_n = a_1 + (n - 1)d$ with $n = 25$.

$$a_{25} = -12 + (25 - 1)(6) = -12 + 24(6) = -12 + 144 = 132$$

b. Solve the equation $a_n = a_1 + (n - 1)d$ for d, given that $n = 15$, $a_1 = 25$, and $a_{15} = -3$.

$$-3 = 25 + (14)d$$
$$d = -2$$

Now find the tenth term.

$$a_n = a_1 + (n - 1)d$$
$$a_{10} = 25 + (9)(-2) = 7 \qquad \bullet \, n = 10, a_1 = 25, d = -2$$

▶ **TRY EXERCISE 16, PAGE 651**

⊙ **ARITHMETIC SERIES**

Consider the arithmetic sequence given by

$$1, 3, 5, \ldots, 2n - 1, \ldots$$

MATH MATTERS

Galileo (1564–1642), using the fact that the sum of a set of odd integers is the square of the number of integers being added (as is shown at the right), was able to show that objects of different weights fall at the same rate. By constructing inclines of various slopes similar to the one shown below, with a track in the center and equal intervals marked along the incline, he measured the distance various balls of different weights traveled in equal intervals of time. He concluded from his observations that the distance an object falls is proportional to the square of the time it takes to fall and does not depend on its weight. Galileo's views were contrary to the prevailing (Aristotelian) theory on this subject, and he lost his post at the University of Pisa because of them.

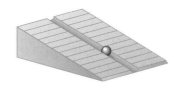

Adding successive terms of this sequence, we generate a sequence of partial sums. The sum of the terms of an arithmetic sequence is called an **arithmetic series.**

$$S_1 = 1$$
$$S_2 = 1 + 3 = 4$$
$$S_3 = 1 + 3 + 5 = 9$$
$$S_4 = 1 + 3 + 5 + 7 = 16$$
$$S_5 = 1 + 3 + 5 + 7 + 9 = 25$$
$$\vdots \qquad \vdots$$
$$S_n = 1 + 3 + \cdots + (2n - 1) = n^2$$

The first five terms of this sequence are 1, 4, 9, 16, 25. It appears from this example that the sum of the first n odd integers is n^2. Shortly, we will be able to prove this result by using the following formula.

Formula for the nth Partial Sum of an Arithmetic Sequence

The **nth partial sum S_n** of an arithmetic sequence a_n with common difference d is

$$S_n = \frac{n}{2}(a_1 + a_n)$$

Proof We write S_n in both forward and reverse order.

$$S_n = a_1 + a_2 + a_3 + \cdots + a_{n-2} + a_{n-1} + a_n$$
$$S_n = a_n + a_{n-1} + a_{n-2} + \cdots + a_3 + a_2 + a_1$$

Add the two partial sums.

$$2S_n = (a_1 + a_n) + (a_2 + a_{n-1}) + (a_3 + a_{n-2}) + \cdots \qquad (1)$$
$$+ (a_{n-2} + a_3) + (a_{n-1} + a_2) + (a_n + a_1)$$

Consider the term $(a_3 + a_{n-2})$. Using the formula for the nth term of an arithmetic sequence, we have

$$a_3 \qquad = a_1 + (3 - 1)d = a_1 + 2d$$
$$a_{n-2} \qquad = a_1 + [(n - 2) - 1]d = a_1 + nd - 3d$$

Thus $\qquad a_3 + a_{n-2} = (a_1 + 2d) + (a_1 + nd - 3d)$
$$= a_1 + (a_1 + nd - d) = a_1 + [a_1 + (n - 1)d]$$
$$= a_1 + a_n$$

In a similar manner, we can show that each term in parentheses in Equation (1) equals $(a_1 + a_n)$. Because there are n such terms, we have

$$2S_n = n(a_1 + a_n)$$
$$S_n = \frac{n}{2}(a_1 + a_n) \qquad \blacklozenge$$

There is an alternative form of the formula for the sum of n terms of an arithmetic sequence.

> **Alternative Formula for the Sum of an Arithmetic Sequence**
>
> The nth partial sum S_n of an arithmetic sequence with common difference d is
>
> $$S_n = \frac{n[2a_1 + (n-1)d]}{2}$$

The proof of this theorem is left as a project.

Alternative to Example 2
a. Find the sum of the first 200 positive even integers.

   ● **40,200**

b. Find the sum of the first 75 terms of the arithmetic sequence whose first three terms are $\frac{1}{2}, \frac{9}{4}, 4$.

   ● $\frac{19,575}{4}$

EXAMPLE 2   **Find a Partial Sum of an Arithmetic Sequence**

a.   Evaluate: $\displaystyle\sum_{i=1}^{100} (2i - 1)$

b.   Find the sum of the first 50 terms of the arithmetic sequence whose first three terms are $2, \frac{13}{4},$ and $\frac{9}{2}$.

Solution

Use the formula $S_n = \dfrac{n}{2}[2a_1 + (n-1)d]$.

a.   We have $a_1 = 1$, $d = 2$, and $n = 100$. Thus

$$S_{100} = \frac{100}{2}[2(1) + (100 - 1)2] = 10{,}000$$

b.   We have $a_1 = 2$, $d = \dfrac{5}{4}$, and $n = 50$. Thus

$$S_{50} = \frac{50}{2}\left[2(2) + (50 - 1)\frac{5}{4}\right] = \frac{6525}{4}$$

▶ **Try Exercise 22, page 651**

The first n positive integers $1, 2, 3, 4, \ldots, n$ are part of an arithmetic sequence with a common difference of 1, $a_1 = 1$, and $a_n = n$. A formula for the sum of the first n positive integers can be found by using the formula for the nth partial sum of an arithmetic sequence.

$$S_n = \frac{n}{2}(a_1 + a_n)$$

Replacing a_1 by 1 and a_n by n yields

$$S_n = \frac{n}{2}(1 + n) = \frac{n(n + 1)}{2}$$

This proves the following theorem.

Sum of the First n Positive Integers

The sum of the first n positive integers is given by

$$S_n = \frac{n(n + 1)}{2}$$

To find the sum of the first 85 positive integers, use $n = 85$.

$$S_{85} = \frac{85(85 + 1)}{2} = 3655$$

● **ARITHMETIC MEANS**

The **arithmetic mean** of two numbers a and b is $\frac{a + b}{2}$. The three numbers a, $\frac{a + b}{2}$, and b form an arithmetic sequence. In general, given two numbers a and b, it is possible to insert k numbers $c_1, c_2, \ldots, c_k$ in such a way that the sequence

$$a, c_1, c_2, \ldots, c_k, b$$

is an arithmetic sequence. This is called *inserting k arithmetic means between a and b*.

Alternative to Example 3
Insert five arithmetic means between 4 and 20.

● $\dfrac{20}{3}, \dfrac{28}{3}, 12, \dfrac{44}{3}, \dfrac{52}{3}$

EXAMPLE 3   **Insert Arithmetic Means**

Insert three arithmetic means between 3 and 13.

Solution

After we insert the three terms, the sequence will be

$$a = 3, c_1, c_2, c_3, b = 13$$

The first term of the sequence is 3, the fifth term is 13, and n is 5. Thus

$$a_n = a_1 + (n - 1)d$$
$$13 = 3 + 4d$$
$$d = \frac{5}{2}$$

The three arithmetic means are

$$c_1 = a + d = 3 + \frac{5}{2} = \frac{11}{2}$$

$$c_2 = a + 2d = 3 + 2\left(\frac{5}{2}\right) = 8$$

$$c_3 = a + 3d = 3 + 3\left(\frac{5}{2}\right) = \frac{21}{2}$$

▶ **TRY EXERCISE 34, PAGE 651**

TOPICS FOR DISCUSSION

1. Discuss what distinguishes an arithmetic sequence from all other types of sequences.

2. Is $a_n = \dfrac{2}{n}$ a possible formula for the nth term of an arithmetic sequence? Why or why not?

3. Discuss the characteristics of an arithmetic series. Give an example of an arithmetic series.

4. Consider the series $\sum_{k=1}^{n} f(k)$. Discuss how you can determine whether this is an arithmetic series.

EXERCISE SET 8.2   *—Suggested Assignment: Exercises 1–47, odd; 50–55.*

In Exercises 1 to 14, find the ninth, twenty-fourth, and nth terms of the arithmetic sequence.

1. 6, 10, 14, ...
   $a_9 = 38$, $a_{24} = 98$, $a_n = 4n + 2$

2. 7, 12, 17, ...
   $a_9 = 47$, $a_{24} = 122$, $a_n = 5n + 2$

3. 6, 4, 2, ...
   $a_9 = -10$, $a_{24} = -40$, $a_n = 8 - 2n$

4. 11, 4, −3, ...
   $a_9 = -45$, $a_{24} = -150$, $a_n = 18 - 7n$

5. −8, −5, −2, ...
   $a_9 = 16$, $a_{24} = 61$, $a_n = 3n - 11$

6. −15, −9, −3, ...
   $a_9 = 33$, $a_{24} = 123$, $a_n = 6n - 21$

7. 1, 4, 7, ...
   $a_9 = 25$, $a_{24} = 70$, $a_n = 3n - 2$

8. −4, 1, 6, ...
   $a_9 = 36$, $a_{24} = 111$, $a_n = 5n - 9$

9. $a, a + 2, a + 4, \dots$ $a_9 = a + 16$,
   $a_{24} = a + 46$, $a_n = a + 2n - 2$

10. $a - 3, a + 1, a + 5, \dots$
   $a_9 = a + 29$, $a_{24} = a + 89$, $a_n = a + 4n - 7$

11. $\log 7, \log 14, \log 28, \dots$
   $a_9 = \log 7 + 8 \log 2$, $a_{24} = \log 7 + 23 \log 2$, $a_n = \log 7 + (n - 1) \log 2$

12. $\ln 4, \ln 16, \ln 64, \dots$
   12. $a_9 = 9 \ln 4$, $a_{24} = 24 \ln 4$, $a_n = n \ln 4$

13. $\log a, \log a^2, \log a^3, \dots$
   $a_9 = 9 \log a$, $a_{24} = 24 \log a$, $a_n = n \log a$

14. $\log_2 5, \log_2 5a, \log_2 5a^2, \dots$
   $a_9 = \log_2 5 + 8 \log_2 a$, $a_{24} = \log_2 5 + 23 \log_2 a$, $a_n = \log_2 5 + (n - 1) \log_2 a$

15. The fourth and fifth terms of an arithmetic sequence are 13 and 15. Find the twentieth term. 45

▶ **16.** The sixth and eighth terms of an arithmetic sequence are −14 and −20. Find the fifteenth term. −41

17. The fifth and seventh terms of an arithmetic sequence are −19 and −29. Find the seventeenth term. −79

18. The fourth and seventh terms of an arithmetic sequence are 22 and 34. Find the twenty-third term. 98

In Exercises 19 to 32, find the nth partial sum of the arithmetic sequence.

19. $a_n = 3n + 2; n = 10$ 185

20. $a_n = 4n - 3; n = 12$ 276

21. $a_n = 3 - 5n; n = 15$ −555

▶ **22.** $a_n = 1 - 2n; n = 20$ −400

23. $a_n = 6n; n = 12$ 468

24. $a_n = 7n; n = 14$ 735

25. $a_n = n + 8; n = 25$ 525

26. $a_n = n - 4; n = 25$ 225

27. $a_n = -n; n = 30$ −465

28. $a_n = 4 - n; n = 40$ −660

29. $a_n = n + x; n = 12$
   $78 + 12x$

30. $a_n = 2n - x; n = 15$
   $240 - 15x$

31. $a_n = nx; n = 20$
   $210x$

32. $a_n = -nx; n = 14$
   $-105x$

In Exercises 33 to 36, insert k arithmetic means between the given numbers.

33. −1 and 23; $k = 5$
   3, 7, 11, 15, 19

▶ **34.** 7 and 19; $k = 5$
   9, 11, 13, 15, 17

35. 3 and $\dfrac{1}{2}$; $k = 4$ $\dfrac{5}{2}, 2, \dfrac{3}{2}, 1$

36. $\dfrac{11}{3}$ and 6; $k = 4$
   $\dfrac{62}{15}, \dfrac{69}{15}, \dfrac{76}{15}, \dfrac{83}{15}$

37. Show that the sum of the first n positive odd integers is n^2.

38. Show that the sum of the first n positive even integers is $n^2 + n$.

39. STACKING LOGS Logs are stacked so that there are 25 logs in the bottom row, 24 logs in the second row, and so on, decreasing by 1 log each row. How many logs are stacked in the sixth row? How many logs are there in all six rows?
20 in the sixth row, 135 in the six rows

40. THEATER SEATING The seating section in a theater has 27 seats in the first row, 29 seats in the second row, and so on, increasing by 2 seats each row for a total of 10 rows. How many seats are in the tenth row, and how many seats are there in the section?
45 seats in the tenth row, 360 seats in the section

41. CONTEST PRIZES A contest offers 15 prizes. The first prize is $5000, and each successive prize is $250 less than the preceding prize. What is the value of the fifteenth prize? What is the total amount of money distributed in prizes? $1500, $48,750

42. PHYSICAL FITNESS An exercise program calls for walking 15 minutes each day for a week. Each week thereafter, the amount of time spent walking increases by 5 minutes per day. In how many weeks will a person be walking 60 minutes each day?
In 10 weeks a person will be walking 60 min a day.

43. PHYSICS An object dropped from a cliff will fall 16 feet the first second, 48 feet the second second, 80 feet the third second, and so on, increasing by 32 feet each second. What is the total distance the object will fall in 7 seconds?
784 ft

44. PHYSICS The distance a ball rolls down a ramp each second is given by the arithmetic sequence whose nth term is $2n - 1$ feet. Find the distance the ball rolls during the tenth second and the total distance the ball travels in 10 seconds.
The distance the ball rolls in the tenth second is 19 ft. The total distance is 100 ft.

CONNECTING CONCEPTS

45. If $f(x)$ is a linear polynomial, show that $f(n)$, where n is a positive integer, is an arithmetic sequence.

46. Find the formula for a_n in terms of a_1 and n for the sequence that is defined recursively by $a_1 = 3, a_n = a_{n-1} + 5$.
$a_n = 5n - 2$

47. Find a formula for a_n in terms of a_1 and n for the sequence that is defined recursively by $a_1 = 4, a_n = a_{n-1} - 3$.
$a_n = 7 - 3n$

48. Suppose a_n and b_n are two sequences such that $a_1 = 4$, $a_n = b_{n-1} + 5$ and $b_1 = 2, b_n = a_{n-1} + 1$. Show that a_n and b_n are arithmetic sequences. Find a_{100}. $a_{100} = 301$

49. Suppose a_n and b_n are two sequences such that $a_1 = 1$, $a_n = b_{n-1} + 7$ and $b_1 = -2, b_n = a_{n-1} + 1$. Show that a_n and b_n are arithmetic sequences. Find a_{50}. $a_{50} = 197$

PREPARE FOR SECTION 8.3

50. For the sequence $2, 4, 8, \ldots, 2^n, \ldots$, what is the ratio of any two successive terms? [8.1] 2

51. Evaluate: $\sum_{n=1}^{4} \dfrac{1}{2^{n-1}}$ [8.1] $\dfrac{15}{8}$

52. Evaluate $S = \dfrac{a(1 - r^n)}{1 - r}$ when $a = 3, r = -2$, and $n = 5$.
[P.2] 33

53. Solve $S - rS = a - ar^2, r \neq 1$, for S. [1.1] $S = a(1 + r)$

54. Write the first three terms of the sequence whose nth term is $a_n = 3\left(-\dfrac{1}{2}\right)^n$. [8.1] $-\dfrac{3}{2}, \dfrac{3}{4}, -\dfrac{3}{8}$

55. Find the first three terms of the sequence of partial sums for the sequence $2, 4, 8, \ldots, 2^n, \ldots$ [8.1] 2, 6, 14

PROJECTS

1. ANGLES OF A TRIANGLE The sum of the interior angles of a triangle is 180°.

  a. Using this fact, what is the sum of the interior angles of a quadrilateral?

  b. What is the sum of the interior angles of a pentagon?

  c. What is the sum of the interior angles of a hexagon?

  d. On the basis of your previous results, what is the apparent formula for the sum of the interior angles of a polygon of n sides?

2. PROVE A FORMULA Prove the Alternative Formula for the Sum of an Arithmetic Sequence.

GEOMETRIC SEQUENCES AND SERIES

GEOMETRIC SEQUENCES

Arithmetic sequences are characterized by a common *difference* between successive terms. A *geometric sequence* is characterized by a common *ratio* between successive terms.

The sequence

$$3, 6, 12, 24, \ldots, 3(2^{n-1}), \ldots$$

is a geometric sequence. Note that the ratio of any two successive terms is 2.

$$\frac{6}{3} = 2 \qquad \frac{12}{6} = 2 \qquad \frac{24}{12} = 2$$

Geometric Sequence

Let r be a nonzero constant real number. A sequence is a **geometric sequence** if

$$\frac{a_{i+1}}{a_i} = r \quad \text{for all positive integers } i.$$

The number r is called the **common ratio.**

Alternative to Example 1

Which of the following are geometric sequences?

a. $-\dfrac{1}{3}, 1, -3, 9, -27, \ldots, -\dfrac{1}{3}(3)^{n-1}, \ldots$

- Yes

b. $16, 9, 2, -5, \ldots, -7n + 23, \ldots$

- No

EXAMPLE 1 Determine Whether a Sequence Is a Geometric Sequence

Which of the following are geometric sequences?

a. $4, -2, 1, \ldots, 4\left(-\dfrac{1}{2}\right)^{n-1}, \ldots$ b. $1, 4, 9, \ldots, n^2, \ldots$

Solution

To determine whether the sequence is a geometric sequence, calculate the ratio of successive terms.

a. $\dfrac{a_{i+1}}{a_i} = \dfrac{4\left(-\dfrac{1}{2}\right)^i}{4\left(-\dfrac{1}{2}\right)^{i-1}} = -\dfrac{1}{2}.$

Because the ratio of successive terms is a constant, the sequence is a geometric sequence.

b. $\dfrac{a_{i+1}}{a_i} = \dfrac{(i+1)^2}{i^2} = \left(1 + \dfrac{1}{i}\right)^2$

Because the ratio of successive terms is not a constant, the sequence is not a geometric sequence.

▶ **TRY EXERCISE 6, PAGE 659**

Consider a geometric sequence in which the first term is a_1 and the common ratio is r. By multiplying each successive term of the geometric sequence by the common ratio, we can derive a formula for the nth term.

$$a_1 = a_1$$
$$a_2 = a_1 r$$
$$a_3 = a_2 r = (a_1 r)r = a_1 r^2$$
$$a_4 = a_3 r = (a_1 r^2)r = a_1 r^3$$

Note the relationship between the number of the term and the number that is the exponent on r. The exponent on r is 1 less than the number of the term. With this observation, we can write a formula for the nth term of a geometric sequence.

The nth Term of a Geometric Sequence

The **nth term of a geometric sequence** with first term a_1 and common ratio r is

$$a_n = a_1 r^{n-1}$$

Alternative to Example 2
Find the nth term of the geometric sequence whose first three terms are
a. 36, 30, 25.
  • $a_n = 36\left(\dfrac{5}{6}\right)^{n-1}$
b. 200, −20, 2.
  • $a_n = 200\left(-\dfrac{1}{10}\right)^{n-1}$

EXAMPLE 2 **Find the nth Term of a Geometric Sequence**

Find the nth term of the geometric sequence whose first three terms are

a. $4, \dfrac{8}{3}, \dfrac{16}{9}, \ldots$ **b.** $5, -10, 20, \ldots$

Solution

a. $r = \dfrac{8/3}{4} = \dfrac{2}{3}$ and $a_1 = 4$. Thus $a_n = 4\left(\dfrac{2}{3}\right)^{n-1}$.

b. $r = \dfrac{-10}{5} = -2$ and $a_1 = 5$. Thus $a_n = 5(-2)^{n-1}$.

▶ **TRY EXERCISE 18, PAGE 660**

● FINITE GEOMETRIC SERIES

Adding the terms of a geometric sequence, we can define the nth partial sum of a geometric sequence in a manner similar to that of an arithmetic sequence. Consider the geometric sequence $1, 2, 4, 8, \ldots, 2^{n-1}, \ldots$

$$S_1 = 1$$
$$S_2 = 1 + 2 = 3$$
$$S_3 = 1 + 2 + 4 = 7$$
$$S_4 = 1 + 2 + 4 + 8 = 15$$
$$\vdots \qquad \vdots$$
$$S_n = 1 + 2 + 4 + 8 + \cdots + 2^{n-1}$$

The first four terms of the sequence of partial sums are 1, 3, 7, and 15.

To find a general formula for S_n, the nth term of the sequence of partial sums of a geometric sequence, let

$$S_n = a_1 + a_1 r + a_1 r^2 + \cdots + a_1 r^{n-1}$$

Multiply each side of this equation by r.

$$S_n = a_1 + a_1 r + a_1 r^2 + \cdots + a_1 r^{n-2} + a_1 r^{n-1}$$
$$rS_n = \qquad a_1 r + a_1 r^2 + \cdots + a_1 r^{n-2} + a_1 r^{n-1} + a_1 r^n$$

Subtract the two equations.

$$S_n - rS_n = a_1 - a_1 r^n$$
$$S_n(1 - r) = a_1(1 - r^n) \qquad \bullet \text{ Factor out the common factors.}$$
$$S_n = \frac{a_1(1 - r^n)}{1 - r} \qquad \bullet \, r \neq 1$$

This proves the following theorem.

The nth Partial Sum of a Geometric Sequence

The **nth partial sum of a geometric sequence** with first term a_1 and common ratio r is

$$S_n = \frac{a_1(1 - r^n)}{1 - r} \quad r \neq 1$$

❓ QUESTION If $r = 1$, what is the nth partial sum of a geometric sequence?

EXAMPLE 3   Find the nth Partial Sum of a Geometric Sequence

Find the partial sum of each geometric sequence.

a. $5, 15, 45, \ldots, 5(3)^{n-1}, \ldots; n = 4$ b. $\displaystyle\sum_{n=1}^{17} 3\left(\frac{3}{4}\right)^{n-1}$

Solution

a.   We have $a_1 = 5$, $r = 3$, and $n = 4$. Thus

$$S_4 = \frac{5[1 - 3^4]}{1 - 3} = \frac{5(-80)}{-2} = 200$$

b.   When $n = 1$, $a_1 = 3$. The first term is 3. The second term is $\dfrac{9}{4}$.

Therefore, the common ratio is $r = \dfrac{3}{4}$. Thus

$$S_{17} = \frac{3[1 - (3/4)^{17}]}{1 - (3/4)} \approx 11.909797$$

▶ **TRY EXERCISE 40, PAGE 660**

Alternative to Example 3
Find the partial sum of each geometric sequence.
a. $-4, 20, -100, \ldots, -4(-5)^{n-1}, \ldots;$
$\quad n = 5$
○ **−2084**

b. $\displaystyle\sum_{n=0}^{6} 5\left(\frac{2}{3}\right)^n$
○ $\dfrac{10{,}295}{729} \approx$ **14.122085**

❓ ANSWER When $r = 1$, the sequence is the constant sequence a_1. The nth partial sum of a constant sequence is na_1.

• INFINITE GEOMETRIC SERIES

Following are two examples of geometric sequences for which $|r| < 1$.

$$3, \frac{3}{4}, \frac{3}{16}, \frac{3}{64}, \frac{3}{256}, \frac{3}{1024}, \cdots \qquad \bullet \; r = \frac{1}{4}$$

$$2, -1, \frac{1}{2}, -\frac{1}{4}, \frac{1}{8}, -\frac{1}{16}, \frac{1}{32}, \cdots \qquad \bullet \; r = -\frac{1}{2}$$

Note that when the absolute value of the common ratio of a geometric sequence is less than 1, the terms of the geometric sequence approach zero as n increases. We write, for $|r| < 1$, $|r|^n \to 0$ as $n \to \infty$.

Consider again the geometric sequence

$$3, \frac{3}{4}, \frac{3}{16}, \frac{3}{64}, \frac{3}{256}, \frac{3}{1024}, \cdots$$

The nth partial sums for $n = 3, 6, 9,$ and 12 are given in **Table 8.1,** along with the values of r^n. As n increases, S_n is closer to 4 and r^n is closer to zero. By finding more values of S_n for larger values of n, we would find that $S_n \to 4$ as $n \to \infty$. As n becomes larger and larger, S_n is the nth partial sum of more and more terms of the sequence. The sum of *all* the terms of a sequence is called an **infinite series**. If the sequence is a geometric sequence, we have an **infinite geometric series**.

TABLE 8.1

n	S_n	r^n
3	3.93750000	0.01562500
6	3.99902344	0.00024414
9	3.99998474	0.00000381
12	3.99999976	0.00000006

Sum of an Infinite Geometric Sequence

If a_n is a geometric sequence with $|r| < 1$ and first term a_1, then the sum of the infinite geometric series is

$$S = \frac{a_1}{1 - r}$$

A formal proof of this formula requires topics that typically are studied in calculus. We can, however, give an intuitive argument. Start with the formula for the nth partial sum of a geometric sequence.

$$S_n = \frac{a_1(1 - r^n)}{1 - r}$$

When $|r| < 1$, $|r|^n \approx 0$ when n is large. Thus

$$S_n = \frac{a_1(1 - r^n)}{1 - r} \approx \frac{a_1(1 - 0)}{1 - r} = \frac{a_1}{1 - r}$$

An infinite series is represented by $\sum\limits_{n=1}^{\infty} a_n$. One application of infinite geometric series concerns repeating decimals. Consider the repeating decimal

$$0.\overline{6} = \frac{6}{10} + \frac{6}{100} + \frac{6}{1000} + \frac{6}{10{,}000} + \cdots$$

The right-hand side is a geometric series with $a_1 = \dfrac{6}{10}$ and common ratio $r = \dfrac{1}{10}$. Thus

$$S = \frac{6/10}{1 - (1/10)} = \frac{6/10}{9/10} = \frac{2}{3}$$

The repeating decimal $0.\overline{6} = \dfrac{2}{3}$. We can write any repeating decimal as a ratio of two integers by using the formula for the sum of an infinite geometric series.

take note

The sum of an infinite geometric series is not defined when $|r| \geq 1$. For instance, the infinite geometric series

$$2 + 4 + 8 + \cdots + 2^n + \cdots$$

with $r = 2$ increases without bound. However, applying the formula $S = \dfrac{a_1}{1 - r}$ with $r = 2$ and $a_1 = 2$ gives $S = -2$, which is not correct.

Alternative to Example 4

a. Evaluate the infinite geometric series

$$\sum_{n=1}^{\infty} \left(\frac{1}{2} \right)^n.$$

  ● 1

b. Write $0.0\overline{45}$ as the ratio of two integers in lowest terms.

  ● $\dfrac{1}{22}$

INSTRUCTOR NOTE

Have students consider $1 - 1 + 1 - 1 + 1 - \cdots$. Writing this with parentheses as $(1 - 1) + (1 - 1) + \cdots$ makes the apparent "sum" 0. However, the apparent "sum" of $1 - (1 - 1) - (1 - 1) \cdots$ is 1. The associative law does not hold for all infinite series.

EXAMPLE 4   **Find the Value of an Infinite Geometric Series**

a. Evaluate the infinite geometric series $\sum\limits_{n=1}^{\infty} \left(-\dfrac{2}{3} \right)^{n-1}$.

b. Write $0.3\overline{45}$ as the ratio of two integers in lowest terms.

Solution

a. To find the first term, we let $n = 1$. Then $a_1 = \left(-\dfrac{2}{3} \right)^{1-1} = \left(-\dfrac{2}{3} \right)^0 = 1$.

The common ratio is $r = -\dfrac{2}{3}$. Thus

$$S = \frac{1}{1 - (-2/3)} = \frac{1}{5/3} = \frac{3}{5}$$

b. $0.3\overline{45} = \dfrac{3}{10} + \left[\dfrac{45}{1000} + \dfrac{45}{100{,}000} + \dfrac{45}{10{,}000{,}000} + \cdots \right]$

The terms in the brackets form an infinite geometric series. Evaluate that series with $a_1 = \dfrac{45}{1000}$ and $r = \dfrac{1}{100}$, and then add the term $\dfrac{3}{10}$.

$$\frac{45}{1000} + \frac{45}{100{,}000} + \frac{45}{10{,}000{,}000} + \cdots = \frac{45/1000}{1 - (1/100)} = \frac{1}{22}$$

Thus $0.3\overline{45} = \dfrac{3}{10} + \dfrac{1}{22} = \dfrac{19}{55}$

▶ **TRY EXERCISE 62, PAGE 660**

• FUTURE VALUE OF AN ANNUITY

In an earlier chapter we discussed compound interest by using exponential functions. As an extension of this idea, suppose that for each of the next 5 years, P dollars are deposited on December 31 into an account earning $i\%$ annual interest compounded annually. Using the compound interest formula, we can find the total value of all the deposits. **Table 8.2** shows the growth of the investment.

TABLE 8.2

Deposit number	Value of each deposit	
1	$P(1 + i)^4$	Value of first deposit after 4 years
2	$P(1 + i)^3$	Value of second deposit after 3 years
3	$P(1 + i)^2$	Value of third deposit after 2 years
4	$P(1 + i)$	Value of fourth deposit after 1 year
5	P	Value of fifth deposit

The total value of the investment after the last deposit, called the **future value** of the investment, is the sum of the values of all the deposits.

$$A = P + P(1 + i) + P(1 + i)^2 + P(1 + i)^3 + P(1 + i)^4$$

This is a geometric series with first term P and common ratio $1 + i$. Thus, using the formula for the nth partial sum of a geometric sequence

$$S = \frac{a_1(1 - r^n)}{1 - r}$$

we have

$$A = \frac{P[1 - (1 + i)^5]}{1 - (1 + i)} = \frac{P[(1 + i)^5 - 1]}{i}$$

Deposits of equal amounts at equal intervals of time are called **annuities.** When the amounts are deposited at the end of a compounding period (as in our example), we have an **ordinary annuity.**

Future Value of an Ordinary Annuity

Let $r = \dfrac{i}{n}$ and $m = nt$, where i is the annual interest rate, n is the number of compounding periods per year, and t is the number of years. Then the future value A of an ordinary annuity after m compounding periods is given by

$$A = \frac{P[(1 + r)^m - 1]}{r}$$

where P is the amount of each deposit.

Alternative to Example 5
A deposit of $50 is made at the end of each month into a savings account that earns 6% annual interest compounded monthly. Find the future value of this savings plan if the deposits are made for 5 years.
- $3488.50

EXAMPLE 5   **Find the Future Value of an Ordinary Annuity**

An employee savings plan allows any employee to deposit $25 at the end of each month into a savings account earning 6% annual interest compounded monthly. Find the future value of this savings plan if an employee makes the deposits for 10 years.

Solution

We are given $P = 25$, $i = 0.06$, $n = 12$, and $t = 10$. Thus,

$$r = \frac{i}{n} = \frac{0.06}{12} = 0.005 \quad \text{and} \quad m = nt = 12(10) = 120$$

$$A = \frac{25[(1 + 0.005)^{120} - 1]}{0.005} \approx 4096.9837$$

The future value after 10 years is $4096.98.

▶ **TRY EXERCISE 70, PAGE 660**

TOPICS FOR DISCUSSION

1. Discuss what distinguishes a geometric sequence from all other types of sequences.

2. Is $a_n = n^2$ a possible formula for the nth term of a geometric sequence? Why or why not?

3. Discuss the characteristics of a geometric series.

4. Consider the series $\sum_{k=1}^{n} f(k)$. Explain how you can determine whether this is a geometric series.

EXERCISE SET 8.3
—Suggested Assignment: Exercises 1–69, every other odd; 75, 79–85.

In Exercises 1 to 12, determine which sequences are geometric. For geometric sequences, find the common ratio.

1. $4, 16, 64, \ldots, 4^n, \ldots$
geometric; $r = 4$

2. $1, 6, 36, \ldots, 6^{n-1}, \ldots$
geometric; $r = 6$

3. $1, \dfrac{1}{2}, \dfrac{1}{3}, \ldots, \dfrac{1}{n}, \ldots$
not geometric

4. $\dfrac{1}{2}, \dfrac{1}{4}, \dfrac{1}{8}, \ldots, \dfrac{1}{2^n}, \ldots$
geometric; $r = \dfrac{1}{2}$

5. $2^x, 2^{2x}, 2^{3x}, \ldots, 2^{nx}, \ldots$
geometric; $r = 2^x$

 6. $e^x, -e^{2x}, e^{3x}, \ldots, (-1)^{n-1}e^{nx}, \ldots$
geometric; $r = -e^x$

7. $3, 6, 12, \ldots, 3(2^{n-1}), \ldots$
geometric; $r = 2$

8. $5, -10, 20, \ldots, 5(-2)^{n-1}, \ldots$
geometric; $r = -2$

9. $x^2, x^4, x^6, \ldots, x^{2n}, \ldots$
geometric; $r = x^2$

10. $3x, 6x^2, 9x^3, \ldots, 3nx^n, \ldots$
not geometric

11. $\ln 5, \ln 10, \ln 15, \ldots, \ln 5n, \ldots$
not geometric

12. $\log x, \log x^2, \log x^4, \ldots, \log x^{2n-1}, \ldots$
geometric; $r = 2$

In Exercises 13 to 32, find the *n*th term of the geometric sequence.

13. $2, 8, 32, \ldots$
2^{2n-1}

14. $1, 5, 25, \ldots$
5^{n-1}

15. $-4, 12, -36, \ldots$
$-4(-3)^{n-1}$

16. $-3, 6, -12, \ldots$
$-3(-2)^{n-1}$

17. $6, 4, \dfrac{8}{3}, \ldots$ $6\left(\dfrac{2}{3}\right)^{n-1}$

▶ 18. $8, 6, \dfrac{9}{2}, \ldots$ $8\left(\dfrac{3}{4}\right)^{n-1}$

19. $-6, 5, -\dfrac{25}{6}, \ldots$ $-6\left(-\dfrac{5}{6}\right)^{n-1}$

20. $-2, \dfrac{4}{3}, -\dfrac{8}{9}, \ldots$ $-2\left(-\dfrac{2}{3}\right)^{n-1}$

21. $9, -3, 1, \ldots$ $\left(-\dfrac{1}{3}\right)^{n-3}$

22. $8, -\dfrac{4}{3}, \dfrac{2}{9}, \ldots$ $8\left(-\dfrac{1}{6}\right)^{n-1}$

23. $1, -x, x^2, \ldots$ $(-x)^{n-1}$

24. $2, 2a, 2a^2, \ldots$ $2a^{n-1}$

25. $c^2, c^5, c^8, \ldots$ c^{3n-1}

26. $-x^2, x^4, -x^6, \ldots$
$-1 \cdot x^2[(-1)^{n-1} \cdot x^{2n-2}]$

27. $\dfrac{3}{100}, \dfrac{3}{10,000}, \dfrac{3}{1,000,000}, \ldots$ $3\left(\dfrac{1}{100}\right)^n$

28. $\dfrac{7}{10}, \dfrac{7}{10,000}, \dfrac{7}{10,000,000}, \ldots$ $7\left(\dfrac{1}{10}\right)^{3n-2}$

29. $0.5, 0.05, 0.005, \ldots$ $5(0.1)^n$

30. $0.4, 0.004, 0.00004, \ldots$ $4(0.1)^{2n-1}$

31. $0.45, 0.0045, 0.000045, \ldots$ $45(0.01)^n$

32. $0.234, 0.000234, 0.000000234, \ldots$ $234(0.001)^n$

33. Find the third term of a geometric sequence whose first term is 2 and whose fifth term is 162. 18

34. Find the fourth term of a geometric sequence whose third term is 1 and whose eighth term is $\dfrac{1}{32}$. $\dfrac{1}{2}$

35. Find the second term of a geometric sequence whose third term is $\dfrac{4}{3}$ and whose sixth term is $-\dfrac{32}{81}$. -2

36. Find the fifth term of a geometric sequence whose fourth term is $\dfrac{8}{9}$ and whose seventh term is $\dfrac{64}{243}$. $\dfrac{16}{27}$

In Exercises 37 to 46, find the sum of the geometric series.

37. $\displaystyle\sum_{n=1}^{5} 3^n$ 363

38. $\displaystyle\sum_{n=1}^{7} 2^n$ 254

39. $\displaystyle\sum_{n=1}^{6} \left(\dfrac{2}{3}\right)^n$ $\dfrac{1330}{729}$

▶ 40. $\displaystyle\sum_{n=1}^{14} \left(\dfrac{4}{3}\right)^n$ $\dfrac{1{,}054{,}609{,}948}{4{,}782{,}969} \approx 220.49$

41. $\displaystyle\sum_{n=0}^{8} \left(-\dfrac{2}{5}\right)^n$ $\dfrac{279{,}091}{390{,}625}$

42. $\displaystyle\sum_{n=0}^{7} \left(-\dfrac{1}{3}\right)^n$ $\dfrac{1640}{2187}$

43. $\displaystyle\sum_{n=1}^{10} (-2)^{n-1}$ -341

44. $\displaystyle\sum_{n=0}^{7} 2(5)^n$ 195,312

45. $\displaystyle\sum_{n=0}^{9} 5(3)^n$ 147,620

46. $\displaystyle\sum_{n=0}^{10} 2(-4)^n$ 1,677,722

In Exercises 47 to 56, find the sum of the infinite geometric series.

47. $\displaystyle\sum_{n=1}^{\infty} \left(\dfrac{1}{3}\right)^n$ $\dfrac{1}{2}$

48. $\displaystyle\sum_{n=1}^{\infty} \left(\dfrac{3}{4}\right)^n$ 3

49. $\displaystyle\sum_{n=1}^{\infty} \left(-\dfrac{2}{3}\right)^n$ $-\dfrac{2}{5}$

50. $\displaystyle\sum_{n=1}^{\infty} \left(-\dfrac{3}{5}\right)^n$ $-\dfrac{3}{8}$

51. $\displaystyle\sum_{n=1}^{\infty} \left(\dfrac{9}{100}\right)^n$ $\dfrac{9}{91}$

52. $\displaystyle\sum_{n=1}^{\infty} \left(\dfrac{7}{10}\right)^n$ $\dfrac{7}{3}$

53. $\displaystyle\sum_{n=1}^{\infty} (0.1)^n$ $\dfrac{1}{9}$

54. $\displaystyle\sum_{n=1}^{\infty} (0.5)^n$ 1

55. $\displaystyle\sum_{n=0}^{\infty} (-0.4)^n$ $\dfrac{5}{7}$

56. $\displaystyle\sum_{n=0}^{\infty} (-0.8)^n$ $\dfrac{5}{9}$

In Exercises 57 to 68, write each rational number as the quotient of two integers in simplest form.

57. $0.\overline{3}$ $\dfrac{1}{3}$

58. $0.\overline{5}$ $\dfrac{5}{9}$

59. $0.\overline{45}$ $\dfrac{5}{11}$

60. $0.\overline{63}$ $\dfrac{7}{11}$

61. $0.\overline{123}$ $\dfrac{41}{333}$

▶ 62. $0.\overline{395}$ $\dfrac{196}{495}$

63. $0.\overline{422}$ $\dfrac{422}{999}$

64. $0.\overline{355}$ $\dfrac{355}{999}$

65. $0.25\overline{4}$ $\dfrac{229}{900}$

66. $0.37\overline{2}$ $\dfrac{67}{180}$

67. $1.20\overline{84}$ $\dfrac{997}{825}$

68. $2.25\overline{90}$ $\dfrac{497}{220}$

69. **TIME VALUE OF MONEY** Find the future value of an ordinary annuity that calls for depositing $100 at the end of every 6 months for 8 years into an account that earns 9% interest compounded semiannually. $2271.93

▶ 70. **TIME VALUE OF MONEY** To save for the replacement of a computer, a business deposits $250 at the end of each month into an account that earns 8% annual interest compounded monthly. Find the future value of the ordinary annuity in 4 years. $14,087.48

CONNECTING CONCEPTS

71. If the sequence a_n is a geometric sequence, make a conjecture about the sequence $\log a_n$ and give a proof.
Because $\log r$ is a constant, the sequence $\log a_n$ is an arithmetic sequence.

72. If the sequence a_n is an arithmetic sequence, make a conjecture about the sequence 2^{a_n} and give a proof.
2^{a_n} is a geometric sequence.

73. ✐   Does $\sum\limits_{i=0}^{\infty} x^i$ $(x \neq 0)$ represent an infinite geometric series? Why or why not? Yes. The common ratio is x.

74. Consider a square with a side of length 1. Construct another square inside the first one by connecting the midpoints of the first square. What is the area of the inscribed square? Continue constructing squares in the same way. Find the area of the nth inscribed square. $a_n = \left(\dfrac{1}{2}\right)^{n-1}$

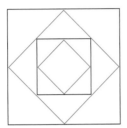

75. The product $P_n = a_1 \cdot a_2 \cdot a_3 \cdots a_n$ is called the nth partial product of a sequence. Find a formula for the nth partial product of the geometric sequence whose nth term is ar^{n-1}.
$a^n r^{[(n-1)n]/2}$

76. Let $f(x) = ab^x$, $a, b > 0$. Show that if x is restricted to positive integers n, then $f(n)$ is a geometric sequence.

77. PHYSICS A ball is dropped from a height of 5 feet. The ball rebounds 80% of the distance after each fall. Use an infinite geometric series to find the total distance the ball will travel. 45 ft

78. PENDULUM The bob of a pendulum swings through an arc of 30 inches on its first swing. Each successive swing is 90% of the length of the previous swing. Find the total distance the bob will travel. 300 in.

79. GENEALOGY Some people can trace their ancestry back 10 generations, which means two parents, four grandparents, eight great-grandparents, and so on. How many grandparents does such a family tree include? 2044

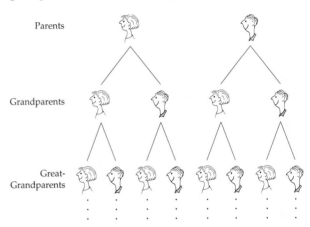

PREPARE FOR SECTION 8.4

80. Show that $\sum\limits_{i=1}^{n} \dfrac{1}{i(i + 1)} = \dfrac{n}{n + 1}$ when $n = 4$. [8.1]

81. Write $k(k + 1)(2k + 1) + 6(k + 1)^2$ as a product of linear factors. [P.4] $(k + 1)(k + 2)(2k + 3)$

82. Simplify: $\dfrac{k}{k + 1} + \dfrac{1}{(k + 1)(k + 2)}$ [P.5] $\dfrac{k + 1}{k + 2}$

83. What is the smallest natural number for which $n^2 > 2n + 1$? [P.1] 3

84. Let $a_n = n$ and $S_n = \dfrac{n(n + 1)}{2}$. Write $S_n + a_{n+1}$ in simplest form. [P.3/8.1] $\dfrac{(n + 1)(n + 2)}{2}$

85. Let $a_n = 2^n$ and $S_n = 2^{n+1} - 2$. Show that $S_n + a_{n+1} = 2(2^{n+1} - 1)$. [P.2/8.1]

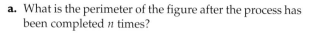

PROJECTS

1. 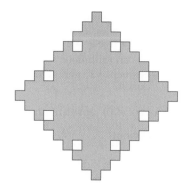 **FRACTALS** An example of a fractal was discussed on page 637. Here is another example of a fractal. Begin with a square with each side 1 unit long. Construct another, smaller square onto the middle third of each side. Continue this procedure of constructing similar but smaller squares on each of the line segments. The figure at the right shows the result after the process has been completed twice.

a. What is the perimeter of the figure after the process has been completed n times?

b. As n approaches infinity, what value does the perimeter approach?

c. What is the area of the figure after the process has been completed n times?

d. As n approaches infinity, what value does the area approach? *Suggestion:* The series in part **c.** is a geometric series after the first term.

SECTION 8.4   # MATHEMATICAL INDUCTION

- **PRINCIPLE OF MATHEMATICAL INDUCTION**
- **EXTENDED PRINCIPLE OF MATHEMATICAL INDUCTION**

Consider the sequence

$$\frac{1}{1 \cdot 2}, \frac{1}{2 \cdot 3}, \frac{1}{3 \cdot 4}, \ldots, \frac{1}{n(n+1)}, \ldots$$

and the sequence of partial sums for this sequence:

$$S_1 = \frac{1}{1 \cdot 2} = \frac{1}{2}$$

$$S_2 = \frac{1}{1 \cdot 2} + \frac{1}{2 \cdot 3} = \frac{2}{3}$$

$$S_3 = \frac{1}{1 \cdot 2} + \frac{1}{2 \cdot 3} + \frac{1}{3 \cdot 4} = \frac{3}{4}$$

$$S_4 = \frac{1}{1 \cdot 2} + \frac{1}{2 \cdot 3} + \frac{1}{3 \cdot 4} + \frac{1}{4 \cdot 5} = \frac{4}{5}$$

❓ QUESTION What does the pattern above suggest for the value of S_5?

❓ ANSWER $S_5 = \dfrac{5}{5+1} = \dfrac{5}{6}$

This pattern suggests the conjecture that

$$S_n = \frac{1}{1 \cdot 2} + \frac{1}{2 \cdot 3} + \frac{1}{3 \cdot 4} + \cdots + \frac{1}{n(n+1)} = \frac{n}{n+1}$$

How can we be sure that the pattern does not break down when $n = 50$ or maybe when $n = 2000$ or some other large number? As we will show, this conjecture is true for all values of n.

As a second example, consider the conjecture that the expression $n^2 - n + 41$ is a prime number for all positive integers n. To test this conjecture, we will try various values of n. See **Table 8.3**. The results suggest that the conjecture is true. But again, how can we be sure? In fact, this conjecture is false when $n = 41$. In that case we have

$$n^2 - n + 41 = (41)^2 - 41 + 41 = (41)^2$$

and $(41)^2$ is not a prime.

The last example illustrates that just verifying a conjecture for a few values of n does not constitute a proof of the conjecture. To prove theorems about statements involving positive integers, a process called *mathematical induction* is used. This process is based on an axiom called the *induction axiom*.

TABLE 8.3

n	$n^2 - n + 41$	
1	41	Prime
2	43	Prime
3	47	Prime
4	53	Prime
5	61	Prime

Induction Axiom

Suppose S is a set of positive integers with the following two properties:

1. 1 is an element of S.

2. If the positive integer k is in S, then $k + 1$ is in S.

Then S contains all the positive integers.

Part 2 of this axiom states that if some positive integer, say, 8, is in S, then $8 + 1$, or 9, is in S. But because 9 is in S, part 2 says that $9 + 1$, or 10, is in S, and so on. Part 1 states that 1 is in S. Thus 2 is in S; thus 3 is in S; thus 4 is in S;.... Therefore all the positive integers are in S.

● PRINCIPLE OF MATHEMATICAL INDUCTION

The induction axiom is used to prove the *Principle of Mathematical Induction*.

INSTRUCTOR NOTE

An induction proof can be likened to knocking over dominoes. First, knock over the first domino. Second, if the dominoes are arranged such that if one of them is knocked over, then so is the next one, then all the dominoes will be knocked over.

Principle of Mathematical Induction

Let P_n be a statement about a positive integer n. If

1. P_1 is true, and

2. the truth of P_k implies the truth of P_{k+1},

then P_n is true for all positive integers.

Part 2 of the Principle of Mathematical Induction is referred to as the **induction hypothesis.** When applying this step, we assume that the statement P_k is true, and then we try to prove that P_{k+1} is also true.

As an example, we will prove that the first conjecture we made in this section is true for all positive integers. Every induction proof has the two distinct parts stated in the theorem. First, we must show that the result is true for $n = 1$. Second, we assume that the statement is true for some positive integer k, and using that assumption, we prove that the statement is true for $n = k + 1$.

Prove that

$$S_n = \frac{1}{1 \cdot 2} + \frac{1}{2 \cdot 3} + \frac{1}{3 \cdot 4} + \cdots + \frac{1}{n(n + 1)} = \frac{n}{n + 1}$$

for all positive integers n.

Proof

1. For $n = 1$,

$$S_1 = \frac{1}{1(1 + 1)} = \frac{1}{2}, \text{ and } \frac{n}{n + 1} = \frac{1}{1 + 1} = \frac{1}{2}$$

The statement is true for $n = 1$.

2. Assume the statement is true for some positive integer k.

$$S_k = \frac{1}{1 \cdot 2} + \frac{1}{2 \cdot 3} + \frac{1}{3 \cdot 4} + \cdots + \frac{1}{k(k + 1)} = \frac{k}{k + 1} \qquad \text{• Induction hypothesis}$$

Now verify that the formula is true when $n = k + 1$. That is, verify that

$$S_{k+1} = \frac{k + 1}{(k + 1) + 1} = \frac{k + 1}{k + 2} \qquad \text{• This is the goal of the induction proof.}$$

It is helpful, when proving a theorem about sums, to note that

$$S_{k+1} = S_k + a_{k+1}$$

Begin by noting that $a_k = \dfrac{1}{k(k + 1)}$; thus, $a_{k+1} = \dfrac{1}{(k + 1)(k + 2)}$.

$$\begin{aligned}
S_{k+1} &= S_k + a_{k+1} \\
&= \frac{k}{k + 1} + \frac{1}{(k + 1)(k + 2)} \qquad \text{• By the induction hypothesis} \\
&\qquad\qquad\qquad\qquad\qquad\qquad\quad \text{and substituting for } a_{k+1} \\
&= \frac{k(k + 2)}{(k + 1)(k + 2)} + \frac{1}{(k + 1)(k + 2)} \\
&= \frac{k(k + 2) + 1}{(k + 1)(k + 2)} = \frac{k^2 + 2k + 1}{(k + 1)(k + 2)} = \frac{(k + 1)^2}{(k + 1)(k + 2)} \\
S_{k+1} &= \frac{k + 1}{k + 2}
\end{aligned}$$

Because we have verified the two parts of the Principle of Mathematical Induction, we can conclude that the statement is true for all positive integers. ◆

Alternative to Example 1
Prove that
$1^2 + 3^2 + 5^2 + \cdots + (2n - 1)^2 = \dfrac{n(2n + 1)(2n - 1)}{3}$.

EXAMPLE I   Prove by Mathematical Induction

Prove that $1^2 + 2^2 + 3^2 + \cdots + n^2 = \dfrac{n(n + 1)(2n + 1)}{6}$.

Solution

Verify the two parts of the Principle of Mathematical Induction.

1. Let $n = 1$.

$$S_1 = 1^2 = 1 = \dfrac{1(1 + 1)(2 \cdot 1 + 1)}{6}$$

2. Assume the statement is true for some positive integer k.

$$S_k = 1^2 + 2^2 + 3^2 + \cdots + k^2 = \dfrac{k(k + 1)(2k + 1)}{6} \qquad \bullet \text{ Induction hypothesis}$$

Verify that the statement is true when $n = k + 1$. Show that

$$S_{k+1} = \dfrac{(k + 1)(k + 2)(2k + 3)}{6}$$

Because $a_k = k^2$, $a_{k+1} = (k + 1)^2$.

$$S_{k+1} = \quad S_k \quad + a_{k+1}$$

$$= \dfrac{k(k + 1)(2k + 1)}{6} + (k + 1)^2$$

$$= \dfrac{k(k + 1)(2k + 1)}{6} + \dfrac{6(k + 1)^2}{6} = \dfrac{k(k + 1)(2k + 1) + 6(k + 1)^2}{6}$$

$$= \dfrac{(k + 1)[k(2k + 1) + 6(k + 1)]}{6} = \dfrac{(k + 1)(2k^2 + 7k + 6)}{6}$$

$$S_{k+1} = \dfrac{(k + 1)(k + 2)(2k + 3)}{6}$$

By the Principle of Mathematical Induction, the statement is true for all positive integers.

▶ **TRY EXERCISE 8, PAGE 668**

INSTRUCTOR NOTE
Students sometimes think that the first step of an inductive proof is unnecessary. But it is necessary to establish that a set S is nonempty. Without doing so, we can prove almost anything. For instance, here is an inductive "proof" that all marbles are red. Assume that the statement is true for $n = k$. Now add a marble to the set and remove one of the other marbles. By the inductive hypothesis, the new set consists entirely of red marbles. Now replace the red marble that was taken out. The new set consists of $k + 1$ red marbles. Thus the statement is true for $n = k + 1$. Therefore, all marbles are red. See the Projects at the end of this section for another example.

Mathematical induction can also be used to prove statements about sequences, products, and inequalities.

Alternative to Example 2
Prove that $\left(1 - \dfrac{1}{2}\right)\left(1 - \dfrac{2}{3}\right) \times$

$\left(1 - \dfrac{3}{4}\right) \cdots \left(1 - \dfrac{n}{n + 1}\right) = \dfrac{1}{(n + 1)!}$.

EXAMPLE 2   Prove a Product Formula by Mathematical Induction

Prove that

$$\left(1 + \dfrac{1}{1}\right)\left(1 + \dfrac{1}{2}\right)\left(1 + \dfrac{1}{3}\right) \cdots \left(1 + \dfrac{1}{n}\right) = n + 1$$

Continued ▶

Solution

1. Verify for $n = 1$.

$$\left(1 + \frac{1}{1}\right) = 2, \text{ and } 1 + 1 = 2$$

2. Assume the statement is true for some positive integer k.

$$P_k = \left(1 + \frac{1}{1}\right)\left(1 + \frac{1}{2}\right)\left(1 + \frac{1}{3}\right)\cdots\left(1 + \frac{1}{k}\right) = k + 1 \qquad \text{• Induction hypothesis}$$

Verify that the statement is true when $n = k + 1$. That is, prove that $P_{k+1} = k + 2$.

$$P_{k+1} = \left(1 + \frac{1}{1}\right)\left(1 + \frac{1}{2}\right)\left(1 + \frac{1}{3}\right)\cdots\left(1 + \frac{1}{k}\right)\left(1 + \frac{1}{k+1}\right)$$

$$= P_k\left(1 + \frac{1}{k+1}\right) = (k+1)\left(1 + \frac{1}{k+1}\right) = k + 1 + 1$$

$$P_{k+1} = k + 2$$

By the Principle of Mathematical Induction, the statement is true for all positive integers.

▶ **TRY EXERCISE 12, PAGE 668**

Alternative to Example 3
Prove that $2n - 1 < 2^n$ for all positive integers.

EXAMPLE 3 **Prove an Inequality by Mathematical Induction**

Prove that $1 + 2n \leq 3^n$ for all positive integers.

Solution

1. Let $n = 1$. Then $1 + 2(1) = 3 \leq 3^1$. The statement is true when n is 1.

2. Assume the statement is true for some positive integer k.

$$1 + 2k \leq 3^k \qquad \text{• Induction hypothesis}$$

Now prove that the statement is true for $n = k + 1$. That is, prove that $1 + 2(k + 1) \leq 3^{k+1}$.

$$3^{k+1} = 3^k(3)$$
$$\geq (1 + 2k)(3) \qquad \text{• Because, by the induction hypothesis,}\ 1 + 2k \leq 3^k.$$
$$= 6k + 3$$
$$> 2k + 2 + 1 \qquad \text{• } 6k > 2k, \text{ and } 3 = 2 + 1.$$
$$= 2(k + 1) + 1$$

Thus $1 + 2(k + 1) \leq 3^{k+1}$.

By the Principle of Mathematical Induction, $1 + 2k \leq 3^k$ for all positive integers.

INSTRUCTOR NOTE
This example shows that sometimes rewriting an expression is not an obvious step. The step

$6k + 3 > 2k + 2 + 1$

is difficult for many students.

▶ **TRY EXERCISE 16, PAGE 668**

CONNECTING CONCEPTS

In Exercises 31 to 35, use mathematical induction to prove each statement.

31. Using a calculator, find the smallest integer N for which $\log N! > N$. Now prove that $\log n! > n$ for all $n > N$.

32. Let a_n be a sequence for which there is a number r and an integer N for which $\dfrac{a_{n+1}}{a_n} < r$ for $n \geq N$. Show that $a_{N+k} < a_N r^k$ for each positive integer k.

33. For constant positive integers m and n, show that $(x^m)^n = x^{mn}$.

34. Prove that $\displaystyle\sum_{i=0}^{n} \dfrac{1}{i!} \leq 3 - \dfrac{1}{n}$ for all positive integers n.

35. Prove that $\left(\dfrac{n+1}{n}\right)^n < 3$ for all integers $n \geq 3$.

PREPARE FOR SECTION 8.5
---

36. Expand $(a + b)^3$. [P.3] $a^3 + 3a^2b + 3ab^2 + b^3$

37. Evaluate $5!$. [8.1] 120

38. Evaluate $0!$. [8.1] 1

39. Evaluate $\dfrac{n!}{k!\,(n-k)!}$ when $n = 6$ and $k = 2$. [8.1] 15

40. Evaluate $\dfrac{n!}{k!\,(n-k)!}$ when $n = 7$ and $k = 3$. [8.1] 35

41. Evaluate $\dfrac{n!}{k!\,(n-k)!}$ when $n = 10$ and $k = 10$. [8.1] 1

PROJECTS
---

1. STEPS IN A MATHEMATICAL INDUCTION PROOF In every proof by mathematical induction, it is important that both parts of the Principle of Mathematical Induction be verified. For instance, consider the formula

$$2 + 4 + 8 + \cdots + 2^n = 2^{n+1} + 1$$

a. Show that if we assume the formula is true for some positive integer k, then the formula is true for $k + 1$.

b. Show that the formula is not true for $n = 1$.

c. Show that the formula is not valid for any value of n by showing that the left side is always an even number and the right side is always an odd number.

d. ✎ Explain how this shows that both steps of the Principle of Mathematical Induction must be verified.

2. THE TOWER OF HANOI The Tower of Hanoi is a game that consists of three pegs and n disks of distinct diameter arranged on one of the pegs such that the largest disk is on the bottom, the next largest is on top of the largest, and so on. The object of the game is to move all the disks from one peg to a second peg. The rules require that only one

disk be moved at a time and that a larger disk may not be placed on a smaller disk. All pegs may be used.

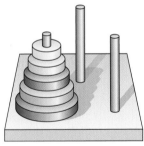

a. Show that it is possible to complete the game in $2^n - 1$ moves.

b. A legend says that in the center of the universe, high priests have the task of moving 64 golden disks from one of three diamond needles by using the rules of the Tower of Hanoi game. When they have completed the transfer, the universe will cease to exist. If one move is made every second, and the priests started 5 billion years ago (the approximate age of Earth), for how many more years does the legend predict the universe will continue to exist?

| SECTION 8.5 | THE BINOMIAL THEOREM |

In certain situations in mathematics it is necessary to write $(a + b)^n$ as the sum of its terms. Because $(a + b)$ is a binomial, this process is called **expanding the binomial.** For small values of n, it is relatively easy to write the expansion by using multiplication.

Earlier in the text we found that

$$(a + b)^1 = a + b$$

$$(a + b)^2 = a^2 + 2ab + b^2$$

$$(a + b)^3 = a^3 + 3a^2b + 3ab^2 + b^3$$

Building on these expansions, we can write a few more.

$$(a + b)^4 = a^4 + 4a^3b + 6a^2b^2 + 4ab^3 + b^4$$

$$(a + b)^5 = a^5 + 5a^4b + 10a^3b^2 + 10a^2b^3 + 5ab^4 + b^5$$

We could continue to build on previous expansions and eventually have quite a comprehensive list of binomial expansions. Instead, however, we will look for a theorem that will enable us to expand $(a + b)^n$ directly without multiplying.

Look at the variable parts of each expansion above. Note that for each $n = 1, 2, 3, 4, 5,$

● The first term is a^n. The exponent on a decreases by 1 for each successive term.

● The exponent on b increases by 1 for each successive term. The last term is b^n.

● The degree of each term is n.

❓ QUESTION   What is the degree of the fourth term of the expansion of $(a + b)^{11}$?

To find a pattern for the coefficients in each expansion of $(a + b)^n$, first note that there are $n + 1$ terms and that the coefficient of the first and last term is 1. To find the remaining coefficients, consider the expansion of $(a + b)^5$.

$$(a + b)^5 = a^5 + 5a^4b + 10a^3b^2 + 10a^2b^3 + 5ab^4 + b^5$$

$$\frac{5}{1} = 5 \qquad \frac{5 \cdot 4}{2 \cdot 1} = 10 \qquad \frac{5 \cdot 4 \cdot 3}{3 \cdot 2 \cdot 1} = 10 \qquad \frac{5 \cdot 4 \cdot 3 \cdot 2}{4 \cdot 3 \cdot 2 \cdot 1} = 5$$

Observe from these patterns that there is a strong relationship to factorials. In fact, we can express each coefficient by using factorial notation.

$$\frac{5!}{1!\,4!} = 5 \qquad \frac{5!}{2!\,3!} = 10 \qquad \frac{5!}{3!\,2!} = 10 \qquad \frac{5!}{4!\,1!} = 5$$

In each denominator the first factorial is the exponent of b, and the second factorial is the exponent of a.

❓ ANSWER   11

In general, we will conjecture that the coefficient of the term $a^{n-k}b^k$ in the expansion of $(a + b)^n$ is $\dfrac{n!}{k!\,(n-k)!}$. Each coefficient of a term of a binomial expansion is called a **binomial coefficient** and is denoted by $\dbinom{n}{k}$.

INSTRUCTOR NOTE

Ask students to evaluate $\dbinom{7}{0}$.

● **1**

Formula for a Binomial Coefficient

The coefficient of the term whose variable part is $a^{n-k}b^k$ in the expansion of $(a + b)^n$ is

$$\binom{n}{k} = \frac{n!}{k!\,(n-k)!}$$

The first term of the expansion of $(a + b)^n$ can be thought of as $a^n b^0$. In this case, we can calculate the coefficient of this term as

$$\binom{n}{0} = \frac{n!}{0!\,(n-0)!} = \frac{n!}{1 \cdot n!} = 1$$

Alternative to Example 1
Evaluate each binomial coefficient.

a. $\dbinom{10}{3}$

 ● **120**

b. $\dbinom{15}{15}$

 ● **1**

EXAMPLE 1 Evaluate a Binomial Coefficient

Evaluate each binomial coefficient. **a.** $\dbinom{9}{6}$ **b.** $\dbinom{10}{10}$

Solution

a. $\dbinom{9}{6} = \dfrac{9!}{6!\,(9-6)!} = \dfrac{9!}{6!\,3!} = \dfrac{9 \cdot 8 \cdot 7 \cdot 6!}{6! \cdot 3 \cdot 2 \cdot 1} = 84$

b. $\dbinom{10}{10} = \dfrac{10!}{10!\,(10-10)!} = \dfrac{10!}{10!\,0!} = 1.$ • Remember that $0! = 1$.

▶ **TRY EXERCISE 4, PAGE 674**

● BINOMIAL THEOREM

We are now ready to state the Binomial Theorem for positive integers.

Binomial Theorem for Positive Integers

If n is a positive integer, then

$$(a + b)^n = \sum_{i=0}^{n} \binom{n}{i} a^{n-i} b^i$$

$$= \binom{n}{0} a^n + \binom{n}{1} a^{n-1} b + \binom{n}{2} a^{n-2} b^2 + \cdots + \binom{n}{n} b^n$$

Alternative to Example 2
Expand $(3x^2 + 2)^3$.

○ $27x^6 + 54x^4 + 36x^2 + 8$

EXAMPLE 2 **Expand the Sum of Two Terms**

Expand: $(2x^2 + 3)^4$

Solution

$$(2x^2 + 3)^4 = \binom{4}{0}(2x^2)^4 + \binom{4}{1}(2x^2)^3(3) + \binom{4}{2}(2x^2)^2(3)^2$$

$$+ \binom{4}{3}(2x^2)(3)^3 + \binom{4}{4}(3)^4$$

$$= 16x^8 + 96x^6 + 216x^4 + 216x^2 + 81$$

▶ **TRY EXERCISE 18, PAGE 674**

Alternative to Example 3
Expand $\left(x - \sqrt{2}\right)^6$.

○ $x^6 - 6\sqrt{2}x^5 + 30x^4 - 40\sqrt{2}x^3 + 60x^2 - 24\sqrt{2}x + 8$

take note

If exactly one of the terms a or b in $(a + b)^n$ is negative, the terms of the expansion alternate in sign.

EXAMPLE 3 **Expand a Difference of Two Terms**

Expand: $\left(\sqrt{x} - 2y\right)^5$

Solution

$$\left(\sqrt{x} - 2y\right)^5 = \binom{5}{0}\left(\sqrt{x}\right)^5 + \binom{5}{1}\left(\sqrt{x}\right)^4(-2y) + \binom{5}{2}\left(\sqrt{x}\right)^3(-2y)^2$$

$$+ \binom{5}{3}\left(\sqrt{x}\right)^2(-2y)^3 + \binom{5}{4}\left(\sqrt{x}\right)(-2y)^4 + \binom{5}{5}(-2y)^5$$

$$= x^{5/2} - 10x^2y + 40x^{3/2}y^2 - 80xy^3 + 80x^{1/2}y^4 - 32y^5$$

▶ **TRY EXERCISE 20, PAGE 674**

● ***i*th TERM OF A BINOMIAL EXPANSION**

The Binomial Theorem also can be used to find a specific term in the expansion of $(a + b)^n$.

Formula for the *i*th Term of a Binomial Expansion

take note

The exponent on b is 1 less than the term number.

The *i*th term of the expansion of $(a + b)^n$ is given by

$$\binom{n}{i - 1}a^{n-i+1}b^{i-1}$$

Alternative to Example 4
Find the sixth term in the expansion of
$(5x^2 - 2y^3)^8$.

● $-224{,}000x^6y^{15}$

EXAMPLE 4   Find the *i*th Term of a Binomial Expansion

Find the fourth term in the expansion of $(2x^3 - 3y^2)^5$.

Solution

With $a = 2x^3$ and $b = -3y^2$, and using the preceding theorem with $i = 4$ and $n = 5$, we have

$$\binom{5}{3}(2x^3)^2(-3y^2)^3 = -1080x^6y^6$$

The fourth term is $-1080x^6y^6$.

▶ **TRY EXERCISE 34, PAGE 674**

● PASCAL'S TRIANGLE

A pattern for the coefficients of the terms of an expanded binomial can be found by writing the coefficients in a triangular array known as **Pascal's Triangle**. See **Figure 8.1.**

Each row begins and ends with the number 1. Any other number in a row is the sum of the two closest numbers above it. For example, $4 + 6 = 10$. Thus each succeeding row can be found from the preceding row.

INSTRUCTOR NOTE

If Pascal's Triangle is written as shown below, each sum of a diagonal is a term of the Fibonacci sequence.

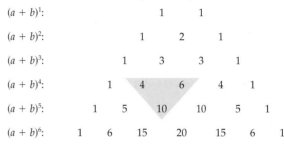

FIGURE 8.1

Pascal's Triangle can be used to expand a binomial for small values of n. For instance, the seventh row of Pascal's Triangle is

$$1 \quad 7 \quad 21 \quad 35 \quad 35 \quad 21 \quad 7 \quad 1$$

Therefore,

$$(a + b)^7 = a^7 + 7a^6b + 21a^5b^2 + 35a^4b^3 + 35a^3b^4 + 21a^2b^5 + 7ab^6 + b^7$$

👥🖊 TOPICS FOR DISCUSSION

1. Discuss the use of the Binomial Theorem.

2. Can the Binomial Theorem be used to expand $(a + b)^n$, n a natural number, for any expressions a and b? Why or why not?

3. What is Pascal's Triangle and how is it related to expanding a binomial?

4. Explain how Pascal's Triangle suggests that $\binom{n-1}{k-1} + \binom{n-1}{k} = \binom{n}{k}$.

EXERCISE SET 8.5

—Suggested Assignment: Exercises 1–53, every other odd; 63–67.
—Answers to Exercises 9–28 are on page AA35.

In Exercises 1 to 8, evaluate the binomial coefficient.

1. $\dbinom{7}{4}$ 35   **2.** $\dbinom{8}{6}$ 28   **3.** $\dbinom{9}{2}$ 36   ▶ **4.** $\dbinom{10}{5}$ 252

5. $\dbinom{12}{9}$ 220   **6.** $\dbinom{6}{5}$ 6   **7.** $\dbinom{11}{0}$ 1   **8.** $\dbinom{14}{14}$ 1

In Exercises 9 to 28, expand the binomial.

9. $(x - y)^6$ **10.** $(a - b)^5$ **11.** $(x + 3)^5$

12. $(x - 5)^4$ **13.** $(2x - 1)^7$ **14.** $(2x + y)^6$

15. $(x + 3y)^6$ **16.** $(x - 4y)^5$ **17.** $(2x - 5y)^4$

▶ **18.** $(3x + 2y)^4$ **19.** $\left(x + \dfrac{1}{x}\right)^6$ ▶ **20.** $\left(2x - \sqrt{y}\right)^7$

21. $(x^2 - 4)^7$ **22.** $(x - y^3)^6$ **23.** $(2x^2 + y^3)^5$

24. $(2x - y^3)^6$ **25.** $\left(\dfrac{2}{x} - \dfrac{x}{2}\right)^4$ **26.** $\left(\dfrac{a}{b} + \dfrac{b}{a}\right)^3$

27. $(s^{-2} + s^2)^6$ **28.** $(2r^{-1} + s^{-1})^5$

In Exercises 29 to 36, find the indicated term without expanding.

29. $(3x - y)^{10}$; eighth term $-3240x^3y^7$

30. $(x + 2y)^{12}$; fourth term $1760x^9y^3$

31. $(x + 4y)^{12}$; third term $1056x^{10}y^2$

32. $(2x - 1)^{14}$; thirteenth term $364x^2$

33. $\left(\sqrt{x} - \sqrt{y}\right)^9$; fifth term $126x^2y^2\sqrt{x}$

34. $(x^{-1/2} + x^{1/2})^{10}$; sixth term 252

35. $\left(\dfrac{a}{b} + \dfrac{b}{a}\right)^{11}$; ninth term $\dfrac{165b^5}{a^5}$

36. $\left(\dfrac{3}{x} - \dfrac{x}{3}\right)^{13}$; seventh term $\dfrac{5148}{x}$

37. Find the term that contains b^8 in the expansion of $(2a - b)^{10}$. $180a^2b^8$

38. Find the term that contains s^7 in the expansion of $(3r + 2s)^9$. $41{,}472r^2s^7$

39. Find the term that contains y^8 in the expansion of $(2x + y^2)^6$. $60x^2y^8$

40. Find the term that contains b^9 in the expansion of $(a - b^3)^8$. $-56a^5b^9$

41. Find the middle term of $(3a - b)^{10}$. $-61{,}236a^5b^5$

42. Find the middle term of $(a + b^2)^8$. $70a^4b^8$

43. Find the two middle terms of $(s^{-1} + s)^9$. $126s^{-1}, 126s$

44. Find the two middle terms of $(x^{1/2} - y^{1/2})^7$. $-35x^2y^{3/2}, 35x^{3/2}y^2$

In Exercises 45 to 50, use the Binomial Theorem to simplify the powers of the complex numbers.

45. $(2 - i)^4$ $-7 - 24i$ **46.** $(3 + 2i)^3$ $-9 + 46i$

47. $(1 + 2i)^5$ $41 - 38i$ **48.** $(1 - 3i)^5$ $316 + 12i$

49. $\left(\dfrac{\sqrt{2}}{2} + i\dfrac{\sqrt{2}}{2}\right)^8$ 1   **50.** $\left(\dfrac{1}{2} + i\dfrac{\sqrt{3}}{2}\right)^6$ 1

CONNECTING CONCEPTS

51. Let n be a positive integer. Expand and simplify $\dfrac{(x + h)^n - x^n}{h}$, where x is any real number and $h \neq 0$.
$nx^{n-1} + \dfrac{n(n-1)x^{n-2}h}{2} + \dfrac{n(n-1)(n-2)x^{n-3}h^2}{6} + \cdots + h^{n-1}$

52. Show that $\dbinom{n}{k} = \dbinom{n}{n-k}$ for all positive integers n and k with $0 \le k \le n$.

53. Show that $\sum_{k=0}^{n} \dbinom{n}{k} = 2^n$. (*Hint:* Use the Binomial Theorem with $x = 1, y = 1$.)

54. Prove that $\dbinom{n}{k} + \dbinom{n}{k+1} = \dbinom{n+1}{k+1}$, n and k integers, $0 \le k \le n$.

55. Prove that $\displaystyle\sum_{i=0}^{n} (-1)^i \binom{n}{i} = 0$.

56. Approximate $(0.98)^8$ by evaluating the first three terms of $(1 - 0.02)^8$. 0.8512

57. Approximate $(1.02)^8$ by evaluating the first three terms of $(1 + 0.02)^8$. 1.1712

There is an extension of the Binomial Theorem called the *Multinomial Theorem.* **This theorem is used in determining probabilities.** *Multinomial Theorem:* **If *n*, *r*, and *k* are positive integers, then the coefficient of $a^r b^k c^{n-r-k}$ in the expansion of $(a + b + c)^n$ is**

$$\frac{n!}{r!\,k!\,(n - r - k)!}$$

In Exercises 58 to 61, use the Multinomial Theorem to find the indicated coefficient.

58. Find the coefficient of $a^2 b^3 c^5$ in the expansion of $(a + b + c)^{10}$. 2520

59. Find the coefficient of $a^5 b^2 c^2$ in the expansion of $(a + b + c)^9$. 756

60. Find the coefficient of $a^4 b^5$ in the expansion of $(a + b + c)^9$. 126

61. Find the coefficient of $a^3 c^5$ in the expansion of $(a + b + c)^8$. 56

PREPARE FOR SECTION 8.6

62. Evaluate: 7! [8.1] 5040

63. Evaluate: 0! [8.1] 1

64. Evaluate $\binom{n}{k}$ when $n = 7$ and $k = 1$. [8.1] 7

65. Evaluate $\binom{n}{k}$ when $n = 8$ and $k = 5$. [8.1] 56

66. Evaluate $\dfrac{n!}{(n - k)!}$ when $n = 10$ and $k = 2$. [8.1] 90

67. Evaluate $\dfrac{n!}{(n - k)!}$ when $n = 6$ and $k = 6$. [8.1] 720

PROJECTS

1. **PASCAL'S TRIANGLE** Write an essay on Pascal's Triangle. Include some of the earliest known examples of the triangle and some of its applications.

2. **SOME OTHER FUNCTIONS** Do some research and determine a definition of positive integers for each of the following types of numbers. Give examples of calculations using each type of number.

    a. Pochammer (m, n) **b.** double factorial $(n!!)$

SECTION **8.6**

PERMUTATIONS AND COMBINATIONS

- **FUNDAMENTAL COUNTING PRINCIPLE**
- **PERMUTATIONS**
- **COMBINATIONS**

● FUNDAMENTAL COUNTING PRINCIPLE

Suppose that an electronics store offers a three-component stereo system for $250. A buyer must choose one amplifier, one tuner, and one pair of speakers. If the store has two models of amplifiers, three models of tuners, and two speaker models, how many different stereo systems could a consumer purchase?

This problem belongs to a class of problems called *counting problems*. The problem is to determine the number of ways in which the conditions of the problem can be satisfied. One way to do this is to make a tree diagram and then count the items on the list. We will organize the list in a table using A_1 and A_2 for the amplifiers; T_1, T_2, and T_3 for the tuners; and S_1 and S_2 for the speakers. See **Figure 8.2.**

By counting the possible systems that can be purchased, we find there are 12 different systems. Another way to arrive at this result is to find the product of the numbers of options available.

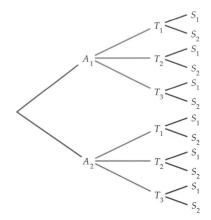

P **FIGURE 8.2**

$$\begin{array}{ccccccc} \text{Number of} & & \text{number of} & & \text{number of} & & \text{number of} \\ \text{amplifiers} & \times & \text{tuners} & \times & \text{speakers} & = & \text{systems} \\ 2 & \times & 3 & \times & 2 & = & 12 \end{array}$$

In some states, a standard car license plate consists of a nonzero digit, followed by three letters, followed by three more digits. What is the maximum number of car license plates of this type that could be issued? If we begin a list of the possible license plates, it soon becomes apparent that listing them all would be very time-consuming and impractical.

1AAA000,   1AAA001,   1AAA002,   1AAA003,…

Instead, the following counting principle is used. This principle forms the basis for all counting problems.

> ### Fundamental Counting Principle
>
> Let $T_1, T_2, T_3, \ldots, T_n$ be a sequence of n conditions. Suppose that T_1 can occur in m_1 ways, T_2 can occur in m_2 ways, T_3 can occur in m_3 ways, and so on until finally T_n can occur in m_n ways. Then the number of ways of satisfying the conditions $T_1, T_2, T_3, \ldots, T_n$ in succession is given by the product
>
> $$m_1 m_2 m_3 \cdots m_n$$

TABLE 8.4

Condition	Number of ways
T_1: a nonzero digit	$m_1 = 9$
T_2: a letter	$m_2 = 26$
T_3: a letter	$m_3 = 26$
T_4: a letter	$m_4 = 26$
T_5: a digit	$m_5 = 10$
T_6: a digit	$m_6 = 10$
T_7: a digit	$m_7 = 10$

To apply the counting principle to the license plate problem, first find the number of ways each condition can be satisfied, as shown in **Table 8.4.** Thus, we have

$$\begin{array}{c} \text{Number of car} \\ \text{license plates} \end{array} = 9 \cdot 26 \cdot 26 \cdot 26 \cdot 10 \cdot 10 \cdot 10 = 158{,}184{,}000$$

? QUESTION Suppose that a license plate begins with two letters. How many different ways could the license plate begin?

Alternative to Example 1
A model railroader is putting together a small railway system consisting of a locomotive, a boxcar, and a caboose. The hobby store offers a choice of four locomotives, seven boxcars, and five cabooses. How many different railway systems can the railroader make?

• **140**

EXAMPLE 1 Apply the Fundamental Counting Principle

An automobile dealer offers three mid-size cars. A customer selecting one of these cars must choose one of three different engines, one of five different colors, and one of four different interior packages. How many different selections can the customer make?

Solution

T_1: mid-size car $m_1 = 3$

T_2: engine $m_2 = 3$

T_3: color $m_3 = 5$

T_4: interior $m_4 = 4$

The number of different selections is $3 \cdot 3 \cdot 5 \cdot 4 = 180$.

▶ **TRY EXERCISE 12, PAGE 681**

• **PERMUTATIONS**

An application of the Fundamental Counting Principle is to determine the number of arrangements of distinct elements in a definite order.

Permutation

A **permutation** is an arrangement of distinct objects in a definite order.

For example, *abc* and *bca* are two of the possible permutations of the three elements *a*, *b*, and *c*.

Consider a race with 10 runners. In how many different orders can the runners finish first, second, and third (assuming no ties)?

Any one of the 10 runners could finish first: $m_1 = 10$

Any one of the remaining 9 runners could be second: $m_2 = 9$

Any one of the remaining 8 runners could be third: $m_3 = 8$

By the Fundamental Counting Principle, there are $10 \cdot 9 \cdot 8 = 720$ possible first-, second-, and third-place finishes for the 10 runners. Using the language of permutations, we would say, "There are 720 permutations of 10 objects (the runners) taken 3 (the possible finishes) at a time."

Permutations occur so frequently in counting problems that a formula, rather than the counting principle, is often used.

INTEGRATING TECHNOLOGY

Some graphing calculators use the notation *nPr* to represent the number of permutations of *n* objects taken *r* at a time. The calculation of the number of permutations of 15 objects taken 4 at a time is shown below.

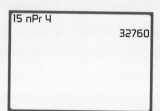

```
15 nPr 4
              32760
```

? ANSWER $26 \times 26 = 676$

Formula for the Number of Permutations of *n* Distinct Objects Taken *r* at a Time

The number of permutations of *n* distinct objects taken *r* at a time is

$$P(n, r) = \frac{n!}{(n - r)!}$$

Alternative to Example 2

In how many ways can first prize, second prize, and third prize be awarded to 100 entrants in a raffle?

● **970,200**

EXAMPLE 2   Find the Number of Permutations

In how many ways can a president, a vice president, a secretary, and a treasurer be selected from a committee of 15 people?

Solution

There are 15 distinct people to place in four positions. Thus $n = 15$ and $r = 4$.

$$P(15, 4) = \frac{15!}{(15 - 4)!} = \frac{15!}{11!} = \frac{15 \cdot 14 \cdot 13 \cdot 12 \cdot 11!}{11!} = 32{,}760$$

▶ **TRY EXERCISE 16, PAGE 681**

Alternative to Example 3

Eight people attend a concert and all sit in the same row containing eight seats.

a. Find the number of ways the group can sit together.
  ● **40,320**

b. Find the number of ways the group can sit together if two people in the group must sit one at each end.
  ● **1440**

c. Find the number of ways the group can sit together if one person in the group must sit at an end.
  ● **10,080**

EXAMPLE 3   Find the Number of Seating Permutations

Six people attend a movie and all sit in the same row containing six seats.

a. Find the number of ways the group can sit together.

b. Find the number of ways the group can sit together if two people in the group must sit side-by-side.

c. Find the number of ways the group can sit together if two people in the group refuse to sit side-by-side.

Solution

a. There are six distinct people to place in six distinct positions. Thus $n = 6$ and $r = 6$.

$$P(6, 6) = \frac{6!}{(6 - 6)!} = \frac{6!}{0!} = \frac{6!}{1} = 720$$

b. Think of the two people who must sit together as a single object and count the number of arrangements of the *five* objects (*AB*), *C*, *D*, *E*, and *F*.

Thus $n = 5$ and $r = 5$.

$$P(5, 5) = \frac{5!}{(5 - 5)!} = \frac{5!}{0!} = \frac{5!}{1} = 120$$

There are also 120 arrangements with A and B reversed [(BA), C, D, E, F]. Thus the total number of arrangements is $120 + 120 = 240$.

c. From part **a.**, there are 720 possible seating arrangements. From part **b.**, there are 240 arrangements with two specific people next to each other. Thus there are $720 - 240 = 480$ arrangements in which two specific people are not seated together.

▶ **TRY EXERCISE 22, PAGE 681**

● COMBINATIONS

Up to this point we have been counting the number of distinct arrangements of objects. In some cases we may be interested in determining the number of ways of selecting objects without regard to the order of the selection. For example, suppose we want to select a committee of three people from five candidates denoted by A, B, C, D, and E. One possible committee is A, C, D. If we select D, C, A, we still have the same committee because the order of the selection is not important. An arrangement of objects for which the order of the selection is not important is a **combination.**

---

take note

Recall that a binomial coefficient is

given by $\binom{n}{r} = \dfrac{n!}{r!\,(n - r)!}$, which is

the same as $C(n, r)$.

Formula for the Number of Combinations of n Objects Taken r at a Time

The number of combinations of n objects taken r at a time is

$$C(n, r) = \frac{n!}{r!\,(n - r)!}$$

Alternative to Example 4

A standard deck of playing cards consists of 52 cards. How many 13-card hands can be chosen from this deck?

● $C(52, 13) = 635{,}013{,}559{,}600$

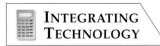 **INTEGRATING TECHNOLOGY**

Some calculators use the notation nCr to represent a combination of n objects taken r at a time.

EXAMPLE 4   Find the Number of Combinations

A standard deck of playing cards consists of 52 cards. How many five-card hands can be chosen from this deck?

Solution

We have $n = 52$ and $r = 5$. Thus

$$C(52, 5) = \frac{52!}{5!\,(52 - 5)!} = \frac{52!}{5!\,47!} = \frac{52 \cdot 51 \cdot 50 \cdot 49 \cdot 48 \cdot 47!}{5 \cdot 4 \cdot 3 \cdot 2 \cdot 1 \cdot 47!} = 2{,}598{,}960$$

▶ **TRY EXERCISE 20, PAGE 681**

Alternative to Example 5
A commemorative album is to feature both color and black-and-white photographs on its dedication page. There are twelve photographs, five of which are black-and-white. If five photographs are chosen to be on the dedication page of the commemorative album, in how many ways can the selection of photographs for the dedication page include exactly two black-and-white photographs?

● **350**

INSTRUCTOR NOTE
Many students have a difficult time distinguishing between a permutation and a combination. A telephone number is a permutation; dialing 2458 is different from dialing 4258. However, in a card game, receiving the ace of hearts, king of hearts, queen of hearts, jack of hearts, and ten of hearts is no different from receiving the queen, king, ace, ten and jack of hearts.

EXAMPLE 5   **Find the Number of Combinations**

A chemist has nine solution samples, of which four are type A and five are type B. If the chemist chooses three of the solutions at random, determine in how many ways the chemist can choose exactly one type A solution.

Solution

The chemist has chosen three solutions, one of which is type A. If one is type A, then two are type B. The number of ways of choosing one type A solution from four type A solutions is $C(4, 1)$.

$$C(4, 1) = \frac{4!}{1!\,(4 - 1)!} = \frac{4!}{1!\,3!} = 4$$

The number of ways of choosing two type B solutions from five type B solutions is $C(5, 2)$.

$$C(5, 2) = \frac{5!}{2!\,(5 - 2)!} = \frac{5!}{2!\,3!} = 10$$

By the counting principle, there are

$$C(4, 1) \cdot C(5, 2) = 4 \cdot 10 = 40$$

ways to choose one type A and two type B solutions.

▶ **TRY EXERCISE 30, PAGE 682**

     The difficult part of counting is determining whether to use the counting principle, the permutation formula, or the combination formula. Following is a summary of guidelines.

Guidelines for Solving Counting Problems

1. The counting principle will always work but is not always the easiest method to apply.

2. When reading a problem, ask yourself, "Is the order of the selection process important?" If the answer is yes, the arrangements are permutations. If the answer is no, the arrangements are combinations.

  TOPICS FOR DISCUSSION

1. Discuss the Fundamental Counting Principle and how it is used.

2. Discuss the difference between a permutation and a combination.

3. Explain why $\binom{n}{k}$ occurs as a coefficient in the binomial formula.

EXERCISE SET 8.6 —*Suggested Assignment: Exercises 1–43, every other odd; 47, 49, 53–59.*

In Exercises 1 to 10, evaluate each quantity.

1. $P(6, 2)$
30

2. $P(8, 7)$
40,320

3. $C(8, 4)$
70

4. $C(9, 2)$
36

5. $P(8, 0)$
1

6. $P(9, 9)$
362,880

7. $C(7, 7)$
1

8. $C(6, 0)$
1

9. $C(10, 4)$
210

10. $P(10, 4)$
5040

11. COMPUTER SYSTEMS A computer manufacturer offers a computer system with three different disk drives, two different monitors, and two different keyboards. How many different computer systems could a consumer purchase from this manufacturer? 12

▶ 12. COLOR MONITORS A computer monitor produces color by blending colors on *palettes*. If a computer monitor has four palettes and each palette has four colors, how many blended colors can be formed? Assume each palette must be used each time. 256

13. COMPUTER SCIENCE A 4-digit binary number is a sequence of four digits consisting of 0 or 1. For instance, 0011 and 1011 are binary numbers. How many four-digit binary numbers are possible? 16

14. COMPUTER MEMORY An integer is stored in a computer's memory as a series of zeros and ones. Each memory unit contains eight spaces for a zero or a one. The first space is used for the sign of the number, and the remaining seven spaces are used for the integer. How many positive integers can be stored in one memory unit of this computer? 128

15. SCHEDULING In how many different ways can six employees be assigned to six different jobs? 720

▶ 16. CONTEST WINNERS First-, second-, and third-place prizes are to be awarded in a dance contest in which 12 contestants are entered. In how many ways can the prizes be awarded? 1320

17. MAILBOXES There are five mailboxes outside a post office. In how many ways can three letters be deposited into the five boxes? 125

18. COMMITTEE MEMBERSHIP How many different committees of three people can be selected from nine people? 84

19. TEST QUESTIONS A professor provides to a class 25 possible essay questions for an upcoming test. Of the 25 questions, the professor will ask 5 of the questions on the exam. How many different tests can the professor prepare? 53,130

▶ 20. TENNIS MATCHES Twenty-six people enter a tennis tournament. How many different first-round matches are possible if each player can be matched with any other player? 325

21. EMPLOYEE INITIALS A company has more than 676 employees. Explain why there must be at least two employees who have the same first and last initials.
Answer on bottom of page.

▶ 22. SEATING ARRANGEMENTS A car holds six passengers, three in the front seat and three in the back seat. How many different seating arrangements of six people are possible if one person refuses to sit in front and one person refuses to sit in back? 216

23. COMMITTEE MEMBERSHIP A committee of six people is chosen from six senators and eight representatives. How many committees are possible if there are to be three senators and three representatives on the committee? 1120

24. ARRANGING NUMBERS The numbers 1, 2, 3, 4, 5, 6 are to be arranged. How many different arrangements are possible under each of the following conditions?

a. All the even numbers come first. 36

b. The arrangements are such that the numbers alternate between even and odd. 72

25. TEST QUESTIONS A true-false examination contains 10 questions. In how many ways can a person answer the questions on this test by just guessing? Assume that all questions are answered. 1024

26. TEST QUESTIONS A twenty-question, four-option multiple-choice examination is given as a pre-employment test. In how many ways could a prospective employee answer the questions on this test by just guessing? Assume that all questions are answered. 4^{20}

27. STATE LOTTERY A state lottery game requires a person to select six different numbers from forty numbers. The order of the selection is not important. In how many ways can this be done? 3,838,380

28. TEST QUESTIONS A student must answer eight of ten questions on an exam. How many different choices can the student make? 45

29. ACCEPTANCE SAMPLING A warehouse receives a shipment of ten computers, of which three are defective. Five

21. There are 676 ways to arrange 26 letters taken 2 at a time. Now, if there are more than 676 employees, then at least two employees will have the same first and last initials.

computers are then randomly selected from the ten and delivered to a store.

a. In how many ways can the store receive no defective computers? 21

b. In how many ways can the store receive one defective computer? 105

c. In how many ways can the store receive all three defective computers? 21

▶ **30.** **CONTEST** Fifteen students, of whom seven are seniors, are selected as semifinalists for a literary award. Of the fifteen students, ten finalists will be selected.

a. In how many ways can ten finalists be selected from the fifteen students? 3003

b. In how many ways can the ten finalists contain three seniors? 280

c. In how many ways can the ten finalists contain at least five seniors? 1722

31. **SERIAL NUMBERS** A television manufacturer uses a code for the serial number of a television set. The first symbol is the letter *A*, *B*, or *C* and represents the location of the manufacturing plant. The next two symbols (01, 02, . . . , 12) represent the month in which the set was manufactured. The next symbol is a 5, a 6, a 7, an 8, or a 9 and represents the year the set was manufactured. The last seven symbols are digits. How many serial numbers are possible? 1.8×10^9

32. **CARD GAMES** Five cards are chosen at random from an ordinary deck of playing cards. In how many ways can the cards be chosen under each of the following conditions?

a. All are hearts. 1287   **b.** All are the same suit. 5148

c. Exactly three are kings. 4512

d. Two or more are aces. 108,336

33. **ACCEPTANCE SAMPLING** A quality control inspector receives a shipment of ten computer disk drives and randomly selects three of the drives for testing. If two of the disk drives in the shipment are defective, find the number of ways in which the inspector could select at most one defective drive. 112

34. **BASKETBALL TEAMS** A basketball team has twelve members. In how many ways can five players be chosen under each of the following conditions?

a. The selection is random. 792

b. The two tallest players are always among the five selected. 120

35. **ARRANGING NUMBERS** The numbers 1, 2, 3, 4, 5, and 6 are arranged in random order. In how many ways can the numbers 1 and 2 appear next to one another in the order 1, 2? 120

36. **OCCUPANCY PROBLEM** Seven identical balls are randomly placed in seven available containers in such a way that two balls are in one container. Of the remaining six containers, each receives at most one ball. Find the number of ways in which this can be accomplished. 42

37. **LINES IN A PLANE** Seven points lie in a plane in such a way that no three points lie on the same line. How many lines are determined by the seven points? 21

38. **CHESS MATCHES** A chess tournament has 12 participants. How many games must be scheduled if every player must play every other player exactly once? 66

39. **CONTEST WINNERS** Eight couples attend a benefit at which two prizes are given. In how many ways can two names be randomly drawn so that the prizes are not awarded to the same couple? 112

40. **GEOMETRY** Suppose there are 12 distinct points on a circle. How many different triangles can be formed with vertices at the given points? 220

41. **TEST QUESTIONS** In how many ways can a student answer a 20-question true-false test if the student marks 10 of the questions true and 10 of the questions false? 184,756

42. **COMMITTEE MEMBERSHIP** From a group of fifteen people, a committee of eight is formed. From the committee a president, a secretary, and a treasurer are selected. Find the number of ways in which the two consecutive operations can be carried out. 2,162,160

43. **COMMITTEE MEMBERSHIP** From a group of twenty people, a committee of twelve is formed. From the committee of twelve, a subcommittee of four people is chosen. Find the number of ways in which the two consecutive operations can be carried out. 62,355,150

44. **CHECKERBOARDS** A checkerboard consists of eight rows and eight columns of squares. Starting at the top left square of a checkerboard, how many possible paths will end at the bottom right square if the only way a player can legally move is right one square or down one square from the current position? $\dfrac{14!}{7!\,7!}$

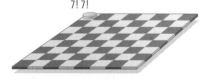

45. ICE CREAM CONES An ice cream store offers 31 flavors of ice cream. How many different triple-decker cones are possible? *Note:* Assume that different orders of the same flavors are *not* different cones. Thus a scoop of rocky road followed by two scoops of mint chocolate is the same as one scoop of mint chocolate followed by one scoop of rocky road followed by a second scoop of mint chocolate. 5456

46. COMPUTER SCREENS A typical computer monitor consists of pixels, each of which can, in some cases, be assigned any one of 2^{16} different colors. If a computer screen has a resolution of 1024 pixels by 768 pixels, how many different images can be displayed on the screen? *Suggestion:* Write your answer as a power of 2. $2^{12,582,912}$

47. DART BOARDS How many different arrangements are there of the integers 1 through 20 on a typical dart board, assuming that 20 is always at the top? 19!

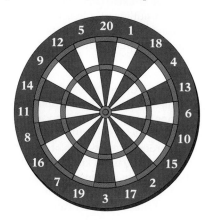

CONNECTING CONCEPTS

48. LINES IN A PLANE Generalize Exercise 37. That is, given n points in a plane, no three of which lie on the same line, how many lines are determined by the n points? $\dfrac{n(n-1)}{2}$ or $\dbinom{n}{2}$

49. BIRTHDAYS Seven people are asked the month of their birth. In how many ways can each of the following conditions exist?

   a. No two people have a birthday in the same month. 3,991,680

   b. At least two people have a birthday in the same month. 31,840,128

50. SUMS OF COINS From a penny, a nickel, a dime, and a quarter, how many different sums of money can be formed using one or more of the coins? 15

51. BIOLOGY Five sticks of equal length are broken into a short piece and a long piece. The ten pieces are randomly arranged in five pairs. In how many ways will each pair consist of a long stick and a short stick? (This exercise actually has a practical side. When cells are exposed to harmful radiation, some chromosomes break. If two long sides unite or two short sides unite, the cell dies.) 120

52. ARRANGING NUMBERS Four random digits are drawn (repetitions are allowed). Among the four digits, in how many ways can two or more repetitions occur? 4960

53. RANDOM WALK An aimless tourist, standing on a street corner, tosses a coin. If the result is heads, the tourist walks one block north. If the result is tails, the tourist walks one block south. At the new corner, the coin is tossed again and the same rule applied. If the coin is tossed ten times, in how many ways will the tourist be back at the original corner? This problem is an elementary example of what is called a *random walk*. Random walk problems have many applications in physics, chemistry, and economics. 252

PREPARE FOR SECTION 8.7

54. What is the Fundamental Counting Principle? [8.6]

55. How many ways can a two-digit number be formed from the digits 1, 2, 3, and 4 if no digit can be repeated in the number? [8.6] 12

56. Evaluate $P(7, 2)$. [8.6] 42

57. Evaluate $C(7, 2)$. [8.6] 21

58. Evaluate $\dbinom{n}{k}p^k q^{n-k}$ when $n = 8$, $k = 5$, $p = \dfrac{1}{4}$, and $q = \dfrac{3}{4}$. [8.1] $\dfrac{189}{8192}$

59. A light switch panel has four switches that control the lights in four different segments of a room. In how many on/off configurations can the four switches be placed? [8.6] 16

PROJECTS

1. **EXPLAIN PERMUTATIONS AND COMBINATIONS** Write an outline of a lesson that you could use to teach permutations and combinations. Include at least five examples of permutations and five examples of combinations.

2. **APPLICATION OF COUNTING** Calculating the number of ways in which balls can be distributed in boxes has a variety of applications. For instance, a traffic engineer may want to know how traffic accidents (the balls) are distributed throughout the days of the week (the boxes). Or a physicist may want to know how electrons (the balls) can be distributed in the energy orbits (the boxes) of an atom. The formula for counting the number of ways in which n distinguishable balls can be placed in k distinguishable boxes, where each box must have at least one ball, is given by

$$\binom{k}{0}k^n - \binom{k}{1}(k-1)^n + \binom{k}{2}(k-2)^n + \cdots + (-1)^{k-1}\binom{k}{k-1}$$

The word *distinguishable* is important. This formula refers to counting under circumstances similar to the situation depicted in the first figure at the top of the next column, where the boxes are numbered and the balls are numbered. The second figure shows a situation that is not covered by this formula. Although the boxes are numbered, the balls are not and are therefore *indistinguishable*.

Box 1

Box 2

Box 3

Box 1

Box 2

Box 3

a. A computer network consists of five computers and three printers. How many possible connections can be made if each computer must be hooked to a printer and all printers are used?

b. A supermarket has four checkout lanes. Assuming shoppers are efficient and will not leave a checkout lane empty, in how many ways can 10 shoppers line up for the checkout lanes?

SECTION 8.7   # INTRODUCTION TO PROBABILITY

- **SAMPLE SPACES**
- **EVENTS**
- **PROBABILITY OF AN EVENT**
- **BINOMIAL PROBABILITIES**

Many events in the world around us have random character, such as the chances of an accident occurring on a certain freeway, the chances of winning a state lottery, and the chances that the nucleus of an atom will undergo fission. By repeatedly observing such events, it is often possible to recognize certain patterns. **Probability** is the mathematical study of random patterns.

When a weather reporter predicts a 30% chance of rain, the forecaster is saying that similar weather conditions have led to rain 30 times out of 100. When a fair coin is tossed, we expect heads to occur $\frac{1}{2}$, or 50%, of the time. The numbers 30% (or 0.3) and $\frac{1}{2}$ are the probabilities of the events.

MATH MATTERS

The beginning of probability theory is frequently associated with letters sent between Pascal (of Pascal's Triangle) and Fermat (Fermat's Last Theorem) in which they discuss the solution of a problem posed to them by Antoine Gombaud, Chevalier de Mere, a French aristocrat who liked to gamble. The basic question was "How many tosses of two dice are necessary to have a better than 50–50 chance of rolling two sixes?" Although the correct analysis of this problem by Fermat and Pascal pre-saged probability theory, historical records indicate that commerce and the need to insure ships, cargo, and lives was another motivating factor to calculating probabilities. The first merchant insurance companies were established in the fourteenth century to insure ships. Life insurance companies were established at the end of the seventeenth century. Lloyd's of London was established sometime before 1690.

Alternative to Example 1
Suppose that among six socks, four are blue and two are green. Three socks are randomly drawn from the six and their colosrs are noted. List the elements in the sample space.

● $B_1B_2B_3$, $B_1B_2B_4$, $B_1B_3B_4$, $B_2B_3B_4$, $B_1B_2G_1$, $B_1B_2G_2$, $B_1B_3G_1$, $B_1B_3G_2$, $B_1B_4G_1$, $B_1B_4G_2$, $B_2B_3G_1$, $B_2B_3G_2$, $B_2B_4G_1$, $B_2B_4G_2$, $B_3B_4G_1$, $B_3B_4G_2$, $B_1G_1G_2$, $B_2G_1G_2$, $B_3G_1G_2$, $B_4G_1G_2$

● SAMPLE SPACES

An activity with an observable outcome is called an **experiment**. Examples of experiments include

1. Flipping a coin and observing the side facing upward

2. Observing the incidence of a disease in a certain population

3. Observing the length of time a person waits in a checkout line in a grocery store

The **sample space** of an experiment is the set of *all possible* outcomes of that experiment.

Consider the experiment of tossing one coin three times and recording the number of occurrences of the upward side of the coin. The sample space is

$$S = \{HHH, HHT, HTH, THH, HTT, THT, TTH, TTT\}$$

EXAMPLE 1   List the Elements of a Sample Space

Suppose that among five batteries, two are defective. Two batteries are randomly drawn from the five and tested for defects. List the elements in the sample space.

Solution

Label the nondefective batteries N_1, N_2, and N_3 and the defective batteries D_1 and D_2. The sample space is

$$S = \{ N_1D_1, N_2D_1, N_3D_1, N_1D_2, N_2D_2, N_3D_2, N_1N_2, N_1N_3, N_2N_3, D_1D_2\}$$

▶ **TRY EXERCISE 6, PAGE 692**

● EVENTS

An **event** E is any subset of a sample space. For the sample space defined in Example 1, several of the events we could define are

E_1: There are no defective batteries.

E_2: At least one battery is defective.

E_3: Both batteries are defective.

Because an event is a subset of the sample space, each of these events can be expressed as a set.

$$E_1 = \{N_1N_2, N_1N_3, N_2N_3\}$$
$$E_2 = \{N_1D_1, N_2D_1, N_3D_1, N_1D_2, N_2D_2, N_3D_2, D_1D_2\}$$
$$E_3 = \{D_1D_2\}$$

There are two methods by which elements are drawn from a sample space: with replacement and without replacement. *With replacement* means that after the element is drawn, it is returned to the sample space. The same element could be selected on the next drawing. When elements are drawn *without replacement*, an element drawn is not returned to the sample space and therefore is not available for any subsequent drawing.

Alternative to Example 2
A two-digit number is formed by choosing from the digits 1, 2, 3, 4, 5, and 6 both with replacement and without replacement. Express each event as a set.
a. E_1: Both digits are odd.
  ○ **With replacement:**
    $E_1 = \{11, 13, 15, 31, 33, 35, 51, 53, 55\}$
    Without replacement:
    $E_1 = \{13, 15, 31, 35, 51, 53\}$
b. E_2: The sum of the digits is greater than 12.
  ○ $\varnothing$

EXAMPLE 2   **List the Elements of an Event**

A two-digit number is formed by choosing from the digits 1, 2, 3, and 4, both with replacement and without replacement. Express each event as a set.

a. E_1: The second digit is greater than or equal to the first digit.

b. E_2: Both digits are less than zero.

Solution

a. With replacement: $E_1 = \{11, 12, 13, 14, 22, 23, 24, 33, 34, 44\}$

Without replacement: $E_1 = \{12, 13, 14, 23, 24, 34\}$

b. $E_2 = \varnothing$
Choosing from the digits 1, 2, 3, and 4, this event is impossible. The impossible event is denoted by the empty set or null set.

▶ **TRY EXERCISE 14, PAGE 692**

● **PROBABILITY OF AN EVENT**

The probability of an event is defined in terms of the concepts of sample space and event.

Probability of an Event

Let $n(S)$ and $n(E)$ represent the number of elements in the sample space S and the number of elements in the event E, respectively. The probability of event E, $P(E)$, is

$$P(E) = \frac{n(E)}{n(S)}$$

Because E is a subset of S, $n(E) \le n(S)$. Thus $P(E) \le 1$. If E is an impossible event, then $E = \varnothing$ and $n(E) = 0$. Thus $P(E) = 0$. If E is an event that *always* occurs, then $E = S$ and $n(E) = n(S)$. Thus $P(E) = 1$. Thus we have, for any event E,

$$0 \le P(E) \le 1$$

❓ **QUESTION** Is it possible for the probability of an event to equal 1.25?

Alternative to Example 3
A coin is tossed four times. What is the probability of each outcome?
a. E_1: Two or more tails will appear.
  ○ $\dfrac{11}{16}$
b. E_2: At least one head will appear.
  ○ $\dfrac{15}{16}$

EXAMPLE 3   **Calculate the Probability of an Event**

A coin is tossed three times. What is the probability of each outcome?

a. E_1: Two or more heads will appear.

b. E_2: At least one tail will appear.

❓ **ANSWER** No. All probabilities must be between 0 and 1, inclusive.

Solution

First determine the number of elements in the sample space. The sample space for this experiment is

$$S = \{HHH, HHT, HTH, THH, HTT, THT, TTH, TTT\}$$

Therefore $n(S) = 8$. Now determine the number of elements in each event. Then calculate the probability of the event by using $P(E) = n(E)/n(S)$.

a. $E_1 = \{HHH, HHT, HTH, THH\}$

$$P(E_1) = \frac{n(E_1)}{n(S)} = \frac{4}{8} = \frac{1}{2}$$

b. $E_2 = \{HHT, HTH, THH, HTT, THT, TTH, TTT\}$

$$P(E_2) = \frac{n(E_2)}{n(S)} = \frac{7}{8}$$

▶ **TRY EXERCISE 22, PAGE 692**

Calculating probabilities by listing and then counting the elements of a sample space is not always practical. Instead, we will use the counting principles developed in the last section to determine the number of elements in the sample space and in an event.

<table>
<tr><td>

Alternative to Example 4
A state lottery game allows a person to choose five integers from 1 to 47 and one MEGA integer from 1 to 27. To win the jackpot, a player must match all five numbers plus the MEGA number.

a. Find the probability that a player will win the jackpot.

⊙ ≈ **0.000000024, which is about one chance in 40 million**

b. A player can win the cost of the lottery ticket by matching just the MEGA number. Find the probability of matching the MEGA number.

⊙ ≈ **0.037**

INSTRUCTOR NOTE
For a lottery (or Las Vegas Keno), the probability of choosing n balls, of which k are "lucky" ($k \le n$), from N balls is

$$\frac{C(n, k) \cdot C(N - n, n - k)}{C(N, k)}$$

</td></tr>
</table>

EXAMPLE 4 Use the Counting Principles to Calculate a Probability

A state lottery game allows a person to choose five numbers from the integers 1 to 40. Repetitions of numbers are not allowed. If three or more numbers match the numbers chosen by the lottery, the player wins a prize. Find the probability that a player will match

a. exactly three numbers

b. exactly four numbers

Solution

The sample space S is the number of ways in which five numbers can be chosen from forty numbers. This is a combination because the order of the drawing is not important.

$$n(S) = C(40, 5) = \frac{40!}{5!\,35!} = 658{,}008$$

We will call the five numbers chosen by the state lottery "lucky" and the remaining thirty-five numbers "unlucky."

a. Let E_1 be the event a player has three lucky and therefore two unlucky numbers. The three lucky numbers are chosen from the five lucky numbers. There are $C(5, 3)$ ways to do this. The two unlucky numbers

Continued ▶

are chosen from the thirty-five unlucky numbers. There are $C(35, 2)$ ways to do this. By the counting principle, the number of ways the event E_1 can occur is

$$N(E_1) = C(5, 3) \cdot C(35, 2) = 10 \cdot 595 = 5950$$

$$P(E_1) = \frac{n(E_1)}{n(S)} = \frac{C(5, 3) \cdot C(35, 2)}{C(40, 5)} = \frac{5950}{658,008} \approx 0.009042$$

b. Let E_2 be the event a player has four lucky numbers and one unlucky number. The number of ways a person can select four lucky numbers and one unlucky number is $C(5, 4) \cdot C(35, 1)$.

$$P(E_2) = \frac{n(E_2)}{n(S)} = \frac{C(5, 4) \cdot C(35, 1)}{C(40, 5)} = \frac{175}{658,008} \approx 0.000266$$

▶ **TRY EXERCISE 32, PAGE 693**

The expression "one or the other of two events occurs" is written as the union of the two sets. For example, suppose an experiment leads to the sample space $S = \{1, 2, 3, 4, 5, 6\}$ and the events are

Draw a number less than four, $E_1 = \{1, 2, 3\}$

Draw an even number, $E_2 = \{2, 4, 6\}$

Then the event $E_1 \cup E_2$ is described by drawing a number less than four *or* an even number. Thus

$$E_1 \cup E_2 = \{1, 2, 3\} \cup \{2, 4, 6\} = \{1, 2, 3, 4, 6\}$$

Two events E_1 and E_2 that cannot occur at the same time are **mutually exclusive** events. Using set notation, if $E_1 \cap E_2 = \varnothing$, then E_1 and E_2 are mutually exclusive.

For example, using the same sample space $\{1, 2, 3, 4, 5, 6\}$, a third event is

Draw an odd number, $E_3 = \{1, 3, 5\}$

Then $E_2 \cap E_3 = \varnothing$ and the events E_2 and E_3 are mutually exclusive. On the other hand,

$$E_1 \cap E_2 = \{2\}$$

so the events E_1 and E_2 are not mutually exclusive.

One of the axioms of probability involves the union of mutually exclusive events.

A Probability Axiom

If E_1 and E_2 are mutually exclusive events, then

$$P(E_1 \cup E_2) = P(E_1) + P(E_2)$$

If the events are not mutually exclusive, the addition rule for probabilities can be used.

Addition Rule for Probabilities

If E_1 and E_2 are two events, then

$$P(E_1 \cup E_2) = P(E_1) + P(E_2) - P(E_1 \cap E_2)$$

The probability axiom and the addition rule are useful when calculating probabilities of events connected by the word *or*.

Using the calculations of Example 4, we can find the probability that a player will have three or four lucky numbers in the lottery. Because the events E_1 and E_2 as defined in Example 4 are mutually exclusive,

$$P(E_1 \cup E_2) = P(E_1) + P(E_2) \approx 0.009042 + 0.000266 = 0.009308$$

As an example of non-mutually exclusive events, draw a card at random from a deck of ordinary playing cards. Find the probability of drawing an ace or a heart.

$$S = \{52 \text{ ordinary playing cards}\}$$

Let $E_1 = \{\text{an ace}\}$ and $E_2 = \{\text{a heart}\}$. Then

$$P(E_1) = \frac{n(E_1)}{n(S)} = \frac{4}{52} = \frac{1}{13} \qquad P(E_2) = \frac{n(E_2)}{n(S)} = \frac{13}{52} = \frac{1}{4}$$

We have $E_1 \cup E_2 = \{\text{an ace } or \text{ a heart}\}$ and $E_1 \cap E_2 = \{\text{ace of hearts}\}$. First, we find $P(E_1 \cap E_2)$.

$$P(E_1 \cap E_2) = \frac{n(E_1 \cap E_2)}{n(S)} = \frac{1}{52}$$

Now we can find $P(E_1 \cup E_2)$.

$$P(E_1 \cup E_2) = P(E_1) + P(E_2) - P(E_1 \cap E_2) = \frac{1}{13} + \frac{1}{4} - \frac{1}{52} = \frac{16}{52} = \frac{4}{13}$$

Two events are **independent** if the outcome of the first event does not influence the outcome of the second event. As an example, consider tossing a fair coin twice. The outcome of the first toss has no bearing on the outcome of the second toss. The two events are independent.

Now consider drawing two cards in succession, without replacement, from a regular deck of playing cards. The probability that the second card drawn will be an ace depends on the card drawn first.

Probability Rule for Independent Events

If E_1 and E_2 are two independent events, then the probability that both E_1 *and* E_2 will occur is

$$P(E_1) \cdot P(E_2)$$

Alternative to Example 5
A card is drawn from an ordinary deck of playing cards, and then a die is rolled. What is the probability that the card will be a spade and the die will show an even number?

● $\dfrac{1}{8}$

MATH MATTERS

Airlines "overbook" flights. That is, they sell more tickets than there are seats on the plane. An airline company can determine the probability that some number of passengers will be "bumped" on a certain flight by using the Binomial Probability Formula. For instance, suppose a plane has 200 seats and the airline sells 240 tickets. If the probability that a person will show up for this flight is 0.8, then the probability that one or more people will have to be bumped is given by

$$\sum_{k=1}^{40} \binom{240}{200+k} 0.8^{200+k} 0.2^{40-k}$$

Using a computer reveals that this sum is approximately 0.08. That is, there is only an 8% chance that someone will have to be bumped, even though the number of tickets sold exceeds the plane's capacity by 20%.

EXAMPLE 5   Calculate a Probability for Independent Events

A coin is tossed and then a die is rolled. What is the probability that the coin will show a head and the die will show a six?

Solution

The events are independent because the result of one does not influence the probability of the other. $P(\text{head}) = \dfrac{1}{2}$ and $P(\text{six}) = \dfrac{1}{6}$. Thus the probability of tossing a head and rolling a six is

$$P(\text{head}) \cdot P(\text{six}) = \frac{1}{2} \cdot \frac{1}{6} = \frac{1}{12}$$

▶ **TRY EXERCISE 34, PAGE 693**

● **BINOMIAL PROBABILITIES**

Some probabilities can be calculated from formulas. One of the most important of these formulas is the *Binomial Probability Formula*. This formula is used to calculate probabilities for *independent* events.

Binomial Probability Formula

Let an experiment consist of n trials for which the probability of success on a single trial is p and the probability of failure is $q = 1 - p$. Then the probability of k successes in n trials is given by

$$\binom{n}{k} p^k q^{n-k}$$

Alternative to Example 6
A multiple-choice test consists of twenty-five questions. For each question there are five possible choices, of which only one is correct. If someone randomly guesses at the answers, what is the probability of guessing fifteen answers correctly?

● ≈ 0.0000115

EXAMPLE 6   Use the Binomial Formula

A multiple-choice exam consists of ten questions. For each question there are four possible choices, of which only one is correct. If someone randomly guesses at the answers, what is the probability of guessing exactly six answers correctly?

Solution

Selecting an answer is one trial of the experiment. Because there are ten questions, $n = 10$. There are four possible choices for each question, of which only one is correct. Therefore,

$$p = \frac{1}{4} \quad \text{and} \quad q = 1 - p = 1 - \frac{1}{4} = \frac{3}{4}$$

A success for this experiment occurs each time a correct answer is guessed. Thus $k = 6$. By the Binomial Probability Formula,

$$P = \binom{10}{6}\left(\frac{1}{4}\right)^6\left(\frac{3}{4}\right)^4 \approx 0.016222$$

The probability of guessing exactly six answers correctly is approximately 0.0162.

▶ **TRY EXERCISE 40, PAGE 693**

Following are five guidelines for calculating probabilities.

Guidelines for Calculating a Probability

1. The word "or" usually means to add the probabilities of each event.

2. The word "and" usually means to multiply the probabilities of each event.

3. The phrase "at least n" means *n or more*. At least 5 is 5 or more.

4. The phrase "at most n" means *n or less*. At most 5 is 5 or less.

5. "Exactly n" means just that. Exactly five heads in seven tosses of a coin means five heads *and therefore* two tails.

 TOPICS FOR DISCUSSION

1. What is the meaning of probability and what are the possible values of a probability?

2. What is the sample space of an experiment? What are events and how are they related to the sample space?

3. Discuss the difference between mutually exclusive events and events that are not mutually exclusive. Give examples of each type.

4. Discuss the Addition Rule for Probabilities and how it is used.

5. What is the Binomial Probability Formula and how is it used?

EXERCISE SET 8.7   *—Suggested Assignment: Exercises 1–45, odd.*

In Exercises 1 to 10, list the elements in the sample space defined by the given experiment.

1. Two people are selected from two senators and three representatives.
$\{S_1R_1, S_1R_2, S_1R_3, S_2R_1, S_2R_2, S_2R_3, R_1R_2, R_1R_3, R_2R_3, S_1S_2\}$

2. A letter is chosen at random from the word "Tennessee."
$\{T, e, n, s\}$

3. A fair coin is tossed and then a random integer between 1 and 4, inclusive, is selected. $\{H1, H2, H3, H4, T1, T2, T3, T4\}$

4. A fair coin is tossed four times. {HHHH, THHH, HTHH, HHHT, TTHH, THHT, HTTH, HHTT, THTH, HTHT, HHTH, HTTT, TTTH, THTT, TTHT, TTTT}

5. Two identical tennis balls are randomly placed in three tennis ball cans.
Answer on page AA35.

▶ **6.** Two people are selected from among one Republican, one Democrat, and one Independent. {RD, RI, DI}

7. Three cards are randomly chosen from the ace of hearts, ace of spades, ace of clubs, and ace of diamonds.
{HSC, HSD, HCD, SCD}

8. Three letters addressed to *A*, *B*, and *C*, respectively, are randomly put into three envelopes addressed to *A*, *B*, and *C*, respectively. {(ABC), (ACB), (BAC), (BCA), (CAB), (CBA)}

9. Two vowels are randomly chosen from a, e, i, o, and u.
{ae, ai, ao, au, ei, eo, eu, io, iu, ou}

10. Three computer disks are randomly chosen from one defective disk and three nondefective disks.
$\{DN_1N_2, DN_1N_3, DN_2N_3, N_1N_2N_3\}$

In Exercises 11 to 15, use the sample space defined by the experiment of tossing a fair coin four times. Express each event as a subset of the sample space.

11. There are no tails. {HHHH}

12. There are exactly two heads. {TTHH, THHT, HTTH, HHTT, THTH, HTHT}

13. There are at most two heads.
{TTTT, HTTT, THTT, TTHT, TTTH, TTHH, THTH, HTHT, THHT, HTTH, HHTT}

▶ **14.** There are more than two heads. {HHHH, HHHT, HHTH, HTHH, THHH}

15. There are 12 tails. ∅

In Exercises 16 to 20, use the sample space defined by the experiment of choosing two random numbers, in succession, from the integers 1, 2, 3, 4, 5, and 6. The numbers are chosen with replacement. Express each event as a subset of the sample space.

16. The sum of the numbers is 7. $\{(1, 6), (2, 5), (3, 4), (4, 3), (5, 2), (6, 1)\}$

17. The two numbers are the same.
$\{(1, 1), (2, 2), (3, 3), (4, 4), (5, 5), (6, 6)\}$

18. The first number is greater than the second number.
$\{(2, 1), (3, 1), (3, 2), (4, 1), (4, 2), (4, 3), (5, 1), (5, 2), (5, 3), (5, 4), (6, 1), (6, 2),$ $(6, 3), (6, 4), (6, 5)\}$

19. The second number is a 4.
$\{(1, 4), (2, 4), (3, 4), (4, 4), (5, 4), (6, 4)\}$

20. The sum of the two numbers is greater than 1.
Answer on page AA35.

In Exercises 21 through 44, calculate the probabilities of the events.

21. **CARD GAMES** From a deck of regular playing cards, one card is chosen at random. Find the probability of each event.

a. The card is a king. $\frac{1}{13}$ **b.** The card is a spade. $\frac{1}{4}$

▶ **22.** **NUMBER THEORY** A single number is chosen from the digits 1, 2, 3, 4, 5, and 6. Find the probability that the number is an even number or a number divisible by 3. $\frac{2}{3}$

23. **ECONOMICS** An economist predicts that the probability of an increase in gross domestic product (GDP) is 0.64 and that the probability of an increase in inflation is 0.55. The economist also predicts that the probability of an increase in GDP *and* inflation is 0.22. Find the probability of an increase in GDP *or* an increase in inflation. 0.97

24. **NUMBER THEORY** Four digits are selected from the digits 1, 2, 3, and 4, and a number is formed. Find the probability that the number is greater than 3000, assuming digits can be repeated. $\frac{1}{2}$

25. **BUILDING INDUSTRY** An owner of a construction company has bid for the contracts on two buildings. If the contractor estimates that the probability of getting the first contract is $\frac{1}{2}$, that of getting the second contract is $\frac{1}{5}$, and that of getting both contracts is $\frac{1}{10}$, find the probability that the contractor will get at least one of the two building contracts. $\frac{3}{5}$

26. **ACCEPTANCE SAMPLING** A shipment of ten calculators contains two defective calculators. Two calculators are chosen from the shipment. Find the probability of each event.

a. Both are defective. $\frac{1}{45}$

b. At least one is defective. $\frac{17}{45}$

27. **NUMBER THEORY** Five random digits are selected from 0 to 9 with replacement. What is the probability (to the nearest hundredth) that 0 does not occur? 0.59

28. **QUEUING THEORY** Six persons are arranged in a line. What is the probability that two specific people, say A and B, are standing next to each other? $\dfrac{1}{3}$

29. **LOTTERY** A box contains 500 envelopes, of which 50 have $100 in cash, 75 have $50 in cash, and 125 have $25 in cash. If an envelope is selected at random from this box, what is the probability that it will contain at least $50? 0.25

30. **JURY SELECTION** A jury of twelve people is selected from thirty people: fifteen women and fifteen men. What is the probability that the jury will have six men and six women? 0.2896

31. **QUEUING THEORY** Three girls and three boys are randomly placed in six adjacent seats. What is the probability that the boys and girls will be in alternating seats? 0.1

▶ **32.** **COMMITTEE MEMBERSHIP** A committee of four is chosen from three accountants and five actuaries. Find the probability that the committee consists of two accountants and two actuaries. $\dfrac{3}{7}$

33. **EXTRASENSORY PERCEPTION** A magician claims to be able to read minds. To test this claim, five cards numbered 1 to 5 are used. A subject selects two cards from the five and concentrates on the numbers. What is the probability that the magician can correctly identify the two cards by just guessing? 0.1

▶ **34.** **CARD GAMES** One card is randomly drawn from a regular deck of playing cards. The card is replaced and another card is drawn. Are the events independent? What is the probability that both cards drawn are aces? yes; $\dfrac{1}{169}$

35. **SCHEDULING** A meeting is scheduled by randomly choosing a weekday and then randomly choosing an hour between 8:00 A.M. and 4:00 P.M. What is the probability that Monday at 8:00 A.M. is chosen? 0.025

36. **NATIONAL DEFENSE** A missile radar detection system consists of two radar screens. The probability that any one of the radar screens will detect an incoming missile is 0.95. If radar detections are assumed to be independent events, what is the probability that a missile that enters the detection space of the radar will be detected? 0.9975

37. **OIL INDUSTRY** An oil drilling venture involves drilling four wells in different parts of the country. For each well, the probability that it will be profitable is 0.10, and the probability that it will be unprofitable is 0.90. If these events are independent, what is the probability of drilling at least one unprofitable well? 0.9999

38. **MANUFACTURING** A manufacturer of CD-ROMs claims that only 1 of every 1000 CD-ROMs manufactured is defective. If this claim is correct and if defective CD-ROMs are independent events, what is the probability that of the next three CD-ROMs produced, all are not defective? 0.997

39. **PREFERENCE TESTING** A software firm is considering marketing two newly designed spreadsheet programs, A and B. To test the appeal of the programs, the firm installs them in four corporations. After 2 weeks, the firm asks each corporation to evaluate each program. If the corporations have no preference, what is the probability that all four will choose product A? $\dfrac{1}{16}$

▶ **40.** **AGRICULTURE** A fruit grower claims that one-fourth of the orange trees in a grove crop have suffered frost damage. Find the probability that among eight orange trees, exactly three have frost damage. 0.2076

41. **QUALITY CONTROL** A quality control inspector receives a shipment of 20 computer monitors. From the 20 monitors, the inspector randomly chooses 5 for inspection. If the probability of a monitor being defective is 0.05, what is the probability that at least one of the monitors chosen by the inspector is defective? 0.2262

42. **LOTTERY** Consider a lottery that sells 1000 tickets and awards two prizes. If you purchase 10 tickets, what is the probability that you will win a prize? 0.02

43. **AIRLINE SCHEDULING** An airline estimates that 75% of the people who make a reservation for a certain flight will actually show up for the flight. Suppose the airline sells 25 tickets on this flight and the plane has room for 20 passengers. What is the probability that 21 or more people with tickets will show up for the flight? 0.2137

44. **AIRLINE SCHEDULING** Suppose that an airplane's engines operate independently and that the probability that any one engine will fail is 0.03. A plane can make a safe landing if at least one-half of its engines operate. Is a safe flight more likely to occur in a two-engine or a four-engine plane? Why? plane with 4 engines

CONNECTING CONCEPTS

45. SPREAD OF A RUMOR A club has nine members. One member starts a rumor by telling it to a second club member, who repeats the rumor to a third person, and so on. At each stage, the recipient of the rumor is chosen at random from the nine club members. What is the probability that the rumor will be told three times without returning to the originator? $\left(\dfrac{7}{8}\right)^2$

46. EXTRASENSORY PERCEPTION As a test for extrasensory perception (ESP), ten cards, five black and five white, are shuffled, and then a person looks at each card. In another room, the ESP subject attempts to guess whether the card is black or white. The ESP subject must guess black five times and white five times. If the ESP subject has no extrasensory perception, what is the probability that the subject will correctly name eight of the ten cards? $\dfrac{25}{252}$

47. TELEPHONE NUMBER EXTENSIONS The telephone extensions at a university are four-digit numbers chosen from the digits 1–9. If two telephone numbers are randomly chosen from the telephone book, what is the probability that the first three digits are different and the fourth digit matches the third digit? $\dfrac{56}{729}$

48. ARRANGING LETTERS OF A WORD Each arrangement of the letters of the word "Tennessee" is written on a piece of paper, and all the pieces of paper are placed in a bowl. One piece of paper is selected at random. What is the probability that the first letter in the arrangement is a T? $\dfrac{1}{9}$

PROJECTS

1. MONTE HALL PROBLEM The grand prize in a game show is behind one of three curtains. A contestant selects one of the three curtains, say, curtain A. To add drama to the show, the game show host reveals a prize behind one of the other curtains. This prize is not the grand prize. Now the contestant has an opportunity to cancel the original choice (curtain A) and choose the remaining closed curtain, or stay with the original choice. For each option, what is the probability that the contestant will now choose the grand prize? *Note:* This problem is sometimes referred to as the *Monte Hall* problem after the game show *Let's Make a Deal.* For more information on this problem, read the Focus on Problem Solving on page 638 and the "Ask Marilyn" column (by syndicated columnist Marilyn vos Savant) in which this problem was discussed (see *Parade* magazine, September 9, 1990, p. 15).

2. BIRTHDAY PROBLEM A famous problem called the *birthday problem* goes like this: Suppose that there are 30 people in a room. What is the probability that at least 2 people have a birthday on the same date? It may surprise you that the answer is approximately 71%. The formula for determining this probability is $1 - \dfrac{P(365, n)}{365^n}$, where n is the number of people in the room and $P(365, n)$ is permutation notation. Use this formula for the following exercises.

a. Find the probability that in a room of 10 people, at least 2 people have the same birthday.

b. Find the probability that in a room of 20 people, at least 2 people have the same birthday.

c. Experiment with different values of n to find how many people need to be in a room before the probability of at least 2 people having the same birthday first exceeds 50%.

3. See our website at **http://college.hmco.com** for a project dealing with overbooking by airlines.

Mathematical Expectation

Expectation E is a number used to determine the fairness of a gambling game. It is defined as the probability of winning a bet times the amount A available to win.

$$E = P \cdot A$$

A game is called *fair* if the expectation of the game equals the amount bet. For example, if you and a friend each bet \$1 on who can guess the side facing up on the flip of a coin, then the expectation is $E = \frac{1}{2} \cdot \$2 = \$1$. Because the amount of your bet equals the expectation, the game is fair.

When a game is *unfair*, it benefits one of the players. If you bet \$1 and your friend bets \$2 on who can guess the flip of a coin, your expectation is $E = \frac{1}{2} \cdot \$3 = \$1.50$. Because your expectation is greater than the amount you bet, the game is advantageous to you. Your friend's expectation is also \$1.50, which is less than the amount your friend bet. This is a disadvantage to your friend.

Keno is a game of chance played in many casinos. In this game, a large basket contains 80 balls numbered from 1 to 80. From these balls, the dealer randomly chooses 20 balls. The number of ways in which the dealer can choose 20 balls from 80 is the number of combinations of 80 things chosen 20 at a time, or $C(80, 20)$.

In one particular game, a gambler can bet \$1 and mark five numbers. The gambler will win a prize if three of the five numbers marked are included in the 20 numbered balls chosen by the dealer. By the counting principle, there are $C(20, 3) \cdot C(60, 2) = 2,017,800$ ways the gambler can do this. The probability of this event is $\frac{C(20, 3) \cdot C(60, 2)}{C(80, 5)} \approx 0.0839$. The amount the gambler wins for this event is \$2 (the \$1 bet plus \$1 from the casino), so the expectation of the gambler is approximately \$.17 ($0.0839 \cdot \$2$).

Each casino has different rules and different methods of awarding prizes. The tables below give the prizes for a \$2 bet for some of the possible choices a gambler can make at four casinos. Complete the Expectation columns. In each case, the Mark column indicates how many numbers the gambler marked, and the Catch column shows how many of the numbers marked by the gambler were also chosen by the dealer.

Casino 1

Mark	Catch	Win	Expectation
6	4	\$8	
6	5	\$176	
6	6	\$2960	

Casino 2

Mark	Catch	Win	Expectation
6	4	\$6	
6	5	\$160	
6	6	\$3900	

Casino 3

Mark	Catch	Win	Expectation
6	4	\$8	
6	5	\$180	
6	6	\$3000	

Casino 4

Mark	Catch	Win	Expectation
6	4	\$6	
6	5	\$176	
6	6	\$3000	

Adding the expectations in each column gives you the total expectation for marking six numbers. Find the total expectation for each casino. Which casino offers the gambler the greatest expectation?

CHAPTER 8 SUMMARY

8.1 Infinite Sequences and Summation Notation

- An infinite sequence is a function whose domain is the positive integers and whose range is the set of real numbers.

- An alternating sequence is one in which the signs of the terms alternate between positive and negative values.

- A recursively defined sequence is one in which each succeeding term of the sequence is defined by using some of the preceding terms.

- If n is a positive integer, then n factorial, $n!$, is the product of the first n positive integers.

$$n! = n(n-1)(n-2) \cdots 3 \cdot 2 \cdot 1$$

- If a_n is a sequence, then $S_n = \sum_{i=1}^{n} a_i$ is the nth partial sum of the sequence.

8.2 Arithmetic Sequences and Series

- Given that d is a real number, the sequence a_n is an arithmetic sequence if $a_{i+1} - a_i = d$ for all i. The number d is called the common difference of the sequence.

- The nth term of an arithmetic sequence with common difference of d is $a_n = a_1 + (n-1)d$.

- If a_n is an arithmetic sequence, then the nth partial sum S_n of the sequence is given by

$$S_n = \frac{n}{2}(a_1 + a_n)$$

8.3 Geometric Sequences and Series

- Given that $r \neq 0$ is a constant real number, the sequence a_n is a geometric sequence if $\dfrac{a_{i+1}}{a_i} = r$ for all positive integers i. The ratio r is called the common ratio of the geometric sequence.

- The nth term of a geometric sequence is $a_n = a_1 r^{n-1}$, where a_1 is the first term of the sequence and r is the common ratio.

- If a_n is a geometric sequence, then the nth partial sum of the sequence is given by

$$S_n = \frac{a_1(1 - r^n)}{1 - r} \quad r \neq 1$$

- If $|r| < 1$, then the sum of an infinite geometric series is given by

$$S = \frac{a_1}{1 - r}$$

8.4 Mathematical Induction

- **Principle of Mathematical Induction**
  Let P_n be a statement that involves positive integers. If
  1. P_1 is true, and
  2. the truth of P_k implies the truth of P_{k+1},
  then P_n is true for all positive integers.

8.5 The Binomial Theorem

- **Binomial Theorem for Positive Integers**
  If n is a positive integer, then

$$(a + b)^n = \sum_{i=0}^{n} \binom{n}{i} a^{n-i} b^i$$

- The ith term of the expansion of $(a + b)^n$ is

$$\binom{n}{i-1} a^{n-i+1} b^{i-1}$$

8.6 Permutations and Combinations

- The Fundamental Counting Principle is used to count the number of ways in which a sequence of n conditions can occur.

- A permutation is an arrangement of distinct objects in a definite order. The formula for the permutations of n distinct objects taken r at a time is

$$P(n, r) = \frac{n!}{(n - r)!}$$

- A combination is an arrangement of objects for which the order of the selection is not important. The formula for the number of combinations of n objects taken r at a time is

$$C(n, r) = \frac{n!}{r!\,(n - r)!}$$

8.7 Introduction to Probability

- Probability is the mathematical study of random patterns. The sample space of an experiment is the set of all possible outcomes of that experiment. An event is any subset of a sample space.

- If S is the sample space of an experiment and E is an event in the sample space, then the probability of the event is given by

$$P(E) = \frac{n(E)}{n(S)}$$

where $n(E)$ and $n(S)$ are the numbers of elements in E and S, respectively.

- **Addition Rule for Probabilities**
  If E_1 and E_2 are two events, then

$$P(E_1 \cup E_2) = P(E_1) + P(E_2) - P(E_1 \cap E_2)$$

- **Probability Rule for Independent Events**
  If E_1 and E_2 are two independent events, then the probability that both E_1 and E_2 will occur is

$$P(E_1) \cdot P(E_2)$$

- **Binomial Probability Formula**
  Let an experiment consist of n trials for which the probability of success on a single trial is p and the probability of failure is $q = 1 - p$. Then the probability of k successes in n trials is given by

$$\binom{n}{k} p^k q^{n-k}$$

CHAPTER 8 TRUE/FALSE EXERCISES

In Exercises 1 to 15, answer true or false. If the statement is false, give an example to show that the statement is false.

1. $0! \cdot 4! = 0$ False; $0! \cdot 4! = 1 \cdot 4 \cdot 3 \cdot 2 \cdot 1 = 24.$

2. $\left(\sum_{i=1}^{3} a_i\right)\left(\sum_{i=1}^{3} b_i\right) = \sum_{i=1}^{3} a_i b_i$ False; $\left(\sum_{i=1}^{3} i\right)\left(\sum_{i=1}^{3} i\right) \neq \sum_{i=1}^{3} i^2.$

3. $\dfrac{n(n-1)(n-2)\cdots(n-k+1)}{k!} = C(n, k)$ True

4. No two terms of a sequence can be equal.
   False; the constant sequence has all terms equal.

5. $1, 8, 27, 64, \ldots, k^3, \ldots$ is a geometric sequence.
   See answer below.

6. $a_1 = 2, a_{n+1} = a_n - 3$ defines an arithmetic sequence. True

7. $0.\overline{9} = 1$ True

8. Adding all the terms of an infinite sequence produces an infinite sum. False; $\sum_{i=1}^{\infty} \frac{1}{2^i} = 1.$

5. False; $\dfrac{(k+1)^3}{k^3} = \left(1 + \dfrac{1}{k}\right)^3$ is not a constant.

9. Because the first step of an induction proof is normally easy, this step can be omitted.
   False; see Project 1, Section 8.4.

10. In the expansion of $(a + b)^8$, the exponent of a for the fifth term is 5. False; the exponent is 4.

11. The counting principle states that if there are n ways to satisfy one condition and m ways to satisfy a second condition, then there are $n + m$ ways to satisfy both conditions.
    False; there are $m \cdot n$ ways.

12. The number of permutations of n things taken r at a time is given by $\dfrac{n!}{r!}$. False; $P(n, r) = \dfrac{n!}{(n-r)!}.$

13. If E is an event in a sample space, then $0 \le P(E) \le 1$, where $P(E)$ is the probability of E. True

14. If A and B are mutually exclusive events, then $P(A \cap B) = 1$. False; $P(A \cap B) = P(\varnothing) = 0.$

15. If a fair coin is tossed five times, then the probability of observing HHHHH is the same as the probability of observing HTHHT. True

CHAPTER 8 REVIEW EXERCISES

—Answers to Exercises 21–40 and 65–68 are on page AA35.

In Exercises 1 to 20, find the third and seventh terms of the sequence defined by a_n.

1. $a_n = n^2$ $a_3 = 9, a_7 = 49$ [8.1]
2. $a_n = n!$ $a_3 = 6, a_7 = 5040$ [8.1]
3. $a_n = 3n + 2$ $a_3 = 11, a_7 = 23$ [8.1]
4. $a_n = 1 - 2n$ $a_3 = -5, a_7 = -13$ [8.1]
5. $a_n = 2^{-n}$ $a_3 = \frac{1}{8}, a_7 = \frac{1}{128}$ [8.1]
6. $a_n = 3^n$ $a_3 = 27, a_7 = 2187$ [8.1]

7. $a_n = \dfrac{1}{n!}$ $a_3 = \dfrac{1}{6}$, $a_7 = \dfrac{1}{5040}$ [8.1]

8. $a_n = \dfrac{1}{n}$ $a_3 = \dfrac{1}{3}$, $a_7 = \dfrac{1}{7}$ [8.1]

9. $a_n = \left(\dfrac{2}{3}\right)^n$ $a_3 = \dfrac{8}{27}$, $a_7 = \dfrac{128}{2187}$ [8.1]

10. $a_n = \left(-\dfrac{4}{3}\right)^n$ $a_3 = -\dfrac{64}{27}$, $a_7 = -\dfrac{16,384}{2187}$ [8.1]

11. $a_1 = 2, a_n = 3a_{n-1}$ $a_3 = 18$, $a_7 = 1458$ [8.1]

12. $a_1 = -1, a_n = 2a_{n-1}$ $a_3 = -4$, $a_7 = -64$ [8.1]

13. $a_1 = 1, a_n = -na_{n-1}$ $a_3 = 6$, $a_7 = 5040$ [8.1]

14. $a_1 = 2, a_n = n^2a_{n-1}$ $a_3 = 72$, $a_7 = 50,803,200$ [8.1]

15. $a_1 = 4, a_n = a_{n-1} + 2$ $a_3 = 8$, $a_7 = 16$ [8.1]

16. $a_1 = 3, a_n = a_{n-1} - 3$ $a_3 = -3$, $a_7 = -15$ [8.1]

17. $a_1 = 1, a_2 = 2, a_n = a_{n-1}a_{n-2}$ $a_3 = 2$, $a_7 = 256$ [8.1]

18. $a_1 = 1, a_2 = 2, a_n = \dfrac{a_{n-1}}{a_{n-2}}$ $a_3 = 2$, $a_7 = 1$ [8.1]

19. $a_1 = -1, a_n = 3na_{n-1}$ $a_3 = -54$, $a_7 = -3,674,160$ [8.1]

20. $a_1 = 2, a_n = -2na_{n-1}$ $a_3 = 48$, $a_7 = 645,120$ [8.1]

21–40. Classify each sequence defined in Exercises 1 to 20 as arithmetic, geometric, or neither.

In Exercises 41 to 56, find the indicated sum of the series. If necessary, round to the nearest ten-thousandth.

41. $\displaystyle\sum_{n=1}^{9} (2n - 3)$ 63 [8.2]

42. $\displaystyle\sum_{i=1}^{11} (1 - 3i)$ -187 [8.2]

43. $\displaystyle\sum_{k=1}^{8} (4k + 1)$ 152 [8.2]

44. $\displaystyle\sum_{i=1}^{10} (i^2 + 3)$ 415 [8.1]

45. $\displaystyle\sum_{n=1}^{6} 3 \cdot 2^n$ 378 [8.3]

46. $\displaystyle\sum_{i=1}^{5} 2 \cdot 4^{i-1}$ 682 [8.3]

47. $\displaystyle\sum_{k=1}^{9} (-1)^k 3^k$ $-14,763$ [8.3]

48. $\displaystyle\sum_{i=1}^{8} (-1)^{i+1} 2^i$ -170 [8.3]

49. $\displaystyle\sum_{i=1}^{10} \left(\dfrac{2}{3}\right)^i$ $\dfrac{116,050}{59,049} \approx 1.9653$ [8.3]

50. $\displaystyle\sum_{i=1}^{11} \left(\dfrac{3}{2}\right)^i$ $\dfrac{525,297}{2048} \approx 256.4927$ [8.3]

51. $\displaystyle\sum_{n=1}^{9} \dfrac{(-1)^{n+1}}{n^2}$ 0.8280 [8.1]

52. $\displaystyle\sum_{k=1}^{5} \dfrac{(-1)^{k+1}}{k!}$ $0.6\overline{3}$ [8.1]

53. $\displaystyle\sum_{n=1}^{\infty} \left(\dfrac{1}{4}\right)^n$ $\dfrac{1}{3}$ [8.3]

54. $\displaystyle\sum_{i=1}^{\infty} \left(-\dfrac{5}{6}\right)^i$ $-\dfrac{5}{11}$ [8.3]

55. $\displaystyle\sum_{k=1}^{\infty} \left(-\dfrac{4}{5}\right)^k$ $-\dfrac{4}{9}$ [8.3]

56. $\displaystyle\sum_{j=0}^{\infty} \left(\dfrac{1}{5}\right)^j$ $\dfrac{5}{4}$ [8.3]

In Exercises 57 to 64, prove each statement by mathematical induction.

57. $\displaystyle\sum_{i=1}^{n} (5i + 1) = \dfrac{n(5n + 7)}{2}$

58. $\displaystyle\sum_{i=1}^{n} (3 - 4i) = n(1 - 2n)$

59. $\displaystyle\sum_{i=0}^{n} \left(-\dfrac{1}{2}\right)^i = \dfrac{2[1 - (-1/2)^{n+1}]}{3}$

60. $\displaystyle\sum_{i=0}^{n} (-1)^i = \dfrac{1 - (-1)^{n+1}}{2}$

61. $n^n \geq n!$

62. $n! > 4^n$, $n \geq 9$

63. 3 is a factor of $n^3 + 2n$ for all positive integers n.

64. Let $a_1 = \sqrt{2}$ and $a_n = \left(\sqrt{2}\right)^{a_{n-1}}$. Prove that $a_n < 2$ for all positive integers n.

In Exercises 65 to 68, use the Binomial Theorem to expand each binomial.

65. $(4a - b)^5$

66. $(x + 3y)^6$

67. $\left(\sqrt{a} + 2\sqrt{b}\right)^8$

68. $\left(2x - \dfrac{1}{2x}\right)^7$

69. Find the fifth term in the expansion of $(3x - 4y)^7$. $241,920x^3y^4$ [8.5]

70. Find the eighth term in the expansion of $(1 - 3x)^9$. $-78,732x^7$ [8.5]

71. **COMPUTER PASSWORDS** A computer password consists of eight letters. How many passwords are possible? Assume there is no difference between lower-case and upper-case letters. 26^8 [8.6]

72. **SERIAL NUMBERS** The serial number on an airplane consists of the letter N, followed by six numerals, followed by one letter. How many serial numbers are possible? $10^6 \cdot 26$ [8.6]

73. **COMMITTEE MEMBERSHIP** From a committee of fifteen members, a president, a vice president, and a treasurer are elected. In how many ways can this be accomplished?   2730 [8.6]

74. **SCHEDULING** The emergency staff for a hospital consists of four supervisors and twelve regular employees. How many shifts of four people can be formed if each shift must contain exactly one supervisor?   880 [8.6]

75. **COMMITTEE MEMBERSHIP** From twelve people, a committee of five people is formed. In how many ways can this be accomplished if there are two people among the twelve who refuse to serve together on the committee?   672 [8.6]

76. **ACCEPTANCE SAMPLING** A shipment of ten calculators contains two defective ones. A quality control inspector randomly chooses four of the calculators for testing. What is the probability that the inspector will choose one defective calculator? $\dfrac{8}{15}$ [8.7]

77. **SUMS OF COINS** A nickel, a dime, and a quarter are tossed. What is the probability that the nickel and dime will show heads and the quarter will show tails? What is the probability that only one of the coins will show tails? $\dfrac{1}{8}, \dfrac{3}{8}$ [8.4]

78. ARRANGEMENTS OF CARDS A deck of ten cards contains five red and five black cards. If four cards are drawn from the deck, what is the probability that two are red and two are black? $\dfrac{10}{21}$ [8.7]

79. NUMBER THEORY For the 1000 numbers from 000 to 999, what is the probability that the middle digit of a number chosen at random is greater than the other two digits? 0.285 [8.7]

80. NUMBER THEORY Two numbers are chosen, with replacement, from the digits 1, 2, 3, 4, 5, and 6, and their sum is recorded. Now two more digits are selected and their sum noted. This process continues until the sum is 7 or the original sum is obtained. If the original sum was 9, what is the probability of obtaining another sum of 9 before obtaining a sum of 7? (*Hint:* Assume the events are independent. The probability can be found by summing an infinite geometric series.) $\dfrac{2}{5}$ [8.7]

81. CARD GAMES Which of the following has the greater probability: drawing an ace and a ten-card (ten, jack, queen, or king) from a regular deck of fifty-two playing cards, or drawing an ace and a ten-card from two decks of regular playing cards? drawing an ace and a ten-card from one deck [8.7]

82. NUMBER THEORY From the digits 1, 2, 3, 4, and 5, two numbers are chosen without replacement. What is the probability that the second number is greater than the first number? $\dfrac{1}{2}$ [8.7]

83. EMPLOYEE BADGES A room contains twelve people who are wearing badges numbered 1 to 12. If three people are randomly selected, what is the probability that the person wearing badge 6 will be included? $\dfrac{1}{4}$ [8.7]

CHAPTER 8 TEST

In Exercises 1 to 3, find the third and fifth terms of the sequence defined by a_n.

1. $a_n = \dfrac{2^n}{n!}$
$a_3 = \dfrac{4}{3},\ a_5 = \dfrac{4}{15}$ [8.1]

2. $a_n = \dfrac{(-1)^{n+1}}{2n}$
$a_3 = \dfrac{1}{6},\ a_5 = \dfrac{1}{10}$ [8.1]

3. $a_1 = 3,\ a_n = 2a_{n-1}$
$a_3 = 12,\ a_5 = 48$ [8.1]

In Exercises 4 to 6, classify each sequence as an arithmetic sequence, a geometric sequence, or neither.

4. $a_n = -2n + 3$
arithmetic [8.3]

5. $a_n = 2n^2$
neither [8.1]

6. $a_n = \dfrac{(-1)^{n-1}}{3^n}$
geometric [8.3]

In Exercises 7 to 9, find the indicated sum of the series.

7. $\displaystyle\sum_{i=1}^{6} \dfrac{1}{i}$ $\dfrac{49}{20}$ [8.1]

8. $\displaystyle\sum_{j=1}^{10} \dfrac{1}{2^j}$ $\dfrac{1023}{1024}$ [8.3]

9. $\displaystyle\sum_{k=1}^{20} (3k - 2)$ 590 [8.2]

10. The third term of an arithmetic sequence is 7 and the eighth term is 22. Find the twentieth term. 58 [8.2]

11. Find the sum of the infinite geometric series given by $\displaystyle\sum_{k=1}^{\infty} \left(\dfrac{3}{8}\right)^k$. $\dfrac{3}{5}$ [8.3]

12. Write $0.\overline{15}$ as the quotient of integers in simplest form.
$\dfrac{5}{33}$ [8.3]

In Exercises 13 and 14, prove the statement by mathematical induction.

13. $\displaystyle\sum_{i=1}^{n} (2 - 3i) = \dfrac{n(1 - 3n)}{2}$

14. $n! > 3^n,\ \ n \geq 7$

15. Write the binomial expansion of $(x - 2y)^5$.
$x^5 - 10x^4y + 40x^3y^2 - 80x^2y^3 + 80xy^4 - 32y^5$ [8.5]

16. Write the binomial expansion of $\left(x + \dfrac{1}{x}\right)^6$.
$x^6 + 6x^4 + 15x^2 + 20 + \dfrac{15}{x^2} + \dfrac{6}{x^4} + \dfrac{1}{x^6}$ [8.5]

17. Find the sixth term in the expansion of $(3x + 2y)^8$.
$48{,}384x^3y^5$ [8.5]

18. Three cards are randomly chosen from a regular deck of playing cards. In how many ways can the cards be chosen? 132,600 [8.6]

19. A serial number consists of seven characters. The first three characters are upper-case letters of the alphabet. The next two characters are selected from the digits 1 through 9. The last two characters are upper-case letters of the alphabet. How many serial numbers are possible if no letter or number can be used twice in the same serial number? 568,339,200 [8.6]

20. Five cards are randomly selected from a deck of cards containing eight black cards and ten red cards. What is the probability that three black cards and two red cards are selected? $\dfrac{5}{17}$ [8.7]

CUMULATIVE REVIEW EXERCISES

1. Solve $|3 - 5x| \le 4$. Write the answer using interval notation. $\left[-\dfrac{1}{5}, \dfrac{7}{5}\right]$ [1.5]

2. Find the linear regression equation for the set $\{(1, 5), (3, 8), (4, 11), (6, 15), (8, 16)\}$. Round values to the nearest tenth. $y = 1.7x + 3.6$ [2.7]

3. Graph: $y = x^2 - x - 2$ [2.1]
Answer on page AA35.

4. Find the value of x in the domain of $F(x) = 5 + \dfrac{x}{3}$ for which $F(x) = -3$. -24 [2.3]

5. Divide $x^3 - 1$ by $x + 1$. $x^2 - x + 1 - \dfrac{2}{x+1}$ [3.1]

6. Solve: $2x^2 - 3x = 4$ $\dfrac{3 \pm \sqrt{41}}{4}$ [1.3]

7. Write $\log_b\left(\dfrac{xy^2}{z^3}\right)$ in terms of the logarithms of x, y, and z.
$\log_b x + 2 \log_b y - 3 \log_b z$ [4.4]

8. Find the eccentricity of the graph of $16x^2 + 25y^2 - 96x + 100y - 156 = 0$. $\dfrac{3}{5}$ [5.2]

9. Solve: $\begin{cases} 2x - 3y = 8 \\ x + 4y = -7 \end{cases}$ $x = 1, y = -2$ [6.1]

10. Given $A = \begin{bmatrix} -1 & 2 \\ 5 & 3 \\ 0 & 3 \end{bmatrix}$ and $B = \begin{bmatrix} 7 & -3 \\ 6 & 5 \\ 1 & -2 \end{bmatrix}$, find $3A - 2B$.
$\begin{bmatrix} -17 & 12 \\ 3 & -1 \\ -2 & 13 \end{bmatrix}$ [7.2]

11. Simplify: $-2\sqrt[4]{80} + 3\sqrt[4]{405}$
$5\sqrt[4]{5}$ [P.2]

12. Does the equation $|x| + |y| = 4$ define y as a function of x? No. [2.2]

13. Find the coordinates of the vertex of $F(x) = -2x^2 + 5x - 2$.
$\left(\dfrac{5}{4}, \dfrac{9}{8}\right)$ [2.4]

14. Let $g(x) = x^2 - x + 4$ and $h(x) = x - 2$. Find $\left(\dfrac{h}{g}\right)(-3)$.
$-\dfrac{5}{16}$ [2.6]

15. Find the horizontal asymptote of the graph of $F(x) = \dfrac{x^3 - 8}{x^5}$. $y = 0$ [3.5]

16. Evaluate: $\log_{\frac{1}{2}} 64$ -6 [4.3]

17. Solve $4^{2x+1} = 3^{x-2}$. Round to the nearest tenth. -2.1 [4.5]

18. Solve: $\begin{cases} x^2 + y^2 + xy = 10 \\ x - y = 1 \end{cases}$ $\left(\dfrac{1+\sqrt{13}}{2}, \dfrac{-1+\sqrt{13}}{2}\right),$ $\left(\dfrac{1-\sqrt{13}}{2}, \dfrac{-1-\sqrt{13}}{2}\right)$ [6.3]

19. Find the product of $\begin{bmatrix} 3 & 2 \\ -2 & 1 \\ 1 & -4 \end{bmatrix}\begin{bmatrix} 2 & 3 & 1 & 1 \\ -2 & 0 & 4 & -3 \end{bmatrix}$.
See answer below.

20. The time t in seconds required for a sky diver to reach a velocity of v feet per second is given by $t = -\dfrac{175}{32}\ln\left(1 - \dfrac{v}{175}\right)$. Determine the velocity of the sky diver after 5 seconds. Round to the nearest mile per hour. 105 mph [4.5]

19. $\begin{bmatrix} 2 & 9 & 11 & -3 \\ -6 & -6 & 2 & -5 \\ 10 & 3 & -15 & 13 \end{bmatrix}$ [7.3]

SOLUTIONS TO THE TRY EXERCISES

Exercise Set P.1, page 15

2. a. Integers: 31, 51

b. Rational numbers: $\dfrac{5}{7}$, 31, $-2\dfrac{1}{2}$, 4.235653907493, 51, 0.888...

c. Irrational number: $\dfrac{5}{\sqrt{7}}$

d. Prime number: 31

e. Real numbers: All the numbers are real numbers.

6. In absolute value, the four smallest integers are 0, 1, 2, and 3. Replacing x in $x^2 - 1$ by these values, we obtain $\{-1, 0, 3, 8\}$.

16. $A \cap B = \{-2, 0, 2\}$ and $A \cap C = \{0, 1, 2, 3\}$. Therefore, $(A \cap B) \cup (A \cap C) = \{-2, 0, 1, 2, 3\}$.

48. $d(z, 5) = |z - 5|$; therefore $|z - 5| > 7$.

54. The interval $(-\infty, 3]$ includes all real numbers from $-\infty$ to 3, including 3. The interval $(2, 6)$ includes all real numbers between 2 and 6, not including 2 and not including 6. Therefore, $(-\infty, 3] \cap (2, 6) = (2, 3]$. The graph is

$$\begin{array}{c}\xleftarrow{\hspace{0.5em}}\!\!+\!\!+\!\!+\!\!+\!\!+\!\!+\!\!(\!\!\!-\!\!]\!\!+\!\!+\!\!\xrightarrow{\hspace{0.5em}}\\ {\scriptstyle -5\;-4\;-3\;-2\;-1\;\;0\;\;1\;\;2\;\;3\;\;4\;\;5}\end{array}$$

64. $\{x \mid -3 \le x < 0\} \cup \{x \mid x \ge 2\}$ is the set of all real numbers between -3 and 0, including -3 but excluding 0, together with (union) all real numbers greater than or equal to 2. The graph is

$$\begin{array}{c}\xleftarrow{\hspace{0.5em}}\!\!+\!\![\!\!-\!\!-\!\!-\!\!-\!\!)\!\!+\!\![\!\!-\!\!-\!\!\xrightarrow{\hspace{0.5em}}\\ {\scriptstyle -5\;-4\;-3\;-2\;-1\;\;0\;\;1\;\;2\;\;3\;\;4\;\;5}\end{array}$$

74. $(z - 2y)^2 - 3z^3$

$$[(-1) - 2(-2)]^2 - 3(-1)^3 = [-1 + 4]^2 - 3(-1)$$
$$= 3^2 + 3$$
$$= 9 + 3 = 12$$

86. Commutative property of addition

90. Substitution

106. $6 + 3[2x - 4(3x - 2)] = 6 + 3[2x - 12x + 8]$
$$= 6 + 3[-10x + 8]$$
$$= 6 - 30x + 24 = -30x + 30$$

Exercise Set P.2, page 31

10. $\dfrac{4^{-2}}{2^{-3}} = \dfrac{2^3}{4^2} = \dfrac{8}{16} = \dfrac{1}{2}$

30. $\dfrac{(-3a^2b^3)^2}{(-2ab^4)^3} = \dfrac{(-3)^{1\cdot2}a^{2\cdot2}b^{3\cdot2}}{(-2)^{1\cdot3}a^{1\cdot3}b^{4\cdot3}}$

$$= \dfrac{9a^4b^6}{-8a^3b^{12}} = -\dfrac{9a}{8b^6}$$

46. $\dfrac{(6.9 \times 10^{27})(8.2 \times 10^{-13})}{4.1 \times 10^{15}} = \dfrac{(6.9)(8.2) \times 10^{27-13}}{4.1 \times 10^{15}}$

$$= \dfrac{56.58 \times 10^{14}}{4.1 \times 10^{15}}$$

$$= 13.8 \times 10^{-1} = 1.38$$

62. $(-5x^{1/3})(-4x^{1/2}) = (-5)(-4)x^{1/3+1/2}$
$$= 20x^{2/6+3/6} = 20x^{5/6}$$

78. $\sqrt{18x^2y^5} = \sqrt{9x^2y^4}\sqrt{2y} = 3|x|y^2\sqrt{2y}$

86. $-3x\sqrt[3]{54x^4} + 2\sqrt[3]{16x^7} = -3x\sqrt[3]{3^3 \cdot 2x^4} + 2\sqrt[3]{2^4x^7}$
$$= -3x\sqrt[3]{3^3x^3}\,\sqrt[3]{2x} + 2\sqrt[3]{2^3x^6}\,\sqrt[3]{2x}$$
$$= -3x(3x\sqrt[3]{2x}) + 2(2x^2\sqrt[3]{2x})$$
$$= -9x^2\sqrt[3]{2x} + 4x^2\sqrt[3]{2x}$$
$$= -5x^2\sqrt[3]{2x}$$

96. $(3\sqrt{5y} - 4)^2 = (3\sqrt{5y} - 4)(3\sqrt{5y} - 4)$
$$= 9 \cdot 5y - 12\sqrt{5y} - 12\sqrt{5y} + 16$$
$$= 45y - 24\sqrt{5y} + 16$$

106. $\dfrac{2}{\sqrt[4]{4y}} = \dfrac{2}{\sqrt[4]{4y}} \cdot \dfrac{\sqrt[4]{4y^3}}{\sqrt[4]{4y^3}} = \dfrac{2\sqrt[4]{4y^3}}{2y} = \dfrac{\sqrt[4]{4y^3}}{y}$

110. $-\dfrac{7}{3\sqrt{2} - 5} = -\dfrac{7}{3\sqrt{2} - 5} \cdot \dfrac{3\sqrt{2} + 5}{3\sqrt{2} + 5}$

$$= \dfrac{-21\sqrt{2} - 35}{18 - 25}$$

$$= \dfrac{-21\sqrt{2} - 35}{-7} = 3\sqrt{2} + 5$$

Exercise Set P.3, page 40

12. a. $-12x^4 - 3x^2 - 11$

b. 4

c. $-12, -3, -11$

d. -12

e. $-12x^4, -3x^2, -11$

24. $(5y^2 - 7y + 3) + (2y^2 + 8y + 1) = 7y^2 + y + 4$

32.
$$\begin{array}{r} 3x^2 - 8x - 5 \\ 5x - 7 \\ \hline -21x^2 + 56x + 35 \\ 15x^3 - 40x^2 - 25x \\ \hline 15x^3 - 61x^2 + 31x + 35 \end{array}$$

56. $(4x^2 - 3y)(4x^2 + 3y) = (4x^2)^2 - (3y)^2 = 16x^4 - 9y^2$

66. $-x^2 - 5x + 4$

$ -(-5)^2 - 5(-5) + 4$ • Replace x by -5.

$= -25 + 25 + 4$ • Simplify.

$= 4$

76. $\dfrac{1}{6}n^3 - \dfrac{1}{2}n^2 + \dfrac{1}{3}n$

$\dfrac{1}{6}(21)^3 - \dfrac{1}{2}(21)^2 + \dfrac{1}{3}(21) = 1330$

It is possible to form 1330 different committees.

78. a. $4.3 \times 10^{-6}(1000)^2 - 2.1 \times 10^{-4}(1000)$

$= 4.09$ seconds

b. $4.3 \times 10^{-6}(5000)^2 - 2.1 \times 10^{-4}(5000)$

$= 106.45$ seconds

c. $4.3 \times 10^{-6}(10,000)^2 - 2.1 \times 10^{-4}(10,000)$

$= 427.9$ seconds

Exercise Set P.4, page 53

6. $6a^3b^2 - 12a^2b + 72ab^3 = 6ab(a^2b - 2a + 12b^2)$

12. $b^2 + 12b - 28 = (b + 14)(b - 2)$

16. $57y^2 + y - 6 = (19y - 6)(3y + 1)$

24. $b^2 - 4ac = 8^2 - 4(16)(-35) = 2304 = 48^2$

The trinomial is factorable over the integers.

36. $8x^6 - 10x^3 - 3 = (4x^3 + 1)(2x^3 - 3)$

40. $81b^2 - 16c^2 = (9b - 4c)(9b + 4c)$

50. $b^2 - 24b + 144 = (b - 12)^2$

56. $b^3 + 64 = (b + 4)(b^2 - 4b + 16)$

66. $a^2y^2 - ay^3 + ac - cy = ay^2(a - y) + c(a - y)$

$= (a - y)(ay^2 + c)$

72. $81y^4 - 16 = (9y^2 - 4)(9y^2 + 4)$

$= (3y - 2)(3y + 2)(9y^2 + 4)$

Exercise Set P.5, page 62

2. $\dfrac{2x^2 - 5x - 12}{2x^2 + 5x + 3} = \dfrac{(2x + 3)(x - 4)}{(2x + 3)(x + 1)} = \dfrac{x - 4}{x + 1}$

16. $\dfrac{x^2 - 16}{x^2 + 7x + 12} \cdot \dfrac{x^2 - 4x - 21}{x^2 - 4x}$

$= \dfrac{(x - 4)(x + 4)(x + 3)(x - 7)}{(x + 3)(x + 4)x(x - 4)} = \dfrac{x - 7}{x}$

30. $\dfrac{3y - 1}{3y + 1} - \dfrac{2y - 5}{y - 3} = \dfrac{(3y - 1)(y - 3)}{(3y + 1)(y - 3)} - \dfrac{(2y - 5)(3y + 1)}{(y - 3)(3y + 1)}$

$= \dfrac{(3y^2 - 10y + 3) - (6y^2 - 13y - 5)}{(3y + 1)(y - 3)}$

$= \dfrac{-3y^2 + 3y + 8}{(3y + 1)(y - 3)}$

42. $\dfrac{3 - \dfrac{2}{a}}{5 + \dfrac{3}{a}} = \dfrac{\left(3 - \dfrac{2}{a}\right)a}{\left(5 + \dfrac{3}{a}\right)a} = \dfrac{3a - 2}{5a + 3}$

60. $\dfrac{e^{-2} - f^{-1}}{ef} = \dfrac{\dfrac{1}{e^2} - \dfrac{1}{f}}{ef} = \dfrac{f - e^2}{e^2f} \div \dfrac{ef}{1}$

$= \dfrac{f - e^2}{e^2f} \cdot \dfrac{1}{ef} = \dfrac{f - e^2}{e^3f^2}$

64. a. $\dfrac{v_1 + v_2}{1 + \dfrac{v_1 v_2}{c^2}} = \dfrac{1.2 \times 10^8 + 2.4 \times 10^8}{1 + \dfrac{(1.2 \times 10^8)(2.4 \times 10^8)}{(6.7 \times 10^8)^2}} \approx 3.4 \times 10^8$ mph

b. $\dfrac{v_1 + v_2}{1 + \dfrac{v_1 \cdot v_2}{c^2}} = \dfrac{c^2(v_1 + v_2)}{c^2\left(1 + \dfrac{v_1 \cdot v_2}{c^2}\right)} = \dfrac{c^2(v_1 + v_2)}{c^2 + v_1 \cdot v_2}$

Exercise Set P.6, page 71

8. $6 - \sqrt{-1} = 6 - i$

18. $(5 - 3i) - (2 + 9i) = 5 - 3i - 2 - 9i = 3 - 12i$

34. $\left(5 + 2\sqrt{-16}\right)\left(1 - \sqrt{-25}\right) = [5 + 2(4i)](1 - 5i)$

$= (5 + 8i)(1 - 5i)$

$= 5 - 25i + 8i - 40i^2$

$= 5 - 25i + 8i - 40(-1)$

$= 5 - 25i + 8i + 40$

$= 45 - 17i$

48. $\dfrac{8 - i}{2 + 3i} = \dfrac{8 - i}{2 + 3i} \cdot \dfrac{2 - 3i}{2 - 3i}$

$= \dfrac{16 - 24i - 2i + 3i^2}{2^2 + 3^2}$

$= \dfrac{16 - 24i - 2i + 3(-1)}{4 + 9}$

$= \dfrac{16 - 26i - 3}{13}$

$= \dfrac{13 - 26i}{13} = \dfrac{13(1 - 2i)}{13}$

$= 1 - 2i$

60. $\dfrac{1}{i^{83}} = \dfrac{1}{i^{80} \cdot i^3} = \dfrac{1}{i^3} = \dfrac{1}{-i}$

$= \dfrac{1}{-i} \cdot \dfrac{i}{i} = \dfrac{i}{-i^2} = \dfrac{i}{-(-1)} = \dfrac{i}{1} = i$

Exercise Set 1.1, page 88

2. $-3y + 20 = 2$

$\quad -3y = -18$ • Subtract 20 from each side.

$\quad\quad y = 6$ • Divide each side by -3.

12. $\dfrac{1}{2}x + 7 - \dfrac{1}{4}x = \dfrac{19}{2}$

$4\left(\dfrac{1}{2}x + 7 - \dfrac{1}{4}x\right) = 4\left(\dfrac{19}{2}\right)$ • Multiply each side by 4.

$\quad\quad 2x + 28 - x = 38$

$\quad\quad\quad\quad\quad x = 38 - 28$ • Collect like terms.

$\quad\quad\quad\quad\quad x = 10$

18. $5(x + 4)(x - 4) = (x - 3)(5x + 4)$

$\quad 5(x^2 - 16) = 5x^2 - 11x - 12$

$\quad 5x^2 - 80 = 5x^2 - 11x - 12$

$\quad -80 + 12 = -11x$

$\quad\quad -68 = -11x$

$\quad\quad \dfrac{68}{11} = x$

24. $2x + \dfrac{1}{3} = \dfrac{6x + 1}{3}$ • Rewrite the left side.

$\dfrac{6x + 1}{3} = \dfrac{6x + 1}{3}$

The left side of this equation is now identical to the right side. Thus the original equation is an identity. The solution set of the original equation consists of all real numbers.

38. $\qquad\qquad |2x - 3| = 21$

$2x - 3 = 21 \quad$ or $\quad 2x - 3 = -21$

$\quad 2x = 24 \qquad\qquad\quad 2x = -18$

$\quad\quad x = 12 \qquad\qquad\quad\quad x = -9$

The solutions of $|2x - 3| = 21$ are -9 and 12.

50. Substitute 175 for P, the number of patents measured in thousands, and solve for x.

$\quad\quad P = 5.4x + 110$

$\quad 175 = 5.4x + 110$

$\quad\quad 65 = 5.4x$ • Subtract 110 from each side.

$\quad\quad\quad x = \dfrac{65}{5.4}$ • Solve for x.

$\quad\quad\quad x \approx 12.04$

Adding 12.04 to 1993 yields 2005.04. Thus, according to the model, the number of patents will first exceed 175,000 in the year 2005.

52. Substitute 22 for m in the given equation and solve for s.

$22 = -\dfrac{1}{2}|s - 55| + 25$ • Substitute 22 for *m*.

$-44 = |s - 55| - 50$ • Multiply each side by -2 to clear the equation of fractions.

$6 = |s - 55|$ • Add 50 to each side.

$s - 55 = 6 \qquad$ or $\qquad s - 55 = -6$

$\quad\quad s = 61 \qquad\qquad\qquad\quad s = 49$

Kate should drive her car at either 61 miles per hour or 49 miles per hour to obtain a gas mileage of 22 miles per gallon.

Exercise Set 1.2, page 98

4. $A = P + Prt$

$A = P(1 + rt)$ • Factor.

$P = \dfrac{A}{(1 + rt)}$ • Solve for *P*.

14. Substitute 105 for w.

SMOG reading grade level $= \sqrt{105} + 3$

$\approx 10.2 + 3$

$= 13.2$

According to the SMOG formula, the estimated reading grade level required to fully understand *A Tale of Two Cities* is 13.2. (*Note:* A different sample of 30 sentences likely would produce a different result. It is for this reason that reading grade levels are often estimated by using several different samples and then computing an average of the results.)

20. $P = 2l + 2w, \qquad w = \dfrac{1}{2}l + 1$

$110 = 2l + 2\left(\dfrac{1}{2}l + 1\right)$ • Substitute for *w*.

$110 = 2l + l + 2$ • Simplify.

$108 = 3l$

$\;36 = l$

$\quad l = 36$ meters

$w = \dfrac{1}{2}l + 1 = \dfrac{1}{2}(36) + 1 = 19$ meters

24. Let $t_1 =$ the time it takes to travel to the island. Let $t_2 =$ the time it takes to make the return trip.

$t_1 + t_2 = 7.5$

$\quad\quad t_2 = 7.5 - t_1$

(continued)

$15t_1 = 10t_2$

$15t_1 = 10(7.5 - t_1)$ • **Substitute for t_2.**

$15t_1 = 75 - 10t_1$

$25t_1 = 75$

$t_1 = 3$ hours

$D = 15t_1 = 15(3) = 45$ nautical miles

32. Let x = the number of glasses of orange juice.

Profit = revenue − cost

$\$2337 = 0.75x - 0.18x$

$2337 = 0.57x$

$x = \dfrac{2337}{0.57}$

$x = 4100$

36. Let x = the amount of money invested at 5%.
Then $7500 - x$ is the amount of money invested at 7%.

5%	x
7%	$7500 - x$

$0.05x + 0.07(7500 - x) = 405$

$0.05x + 525 - 0.07x = 405$

$-0.02x = -120$

$x = 6000$

$7500 - x = 1500$

$6000 was invested at 5%. $1500 was invested at 7%.

40. Let x = the number of liters of the 40% solution to be mixed with the 24% solution.

0.40	x
0.24	4
0.30	$4 + x$

$0.40x + 0.24(4) = 0.30(4 + x)$

$0.40x + 0.96 = 1.2 + 0.30x$

$0.10x = 0.24$

$x = 2.4$

Thus 2.4 liters of 40% sulfuric acid should be mixed with 4 liters of a 24% sulfuric acid solution to produce the 30% solution.

50. Let x = the number of hours needed to print the report if both the printers are used.

Printer A prints $\dfrac{1}{3}$ of the report every hour.

Printer B prints $\dfrac{1}{4}$ of the report every hour.

Thus

$\dfrac{1}{3}x + \dfrac{1}{4}x = 1$

$4x + 3x = 12 \cdot 1$

$7x = 12$

$x = \dfrac{12}{7} \approx 1.71$

It would take approximately 1.71 hours to print the report.

Exercise Set 1.3, page 113

6. $12x^2 - 41x + 24 = 0$

$(4x - 3)(3x - 8) = 0$ • **Factor.**

$4x - 3 = 0$ or $3x - 8 = 0$ • **Apply the zero product property.**

$x = \dfrac{3}{4}$ $x = \dfrac{8}{3}$

A check shows that $\dfrac{3}{4}$ and $\dfrac{8}{3}$ are both solutions of $12x^2 - 41x + 24 = 0$.

20. $(x + 2)^2 + 28 = 0$

$(x + 2)^2 = -28$

$\sqrt{(x + 2)^2} = \sqrt{-28}$

$x + 2 = \pm i\sqrt{28} = \pm 2i\sqrt{7}$

$x = -2 \pm 2i\sqrt{7}$

The solutions are $-2 - 2i\sqrt{7}$ and $-2 + 2i\sqrt{7}$.

26. $x^2 - 6x + 10 = 0$

$x^2 - 6x = -10$

$x^2 - 6x + 9 = -10 + 9$ • **Add** $\left[\dfrac{1}{2}(-6)\right]^2$ **to each side.**

$(x - 3)^2 = -1$ • **Factor the left side.**

$\sqrt{(x - 3)^2} = \pm\sqrt{-1}$ • **The square root procedure.**

$x - 3 = \pm i$

$x = 3 \pm i$

The solutions are $3 - i$ and $3 + i$.

30. $2x^2 + 10x - 3 = 0$

$2x^2 + 10x = 3$

$2(x^2 + 5x) = 3$

$x^2 + 5x = \dfrac{3}{2}$ • **Divide each side by 2.**

$x^2 + 5x + \dfrac{25}{4} = \dfrac{3}{2} + \dfrac{25}{4}$ • **Complete the square.**

$\left(x + \dfrac{5}{2}\right)^2 = \dfrac{31}{4}$

$x + \dfrac{5}{2} = \pm\sqrt{\dfrac{31}{4}}$

$x = -\dfrac{5}{2} \pm \dfrac{\sqrt{31}}{2}$

$x = \dfrac{-5 + \sqrt{31}}{2}$ or $x = \dfrac{-5 - \sqrt{31}}{2}$

38. $2x^2 + 4x - 1 = 0$

$x = \dfrac{-4 \pm \sqrt{4^2 - 4(2)(-1)}}{4}$

$x = \dfrac{-4 \pm \sqrt{16 + 8}}{4} = \dfrac{-4 \pm \sqrt{24}}{4}$

$$x = \frac{-4 \pm 2\sqrt{6}}{4} = \frac{-2 \pm \sqrt{6}}{2}$$

$$x = \frac{-2 + \sqrt{6}}{2} \quad \text{or} \quad x = \frac{-2 - \sqrt{6}}{2}$$

48. $x^2 + 3x - 11 = 0$

$b^2 - 4ac = 3^2 - 4(1)(-11) = 9 + 44 = 53 > 0$

Thus the equation has two distinct real roots.

58. Home plate, first base, and second base form a right triangle. The legs of this right triangle each measure 90 ft. The distance from home plate to second base is the length of the hypotenuse c of this right triangle.

$$c^2 = 90^2 + 90^2$$
$$c^2 = 16{,}200$$
$$c = \sqrt{16{,}200}$$
$$c \approx 127.3$$

To the nearest tenth of a foot, the distance from home plate to second base is 127.3 feet. (*Note:* We have not considered $-\sqrt{16{,}200}$ as a solution because we know that the distance must be positive.)

70. Let w be the width, in inches, of the new candy bar. Then the length, in inches, of the new candy bar is $2.5w$, and the height is 0.5 inch. The volume of the original candy bar is $5 \cdot 2 \cdot 0.5 = 5$ cubic inches. Thus the volume of the new candy bar is $0.80(5) = 4$ cubic inches. Substitute in the formula for the volume of a rectangular solid to produce

$$lwh = V$$
$$(2.5w)(w)(0.5) = 4$$
$$1.25w^2 = 4$$
$$w^2 = 3.2$$
$$w = \sqrt{3.2}$$
$$\approx 1.8$$

The width of the new candy bar should be about 1.8 inches and the length $2.5(1.8) \approx 4.5$ inches.

72. When the ball hits the ground, $h = 0$. Thus we need to solve $0 = -16t^2 + 52t + 4.5$ for t.

$$0 = -16t^2 + 52t + 4.5$$
$$t = \frac{-(52) \pm \sqrt{(52)^2 - 4(-16)(4.5)}}{2(-16)}$$
$$= \frac{-52 \pm \sqrt{2992}}{-32}$$
$$\approx 3.3$$

The ball will hit the ground in about 3.3 seconds. Disregard the negative solution because the time must be positive.

Exercise Set 1.4, page 125

6.
$$x^4 - 36x^2 = 0$$
$$x^2(x^2 - 36) = 0$$
$$x^2(x - 6)(x + 6) = 0$$
$$x = 0, x = 6, x = -6$$

14. Multiply each side of the equation by $(y + 2)(y - 4)$ to clear the equation of fractions.

$$\frac{4}{y + 2} = \frac{7}{y - 4} \qquad y \neq -2, y \neq 4$$

$$(y + 2)(y - 4)\left(\frac{4}{y + 2}\right) = (y + 2)(y - 4)\left(\frac{7}{y - 4}\right)$$

$$(y - 4)4 = (y + 2)7$$
$$4y - 16 = 7y + 14$$
$$4y - 7y = 14 + 16$$
$$-3y = 30$$
$$y = -10$$

Check to verify that -10 is the solution.

28. $\sqrt{10 - x} = 4$ *Check:* $\sqrt{10 - (-6)} = 4$

$$10 - x = 16 \qquad\qquad \sqrt{16} = 4$$
$$-x = 6 \qquad\qquad\quad 4 = 4$$
$$x = -6$$

The solution is -6.

30.
$$x = \sqrt{5 - x} + 5$$
$$(x - 5)^2 = \left(\sqrt{5 - x}\right)^2$$
$$x^2 - 10x + 25 = 5 - x$$
$$x^2 - 9x + 20 = 0$$
$$(x - 5)(x - 4) = 0$$
$$x = 5 \quad \text{or} \quad x = 4$$

Check: $5 = \sqrt{5 - 5} + 5$ $4 = \sqrt{5 - 4} + 5$

$$5 = 0 + 5 \qquad\qquad 4 = 1 + 5$$
$$5 = 5 \qquad\qquad\quad 4 = 6 \quad \text{False}$$

The solution is 5.

34.
$$\sqrt{x + 7} - 2 = \sqrt{x - 9}$$
$$\left(\sqrt{x + 7} - 2\right)^2 = \left(\sqrt{x - 9}\right)^2$$
$$x + 7 - 4\sqrt{x + 7} + 4 = x - 9$$
$$-4\sqrt{x + 7} = -20$$
$$\left(\sqrt{x + 7}\right)^2 = (5)^2$$
$$x + 7 = 25$$
$$x = 18$$

Check: $\sqrt{18 + 7} - 2 = \sqrt{18 - 9}$

$$\sqrt{25} - 2 = \sqrt{9}$$

(continued)

$$5 - 2 = 3$$
$$3 = 3$$

The solution is 18.

42. $x^4 - 10x^2 + 9 = 0$ • Let $u = x^2$.

$u^2 - 10u + 9 = 0$

$(u - 9)(u - 1) = 0$

$u = 9$ or $u = 1$

$x^2 = 9$ $x^2 = 1$

$x = \pm 3$ $x = \pm 1$

The solutions are 3, −3, 1, and −1.

50. $6x^{2/3} - 7x^{1/3} - 20 = 0$ • Let $u = x^{1/3}$.

$6u^2 - 7u - 20 = 0$

$(3u + 4)(2u - 5) = 0$

$u = -\dfrac{4}{3}$ or $u = \dfrac{5}{2}$

$x^{1/3} = -\dfrac{4}{3}$ $x^{1/3} = \dfrac{5}{2}$

$(x^{1/3})^3 = \left(-\dfrac{4}{3}\right)^3$ $(x^{1/3})^3 = \left(\dfrac{5}{2}\right)^3$

$x = -\dfrac{64}{27}$ $x = \dfrac{125}{8}$

The solutions are $-\dfrac{64}{27}$ and $\dfrac{125}{8}$.

60. Sandy is to receive $\dfrac{1}{2}$ of an adult dosage of a particular medication. Substituting into Young's rule yields:

$$\dfrac{1}{2} = \dfrac{x}{x + 12}$$

$$2(x + 12)\dfrac{1}{2} = 2(x + 12)\left(\dfrac{x}{x + 12}\right)$$

$$x + 12 = 2x$$

$$12 = x$$

Sandy is 12 years old.

62. Substitute 4 for the reading grade level in the SMOG formula to produce

$4 = \sqrt{w} + 3$

$1 = \sqrt{w}$ • Subtract 3 from each side.

$1 = w$ • Square each side.

The writer should strive for a maximum of one word with three or more syllables in any sample of 30 sentences.

---

6. $-4(x - 5) \geq 2x + 15$

$-4x + 20 \geq 2x + 15$

$-6x \geq -5$

$x \leq \dfrac{5}{6}$

The solution set is $\left\{ x \,\middle|\, x \leq \dfrac{5}{6} \right\}$.

10. $2x + 5 > -16$ and $2x + 5 < 9$

$2x > -21$ and $2x < 4$

$x > -\dfrac{21}{2}$ and $x < 2$

$\left\{ x \,\middle|\, x > -\dfrac{21}{2} \right\} \cap \{x \,|\, x < 2\} = \left\{ x \,\middle|\, -\dfrac{21}{2} < x < 2 \right\}$

The solution set is $\left\{ x \,\middle|\, -\dfrac{21}{2} < x < 2 \right\}$.

18. $|2x - 9| < 7$

$-7 < 2x - 9 < 7$

$2 < \quad 2x \quad < 16$

$1 < \quad x \quad < 8$

In interval notation, the solution set is $(1, 8)$.

34. $x^2 + 5x + 6 < 0$

$(x + 2)(x + 3) = 0$

$x = -2$ and $x = -3$ • Critical values

Use a test number from each of the intervals $(-\infty, -3)$, $(-3, -2)$, and $(-2, \infty)$ to determine where $x^2 + 5x + 6$ is negative.

In interval notation, the solution set is $(-3, -2)$.

46. $\dfrac{3x + 1}{x - 2} \geq 4$

$\dfrac{3x + 1}{x - 2} - 4 \geq 0$

$\dfrac{3x + 1 - 4(x - 2)}{x - 2} \geq 0$

$$\frac{-x + 9}{x - 2} \geq 0$$

$x = 2$ and $x = 9$ • **Critical values**

Use a test number from each of the intervals $(-\infty, 2)$, $(2, 9)$, and $(9, \infty)$ to determine where $\frac{-x + 9}{x - 2}$ is positive. The solution set is $(2, 9]$.

52. Let $m =$ the number of miles driven.

Company A: $29 + 0.12m$
Company B: $22 + 0.21m$

$29 + 0.12m < 22 + 0.21m$
$\qquad 77.\overline{7} < m$

Company A is less expensive if you drive at least 78 miles.

54. Substitute 6.50 for P. Then solve the following inequality.

$0.218t + 4.02 > 6.50$
$\quad 0.218t > 2.48$
$\qquad t > \dfrac{2.48}{0.218} \approx 11.38$

Adding 11.38 to 1994 yields 2005.38. According to the given mathematical model, we should first expect to see the average price of a movie ticket exceed \$6.50 in the year 2005.

58. $41 \leq \qquad F \qquad \leq 68$

$41 \leq \dfrac{9}{5}C + 32 \leq 68$

$\quad 9 \leq \quad \dfrac{9}{5}C \quad \leq 36$

$\dfrac{5}{9}(9) \leq \left(\dfrac{5}{9}\right)\left(\dfrac{9}{5}\right)C \leq \dfrac{5}{9}(36)$

$\quad 5 \leq \qquad C \qquad \leq 20$

The Celsius temperature is between 5°C and 20°C, inclusive.

66. We need to solve:

$$\frac{0.00014x^2 + 12x + 400{,}000}{x} < 30 \qquad \text{(I)}$$

Because $x > 0$, we can multiply both sides by x to produce

$0.00014x^2 + 12x + 400{,}000 < 30x$
$0.00014x^2 - 18x + 400{,}000 < 0$

Use the quadratic formula to find the critical values.

$$x = \frac{-(-18) \pm \sqrt{(-18)^2 - 4(0.00014)(400{,}000)}}{2(0.00014)}$$

$$= \frac{18 \pm \sqrt{100}}{0.00028}$$

Use a calculator to find that the critical values are approximately 28,571.4 and 100,000. A test value can be

used to show that our original inequality (I) is true on the interval (28,571.4, 100,000). Thus the company should manufacture from 28,572 to 99,999 pairs of running shoes if it wishes to bring the average cost below \$30 per pair.

Exercise Set 1.6, page 150

22. $d = kw$

$\quad 6 = k \cdot 80$

$\dfrac{6}{80} = k$

$\quad k = \dfrac{3}{40}$

Thus $d = \dfrac{3}{40} \cdot 100 = 7.5$ inches.

26. $r = kv^2$

$\quad 140 = k \cdot 60^2$

$\dfrac{140}{60^2} = k$

$\dfrac{7}{180} = k$

Thus $r = \dfrac{7}{180} \cdot 65^2 \approx 164.3$ feet.

30. The general variation is

$$f = \frac{k}{l}$$

where f is the frequency, in vibrations per second, of the vibrating string and l is the length of the string in inches. We are given that $f = 144$ when $l = 20$ inches.

Solving $144 = \dfrac{k}{20}$ for k yields $k = 2880$. Thus the specific variation is $f = \dfrac{2880}{l}$. When $l = 18$ inches, we find

$f = \dfrac{2880}{18} = 160$. The frequency of a guitar string with a length of 18 inches is 160 vibrations per second. (*Note:* We have assumed that the tension is the same for both strings.)

32. $I = \dfrac{k}{d^2}$

$\quad 50 = \dfrac{k}{10^2}$

$5000 = k$

Thus $I = \dfrac{5000}{d^2} = \dfrac{5000}{15^2} = \dfrac{5000}{225} \approx 22.2$ footcandles.

34. $L = kwd^2$

$200 = k \cdot 2 \cdot 6^2$

$k = \dfrac{200}{2 \cdot 6^2} = \dfrac{25}{9}$

Thus $L = \dfrac{25}{9} \cdot 4 \cdot 4^2 = \dfrac{1600}{9} \approx 178$ pounds.

38. $L = k\dfrac{wd^2}{l}$

$800 = k\dfrac{4 \cdot 8^2}{12}$

$\dfrac{12 \cdot 800}{4 \cdot 8^2} = k$

$37.5 = k$

Thus $L = 37.5\dfrac{3.5 \cdot 6^2}{16} = 295.3125 \approx 295$ pounds.

Exercise Set 2.1, page 174

6. $d = \sqrt{(x_2 - x_1)^2 + (y_2 - y_1)^2}$

$d = \sqrt{[-10 - (-5)]^2 + (14 - 8)^2}$

$= \sqrt{(-5)^2 + 6^2} = \sqrt{25 + 36}$

$= \sqrt{61}$

26.

30.

32.
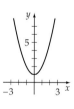

40. y-intercept: $\left(0, -\dfrac{15}{4}\right)$

x-intercept: $(5, 0)$

64. $r = \sqrt{(1 - (-2))^2 + (7 - 5)^2}$

$= \sqrt{9 + 4} = \sqrt{13}$

Using the standard form

$(x - h)^2 + (y - k)^2 = r^2$

with $h = -2, k = 5$, and $r = \sqrt{13}$ yields

$(x + 2)^2 + (y - 5)^2 = \left(\sqrt{13}\right)^2$

66. $x^2 + y^2 - 6x - 4y + 12 = 0$

$x^2 - 6x + y^2 - 4y = -12$

$x^2 - 6x + 9 + y^2 - 4y + 4 = -12 + 9 + 4$

$(x - 3)^2 + (y - 2)^2 = 1^2$

center $(3, 2)$, radius 1

Exercise Set 2.2, page 190

2. Given $g(x) = 2x^2 + 3$

   a. $g(3) = 2(3)^2 + 3 = 18 + 3 = 21$

   b. $g(-1) = 2(-1)^2 + 3 = 2 + 3 = 5$

   c. $g(0) = 2(0)^2 + 3 = 0 + 3 = 3$

   d. $g\left(\dfrac{1}{2}\right) = 2\left(\dfrac{1}{2}\right)^2 + 3 = \dfrac{1}{2} + 3 = \dfrac{7}{2}$

   e. $g(c) = 2(c)^2 + 3 = 2c^2 + 3$

   f. $g(c + 5) = 2(c + 5)^2 + 3 = 2c^2 + 20c + 50 + 3$

   $= 2c^2 + 20c + 53$

10. a. Because $0 \le 0 \le 5, Q(0) = 4$.

   b. Because $6 < e < 7, Q(e) = -e + 9$.

   c. Because $1 < n < 2, Q(n) = 4$.

   d. Because $1 < m \le 2, 8 < m^2 + 7 \le 11$. Thus

   $Q(m^2 + 7) = \sqrt{(m^2 + 7) - 7} = \sqrt{m^2} = m$

14. $x^2 - 2y = 2$ • Solve for y.

$-2y = -x^2 + 2$

$y = \dfrac{1}{2}x^2 - 1$

y is a function of x because each x value will yield one and only one y value.

28. Domain is the set of all real numbers.

40. Domain is the set of all real numbers.

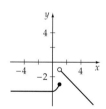

48. a. $[0, \infty)$

   b. Since \$31,250 is between \$27,950 and \$67,700 use $T(x) = 0.27(x - 27,950) + 3892.50$. Then, $T(31,250) = 0.27(31,250 - 27,950) + 3892.50 = \$4783.50$.

   c. Since \$72,000 is between \$67,700 and \$141,250 use $T(x) = 0.30(x - 67,700) + 14,625$. Then, $T(72,000) = 0.30(72,000 - 67,700) + 14,625 = \$15,915$.

50. a. This is the graph of a function. Every vertical line intersects the graph in at most one point.

   b. This is not the graph of a function. Some vertical lines intersect the graph at two points.

   c. This is not the graph of a function. The vertical line at $x = -2$ intersects the graph at more than one point.

   d. This is the graph of a function. Every vertical line intersects the graph at exactly one point.

66. $v(t) = 44,000 - 4200t, 0 \le t \le 8$

68. a. $V(x) = (30 - 2x)^2 x$
$$= (900 - 120x + 4x^2)x$$
$$= 900x - 120x^2 + 4x^3$$

b. Domain: $\{x \mid 0 < x < 15\}$

72. $d(A, B) = \sqrt{1 + x^2}$. The time required to swim from A to B at 2 mph is $\dfrac{\sqrt{1 + x^2}}{2}$ hours.

$d(B, C) = 3 - x$. The time required to run from B to C at 8 mph is $\dfrac{3 - x}{8}$ hours.

Thus the total time to reach point C is

$$t = \frac{\sqrt{1 + x^2}}{2} + \frac{3 - x}{8} \text{ hours}$$

Exercise Set 2.3, page 207

2. $m = \dfrac{1 - 4}{5 - (-2)} = -\dfrac{3}{7}$

16. $m = -1$
$b = 1$

28. $y - 5 = -2(x - 0)$
$y = -2x + 5$

42. $f(x) = \dfrac{2x}{3} + 2$

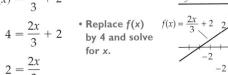

$4 = \dfrac{2x}{3} + 2$ • Replace $f(x)$ by 4 and solve for x.

$2 = \dfrac{2x}{3}$

$3 = x$

When $x = 3, f(x) = 4$.

46. $f(x) = 0$
$-2x - 4 = 0$
$-2x = 4$
$x = -2$

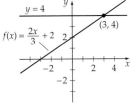

50. $f_1(x) = f_2(x)$
$-2x - 11 = 3x + 7$
$-5x - 11 = 7$
$-5x = 18$
$x = -\dfrac{18}{5} = -3.6$

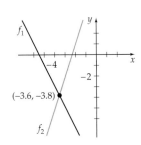

56. a. Using the data for 1997 and 2003, two ordered pairs on the line are (1997, 531.0) and (2003, 725.0). Find the slope of the line.

$$m = \frac{725.0 - 531.0}{2003 - 1997} \approx 32.3$$

Use the point-slope formula to find the equation of the line between the given points.

$$y - y_1 = m(x - x_1)$$
$$y - 531.0 = 32.3(x - 1997)$$
$$y - 531.0 = 32.3x - 64,503.1$$
$$y = 32.3x - 64,038.7$$

Using functional notation, the linear function is $C(t) = 35.6t - 70,585.4$.

b. To find the year when consumer debt first exceeds $850 billion, let $C(t) = 850$ and solve for t.

$$C(t) = 32.3t - 64,038.7$$
$$850 = 32.3t - 64,038.7$$
$$64,888.7 = 32.3t$$
$$2008 \approx t$$

According to the model, revolving consumer debt will first exceed $850 billion in 2008.

66.
$$P(x) = R(x) - C(x)$$
$$P(x) = 124x - (78.5x + 5005)$$
$$P(x) = 45.5x - 5005$$
$$45.5x - 5005 = 0$$
$$45.5x = 5005$$
$$x = 110 \qquad \text{• The break-even point}$$

78. a. The slope of the radius from $(0, 0)$ to $(\sqrt{15}, 1)$ is $\dfrac{1}{\sqrt{15}}$. The slope of the linear path of the rock is $-\sqrt{15}$. The path of the rock is given by

$$y - 1 = -\sqrt{15}(x - \sqrt{15})$$
$$y - 1 = -\sqrt{15}x + 15$$
$$y = -\sqrt{15}x + 16$$

Every point on the wall has a y value of 14. Thus

$$14 = -\sqrt{15}x + 16$$
$$-2 = -\sqrt{15}x$$
$$x = \frac{2}{\sqrt{15}} \approx 0.52$$

The rock hits the wall at $(0.52, 14)$.

Exercise Set 2.4, page 222

10. $f(x) = x^2 + 6x - 1$

$\quad\quad = x^2 + 6x + 9 + (-1 - 9)$

$\quad\quad = (x + 3)^2 - 10$

vertex $(-3, -10)$

axis of symmetry $x = -3$

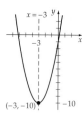

20. $h = -\dfrac{b}{2a} = -\dfrac{-6}{2(1)} = 3$

$k = f(3) = 3^2 - 6(3) = -9$

vertex $(3, -9)$

$f(x) = (x - 3)^2 - 9$

32. Determine the y-coordinate of the vertex of the graph of $f(x) = 2x^2 + 6x - 5$.

$f(x) = 2x^2 + 6x - 5$ $\quad$ • $a = 2, b = 6, c = -5$.

$h = -\dfrac{b}{2a} = -\dfrac{6}{2(2)} = -\dfrac{3}{2}$ $\quad$ • Find the x-coordinate of the vertex.

$k = f\left(-\dfrac{3}{2}\right) = 2\left(-\dfrac{3}{2}\right)^2 + 6\left(-\dfrac{3}{2}\right) - 5 = -\dfrac{19}{2}$

$\quad\quad\quad$ • Find the y-coordinate of the vertex.

The vertex is $\left(-\dfrac{3}{2}, -\dfrac{19}{2}\right)$. Because the parabola opens

up, $-\dfrac{19}{2}$ is the minimum value of f. Therefore, the range

of f is $\left\{y \,|\, y \geq -\dfrac{19}{2}\right\}$. To determine the values of x for

which $f(x) = 15$, replace $f(x)$ by $2x^2 + 6x - 5$ and solve

for x.

$\quad\quad\quad\quad f(x) = 15$

$\quad\quad 2x^2 + 6x - 5 = 15$ $\quad$ • Replace $f(x)$ by $2x^2 + 6x - 5$.

$\quad\quad 2x^2 + 6x - 20 = 0$ $\quad$ • Solve for x.

$\quad\quad 2(x - 2)(x + 5) = 0$ $\quad$ • Factor.

$\quad\quad x - 2 = 0 \quad\quad x + 5 = 0$ $\quad$ • Use the Principle of Zero

$\quad\quad\quad x = 2 \quad\quad\quad x = -5$ $\quad\quad$ Products to solve for x.

The values of x for which $f(x) = 15$ are 2 and -5.

36. $f(x) = -x^2 - 6x$

$\quad\quad = -(x^2 + 6x)$

$\quad\quad = -(x^2 + 6x + 9) + 9$

$\quad\quad = -(x + 3)^2 + 9$

Maximum value of f is 9 when $x = -3$.

46. a. $l + w = 240$, so $w = 240 - l$.

$\quad$ **b.** $A = lw = l(240 - l) = 240l - l^2$

c. The l value of the vertex point of the graph of $A = 240l - l^2$ is

$-\dfrac{b}{2a} = -\dfrac{240}{2(-1)} = 120$

Thus $l = 120$ meters and $w = 240 - 120 = 120$ meters are the dimensions that produce the greatest area.

68. Let x = the number of parcels.

$\quad$ **a.** $R(x) = xp = x(22 - 0.01x) = -0.01x^2 + 22x$

$\quad$ **b.** $P(x) = R(x) - C(x)$

$\quad\quad\quad = (-0.01x^2 + 22x) - (2025 + 7x)$

$\quad\quad\quad = -0.01x^2 + 15x - 2025$

$\quad$ **c.** $-\dfrac{b}{2a} = -\dfrac{15}{2(-0.01)} = 750$

The maximum profit is

$P(750) = -0.01(750)^2 + 15(750) - 2025 = \$3600$

$\quad$ **d.** The price per parcel that yields the maximum profit is

$p(750) = 22 - 0.01(750) = \$14.50$

$\quad$ **e.** The break-even point(s) occur when $R(x) = C(x)$.

$\quad\quad -0.01x^2 + 22x = 2025 + 7x$

$\quad\quad\quad 0 = 0.01x^2 - 15x + 2025$

$\quad\quad\quad x = \dfrac{-(-15) \pm \sqrt{(-15)^2 - 4(0.01)(2025)}}{2(0.01)}$

$x = 150$ and $x = 1350$ are the break-even points.

Thus the minimum number of parcels the air freight company must ship to break even is 150.

70. $h(t) = -16t^2 + 64t + 80$

$\quad\quad t = -\dfrac{b}{2a} = -\dfrac{64}{2(-16)} = 2$

$\quad h(2) = -16(2)^2 + 64(2) + 80$

$\quad\quad\quad = -64 + 128 + 80 = 144$

$\quad$ **a.** The vertex $(2, 144)$ gives us the maximum height of 144 feet.

$\quad$ **b.** The vertex of the graph of h is $(2, 144)$, so the time when the projectile achieves this maximum height is at time $t = 2$ seconds.

$\quad$ **c.** $-16t^2 + 64t + 80 = 0$ $\quad$ • Solve for t with $h = 0$.

$\quad\quad -16(t^2 - 4t - 5) = 0$

$\quad\quad -16(t + 1)(t - 5) = 0$

$\quad\quad t = -1 \quad\quad\quad t - 5 = 0$

$\quad\quad\quad$ no $\quad\quad\quad\quad\quad t = 5$

The projectile will have a height of 0 feet at time $t = 5$ seconds.

Exercise Set 2.5, page 238

14. The graph is symmetric with respect to the x-axis, because replacing y with $-y$ leaves the equation unaltered. The graph is not symmetric with respect to the y-axis, because replacing x with $-x$ alters the equation.

24. The graph is symmetric with respect to the origin because $(-y) = (-x)^3 - (-x)$ simplifies to $-y = -x^3 + x$, which is equivalent to the original equation $y = x^3 - x$.

44. Even, because $h(-x) = (-x)^2 + 1 = x^2 + 1 = h(x)$.

58.

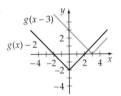

68.

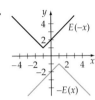

70.

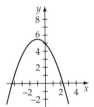

72. a.

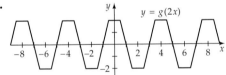

b.

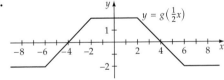

Exercise Set 2.6, page 251

10. $f(x) + g(x) = \sqrt{x-4} - x$ Domain: $\{x \mid x \geq 4\}$

$f(x) - g(x) = \sqrt{x-4} + x$ Domain: $\{x \mid x \geq 4\}$

$f(x)g(x) = -x\sqrt{x-4}$ Domain: $\{x \mid x \geq 4\}$

$\dfrac{f(x)}{g(x)} = -\dfrac{\sqrt{x-4}}{x}$ Domain: $\{x \mid x \geq 4\}$

14. $(f+g)(x) = (x^2 - 3x + 2) + (2x - 4) = x^2 - x - 2$

$(f+g)(-7) = (-7)^2 - (-7) - 2 = 49 + 7 - 2 = 54$

30. $\dfrac{f(x+h) - f(x)}{h} = \dfrac{[4(x+h) - 5] - (4x - 5)}{h}$

$= \dfrac{4x + 4(h) - 5 - 4x + 5}{h}$

$= \dfrac{4(h)}{h} = 4$

38. $(g \circ f)(x) = g[f(x)] = g[2x - 7]$

$= 3[2x - 7] + 2 = 6x - 19$

$(f \circ g)(x) = f[g(x)] = f[3x + 2]$

$= 2[3x + 2] - 7 = 6x - 3$

50. $(f \circ g)(4) = f[g(4)]$

$= f[4^2 - 5(4)]$

$= f[-4] = 2(-4) + 3 = -5$

66. a. $l = 3 - 0.5t$ for $0 \leq t \leq 6$. $l = -3 + 0.5t$ for $t > 6$. In either case, $l = |3 - 0.5t|$. $w = |2 - 0.2t|$ as in Example 7.

b. $A(t) = |3 - 0.5t||2 - 0.2t|$

c. A is decreasing on $[0, 6]$ and on $[8, 10]$. A is increasing on $[6, 8]$ and on $[10, 14]$.

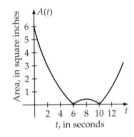

d. The highest point on the graph of A for $0 \leq t \leq 14$ occurs when $t = 0$ seconds.

72. a. On $[2, 3]$,

$a = 2$

$\Delta t = 3 - 2 = 1$

$s(a + \Delta t) = s(3) = 6 \cdot 3^2 = 54$

$s(a) = s(2) = 6 \cdot 2^2 = 24$

$\text{Average velocity} = \dfrac{s(a + \Delta t) - s(a)}{\Delta t}$

$= \dfrac{s(3) - s(2)}{1}$

$= 54 - 24 = 30$ feet per second

This is identical to the slope of the line through $(2, f(2))$ and $(3, f(3))$ because

$m = \dfrac{s(3) - s(2)}{3 - 2} = s(3) - s(2) = 54 - 24 = 30$

b. On $[2, 2.5]$,

$a = 2$

$\Delta t = 2.5 - 2 = 0.5$

$s(a + \Delta t) = s(2.5) = 6(2.5)^2 = 37.5$

$$\text{Average velocity} = \frac{s(2.5) - s(2)}{0.5}$$

$$= \frac{37.5 - 24}{0.5}$$

$$= \frac{13.5}{0.5} = 27 \text{ feet per second}$$

c. On $[2, 2.1]$,

$a = 2$

$\Delta t = 2.1 - 2 = 0.1$

$s(a + \Delta t) = s(2.1) = 6(2.1)^2 = 26.46$

$$\text{Average velocity} = \frac{s(2.1) - s(2)}{0.1}$$

$$= \frac{26.46 - 24}{0.1}$$

$$= \frac{2.46}{0.1} = 24.6 \text{ feet per second}$$

d. On $[2, 2.01]$,

$a = 2$

$\Delta t = 2.01 - 2 = 0.01$

$s(a + \Delta t) = s(2.01) = 6(2.01)^2 = 24.2406$

$$\text{Average velocity} = \frac{s(2.01) - s(2)}{0.01}$$

$$= \frac{24.2406 - 24}{0.01}$$

$$= \frac{0.2406}{0.01} = 24.06 \text{ feet per second}$$

e. On $[2, 2.001]$,

$a = 2$

$\Delta t = 2.001 - 2 = 0.001$

$s(a + \Delta t) = s(2.001) = 6(2.001)^2 = 24.024006$

$$\text{Average velocity} = \frac{s(2.001) - s(2)}{0.001}$$

$$= \frac{24.024006 - 24}{0.001}$$

$$= \frac{0.024006}{0.001} = 24.006 \text{ feet per second}$$

f. On $[2, 2 + \Delta t]$,

$$\frac{s(2 + \Delta t) - s(2)}{\Delta t} = \frac{6(2 + \Delta t)^2 - 24}{\Delta t}$$

$$= \frac{6(4 + 4(\Delta t) + (\Delta t)^2) - 24}{\Delta t}$$

$$= \frac{24 + 24(\Delta t) + 6(\Delta t)^2 - 24}{\Delta t}$$

$$= \frac{24\Delta t + 6(\Delta t)^2}{\Delta t} = 24 + 6(\Delta t)$$

As Δt approaches zero, the average velocity approaches 24 feet per second.

Exercise Set 2.7, page 263

18. Enter the data in the table. Then use your calculator to find the linear regression equation.

   a. The linear regression equation is

$$y = -72.06131724x + 14926.16191$$

   b. Evaluate the linear regression equation when $x = 55$.

$$y = -72.06131724(55) + 14926.16191$$

$$\approx 10{,}962.79$$

   The approximate trade-in value of the car is \$10,963.

32. Enter the data in the table. Then use your calculator to find the quadratic regression model.

   a. $y = 0.05208x^2 - 3.56026x + 82.32999$

   b. The speed at which the bird has minimum oxygen consumption is the x-coordinate of the vertex of the graph of the regression equation. Recall that the x-coordinate of the vertex is given by $x = -\dfrac{b}{2a}$.

$$x = -\frac{b}{2a} = -\frac{-3.56026}{2(0.05208)}$$

$$\approx 34$$

   The speed that minimizes oxygen consumption is approximately 34 kilometers per hour.

Exercise Set 3.1, page 287

2.

$$
\require{enclose}
\begin{array}{r}
6x^2 - 9x + 28 \\
x + 4 \enclose{longdiv}{6x^3 + 15x^2 - 8x + 2} \\
\underline{6x^3 + 24x^2} \\
-9x^2 - 8x \\
\underline{-9x^2 - 36x} \\
28x + 2 \\
\underline{28x + 112} \\
-110
\end{array}
$$

$$\frac{6x^3 + 15x^2 - 8x + 2}{x + 4} = 6x^2 - 9x + 28 - \frac{110}{x + 4}$$

12.

$$
\begin{array}{r|rrrr}
5 & 5 & 6 & -8 & 1 \\
  &   & 25 & 155 & 735 \\
\hline
  & 5 & 31 & 147 & 736
\end{array}
$$

$$\frac{5x^3 + 6x^2 - 8x + 1}{x - 5} = 5x^2 + 31x + 147 + \frac{736}{x - 5}$$

26. $3 \lfloor 2 \quad -1 \quad 3 \quad -1$

$\qquad \quad 6 \quad 15 \quad 54$

$\qquad \overline{2 \quad 5 \quad 18 \quad 53}$

$P(c) = P(3) = 53$

36. $-6 \lfloor 1 \quad 4 \quad -27 \quad -90$

$\qquad \quad -6 \quad 12 \quad 90$

$\qquad \overline{1 \quad -2 \quad -15 \quad 0}$

A remainder of 0 indicates that $x + 6$ is a factor of $P(x)$.

56. $-1 \lfloor 1 \quad 5 \quad 3 \quad -5 \quad -4$

$\qquad \quad -1 \quad -4 \quad 1 \quad 4$

$\qquad \overline{1 \quad 4 \quad -1 \quad -4 \quad 0}$

The reduced polynomial is $x^3 + 4x^2 - x - 4$.
$x^4 + 5x^3 + 3x^2 - 5x - 4 = (x + 1)(x^3 + 4x^2 - x - 4)$

Section 3.2, page 301

2. Because $a_n = -2$ is negative and $n = 3$ is odd, the graph of P goes up to the far left and down to the far right.

22. $P(x) = x^3 - 6x^2 + 8x$

$\qquad = x(x^2 - 6x + 8)$

$\qquad = x(x - 2)(x - 4)$

The factor x can be written as $(x - 0)$. Apply the factor theorem to determine that the real zeros of P are 0, 2, and 4.

28. $0 \lfloor 4 \quad -1 \quad -6 \quad 1$

$\qquad \quad 0 \quad 0 \quad 0$

$\qquad \overline{4 \quad -1 \quad -6 \quad 1} \qquad \bullet \; P(0) = 1$

$1 \lfloor 4 \quad -1 \quad -6 \quad 1$

$\qquad \quad 4 \quad 3 \quad -3$

$\qquad \overline{4 \quad 3 \quad -3 \quad -2} \qquad \bullet \; P(1) = -2$

Because P is a polynomial function, the graph of P is continuous. Also, $P(0)$ and $P(1)$ have opposite signs. Thus by the Zero Location Theorem we know that P must have a real zero between 0 and 1.

34. The exponent of $(x + 2)$ is 1, which is odd. Thus the graph of P crosses the x-axis at the x-intercept $(-2, 0)$. The exponent of $(x - 6)^2$ is even. Thus the graph of P intersects but does not cross the x-axis at $(6, 0)$.

42. *Far-left and far-right behavior.* The leading term of $P(x) = x^3 + 2x^2 - 3x$ is $1x^3$. The leading coefficient 1 is positive and the degree of the polynomial 3 is odd. Thus the graph of P goes down to its far left and up to its far right.

The y-intercept. $P(0) = 0^3 + 2(0)^2 - 3(0) = 0$. The y-intercept is $(0, 0)$.

The x-intercept(s). Try to factor $x^3 + 2x^2 - 3x$.

$x^3 + 2x^2 - 3x = x(x^2 + 2x - 3)$

$\qquad \qquad \qquad \quad = x(x + 3)(x - 1)$

Use the Factor Theorem to determine that $(0, 0)$, $(-3, 0)$, and $(1, 0)$ are the x-intercepts. Apply the Even and Odd Powers of $(x - c)$ Theorem to determine that the graph of P will cross the x-axis at each of its x-intercepts.

Additional points: $(-2, 6)$, $(-1, 4)$, $(0.5, -0.875)$, $(1.5, 3.375)$

Symmetry: The function P is not an even or an odd function. Thus the graph of P is *not* symmetric with respect to either the y-axis or the origin.

Sketch the graph.

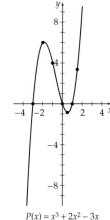

$P(x) = x^3 + 2x^2 - 3x$

48. The volume of the box is $V = lwh$, with $h = x$, $l = 18 - 2x$, and $w = \dfrac{42 - 3x}{2}$. Therefore, the volume is

$$V(x) = (18 - 2x)\left(\frac{42 - 3x}{2}\right)x$$

$$= 3x^3 - 69x^2 + 378x$$

Use a graphing utility to graph $V(x)$. The graph is shown below. The value of x that produces the maximum volume is 3.571 inches (to the nearest 0.001 inch). *Note:* Your x-value may differ slightly from 3.5705971 depending on the values you use for Xmin and Xmax. The maximum volume is approximately 606.6 cubic inches.

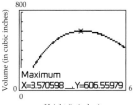

Height (in inches)

Section 3.3, page 316

10. $p = \pm 1, \pm 2, \pm 4, \pm 8$

$q = \pm 1, \pm 3$

$\dfrac{p}{q} = \pm 1, \pm 2, \pm 4, \pm 8, \pm \dfrac{1}{3}, \pm \dfrac{2}{3}, \pm \dfrac{4}{3}, \pm \dfrac{8}{3}$

18.

$$
\begin{array}{r|rrrr}
1 & 1 & 0 & -19 & -28 \\
  &   & 1 & 1 & -18 \\
\hline
  & 1 & 1 & -18 & -46
\end{array}
$$

$$
\begin{array}{r|rrrr}
2 & 1 & 0 & -19 & -28 \\
  &   & 2 & 4 & -30 \\
\hline
  & 1 & 2 & -15 & -58
\end{array}
$$

$$
\begin{array}{r|rrrr}
3 & 1 & 0 & -19 & -28 \\
  &   & 3 & 9 & -30 \\
\hline
  & 1 & 3 & -10 & -58
\end{array}
$$

$$
\begin{array}{r|rrrr}
4 & 1 & 0 & -19 & -28 \\
  &   & 4 & 16 & -12 \\
\hline
  & 1 & 4 & -3 & -40
\end{array}
$$

$$
\begin{array}{r|rrrr}
5 & 1 & 0 & -19 & -28 \\
  &   & 5 & 25 & 30 \\
\hline
  & 1 & 5 & 6 & 2
\end{array}
$$

None of these numbers are negative, so 5 is an upper bound.

$$
\begin{array}{r|rrrr}
-1 & 1 & 0 & -19 & -28 \\
   &   & -1 & 1 & 18 \\
\hline
   & 1 & -1 & -18 & -10
\end{array}
$$

$$
\begin{array}{r|rrrr}
-2 & 1 & 0 & -19 & -28 \\
   &   & -2 & 4 & 30 \\
\hline
   & 1 & -2 & -15 & 2
\end{array}
$$

$$
\begin{array}{r|rrrr}
-3 & 1 & 0 & -19 & -28 \\
   &   & -3 & 9 & 30 \\
\hline
   & 1 & -3 & -10 & 2
\end{array}
$$

$$
\begin{array}{r|rrrr}
-4 & 1 & 0 & -19 & -28 \\
   &   & -4 & 16 & 12 \\
\hline
   & 1 & -4 & -3 & -16
\end{array}
$$

$$
\begin{array}{r|rrrr}
-5 & 1 & 0 & -19 & -28 \\
   &   & -5 & 25 & -30 \\
\hline
   & 1 & -5 & 6 & -58
\end{array}
$$

These numbers alternate in sign, so -5 is a lower bound.

28. $P(x)$ has one positive real zero because P has one variation in sign.

$P(-x) = (-x)^3 - 19(-x) - 30 = -x^3 + 19x - 30$

$P(x)$ has two or no negative real zeros because $P(-x) = -x^3 + 19x - 30$ has two variations in sign.

38. $P(x)$ has one positive and two or no negative real zeros (see Exercise 28 above).

$$
\begin{array}{r|rrrr}
5 & 1 & 0 & -19 & -30 \\
  &   & 5 & 25 & 30 \\
\hline
  & 1 & 5 & 6 & 0
\end{array}
$$

The reduced polynomial is $x^2 + 5x + 6 = (x + 3)(x + 2)$, which has -3 and -2 as zeros. Thus the zeros of $P(x) = x^3 - 19x - 30$ are -3, -2, and 5.

68. The volume of the tank is equal to the volume of the two hemispheres plus the volume of the cylinder. Thus

$$\frac{4}{3}\pi x^3 + 6\pi x^2 = 9\pi$$

Dividing each term by π and multiplying by 3 produces

$$4x^3 + 18x^2 = 27$$

Intersection Method   Use a graphing utility to graph $y = 4x^3 + 18x^2$ and $y = 27$ on the same screen, with

$x > 0$. The x-coordinate of the point of intersection of the two graphs is the desired solution. The graphs intersect at $x \approx 1.098$ (rounded to the nearest thousandth of a foot). The length of the radius is approximately 1.098 feet.

72. We need to find the natural number solution of $n^3 - 3n^2 + 2n = 504$, which can be written as

$$n^3 - 3n^2 + 2n - 504 = 0$$

The constant term has many natural number divisors, but the following synthetic division shows that 10 is an upper bound for the zeros of $P(n) = n^3 - 3n^2 + 2n - 504$.

$$
\begin{array}{r|rrrr}
10 & 1 & -3 & 2 & -504 \\
   &   & 10 & 70 & 720 \\
\hline
   & 1 & 7 & 72 & 216
\end{array}
$$

The following synthetic division shows that 9 is a zero of $P(n)$.

$$
\begin{array}{r|rrrr}
9 & 1 & -3 & 2 & -504 \\
  &   & 9 & 54 & 504 \\
\hline
  & 1 & 6 & 56 & 0
\end{array}
$$

Thus the given group of cards consists of exactly nine cards. There is no need to seek additional solutions, because any increase (decrease) in the number of cards will increase (decrease) the number of ways one can select three cards from the group of cards.

Section 3.4, page 327

2. Use the Rational Zero Theorem to determine the possible rational zeros.

$$\frac{p}{q} = \pm 1, \pm 5$$

The following synthetic division shows that 1 is a zero of $P(x)$.

$$
\begin{array}{r|rrrr}
1 & 1 & -3 & 7 & -5 \\
  &   & 1 & -2 & 5 \\
\hline
  & 1 & -2 & 5 & 0
\end{array}
$$

Use the quadratic formula to find the zeros of the reduced polynomial $x^2 - 2x + 5$.

$$x = \frac{-(-2) \pm \sqrt{(-2)^2 - 4(1)(5)}}{2(1)} = 1 \pm 2i$$

The zeros of $P(x) = x^3 - 3x^2 + 7x - 5$ are 1, $1 - 2i$, and $1 + 2i$.

The linear factored form of $P(x)$ is

$$P(x) = (x - 1)(x - [1 - 2i])(x - [1 + 2i])$$

or

$$P(x) = (x - 1)(x - 1 + 2i)(x - 1 - 2i)$$

12.

$$
\begin{array}{r|rrrr}
5+3i & 3 & -29 & 92 & 34 \\
 & & 15+9i & -97+3i & -34 \\
\hline
 & 3 & -14+9i & -5+3i & 0 \\
\end{array}
$$

$$
\begin{array}{r|rrr}
5-3i & 3 & -14+9i & -5+3i \\
 & & 15-9i & 5-3i \\
\hline
 & 3 & 1 & 0 \\
\end{array}
$$

The reduced polynomial $3x+1$ has $-\dfrac{1}{3}$ as a zero. The zeros of $3x^3 - 29x^2 + 92x + 34$ are $5+3i$, $5-3i$, and $-\dfrac{1}{3}$.

16.

$$
\begin{array}{r|rrrrrr}
3i & 1 & -6+0i & 22+0i & -64+0i & 117+0i & -90 \\
 & & 0+3i & -9-18i & 54+39i & -117-30i & 90 \\
\hline
\end{array}
$$

$$
\begin{array}{r|rrrrrr}
-3i & 1 & -6+3i & 13-18i & -10+39i & 0-30i & 0 \\
 & & 0-3i & 0+18i & 0-39i & 30i & \\
\hline
 & 1 & -6 & 13 & -10 & 0 & \\
\end{array}
$$

$$\frac{p}{q} = \pm 1, \pm 2, \pm 5, \pm 10$$

$$
\begin{array}{r|rrrr}
2 & 1 & -6 & 13 & -10 \\
 & & 2 & -8 & 10 \\
\hline
 & 1 & -4 & 5 & 0 \\
\end{array}
$$

Use the quadratic formula to solve $x^2 - 4x + 5 = 0$.

$$x = \frac{-(-4) \pm \sqrt{(-4)^2 - 4(1)(5)}}{2(1)} = \frac{4 \pm \sqrt{-4}}{2}$$

$$= \frac{4 \pm 2i}{2} = 2 \pm i$$

The zeros of $x^5 - 6x^4 + 22x^3 - 64x^2 + 117x - 90$ are $3i$, $-3i$, 2, $2+i$, and $2-i$.

24. The graph of $P(x) = 4x^3 + 3x^2 + 16x + 12$ is shown below. Applying Descartes' Rule of Signs, we find that the real zeros are all negative numbers. From the Upper- and Lower-Bound Theorem there is no real zero less than -1, and from the Rational Zero Theorem the possible rational zeros (that are negative and greater than -1) are $\dfrac{p}{q} = -\dfrac{1}{2}, -\dfrac{1}{4}$, and $-\dfrac{3}{4}$. From the graph, it appears that $-\dfrac{3}{4}$ is a zero.

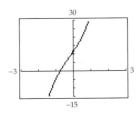

Use synthetic division with $c = -\dfrac{3}{4}$.

$$
\begin{array}{r|rrrr}
-\frac{3}{4} & 4 & 3 & 16 & 12 \\
 & & -3 & 0 & -12 \\
\hline
 & 4 & 0 & 16 & 0 \\
\end{array}
$$

Thus $-\dfrac{3}{4}$ is a zero, and by the Factor Theorem,

$$4x^3 + 3x^2 + 16x + 12 = \left(x + \frac{3}{4}\right)(4x^2 + 16) = 0$$

Solve $4x^2 + 16 = 0$ to find that $x = -2i$ and $x = 2i$. The solutions of the original equation are $-\dfrac{3}{4}$, $-2i$, and $2i$.

42. Because P has real coefficients, use the Conjugate Pair Theorem.

$$
\begin{aligned}
P &= (x - [3 + 2i])(x - [3 - 2i])(x - 7) \\
&= (x - 3 - 2i)(x - 3 + 2i)(x - 7) \\
&= (x^2 - 6x + 13)(x - 7) \\
&= x^3 - 13x^2 + 55x - 91
\end{aligned}
$$

Section 3.5, page 341

2. Set the denominator equal to zero.

$$x^2 - 4 = 0$$
$$(x - 2)(x + 2) = 0$$
$$x = 2 \quad \text{or} \quad x = -2$$

The vertical asymptotes are $x = 2$ and $x = -2$.

6. The horizontal asymptote is $y = 0$ (x-axis) because the degree of the denominator is larger than the degree of the numerator.

10. Vertical asymptote: $x - 2 = 0$

$$x = 2$$

Horizontal asymptote: $y = 0$

No x-intercepts.

y-intercept: $\left(0, -\dfrac{1}{2}\right)$

26. Vertical asymptote:

$$x^2 - 6x + 9 = 0$$
$$(x - 3)(x - 3) = 0$$
$$x = 3$$

The horizontal asymptote is $y = \dfrac{1}{1} = 1$ (the Theorem on Horizontal Asymptotes) because the numerator and denominator both have degree 2. The graph crosses the horizontal asymptote at $\left(\dfrac{3}{2}, 1\right)$. The graph intersects, but does not cross, the x-axis at $(0, 0)$. See the graph on the following page.

32.

$$x^2 - 3x + 5 \overline{)x^3 - 2x^2 + 3x + 4}$$
$$\underline{x^3 - 3x^2 + 5x}$$
$$x^2 - 2x + 4$$
$$\underline{x^2 - 3x + 5}$$
$$x - 1$$

$$F(x) = x + 1 + \frac{x - 1}{x^2 - 3x + 5}$$

Slant asymptote: $y = x + 1$

48. $F(x) = \dfrac{x^2 - x - 12}{x^2 - 2x - 8} = \dfrac{(x - 4)(x + 3)}{(x - 4)(x + 2)} = \dfrac{x + 3}{x + 2}, \, x \neq 4$

The function F is undefined at $x = 4$. Thus the graph of F is the graph of $y = \dfrac{x + 3}{x + 2}$ with an open circle at $\left(4, \dfrac{7}{6} \right)$. The height of the open circle was found by evaluating $y = \dfrac{x + 3}{x + 2}$ at $x = 4$.

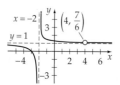

56. a.

$$\overline{C}(1000) = \frac{0.0006(1000)^2 + 9(1000) + 401{,}000}{1000}$$
$$= \$410.60$$

$$\overline{C}(10{,}000) = \frac{0.0006(10{,}000)^2 + 9(10{,}000) + 401{,}000}{10{,}000}$$
$$= \$55.10$$

$$\overline{C}(100{,}000) = \frac{0.0006(100{,}000)^2 + 9(100{,}000) + 401{,}000}{100{,}000}$$
$$= \$73.01$$

b. Graph $\overline{C}$ and use the minimum feature of a graphing utility.

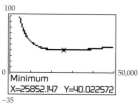

The minimum average cost per telephone is $40.02. The minimum is achieved by producing approximately 25,852 telephones.

Exercise Set 4.1, page 364

10. Because the graph of the given function is a line that passes through $(0, 6)$, $(2, 3)$, and $(6, -3)$, the graph of the inverse will be a line that passes through $(6, 0)$, $(3, 2)$, and $(-3, 6)$. See the following figure. Notice that the line shown below is a reflection of the line given in Exercise 10 across the line given by $y = x$.

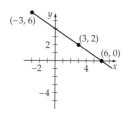

20. Check to see if $f[g(x)] = x$ for all x in the domain of g and $g[f(x)] = x$ for all x in the domain of f. The following shows that $f[g(x)] = x$ for all real numbers x.

$$f[g(x)] = f[2x + 3]$$
$$= \frac{1}{2}(2x + 3) - \frac{3}{2}$$
$$= x + \frac{3}{2} - \frac{3}{2}$$
$$= x$$

The following shows that $g[f(x)] = x$ for all real numbers x.

$$g[f(x)] = g\left[\frac{1}{2}x - \frac{3}{2} \right]$$
$$= 2\left(\frac{1}{2}x - \frac{3}{2} \right) + 3$$
$$= x - 3 + 3$$
$$= x$$

Thus f and g are inverses.

28.

$$f(x) = 4x - 8$$
$$y = 4x - 8 \qquad \bullet \text{ Replace } f(x) \text{ by } y.$$
$$x = 4y - 8 \qquad \bullet \text{ Interchange } x \text{ and } y.$$
$$x + 8 = 4y \qquad \bullet \text{ Solve for } y.$$
$$\frac{1}{4}(x + 8) = y$$
$$y = \frac{1}{4}x + 2$$
$$f^{-1}(x) = \frac{1}{4}x + 2 \qquad \bullet \text{ Replace } y \text{ by } f^{-1}(x).$$

34. $f(x) = \dfrac{x}{x-2}, x \neq 2$

$y = \dfrac{x}{x-2}$ • Replace $f(x)$ by y.

$x = \dfrac{y}{y-2}$ • Interchange x and y.

$x(y-2) = y$

$xy - 2x = y$ • Solve for y.

$xy - y = 2x$

$y(x-1) = 2x$

$y = \dfrac{2x}{x-1}$

$f^{-1}(x) = \dfrac{2x}{x-1}, x \neq 1$ • Replace y by $f^{-1}(x)$ and indicate any restrictions.

40. $f(x) = \sqrt{4-x}, x \leq 4$

$y = \sqrt{4-x}$ • Replace $f(x)$ by y.

$x = \sqrt{4-y}$ • Interchange x and y.

$x^2 = 4 - y$ • Solve for y.

$x^2 - 4 = -y$

$-x^2 + 4 = y$

$f^{-1}(x) = -x^2 + 4, x \geq 0$ • Replace y by $f^{-1}(x)$ and indicate any restrictions.

The range of f is $\{y \mid y \geq 0\}$. Therefore, the domain of f^{-1} is $\{x \mid x \geq 0\}$, as indicated above.

50. $K(x) = 1.3x - 4.7$

$y = 1.3x - 4.7$ • Replace $K(x)$ by y.

$x = 1.3y - 4.7$ • Interchange x and y.

$x + 4.7 = 1.3y$ • Solve for y.

$\dfrac{x + 4.7}{1.3} = y$

$K^{-1}(x) = \dfrac{x + 4.7}{1.3}$ • Replace y by $K^{-1}(x)$.

The function $K^{-1}(x) = \dfrac{x + 4.7}{1.3}$ can be used to convert a United Kingdom men's shoe size to its equivalent U.S. shoe size.

Exercise Set 4.2, page 376

2. $f(3) = 5^3 = 5 \cdot 5 \cdot 5 = 125$

$f(-2) = 5^{-2} = \dfrac{1}{5^2} = \dfrac{1}{5 \cdot 5} = \dfrac{1}{25}$

22. The graph of $f(x) = \left(\dfrac{5}{2}\right)^x$ has a y-intercept of $(0, 1)$ and the graph passes through $\left(1, \dfrac{5}{2}\right)$. Plot a few additional points, such as $\left(-1, \dfrac{2}{5}\right)$ and $\left(2, \dfrac{25}{4}\right)$. Because the base $\dfrac{5}{2}$ is greater than 1, we know that the graph must have all the properties of an increasing exponential function. Draw a smooth increasing curve through the points. The graph should be asymptotic to the negative portion of the x-axis, as shown in the following figure.

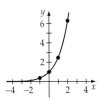

28. Because $F(x) = 6^{x+5} = f(x+5)$, the graph of $F(x)$ can be produced by shifting the graph of f horizontally to the left 5 units.

30. Because $F(x) = -\left[\left(\dfrac{5}{2}\right)^x\right] = -f(x)$, the graph of $F(x)$ can be produced by reflecting the graph of f across the x-axis.

44. a. $A(45) = 200e^{-0.014(45)}$

≈ 106.52

After 45 minutes the patient will have about 107 milligrams of medication in his or her bloodstream.

b. Use a graphing calculator to graph $y = 200e^{-0.014x}$ and $y = 50$ in the same viewing window as shown below.

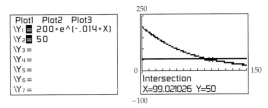

The x-coordinate (which represents time in minutes) of the point of intersection is about 99.02. Thus it will take about 99 minutes before the patient's medication level is reduced to 50 milligrams.

54. a. $P(0) = \dfrac{3600}{1 + 7e^{-0.05(0)}}$

$= \dfrac{3600}{1 + 7}$

$= \dfrac{3600}{8}$

$= 450$

Immediately after the lake was stocked, the lake contained 450 bass.

b. $P(12) = \dfrac{3600}{1 + 7e^{-0.05(12)}}$

≈ 743.54

After 1 year (12 months) there were about 744 bass in the lake.

c. As $t \to \infty$, $7e^{-0.05t} = \dfrac{7}{e^{0.05t}}$ approaches 0. Thus as $t \to \infty$,

$P(t) = \dfrac{3600}{1 + 7e^{-0.05t}}$ will approach $\dfrac{3600}{1 + 0} = 3600$. As time goes by the bass population will increase, approaching 3600.

Exercise Set 4.3, page 391

4. The exponential form of $\log_b x = y$ is $b^y = x$. Thus the exponential form of $\log_4 64 = 3$ is $4^3 = 64$.

12. The logarithmic form of $b^y = x$ is $y = \log_b x$. Thus the logarithmic form of $5^3 = 125$ is $3 = \log_5 125$.

28. $\log 1{,}000{,}000 = \log_{10} 10^6 = 6$

32. To graph $y = \log_6 x$, use the equivalent exponential equation $x = 6^y$. Choose some y-values, such as $-1, 0, 1$, and calculate the corresponding x-values. This yields the ordered pairs $\left(\dfrac{1}{6}, -1\right)$, $(1, 0)$, and $(6, 1)$. Plot these ordered pairs and draw a smooth curve through the points to produce the following graph.

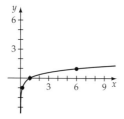

40. $\log_4(5 - x)$ is defined only for $5 - x > 0$, which is equivalent to $x < 5$. Using interval notation, the domain of $k(x) = \log_4(5 - x)$ is $(-\infty, 5)$.

50. The graph of $f(x) = \log_6(x + 3)$ can be produced by shifting the graph of $f(x) = \log_6 x$ (from Exercise 32) 3 units to the left. See the figure at the top of the next column.

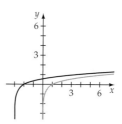

70. a. $S(0) = 5 + 29 \ln(0 + 1) = 5 + 0 = 5$. When starting, the student had an average typing speed of 5 words per minute. $S(3) = 5 + 29 \ln(3 + 1) \approx 45.2$. After 3 months the student's average typing speed was about 45 words per minute.

b. Use the intersection feature of a graphing utility to find the x-coordinate of the point of intersection of the graphs of $y = 5 + 29 \ln(x + 1)$ and $y = 65$.

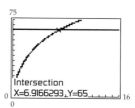

The graphs intersect at about $(6.9, 65)$. The student will achieve a typing speed of 65 words per minute in about 6.9 months.

Exercise Set 4.4, page 403

2. $\ln \dfrac{z^3}{\sqrt{xy}} = \ln z^3 - \ln \sqrt{xy}$

$= \ln z^3 - \ln(xy)^{1/2}$

$= 3 \ln z - \dfrac{1}{2} \ln(xy)$

$= 3 \ln z - \dfrac{1}{2}(\ln x + \ln y)$

$= 3 \ln z - \dfrac{1}{2} \ln x - \dfrac{1}{2} \ln y$

10. $3 \log_2 t - \dfrac{1}{3} \log_2 u + 4 \log_2 v = \log_2 t^3 - \log_2 u^{1/3} + \log_2 v^4$

$= \log_2 \dfrac{t^3}{u^{1/3}} + \log_2 v^4$

$= \log_2 \dfrac{t^3 v^4}{u^{1/3}}$

$= \log_2 \dfrac{t^3 v^4}{\sqrt[3]{u}}$

16. $\log_5 37 = \dfrac{\log 37}{\log 5} \approx 2.2436$

24. $\log_8(5 - x) = \dfrac{\ln(5 - x)}{\ln 8}$, so enter $\dfrac{\ln(5 - x)}{\ln 8}$ into Y1 on a graphing calculator.

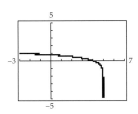

48. $\text{pH} = -\log[H^+] = -\log(1.26 \times 10^{-3}) \approx 2.9$

50.
$$\text{pH} = -\log[H^+]$$
$$5.6 = -\log[H^+]$$
$$-5.6 = \log[H^+]$$
$$10^{-5.6} = H^+$$

The hydronium-ion concentration is $10^{-5.6} \approx 2.51 \times 10^{-6}$ mole per liter.

56. $M = \log\left(\dfrac{I}{I_0}\right) = \log\left(\dfrac{398{,}107{,}000 I_0}{I_0}\right) = \log(398{,}107{,}000)$

≈ 8.6

58. $\log\left(\dfrac{I}{I_0}\right) = 9.5$

$\dfrac{I}{I_0} = 10^{9.5}$

$I = 10^{9.5} I_0$

$I \approx 3{,}162{,}277{,}660 I_0$

60. In Example 7 we noticed that if an earthquake has a Richter scale magnitude of M_1 and a smaller earthquake has a Richter scale magnitude of M_2, then the first earthquake is $10^{M_1 - M_2}$ times as intense as the smaller earthquake. In this exercise, $M_1 = 9.5$ and $M_2 = 8.3$. Thus $10^{M_1 - M_2} = 10^{9.5 - 8.3} = 10^{1.2} \approx 15.8$. The 1960 earthquake in Chile was about 15.8 times as intense as the San Francisco earthquake of 1906.

64. $M = \log A + 3 \log 8t - 2.92$

$= \log 26 + 3\log[8 \cdot 17] - 2.92$ • Substitute 26 for A and 17 for t.

$\approx 1.4150 + 6.4006 - 2.92$

≈ 4.9

Exercise Set 4.5, page 415

2. $3^x = 243$

$3^x = 3^5$

$x = 5$

10.
$$6^x = 50$$
$$\log(6^x) = \log 50$$
$$x \log 6 = \log 50$$
$$x = \dfrac{\log 50}{\log 6} \approx 2.18$$

18.
$$3^{x-2} = 4^{2x+1}$$
$$\log 3^{x-2} = \log 4^{2x+1}$$
$$(x - 2)\log 3 = (2x + 1)\log 4$$
$$x \log 3 - 2\log 3 = 2x \log 4 + \log 4$$
$$x \log 3 - 2\log 3 - 2x \log 4 = \log 4$$
$$x \log 3 - 2x \log 4 = \log 4 + 2\log 3$$
$$x(\log 3 - 2\log 4) = \log 4 + 2\log 3$$
$$x = \dfrac{\log 4 + 2\log 3}{\log 3 - 2\log 4}$$
$$x \approx -2.141$$

22. $\log(x^2 + 19) = 2$

$x^2 + 19 = 10^2$

$x^2 + 19 = 100$

$x^2 = 81$

$x = \pm 9$

A check shows that 9 and -9 are both solutions of the original equation.

26. $\log_3 x + \log_3(x + 6) = 3$

$\log_3[x(x + 6)] = 3$

$3^3 = x(x + 6)$

$27 = x^2 + 6x$

$x^2 + 6x - 27 = 0$

$(x + 9)(x - 3) = 0$

$x = -9$ or $x = 3$

Because $\log_3 x$ is defined only for $x > 0$, the only solution is $x = 3$.

36. $\ln x = \dfrac{1}{2}\ln\left(2x + \dfrac{5}{2}\right) + \dfrac{1}{2}\ln 2$

$= \dfrac{1}{2}\left[\ln\left(2x + \dfrac{5}{2}\right) + \ln 2\right]$

$\ln x = \dfrac{1}{2}\ln\left[2\left(2x + \dfrac{5}{2}\right)\right]$

$\ln x = \dfrac{1}{2}\ln(4x + 5)$

$\ln x = \ln(4x + 5)^{1/2}$

$x = \sqrt{4x + 5}$

$x^2 = 4x + 5$

$0 = x^2 - 4x - 5$

$0 = (x - 5)(x + 1)$

$x = 5$ or $x = -1$

Check: $\ln 5 = \dfrac{1}{2}\ln\left(10 + \dfrac{5}{2}\right) + \dfrac{1}{2}\ln 2$

$1.6094 \approx 1.2629 + 0.3466$

Because $\ln(-1)$ is not defined, -1 is not a solution. Thus the only solution is $x = 5$.

40. $\dfrac{10^x + 10^{-x}}{2} = 8$

$10^x + 10^{-x} = 16$

$10^x(10^x + 10^{-x}) = (16)10^x$ • **Multiply each side**

$10^{2x} + 1 = 16(10^x)$ **by 10^x.**

$10^{2x} - 16(10^x) + 1 = 0$

$u^2 - 16u + 1 = 0$ • **Let $u = 10^x$.**

$u = \dfrac{16 \pm \sqrt{16^2 - 4(1)(1)}}{2} = 8 \pm 3\sqrt{7}$

$10^x = 8 \pm 3\sqrt{7}$ • **Replace u with 10^x.**

$\log 10^x = \log(8 \pm 3\sqrt{7})$

$x = \log(8 \pm 3\sqrt{7}) \approx \pm 1.20241$

68. a. $t = \dfrac{9}{24}\ln\dfrac{24 + v}{24 - v}$

$1.5 = \dfrac{9}{24}\ln\dfrac{24 + v}{24 - v}$

$4 = \ln\dfrac{24 + v}{24 - v}$

$e^4 = \dfrac{24 + v}{24 - v}$ • **$N = \ln M$ means $e^N = M$.**

$(24 - v)e^4 = 24 + v$

$-v - ve^4 = 24 - 24e^4$

$v(-1 - e^4) = 24 - 24e^4$

$v = \dfrac{24 - 24e^4}{-1 - e^4} \approx 23.14$

The velocity is about 23.14 feet per second.

b. The vertical asymptote is $v = 24$.

c. Due to the air resistance, the object cannot reach or exceed a velocity of 24 feet per second.

Exercise Set 4.6, page 430

4. a. $P = 12,500, r = 0.08, t = 10, n = 1.$

$A = 12,500\left(1 + \dfrac{0.08}{1}\right)^{10} \approx \$26,986.56$

b. $n = 365$

$A = 12,500\left(1 + \dfrac{0.08}{365}\right)^{3650} \approx \$27,816.82$

c. $n = 8760$

$A = 12,500\left(1 + \dfrac{0.08}{8760}\right)^{87600} \approx \$27,819.16$

6. $P = 32,000, r = 0.08, t = 3.$

$A = Pe^{rt} = 32,000e^{3(0.08)} \approx \$40,679.97$

10. $t = \dfrac{\ln 3}{r}$ $r = 0.055$

$t = \dfrac{\ln 3}{0.055}$

$t \approx 20$ years (to the nearest year)

18. a. $P(12) = 20,899(1.027)^{12} \approx 28,722$ thousands, or 28,772,000.

b. P is in thousands, so

$35,000 = 20,899(1.027)^t$

$\dfrac{35,000}{20,899} = 1.027^t$

$\ln\left(\dfrac{35,000}{20,899}\right) = t \ln 1.027$

$\dfrac{\ln\left(\dfrac{35,000}{20,899}\right)}{\ln 1.027} = t$

$19.35 \approx t$

According to the growth function, the population will first exceed 35 million in 19.35 years—that is, in the year $1991 + 19 = 2010$.

20. $N(t) = N_0 e^{kt}$

$N(138) = N_0 e^{138k}$

$0.5N_0 = N_0 e^{138k}$

$0.5 = e^{138k}$

$\ln 0.5 = 138k$

$k = \dfrac{\ln 0.5}{138} \approx -0.005023$

$N(t) = N_0(0.5)^{t/138} \approx N_0 e^{-0.005023t}$

24. $N(t) = N_0(0.5)^{t/5730}$

$0.65N_0 = N_0(0.5)^{t/5730}$

$0.65 = (0.5)^{t/5730}$

$\ln 0.65 = \ln(0.5)^{t/5730}$

$t = 5730\dfrac{\ln 0.65}{\ln 0.5} \approx 3600$

The bone is approximately 3600 years old.

32. a.

b. Here is an algebraic solution. An approximate solution can be obtained from the graph.

$$v = 64(1 - e^{-t/2})$$

$$50 = 64(1 - e^{-t/2})$$

$$\frac{50}{64} = (1 - e^{-t/2})$$

$$1 - \frac{50}{64} = e^{-t/2}$$

$$\ln\left(1 - \frac{50}{64}\right) = -\frac{t}{2}$$

$$t = -2\ln\left(1 - \frac{50}{64}\right) \approx 3.0$$

The velocity is 50 feet per second in approximately 3.0 seconds.

c. As $t \to \infty$, $e^{-t/2} \to 0$. Therefore, $64(1 - e^{-t/2}) \to 64$. The horizontal asymptote is $v = 64$.

d. Because of the air resistance, the velocity of the object will never reach or exceed 64 feet per second.

48. a. Represent the year 2001 by $t = 0$; then the year 2002 will be represented by $t = 1$. Use the following substitutions: $P_0 = 240$, $P(1) = 310$, $c = 3400$, and

$$a = \frac{c - P_0}{P_0} = \frac{3400 - 240}{240} \approx 13.16667.$$

$$P(t) = \frac{c}{1 + ae^{-bt}}$$

$$P(1) = \frac{3400}{1 + 13.16667e^{-b(1)}}$$

$$310 = \frac{3400}{1 + 13.16667e^{-b}}$$

$$310(1 + 13.16667e^{-b}) = 3400$$

$$1 + 13.16667e^{-b} = \frac{3400}{310}$$

$$13.16667e^{-b} = \frac{3400}{310} - 1$$

$$13.16667e^{-b} \approx 9.96774$$

$$e^{-b} \approx \frac{9.96774}{13.16667}$$

$$-b \approx \ln\frac{9.96774}{13.16667}$$

$$b \approx 0.27833$$

Using $a = 13.16667$, $b = 0.27833$, and $c = 3400$ gives the following logistic model.

$$P(t) \approx \frac{3400}{1 + 13.16667e^{-0.27833t}}$$

b. Because 2008 is 7 years past 2001, the year 2008 is represented by $t = 7$.

$$P(7) \approx \frac{3400}{1 + 13.16667e^{-0.27833(7)}} \approx 1182$$

According to the model there will be about 1182 groundhogs in 2008.

Exercise Set 4.7, page 444

4. The following scatter plot suggests that the data can be modeled by an increasing function that is concave down. Thus the most suitable model for the data is an increasing logarithmic function.

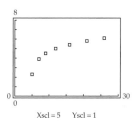

Xscl = 5   Yscl = 1

22. From the scatter plot in the following figure, it appears that the data can be closely modeled by a decreasing exponential function of the form $y = ab^x$, with $b < 1$.

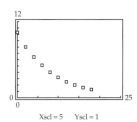

Xscl = 5   Yscl = 1

The calculator display in the following figure shows that the exponential regression equation is $y \approx 10.1468(0.89104)^x$, where x is the altitude in kilometers and y is the pressure in newtons per square centimeter.

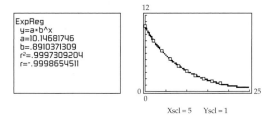

Xscl = 5   Yscl = 1

The correlation coefficient $r \approx -0.99987$ is close to -1. This indicates that the function $y \approx 10.1468(0.89104)^x$ provides a good fit for the data. The graph of y shown above also indicates that the regression function provides a good model for the data. When $x = 24$ kilometers, the atmospheric pressure is about $10.1468(0.89104)^{24} \approx 0.6$ newton per square centimeter.

24. a. Use a graphing utility to perform an exponential regression and a logarithmic regression. For the given data, the logarithmic function $y = 61.735786 - 4.1044761 \ln x$ provides a slightly better fit than does the exponential regression function, as determined by comparing the correlation coefficients. See the calculator displays below.

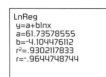

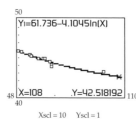

Xscl = 10   Yscl = 1

b. To predict the world record time in 2008, evaluate $y = 61.735786 - 4.104476 \ln x$ at $x = 108$. The graph on the right above shows that the predicted world record time in the men's 400-meter race for the year 2008 is about 42.52 seconds.

26. a. Use a graphing utility to perform a logistic regression on the data. The following figure shows the results obtained by using a TI-83 graphing calculator.

```
Logistic
y=c/(1+ae^(-bx))
a=2.245804979
b=.0434109644
c=1541897.467
```

The logistic regression function for the data is
$$P(t) \approx \frac{1{,}541{,}897}{1 + 2.24580e^{-0.043411t}}.$$

b. The year 2010 is represented by $t = 60$.
$$P(60) = \frac{1{,}541{,}897}{1 + 2.24580e^{-0.043411(60)}} \approx 1{,}320{,}000$$

The logistic regression function predicts that Hawaii's population will be about 1,320,000 in 2010.

c. The carrying capacity, to the nearest thousand, of the logistic model is 1,542,000 people.

Exercise Set 5.1, page 468

4. Comparing $x^2 = 4py$ with $x^2 = -\dfrac{1}{4}y$, we have $4p = -\dfrac{1}{4}$ or $p = -\dfrac{1}{16}$.

vertex $(0, 0)$

focus $\left(0, -\dfrac{1}{16}\right)$

directrix $y = \dfrac{1}{16}$

20. $x^2 + 5x - 4y - 1 = 0$

$$x^2 + 5x = 4y + 1$$

$$x^2 + 5x + \frac{25}{4} = 4y + 1 + \frac{25}{4} \qquad \bullet \text{ Complete the square.}$$

$$\left(x + \frac{5}{2}\right)^2 = 4\left(y + \frac{29}{16}\right) \qquad \bullet \ h = -\frac{5}{2}, k = -\frac{29}{16}$$

$$4p = 4$$

$$p = 1 \qquad \bullet \text{ Compare to } (x - h)^2 = 4p(y - k)^2.$$

vertex $\left(-\dfrac{5}{2}, -\dfrac{29}{16}\right)$

focus $(h, k + p) = \left(-\dfrac{5}{2}, -\dfrac{13}{16}\right)$

directrix $y = k - p = -\dfrac{45}{16}$

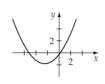

28. vertex $(0, 0)$, focus $(5, 0)$; $p = 5$ because focus is $(p, 0)$.

$$y^2 = 4px$$
$$y^2 = 4(5)x$$
$$y^2 = 20x$$

30. vertex $(2, -3)$, focus $(0, -3)$

$(h, k) = (2, -3)$, so $h = 2$ and $k = -3$.

Focus is $(h + p, k) = (2 + p, -3) = (0, -3)$.

Therefore, $2 + p = 0$ and $p = -2$.

$$(y - k)^2 = 4p(x - h)$$
$$(y + 3)^2 = 4(-2)(x - 2)$$
$$(y + 3)^2 = -8(x - 2)$$

38.
$$x^2 = 4py$$
$$40.5^2 = 4p(16)$$
$$p = \frac{40.5^2}{64}$$
$$p \approx 25.6 \text{ feet}$$

Exercise Set 5.2, page 480

20. $25x^2 + 12y^2 = 300$

$$\frac{x^2}{12} + \frac{y^2}{25} = 1 \qquad \bullet\, a^2 = 25, b^2 = 12, c^2 = 25 - 12$$
$$a = 5, b = 2\sqrt{3}, c = \sqrt{13}$$

center $(0, 0)$

vertices $(0, 5)$ and $(0, -5)$

foci $\left(0, \sqrt{13}\right)$ and $\left(0, -\sqrt{13}\right)$

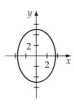

26.
$$9x^2 + 16y^2 + 36x - 16y - 104 = 0$$
$$9x^2 + 36x + 16y^2 - 16y - 104 = 0$$
$$9(x^2 + 4x) + 16(y^2 - y) = 104$$
$$9(x^2 + 4x + 4) + 16\left(y^2 - y + \frac{1}{4}\right) = 104 + 36 + 4$$
$$9(x + 2)^2 + 16\left(y - \frac{1}{2}\right)^2 = 144$$
$$\frac{(x + 2)^2}{16} + \frac{\left(y - \frac{1}{2}\right)^2}{9} = 1$$

center $\left(-2, \frac{1}{2}\right)$

$a = 4, b = 3,$
$c = \sqrt{4^2 - 3^2} = \sqrt{7}$

vertices $\left(2, \frac{1}{2}\right)$ and $\left(-6, \frac{1}{2}\right),$

foci $\left(-2 + \sqrt{7}, \frac{1}{2}\right)$ and

$\left(-2 - \sqrt{7}, \frac{1}{2}\right)$

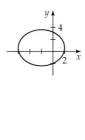

42. Center $(-4, 1) = (h, k)$. Therefore, $h = -4$ and $k = 1$. Length of minor axis is 8, so $2b = 8$ or $b = 4$. The equation of the ellipse is of the form

$$\frac{(x - h)^2}{a^2} + \frac{(y - k)^2}{b^2} = 1$$

$$\frac{(x + 4)^2}{a^2} + \frac{(y - 1)^2}{16} = 1 \qquad \bullet\, h = -4, k = 1, b = 4$$

$$\frac{(0 + 4)^2}{a^2} + \frac{(4 - 1)^2}{16} = 1 \qquad \bullet\, \text{The point } (0, 4) \text{ is on the graph. Thus } x = 0 \text{ and } y = 4 \text{ satisfy the equation.}$$

$$\frac{16}{a^2} + \frac{9}{16} = 1 \qquad \bullet\, \text{Solve for } a^2.$$

$$\frac{16}{a^2} = \frac{7}{16}$$

$$a^2 = \frac{256}{7}$$

$$\frac{(x + 4)^2}{256/7} + \frac{(y - 1)^2}{16} = 1$$

48. Because the foci are $(0, -3)$ and $(0, 3)$, $c = 3$ and the center is $(0, 0)$, the midpoint of the line segment between $(0, -3)$ and $(0, 3)$.

$$e = \frac{c}{a}$$
$$\frac{1}{4} = \frac{3}{a} \qquad \bullet\, e = \frac{1}{4}$$
$$a = 12$$
$$3^2 = 12^2 - b^2 \qquad \bullet\, c^2 = a^2 - b^2$$
$$b^2 = 144 - 9 = 135 \qquad \bullet\, \text{Solve for } b^2.$$

The equation of the ellipse is $\dfrac{x^2}{135} + \dfrac{y^2}{144} = 1$.

56. The mean distance is $a = 67.08$ million miles.

Aphelion $= a + c = 67.58$ million miles

Thus $c = 67.58 - a = 0.50$ million miles.

$b = \sqrt{a^2 - c^2} = \sqrt{67.08^2 - 0.50^2} \approx 67.078$

An equation of the orbit of Venus is

$$\frac{x^2}{67.08^2} + \frac{y^2}{67.078^2} = 1$$

58. The length of the semimajor axis is 50 feet. Thus

$$c^2 = a^2 - b^2$$
$$32^2 = 50^2 - b^2$$
$$b^2 = 50^2 - 32^2$$
$$b = \sqrt{50^2 - 32^2}$$
$$b \approx 38.4 \text{ feet}$$

Exercise Set 5.3, page 495

4. $\dfrac{y^2}{25} - \dfrac{x^2}{36} = 1$

$a^2 = 25 \quad b^2 = 36 \quad c^2 = a^2 + b^2 = 25 + 36 = 61$
$a = 5 \qquad b = 6 \qquad c = \sqrt{61}$

Transverse axis is on y-axis because y^2 term is positive.

center $(0, 0)$

foci $\left(0, \sqrt{61}\right)$ and $\left(0, -\sqrt{61}\right)$

asymptotes $y = \dfrac{5}{6}x$ and

$y = -\dfrac{5}{6}x$

vertices $(0, 5)$ and $(0, -5)$

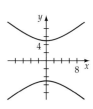

26. $16x^2 - 9y^2 - 32x - 54y + 79 = 0$

$16(x^2 - 2x + 1) - 9(y^2 + 6y + 9) = -79 + 16 - 81$

$$= -144$$

$$\frac{(y + 3)^2}{16} - \frac{(x - 1)^2}{9} = 1$$

Transverse axis is parallel to y-axis because y^2 term is positive. Center is at $(1, -3)$; $a^2 = 16$ so $a = 4$.

vertices $(h, k + a) = (1, 1)$

$\qquad\qquad (h, k - a) = (1, -7)$

$c^2 = a^2 + b^2 = 16 + 9 = 25$

$c = \sqrt{25} = 5$

foci $(h, k + c) = (1, 2)$

$\qquad (h, k - c) = (1, -8)$

Because $b^2 = 9$ and $b = 3$, the asymptotes are

$y + 3 = \dfrac{4}{3}(x - 1)$ and

$y + 3 = -\dfrac{4}{3}(x - 1).$

48. Because the vertices are $(2, 3)$ and $(-2, 3)$, $a = 2$ and the center is $(0, 3)$.

$e = \dfrac{c}{a} \qquad\qquad c^2 = a^2 + b^2$

$\qquad\qquad\qquad\quad 5^2 = 2^2 + b^2$

$\dfrac{5}{2} = \dfrac{c}{2} \qquad\qquad b^2 = 25 - 4 = 21$

$c = 5$

Substituting into the standard equation yields

$\dfrac{x^2}{4} - \dfrac{(y - 3)^2}{21} = 1.$

54. a. Because the transmitters are 300 miles apart, $2c = 300$ and $c = 150$.

$2a = $ rate $\times$ time

$2a = 0.186 \times 800 = 148.8$ miles

Thus $a = 74.4$ miles.

$b = \sqrt{c^2 - a^2}$

$\quad = \sqrt{150^2 - 74.4^2} \approx 130.25$ miles

The ship is located on the hyperbola given by

$\dfrac{x^2}{74.4^2} - \dfrac{y^2}{130.25^2} = 1$

b. The ship will reach the coastline when $x < 0$ and $y = 0$. Thus

$\dfrac{x^2}{74.4^2} - \dfrac{0^2}{130.25^2} = 1$

$\dfrac{x^2}{74.4^2} = 1$

$x^2 = 74.4^2$

$x = -74.4$

The ship reaches the coastline 74.4 miles to the left of the origin at the point $(-74.4, 0)$.

Exercise Set 6.1, page 513

6. $\begin{cases} 8x + 3y = -7 & (1) \\ \quad\quad x = 3y + 15 & (2) \end{cases}$

$8(3y + 15) + 3y = -7$ • **Replace x in Eq. (1).**

$24y + 120 + 3y = -7$ • **Simplify.**

$27y = -7$

$y = -\dfrac{127}{27}$

$x = 3\left(-\dfrac{127}{27}\right) + 15 = \dfrac{8}{9}$ • **Substitute** $-\dfrac{127}{27}$ **for y in Eq. (2).**

The solution is $\left(\dfrac{8}{9}, -\dfrac{127}{27}\right)$.

18. $\begin{cases} 3x - 4y = 8 & (1) \\ 6x - 8y = 9 & (2) \end{cases}$

$8y = 6x - 9$ • **Solve Eq. (2) for y.**

$y = \dfrac{3}{4}x - \dfrac{9}{8}$

$3x - 4\left(\dfrac{3}{4}x - \dfrac{9}{8}\right) = 8$ • **Replace y in Eq. (1).**

$3x - 3x + \dfrac{9}{2} = 8$ • **Simplify.**

$\dfrac{9}{2} = 8$

This is a false equation. Therefore, the system of equations is inconsistent and has no solution.

20. $\begin{cases} 5x + 2y = 2 & (1) \\ \quad\quad y = -\dfrac{5}{2}x + 1 & (2) \end{cases}$

$5x + 2\left(-\dfrac{5}{2}x + 1\right) = 2$ • **Replace y in Eq. (1).**

$5x - 5x + 2 = 2$ • **Simplify.**

$2 = 2$

This is a true statement; therefore, the system of equations is dependent. Let $x = c$. Then $y = -\dfrac{5}{2}c + 1$. Thus the solutions are $\left(c, -\dfrac{5}{2}c + 1\right)$.

24. $\begin{cases} 3x - 8y = -6 & (1) \\ -5x + 4y = 10 & (2) \end{cases}$

$3x - 8y = -6$

$\underline{-10x + 8y = 20}$ • **2 times Eq. (2)**

$-7x \qquad = 14$

$x = -2$

$3(-2) - 8y = -6$ • **Substitute -2 for x in Eq. (1).**
Solve for y.

$-8y = 0$

$y = 0$

The solution is $(-2, 0)$.

28. $\begin{cases} 4x + 5y = 2 & (1) \\ 8x - 15y = 9 & (2) \end{cases}$

$12x + 15y = 6$ • **3 times Eq. (1)**

$\underline{8x - 15y = 9}$

$20x \qquad = 15$

$x = \dfrac{3}{4}$

$4\left(\dfrac{3}{4}\right) + 5y = 2$ • **Substitute $\dfrac{3}{4}$ for x in Eq. (1).**

$3 + 5y = 2$ • **Solve for y.**

$y = -\dfrac{1}{5}$

The solution is $\left(\dfrac{3}{4}, -\dfrac{1}{5}\right)$.

42. Solve the system of equations $\begin{cases} x = 25p - 500 \\ x = -7p + 1100 \end{cases}$

by the substitution method.

$25p - 500 = -7p + 1100$

$32p = 1600$

$p = 50$

The equilibrium price is \$50.

46. Let r = the rate of the canoeist.
Let w = the rate of the current.
Rate of canoeist with the current: $r + w$
Rate of canoeist against the current: $r - w$

$r \cdot t = d$

$(r + w) \cdot 2 = 12$ (1)

$(r - w) \cdot 4 = 12$ (2)

$r + w = 6$ • **Divide Eq. (1) by 2.**

$\underline{r - w = 3}$ • **Divide Eq. (2) by 4.**

$2r \qquad = 9$

$r = 4.5$

$4.5 + w = 6$

$w = 1.5$

Rate of canoeist = 4.5 miles per hour
Rate of current = 1.5 miles per hour

Exercise Set 6.2, page 527

12. $\begin{cases} 3x + 2y - 5z = 6 & (1) \\ 5x - 4y + 3z = -12 & (2) \\ 4x + 5y - 2z = 15 & (3) \end{cases}$

$15x + 10y - 25z = 30$ • **5 times Eq. (1)**

$\underline{-15x + 12y - 9z = 36}$ • **-3 times Eq. (2)**

$22y - 34z = 66$ • **Divide by 2.**

$11y - 17z = 33$ (4)

$12x + 8y - 20z = 24$ • **4 times Eq. (1)**

$\underline{-12x - 15y + 6z = -45}$ • **-3 times Eq. (3)**

$-7y - 14z = -21$ • **Divide by -7.**

$y + 2z = 3$ (5)

$11y - 17z = 33$ (4)

$\underline{-11y - 22z = -33}$ • **-11 times Eq. (5)**

$-39z = 0$

$z = 0$ (6)

$11y - 17(0) = 33$

$y = 3$

$3x + 2(3) - 5(0) = 6$

$x = 0$

The solution is $(0, 3, 0)$.

16. $\begin{cases} 2x + 3y + 2z = 14 & (1) \\ x - 3y + 4z = 4 & (2) \\ -x + 12y - 6z = 2 & (3) \end{cases}$

$2x + 3y + 2z = 14$ (1)

$\underline{-2x + 6y - 8z = -8}$ • **-2 times Eq. (2)**

$9y - 6z = 6$ • **Divide by 3.**

$3y - 2z = 2$ (4)

$2x + 3y + 2z = 14$ (1)

$\underline{-2x + 24y - 12z = 4}$ • **2 times Eq. (3)**

$27y - 10z = 18$ (5)

$-27y + 18z = -18$ • **-9 times Eq. (4)**

$\underline{27y - 10z = 18}$ (5)

$8z = 0$

$z = 0$ (6)

$3y - 2(0) = 2$ • **Substitute $z = 0$ in Eq. (4).**

$y = \dfrac{2}{3}$

$2x + 3\left(\dfrac{2}{3}\right) + 2(0) = 14$ • **Substitute $y = \dfrac{2}{3}$ and $z = 0$ in Eq. (1).**

$x = 6$

The solution is $\left(6, \dfrac{2}{3}, 0\right)$.

18. $\begin{cases} 2x + 3y - 6z = 4 & (1) \\ 3x - 2y - 9z = -7 & (2) \\ 2x + 5y - 6z = 8 & (3) \end{cases}$

$\begin{aligned} 6x + 9y - 18z &= 12 \\ -6x + 4y + 18z &= 14 \\ \hline 13y &= 26 \\ y &= 2 \quad (4) \end{aligned}$ • **3 times Eq. (1)**   • **−2 times Eq. (2)**

$\begin{aligned} 2x + 3y - 6z &= 4 \quad (1) \\ -2x - 5y + 6z &= -8 \\ \hline -2y &= -4 \\ y &= 2 \quad (5) \end{aligned}$ • **−1 times Eq. (3)**

$\begin{aligned} y &= 2 \quad (4) \\ -y &= -2 \\ \hline 0 &= 0 \quad (6) \end{aligned}$ • **−1 times Eq. (5)**

The equations are dependent. Let $z = c$.

$2x + 3(2) - 6c = 4$ • **Substitute $y = 2$ and $z = c$ in Eq. (1).**

$x = 3c - 1$

The solutions are $(3c - 1, 2, c)$.

20. $\begin{cases} x - 3y + 4z = 9 & (1) \\ 3x - 8y - 2z = 4 & (2) \end{cases}$

$\begin{aligned} -3x + 9y - 12z &= -27 \\ 3x - 8y - 2z &= 4 \quad (2) \\ \hline y - 14z &= -23 \quad (3) \end{aligned}$ • **−3 times Eq. (1)**

$y = 14z - 23$ • **Solve Eq. (3) for y.**

$x - 3(14z - 23) + 4z = 9$ • **Substitute $14z - 23$ for y in Eq. (1).**

$x = 38z - 60$ • **Solve for x.**

Let $z = c$. The solutions are $(38c - 60, 14c - 23, c)$.

32. $\begin{cases} 5x + 2y + 3z = 0 & (1) \\ 3x + y - 2z = 0 & (2) \\ 4x - 7y + 5z = 0 & (3) \end{cases}$

$\begin{aligned} 15x + 6y + 9z &= 0 \\ -15x - 5y + 10z &= 0 \\ \hline y + 19z &= 0 \quad (4) \end{aligned}$ • **3 times Eq. (1)**   • **−5 times Eq. (2)**

$\begin{aligned} 20x + 8y + 12z &= 0 \\ -20x + 35y - 25z &= 0 \\ \hline 43y - 13z &= 0 \quad (5) \end{aligned}$ • **4 times Eq. (1)**   • **−5 times Eq. (3)**

$\begin{aligned} -43y - 817z &= 0 \\ 43y - 13z &= 0 \quad (5) \\ \hline -830z &= 0 \\ z &= 0 \quad (6) \end{aligned}$ • **−43 times Eq. (4)**

Solving by back substitution, the only solution is $(0, 0, 0)$.

36. $x^2 + y^2 + ax + by + c = 0$

$\begin{cases} 0 + 36 + a(0) + b(6) + c = 0 \\ 1 + 25 + a(1) + b(5) + c = 0 \\ 49 + 1 + a(-7) + b(-1) + c = 0 \end{cases}$ • **Let $x = 0$, $y = 6$.**   • **Let $x = 1$, $y = 5$.**   • **Let $x = -7$, $y = -1$.**

$\begin{cases} 6b + c = -36 & (1) \\ a + 5b + c = -26 & (2) \\ -7a - b + c = -50 & (3) \end{cases}$

$\begin{aligned} 7a + 35b + 7c &= -182 \\ -7a - b + c &= -50 \quad (3) \\ \hline 34b + 8c &= -232 \\ 17b + 4c &= -116 \quad (4) \end{aligned}$ • **7 times Eq. (2)**

$\begin{aligned} -24b - 4c &= 144 \\ 17b + 4c &= -116 \quad (4) \\ \hline -7b &= 28 \\ b &= -4 \end{aligned}$ • **−4 times Eq. (1)**

$17(-4) + 4c = -116$ • **Substitute −4 for b in Eq. (4).**

$c = -12$

$-7a - (-4) - 12 = -50$ • **Substitute −4 for b and −12 for c in Eq. (3).**

$a = 6$

An equation of the circle whose graph passes through the three given points is $x^2 + y^2 + 6x - 4y - 12 = 0$.

42. Let x_1, x_2, x_3, and x_4 represent the numbers of cars per hour that travel AB, BC, CD, and DA, respectively. Using the principle that the number of cars entering an intersection must equal the number of cars leaving the intersection, we can write the following equations.

A: $75 + x_4 = x_1 + 60$

B: $x_1 + 50 = x_2 + 100$

C: $x_2 + 45 = x_3 + 50$

D: $x_3 + 80 = x_4 + 40$

The equations for the traffic intersections result in the following system of equations.

$\begin{cases} x_1 - x_4 = 15 & (1) \\ x_1 - x_2 = 50 & (2) \\ x_2 - x_3 = 5 & (3) \\ x_3 - x_4 = -40 & (4) \end{cases}$

Subtracting Equation (2) from Equation (1) gives

$\begin{aligned} x_1 - x_4 &= 15 \\ x_1 - x_2 &= 50 \\ \hline x_2 - x_4 &= -35 \quad (5) \end{aligned}$

Adding Equation (3) and Equation (4) gives

$\begin{aligned} x_2 - x_3 &= 5 \\ x_3 - x_4 &= -40 \\ \hline x_2 - x_4 &= -35 \quad (6) \end{aligned}$

Because Equation (5) and Equation (6) are the same, the system of equations is dependent. Because we want to know the cars per hour between B and C, solve the system in terms of x_2.

$$x_1 = x_2 + 50$$
$$x_3 = x_2 - 5$$
$$x_4 = x_2 + 35$$

Because there cannot be a negative number of cars per hour between two intersections, to ensure that $x_3 \geq 0$, we must have $x_2 \geq 5$. The minimum number of cars traveling between B and C is 5 cars per hour.

Exercise Set 6.3, page 536

8. $\begin{cases} x - 2y = 3 & (1) \\ xy = -1 & (2) \end{cases}$

$x = 2y + 3$ • Solve Eq. (1) for x.

$(2y + 3)y = -1$ • Replace x by $2y + 3$ in Eq. (2).

$2y^2 + 3y + 1 = 0$ • Solve for y.

$(2y + 1)(y + 1) = 0$

$y = -\dfrac{1}{2}$ or $y = -1$

$x - 2\left(-\dfrac{1}{2}\right) = 3$ $x - 2(-1) = 3$ • Substitute for y in Eq. (1).

$\phantom{x - 2\left(-\dfrac{1}{2}\right)}x = 2$ $x = 1$

The solutions are $\left(2, -\dfrac{1}{2}\right)$ and $(1, -1)$.

16. $\begin{cases} 3x^2 - 2y^2 = 19 & (1) \\ x^2 - y^2 = 5 & (2) \end{cases}$

$3x^2 - 2y^2 = 19$ (1)

$\underline{-3x^2 + 3y^2 = -15}$ • Multiply Eq. (2) by -3.

$\phantom{-3x^2 + {}}y^2 = 4$ • Add the equations.

$\phantom{-3x^2 + {}}y = \pm 2$ • Solve for y.

$x^2 - (-2)^2 = 5$ • Substitute -2 for y in Eq. (2).

$x^2 - 4 = 5$

$x^2 = 9$

$x = \pm 3$

$x^2 - 2^2 = 5$ • Substitute 2 for y in Eq. (2).

$x^2 - 4 = 5$

$x^2 = 9$

$x = \pm 3$

The solutions are $(3, -2)$, $(-3, -2)$, $(3, 2)$, $(-3, 2)$.

20. $\begin{cases} 2x^2 + 3y^2 = 11 & (1) \\ 3x^2 + 2y^2 = 19 & (2) \end{cases}$

Use the elimination method to eliminate y^2.

$4x^2 + 6y^2 = 22$ • 2 times Eq. (1)

$\underline{-9x^2 - 6y^2 = -57}$ • -3 times Eq. (2)

$-5x^2 = -35$

$x^2 = 7$

$2(7) + 3y^2 = 11$ • Substitute for x in Eq. (1).

$\phantom{2(7) + {}}3y^2 = -3$

$y^2 = -1$

$y^2 = -1$ has no real number solutions. The graphs of the equations do not intersect. The system is inconsistent and has no solution.

28. $\begin{cases} (x + 2)^2 + (y - 3)^2 = 10 \\ (x - 3)^2 + (y + 1)^2 = 13 \end{cases}$

$x^2 + 4x + 4 + y^2 - 6y + 9 = 10$ (1)

$\underline{x^2 - 6x + 9 + y^2 + 2y + 1 = 13}$ (2)

$10x - 5 - 8y + 8 = -3$ • Subtract.

$10x - 8y = -6$

$y = \dfrac{5x + 3}{4}$ (3)   • Solve for y.

$(x + 2)^2 + \left(\dfrac{5x - 9}{4}\right)^2 = 10$ • Substitute for y.

$x^2 + 4x + 4 + \dfrac{25x^2 - 90x + 81}{16} = 10$ • Solve for x.

$16x^2 + 64x + 64 + 25x^2 - 90x + 81 = 160$

$41x^2 - 26x - 15 = 0$

$(41x + 15)(x - 1) = 0$

$x = -\dfrac{15}{41}$ or $x = 1$

$y = \dfrac{5}{4}\left(-\dfrac{15}{41}\right) + \dfrac{3}{4}$ or $y = \dfrac{5(1) + 3}{4}$ • Substitute for x into Eq. (3).

$y = \dfrac{12}{41}$ or $y = 2$

The solutions are $\left(-\dfrac{15}{41}, \dfrac{12}{41}\right)$ and $(1, 2)$.

Exercise Set 6.4, page 544

14. $\dfrac{7x + 44}{x^2 + 10x + 24} = \dfrac{7x + 44}{(x + 4)(x + 6)} = \dfrac{A}{x + 4} + \dfrac{B}{x + 6}$

$7x + 44 = A(x + 6) + B(x + 4)$

$7x + 44 = (A + B)x + (6A + 4B)$

$\begin{cases} 7 = A + B \\ 44 = 6A + 4B \end{cases}$

The solution is $A = 8$, $B = -1$.

$\dfrac{7x + 44}{x^2 + 10x + 24} = \dfrac{8}{x + 4} + \dfrac{-1}{x + 6}$

22. $\dfrac{x - 18}{x(x - 3)^2} = \dfrac{A}{x} + \dfrac{B}{x - 3} + \dfrac{C}{(x - 3)^2}$

$x - 18 = A(x - 3)^2 + Bx(x - 3) + Cx$

$x - 18 = Ax^2 - 6Ax + 9A + Bx^2 - 3Bx + Cx$

$x - 18 = (A + B)x^2 + (-6A - 3B + C)x + 9A$

$\begin{cases} 0 = A + B \\ 1 = -6A - 3B + C \\ -18 = 9A \end{cases}$

The solution is $A = -2$, $B = 2$, $C = -5$.

$\dfrac{x - 18}{x(x - 3)^2} = \dfrac{-2}{x} + \dfrac{2}{x - 3} + \dfrac{-5}{(x - 3)^2}$

24. $x^3 - x^2 + 10x - 10 = (x - 1)(x^2 + 10)$

$\dfrac{9x^2 - 3x + 49}{(x - 1)(x^2 + 10)} = \dfrac{A}{x - 1} + \dfrac{Bx + C}{x^2 + 10}$

$9x^2 - 3x + 49 = A(x^2 + 10) + (Bx + C)(x - 1)$

$9x^2 - 3x + 49 = (A + B)x^2 + (-B + C)x + (10A - C)$

$\begin{cases} 9 = A + B \\ -3 = -B + C \\ 49 = 10A - C \end{cases}$

The solution is $A = 5$, $B = 4$, $C = 1$.

$\dfrac{9x^2 - 3x + 49}{x^3 - x^2 + 10x - 10} = \dfrac{5}{x - 1} + \dfrac{4x + 1}{x^2 + 10}$

30. $\dfrac{2x^3 + 9x + 1}{(x^2 + 7)^2} = \dfrac{Ax + B}{x^2 + 7} + \dfrac{Cx + D}{(x^2 + 7)^2}$

$2x^3 + 9x + 1 = (Ax + B)(x^2 + 7) + Cx + D$

$2x^3 + 9x + 1 = Ax^3 + Bx^2 + (7A + C)x + (7B + D)$

$\begin{cases} 2 = A \\ 0 = B \\ 9 = 7A + C \\ 1 = 7B + D \end{cases}$

The solutions are $A = 2$, $B = 0$, $C = -5$, $D = 1$.

$\dfrac{2x^3 + 9x + 1}{x^4 + 14x^2 + 49} = \dfrac{2x}{x^2 + 7} + \dfrac{-5x + 1}{(x^2 + 7)^2}$

34.

$$2x^2 + 3x - 2 \overline{\smash{\big)}\, 2x^3 + 5x^2 + 3x - 8} \quad \overset{x + 1}{}$$

$\underline{2x^3 + 3x^2 - 2x}$

$2x^2 + 5x - 8$

$\underline{2x^2 + 3x - 2}$

$2x - 6$

$\dfrac{2x^3 + 5x^2 + 3x - 8}{2x^2 + 3x - 2} = x + 1 + \dfrac{2x - 6}{2x^2 + 3x - 2}$

$\dfrac{2x - 6}{(2x - 1)(x + 2)} = \dfrac{A}{2x - 1} + \dfrac{B}{x + 2}$

$2x - 6 = A(x + 2) + B(2x - 1)$

$2x - 6 = Ax + 2A + 2Bx - B$

$2x - 6 = (A + 2B)x + (2A - B)$

$\begin{cases} 2 = A + 2B \\ -6 = 2A - B \end{cases}$

The solutions are $A = -2$, $B = 2$.

$\dfrac{2x^3 + 5x^2 + 3x - 8}{2x^2 + 3x - 2} = x + 1 + \dfrac{-2}{2x - 1} + \dfrac{2}{x + 2}$

Exercise Set 6.5, page 551

6.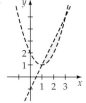

12.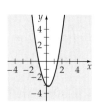

20.

28.

38.

42.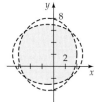

44.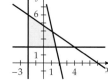

Exercise Set 6.6, page 559

12. $C = 4x + 3y$

(x, y)	C
(0, 8)	24
(2, 4)	20
(5, 2)	26
(11, 0)	44
(20, 0)	80
(20, 20)	140
(0, 20)	60

• Minimum

22. x = hours of machine 1 use

y = hours of machine 2 use

Cost $= 28x + 25y$

Constraints: $\begin{cases} 4x + 3y \geq 60 \\ 5x + 10y \geq 100 \\ x \geq 0, y \geq 0 \end{cases}$

(x, y)	Cost
(0, 20)	500
(12, 4)	436
(20, 0)	560

• Minimum

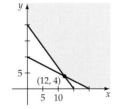

To achieve the minimum cost, use machine 1 for 12 hours and machine 2 for 4 hours.

24. Let x = number of standard models.

Let y = number of deluxe models.

Profit $= 25x + 35y$

Constraints: $\begin{cases} x + 3y \leq 24 \\ x + y \leq 10 \\ 2x + y \leq 16 \\ x \geq 0, y \geq 0 \end{cases}$

(x, y)	Profit
(0, 0)	0
(0, 8)	280
(6, 4)	290
(3, 7)	320
(8, 0)	200

• Maximum

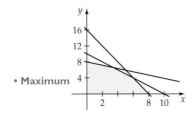

To maximize profits, produce three standard models and seven deluxe models.

Exercise Set 7.1, page 578

6. $\begin{bmatrix} 1 & 2 & 4 & 1 \\ 2 & 2 & 7 & 3 \\ 3 & 6 & 8 & -1 \end{bmatrix} \xrightarrow[-3R_1 + R_3]{-2R_1 + R_2} \begin{bmatrix} 1 & 2 & 4 & 1 \\ 0 & -2 & -1 & 1 \\ 0 & 0 & -4 & -4 \end{bmatrix}$

$\begin{bmatrix} 1 & 2 & 4 & 1 \\ 0 & -2 & -1 & 1 \\ 0 & 0 & -4 & -4 \end{bmatrix} \xrightarrow{-\frac{1}{2}R_2} \begin{bmatrix} 1 & 2 & 4 & 1 \\ 0 & 1 & \frac{1}{2} & -\frac{1}{2} \\ 0 & 0 & -4 & -4 \end{bmatrix}$

$\begin{bmatrix} 1 & 2 & 4 & 1 \\ 0 & 1 & \frac{1}{2} & -\frac{1}{2} \\ 0 & 0 & -4 & -4 \end{bmatrix} \xrightarrow{-\frac{1}{4}R_3} \begin{bmatrix} 1 & 2 & 4 & 1 \\ 0 & 1 & \frac{1}{2} & -\frac{1}{2} \\ 0 & 0 & 1 & 1 \end{bmatrix}$

14. $\begin{bmatrix} 1 & -3 & 1 & 8 \\ 2 & -5 & -3 & 2 \\ 1 & 4 & 1 & 1 \end{bmatrix} \xrightarrow[-1R_1 + R_3]{-2R_1 + R_2} \begin{bmatrix} 1 & -3 & 1 & 8 \\ 0 & 1 & -5 & -14 \\ 0 & 7 & 0 & -7 \end{bmatrix}$

$\xrightarrow{-7R_2 + R_3} \begin{bmatrix} 1 & -3 & 1 & 8 \\ 0 & 1 & -5 & -14 \\ 0 & 0 & 35 & 91 \end{bmatrix}$

$\xrightarrow{\frac{1}{35}R_3} \begin{bmatrix} 1 & -3 & 1 & 8 \\ 0 & 1 & -5 & -14 \\ 0 & 0 & 1 & \frac{13}{5} \end{bmatrix}$

$\begin{cases} x - 3y + z = 8 \\ y - 5z = -14 \\ z = \dfrac{13}{5} \end{cases}$

By back substitution, the solution is $\left(\dfrac{12}{5}, -1, \dfrac{13}{5} \right)$.

18. $\begin{bmatrix} 3 & -5 & 2 & 4 \\ 1 & -3 & 2 & 4 \\ 5 & -11 & 6 & 12 \end{bmatrix} \xrightarrow{R_2 \leftrightarrow R_1} \begin{bmatrix} 1 & -3 & 2 & 4 \\ 3 & -5 & 2 & 4 \\ 5 & -11 & 6 & 12 \end{bmatrix}$

$\xrightarrow[-5R_1 + R_3]{-3R_1 + R_2} \begin{bmatrix} 1 & -3 & 2 & 4 \\ 0 & 4 & -4 & -8 \\ 0 & 4 & -4 & -8 \end{bmatrix} \xrightarrow{\frac{1}{4}R_2} \begin{bmatrix} 1 & -3 & 2 & 4 \\ 0 & 1 & -1 & -2 \\ 0 & 4 & -4 & -8 \end{bmatrix}$

$\xrightarrow{-4R_2 + R_3} \begin{bmatrix} 1 & -3 & 2 & 4 \\ 0 & 1 & -1 & -2 \\ 0 & 0 & 0 & 0 \end{bmatrix}$

$\begin{cases} x - 3y + 2z = 4 \quad (1) \\ y - z = -2 \quad (2) \\ 0 = 0 \quad (3) \end{cases}$

$y - z = -2$ or $y = z - 2$

$x - 3(z - 2) + 2z = 4$ • **Substitute z − 2 for y in Eq. (1).**

$x - 3z + 6 + 2z = 4$

$x = z - 2$

Let $z = c$. The solutions are $(c - 2, c - 2, c)$.

20. $\begin{bmatrix} 2 & 5 & 2 & | & -1 \\ 1 & 2 & -3 & | & 5 \\ 5 & 12 & 1 & | & 10 \end{bmatrix} \xrightarrow{R_2 \leftrightarrow R_1} \begin{bmatrix} 1 & 2 & -3 & | & 5 \\ 2 & 5 & 2 & | & -1 \\ 5 & 12 & 1 & | & 10 \end{bmatrix}$

$\xrightarrow[-5R_1 + R_3]{-2R_1 + R_2} \begin{bmatrix} 1 & 2 & -3 & | & 5 \\ 0 & 1 & 8 & | & -11 \\ 0 & 2 & 16 & | & -15 \end{bmatrix}$

$\xrightarrow{-2R_2 + R_3} \begin{bmatrix} 1 & 2 & -3 & | & 5 \\ 0 & 1 & 8 & | & -11 \\ 0 & 0 & 0 & | & 7 \end{bmatrix}$

$\begin{cases} x + 2y - 3z = 5 \\ y + 8z = -11 \\ 0 = 7 \end{cases}$

Because $0 = 7$ is a false equation, the system of equations has no solution.

36. $\begin{bmatrix} 1 & -1 & 3 & -5 & | & 10 \\ 2 & -3 & 4 & 1 & | & 7 \\ 3 & 1 & -2 & -2 & | & 6 \end{bmatrix}$

$\xrightarrow[-3R_1 + R_3]{-2R_1 + R_2} \begin{bmatrix} 1 & -1 & 3 & -5 & | & 10 \\ 0 & -1 & -2 & 11 & | & -13 \\ 0 & 4 & -11 & 13 & | & -24 \end{bmatrix}$

$\xrightarrow{-1R_2} \begin{bmatrix} 1 & -1 & 3 & -5 & | & 10 \\ 0 & 1 & 2 & -11 & | & 13 \\ 0 & 4 & -11 & 13 & | & -24 \end{bmatrix}$

$\xrightarrow{-4R_2 + R_3} \begin{bmatrix} 1 & -1 & 3 & -5 & | & 10 \\ 0 & 1 & 2 & -11 & | & 13 \\ 0 & 0 & -19 & 57 & | & -76 \end{bmatrix}$

$\xrightarrow{-\frac{1}{19}R_3} \begin{bmatrix} 1 & -1 & 3 & -5 & | & 10 \\ 0 & 1 & 2 & -11 & | & 13 \\ 0 & 0 & 1 & -3 & | & 4 \end{bmatrix}$

$\begin{cases} t - u + 3v - 5w = 10 & (1) \\ u + 2v - 11w = 13 & (2) \\ v - 3w = 4 & (3) \end{cases}$

$v = 3w + 4$

$u + 2(3w + 4) - 11w = 13$ • Substitute $3w + 4$

$u = 5w + 5$ for v in Eq. 2.

$t - (5w + 5) + 3(3w + 4) - 5w = 10$ • Substitute

$t = w + 3$ $5w + 5$ for u
and $3w + 4$ for v
in Eq. (1).

Let w be any real number c. The solution of the system of equations is $(c + 3, 5c + 5, 3c + 4, c)$.

44. Because there are four given points, the degree of the interpolating polynomial will be at most 3. The form of the polynomial will be $p(x) = a_3x^3 + a_2x^2 + a_1x + a_0$. Use this polynomial to create a system of equations.

$p(x) = a_3x^3 + a_2x^2 + a_1x + a_0$

$p(-1) = a_3(-1)^3 + a_2(-1)^2 + a_1(-1) + a_0$
$= -a_3 + a_2 - a_1 + a_0 = -5$

$p(0) = a_3(0)^3 + a_2(0)^2 + a_1(0) + a_0 = a_0 = 0$

$p(1) = a_3(1)^3 + a_2(1)^2 + a_1(1) + a_0$
$= a_3 + a_2 + a_1 + a_0 = 1$

$p(2) = a_3(2)^3 + a_2(2)^2 + a_1(2) + a_0$
$= 8a_3 + 4a_2 + 2a_1 + a_0 = 4$

The system of equations and the associated augmented matrix are

$\begin{cases} -a_3 + a_2 - a_1 + a_0 = -5 \\ a_0 = 0 \\ a_3 + a_2 + a_1 + a_0 = 1 \\ 8a_3 + 4a_2 + 2a_1 + a_0 = 4 \end{cases}$ $\begin{bmatrix} -1 & 1 & -1 & 1 & | & -5 \\ 0 & 0 & 0 & 1 & | & 0 \\ 1 & 1 & 1 & 1 & | & 1 \\ 8 & 4 & 2 & 1 & | & 4 \end{bmatrix}$

The augmented matrix in row echelon form and the resulting system of equations are

$\begin{bmatrix} 1 & 0.5 & 0.25 & 0.125 & | & 0.5 \\ 0 & 1 & -0.5 & 0.75 & | & -3 \\ 0 & 0 & 1 & 0.5 & | & 2 \\ 0 & 0 & 0 & 1 & | & 0 \end{bmatrix}$

$\begin{cases} a_1 + 0.5a_2 + 0.25a_3 + 0.125a_4 = 0.5 \\ a_2 - 0.5a_3 + 0.75a_4 = -3 \\ a_3 + 0.5a_4 = 2 \\ a_4 = 0 \end{cases}$

Solving the system of equations by back substitution yields $a_0 = 0, a_1 = 2, a_2 = -2,$ and $a_3 = 1$. The interpolating polynomial is $p(x) = x^3 - 2x^2 + 2x$.

Exercise Set 7.2, page 595

6. a. $A + B = \begin{bmatrix} 2 & -2 \\ 3 & 4 \\ 1 & 0 \end{bmatrix} + \begin{bmatrix} -1 & 8 \\ 2 & -2 \\ -4 & 3 \end{bmatrix} = \begin{bmatrix} 1 & 6 \\ 5 & 2 \\ -3 & 3 \end{bmatrix}$

b. $A - B = \begin{bmatrix} 2 & -2 \\ 3 & 4 \\ 1 & 0 \end{bmatrix} - \begin{bmatrix} -1 & 8 \\ 2 & -2 \\ -4 & 3 \end{bmatrix} = \begin{bmatrix} 3 & -10 \\ 1 & 6 \\ 5 & -3 \end{bmatrix}$

c. $2B = 2\begin{bmatrix} -1 & 8 \\ 2 & -2 \\ -4 & 3 \end{bmatrix} = \begin{bmatrix} -2 & 16 \\ 4 & -4 \\ -8 & 6 \end{bmatrix}$

d. $2A - 3B = 2\begin{bmatrix} 2 & -2 \\ 3 & 4 \\ 1 & 0 \end{bmatrix} - 3\begin{bmatrix} -1 & 8 \\ 2 & -2 \\ -4 & 3 \end{bmatrix} = \begin{bmatrix} 7 & -28 \\ 0 & 14 \\ 14 & -9 \end{bmatrix}$

16. $AB = \begin{bmatrix} -1 & 2 & 0 \\ 2 & -1 & 1 \\ -2 & 2 & -1 \end{bmatrix} \begin{bmatrix} 2 & -1 & 0 \\ 1 & 5 & -1 \\ 0 & -1 & 3 \end{bmatrix}$

$= \begin{bmatrix} (-1)(2) + (2)(1) & + (0)(0) \\ (2)(2) & + (-1)(1) + (1)(0) \\ (-2)(2) + (2)(1) & + (-1)(0) \end{bmatrix}$

$\begin{matrix} (-1)(-1) + (2)(5) & + (0)(-1) \\ (2)(-1) & + (-1)(5) + (1)(-1) \\ (-2)(-1) + (2)(5) & + (-1)(-1) \end{matrix}$

$\begin{matrix} (-1)(0) + (2)(-1) & + (0)(3) \\ (2)(0) & + (-1)(-1) + (1)(3) \\ (-2)(0) + (2)(-1) & + (-1)(3) \end{matrix}$

$= \begin{bmatrix} 0 & 11 & -2 \\ 3 & -8 & 4 \\ -2 & 13 & -5 \end{bmatrix}$

$BA = \begin{bmatrix} 2 & -1 & 0 \\ 1 & 5 & -1 \\ 0 & -1 & 3 \end{bmatrix} \begin{bmatrix} -1 & 2 & 0 \\ 2 & -1 & 1 \\ -2 & 2 & -1 \end{bmatrix}$

$= \begin{bmatrix} (2)(-1) + (-1)(2) + (0)(-2) \\ (1)(-1) + (5)(2) & + (-1)(-2) \\ (0)(-1) + (-1)(2) + (3)(-2) \end{bmatrix}$

$\begin{matrix} (2)(2) + (-1)(-1) + (0)(2) \\ (1)(2) + (5)(-1) & + (-1)(2) \\ (0)(2) + (-1)(-1) + (3)(2) \end{matrix}$

$\begin{matrix} (2)(0) + (-1)(1) + (0)(-1) \\ (1)(0) + (5)(1) & + (-1)(-1) \\ (0)(0) + (-1)(1) + (3)(-1) \end{matrix}$

$= \begin{bmatrix} -4 & 5 & -1 \\ 11 & -5 & 6 \\ -8 & 7 & -4 \end{bmatrix}$

36. $\begin{bmatrix} 2 & 0 & 5 \\ 3 & -5 & 1 \\ 4 & -7 & 6 \end{bmatrix} \begin{bmatrix} x \\ y \\ z \end{bmatrix} = \begin{bmatrix} 9 \\ 7 \\ 14 \end{bmatrix}$

$\begin{bmatrix} 2x & + 5z \\ 3x - 5y + & z \\ 4x - 7y + 6z \end{bmatrix} = \begin{bmatrix} 9 \\ 7 \\ 14 \end{bmatrix}$ • **Multiply the matrices.**

$\begin{cases} 2x & + 5z = 9 \\ 3x - 5y + & z = 7 \\ 4x - 7y + 6z = 14 \end{cases}$ • **Use equality of matrices to write the system of equations.**

56. $\overset{A}{[0.25} \quad \overset{B}{0.75]} \begin{bmatrix} 0.98 & 0.02 \\ 0.05 & 0.95 \end{bmatrix}^5 \approx \overset{A}{[0.391} \quad \overset{B}{0.609]}$

After 5 months, store A has approximately 39.1% of the town's customers.

6. $\begin{bmatrix} 1 & 3 & -2 & | & 1 & 0 & 0 \\ -1 & -5 & 6 & | & 0 & 1 & 0 \\ 2 & 6 & -3 & | & 0 & 0 & 1 \end{bmatrix}$

$\xrightarrow[\substack{R_1 + R_2 \\ -2R_1 + R_3}]{} \begin{bmatrix} 1 & 3 & -2 & | & 1 & 0 & 0 \\ 0 & -2 & 4 & | & 1 & 1 & 0 \\ 0 & 0 & 1 & | & -2 & 0 & 1 \end{bmatrix}$

$\xrightarrow[-\frac{1}{2}R_2]{} \begin{bmatrix} 1 & 3 & -2 & | & 1 & 0 & 0 \\ 0 & 1 & -2 & | & -\frac{1}{2} & -\frac{1}{2} & 0 \\ 0 & 0 & 1 & | & -2 & 0 & 1 \end{bmatrix}$

$\xrightarrow[\substack{2R_3 + R_2 \\ 2R_3 + R_1}]{} \begin{bmatrix} 1 & 3 & 0 & | & -3 & 0 & 2 \\ 0 & 1 & 0 & | & -\frac{9}{2} & -\frac{1}{2} & 2 \\ 0 & 0 & 1 & | & -2 & 0 & 1 \end{bmatrix}$

$\xrightarrow[-3R_2 + R_1]{} \begin{bmatrix} 1 & 0 & 0 & | & \frac{21}{2} & \frac{3}{2} & -4 \\ 0 & 1 & 0 & | & -\frac{9}{2} & -\frac{1}{2} & 2 \\ 0 & 0 & 1 & | & -2 & 0 & 1 \end{bmatrix}$

The inverse matrix is $\begin{bmatrix} \frac{21}{2} & \frac{3}{2} & -4 \\ -\frac{9}{2} & -\frac{1}{2} & 2 \\ -2 & 0 & 1 \end{bmatrix}$.

10. $\begin{bmatrix} 1 & -2 & 2 & | & 1 & 0 & 0 \\ 2 & -3 & 1 & | & 0 & 1 & 0 \\ 3 & -6 & 6 & | & 0 & 0 & 1 \end{bmatrix}$

$\xrightarrow[\substack{-2R_1 + R_2 \\ -3R_1 + R_3}]{} \begin{bmatrix} 1 & -2 & 2 & | & 1 & 0 & 0 \\ 0 & 1 & -3 & | & -2 & 1 & 0 \\ 0 & 0 & 0 & | & -3 & 0 & 1 \end{bmatrix}$

Because there are zeros in a row of the original matrix, the matrix does not have an inverse.

20. $\begin{bmatrix} 1 & 2 & -1 \\ 2 & 3 & -1 \\ 3 & 6 & -2 \end{bmatrix} \begin{bmatrix} x \\ y \\ z \end{bmatrix} = \begin{bmatrix} 5 \\ 8 \\ 14 \end{bmatrix}$

The inverse of the coefficient matrix is

$\begin{bmatrix} 0 & 2 & -1 \\ -1 & -1 & 1 \\ -3 & 0 & 1 \end{bmatrix}$

Multiplying each side of the equation by the inverse, we have

$\begin{bmatrix} x \\ y \\ z \end{bmatrix} = \begin{bmatrix} 0 & 2 & -1 \\ -1 & -1 & 1 \\ -3 & 0 & 1 \end{bmatrix} \begin{bmatrix} 5 \\ 8 \\ 14 \end{bmatrix} = \begin{bmatrix} 2 \\ 1 \\ -1 \end{bmatrix}$

The solution is $(2, 1, -1)$.

26. Write a system of equations.

$$x_1 = \frac{40 + 40 + 25 + x_2}{4} = \frac{105 + x_2}{4}$$

$$x_2 = \frac{25 + 60 + 40 + x_1}{4} = \frac{125 + x_1}{4}$$

Rewrite the system of equations.

$$4x_1 - x_2 = 105$$
$$-x_1 + 4x_2 = 125$$

Solve the system of equations using an inverse matrix.

$$\begin{bmatrix} 4 & -1 \\ -1 & 4 \end{bmatrix}\begin{bmatrix} x_1 \\ x_2 \end{bmatrix} = \begin{bmatrix} 105 \\ 125 \end{bmatrix}$$

$$\begin{bmatrix} \frac{4}{15} & \frac{1}{15} \\ \frac{1}{15} & \frac{4}{15} \end{bmatrix}\begin{bmatrix} 4 & -1 \\ -1 & 4 \end{bmatrix}\begin{bmatrix} x_1 \\ x_2 \end{bmatrix} = \begin{bmatrix} \frac{4}{15} & \frac{1}{15} \\ \frac{1}{15} & \frac{4}{15} \end{bmatrix}\begin{bmatrix} 105 \\ 125 \end{bmatrix}$$

$$\begin{bmatrix} x_1 \\ x_2 \end{bmatrix} = \begin{bmatrix} \frac{109}{3} \\ \frac{121}{3} \end{bmatrix}$$

The temperatures, to the nearest tenth of a degree, are $x_1 = 36.3°F$ and $x_2 = 40.3°F$.

Exercise Set 7.4, page 621

2. $\begin{vmatrix} 2 & 9 \\ -6 & 2 \end{vmatrix} = 2 \cdot 2 - (-6)(9) = 4 + 54 = 58$

14. $M_{13} = \begin{vmatrix} 1 & 3 \\ 6 & -2 \end{vmatrix} = 1(-2) - 6(3) = -2 - 18 = -20$

$C_{13} = (-1)^{1+3} \cdot M_{13} = 1 \cdot M_{13} = 1(-20) = -20$

20. Expanding by cofactors of row 1 yields

$\begin{vmatrix} 3 & -2 & 0 \\ 2 & -3 & 2 \\ 8 & -2 & 5 \end{vmatrix} = 3C_{11} + (-2)C_{12} + 0 \cdot C_{13}$

$= 3\begin{vmatrix} -3 & 2 \\ -2 & 5 \end{vmatrix} + 2\begin{vmatrix} 2 & 2 \\ 8 & 5 \end{vmatrix} + 0\begin{vmatrix} 2 & -3 \\ 8 & -2 \end{vmatrix}$

$= 3(-15 + 4) + 2(10 - 16) + 0$

$= 3(-11) + 2(-6) = -33 + (-12)$

$= -45$

42. Let $D = \begin{vmatrix} 3 & -2 & -1 \\ 1 & 2 & 4 \\ 2 & -2 & 3 \end{vmatrix}$. Then

$D \overset{R_1 \leftrightarrow R_2}{=} -\begin{vmatrix} 1 & 2 & 4 \\ 3 & -2 & -1 \\ 2 & -2 & 3 \end{vmatrix} \overset{\substack{-3R_1 + R_2 \\ -2R_1 + R_3}}{=} -\begin{vmatrix} 1 & 2 & 4 \\ 0 & -8 & -13 \\ 0 & -6 & -5 \end{vmatrix}$

$\overset{-\frac{1}{8}R_2}{=} 8\begin{vmatrix} 1 & 2 & 4 \\ 0 & 1 & \frac{13}{8} \\ 0 & -6 & -5 \end{vmatrix} \overset{6R_2 + R_3}{=} 8\begin{vmatrix} 1 & 2 & 4 \\ 0 & 1 & \frac{13}{8} \\ 0 & 0 & \frac{19}{4} \end{vmatrix}$

$= 8(1)(1)\left(\frac{19}{4}\right) = 38$

Exercise Set 7.5, page 627

4. $x_1 = \dfrac{\begin{vmatrix} 9 & 5 \\ 8 & 7 \end{vmatrix}}{\begin{vmatrix} 2 & 5 \\ 5 & 7 \end{vmatrix}} = \dfrac{63 - 40}{14 - 25} = \dfrac{23}{-11} = -\dfrac{23}{11}$

$x_2 = \dfrac{\begin{vmatrix} 2 & 9 \\ 5 & 8 \end{vmatrix}}{\begin{vmatrix} 2 & 5 \\ 5 & 7 \end{vmatrix}} = \dfrac{16 - 45}{14 - 25} = \dfrac{-29}{-11} = \dfrac{29}{11}$

The solution is $\left(-\dfrac{23}{11}, \dfrac{29}{11}\right)$.

24. $x_3 = \dfrac{\begin{vmatrix} 2 & 5 & -3 & -3 \\ 1 & 7 & 4 & -1 \\ 4 & 0 & 3 & 1 \\ 3 & 2 & 0 & 0 \end{vmatrix}}{\begin{vmatrix} 2 & 5 & -5 & -3 \\ 1 & 7 & 8 & -1 \\ 4 & 0 & 1 & 1 \\ 3 & 2 & -1 & 0 \end{vmatrix}} = \dfrac{157}{168}$

Exercise Set 8.1, page 644

6. $a_n = \dfrac{(-1)^{n+1}}{n(n + 1)}, a_1 = \dfrac{(-1)^{1+1}}{1(1 + 1)} = \dfrac{1}{2},$

$a_2 = \dfrac{(-1)^{2+1}}{2(2 + 1)} = -\dfrac{1}{6}, a_3 = \dfrac{(-1)^{3+1}}{3(3 + 1)} = \dfrac{1}{12},$

$a_8 = \dfrac{(-1)^{8+1}}{8(8 + 1)} = -\dfrac{1}{72}$

28. $a_1 = 1, a_2 = 2^2 \cdot a_1 = 4 \cdot 1 = 4, a_3 = 3^2 \cdot a_2 = 9 \cdot 4 = 36$

42. $\dfrac{12!}{4! \, 8!} = \dfrac{12 \cdot 11 \cdot 10 \cdot 9 \cdot 8!}{4! \, 8!} = \dfrac{12 \cdot 11 \cdot 10 \cdot 9}{4 \cdot 3 \cdot 2 \cdot 1} = 495$

52. $\displaystyle\sum_{i=1}^{6} (2i + 1)(2i - 1) = \sum_{i=1}^{6} (4i^2 - 1)$

$= (4 \cdot 1^2 - 1) + (4 \cdot 2^2 - 1)$

$\quad + (4 \cdot 3^2 - 1) + (4 \cdot 4^2 - 1)$

$\quad + (4 \cdot 5^2 - 1) + (4 \cdot 6^2 - 1)$

$= 3 + 15 + 35 + 63 + 99 + 143$

$= 358$

Exercise Set 8.2, page 651

16. $a_6 = -14$, $a_8 = -20$

$$a_8 = a_6 + 2d$$

$$\frac{a_8 - a_6}{2} = d \qquad \text{• Solve for } d.$$

$$\frac{-20 - (-14)}{2} = d$$

$$-3 = d$$

$$a_n = a_1 + (n - 1)d$$

$$a_6 = a_1 + (6 - 1)(-3)$$

$$-14 = a_1 + (-15)$$

$$a_1 = 1$$

$$a_{15} = 1 + (15 - 1)(-3) = 1 + (14)(-3) = -41$$

22. $S_{20} = \dfrac{20}{2}(a_1 + a_{20})$

$$a_1 = 1 - 2(1) = -1$$

$$a_{20} = 1 - 2(20) = -39$$

$$S_{20} = 10[-1 + (-39)] = 10(-40) = -400$$

34. $a = 7$, c_1, c_2, c_3, c_4, c_5, $b = 19$

$$a_n = a_1 + (n - 1)d$$

$$19 = 7 + (7 - 1)d \qquad \text{• There are seven terms, so } n = 7.$$

$$19 = 7 + 6d$$

$$d = 2$$

$$c_1 = a_1 + d = 7 + 2 = 9$$

$$c_2 = a_1 + 2d = 7 + 4 = 11$$

$$c_3 = a_1 + 3d = 7 + 6 = 13$$

$$c_4 = a_1 + 4d = 7 + 8 = 15$$

$$c_5 = a_1 + 5d = 7 + 10 = 17$$

Exercise Set 8.3, page 659

6. $\dfrac{a_{i+1}}{a_i} = \dfrac{(-1)^i e^{(i+1)x}}{(-1)^{i-1} e^{ix}} = -e^{(i+1)x - ix} = -e^x$

Because x is a constant, $-e^x$ is a constant and the sequence is a geometric sequence.

18. $\dfrac{a_2}{a_1} = \dfrac{6}{8} = \dfrac{3}{4} = r$

$$a_n = a_1 r^{n-1}$$

$$a_n = 8\left(\frac{3}{4}\right)^{n-1}$$

40. $r = \dfrac{4}{3}$, $a_1 = \dfrac{4}{3}$, $n = 14$

$$S_n = \frac{a_1(1 - r^n)}{1 - r}$$

$$S_{14} = \frac{\dfrac{4}{3}\left[1 - \left(\dfrac{4}{3}\right)^{14}\right]}{1 - \dfrac{4}{3}} = \frac{\dfrac{4}{3}\left[\dfrac{-263{,}652{,}487}{4{,}782{,}969}\right]}{-\dfrac{1}{3}} \approx 220.49$$

62. $0.3\overline{95} = \dfrac{3}{10} + \dfrac{95}{1000} + \dfrac{95}{100{,}000} + \cdots = \dfrac{3}{10} + \dfrac{\dfrac{95}{1000}}{1 - \dfrac{1}{100}}$

$$= \frac{3}{10} + \frac{95}{990} = \frac{392}{990} = \frac{196}{495}$$

70. $A = \dfrac{P[(1 + r)^m - 1]}{r}$; $P = 250$, $r = \dfrac{0.08}{12}$, $m = 12(4)$

$$A = \frac{250\left[\left(1 + \dfrac{0.08}{12}\right)^{48} - 1\right]}{\dfrac{0.08}{12}} \approx 14{,}087.48$$

Exercise Set 8.4, page 668

8. $S_n = 2 + 6 + 12 + \cdots + n(n + 1) = \dfrac{n(n + 1)(n + 2)}{3}$

1. When $n = 1$, $S_1 = 1(1 + 1) = 2$; $\dfrac{1(1 + 1)(1 + 2)}{3} = 2$.

   Therefore, the statement is true for $n = 1$.

2. Assume the statement is true for $n = k$.

$$S_k = 2 + 6 + 12 + \cdots + k(k + 1)$$

$$= \frac{k(k + 1)(k + 2)}{3} \qquad \text{• Induction hypothesis}$$

   Prove the statement is true for $n = k + 1$. That is, prove

$$S_{k+1} = \frac{(k + 1)(k + 2)(k + 3)}{3}.$$

   Because $a_k = k(k + 1)$ and $a_{k+1} = (k + 1)(k + 2)$,

$$S_{k+1} = S_k + a_{k+1} = \frac{k(k + 1)(k + 2)}{3} + (k + 1)(k + 2)$$

$$= \frac{k(k + 1)(k + 2) + 3(k + 1)(k + 2)}{3}$$

$$= \frac{(k + 1)(k + 2)(k + 3)}{3} \qquad \text{• Factor out } (k + 1) \text{ and } (k + 2) \text{ from each term.}$$

   By the Principle of Mathematical Induction, the statement is true for all positive integers n.

12. $P_n = \left(1 - \dfrac{1}{2}\right)\left(1 - \dfrac{1}{3}\right)\cdots\left(1 - \dfrac{1}{n+1}\right) = \dfrac{1}{n+1}$

1. Let $n = 1$; then $P_1 = \left(1 - \dfrac{1}{2}\right) = \dfrac{1}{2}$; $\dfrac{1}{1+1} = \dfrac{1}{2}$.

   The statement is true for $n = 1$.

2. Assume the statement is true for $n = k$.

   $P_k = \left(1 - \dfrac{1}{2}\right)\left(1 - \dfrac{1}{3}\right)\cdots\left(1 - \dfrac{1}{k+1}\right) = \dfrac{1}{k+1}$

   Prove the statement is true for $n = k + 1$. That is, prove

   $P_{k+1} = \left(1 - \dfrac{1}{2}\right)\left(1 - \dfrac{1}{3}\right)\cdots\left(1 - \dfrac{1}{k+1}\right)\left(1 - \dfrac{1}{k+2}\right)$

   $= \dfrac{1}{k+2}$

   Because $a_k = \left(1 - \dfrac{1}{k+1}\right)$ and $a_{k+1} = \left(1 - \dfrac{1}{k+2}\right)$,

   $P_{k+1} = P_k \cdot a_{k+1} = \dfrac{1}{k+1} \cdot \left(1 - \dfrac{1}{k+2}\right)$

   $= \dfrac{1}{k+1} \cdot \dfrac{k+1}{k+2} = \dfrac{1}{k+2}$

   By the Principle of Mathematical Induction, the statement is true for all positive integers n.

16. If $a > 1$, show that $a^{n+1} > a^n$ for all positive integers n.

1. Because $a > 1$, $a \cdot a > a \cdot 1$ or $a^2 > a$. Thus the statement is true when $n = 1$.

2. Assume the statement is true for $n = k$.

   $a^{k+1} > a^k$ • **Induction hypothesis**

   Prove the statement is true for $n = k + 1$. That is, prove $a^{k+2} > a^{k+1}$.

   Because $a^{k+1} > a^k$ and $a > 0$,

   $a(a^{k+1}) > a(a^k)$

   $a^{k+2} > a^{k+1}$

   By the Principle of Mathematical Induction, the statement is true for all positive integers n.

20. 1. Let $n = 1$. Because $\log_{10} 1 = 0$,

   $\log_{10} 1 < 1$

   The inequality is true for $n = 1$.

2. Assume $\log_{10} k < k$ is true for some positive integer k (induction hypothesis). Prove the inequality is true for $n = k + 1$. That is, prove $\log_{10}(k + 1) < k + 1$ is true when $n = k + 1$.

   $\log_{10}(k + 1) \leq \log_{10}(k + k)$

   $= \log_{10} 2k = \log_{10} 2 + \log_{10} k < 1 + k$

Thus $\log_{10}(k + 1) < k + 1$. By the Principle of Mathematical Induction, $\log_{10} n < n$ for all positive integers n.

Exercise Set 8.5, page 674

4. $\dbinom{10}{5} = \dfrac{10!}{5!\,5!} = \dfrac{10 \cdot 9 \cdot 8 \cdot 7 \cdot 6 \cdot 5!}{5!\,5!} = \dfrac{10 \cdot 9 \cdot 8 \cdot 7 \cdot 6}{5 \cdot 4 \cdot 3 \cdot 2 \cdot 1}$

$= 252$

18. $(3x + 2y)^4$

$= (3x)^4 + 4(3x)^3(2y) + 6(3x)^2(2y)^2 + 4(3x)(2y)^3 + (2y)^4$

$= 81x^4 + 216x^3y + 216x^2y^2 + 96xy^3 + 16y^4$

20. $\left(2x - \sqrt{y}\right)^7 = \dbinom{7}{0}(2x)^7 + \dbinom{7}{1}(2x)^6\left(-\sqrt{y}\right)$

$+ \dbinom{7}{2}(2x)^5\left(-\sqrt{y}\right)^2 + \dbinom{7}{3}(2x)^4\left(-\sqrt{y}\right)^3$

$+ \dbinom{7}{4}(2x)^3\left(-\sqrt{y}\right)^4 + \dbinom{7}{5}(2x)^2\left(-\sqrt{y}\right)^5$

$+ \dbinom{7}{6}(2x)\left(-\sqrt{y}\right)^6 + \dbinom{7}{7}\left(-\sqrt{y}\right)^7$

$= 128x^7 - 448x^6\sqrt{y} + 672x^5y - 560x^4y\sqrt{y}$

$+ 280x^3y^2 - 84x^2y^2\sqrt{y}$

$+ 14xy^3 - y^3\sqrt{y}$

34. $\dbinom{10}{6-1}(x^{-1/2})^{10-6+1}(x^{1/2})^{6-1} = \dbinom{10}{5}(x^{-1/2})^5(x^{1/2})^5 = 252$

Exercise Set 8.6, page 681

12. Because there are four palettes and each palette contains four colors, by the counting principle there are $4 \cdot 4 \cdot 4 \cdot 4 = 256$ possible colors.

16. There are three possible finishes (first, second, and third) for the 12 contestants. Because the order of finish is important, these are the permutations of the 12 contestants selected 3 at a time.

$P(12, 3) = \dfrac{12!}{(12-3)!} = \dfrac{12!}{9!} = 12 \cdot 11 \cdot 10 = 1320$

There are 1320 possible finishes.

20. Player A matched against Player B is the same tennis match as Player B matched against Player A. Therefore, this is a combination of 26 players selected 2 at a time.

$C(26, 2) = \dfrac{26!}{2!(26-2)!} = \dfrac{26!}{2!\,24!} = \dfrac{26 \cdot 25 \cdot 24!}{2 \cdot 1 \cdot 24!} = 325$

There are 325 possible first-round matches.

22. The person who refuses to sit in the back seat can be placed in any one of the three front seats. Similarly, the person who refuses to sit in the front can be placed in any of the three back seats. The remaining four people can sit in any of the remaining seats. The number of seating arrangements is

$3 \cdot 3 \cdot 4 \cdot 3 \cdot 2 \cdot 1 = 216$

30. a. The number of ways in which 10 finalists can be selected from 15 semifinalists is the combination of 15 students selected 10 at a time.

$C(15, 10) = 3003$

There are 3003 ways in which the finalists can be chosen.

b. The number of ways in which the 10 finalists can include 3 seniors is the product of the combination of 7 seniors selected 3 at a time and the combination of 8 remaining students selected 7 at a time.

$C(7, 3)C(8, 7) = 35 \cdot 8 = 280$

There are 280 ways in which the finalists can include 3 seniors.

c. "At least five seniors" means 5 or 6 or 7 seniors are finalists (there are only 7 seniors). Because the events are related by "or," sum the number of ways each event can occur.

$C(7, 5)C(8, 5) + C(7, 6)C(8, 4) + C(7, 7)C(8, 3)$
$= 21 \cdot 56 + 7 \cdot 70 + 1 \cdot 56 = 1176 + 490 + 56 = 1722$

There are 1722 ways in which the finalists can include at least 5 seniors.

Exercise Set 8.7, page 692

6. Let R represent the Republican, D the Democrat, and I the Independent. The sample space is

{(R, D), (R, I), (D, I)}

14. {HHHT, HHTH, HTHH, THHH, HHHH}

22. Let $E = \{2, 4, 6\}$, $T = \{3, 6\}$, and $S = \{1, 2, 3, 4, 5, 6\}$.

$E \cup T = \{2, 3, 4, 6\}$

$P(E \cup T) = \dfrac{N(E \cup T)}{N(S)} = \dfrac{4}{6} = \dfrac{2}{3}$

32. $\dfrac{C(3, 2) \cdot C(5, 2)}{C(8, 4)} = \dfrac{3 \cdot 10}{70} = \dfrac{3}{7}$

34. Yes, because the card was replaced. The probability of an ace on each draw is $\dfrac{4}{52} = \dfrac{1}{13}$.

$P(2 \text{ aces}) = \dfrac{1}{13} \cdot \dfrac{1}{13} = \dfrac{1}{169}$

40. This is a binomial experiment; $p = \dfrac{1}{4}$, $q = \dfrac{3}{4}$, $n = 8$, and $k = 3$.

$\dbinom{8}{3}\left(\dfrac{1}{4}\right)^{3}\left(\dfrac{3}{4}\right)^{5} = 56\left(\dfrac{1}{64}\right)\left(\dfrac{243}{1024}\right) \approx 0.2076$

ANSWERS TO SELECTED EXERCISES

Exercise Set P.1, page 15

1. Integers: $0, -44, \sqrt{81}, 53$; Rational numbers: $-\dfrac{1}{5}, 0, -44, 3.14, \sqrt{81}, 53$; Irrational numbers: $\pi, 5.05005000500005\ldots$; Prime number: 53;

Real numbers: All the numbers are real numbers. **3.** $2, 4, 6, 8$ **5.** $3, 5, 7, 9$ **7.** $0, 1, 2, 3$ **9.** $\{-3, -2, -1, 0, 1, 2, 3, 4, 6\}$

11. $\{0, 1, 2, 3\}$ **13.** $\varnothing$ **15.** $\{1, 3\}$ **17.** $\{-2, 0, 1, 2, 3, 4, 6\}$ **19.** $\{x \mid -2 < x < 3\}$,

21. $\{x \mid -5 \le x \le -1\}$, **23.** $\{x \mid x \ge 2\}$,

25. $(3, 5)$, **27.** $[-2, \infty)$, **29.** $[0, 1]$,

31. -5 **33.** 12 **35.** $\pi^2 + 10$ **37.** 9 **39.** $3x - 1$ **41.** $|x - 3|$ **43.** $|x + 2| = 4$ **45.** $|m - n|$ **47.** $|a - 4| < 5$

49. $|x + 2| > 4$ **51.** **53.** **55.**

57. **59.** **61.**

63. **65.** **67.** 8 **69.** 12 **71.** -72 **73.** 19 **75.** 13 **77.** -3

79. Associative property of multiplication **81.** Distributive property **83.** Commutative property of multiplication **85.** Identity property of multiplication **87.** Reflexive property of equality **89.** Transitive property of equality **91.** Inverse property of multiplication

93. $6x$ **95.** $3x + 6$ **97.** $\dfrac{3}{2}a$ **99.** $6x - 13$ **101.** $-12x + 6y + 5$ **103.** $2a$ **105.** $21a + 6$ **107.** 6 square inches

109. \$5150 **111.** 66 beats per minute **113.** 100 feet **115.** A **117.** $\varnothing$ **119.** B is a subset of A.
121. No. $(8 \div 4) \div 2 = 2 \div 2 = 1, 8 \div (4 \div 2) = 8 \div 2 = 4$ **123.** All but the multiplicative inverse property **125.** $x + 7$
127. $|x - 2| < |x - 6|$ **129.** $|x - 3| > |x + 7|$ **131.** $2 < |x - 4| < 7$

Prepare for Section P.2, page 18

133. 32 **134.** $\dfrac{1}{16}$ **135.** 64 **136.** $314{,}000$ **137.** False **138.** False

Exercise Set P.2, page 31

1. -125 **3.** 1 **5.** $\dfrac{1}{16}$ **7.** 32 **9.** 27 **11.** -2 **13.** $\dfrac{2}{x^4}$ **15.** $6a^3b^8$ **17.** $\dfrac{3}{4a^4}$ **19.** $\dfrac{2y^2}{3x^2}$ **21.** $\dfrac{12}{a^3b}$ **23.** $-18m^5n^6$ **25.** $\dfrac{1}{x^6}$

27. $\dfrac{1}{4a^4b^2}$ **29.** $2x$ **31.** $\dfrac{b^{10}}{a^{10}}$ **33.** 2.011×10^{12} **35.** 5.62×10^{-10} **37.** $31{,}400{,}000$ **39.** -0.0000023 **41.** 2.7×10^8 **43.** 1.5×10^{-11}

45. 7.2×10^{12} **47.** 8×10^{-16} **49.** 8 **51.** -16 **53.** $\dfrac{1}{27}$ **55.** $\dfrac{2}{3}$ **57.** 16 **59.** $8ab^2$ **61.** $-12x^{11/12}$ **63.** $3x^2y^3$ **65.** $\dfrac{4z^{2/5}}{3}$

67. $6x^{5/6}y^{5/6}$ **69.** $\dfrac{3a^{1/12}}{b}$ **71.** $3\sqrt{5}$ **73.** $2\sqrt[3]{3}$ **75.** $-3\sqrt[3]{5}$ **77.** $2|x|y\sqrt{6y}$ **79.** $2ay^2\sqrt[3]{2y}$ **81.** $-13\sqrt{2}$ **83.** $-10\sqrt[4]{3}$

85. $17y\sqrt[3]{4y}$ **87.** $-14x^2y\sqrt[3]{y}$ **89.** $17 + 7\sqrt{5}$ **91.** -7 **93.** $12z + \sqrt{z} - 6$ **95.** $x + 4\sqrt{x} + 4$ **97.** $x + 4\sqrt{x - 3} + 1$ **99.** $\sqrt{2}$

101. $\dfrac{\sqrt{10}}{6}$ **103.** $\dfrac{3\sqrt[3]{4}}{2}$ **105.** $\dfrac{2\sqrt[3]{x}}{x}$ **107.** $-\dfrac{3\sqrt{3} - 12}{13}$ **109.** $\dfrac{3\sqrt{5} - 3}{4}$ **111.** $\dfrac{3\sqrt{5} - 3\sqrt{x}}{5 - x}$ **113.** $\approx 2.21 \times 10^4$ dollars

115. $\approx 3.13 \times 10^7$ **117.** $\approx 1.38 \times 10^{-2}$ **119.** 8 minutes **121.** \$22,688 **123.** ≈ 8.91 billion **125. a.** 56% **b.** 24%

127. No. $2 < 3$, but $\dfrac{1}{2} > \dfrac{1}{3}$. **129.** $\dfrac{8}{5}$ **131.** $-\dfrac{19}{12}$ **133.** $\dfrac{1}{\sqrt{4 + h} + 2}$ **135.** $\dfrac{1}{\sqrt{n^2 + 1} + n}$ **137.** 2

Prepare for Section P.3, page 34

138. $-6a + 12b$ **139.** $-4x + 19$ **140.** $3x^2 - 3x - 6$ **141.** $-x^2 - 5x - 1$ **142.** False   **143.** False

Exercise Set P.3, page 40

1. D   **3.** H   **5.** G   **7.** B   **9.** J   **11. a.** $x^2 + 2x - 7$ **b.** 2   **c.** $1, 2, -7$ **d.** 1   **e.** $x^2, 2x, -7$ **13. a.** $x^3 - 1$ **b.** 3   **c.** $1, -1$
d. 1   **e.** $x^3, -1$ **15. a.** $2x^4 + 3x^3 + 4x^2 + 5$ **b.** 4   **c.** $2, 3, 4, 5$ **d.** 2   **e.** $2x^4, 3x^3, 4x^2, 5$ **17.** 3   **19.** 5   **21.** 2
23. $5x^2 + 11x + 3$ **25.** $9w^3 + 8w^2 - 2w + 6$ **27.** $-2r^2 + 3r^2 - 12$ **29.** $-3u^2 - 2u + 4$ **31.** $8x^3 + 18x^2 - 67x + 40$
33. $6x^4 - 19x^3 + 26x^2 - 29x + 10$ **35.** $10x^2 + 22x + 4$ **37.** $y^2 + 3y + 2$ **39.** $4z^2 - 19z + 12$ **41.** $a^2 + 3a - 18$
43. $10x^2 - 57xy + 77y^2$ **45.** $18x^2 + 55xy + 25y^2$ **47.** $6p^2 - 11pq - 35q^2$ **49.** $12d^2 + 4d - 8$ **51.** $r^3 + s^3$ **53.** $60c^3 - 49c^2 + 4$
55. $9x^2 - 25$ **57.** $9x^4 - 6x^2y + y^2$ **59.** $16w^2 + 8wz + z^2$ **61.** $x^2 + 10x + 25 - y^2$ **63.** 29   **65.** -17 **67.** -1 **69.** 33
71. a. 1.6 pounds   **b.** 3.6 pounds   **73. a.** 72π cubic inches   **b.** 300π cubic centimeters   **75. a.** 0.076 second   **b.** 0.085 second
77. 11,175 matches   **79.** 14.8 seconds; 90.4 seconds   **81.** Yes. The ball is approximately 4.4 feet high when it crosses home plate.   **83.** 15
85. $a^3 - 3a^2b + 3ab^2 - b^3$ **87.** $y^3 + 6y^2 + 12y + 8$ **89.** $27x^3 + 135x^2y + 225xy^2 + 125y^3$

Prepare for Section P.4, page 43

90. $3x^2$ **91.** $-36x^6$ **92. a.** $(x^2)^3$ **b.** $(x^3)^2$ **93.** $3b^3$ **94.** 7   **95.** 1

Exercise Set P.4, page 53

1. $5(x + 4)$ **3.** $-3x(5x + 4)$ **5.** $2xy(5x + 3 - 7y)$ **7.** $(x - 3)(2a + 3b)$ **9.** $(x + 3)(x + 4)$ **11.** $(a - 12)(a + 2)$ **13.** $(6x + 1)(x + 4)$
15. $(17x + 4)(3x - 1)$ **17.** $(3x + 8y)(2x - 5y)$ **19.** $(x^2 + 5)(x^2 + 1)$ **21.** $(6x^2 + 5)(x^2 + 3)$ **23.** factorable over the integers
25. not factorable over the integers   **27.** not factorable over the integers   **29.** $(x^2 - 3)(x^2 + 2)$ **31.** $(xy - 4)(xy + 2)$
33. $(3x^2 - 1)(x^2 + 4)$ **35.** $(3x^3 - 4)(x^3 + 2)$ **37.** $(x - 3)(x + 3)$ **39.** $(2a - 7)(2a + 7)$ **41.** $(1 - 10x)(1 + 10x)$ **43.** $(x^2 - 3)(x^2 + 3)$
45. $(x + 3)(x + 7)$ **47.** $(x + 5)^2$ **49.** $(a - 7)^2$ **51.** $(2x + 3)^2$ **53.** $(z^2 + 2w^2)^2$ **55.** $(x - 2)(x^2 + 2x + 4)$
57. $(2x - 3y)(4x^2 + 6xy + 9y^2)$ **59.** $(2 - x^2)(4 + 2x^2 + x^4)$ **61.** $(x - 3)(x^2 - 3x + 3)$ **63.** $(3x + 1)(x^2 + 2)$ **65.** $(x - 1)(ax + b)$
67. $(3w + 2)(2w^2 - 5)$ **69.** $2(3x - 1)(3x + 1)$ **71.** $(2x - 1)(2x + 1)(4x^2 + 1)$ **73.** $a(3x - 2y)(4x - 5y)$ **75.** $b(3x + 4)(x - 1)(x + 1)$
77. $2b(6x + y)^2$ **79.** $(w - 3)(w^2 - 12w + 39)$ **81.** $(x + 3y - 1)(x + 3y + 1)$ **83.** not factorable over the integers   **85.** $(2x - 5)^2(3x + 5)$
87. $(2x - y)(2x + y + 1)$ **89.** 8   **91.** 64   **93.** $(x^n - 1)(x^n + 1)(x^{2n} + 1)$ **95.** $\pi(R - r)(R + r)$ **97.** $r^2(4 - \pi)$

Prepare for Section P.5, page 55

99. $\dfrac{8}{5}$ **100.** $\dfrac{xz}{wy}$ **101.** $x + 3$ **102.** $2x(2x - 3)$ **103.** $(x - 6)(x + 1)$ **104.** $(x - 4)(x^2 + 4x + 16)$

Exercise Set P.5, page 62

1. $\dfrac{x + 4}{3}$ **3.** $\dfrac{x - 3}{x - 2}$ **5.** $\dfrac{a^2 - 2a + 4}{a - 2}$ **7.** $-\dfrac{x + 8}{x + 2}$ **9.** $-\dfrac{4y^2 + 7}{y + 7}$ **11.** $-\dfrac{8}{a^3b}$ **13.** $\dfrac{10}{27q^2}$ **15.** $\dfrac{x(3x + 7)}{2x + 3}$ **17.** $\dfrac{x + 3}{2x + 3}$
19. $\dfrac{(2y + 3)(3y - 4)}{(2y - 3)(y + 1)}$ **21.** $\dfrac{1}{a - 8}$ **23.** $\dfrac{3p - 2}{r}$ **25.** $\dfrac{8x(x - 4)}{(x - 5)(x + 3)}$ **27.** $\dfrac{3y - 4}{y + 4}$ **29.** $\dfrac{7z(2z - 5)}{(2z - 3)(z - 5)}$ **31.** $\dfrac{-2x^2 + 14x - 3}{(x - 3)(x + 3)(x + 4)}$
33. $\dfrac{(2x - 1)(x + 5)}{x(x - 5)}$ **35.** $\dfrac{-q^2 + 12q + 5}{(q - 3)(q + 5)}$ **37.** $\dfrac{3x^2 - 7x - 13}{(x + 3)(x + 4)(x - 3)(x - 4)}$ **39.** $\dfrac{(x + 2)(3x - 1)}{x^2}$ **41.** $\dfrac{4x + 1}{x - 1}$ **43.** $\dfrac{x - 2y}{y(y - x)}$
45. $\dfrac{(5x + 9)(x + 3)}{(x + 2)(4x + 3)}$ **47.** $\dfrac{(b + 3)(b - 1)}{(b - 2)(b + 2)}$ **49.** $\dfrac{x - 1}{x}$ **51.** $2 - m^2$ **53.** $\dfrac{-x^2 + 5x + 1}{x^2}$ **55.** $\dfrac{-x - 7}{x^2 + 6x - 3}$ **57.** $\dfrac{2x - 3}{x + 3}$ **59.** $\dfrac{a + b}{ab(a - b)}$
61. $\dfrac{(b - a)(b + a)}{ab(a^2 + b^2)}$ **63. a.** ≈ 136.55 miles per hour   **b.** $\dfrac{2v_1v_2}{v_1 + v_2}$ **65.** 0.040   **67.** 9446 kilometers per second   **69.** $\dfrac{2x + 1}{x(x + 1)}$
71. $\dfrac{3x^2 - 4}{x(x - 2)(x + 2)}$ **73.** $\dfrac{x^2 + 9x + 25}{(x + 5)^2}$ **75.** $\dfrac{x(1 - 4xy)}{(1 - 2xy)(1 + 2xy)}$ **77.** $R\left[\dfrac{(1 + i)^n - 1}{i(1 + i)^n}\right]$

Prepare for Section P.6, page 65

79. $15x^2 - 22x + 8$ **80.** $25x^2 - 20x + 4$ **81.** $4\sqrt{6}$ **82.** $-54 + \sqrt{5}$ **83.** $\dfrac{17 + 8\sqrt{2}}{7}$ **84.** b

Exercise Set P.6, page 71

1. $9i$ **3.** $7i\sqrt{2}$ **5.** $4 + 9i$ **7.** $5 + 7i$ **9.** $8 - 3i\sqrt{2}$ **11.** $11 - 5i$ **13.** $-7 + 4i$ **15.** $8 - 5i$ **17.** -10 **19.** $-2 + 16i$ **21.** -40
23. -10 **25.** $19i$ **27.** $20 - 10i$ **29.** $22 - 29i$ **31.** 41   **33.** $12 - 5i$ **35.** $-114 + 42i\sqrt{2}$ **37.** $-6i$ **39.** $3 - 6i$ **41.** $\dfrac{7}{53} - \dfrac{2}{53}i$

43. $1 + i$ **45.** $\dfrac{15}{41} - \dfrac{29}{41}i$ **47.** $\dfrac{5}{13} + \dfrac{12}{13}i$ **49.** $2 + 5i$ **51.** $-16 - 30i$ **53.** $-11 - 2i$ **55.** $-i$ **57.** -1 **59.** $-i$ **61.** -1
63. $\dfrac{1}{2} + \dfrac{\sqrt{3}}{2}i$ **65.** $-\dfrac{3}{2} + \dfrac{\sqrt{3}}{2}i$ **67.** $\dfrac{1}{2} + \dfrac{1}{2}i$ **69.** $(x + 4i)(x - 4i)$ **71.** $(z + 5i)(z - 5i)$ **73.** $(2x + 9i)(2x - 9i)$ **79.** 0

Chapter P True/False Exercises, page 76

1. True **2.** False; if $a = \dfrac{1}{2}$, then $\left(\dfrac{1}{2}\right)^2 = \dfrac{1}{4} < \dfrac{1}{2}$. **3.** True **4.** False; $\sqrt{2} + \left(-\sqrt{2}\right) = 0$, which is a rational number.
5. False. $\sqrt{-2}\sqrt{-6} = -4$ $(2 \oplus 4) \oplus 6 \neq 2 \oplus (4 \oplus 6)$. **6.** False; $x > a$ is written as (a, ∞). **7.** False; $\sqrt{(-2)^2} \neq -2$. **8.** False. Let $a = 2$
and $b = 3$. **9.** False. Let $a = 1$ and $b = 2$. **10.** False. $\sqrt{-2} \cdot \sqrt{-8} = i\sqrt{2} \cdot i\sqrt{8} = i^2\sqrt{16} = -4$.

Chapter P Review Exercises, page 76

1. integer, rational number, real number, prime number [P.1] **2.** irrational number, real number [P.1] **3.** rational number, real number [P.1]
4. rational number, real number [P.1] **5.** $\{1, 2, 3, 5, 7, 11\}$ [P.1] **6.** $\{5\}$ [P.1] **7.** Distributive property [P.1] **8.** Commutative property of
addition [P.1] **9.** Associative property of multiplication [P.1] **10.** Closure property of addition [P.1] **11.** Identity property of addition [P.1]
12. Identity property of multiplication [P.1] **13.** Symmetric property of equality [P.1] **14.** Transitive property of equality [P.1]
15. $(-4, 2]$ [P.1] **16.** $(-\infty, -1] \cup (3, \infty)$ [P.1]
17. $-3 \le x < 2$ [P.1] **18.** $x > -1$ [P.1] **19.** 7 [P.1] **20.** $\pi - 2$ [P.1]
21. $4 - \pi$ [P.1] **22.** 11 [P.1] **23.** 17 [P.1] **24.** $\sqrt{5} + \sqrt{2}$ [P.1] **25.** -36 [P.1] **26.** $\dfrac{2}{27}$ [P.2] **27.** $12x^8y^3$ [P.2] **28.** $\dfrac{4a^2b^8}{9c^4}$ [P.2]
29. 5 [P.2] **30.** -9 [P.2] **31.** $x^{17/12}$ [P.2] **32.** $4x^{1/2}$ [P.2] **33.** $x^{3/4}y^2$ [P.2] **34.** $x - y$ [P.2] **35.** $4ab^3\sqrt{3b}$ [P.2] **36.** $2a\sqrt{3ab}$ [P.2]
37. $6x\sqrt{2y}$ [P.2] **38.** $3xy^2\sqrt{2xy}$ [P.2] **39.** $\dfrac{3y\sqrt{15y}}{5}$ [P.2] **40.** $-\dfrac{2\sqrt{10xyz}}{5z^2}$ [P.2] **41.** $\dfrac{7\sqrt[3]{4x}}{2}$ [P.2] **42.** $\dfrac{5\sqrt[3]{3y^2}}{3}$ [P.2] **43.** $-3y^2\sqrt[3]{5x^2y}$ [P.2]
44. $-5y^2\sqrt[3]{2x}$ [P.2] **45.** 6.2×10^5 [P.2] **46.** 1.7×10^{-6} [P.2] **47.** $35{,}000$ [P.2] **48.** 0.000000431 [P.2] **49.** $-a^2 - 2a - 1$ [P.3]
50. $2b^2 + 8b - 8$ [P.3] **51.** $6x^4 + 5x^3 - 13x^2 + 22x - 20$ [P.3] **52.** $27y^3 - 135y^2 + 225y - 125$ [P.3] **53.** $3(x + 5)^2$ [P.4]
54. $(5x - 3y)^2$ [P.4] **55.** $4(5a^2 - b^2)$ [P.4] **56.** $2(2a + 5)(4a^2 - 10a + 25)$ [P.4] **57.** $\dfrac{3x - 2}{x + 4}$ [P.5] **58.** $\dfrac{2x - 5}{4x^2 - 10x + 25}$ [P.5]
59. $\dfrac{2x + 3}{2x - 5}$ [P.5] **60.** $\dfrac{2x + 1}{x + 3}$ [P.5] **61.** $\dfrac{x(3x + 10)}{(x + 3)(x - 3)(x + 4)}$ [P.5] **62.** $\dfrac{x(5x - 7)}{(x + 3)(x + 4)(2x - 1)}$ [P.5] **63.** $\dfrac{2x - 9}{3x - 17}$ [P.5] **64.** $\dfrac{x + 4}{5x + 8}$ [P.5]
65. $5 + 8i$ [P.6] **66.** $2 - 3i\sqrt{2}$ [P.6] **67.** $6 - i$ [P.6] **68.** $-2 + 10i$ [P.6] **69.** $8 + 6i$ [P.6] **70.** $29 + 22i$ [P.6] **71.** $8 + 6i$ [P.6]
72. i [P.6] **73.** $-3 - 2i$ [P.6] **74.** $-\dfrac{14}{25} - \dfrac{23}{25}i$ [P.6]

Chapter P Test, page 78

1. Distributive property [P.1] **2.** $\{0, 1, 2, 3, 4, 5, 6, 7, 8, 9\}$ [P.1] **3.** 7 [P.1] **4.** $\dfrac{4}{9x^4y^2}$ [P.2] **5.** $\dfrac{96bc^2}{a^5}$ [P.2] **6.** 1.37×10^{-3} [P.2] **7.** $\dfrac{x^{5/6}}{y^{9/4}}$ [P.2]
8. $7xy\sqrt[3]{3xy}$ [P.2] **9.** $\dfrac{\sqrt[4]{8x}}{2}$ [P.2] **10.** $\dfrac{3\sqrt{x} - 6}{x - 4}$ [P.2] **11.** $x^3 - 2x^2 + 5xy - 2x^2y - 2y^2$ [P.3] **12.** -94 [P.3] **13.** $(7x - 1)(x + 5)$ [P.4]
14. $(a - 4b)(3x - 2)$ [P.4] **15.** $2x(2x - y)(4x^2 + 2xy + y^2)$ [P.4] **16.** $-\dfrac{x + 3}{x + 5}$ [P.5] **17.** $\dfrac{(x - 6)(x + 1)}{(x + 3)(x - 2)(x - 3)}$ [P.5] **18.** $\dfrac{x(x + 2)}{x - 3}$ [P.5]
19. $\dfrac{3a^2 - 3ab - 10a + 5b}{a(2a - b)}$ [P.5] **20.** $\dfrac{x(2x - 1)}{2x + 1}$ [P.5] **21.** $7 + 2i\sqrt{5}$ [P.6] **22.** $2 + 2i$ [P.6] **23.** $22 - 3i$ [P.6] **24.** $\dfrac{11}{26} + \dfrac{23}{26}i$ [P.6] **25.** i [P.6]

Exercise Set 1.1, page 88

1. 15 **3.** -4 **5.** $\dfrac{9}{2}$ **7.** $\dfrac{108}{23}$ **9.** $\dfrac{2}{9}$ **11.** 12 **13.** 16 **15.** 9 **17.** $\dfrac{1}{2}$ **19.** $\dfrac{22}{13}$ **21.** $\dfrac{95}{18}$ **23.** identity **25.** conditional
equation **27.** contradiction **29.** identity **31.** conditional equation **33.** $-4, 4$ **35.** $7, 3$ **37.** $8, -3$ **39.** $2, -8$ **41.** $20, -12$
43. no solution **45.** $12, -18$ **47.** $\dfrac{a + b}{2}, \dfrac{a - b}{2}$ **49.** 2008 **51.** after 3 hours and after 5 hours 24 minutes **53.** 72 square yards
55. 15 minutes **57.** maximum 166 beats per minute, minimum 127 beats per minute **61.** $\{x \,|\, x \ge -4\}$ **63.** $\{x \,|\, x \le -7\}$ **65.** $\left\{x \,\middle|\, x \ge -\dfrac{7}{2}\right\}$

A4   Answers to Selected Exercises

Prepare for Section 1.2, page 90

67. $23\frac{1}{2}$ **68.** $\frac{4}{15}$ **69.** the distributive property   **70.** the associative property of multiplication   **71.** $\frac{11}{15}x$ **72.** $\frac{ab}{a+b}$

Exercise Set 1.2, page 98

1. $h = \frac{3V}{\pi r^2}$ **3.** $t = \frac{I}{Pr}$ **5.** $m_1 = \frac{Fd^2}{Gm_2}$ **7.** $d = \frac{a_n - a_1}{n-1}$ **9.** $r = \frac{S - a_1}{S}$ **11.** 88.8   **13.** 9.5   **15.** 11.2   **17.** 100   **19.** 30 feet by 57 feet
21. 12 centimeters, 36 centimeters, 36 centimeters   **23.** 240 meters   **25.** 2 hours   **27.** 3 miles   **29.** 98   **31.** 850   **33.** $937.50
35. $7600 invested at 8%, $6400 invested at 6.5%   **37.** $3750   **39.** $18\frac{2}{11}$ grams   **41.** 64 liters   **43.** 1200 at $14 and 1800 at $25
45. $6\frac{2}{3}$ pounds of the $12 coffee and $13\frac{1}{3}$ pounds of the $9 coffee   **47.** 10 grams   **49.** 7.875 hours   **51.** $10.05 for book, $0.05 for
bookmark   **53.** 6.25 feet   **55.** 40 pounds   **57.** 1384 feet   **59.** 84 years old
Prepare for Section 1.3, page 102
61. $(x + 6)(x - 7)$ **62.** $(2x + 3)(3x - 5)$ **63.** $3 + 4i$ **64.** 1   **65.** 1   **66.** 0

Exercise Set 1.3, page 113

1. $-3, 5$ **3.** $-\frac{1}{2}, 1$ **5.** $-24, \frac{3}{8}$ **7.** $0, \frac{7}{3}$ **9.** $2, 8$ **11.** ± 9 **13.** $\pm 2\sqrt{6}$ **15.** $\pm 2i$ **17.** $-1, 11$ **19.** $3 \pm 4i$ **21.** $-3 \pm 2\sqrt{2}$
23. $-3, 5$ **25.** $-2 \pm i$ **27.** $\frac{-3 \pm \sqrt{13}}{2}$ **29.** $\frac{-2 \pm \sqrt{6}}{2}$ **31.** $\frac{4 \pm \sqrt{13}}{3}$ **33.** $-3, 5$ **35.** $\frac{-1 \pm \sqrt{5}}{2}$ **37.** $\frac{-2 \pm \sqrt{2}}{2}$ **39.** $\frac{5}{6} \pm \frac{\sqrt{11}}{6}i$
41. $\frac{-3 \pm \sqrt{41}}{4}$ **43.** $-\frac{5}{6}, \frac{7}{4}$ **45.** $-2, \frac{4}{5}$ **47.** 81; two real solutions   **49.** -116; no real solutions   **51.** 0; one real solution   **53.** 2116;
two real solutions   **55.** -111; no real solutions   **57.** 26.8 centimeters   **59.** width 43.2 inches; height 32.4 inches   **61.** 1996   **63.** 5800 or
11,000 racquets   **65.** 12 feet by 48 feet or 32 feet by 18 feet   **67.** 0.3 miles and 3.9 miles   **69.** 1.7 seconds   **71.** 1.8 seconds and
11.9 seconds   **73.** No   **75.** 9 people   **77.** 2006   **79. a.** 44.8 million pounds   **b.** 2007   **81. a.** $l = \left(\frac{1 + \sqrt{5}}{2}\right)w$ **b.** 163.4 feet
c. Answers will vary.   **83.** Yes   **85.** Yes
Prepare for Section 1.4, page 117
87. $x(x + 4)(x - 4)$ **88.** $x^2(x + 6)(x - 6)$ **89.** 4   **90.** 64   **91.** $x + 2\sqrt{x - 5} - 4$ **92.** $x - 4\sqrt{x + 3} + 7$

Exercise Set 1.4, page 125

1. $0, \pm 5$ **3.** $2, \pm 1$ **5.** $0, \pm 3$ **7.** $0, -5, 8$ **9.** $0, \pm 4$ **11.** $2, -1 \pm i\sqrt{3}$ **13.** 31   **15.** 2   **17.** no solution   **19.** no solution
21. $\frac{7}{2}$ **23.** -12 **25.** 1   **27.** 40   **29.** 3   **31.** 7   **33.** 7   **35.** 9   **37.** $\frac{5}{2}$ **39.** $1, -6$ **41.** $\pm\sqrt{7}, \pm\sqrt{2}$ **43.** $\pm 2, \pm\frac{\sqrt{6}}{2}$
45. $\sqrt[3]{2}, -\sqrt[3]{3}$ **47.** 1, 16   **49.** $-\frac{1}{27}, 64$ **51.** $\pm\frac{\sqrt{15}}{3}$ **53.** ± 1 **55.** $\frac{256}{81}, 16$ **57.** $13\frac{1}{3}$ hours   **59.** 8 games   **61.** 9 words with
three or more syllables   **63.** 3 inches   **65.** 10.5 millimeters   **67.** 87 feet   **69. a.** 8.93 inches   **b.** $5\sqrt{3}$ inches
71. $s = \left(\frac{-275 + 5\sqrt{3025 + 176T}}{2}\right)^2$
Prepare for Section 1.5, page 128
73. $\{x \mid x > 5\}$ **74.** 38   **75.** 2   **76.** $(2x + 3)(5x - 3)$ **77.** $\frac{7}{2}$ **78.** $\frac{5}{2}, 3$

Exercise Set 1.5, page 140

1. $\{x \mid x < 4\}$,   **3.** $\{x \mid x < -6\}$,

5. $\left\{x \mid x \geq -\frac{13}{8}\right\}$,   **7.** $\{x \mid x < 2\}$,

9. $\left\{x \mid -\frac{3}{4} < x \leq 4\right\}$,   **11.** $\left\{x \mid \frac{1}{3} \leq x \leq \frac{11}{3}\right\}$,

13. $\{x \,|\, x < -3 \text{ or } x \ge -1\}$,   **15.** $\{x \,|\, x < 1\}$,   **17.** $\left(-\infty, -\dfrac{3}{2}\right) \cup \left(\dfrac{5}{2}, \infty\right)$

19. $(-\infty, -8] \cup [2, \infty)$ **21.** $\left[-\dfrac{4}{3}, 8\right]$ **23.** $(-\infty, -4] \cup \left[\dfrac{28}{5}, \infty\right)$ **25.** $(-\infty, \infty)$ **27.** $\{4\}$ **29.** $(-\infty, -7) \cup (0, \infty)$ **31.** $[-4, 4]$

33. $(-5, -2)$ **35.** $(-\infty, -4] \cup [7, \infty)$ **37.** $(-4, 1)$ **39.** $\left[-\dfrac{29}{2}, -8\right)$ **41.** $\left[-4, -\dfrac{7}{2}\right)$ **43.** $(-\infty, -1) \cup (2, 4)$

45. $(-\infty, 5) \cup [12, \infty)$ **47.** $\left(-\dfrac{2}{3}, 0\right) \cup \left(\dfrac{5}{2}, \infty\right)$ **49.** $(-\infty, 5)$ **51.** if you write more than 57 checks a month   **53.** $0 < h \le 26$ inches

55. at least 34 sales   **57.** $20° \le C \le 40°$ **59.** $\{12, 14, 16\}, \{14, 16, 18\}$ **61.** 130.0 to 137.5 centimeters   **63.** $(0, 210)$ **65.** at least 9791 books   **67.** maximum radius 4.480 inches, minimum radius 4.432 inches   **69.** $(-\infty, 3) \cup (3, 6) \cup (6, \infty)$ **71.** $(-3, \infty)$ **73.** $(-5, -1) \cup (1, 5)$ **75.** $(-7, -3] \cup [3, 7)$ **77.** $(a - \delta, a) \cup (a, a + \delta)$ **79.** more than 1 second but less than 3 seconds

Prepare for Section 1.6, page 143

81. 65   **82.** 45   **83.** 27   **84.** 28.125   **85.** The area becomes 4 times as large.   **86.** No. The volume becomes 9 times as large.

Exercise Set 1.6, page 150

1. $d = kt$ **3.** $y = \dfrac{k}{x}$ **5.** $m = knp$ **7.** $V = klwh$ **9.** $A = ks^2$ **11.** $F = \dfrac{km_1m_2}{d^2}$ **13.** $y = kx, k = \dfrac{4}{3}$ **15.** $r = kt^2, k = \dfrac{1}{81}$

17. $T = krs^2, k = \dfrac{7}{25}$ **19.** $V = klwh, k = 1$ **21.** 1.02 liters   **23.** 62 semester hours   **25.** 11.7 fluid ounces   **27. a.** 3.3 seconds   **b.** 3.7 feet   **29.** 40 revolutions per minute   **31.** 112 decibels   **33. a.** 9 times larger   **b.** 3 times larger   **c.** 27 times larger   **35.** 6 times larger   **37.** 2.97   **39.** 3950 pounds   **41.** 142 million miles

Chapter 1 True/False Exercises, page 155

1. False; $(-3)^2 = 9$.   **2.** False; one has solution set $\{3\}$, and the other has solution set $\{3, -4\}$.   **3.** True   **4.** True   **5.** False; $100 > 1$ but $\dfrac{1}{100} \not> \dfrac{1}{1}$.   **6.** False; the discriminant is $b^2 - 4ac$.   **7.** False; $\sqrt{1} + \sqrt{1} = 1 + 1 = 2$ but $1 + 1 = 2 \ne 2^2$.   **8.** True   **9.** False; $3x^2 - 48 = 0$ has roots of 4 and -4.   **10.** True

Chapter 1 Review Exercises, page 155

1. $\dfrac{3}{2}$ [1.1]   **2.** $\dfrac{11}{3}$ [1.1]   **3.** $\dfrac{1}{2}$ [1.1]   **4.** $\dfrac{11}{4}$ [1.1]   **5.** $-\dfrac{38}{15}$ [1.4]   **6.** $-\dfrac{1}{2}$ [1.4]   **7.** $3, 2$ [1.3]   **8.** $\dfrac{4}{3}, -\dfrac{3}{2}$ [1.3]   **9.** $\dfrac{1 \pm \sqrt{13}}{6}$ [1.3]

10. $\dfrac{1}{2} \pm \dfrac{\sqrt{3}}{2}i$ [1.3]   **11.** $0, \dfrac{5}{3}$ [1.4]   **12.** $0, \pm 2$ [1.4]   **13.** $\pm\dfrac{2\sqrt{3}}{3}, \pm\dfrac{\sqrt{10}}{2}$ [1.4]   **14.** $\dfrac{4}{9}$ [1.4]   **15.** $-5, 3$ [1.4]   **16.** $6, -4$ [1.4]

17. 4 [1.4]   **18.** 7 [1.4]   **19.** -4 [1.4]   **20.** 0 [1.4]   **21.** $-2, -4$ [1.4]   **22.** $\dfrac{11}{4}, \dfrac{9}{4}$ [1.4]   **23.** $5, 1$ [1.1]   **24.** $-1, -9$ [1.1]   **25.** $2, -3$ [1.1]

26. $5, -\dfrac{1}{3}$ [1.1]   **27.** $-2, -1$ [1.4]   **28.** $1, -4, \dfrac{4}{3}$ [1.4]   **29.** $(-\infty, 2]$ [1.5]   **30.** $\left[\dfrac{6}{7}, \infty\right)$ [1.5]   **31.** $[-5, 2]$ [1.5]   **32.** $(-\infty, -1) \cup (3, \infty)$ [1.5]

33. $\left[\dfrac{145}{9}, 35\right]$ [1.5]   **34.** $(86, 149)$ [1.5]   **35.** $(-\infty, 0] \cup [3, 4]$ [1.5]   **36.** $(-7, 0) \cup (3, \infty)$ [1.5]   **37.** $(-\infty, -3) \cup (4, \infty)$ [1.5]

38. $(-\infty, -7) \cup [0, 5]$ [1.5]   **39.** $\left(-\infty, \dfrac{5}{2}\right] \cup (3, \infty)$ [1.5]   **40.** $\left[\dfrac{5}{2}, 5\right)$ [1.5]   **41.** $\left(\dfrac{2}{3}, 2\right)$ [1.5]   **42.** $(-\infty, 1] \cup [2, \infty)$ [1.5]

43. $(1, 2) \cup (2, 3)$ [1.5]   **44.** $(a - b, a) \cup (a, a + b)$ [1.5]   **45.** $h = \dfrac{V}{\pi r^2}$ [1.2]   **46.** $t = \dfrac{A - P}{Pr}$ [1.2]   **47.** $b_1 = \dfrac{2A - hb_2}{h}$ [1.2]

48. $w = \dfrac{P - 2l}{2}$ [1.2]   **49.** $m = \dfrac{e}{c^2}$ [1.2]   **50.** $m_1 = \dfrac{Fs^2}{Gm_2}$ [1.2]   **51.** 80 [1.2]   **52.** width $= 12$ feet by length $= 15$ feet [1.2]

53. 24 nautical miles [1.2]   **54.** $20.00 [1.2]   **55.** $1750 in the 4% account, $3750 in the 6% account [1.2]   **56.** Price of calculator is $20.50. Price of battery is $0.50. [1.2]   **57.** $864 [1.2]   **58.** length $= 12$ inches by width $= 8$ inches, or length $= 8$ inches by width $= 12$ inches [1.2]   **59.** 18 hours [1.4]   **60.** 4024 adult tickets, 502 student tickets [1.2]   **61.** ≈ 13 feet [1.2]   **62.** $(12, 24)$ The revenue is greater than $576 when the price is between $12 and $24. [1.5]   **63. a.** $|B - 218| > 48$ [1.5]   **b.** $(0, 170) \cup (266, \infty)$ **64.** more than $425 but less than $725 [1.5]   **65.** $0 < h \le 23.5$ inches [1.5]   **66.** $[27, 82]$ [1.5]   **67.** 9.39 to 9.55 inches [1.5]   **68.** more than 0.6 miles but less than 3.6 miles from the city center [1.5]   **69.** 1.64 meters per second squared [1.6]   **70.** 89.9 tons [1.6]

Chapter 1 Test, page 158

1. 3 [1.1]   **2.** −5, 11 [1.1]   **3.** $-\dfrac{1}{2}, \dfrac{8}{3}$ [1.3]   **4.** $\dfrac{4 \pm \sqrt{14}}{2}$ [1.3]   **5.** $\dfrac{5 \pm \sqrt{37}}{6}$ [1.3]   **6.** discriminant: 1; two real solutions [1.3]

7. $x = \dfrac{c - cd}{a - c}, a \neq c$ [1.2]   **8.** 3 [1.4]   **9.** $\dfrac{8}{27}, -64$ [1.4]   **10.** $-\dfrac{14}{3}$ [1.4]   **11. a.** $\{x \mid x \leq 8\}$ [1.5]   **b.** $[-2, 5)$ [1.5]   **12.** $[-4, -1) \cup [3, \infty)$ [1.5]

13. from $10\dfrac{7}{8}$ inches to $11\dfrac{7}{16}$ inches [1.5]   **14.** 2 miles per hour [1.2]   **15.** 2.25 liters [1.2]   **16.** 15 hours [1.4]   **17.** more than 100 miles [1.5]

18. more than 14.7 feet but less than 145.0 feet from a side line [1.5]   **19.** more than 1.25 miles but less than 10 miles from the city center [1.5]
20. 4.4 miles per second [1.6]

Cumulative Review Exercises, page 159

1. −11 [P.1]   **2.** 1.7×10^{-4} [P.2]   **3.** $8x^2 - 30x + 41$ [P.3]   **4.** $(8x - 5)(x + 3)$ [P.4]   **5.** $\dfrac{2x + 17}{x - 4}$ [P.5]   **6.** $a^{11/12}$ [P.2]   **7.** 29 [P.6]   **8.** $\dfrac{10}{3}$ [1.1]

9. $\dfrac{2 \pm \sqrt{10}}{2}$ [1.3]   **10.** 1, 5 [1.1]   **11.** 5 [1.4]   **12.** −6, 0, 6 [1.4]   **13.** $\pm\sqrt{3}, \pm\dfrac{\sqrt{10}}{2}$ [1.4]   **14.** $\{x \mid x \leq -1 \text{ or } x > 1\}$ [1.5]

15. $(-\infty, 4] \cup [8, \infty)$ [1.5]   **16.** $\left\{x \mid \dfrac{10}{7} \leq x < \dfrac{3}{2}\right\}$ [1.5]   **17.** length 58 feet, width 42 feet [1.2]   **18.** 9475 to 24,275 printers [1.5]

19. 68 to 100 [1.5]   **20.** between 14.3% and 23.1% [1.5]

Exercise Set 2.1, page 174

1.
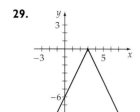
3. a.

b. 23.4 beats per minute   **5.** $7\sqrt{5}$ **7.** $\sqrt{1261}$ **9.** $\sqrt{89}$ **11.** $\sqrt{38 - 12\sqrt{6}}$
13. $2\sqrt{a^2 + b^2}$ **15.** $-x\sqrt{10}$ **17.** (12, 0), (−4, 0)   **19.** (3, 2)   **21.** (6, 4)
23. (−0.875, 3.91)   **25.**
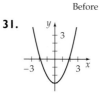
27.
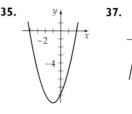

29.
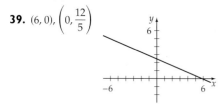
31.   **33.**   **35.**   **37.**
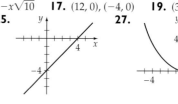

39. $(6, 0), \left(0, \dfrac{12}{5}\right)$
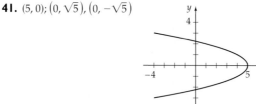
41. $(5, 0); (0, \sqrt{5}), (0, -\sqrt{5})$
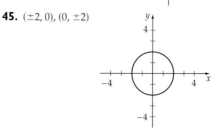

43. $(-4, 0); (0, 4), (0, -4)$
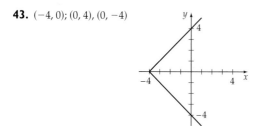
45. $(\pm 2, 0), (0, \pm 2)$

47. $(\pm 4, 0), (0, \pm 4)$

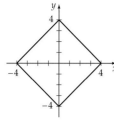

49. center $(0, 0)$, radius 6 **51.** center $(1, 3)$, radius 7 **53.** center $(-2, -5)$, radius 5
55. center $(8, 0)$, radius $\dfrac{1}{2}$ **57.** $(x - 4)^2 + (y - 1)^2 = 2^2$

59. $\left(x - \dfrac{1}{2}\right)^2 + \left(y - \dfrac{1}{4}\right)^2 = (\sqrt{5})^2$ **61.** $(x - 0)^2 + (y - 0)^2 = 5^2$

63. $(x - 1)^2 + (y - 3)^2 = 5^2$ **65.** center $(3, 0)$, radius 2 **67.** center $(7, -4)$, radius 3
69. center $\left(-\dfrac{1}{2}, 0\right)$, radius 4 **71.** center $\left(\dfrac{1}{2}, -\dfrac{3}{2}\right)$, radius $\dfrac{5}{2}$

73. $(x + 1)^2 + (y - 7)^2 = 25$ **75.** $(x - 7)^2 + (y - 11)^2 = 121$ **77.** **79.** **81.**

83. **85.** **87.** $(13, 5)$ **89.** $(7, -6)$ **91.** $x^2 - 6x + y^2 - 8y = 0$ **93.** $9x^2 + 25y^2 = 225$
95. $(x + 3)^2 + (y - 3)^2 = 3^2$

Prepare for Section 2.2, page 176

97. -4 **98.** $D = \{-3, -2, -1, 0, 2\}$; $R = \{1, 2, 4, 5\}$ **99.** $\sqrt{58}$ **100.** $x \geq 3$ **101.** $-2, 3$ **102.** 13

Exercise Set 2.2, page 190

1. a. 5 **b.** -4 **c.** -1 **d.** 1 **e.** $3k - 1$ **f.** $3k + 5$ **3. a.** $\sqrt{5}$ **b.** 3 **c.** 3 **d.** $\sqrt{21}$ **e.** $\sqrt{r^2 + 2r + 6}$ **f.** $\sqrt{c^2 + 5}$
5. a. $\dfrac{1}{2}$ **b.** $\dfrac{1}{2}$ **c.** $\dfrac{5}{3}$ **d.** 1 **e.** $\dfrac{1}{c^2 + 4}$ **f.** $\dfrac{1}{|2 + h|}$ **7. a.** 1 **b.** 1 **c.** -1 **d.** -1 **e.** 1 **f.** -1 **9. a.** -11 **b.** 6
c. $3c + 1$ **d.** $-k^2 - 2k + 10$ **11.** Yes **13.** No **15.** No **17.** Yes **19.** No **21.** Yes **23.** Yes **25.** Yes **27.** all real numbers
29. all real numbers **31.** $\{x \mid x \neq -2\}$ **33.** $\{x \mid x \geq -7\}$ **35.** $\{x \mid -2 \leq x \leq 2\}$ **37.** $\{x \mid x > -4\}$ **39.**

41. **43.** **45.**

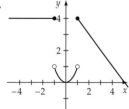 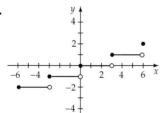 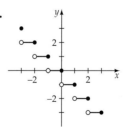

47. a. \$1.05 **b.**

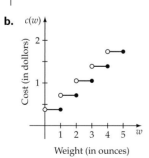

49. a, b, and **d.** **51.** decreasing on $(-\infty, 0]$; increasing on $[0, \infty)$
53. increasing on $(-\infty, \infty)$ **55.** decreasing on $(-\infty, -3]$; increasing on $[-3, 0]$; decreasing on $[0, 3]$; increasing on $[3, \infty)$ **57.** constant on $(-\infty, 0]$; increasing on $[0, \infty)$
59. decreasing on $(-\infty, 0]$; constant on $[0, 1]$; increasing on $[1, \infty)$ **61.** g and F
63. a. $w = 25 - l$ **b.** $A = 25l - l^2$ **65.** $v(t) = 80{,}000 - 6500t, \ 0 \leq t \leq 10$
67. a. $C(x) = 2000 + 22.80x$ **b.** $R(x) = 37.00x$ **c.** $P(x) = 14.20x - 2000$
69. $h = 15 - 5r$ **71.** $d = \sqrt{(3t)^2 + 50^2}$ **73.** $d = \sqrt{(45 - 8t)^2 + (6t)^2}$
75. a. $L(x) = \left(\dfrac{1}{4\pi} + \dfrac{1}{16}\right)x^2 - \dfrac{5}{2}x + 25$ **b.** 25, 17.27, 14.09, 15.46, 21.37, 31.83
c. $[0, 20]$ **77. a.** $A(x) = \sqrt{900 + x^2} + \sqrt{400 + (40 - x)^2}$
b. 74.72, 67.68, 64.34, 64.79, 70 **c.** $[0, 40]$ **79.** 275, 375, 385, 390, 394

81. $c = -2$ or $c = 3$ **83.** 1 is not in the range of f.

85. 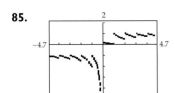   **87.** 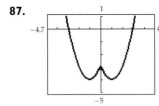   **89.**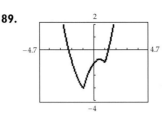

91. 4   **93.** 2   **95. a.** 36
b. 13   **c.** 12   **d.** 30
e. $13k - 2$ **f.** $8k - 11$
97. $4\sqrt{21}$ **99.** 1, −3

101.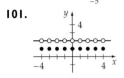

Prepare for Section 2.3, page 197

103. 7   **104.** −1   **105.** $-\dfrac{8}{5}$ **106.** $y = -2x + 9$ **107.** $y = \dfrac{3}{5}x - 3$ **108.** 2

Exercise Set 2.3, page 207

1. $-\dfrac{3}{2}$ **3.** $-\dfrac{1}{2}$ **5.** The line does not have slope.   **7.** 6   **9.** $\dfrac{9}{19}$ **11.** $\dfrac{f(3 + h) - f(3)}{h}$ **13.** $\dfrac{f(h) - f(0)}{h}$ **15.**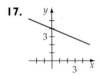

17.   **19.**   **21.** 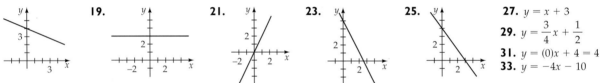   **23.**   **25.** 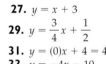   **27.** $y = x + 3$
29. $y = \dfrac{3}{4}x + \dfrac{1}{2}$
31. $y = (0)x + 4 = 4$
33. $y = -4x - 10$

35. $y = -\dfrac{3}{4}x + \dfrac{13}{4}$ **37.** $y = \dfrac{12}{5}x - \dfrac{29}{5}$ **39.** −2   **41.** $-\dfrac{1}{2}$ **43.** −4   **45.** 4   **47.** −20   **49.** $\dfrac{1}{3}$ **51.** $\dfrac{16}{3}$ **53.** $m = 2.875$. The
value of the slope indicates that the speed of sound in water increases 2.875 feet per second for a 1-degree increase in temperature.
55. a. $H(c) = 1.45c$ **b.** 26 miles per gallon   **57. a.** $N(t) = 2500t - 4{,}962{,}000$ **b.** 2008   **59. a.** $B(d) = 30d - 300$ **b.** The value of
the slope means that a 1-inch increase in the diameter of a log 32 feet long results in an increase of 30 board-feet of lumber that can be obtained
from the log.   **c.** 270 board-feet   **61.** line A, Michelle; line B, Amanda; line C, distance between Michelle and Amanda
63. a. $y = 1.842x - 18.947$ **b.** 147   **65.** $P(x) = 40.50x - 1782$, $x = 44$, the break-even point   **67.** $P(x) = 79x - 10{,}270$, $x = 130$, the break-
even point   **69. a.** \$275   **b.** \$283   **c.** \$355   **d.** \$8   **71. a.** $C(t) = 19{,}500.00 + 6.75t$ **b.** $R(t) = 55.00t$ **c.** $P(t) = 48.25t - 19{,}500.00$
d. approximately 405 days   **73.** $y = -\dfrac{3}{4}x + \dfrac{15}{4}$ **75.** $y = x + 1$ **77.** −5 ft   **79. a.** $Q = (3, 10)$, $m = 5$ **b.** $Q = (2.1, 5.41)$, $m = 4.1$

c. $Q = (2.01, 5.0401)$, $m = 4.01$ **d.** 4   **85.** $y = -2x + 11$ **87.** $5x + 3y = 15$ **89.** $3x + y = 17$ **93.** $\left(\dfrac{9}{2}, \dfrac{81}{4}\right)$

Prepare for Section 2.4, page 213

95. $(3x - 2)(x + 4)$ **96.** $x^2 - 8x + 16 = (x - 4)^2$ **97.** 26   **98.** $-\dfrac{1}{2}, 1$ **99.** $\dfrac{-3 \pm \sqrt{17}}{2}$ **100.** 1, 3

Exercise Set 2.4, page 222

1. d   **3.** b   **5.** g   **7.** c   **9.** $f(x) = (x + 2)^2 - 3$ **11.** $f(x) = (x - 4)^2 - 11$ **13.** $f(x) = \left(x - \left(-\dfrac{3}{2}\right)\right)^2 - \dfrac{5}{4}$

vertex: $(-2, -3)$ vertex: $(4, -11)$ vertex: $\left(-\dfrac{3}{2}, -\dfrac{5}{4}\right)$

axis of symmetry: $x = -2$ axis of symmetry: $x = 4$ axis of symmetry: $x = -\dfrac{3}{2}$

15. $f(x) = -(x - 2)^2 + 6$ **17.** $f(x) = -3\left(x - \dfrac{1}{2}\right)^2 + \dfrac{31}{4}$ **19.** vertex: $(5, -25)$, $f(x) = (x - 5)^2 - 25$

21. vertex: $(0, -10)$, $f(x) = x^2 - 10$

vertex: $(2, 6)$ vertex: $\left(\dfrac{1}{2}, \dfrac{31}{4}\right)$ **23.** vertex: $(3, 10)$, $f(x) = -(x - 3)^2 + 10$

25. vertex: $\left(\dfrac{3}{4}, \dfrac{47}{8}\right)$, $f(x) = 2\left(x - \dfrac{3}{4}\right)^2 + \dfrac{47}{8}$

axis of symmetry: $x = 2$ axis of symmetry: $x = \dfrac{1}{2}$ **27.** vertex: $\left(\dfrac{1}{8}, \dfrac{17}{16}\right)$, $f(x) = -4\left(x - \dfrac{1}{8}\right)^2 + \dfrac{17}{16}$

    29. $\{y \mid y \geq -2\}$, -1 and 3 **31.** $\left\{y \mid y \leq \dfrac{17}{8}\right\}$, 1 and $\dfrac{3}{2}$

33. No, $3 \notin \left\{y \mid y \geq \dfrac{15}{4}\right\}$ **35.** -16, minimum   **37.** 11, maximum

39. $-\dfrac{1}{8}$, minimum   **41.** -11, minimum   **43.** 35, maximum

45. a. 27 feet   **b.** $22\dfrac{5}{16}$ feet   **c.** 20.1 feet from the center   **47. a.** $w = \dfrac{600 - 2l}{3}$ **b.** $A = 200l - \dfrac{2}{3}l^2$ **c.** $w = 100$ feet, $l = 150$ feet

49. a. 12:43 P.M.   **b.** $91°$F   **51.** 1993, 2500 homes   **53.** Yes   **55. a.** 41 miles per gallon   **b.** 34 miles per gallon   **57.** y-intercept $(0, 0)$;
x-intercepts $(0, 0)$ and $(-6, 0)$ **59.** y-intercept $(0, -6)$; no x-intercepts   **61.** 740 units yield a maximum revenue of \$109,520.   **63.** 85 units
yield a maximum profit of \$24.25.   **65.** $P(x) = -0.1x^2 + 50x - 1840$, break-even points: $x = 40$ and $x = 460$ **67. a.** $R(x) = -0.25x^2 + 30.00x$
b. $P(x) = -0.25x^2 + 27.50x - 180$ **c.** \$576.25   **d.** 55   **69. a.** $t = 4$ seconds   **b.** 256 feet   **c.** $t = 8$ seconds   **71.** 30 feet

73. $r = \dfrac{48}{4 + \pi} \approx 6.72$ feet, $h = r \approx 6.72$ feet   **77.** $f(x) = \dfrac{3}{4}x^2 - 3x + 4$ **79. a.** $w = 16 - x$ **b.** $A = 16x - x^2$ **81.** The discriminant is
$b^2 - 4(1)(-1) = b^2 + 4$, which is positive for all b.   **83.** increases the height of each point on the graph by c units   **85.** 4, 4

Prepare for Section 2.5, page 227

89. $x = -2$ **92.** $3, -1, -3, -3, -1$ **93.** $(0, b)$ **94.** $(0, 0)$

Exercise Set 2.5, page 238

1. 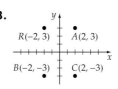   **3.**   **5.**   **7.**   **9.**   **11.**

13. a. No   **b.** Yes   **15. a.** No   **b.** No   **17. a.** Yes   **b.** Yes   **19. a.** Yes   **b.** Yes   **21. a.** Yes   **b.** Yes   **23.** No   **25.** Yes

27. Yes **29.** Yes **31.**   **33.** 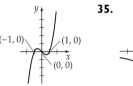 **35.** 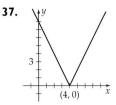 **37.**

39. 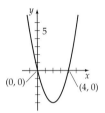 **41.**   **43.** even **45.** odd **47.** even **49.** even **51.** even **53.** even **55.** neither
57. a., b. 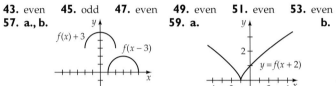 **59. a.**   **b.**

61. a. $(-5, 5), (-3, -2), (-2, 0)$ **b.** $(-2, 6), (0, -1), (1, 1)$ **63. a.** 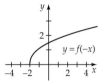 **b.**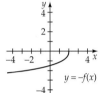

65. a. $(1, 3), (-2, -4)$ **b.** $(-1, -3), (2, 4)$ **67. a., b.**   **69.**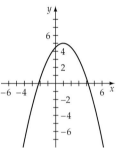

71. a. 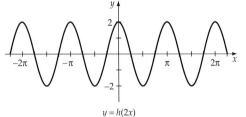 **b.**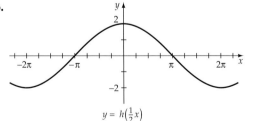

73. a. 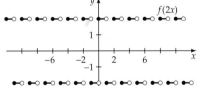 **b.**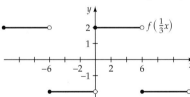

75. 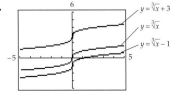 **77.** 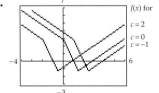 **79.**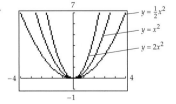

81.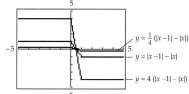

83. a. 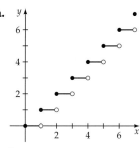 **b.**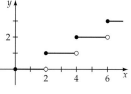

c. 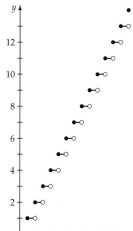 **85. a.** $f(x) = \dfrac{2}{(x+1)^2+1} + 1$ **b.** $f(x) = -\dfrac{2}{(x-2)^2+1}$

Prepare for Section 2.6, page 242

87. $x^2 + 1$ **88.** $6x^3 - 11x^2 + 7x - 6$ **89.** $18a^2 - 15a + 2$ **90.** $2h^2 + 3h$ **91.** all real numbers except $x = 1$ **92.** $[4, \infty)$

Exercise Set 2.6, page 251

1. $f(x) + g(x) = x^2 - x - 12$, Domain is the set of all real numbers.
$f(x) - g(x) = x^2 - 3x - 18$, Domain is the set of all real numbers.
$f(x) \cdot g(x) = x^3 + x^2 - 21x - 45$, Domain is the set of all real numbers.
$\dfrac{f(x)}{g(x)} = x - 5$, Domain $\{x \mid x \neq -3\}$

3. $f(x) + g(x) = 3x + 12$, Domain is the set of all real numbers.
$f(x) - g(x) = x + 4$, Domain is the set of all real numbers.
$f(x) \cdot g(x) = 2x^2 + 16x + 32$, Domain is the set of all real numbers.
$\dfrac{f(x)}{g(x)} = 2$, Domain $\{x \mid x \neq -4\}$

5. $f(x) + g(x) = x^3 - 2x^2 + 8x$, Domain is the set of all real numbers.
$f(x) - g(x) = x^3 - 2x^2 + 6x$, Domain is the set of all real numbers
$f(x) \cdot g(x) = x^4 - 2x^3 + 7x^2$, Domain is the set of all real numbers.
$\dfrac{f(x)}{g(x)} = x^2 - 2x + 7$, Domain $\{x \mid x \neq 0\}$

7. $f(x) + g(x) = 4x^2 + 7x - 12$, Domain is the set of all real numbers.
$f(x) - g(x) = x - 2$, Domain is the set of all real numbers.
$f(x) \cdot g(x) = 4x^4 + 14x^3 - 12x^2 - 41x + 35$, Domain is the set of all real numbers.
$\dfrac{f(x)}{g(x)} = 1 + \dfrac{x - 2}{2x^2 + 3x - 5}$, Domain $\left\{ x \mid x \neq 1, x \neq -\dfrac{5}{2} \right\}$

9. $f(x) + g(x) = \sqrt{x - 3} + x$, Domain $\{x \mid x \geq 3\}$
$f(x) - g(x) = \sqrt{x - 3} - x$, Domain $\{x \mid x \geq 3\}$
$f(x) \cdot g(x) = x\sqrt{x - 3}$, Domain $\{x \mid x \geq 3\}$
$\dfrac{f(x)}{g(x)} = \dfrac{\sqrt{x - 3}}{x}$, Domain $\{x \mid x \geq 3\}$

11. $f(x) + g(x) = \sqrt{4 - x^2} + 2 + x$, Domain $\{x \mid -2 \leq x \leq 2\}$
$f(x) - g(x) = \sqrt{4 - x^2} - 2 - x$, Domain $\{x \mid -2 \leq x \leq 2\}$
$f(x) \cdot g(x) = \left(\sqrt{4 - x^2}\right)(2 + x)$, Domain $\{x \mid -2 \leq x \leq 2\}$
$\dfrac{f(x)}{g(x)} = \dfrac{\sqrt{4 - x^2}}{2 + x}$ Domain $\{x \mid -2 < x \leq 2\}$

13. 18 **15.** $-\dfrac{9}{4}$ **17.** 30 **19.** 12 **21.** 300 **23.** $-\dfrac{384}{125}$ **25.** $-\dfrac{5}{2}$ **27.** $-\dfrac{1}{4}$ **29.** 2 **31.** $2x + h$ **33.** $4x + 2h + 4$

35. $-8x - 4h$ **37.** $(g \circ f)(x) = 6x + 3$ **39.** $(g \circ f)(x) = x^2 + 4x + 1$ **41.** $(g \circ f)(x) = -5x^3 - 10x$ **43.** $(g \circ f)(x) = \dfrac{1 - 5x}{x + 1}$
$(f \circ g)(x) = 6x - 16$ $(f \circ g)(x) = x^2 + 8x + 11$ $(f \circ g)(x) = -125x^3 - 10x$
$(f \circ g)(x) = \dfrac{2}{3x - 4}$

45. $(g \circ f)(x) = \dfrac{\sqrt{1 - x^2}}{|x|}$ **47.** $(g \circ f)(x) = -\dfrac{2|5 - x|}{3}$ **49.** 66 **51.** 51 **53.** -4 **55.** 41 **57.** $-\dfrac{3848}{625}$ **59.** $6 + 2\sqrt{3}$
$(f \circ g)(x) = \dfrac{1}{x - 1}$ $(f \circ g)(x) = \dfrac{3|x|}{|5x + 2|}$

61. $16c^2 + 4c - 6$ **63.** $9k^4 + 36k^3 + 45k^2 + 18k - 4$ **65. a.** $A(t) = \pi(1.5t)^2$, $A(2) = 9\pi$ square feet ≈ 28.27 square feet **b.** $V(t) = 2.25\pi t^3$, $V(3) = 60.75\pi$ cubic feet ≈ 190.85 cubic feet **67. a.** $d(t) = \sqrt{(48 - t)^2 - 4^2}$ **b.** $s(35) = 13$ feet, $d(35) \approx 12.37$ feet **69.** $(Y \circ F)(x)$ converts x inches to yards. **71. a.** 99.8; this is identical to the slope of the line through $(0, C(0))$ and $(1, C(1))$. **b.** 156.2 **c.** -49.7 **d.** -30.8 **e.** -16.4 **f.** 0

Prepare for Section 2.7, page 254

83. slope: $-\dfrac{1}{3}$; y-intercept: $(0, 4)$ **84.** slope: $\dfrac{3}{4}$; y-intercept: $(0, -3)$ **85.** $y = -0.45x + 2.3$ **86.** $y = -\dfrac{2}{3}x - 2$ **87.** 19 **88.** 3

Exercise Set 2.7, page 263

1. no linear relationship **3.** linear **5.** Figure A **7.** $y = 2.00862069x + 0.5603448276$ **9.** $y = -0.7231182796x + 9.233870968$
11. $y = 2.222641509x - 7.364150943$ **13.** $y = 1.095779221x^2 - 2.69642857x + 1.136363636$
15. $y = -0.2987274717x^2 - 3.20998141x + 3.416463667$ **17. a.** $y = 23.55706665x - 24.4271215$ **b.** 1247.7 centimeters
19. a. $y = 1.671510024x + 16.32830605$ **b.** 46.4 centimeters **21. a.** $y = 0.1628623408x - 0.6875682232$ **b.** 25 **23.** No, because the linear correlation coefficient is close to 0. **25. a.** Yes, there is a strong linear correlation. **b.** $y = -0.9033088235x + 78.62573529$
c. 56 years **27.** $r^2 \approx 0.667$. The coefficient of determination means that approximately 66.7% of the variation in EPA mileage estimates can be attributed to the horsepower of the car. **29.** $y = -0.6328671329x^2 + 33.6160839x - 379.4405594$
31. a. $y = -0.0165034965x^2 + 1.366713287x + 5.685314685$ **b.** 32.8 miles per gallon
33. a. 5 pound: $s = 0.6130952381t^2 - 0.0714285714t + 0.1071428571$
10 pound: $s = 0.6091269841t^2 - 0.0011904762t - 0.3$
15 pound: $s = 0.5922619048t^2 + 0.3571428571t - 1.520833333$
b. All the regression equations are approximately the same. Therefore, the equations of motion of the three masses are the same.
35. quadratic; r^2 is closer to 1 for the quadratic model.

Chapter 2 True/False Exercises, page 271

1. False. Let $f(x) = x^2$. Then $f(3) = f(-3) = 9$, but $3 \neq -3$. **2.** False. Consider $f(x) = x + 1$ and $g(x) = x^2 - 2$. **3.** True **4.** True
5. False. Let $f(x) = 3x$. $[f(x)]^2 = 9x^2$, whereas $f[f(x)] = f(3x) = 3(3x) = 9x$. **6.** False. Let $f(x) = x^2$. Then $f(1) = 1$, $f(2) = 4$. Thus $\dfrac{f(2)}{f(1)} = 4 \neq \dfrac{2}{1}$. **7.** True **8.** False. Let $f(x) = |x|$. Then $f(-1 + 3) = f(2) = 2$. $f(-1) + f(3) = 1 + 3 = 4$. **9.** True **10.** True **11.** True
12. True **13.** True **14.** False. The coefficient of determination is r^2 and therefore nonnegative.

Chapter 2 Review Exercises, page 272

1. $\sqrt{181}$ [2.1] **2.** $\sqrt{80} = 4\sqrt{5}$ [2.1] **3.** $\left(-\dfrac{1}{2}, 10\right)$ [2.1] **4.** $(2, -2)$ [2.1] **5.** center $(3, -4)$, radius 9 [2.1] **6.** center $(-5, -2)$,
radius 3 [2.1] **7.** $(x - 2)^2 + (y + 3)^2 = 5^2$ [2.1] **8.** $(x + 5)^2 + (y - 1)^2 = 8^2$, radius $= |-5 - (3)| = 8$ [2.1] **9. a.** 2 **b.** 10 **c.** $3t^2 + 4t - 5$
d. $3x^2 + 6xh + 3h^2 + 4x + 4h - 5$ **e.** $9t^2 + 12t - 15$ **f.** $27t^2 + 12t - 5$ [2.2] **10. a.** $\sqrt{55}$ **b.** $\sqrt{39}$ **c.** 0 **d.** $\sqrt{64 - x^2}$
e. $2\sqrt{64 - t^2}$ **f.** $2\sqrt{16 - t^2}$ [2.2] **11. a.** 5 **b.** -11 **c.** $x^2 - 12x + 32$ **d.** $x^2 + 4x - 8$ [2.6] **12. a.** 79 **b.** 56 **c.** $2x^2 - 4x + 9$
d. $2x^2 + 6$ [2.6] **13.** $8x + 4h - 3$ [2.6] **14.** $3x^2 + 3xh + h^2 - 1$ [2.6] **15.** [2.2] **16.** [2.2]

increasing on $[3, \infty)$
decreasing on $(-\infty, 3]$

f is increasing on $[0, \infty)$
f is decreasing on $(-\infty, 0]$

17. 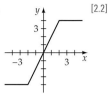 [2.2]

increasing on $[-2, 2]$
constant on $(-\infty, -2] \cup [2, \infty)$

18. 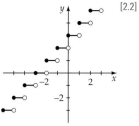 [2.2]

f is constant on..., $[-6, -5)$,
$[-5, -4), [-4, -3), [-3, -2)$,
$[-2, -1), [-1, 0), [0, 1), \ldots$

19. 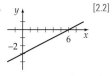 [2.2]

increasing on $(-\infty, \infty)$

20. 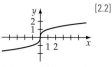 [2.2]

f is increasing on $(-\infty, \infty)$

21. Domain: $\{x \mid x \text{ is a real number}\}$ [2.2]   **22.** Domain: $\{x \mid x \le 6\}$ [2.2]   **23.** Domain: $\{x \mid -5 \le x \le 5\}$ [2.2]   **24.** Domain: $\{x \mid x \ne -3, x \ne 5\}$ [2.2]

25. $y = -2x + 1$ [2.3]   **26.** $y = \dfrac{11}{7}x$ [2.3]   **27.** $y = \dfrac{3}{4}x + \dfrac{19}{2}$ [2.3]   **28.** $y = \dfrac{5}{2}x + \dfrac{1}{2}$ [2.3]   **29.** $f(x) = (x + 3)^2 + 1$ [2.4]

30. $f(x) = 2(x + 1)^2 + 3$ [2.4]   **31.** $f(x) = -(x + 4)^2 + 19$ [2.4]   **32.** $f(x) = 4\left(x - \dfrac{3}{4}\right)^2 - \dfrac{5}{4}$ [2.4]   **33.** $f(x) = -3\left(x - \dfrac{2}{3}\right)^2 - \dfrac{11}{3}$ [2.4]

34. $f(x) = (x - 3)^2 + 0$ [2.4]   **35.** $(1, 8)$ [2.4]   **36.** $(0, -10)$ [2.4]   **37.** $(5, 161)$ [2.4]   **38.** $(-4, 30)$ [2.4]   **39.** $\dfrac{4\sqrt{5}}{5}$ [2.3]

40. a. $R = 13x$ **b.** $P = 12.5x - 1050$ **c.** $x = 84$ [2.3]   **41.** 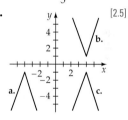 [2.5]

42. [2.5]

43. symmetric to the y-axis [2.5]   **44.** symmetric to the x-axis [2.5]   **45.** symmetric to the origin [2.5]   **46.** symmetric to the x-axis, the y-axis, and the origin [2.5]   **47.** symmetric to the x-axis, the y-axis, and the origin [2.5]   **48.** symmetric to the origin [2.5]   **49.** symmetric to the x-axis, the y-axis, and the origin [2.5]   **50.** symmetric to the origin [2.5]

51.

a. Domain is the set of all real numbers.
Range: $\{y \mid y \le 4\}$
b. even [2.5]

52.

a. Domain is the set of all real numbers.
Range is the set of all real numbers.
b. g is neither even nor odd [2.5]

53.

a. Domain is the set of all real numbers.
Range: $\{y \mid y \ge 4\}$
b. even [2.5]

54.

a. Domain: $\{x \mid -4 \le x \le 4\}$
Range: $\{y \mid 0 \le y \le 4\}$
b. even [2.5]

55.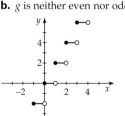

a. Domain is the set of all real numbers.
Range is the set of all real numbers.
b. odd [2.5]

56.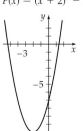

a. Domain: $\{x \mid x \text{ is a real number}\}$
Range: $\{y \mid y \text{ is an even integer}\}$
b. g is neither even nor odd [2.5]

57. $F(x) = (x + 2)^2 - 11$ [2.5]

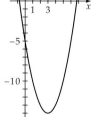

58. $A(x) = (x - 3)^2 - 14$ [2.5]

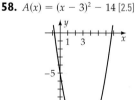

59. $P(x) = 3(x - 0)^2 - 4$ [2.5]   **60.** $G(x) = 2(x - 2)^2 - 5$ [2.5]   **61.** $W(x) = -4\left(x + \dfrac{3}{4}\right)^2 + \dfrac{33}{4}$ [2.5]   **62.** $T(x) = -2\left(x + \dfrac{5}{2}\right)^2 + \dfrac{25}{2}$

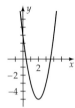
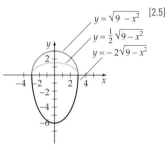
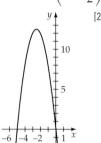

[2.5]

63.   [2.5]   **64.**   [2.5]   **65.**   [2.5]

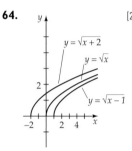

66.   [2.2]   **67.**   [2.2]   **68.**   [2.2]

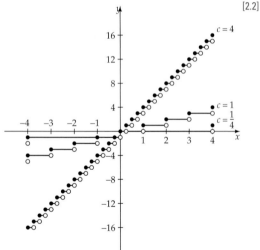
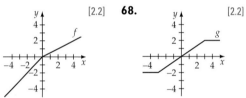

69. $f(x) + g(x) = x^2 + x - 6$, Domain is the set of all real numbers.
$f(x) - g(x) = x^2 - x - 12$, Domain is the set of all real numbers.
$f(x) \cdot g(x) = x^3 + 3x^2 - 9x - 27$, Domain is the set of all real numbers.
$\dfrac{f(x)}{g(x)} = x - 3$, Domain $\{x \mid x \neq -3\}$ [2.6]

70. $(f + g)(x) = x^3 + x^2 - 2x + 12$, Domain is the set of all real numbers.
$(f - g)(x) = x^3 - x^2 + 2x + 4$, Domain is the set of all real numbers.
$(fg)(x) = x^5 - 2x^4 + 4x^3 + 8x^2 - 16x + 32$, Domain is the set of all real numbers.
$\left(\dfrac{f}{g}\right)(x) = x + 2$, Domain is the set of all real numbers. [2.6]

71. 25, 25 [2.4]   **72.** -5 and 5 [2.4]   **73. a.** 18 feet per second   **b.** 15 feet per second   **c.** 13.5 feet per second   **d.** 12.03 feet per second
e. 12 feet per second [2.4]   **74. a.** 17 feet per second   **b.** 15 feet per second   **c.** 14 feet per second   **d.** 13.02 feet per second
e. 13 feet per second [2.4]   **75. a.** $y = 0.0180247x + 0.0005005$ **b.** Yes. $r = 0.999$, which is very close to 1.   **c.** 1.8 seconds [2.7]
76. a. $y = 0.0047952048x^2 - 1.756843157x + 180.4065934$ **b.** No   **c.** The regression line is a model of the data and is not based on physical
principles. [2.7]

Chapter 2 Test, page 274

1. midpoint $(1, 1)$; length $2\sqrt{13}$ [2.1]   **2.** $(-4, 0); \left(0, \sqrt{2}\right), \left(0, -\sqrt{2}\right)$ [2.1]   **3.**   [2.1]

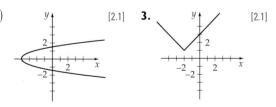

4. center $(2, -1)$; radius 3 [2.1]   **5.** domain $\{x \mid x \geq 4 \text{ or } x \leq -4\}$ [2.2]   **6.**

[2.2]   **7. a.** $R = 12.00x$ **b.** $P = 11.25x - 875$
c. $x = 78$ [2.4]

a. increasing on $(-\infty, 2]$
b. not consistent on any interval
c. decreasing on $[2, \infty)$

8.

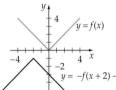

[2.5]   **9. a.** even   **b.** odd   **c.** neither [2.5]   **10.** $y = -\dfrac{2}{3}x + \dfrac{2}{3}$ [2.3]   **11.** -12, minimum [2.4]

12. $x^2 + x - 3; \dfrac{x^2 - 1}{x - 2}, x \neq 2$ [2.6]   **13.** $2x + h$ [2.6]   **14.** $4x^2 + 16x + 15$ [2.6]

15. a. 25 feet per second   **b.** 22.5 feet per second   **c.** 20.05 feet per second [2.6]
16. a. $y = -7.98245614x + 767.122807$ **b.** 57 calories [2.7]

Cumulative Review Exercises, page 275

1. Commutative Property of Addition [P.1]   **2.** $\dfrac{6}{\pi}, \sqrt{2}$ [P.1]   **3.** $8x - 33$ [P.1]   **4.** $128x^5y^{10}$ [P.2]   **5.** $\dfrac{4}{3b^2}$ [P.2]   **6.** $6x^2 - 5x - 21$ [P.3]

7. $\dfrac{x + 9}{x + 3}$ [P.5]   **8.** $\dfrac{-2}{(2x - 1)(x - 1)}$ [P.5]   **9.** 0 [1.1]   **10.** $\dfrac{1 \pm \sqrt{5}}{2}$ [1.3]   **11.** $-\dfrac{7}{2}, 1$ [1.3]   **12.** $x = -\dfrac{2}{3}y + 5$ [1.1]   **13.** $\pm\sqrt{2}, \pm i$ [1.4]

14. $x > -4$ [1.5]   **15.** $\sqrt{17}$ [2.1]   **16.** -15 [2.2]   **17.** $y = -\dfrac{1}{2}x - 2$ [2.3]   **18.** 100 ounces [1.1]   **19.** Yes [2.4]   **20.** $0.04°F$ per minute [2.3]

Exercise Set 3.1, page 287

1. $5x^2 - 9x + 10 - \dfrac{10}{x + 3}$ **3.** $x^3 + 2x^2 - x + 1 + \dfrac{1}{x - 2}$ **5.** $x^2 + 4x + 10 + \dfrac{25}{x - 3}$ **7.** $x^3 + 7x^2 + 31x + 119 + \dfrac{475}{x - 4}$

9. $x^4 + 2x^3 + 2x - 1 - \dfrac{8}{x - 1}$ **11.** $4x^2 + 3x + 12 + \dfrac{17}{x - 2}$ **13.** $4x^2 - 4x + 2 + \dfrac{1}{x + 1}$ **15.** $x^4 + 4x^3 + 6x^2 + 24x + 101 + \dfrac{403}{x - 4}$

17. $x^4 + x^3 + x^2 + x + 1$ **19.** $8x^2 + 6$ **21.** $x^7 + 2x^6 + 5x^5 + 10x^4 + 21x^3 + 42x^2 + 85x + 170 + \dfrac{344}{x - 2}$

23. $x^5 - 3x^4 + 9x^3 - 27x^2 + 81x - 242 + \dfrac{716}{x + 3}$ **25.** 25 **27.** 45 **29.** -2230 **31.** -80 **33.** -187 **35.** Yes   **37.** No
39. Yes   **41.** Yes   **43.** No   **55.** $(x - 2)(x^2 + 3x + 7)$ **57.** $(x - 4)(x^3 + 3x^2 + 3x + 1)$ **59. a.** $19,968   **b.** $23,007   **61. a.** 336
b. 336; They are the same.   **63. a.** 100 cards   **b.** 610 cards   **65. a.** 400 people per square mile   **b.** 240 people per square mile
67. a. 304 cubic inches   **b.** 892 cubic inches   **69.** 13   **71.** Yes

Prepare for Section 3.2, page 289

73. 2 **74.** $\dfrac{9}{8}$ **75.** $[-1, \infty)$ **76.** $[1, \infty)$ **77.** $(x + 1)(x - 1)(x + 2)(x - 2)$ **78.** $\left(\dfrac{2}{3}, 0\right), \left(-\dfrac{1}{2}, 0\right)$

Exercise Set 3.2, page 301

1. up to the far left, up to the far right   **3.** down to the far left, up to the far right   **5.** down to the far left, down to the far right
7. down to the far left, up to the far right   **9.** $a < 0$ **11.** Vertex is $(-2, -5)$, minimum is -5.   **13.** Vertex is $(-4, 17)$, maximum is 17.
15. relative maximum $y \approx 5.0$ at   **17.** relative maximum $y \approx 31.0$ at   **19.** relative maximum $y \approx 2.0$ at $x \approx 1.0$,
$x \approx -2.1$, relative minimum $x \approx -2.0$, relative minimum   relative minima $y \approx -14.0$ at $x \approx -1.0$
$y \approx -16.9$ at $x \approx 1.4$ $y \approx -77.0$ at $x \approx 4.0$ and $y \approx -14.0$ at $x \approx 3.0$

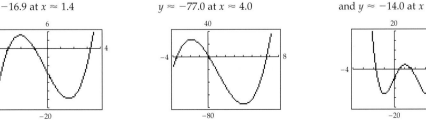

21. $-3, 0, 5$ **23.** $-3, -2, 2, 3$ **25.** $-2, -1, 0, 1, 2$ **33.** crosses the x-axis at $(-1, 0)$, $(1, 0)$, and $(3, 0)$ **35.** crosses the x-axis at $(7, 0)$;

intersects but does not cross at $(3, 0)$ **37.** crosses the x-axis at $(1, 0)$; intersects but does not cross at $\left(\dfrac{3}{2}, 0\right)$ **39.** crosses the x-axis at $(0, 0)$; intersects but does not cross at $(3, 0)$

41. 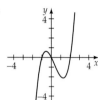   **43.** 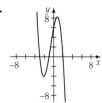   **45.**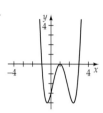

47. a. $V(x) = x(15 - 2x)(10 - 2x) = 4x^3 - 50x^2 + 150x$ **b.** 1.96 inches   **49.** 2.137 inches   **51.** \$464,000   **53. a.** 1918   **b.** 9.5 marriages per thousand population   **55. a.** 20.69 milligrams   **b.** 118 minutes   **57. a.** 3.24 inches   **b.** 4 feet from either end; 3.84 inches   **c.** 3.24 inches   **59.** between 3 and 4   **61.** $(5, 0)$ **63.** Shift the graph of $y = x^3$ horizontally 2 units to the right and vertically upward 1 unit.

Prepare for Section 3.3, page 305

65. $\dfrac{2}{3}, \dfrac{7}{2}$ **66.** $2x^2 - x + 6 - \dfrac{19}{x + 2}$ **67.** $3x^3 + 9x^2 + 6x + 15 + \dfrac{40}{x - 3}$ **68.** 1, 2, 3, 4, 6, 12   **69.** $\pm 1, \pm 3, \pm 9, \pm 27$
70. $P(-x) = -4x^3 - 3x^2 + 2x + 5$

Exercise Set 3.3, page 316

1. 3 (multiplicity 2), -5 (multiplicity 1)   **3.** 0 (multiplicity 2), $-\dfrac{5}{3}$ (multiplicity 2)   **5.** 2 (multiplicity 1), -2 (multiplicity 1), -3 (multiplicity 2)

7. $\pm 1, \pm 2, \pm 4, \pm 8$ **9.** $\pm 1, \pm 2, \pm 3, \pm 4, \pm 6, \pm 12, \pm\dfrac{1}{2}, \pm\dfrac{3}{2}$ **11.** $\pm 1, \pm 2, \pm 4, \pm\dfrac{1}{2}, \pm\dfrac{1}{3}, \pm\dfrac{2}{3}, \pm\dfrac{4}{3}, \pm\dfrac{1}{6}$ **13.** $\pm 1, \pm 7, \pm\dfrac{1}{2}, \pm\dfrac{7}{2},$

$\pm\dfrac{1}{4}, \pm\dfrac{7}{4}$ **15.** $\pm 1, \pm 2, \pm 4, \pm 8, \pm 16, \pm 32$ **17.** upper bound 2, lower bound -5 **19.** upper bound 4, lower bound -4

21. upper bound 1, lower bound -4 **23.** upper bound 4, lower bound -2 **25.** upper bound 2, lower bound -1 **27.** one positive zero, two or no negative zeros   **29.** two or no positive zeros, one negative zero   **31.** one positive zero, three or one negative zeros

33. three or one positive zeros, one negative zero   **35.** one positive zero, no negative zeros   **37.** $2, -1, -4$ **39.** $3, -4, \dfrac{1}{2}$

41. $\dfrac{1}{2}, -\dfrac{1}{3}, -2$ (multiplicity 2)   **43.** $\dfrac{1}{2}, 4, \sqrt{3}, -\sqrt{3}$ **45.** $6, 1 + \sqrt{5}, 1 - \sqrt{5}$ **47.** $5, \dfrac{1}{2}, 2 + \sqrt{3}, 2 - \sqrt{3}$

49. $1, -1, -2, -\dfrac{2}{3}, 3 + \sqrt{3}, 3 - \sqrt{3}$ **51.** $2, -1$ (multiplicity 2)   **53.** $0, -2, 1 + \sqrt{2}, 1 - \sqrt{2}$ **55.** -1 (multiplicity 3), 2

57. $-\dfrac{3}{2}, 1$ (multiplicity 2), 8   **59.** $n = 9$ inches   **61.** $x = 4$ inches   **63. a.** 26 pieces   **b.** 7 cuts   **65.** 7 rows   **67.** $x = 0.084$ inch

69. 1977 and 1986   **71.** 16.9 feet   **73. a.** 73 seconds   **b.** 93,000 digits   **75.** $B = 15$. The absolute value of each of the given zeros is less than B.   **77.** $B = 11$. The absolute value of each of the zeros is less than B.

79. $3 + 2i$ **80.** $2 - i\sqrt{5}$ **81.** $x^3 - 8x^2 + 19x - 12$ **82.** $x^2 - 4x + 5$ **83.** $-3i, 3i$ **84.** $\dfrac{1}{2} - \dfrac{1}{2}i\sqrt{19}, \dfrac{1}{2} + \dfrac{1}{2}i\sqrt{19}$

Exercise Set 3.4, page 327

1. $2, -3, 2i, -2i; P(x) = (x - 2)(x + 3)(x - 2i)(x + 2i)$ **3.** $\dfrac{1}{2}, -3, 1 + 5i, 1 - 5i; P(x) = \left(x - \dfrac{1}{2}\right)(x + 3)(x - 1 - 5i)(x - 1 + 5i)$

5. 1 (multiplicity 3), $3 + 2i, 3 - 2i; P(x) = (x - 1)^3(x - 3 - 2i)(x - 3 + 2i)$

7. $-3, -\dfrac{1}{2}, 2 + i, 2 - i; P(x) = (x + 3)\left(x + \dfrac{1}{2}\right)(x - 2 - i)(x - 2 + i)$

9. $4, 2, \dfrac{1}{2} + \dfrac{3}{2}i, \dfrac{1}{2} - \dfrac{3}{2}i; P(x) = (x - 4)(x - 2)\left(x - \dfrac{1}{2} - \dfrac{3}{2}i\right)\left(x - \dfrac{1}{2} + \dfrac{3}{2}i\right)$ **11.** $1 - i, \dfrac{1}{2}$ **13.** $i, -3$ **15.** $2 + 3i, i, -i$

17. $1 - 3i, 1 + 2i, 1 - 2i$ **19.** $2i, 1$ (multiplicity 3)   **21.** $5 - 2i, \dfrac{7}{2} + \dfrac{\sqrt{3}}{2}i, \dfrac{7}{2} - \dfrac{\sqrt{3}}{2}i$ **23.** $\dfrac{3}{2}, -\dfrac{1}{2} + \dfrac{\sqrt{7}}{2}i, -\dfrac{1}{2} - \dfrac{\sqrt{7}}{2}i$ **25.** $-\dfrac{2}{3}, \dfrac{3}{4}, \dfrac{5}{2}$

27. $-i, i, 2$ (multiplicity 2)   **29.** -3 (multiplicity 2), 1 (multiplicity 2)   **31.** $P(x) = x^3 - 3x^2 - 10x + 24$ **33.** $P(x) = x^3 - 3x^2 + 4x - 12$

35. $P(x) = x^4 - 10x^3 + 63x^2 - 214x + 290$ **37.** $P(x) = x^5 - 22x^4 + 212x^3 - 1012x^2 + 2251x - 1830$ **39.** $P(x) = 4x^3 - 19x^2 + 224x - 159$

41. $P(x) = x^3 + 13x + 116$ **43.** $P(x) = x^4 - 18x^3 + 131x^2 - 458x + 650$ **45.** $P(x) = x^5 - 4x^4 + 16x^3 - 18x^2 - 97x + 102$

47. $P(x) = 3x^3 - 12x^2 + 3x + 18$ **49.** $P(x) = -2x^4 + 4x^3 + 36x^2 - 140x + 150$ **51.** The Conjugate Pair Theorem does not apply because some of the coefficients of the polynomial are not real numbers.

Prepare for Section 3.5, page 328

53. $\dfrac{x - 3}{x - 5}$ **54.** $-\dfrac{3}{2}$ **55.** $\dfrac{1}{3}$ **56.** $x = 0, -3, \dfrac{5}{2}$ **57.** The degree of the numerator is 3. The degree of the denominator is 2.

58. $x + 4 + \dfrac{7x - 11}{x^2 - 2x}$

Exercise Set 3.5, page 341

1. $x = 0, x = -3$ **3.** $x = -\dfrac{1}{2}, x = \dfrac{4}{3}$ **5.** $y = 4$ **7.** $y = 30$

9. $x = -4, y = 0$ **11.** $x = 3, y = 0$ **13.** $x = 0, y = 0$ **15.** $x = -4, y = 1$ **17.** $x = 2, y = -1$

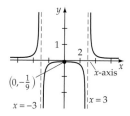   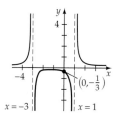   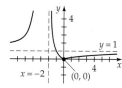   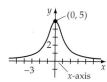   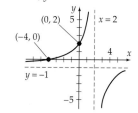

19. $x = 3, x = -3, y = 0$ **21.** $x = -3, x = 1, y = 0$ **23.** $x = -2, y = 1$ **25.** no vertical asymptote; horizontal asymptote: $y = 0$

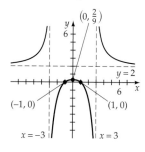   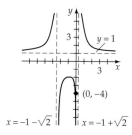   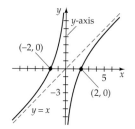

27. $x = 3, x = -3, y = 2$ **29.** $x = -1 + \sqrt{2}, x = -1 - \sqrt{2}, y = 1$ **31.** $y = 3x - 7$ **33.** $y = x$ **35.** $x = 0, y = x$

37. $x = -3, y = x - 6$ **39.** $x = 4, y = 2x + 13$ **41.** $x = -2, y = x - 3$ **43.** $x = 2, x = -2, y = x$

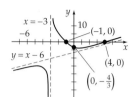 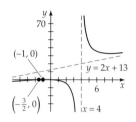 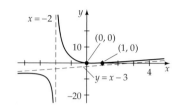 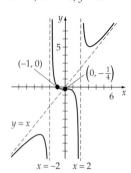

45.   **47.**   **49.**   **51.**

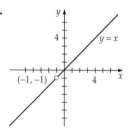 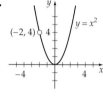 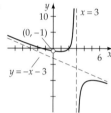 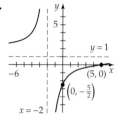

53. a. \$76.43, \$8.03, \$1.19   **b.** $y = 0.43$. As the number of golf balls produced increases, the average cost per golf ball approaches \$.43.

55. a. \$1333.33   **b.** \$8000   **c.**   **57. a.** $R(0) \approx 38.8\%, R(7) \approx 39.9\%, R(12) \approx 40.9\%$ **b.** $\approx 44.7\%$

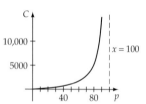

59. a. 26,923, 68,293, 56,000   **b.** 2001   **c.** The population will approach 0.   **61. a.** 3.8 centimeters

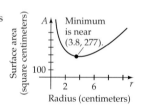

b. No   **c.** As the radius r increases without bound, the surface area approaches twice the area of a circle with radius r.   **63.** $(-2, 2)$
65. $(0, 1)$ and $(-4, 1)$

Chapter 3 True/False Exercises, page 347

1. False; $P(x) = x - i$ has a zero of i, but it does not have a zero of $-i$.   **2.** False; Descartes' Rule of Signs indicates that $P(x) = x^3 - x^2 + x - 1$
has three or one positive zeros. In fact, P has only one positive zero.   **3.** True   **4.** True   **5.** False; $F(x) = \dfrac{x}{x^2 + 1}$ does not have a vertical
asymptote.   **6.** False; $F(x) = \dfrac{(x-2)^2}{(x-3)(x-2)} = \dfrac{x-2}{x-3}, x \neq 2$. The graph of F has a hole at $x = 2$.   **7.** True   **8.** True   **9.** True   **10.** True

11. True   **12.** False; $P(x) = x^2 + 1$ does not have a real zero.

Chapter 3 Review Exercises, page 348

1. $4x^2 + x + 8 + \dfrac{22}{x-3}$ [3.1]   **2.** $5x^2 + 5x - 13 - \dfrac{11}{x-1}$ [3.1]   **3.** $3x^2 - 6x + 7 - \dfrac{13}{x+2}$ [3.1]   **4.** $2x^2 + 8x + 20$ [3.1]   **5.** $3x^2 + 5x - 11$ [3.1]

6. $x^3 + 2x^2 - 8x - 9$ [3.1]   **7.** 77 [3.1]   **8.** 22 [3.1]   **9.** 33 [3.1]   **10.** 558 [3.1]

The verifications in Exercises 11–14 make use of the concepts from Section 3.1.

15. [3.2] **16.** [3.2] **17.** [3.2] **18.** [3.2] **19.** 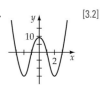 [3.2]

20. [3.2] **21.** $\pm 1, \pm 2, \pm 3, \pm 6$ [3.3] **22.** $\pm 1, \pm 2, \pm 3, \pm 5, \pm 6, \pm 10, \pm 15, \pm 30, \pm \frac{1}{2}, \pm \frac{3}{2}, \pm \frac{5}{2}, \pm \frac{15}{2}$ [3.3]

23. $\pm 1, \pm 2, \pm 3, \pm 4, \pm 6, \pm 12, \pm \frac{1}{3}, \pm \frac{2}{3}, \pm \frac{4}{3}, \pm \frac{1}{5}, \pm \frac{2}{5}, \pm \frac{3}{5}, \pm \frac{4}{5}, \pm \frac{6}{5}, \pm \frac{12}{5}, \pm \frac{1}{15}, \pm \frac{2}{15}, \pm \frac{4}{15}$ [3.3] **24.** $\pm 1, \pm 2, \pm 4, \pm 8, \pm 16, \pm 32, \pm 64$

[3.3] **25.** ± 1 [3.3] **26.** $\pm 1, \pm 2, \pm \frac{1}{6}, \pm \frac{1}{3}, \pm \frac{1}{2}, \pm \frac{2}{3}$ [3.3] **27.** no positive real zeros and three or one negative real zeros [3.3]

28. three or one positive real zeros, one negative real zero [3.3] **29.** one positive real zero and one negative real zero [3.3]

30. five, three, or one positive real zeros, no negative real zeros [3.3] **31.** $1, -2, -5$ [3.3] **32.** $2, 5, 3$ [3.3] **33.** -2 (multiplicity 2), $-\frac{1}{2}, -\frac{4}{3}$

[3.3] **34.** $-\frac{1}{2}, -3, i, -i$ [3.4] **35.** 1 (multiplicity 4) [3.3] **36.** $-\frac{1}{2}, 2 + 3i, 2 - 3i$ [3.4] **37.** $-1, 3, 1 + 2i$ [3.4] **38.** $-5, 2, 2 - i$ [3.4]

39. $P(x) = 2x^3 - 3x^2 - 23x + 12$ [3.4] **40.** $P(x) = x^4 + x^3 - 5x^2 + x - 6$ [3.4] **41.** $P(x) = x^4 - 3x^3 + 27x^2 - 75x + 50$ [3.4]
42. $P(x) = x^4 + 2x^3 + 6x^2 + 32x + 40$ [3.4] **43.** vertical asymptote: $x = -2$, horizontal asymptote: $y = 3$ [3.5]
44. vertical asymptotes: $x = -3, x = 1$, horizontal asymptote: $y = 2$ [3.5] **45.** vertical asymptote: $x = -1$, slant asymptote: $y = 2x + 3$ [3.5]
46. no vertical asymptote, horizontal asymptote: $y = 3$ [3.5]

47. 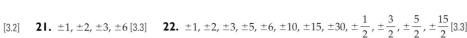 [3.5] **48.** [3.5] **49.** [3.5] **50.** [3.5]

51. 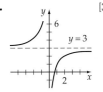 [3.5] **52.** [3.5] **53.** 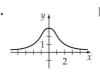 [3.5] **54.** 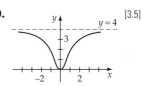 [3.5]

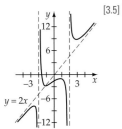 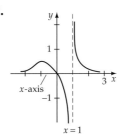 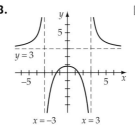 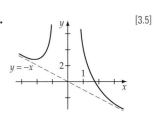

55. a. \$12.59, \$6.43 **b.** $y = 5.75$. As the number of skateboards produced increases, the average cost per skateboard approaches \$5.75. [3.5]
56. a. 15°F **b.** 2.4°F **c.** 0°F [3.5] **57. a.** As the radius of the blood vessel approaches 0, the resistance gets larger. **b.** As the radius of
the blood vessel gets larger, the resistance approaches zero. [3.5]

Chapter 3 Test, page 349

1. $3x^2 - x + 6 - \frac{13}{x + 2}$ [3.1] **2.** 43 [3.1] **3.** The verification for Exercise 3 makes use of the concepts from Section 3.1. **4.** up to the far left

and down to the far right [3.2] **5.** $0, \frac{2}{3}, -3$ [3.2] **6.** $P(1) < 0, P(2) > 0$. Therefore, by the Zero Location Theorem, the continuous polynomial function P has a zero between 1 and 2. [3.2]   **7.** 2 (multiplicity 2), -2 (multiplicity 2), $\frac{3}{2}$ (multiplicity 1), -1 (multiplicity 3) [3.3]

8. $\pm 1, \pm 3, \pm \frac{1}{2}, \pm \frac{3}{2}, \pm \frac{1}{3}, \pm \frac{1}{6}$ [3.3]   **9.** upper bound 4, lower bound -5 [3.3]   **10.** four, two, or zero positive zeros, no negative zero [3.3]

11. $\frac{1}{2}, 3, -2$ [3.3]   **12.** $2 - 3i, -\frac{2}{3}, -\frac{5}{2}$ [3.4]   **13.** 0, 1 (multiplicity 2), $2 + i, 2 - i$ [3.4]   **14.** $P(x) = x^4 - 5x^3 + 8x^2 - 6x$ [3.4]   **15.** vertical

asymptotes: $x = 3, x = 2$ [3.5]   **16.** horizontal asymptote: $y = \frac{3}{2}$ [3.5]   **17.** [3.5]   **18.** [3.5]

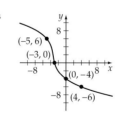

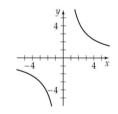

19. a. 5 words per minute, 16 words per minute, 25 words per minute   **b.** 70 words per minute [3.5]   **20.** 2.42 inches, 487.9 cubic inches [3.3]

Cumulative Review Exercises, page 351

1. $-1 + 2i$ [P.6]   **2.** $\frac{1 \pm \sqrt{5}}{2}$ [1.3]   **3.** 2, 10 [1.4]   **4.** $\{x \mid -8 \le x \le 14\}$ [1.5]   **5.** $\sqrt{281}$ [2.1]   **6.** Translate the graph of $y = x^2$ to the right

2 units and 4 units up. [2.5]   **7.** $2x + h - 2$ [2.6]   **8.** $32x^2 - 92x + 60$ [2.6]   **9.** $x^3 - x^2 + x + 11$ [2.6]   **10.** $4x^3 - 8x^2 + 14x - 32 + \frac{59}{x + 2}$
[3.1]   **11.** 141 [3.1]   **12.** The graph goes down. [3.2]   **13.** 0.3997 [3.2]   **14.** $\pm 1, \pm 2, \pm 4, \pm \frac{1}{3}, \pm \frac{2}{3}, \pm \frac{4}{3}$
[3.3]   **15.** zero positive real zeros, three or one negative real zeros [3.3]   **16.** $-2, 1 + 2i, 1 - 2i$ [3.4]   **17.** $P(x) = x^3 - 4x^2 - 2x + 20$ [3.4]
18. $(x - 2)(x + 3i)(x - 3i)$ [3.4]
19. vertical asymptotes: $x = -3, x = 2$; horizontal asymptote: $y = 4$ [3.5]   **20.** $y = x + 4$ [3.5]

Exercise Set 4.1, page 364

1. 3   **3.** -3 **5.** 3   **7.** range   **9.** Yes   **11.** Yes   **13.** Yes

15. No   **17.** Yes   **19.** Yes   **21.** No   **23.** $\{(1, -3), (2, -2), (5, 1), (-7, 4)\}$ **25.** $\{(1, 0), (2, 1), (4, 2), (8, 3), (16, 4)\}$

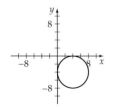

27. $f^{-1}(x) = \frac{1}{2}x - 2$ **29.** $f^{-1}(x) = \frac{1}{3}x + \frac{7}{3}$ **31.** $f^{-1}(x) = -\frac{1}{2}x + \frac{5}{2}$ **33.** $f^{-1}(x) = \frac{x}{x - 2}, x \ne 2$ **35.** $f^{-1}(x) = \frac{x + 1}{1 - x}, x \ne 1$
37. $f^{-1}(x) = \sqrt{x - 1}, x \ge 1$ **39.** $f^{-1}(x) = x^2 + 2, x \ge 0$ **41.** $f^{-1}(x) = \sqrt{x + 4} - 2, x \ge -4$ **43.** $f^{-1}(x) = -\sqrt{x + 5} - 2, x \ge -5$
45. $V^{-1}(x) = \sqrt[3]{x}$. V^{-1} finds the length of a side of a cube given the volume.
47. Yes. Yes. A conversion function is a nonconstant linear function. All nonconstant linear functions have inverses that are also functions.

49. $s^{-1}(x) = \dfrac{1}{2}x - 12$ **51.** $E^{-1}(s) = 20s - 50,000$. From the monthly earnings s the executive can find $E^{-1}(s)$, the value of the software sold.

53. 44205833; $f^{-1}(x) = \dfrac{1}{2}x + \dfrac{1}{2}$, $f^{-1}(44205833) = 22102917$

55. Because the function is increasing and 4 is between 2 and 5, c must be between 7 and 12. **57.** between 2 and 5

59. between 3 and 7 **61.** $f^{-1}(x) = \dfrac{x - b}{a}$, $a \neq 0$ **63.** The reflection of f across the line given by $y = x$ yields f. Thus f is its own inverse.

65. Yes **67.** No

Prepare for Section 4.2, page 367

69. 8 **70.** $\dfrac{1}{81}$ **71.** $\dfrac{17}{8}$ **72.** $\dfrac{40}{9}$ **73.** $\dfrac{1}{10}$, 1, 10, and 100 **74.** 2, 1, $\dfrac{1}{2}$, and $\dfrac{1}{4}$

Exercise Set 4.2, page 376

1. $f(0) = 1; f(4) = 81$ **3.** $g(-2) = \dfrac{1}{100}; g(3) = 1000$ **5.** $h(2) = \dfrac{9}{4}; h(-3) = \dfrac{8}{27}$ **7.** $j(-2) = 4; j(4) = \dfrac{1}{16}$ **9.** 9.19 **11.** 9.03 **13.** 9.74

15. a. $k(x)$ **b.** $g(x)$ **c.** $h(x)$ **d.** $f(x)$

17. 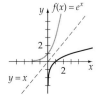 **19.** 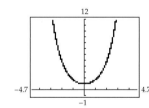 **21.** 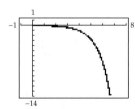 **23.**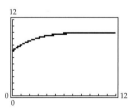

25. Shift the graph of f vertically upward 2 units. **27.** Shift the graph of f horizontally to the right 2 units.
29. Reflect the graph of f across the y-axis. **31.** Stretch the graph of f vertically away from the x-axis by a factor of 2.
33. Reflect the graph of f across the y-axis and then shift this graph vertically upward 2 units.

35. no horizontal asymptote **37.** no horizontal asymptote

39. horizontal asymptote: $y = 0$ 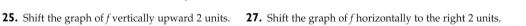 **41.** horizontal asymptote: $y = 10$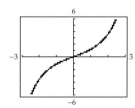

43. a. 122 million connections **b.** 2006 **45. a.** 233 items per month; 59 items per month **b.** The demand will approach
25 items per month. **47. a.** 0.53 **b.** 0.89 **c.** 5.2 minutes **d.** There is a 98% probability that at least one customer will arrive between
10:00 A.M. and 10:05.2 A.M. **49. a.** 8.7% **b.** 2.6% **51. a.** 6400; 409,600 **b.** 11.6 hours **53. a.** 515,000 people **b.** 1997
55. a. 363 beneficiaries; 88,572 beneficiaries **b.** 13 rounds **57. a.** 141°F **b.** after 28.3 minutes **59. a.** 261.63 vibrations per second
b. No. The function $f(n)$ is not a linear function. Therefore, the graph of $f(n)$ does not increase at a constant rate.

63.   **65.** $(-\infty, \infty)$ **67.** $[0, \infty)$

68. 4   **69.** 3   **70.** 5   **71.** $f^{-1}(x) = \dfrac{3x}{2 - x}$ **72.** $\{x \mid x \geq 2\}$ **73.** the set of all positive real numbers

Exercise Set 4.3, page 391

1. $10^1 = 10$ **3.** $8^2 = 64$ **5.** $7^0 = x$ **7.** $e^4 = x$ **9.** $e^0 = 1$ **11.** $\log_3 9 = 2$ **13.** $\log_4 \dfrac{1}{16} = -2$ **15.** $\log_b y = x$ **17.** $\ln y = x$

19. $\log 100 = 2$ **21.** 2   **23.** -5 **25.** 3   **27.** -2 **29.** -4 **31.**

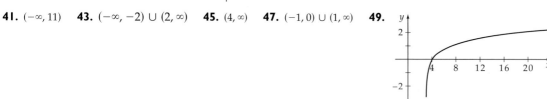

33.   **35.**   **37.**   **39.** $(3, \infty)$

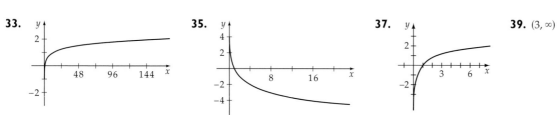

41. $(-\infty, 11)$ **43.** $(-\infty, -2) \cup (2, \infty)$ **45.** $(4, \infty)$ **47.** $(-1, 0) \cup (1, \infty)$ **49.**

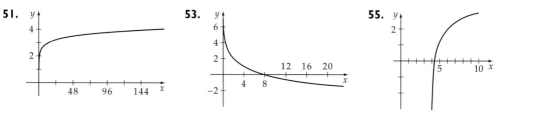

51.   **53.**   **55.**

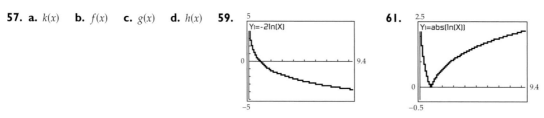

57. a. $k(x)$ **b.** $f(x)$ **c.** $g(x)$ **d.** $h(x)$ **59.**   **61.**

63.   **65.**   **67.**

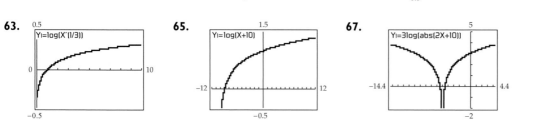

69. a. 2.0%   **b.** 45 months   **71. a.** 3298 units; 3418 units; 3490 units   **b.** 2750 units   **73.** 2.05 square meters
75. a. Answers will vary.   **b.** 96 digits   **c.** 3385 digits   **d.** 6,320,430 digits   **77.** f and g are inverse functions.
79. range of f: $\{y \mid -1 < y < 1\}$; range of g: all real numbers

Prepare for Section 4.4, page 394

81. ≈ 0.77815 for each expression   **82.** ≈ 0.98083 for each expression   **83.** ≈ 1.80618 for each expression
84. ≈ 3.21888 for each expression   **85.** ≈ 1.60944 for each expression   **86.** ≈ 0.90309 for each expression

Exercise Set 4.4, page 403

1. $\log_b x + \log_b y + \log_b z$ **3.** $\ln x - 4 \ln z$ **5.** $\frac{1}{2} \log_2 x - 3 \log_2 y$ **7.** $\frac{1}{2} \log_7 x + \frac{1}{2} \log_7 z - 2 \log_7 y$ **9.** $\log[x^2(x + 5)]$ **11.** $\ln(x + y)$

13. $\log\left[x^3 \cdot \sqrt[3]{y}\,(x + 1)\right]$ **15.** 1.5395   **17.** 0.8672   **19.** -0.6131 **21.** 0.6447   **23.**

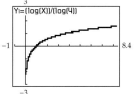

25.

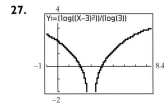

27.

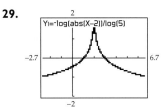

29.

31. False; $\log 10 + \log 10 = 2$ but $\log(10 + 10) = \log 20 \neq 2$.   **33.** True   **35.** False; $\log 100 - \log 10 = 1$ but $\log(100 - 10) = \log 90 \neq 1$.
37. False; $\dfrac{\log 100}{\log 10} = \dfrac{2}{1} = 2$ but $\log 100 - \log 10 = 1$.   **39.** False; $(\log 10)^2 = 1$ but $2 \log 10 = 2$.   **41.** 2   **43.** 500^{501}
45. $1:870{,}551$; $1:757{,}858$; $1:659{,}754$; $1:574{,}349$; $1:500{,}000$ **47.** 10.4; base   **49.** 3.16×10^{-10} mole per liter
51. a. 82.0 decibels   **b.** 40.3 decibels   **c.** 115.0 decibels   **d.** 152.0 decibels   **53.** 10 times more intense   **55.** 5
57. $10^{6.5} I_0$ or about $3{,}162{,}277.7 I_0$ **59.** 100 to 1   **61.** $10^{1.8}$ to 1 or about 63 to 1   **63.** 5.5   **65. a.** $M \approx 6$ **b.** $M \approx 4$ **c.** The results are
close to the magnitudes produced by the amplitude-time-difference formula.

Prepare for Section 4.5, page 406

66. $\log_3 729 = 6$ **67.** $5^4 = 625$ **68.** $\log_a b = x + 2$ **69.** $x = \dfrac{4a}{7b + 2c}$ **70.** $x = \dfrac{3}{44}$ **71.** $x = \dfrac{100(A - 1)}{A + 1}$

Exercise Set 4.5, page 415

1. 6   **3.** $-\dfrac{3}{2}$ **5.** $-\dfrac{6}{5}$ **7.** 3   **9.** $\dfrac{\log 70}{\log 5}$ **11.** $-\dfrac{\log 120}{\log 3}$ **13.** $\dfrac{\log 315 - 3}{2}$ **15.** $\ln 10$ **17.** $\dfrac{\ln 2 - \ln 3}{\ln 6}$ **19.** $\dfrac{3 \log 2 - \log 5}{2 \log 2 + \log 5}$

21. 7   **23.** 4   **25.** $2 + 2\sqrt{2}$ **27.** $\dfrac{199}{95}$ **29.** -1 **31.** 3   **33.** 10^{10} **35.** 2   **37.** 5   **39.** $\log\left(20 + \sqrt{401}\right)$ **41.** $\dfrac{1}{2} \log\left(\dfrac{3}{2}\right)$

43. $\ln\left(15 \pm 4\sqrt{14}\right)$ **45.** $\ln\left(1 + \sqrt{65}\right) - \ln 8$ **47.** 1.61   **49.** 0.96   **51.** 2.20   **53.** -1.93 **55.** -1.34

57. a. 8500, 10,285   **b.** in 6 years   **59. a.** 60°F   **b.** 27 minutes   **61. a.**

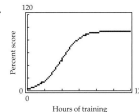

Hours of training

b. 48 hours
c. $P = 100$
d. As the number of hours of
training increases, the test
scores approach 100%.

63. a.

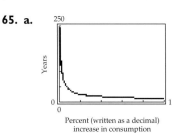

Number of bison vs *Years* (axes: 0 to 1200, 0 to 100)

b. in 27 years or the year 2026   **c.** $B = 1000$ **d.** As the number of years increases, the bison population approaches but never reaches or exceeds 1000.

65. a.

Years (0 to 250) vs *Percent (written as a decimal) increase in consumption* (0 to 1)

b. 78 years   **c.** 1.9%

67. a. 116 feet per second   **b.** $v = 150$ **c.** The velocity of the package approaches but never reaches or exceeds 150 feet per second.
69. a. 1.72 seconds   **b.** $v = 100$ **c.** The object cannot fall faster than 100 feet per second.

71. a.

Distance (in feet) (0 to 500) vs *Time (in seconds)* (0 to 4)

b. 2.6 seconds   **73.** 138

75. The second step; because $\log 0.5 < 0$, the inequality sign must be reversed.   **77.** $x = \dfrac{y}{y-1}$ **79.** $e^{0.336} \approx 1.4$

Prepare for Section 4.6, page 419

81. 1220.39   **82.** 824.96   **83.** -0.0495 **84.** 1340   **85.** 0.025   **86.** 12.8

Exercise Set 4.6, page 430

1. a. $9724.05   **b.** $11,256.80   **3. a.** $48,885.72   **b.** $49,282.20   **c.** $49,283.30   **5.** $24,730.82   **7.** 8.8 years   **9.** $t = \dfrac{\ln 3}{r}$

11. 14 years   **13. a.** 2200 bacteria   **b.** 17,600 bacteria   **15. a.** $N(t) \approx 22,600e^{0.01368t}$ **b.** 27,700   **17. a.** 10,755,000   **b.** 2042

19. a.

Micrograms of Na (A, 0 to 4) vs *Time (in hours)* (30, 60, 90)

b. 3.18 micrograms   **c.** ≈ 15.07 hours   **d.** ≈ 30.14 hours   **21.** ≈ 6601 years ago

23. ≈ 2378 years old   **25. a.** 0.056   **b.** 42°F   **c.** 54 minutes   **27. a.** 211 hours   **b.** 1386 hours   **29.** 3.1 years

31. a.

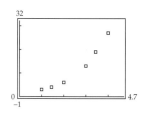

b. 0.98 second   **c.** $v = 32$ **d.** As time increases, the velocity approaches but never reaches or exceeds 32 feet per second.

33. a.

b. 2.5 seconds   **c.** ≈ 24.56 feet per second   **d.** The average speed of the object was approximately 24.56 feet per second during the period from $t = 1$ to $t = 2$ seconds.

35. a. 1900   **b.** 0.16   **c.** 200   **37. a.** 157,500   **b.** 0.04   **c.** 45,000   **39. a.** 2400   **b.** 0.12   **c.** 300

41. $P(t) \approx \dfrac{5500}{1 + 12.75e^{-0.37263t}}$ **43.** $P(t) \approx \dfrac{100}{1 + 4.55556e^{-0.22302t}}$ **45. a.** $158,000, $163,000   **b.** $625,000

47. a. $P(t) \approx \dfrac{1600}{1 + 4.12821e^{-0.06198t}}$ **b.** about 497 wolves   **49. a.** $P(t) \approx \dfrac{8500}{1 + 4.66667e^{-0.14761t}}$ **b.** 2010   **51.** 45 hours

53. a. 0.71 gram   **b.** 0.96 gram   **c.** 0.52 gram   **55. a.** 1.7%   **b.** 13.9%   **c.** 19.0%   **d.** 19.5%   **e.** 1.5%; $P \to 0$
57. 13,715,120,270 centuries

Prepare for Section 4.7, page 435

59. decreasing   **60.** decreasing   **61.** 36   **62.** 840   **63.** 15.8   **64.** $P = 55$

Exercise Set 4.7, page 444

1. increasing exponential function   **3.** decreasing exponential function; decreasing logarithmic function   **5.** decreasing logarithmic function

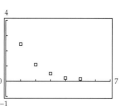

7. $y \approx 0.99628(1.20052)^x$; $r \approx 0.85705$ **9.** $y \approx 1.81505(0.51979)^x$; $r \approx -0.99978$ **11.** $y \approx 4.89060 - 1.35073 \ln x$; $r \approx -0.99921$

13. $y \approx 14.05858 + 1.76393 \ln x$; $r \approx 0.99983$ **15.** $y \approx \dfrac{235.58598}{1 + 1.90188e^{-0.05101x}}$ **17.** $y \approx \dfrac{2098.68307}{1 + 1.19794e^{-0.06004x}}$

19. a. $y \approx 5.48184(1.00356)^x$; 6.78%   **b.** 69 months   **21. a.** $T \approx 0.06273(1.07078)^F$ **b.** 5.3 hours   **23. a.** $T \approx 0.07881(1.07259)^F$
b. 7.5 hours; 2.2 hours   **25. a.** $N(t) \approx 1500.093(1.940)^t$ **b.** 2005   **27. a.** $p \approx 7.862(1.026)^y$ **b.** 36 centimeters
29. a. LinReg: pH $\approx 0.01353q + 7.02852$, $r \approx 0.956627$; LnReg: pH $\approx 6.10251 + 0.43369 \ln q$, $r \approx 0.999998$. The logarithmic model provides a better fit.   **b.** 126.0   **31. a.** $p \approx 3200(0.91894)^t$; 2012   **b.** No. The model fits the data perfectly because there are only two data points.

33. a. ExpReg: $a \approx 8000(1.10657)^t$; 550,500,000 automobiles   **b.** 2004   **35. a.** logistic: distance in feet $\approx \dfrac{71.84158}{1 + 13.77825e^{-0.07915t}}$;

logarithmic: distance in feet $\approx -22.58293 + 20.91655 \ln t$ **b.** logistic growth model   **c.** 71.65 feet
37. a. LinReg: $w \approx 10.17227t + 16.45111$, $r \approx 0.95601$; LnReg: $w \approx 18.26750 + 31.03499 \ln t$, $r \approx 0.99996$ **b.** The logarithmic model provides a better fit.   **c.** 89.7 cubic yards   **39.** A and B have different exponential regression functions.   **41. a.** ExpReg: $y \approx 1.81120(1.61740)^x$, $r \approx 0.96793$; PwrReg: $y \approx 2.09385(x)^{1.40246}$, $r \approx 0.99999$ **b.** The power regression function provides the better fit.

Chapter 4 True/False Exercises, page 453

1. False. $f(x) = x^2$ does not have an inverse function.   **2.** False. Let $f(x) = 2x$, $g(x) = 3x$. Then $f(g(0)) = 0$ and $g(f(0)) = 0$, but f and g are not inverse functions.   **3.** True   **4.** True   **5.** True   **6.** False; f is not defined for negative values of x, and thus $g(f(x))$ is undefined for negative values of x.   **7.** False; $h(x)$ is not an increasing function for $0 < b < 1$.   **8.** False; $j(x)$ is not an increasing function for $0 < b < 1$.   **9.** True   **10.** True   **11.** True   **12.** True   **13.** False; $\log x + \log y = \log(xy)$.   **14.** True   **15.** True   **16.** True

Chapter 4 Review Exercises, page 454

1. Yes [4.1]   **2.** Yes [4.1]   **3.** Yes [4.1]   **4.** No [4.1]

5. $f^{-1}(x) = \dfrac{x + 4}{3}$ [4.1]   **6.** $g^{-1}(x) = -\dfrac{1}{2}x + \dfrac{3}{2}$ [4.1]   **7.** $h^{-1}(x) = -2x - 4$ [4.1]   **8.** $k^{-1}(x) = k(x) = \dfrac{1}{x}$ [4.1]

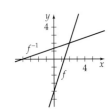   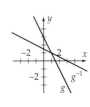   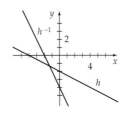

9. 2 [4.3]   **10.** 4 [4.3]   **11.** 3 [4.3]   **12.** π [4.3]   **13.** -2 [4.5]   **14.** 8 [4.5]   **15.** -3 [4.5]   **16.** -4 [4.5]
17. ± 1000 [4.5]   **18.** $\pm 10^{10}$ [4.5]   **19.** 7 [4.5]   **20.** ± 8 [4.5]

21. [4.2]   **22.** [4.2]   **23.** [4.2]   **24.** [4.2]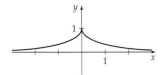

25. [4.2]   **26.** [4.2]   **27.** [4.3]   **28.** [4.3]

29. [4.3] 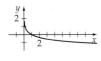   **30.** [4.3] 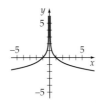   **31.** [4.2]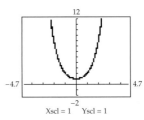

32. [4.2] 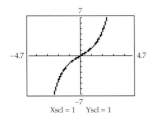   **33.** $4^3 = 64$ [4.3]   **34.** $\left(\dfrac{1}{2}\right)^{-3} = 8$ [4.3]   **35.** $(\sqrt{2})^4 = 4$ [4.3]

36. $e^0 = 1$ [4.3]   **37.** $\log_5 125 = 3$ [4.3]   **38.** $\log_2 1024 = 10$ [4.3]   **39.** $\log_{10} 1 = 0$ [4.3]   **40.** $\log_8 2\sqrt{2} = \dfrac{1}{2}$ [4.3]

41. $2 \log_b x + 3 \log_b y - \log_b z$ [4.4]   **42.** $\frac{1}{2} \log_b x - 2 \log_b y - \log_b z$ [4.4]   **43.** $\ln x + 3 \ln y$ [4.4]   **44.** $\frac{1}{2} \ln x + \frac{1}{2} \ln y - 4 \ln z$ [4.4]

45. $\log\left(x^2 \sqrt[3]{x+1}\right)$ [4.4]   **46.** $\log \dfrac{x^5}{(x+5)^2}$ [4.4]   **47.** $\ln \dfrac{\sqrt{2xy}}{z^3}$ [4.4]   **48.** $\ln \dfrac{xz}{y}$ [4.4]   **49.** 2.86754 [4.4]   **50.** 3.35776 [4.4]

51. -0.117233 [4.4]   **52.** -0.578989 [4.4]   **53.** $\dfrac{\ln 30}{\ln 4}$ [4.5]   **54.** $\dfrac{\log 41}{\log 5} - 1$ [4.5]   **55.** 4 [4.5]   **56.** $\dfrac{1}{6} e$ [4.5]   **57.** 4 [4.5]   **58.** 15 [4.5]

59. $\dfrac{\ln 3}{2 \ln 4}$ [4.5]   **60.** $\dfrac{\ln(8 \pm 3\sqrt{7})}{\ln 5}$ [4.5]   **61.** 10^{1000} [4.5]   **62.** $e^{(e^2)}$ [4.5]   **63.** 1,000,005 [4.5]   **64.** $\dfrac{15 + \sqrt{265}}{2}$ [4.5]   **65.** 81 [4.5]

66. $\pm\sqrt{5}$ [4.5]   **67.** 4 [4.5]   **68.** 5 [4.5]   **69.** 7.7 [4.4]   **70.** 5.0 [4.4]   **71.** 3162 to 1 [4.4]   **72.** 2.8 [4.4]   **73.** 4.2 [4.4]
74. $\approx 3.98 \times 10^{-6}$ [4.4]   **75. a.** \$20,323.79   **b.** \$20,339.99 [4.6]   **76. a.** \$25,646.69   **b.** \$25,647.32 [4.6]   **77.** \$4,438.10 [4.6]
78. a. 69.9%   **b.** 6 days   **c.** 19 days [4.6]   **79.** $N(t) \approx e^{0.8047t}$ [4.6]   **80.** $N(t) \approx 2e^{0.5682t}$ [4.6]   **81.** $N(t) \approx 3.783 e^{0.0558t}$ [4.6]
82. $N(t) \approx e^{-0.6931t}$ [4.6]   **83. a.** $P(t) \approx 25,200 e^{0.06155789t}$ **b.** 38,800 [4.6]   **84.** 340 years [4.6]
85. a. linear: $P \approx -63,121t + 7,599,401$, $r \approx -0.93813$; exponential: $P \approx 64,717,271(0.96174359)^t$, $r \approx -0.95227$;
logarithmic: $P \approx 29,163,839 - 6,052,741 \ln t$, $r \approx -0.94256$ **b.** The exponential equation provides a better fit for the data.
c. 1,040,000 [4.7]   **86. a.** linear: $R \approx -0.475297t + 53.1037$, $r \approx -0.98118$; exponential: $R \approx 207.544(0.966206)^t$, $r \approx -0.99660$;
logarithmic: $R \approx 181.202 - 38.0586 \ln t$, $r \approx -0.99073$ **b.** The exponential equation provides a better fit for the data.

c. 5.1 per 1000 live births [4.7]   **87. a.** $P(t) \approx \dfrac{1400}{1 + \dfrac{17}{3} e^{-0.22458t}}$ **b.** 1070 [4.6]   **88. a.** $21\dfrac{1}{3}$ **b.** $P(t) \to 128$ [4.6]

Chapter 4 Test, page 456

1. $f^{-1}(x) = \dfrac{1}{2} x + \dfrac{3}{2}$ [4.1]   **2.** $f^{-1}(x) = \dfrac{8x}{4x - 1}$

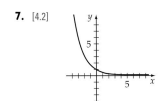

Domain f^{-1}: all real numbers

except $\dfrac{1}{4}$

Range f^{-1}: all real numbers except 2 [4.1]

3. a. $b^c = 5x - 3$ [4.3]   **b.** $\log_3 y = \dfrac{x}{2}$ [4.3]   **4.** $2 \log_b z - 3 \log_b y - \dfrac{1}{2} \log_b x$ [4.4]   **5.** $\log \dfrac{2x+3}{(x-2)^3}$ [4.4]   **6.** 1.7925 [4.4]

7. [4.2]   **8.** [4.3]

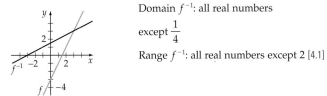

9. 1.9206 [4.5]   **10.** $\dfrac{5 \ln 4}{\ln 28}$ [4.5]   **11.** 1 [4.5]   **12.** -3 [4.5]

13. a. \$29,502.36   **b.** \$29,539.62 [4.6]   **14.** 17.36 years [4.6]   **15. a.** 7.6   **b.** 63 to 1 [4.4]   **16. a.** $P(t) \approx 34,600 e^{0.04667108t}$ **b.** 55,000 [4.6]
17. 690 years [4.6]   **18. a.** $y \approx 1.67199(2.47188)^x$ **b.** 1945 [4.7]   **19. a.** $R(t) \approx 1.74830 + 0.78089 \ln x$; 2.73%   **b.** 2.6 years [4.7]
20. a. $P(t) \approx \dfrac{1100}{1 + 5.875 e^{-0.20429t}}$ **b.** ≈ 457 raccoons [4.6]

Cumulative Review Exercises, page 457

1. $[2, 6]$ [1.1]   **2.** $\{x \mid 3 < x \le 6\}$ [1.5]   **3.** 7.8 [2.1]   **4.** 38.25 feet [2.4]   **5.** $4x^2 + 4x - 4$ [2.6]   **6.** $f^{-1}(x) = \dfrac{1}{3} x + \dfrac{5}{3}$ [4.1]

7. 3500 pounds [1.6]   **8.** 3 or 1 positive real zeros; 1 negative real zero [3.3]   **9.** $1, 4, -\sqrt{3}, \sqrt{3}$ [3.3]   **10.** $P(x) = x^3 - 4x^2 + 6x - 4$ [3.4]
11. vertical asymptote: $x = 4$, horizontal asymptote: $y = 3$ [3.5]   **12.** Domain: all real numbers; Range: $\{y \mid 0 < y \le 4\}$ [3.5]
13. decreasing function [4.2]   **14.** $4^y = x$ [4.3]   **15.** $\log_5 125 = 3$ [4.3]   **16.** 7.1 [4.4]   **17.** 2.0149 [4.5]   **18.** 510 years old [4.6]

19. a. $y \approx 84.41319 + 4.88166 \ln x$ **b.** 99.28 meters [4.7]   **20. a.** $P(x) \approx \dfrac{450}{1 + 1.8125 e^{-0.13882x}}$ **b.** 310 wolves [4.7]

Exercise Set 5.1, page 468

1. vertex: $(0, 0)$

focus: $(0, -1)$

directrix: $y = 1$

3. vertex: $(0, 0)$

focus: $\left(\dfrac{1}{12}, 0\right)$

directrix: $x = -\dfrac{1}{12}$

5. vertex: $(2, -3)$

focus: $(2, -1)$

directrix: $y = -5$

7. vertex: $(2, -4)$

focus: $(1, -4)$

directrix: $x = 3$

9. vertex: $(-4, 1)$

focus: $\left(-\dfrac{7}{2}, 1\right)$

directrix: $x = -\dfrac{9}{2}$

 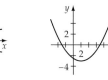

11. vertex: $(2, 2)$

focus: $\left(2, \dfrac{5}{2}\right)$

directrix: $y = \dfrac{3}{2}$

13. vertex: $(-4, -10)$

focus: $\left(-4, -\dfrac{39}{4}\right)$

directrix: $y = -\dfrac{41}{4}$

15. vertex: $\left(-\dfrac{7}{4}, \dfrac{3}{2}\right)$

focus: $\left(-2, \dfrac{3}{2}\right)$

directrix: $x = -\dfrac{3}{2}$

17. vertex: $(-5, -3)$

focus: $\left(-\dfrac{9}{2}, -3\right)$

directrix: $x = -\dfrac{11}{2}$

19. vertex: $\left(-\dfrac{3}{2}, \dfrac{13}{12}\right)$

focus: $\left(-\dfrac{3}{2}, \dfrac{1}{3}\right)$

directrix: $y = \dfrac{11}{6}$

   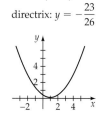

21. vertex: $\left(2, -\dfrac{5}{4}\right)$

focus: $\left(2, -\dfrac{3}{4}\right)$

directrix: $y = -\dfrac{7}{4}$

23. vertex: $\left(\dfrac{9}{2}, -1\right)$

focus: $\left(\dfrac{35}{8}, -1\right)$

directrix: $x = \dfrac{37}{8}$

25. vertex: $\left(1, \dfrac{1}{9}\right)$

focus: $\left(1, \dfrac{31}{36}\right)$

directrix: $y = -\dfrac{23}{26}$

27. $x^2 = -16y$ **29.** $(x + 1)^2 = 4(y - 2)$ **31.** $(x - 3)^2 = 4(y + 4)$

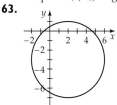

33. $(x + 4)^2 = 4(y - 1)$ **35.** vertex: $(250, 20)$, focus: $\left(\dfrac{3240}{13}, 20\right)$ **37.** on axis 4 feet above vertex   **39.** 6.0 inches   **41. a.** 5900 square feet

b. 56,800 square feet   **43.** $a = 1.5$ inches   **45.** $(-0.3660, -0.3660)$ and $(1.3660, 1.3660)$ **47.** $(-1.5616, 3.8769)$ and $(2.5616, 12.1231)$

49. 4   **51.** $4|p|$ **53.**   **55.**   **57.** $x^2 + y^2 - 8x - 8y - 2xy = 0$

Prepare for Section 5.2, page 470

58. midpoint: $(2, 3)$; length: $2\sqrt{13}$ **59.** $-8, 2$ **60.** $1 \pm \sqrt{3}$ **61.** $x^2 - 8x + 16 = (x - 4)^2$ **62.** $y = \pm\sqrt{4 - (x - 2)^2}$

63.

Exercise Set 5.2, page 480

1. vertices: $(0, 5)$, $(0, -5)$
center: $(0, 0)$

foci: $(0, 3)$, $(0, -3)$

3. vertices: $(3, 0)$, $(-3, 0)$
center: $(0, 0)$

foci: $\left(\sqrt{5}, 0\right)$, $\left(-\sqrt{5}, 0\right)$

5. vertices: $(0, 3)$, $(0, -3)$
center: $(0, 0)$

foci: $\left(0, \sqrt{2}\right)$, $\left(0, -\sqrt{2}\right)$

7. vertices: $(0, 4)$, $(0, -4)$
center: $(0, 0)$

foci: $\left(0, \dfrac{\sqrt{55}}{2}\right)$, $\left(0, -\dfrac{\sqrt{55}}{2}\right)$

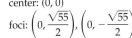

9. vertices: $(8, -2)$, $(-2, -2)$
center: $(3, -2)$
foci: $(6, -2)$, $(0, -2)$

11. vertices: $(-2, 5)$, $(-2, -5)$
center: $(-2, 0)$
foci: $(-2, 4)$, $(-2, -4)$

13. vertices: $\left(1 + \sqrt{21}, 3\right)$, $\left(1 - \sqrt{21}, 3\right)$
center: $(1, 3)$
foci: $\left(1 + \sqrt{17}, 3\right)$, $\left(1 - \sqrt{17}, 3\right)$

15. vertices: $(1, 2)$, $(1, -4)$
center: $(1, -1)$

foci: $\left(1, -1 + \dfrac{\sqrt{65}}{3}\right)$, $\left(1, -1 - \dfrac{\sqrt{65}}{3}\right)$

17. vertices: $(2, 0)$, $(-2, 0)$
center: $(0, 0)$

foci: $(1, 0)$, $(-1, 0)$

19. vertices: $(0, 5)$, $(0, -5)$
center: $(0, 0)$

foci: $(0, 3)$, $(0, -3)$

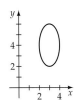

21. vertices: $(0, 4)$, $(0, -4)$
center: $(0, 0)$

foci: $\left(0, \dfrac{\sqrt{39}}{2}\right)$, $\left(0, -\dfrac{\sqrt{39}}{2}\right)$

23. vertices: $(3, 6)$, $(3, 2)$
center: $(3, 4)$

foci: $\left(3, 4 + \sqrt{3}\right)$, $\left(3, 4 - \sqrt{3}\right)$

25. vertices: $(-1, -3)$, $(5, -3)$
center: $(2, -3)$

foci: $(0, -3)$, $(4, -3)$

27. vertices: $(2, 4)$, $(2, -4)$

center: $(2, 0)$

foci: $\left(2, \sqrt{7}\right)$, $\left(2, -\sqrt{7}\right)$

29. vertices: $(-1, 6)$, $(-1, -4)$

center: $(-1, 1)$

foci: $(-1, 4)$, $(-1, -2)$

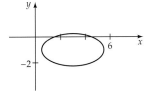

31. vertices: $\left(\dfrac{11}{2}, -1\right)$, $\left(\dfrac{1}{2}, -1\right)$

center: $(3, -1)$

foci: $\left(3 + \dfrac{\sqrt{17}}{2}, -1\right)$, $\left(3 - \dfrac{\sqrt{17}}{2}, -1\right)$

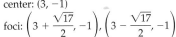

33. $\dfrac{x^2}{25} + \dfrac{y^2}{9} = 1$ **35.** $\dfrac{x^2}{36} + \dfrac{y^2}{16} = 1$ **37.** $\dfrac{x^2}{36} + \dfrac{y^2}{81/8} = 1$ **39.** $\dfrac{(x+2)^2}{16} + \dfrac{(y-4)^2}{7} = 1$ **41.** $\dfrac{(x-2)^2}{25/24} + \dfrac{(y-4)^2}{25} = 1$

43. $\dfrac{(x-5)^2}{16} + \dfrac{(y-1)^2}{25} = 1$ **45.** $\dfrac{x^2}{25} + \dfrac{y^2}{21} = 1$ **47.** $\dfrac{x^2}{20} + \dfrac{y^2}{36} = 1$ **49.** $\dfrac{(x-1)^2}{25} + \dfrac{(y-3)^2}{21} = 1$ **51.** $\dfrac{x^2}{80} + \dfrac{y^2}{144} = 1$

53. 41 centimeters from the emitter   **55.** $\dfrac{x^2}{884.74^2} + \dfrac{y^2}{883.35^2} = 1$ **57.** 40 feet   **59.** $\dfrac{\left(x - \dfrac{9\sqrt{15}}{2}\right)^2}{324} + \dfrac{y^2}{81/4} = 1$ **61.** 1512

63. a. $\dfrac{x^2}{307.5^2} + \dfrac{y^2}{255^2} = 1$ **b.** 246,300 square feet

65. $y = \dfrac{-36 \pm \sqrt{1296 - 36(16x^2 - 108)}}{18}$ **67.** $y = \dfrac{54 \pm \sqrt{2916 - 36(16x^2 - 64x + 1)}}{18}$ **69.** $y = \dfrac{-18 \pm \sqrt{324 - 36(4x^2 + 24x + 44)}}{18}$

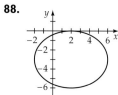 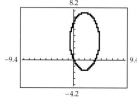 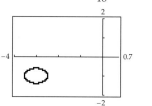

71. $\dfrac{x^2}{36} + \dfrac{y^2}{27} = 1$ **73.** $\dfrac{(x-1)^2}{16} + \dfrac{(y-2)^2}{12} = 1$ **75.** $\dfrac{9}{2}$ **79.** $x = \pm\dfrac{9\sqrt{5}}{5}$

Prepare for Section 5.3, page 484

83. midpoint: $(1, -1)$; length: $2\sqrt{13}$ **84.** $-4, 2$ **85.** $\sqrt{2}$ **86.** $4(x^2 + 6x + 9) = 4(x+3)^2$ **87.** $y = \pm\dfrac{3}{2}\sqrt{x^2 - 4}$

88.

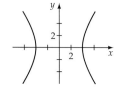

Exercise Set 5.3 page 495

1. center: $(0, 0)$

vertices: $(\pm 4, 0)$

foci: $\left(\pm\sqrt{41}, 0\right)$

asymptotes: $y = \pm\dfrac{5}{4}x$

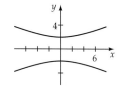

3. center: $(0, 0)$

vertices: $(0, \pm 2)$

foci: $\left(0, \pm\sqrt{29}\right)$

asymptotes: $y = \pm\dfrac{2}{5}x$

5. center: $(0, 0)$

vertices: $\left(\pm\sqrt{7}, 0\right)$

foci: $(\pm 4, 0)$

asymptotes: $y = \pm\dfrac{3\sqrt{7}}{7}x$

7. center: $(0, 0)$

vertices: $\left(\pm\dfrac{3}{2}, 0\right)$

foci: $\left(\pm\dfrac{\sqrt{73}}{2}, 0\right)$

asymptotes: $y = \pm\dfrac{8}{3}x$

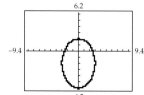

9. center: $(3, -4)$
vertices: $(7, -4), (-1, -4)$
foci: $(8, -4), (-2, -4)$
asymptotes: $y + 4 = \pm\dfrac{3}{4}(x - 3)$

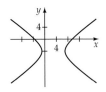

11. center: $(1, -2)$
vertices: $(1, 0), (1, -4)$
foci: $\left(1, -2 \pm 2\sqrt{5}\right)$
asymptotes: $y + 2 = \pm\dfrac{1}{2}(x - 1)$

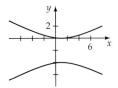

13. center: $(-2, 0)$
vertices: $(1, 0), (-5, 0)$
foci: $\left(-2 \pm \sqrt{34}, 0\right)$
asymptotes: $y = \pm\dfrac{5}{3}(x + 2)$

15. center: $(1, -1)$
vertices: $\left(\dfrac{7}{3}, -1\right), \left(-\dfrac{1}{3}, -1\right)$
foci: $\left(1 \pm \dfrac{\sqrt{97}}{3}, -1\right)$
asymptotes: $y + 1 = \pm\dfrac{9}{4}(x - 1)$

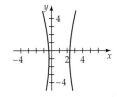

17. center: $(0, 0)$
vertices: $(\pm 3, 0)$
foci: $\left(\pm 3\sqrt{2}, 0\right)$
asymptotes: $y = \pm x$

19. center: $(0, 0)$
vertices: $(0, \pm 3)$
foci: $(0, \pm 5)$
asymptotes: $y = \pm\dfrac{3}{4}x$

21. center: $(0, 0)$
vertices: $\left(0, \pm\dfrac{2}{3}\right)$
foci: $\left(0, \pm\dfrac{\sqrt{5}}{3}\right)$
asymptotes: $y = \pm 2x$

23. center: $(3, 4)$
vertices: $(3, 6), (3, 2)$
foci: $\left(3, 4 \pm 2\sqrt{2}\right)$
asymptotes: $y - 4 = \pm(x - 3)$

25. center: $(-2, -1)$
vertices: $(-2, 2), (-2, -4)$
foci: $\left(-2, -1 \pm \sqrt{13}\right)$
asymptotes: $y + 1 = \pm\dfrac{3}{2}(x + 2)$

27. $y = \dfrac{-6 \pm \sqrt{36 + 4(4x^2 + 32x + 39)}}{-2}$

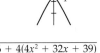
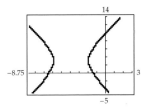

29. $y = \dfrac{64 \pm \sqrt{4096 + 64(9x^2 - 36x + 116)}}{-32}$

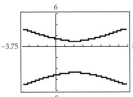

31. $y = \dfrac{18 \pm \sqrt{324 + 36(4x^2 + 8x - 6)}}{-18}$

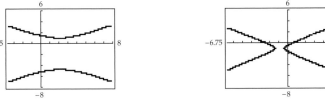

33. $\dfrac{x^2}{9} - \dfrac{y^2}{7} = 1$ **35.** $\dfrac{y^2}{20} - \dfrac{x^2}{5} = 1$

37. $\dfrac{y^2}{9} - \dfrac{x^2}{36/7} = 1$ **39.** $\dfrac{y^2}{16} - \dfrac{x^2}{64} = 1$ **41.** $\dfrac{(x - 4)^2}{4} - \dfrac{(y - 3)^2}{5} = 1$ **43.** $\dfrac{(x - 4)^2}{144/41} - \dfrac{(y + 2)^2}{225/41} = 1$ **45.** $\dfrac{(y - 2)^2}{3} - \dfrac{(x - 7)^2}{12} = 1$

47. $\dfrac{(y - 7)^2}{1} - \dfrac{(x - 1)^2}{3} = 1$ **49.** $\dfrac{x^2}{4} - \dfrac{y^2}{12} = 1$ **51.** $\dfrac{(x - 4)^2}{36/7} - \dfrac{(y - 1)^2}{4} = 1$ and $\dfrac{(y - 1)^2}{36/7} - \dfrac{(x - 4)^2}{4} = 1$ **53. a.** $\dfrac{x^2}{2162.25} - \dfrac{y^2}{13,462.75} = 1$

b. 221 miles   **55.** $y^2 - x^2 = 10{,}000^2$, hyperbola   **57.** ellipse   **59.** parabola   **61.** parabola

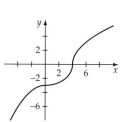

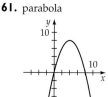

63. ellipse   **65.** $\dfrac{x^2}{1} - \dfrac{y^2}{3} = 1$ **67.** $\dfrac{y^2}{9} - \dfrac{x^2}{7} = 1$ **69.** $x = \pm\dfrac{16\sqrt{41}}{41}$ **73.**

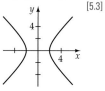

Chapter 5 True/False Exercises, page 500

1. False; a parabola has no asymptotes.   **2.** True   **3.** False; by keeping the foci fixed and varying the asymptotes, we can make the conjugate axis any size needed.   **4.** False; $\dfrac{x^2}{25} + \dfrac{y^2}{9} = 1$ and $\dfrac{x^2}{36} + \dfrac{y^2}{20} = 1$ have the same c's but different a's.   **5.** False; parabolas have no asymptotes.   **6.** True   **7.** False; the graph of a parabola can be a function.   **8.** True   **9.** True

Chapter 5 Review Exercises, page 500

1. vertices: $(\pm 2, 0)$ **3.** vertices: $(-1, -1), (7, -1)$ **5.** vertex: $(-2, 1)$ **7.** vertices: $(-2, -2), (-2, 4)$

center: $(0, 0)$ center: $(3, -1)$ focus: $\left(-\dfrac{29}{16}, 1\right)$ center: $(-2, 1)$

foci: $\left(\pm 2\sqrt{2}, 0\right)$ foci: $\left(3 \pm 2\sqrt{3}, -1\right)$ directrix: $x = -\dfrac{35}{16}$ foci: $\left(-2, 1 \pm \sqrt{5}\right)$

asymptotes: $y = \pm x$

[5.3]   [5.2]   [5.1]   [5.2]

9. vertices: $\left(-5, \dfrac{2}{3}\right), \left(7, \dfrac{2}{3}\right)$ **11.** vertex: $\left(-\dfrac{7}{2}, -1\right)$ **13.** $\dfrac{(x-2)^2}{25} + \dfrac{(y-3)^2}{16} = 1$ [5.2]   **15.** $\dfrac{(x+2)^2}{4} - \dfrac{(y-2)^2}{5} = 1$ [5.2]

center: $\left(1, \dfrac{2}{3}\right)$ focus: $\left(-\dfrac{7}{2}, -3\right)$

foci: $\left(1 \pm 2\sqrt{13}, \dfrac{2}{3}\right)$ directrix: $y = 1$

asymptotes: $y - \dfrac{2}{3} = \pm\dfrac{2}{3}(x - 1)$

[5.3]   [5.1]

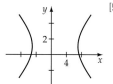

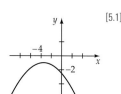

17. $x^2 = \dfrac{3}{2}(y + 2)$ or $(y + 2)^2 = 12x$ [5.1]   **19.** $\dfrac{x^2}{36} - \dfrac{y^2}{4/9} = 1$ [5.3]   **21.** $(y - 3)^2 = -8x$ [5.1]   **23.** $\dfrac{(x-1)^2}{25} + \dfrac{(y-1)^2}{9} = 1$ [5.2]

Chapter 5 Test, page 501

1. focus: $(0, 2)$
vertex: $(0, 0)$
directrix: $y = -2$
[5.1]

2. focus: $(-2, 4)$
vertex: $(-2, 1)$
directrix: $y = -2$
[5.1]

3. $(y + 2)^2 = -8(x - 1)$ [5.1]

4. 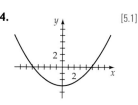 [5.1]

5. vertices: $(0, 8)$, $(0, -8)$
foci: $\left(0, \sqrt{55}\right), \left(0, -\sqrt{55}\right)$ [5.2]

6. 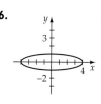 [5.2]

7. vertices: $(3, 4)$, $(3, -6)$
foci: $(3, 3)$, $(3, -5)$ [5.2]

8. $\dfrac{x^2}{45} + \dfrac{(y + 3)^2}{9} = 1$ [5.2]

9. $\dfrac{4}{5}$ [5.3]

10. 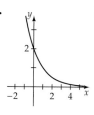 [5.3]

11. vertices: $(6, 0)$, $(-6, 0)$
foci: $(-10, 0)$, $(10, 0)$
asymptotes: $y = \pm \dfrac{4}{3} x$ [5.3]

12. [5.3]

13. vertices: $(-5, 10)$, $(-5, -2)$
foci: $\left(-5, 4 + 3\sqrt{5}\right), \left(-5, 4 - 3\sqrt{5}\right)$ [5.3]

14. $\dfrac{(x + 4)^2}{4} - \dfrac{(y + 3)^2}{30} = 1$

15. $(y - 4)^2 = -16(x - 2)$

Cumulative Review Exercises, page 502

1. $\pm 2, \pm i\sqrt{2}$ [1.4]

2. $\dfrac{-x + 7}{(x - 1)(x + 2)}$ [P.5]

3. $-4 - h$ [2.6]

4. -19 [2.6]

5. 6 [3.4]

6. $y = -\dfrac{3}{2} x - \dfrac{5}{2}$ [2.3]

7. $x = -3, y = 2$ [3.5]

8. $\sqrt{29}$ [2.1]

9. [4.2]

10. 1 [4.5]

11. 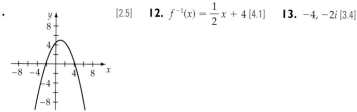 [2.5]

12. $f^{-1}(x) = \dfrac{1}{2} x + 4$ [4.1]

13. $-4, -2i$ [3.4]

14. odd [2.5]

15. origin [2.5]

16. 1.465 [4.5]

17. $(-4, 1)$ [1.5]

18. all real numbers except -2 and 2 [2.2]

19. $A(d) = \dfrac{d^2}{2}$ [2.2]

20. 4.8 s [4.2]

Exercise Set 6.1, page 513

1. $(2, -4)$
3. $\left(-\dfrac{6}{5}, \dfrac{27}{5}\right)$
5. $(3, 4)$
7. $(1, -1)$
9. $(3, -4)$
11. $(2, 5)$
13. $(-1, -1)$
15. $\left(\dfrac{62}{25}, \dfrac{34}{25}\right)$
17. no solution

19. $\left(c, -\dfrac{4}{3} c + 2\right)$
21. $(2, -4)$
23. $(0, 3)$
25. $\left(\dfrac{3}{5} c, c\right)$
27. $\left(-\dfrac{1}{2}, \dfrac{2}{3}\right)$
29. no solution
31. $(-6, 3)$
33. $\left(2, -\dfrac{3}{2}\right)$

35. $\left(2\sqrt{3}, 3\right)$
37. $\left(\dfrac{38}{17\pi}, \dfrac{3}{17}\right)$
39. $\left(\sqrt{2}, \sqrt{3}\right)$
41. \$125
43. plane: 120 mph, wind: 30 mph

45. boat: 25 mph, current: 5 mph
47. \$12 per kilogram for iron, \$16 per kilogram for lead

49. 8 grams of 40% gold, 12 grams of 60% gold
51. $\dfrac{9}{5}$ square units
53. 8
55. 42, 56, 70; 40, 42, 58; 42, 144, 150; 42, 440, 442

57. 90 people
59. $(63,800, 12,760)$ The point indicates that a person with an adjusted gross income of \$63,800 would pay the same tax using either method.
61. \$14,000 at 6%, \$11,000 at 6.5%
63. $x = -\dfrac{58}{17}, y = \dfrac{52}{17}$
65. $x = -2, y = -1$
67. $x = \dfrac{153}{26}, y = \dfrac{151}{26}$

69. $x = 2 + 3i, y = 1 - 2i$
71. $x = 3 - 5i, y = 4i$

Prepare for Section 6.2, page 516

72. $y = \dfrac{2}{5}x - 3$ **73.** $z = -c + 13$ **74.** $\left(\dfrac{18}{5}, 4\right)$ **75.** $(2, -5)$ **76.** $(-2, -10)$ **77.** $(c, -4c + 9)$

Exercise Set 6.2, page 527

1. $(2, -1, 3)$ **3.** $(2, 0, -3)$ **5.** $(2, -3, 1)$ **7.** $(-5, 1, -1)$ **9.** $(3, -5, 0)$ **11.** $(0, 2, 3)$ **13.** $(5c - 25, 48 - 9c, c)$ **15.** $(3, -1, 0)$

17. no solution   **19.** $\left(\dfrac{1}{11}(50 - 11c), \dfrac{1}{11}(11c - 18), c\right)$ **21.** no solution   **23.** $\left(\dfrac{1}{29}(25 + 4c), \dfrac{1}{29}(55 - 26c), c\right)$ **25.** $(0, 0, 0)$

27. $\left(\dfrac{5}{14}c, \dfrac{4}{7}c, c\right)$ **29.** $(-11c, -6c, c)$ **31.** $(0, 0, 0)$ **33.** $y = 2x^2 - x - 3$ **35.** $x^2 + y^2 - 4x + 2y - 20 = 0$

37. center $(-7, -2)$, radius 13   **39.** 500 cars per hour   **41.** AC: 258 to 308, CD: 209 to 259, BD: 262 to 312   **43.** $d_1 = 9$ inches,

$d_2 = 3$ inches, $d_3 = 4$ inches   **45.** $(3, 5, 2, -3)$ **47.** $(1, -2, -1, 3)$ **49.** $(14a - 7b - 8, -6a + 2b + 5, a, b)$ **51.** $A = -\dfrac{13}{2}$

53. $A \neq -3, A \neq 1$ **55.** $A = -3$ **57.** $3x - 5y - 2z = -2$

Prepare for Section 6.3, page 530

58. $-1 \pm \sqrt{3}$ **59.** $(1, -3)$ **60.** parabola   **61.** hyperbola   **62.** 2   **63.** 4

Exercise Set 6.3, page 536

1. $(1, 0), (2, 2)$ **3.** $\left(\dfrac{2 + \sqrt{2}}{2}, \dfrac{-6 + \sqrt{2}}{2}\right), \left(\dfrac{2 - \sqrt{2}}{2}, \dfrac{-6 - \sqrt{2}}{2}\right)$ **5.** $(5, 18)$ **7.** $(4, 6), (6, 4)$ **9.** $\left(-\dfrac{3}{2}, -4\right), (2, 3)$

11. $\left(\dfrac{19}{29}, -\dfrac{11}{29}\right), (1, 1)$ **13.** $(-2, 9), (1, -3), (-1, 1)$ **15.** $(-2, 1), (-2, -1), (2, 1), (2, -1)$ **17.** $(4, 2), (-4, 2), (4, -2), (-4, -2)$

19. no real number solution   **21.** $\left(\dfrac{12}{5}, \dfrac{1}{5}\right), (2, 1)$ **23.** $\left(\dfrac{26}{5}, -\dfrac{3}{5}\right), (1, -2)$ **25.** $\left(\dfrac{39}{10}, -\dfrac{7}{10}\right), (3, 2)$

27. $\left(\dfrac{-3 + \sqrt{3}}{2}, \dfrac{1 + \sqrt{3}}{2}\right), \left(\dfrac{-3 - \sqrt{3}}{2}, \dfrac{1 - \sqrt{3}}{2}\right)$ **29.** $\left(\dfrac{19}{13}, \dfrac{22}{13}\right), (1, 4)$ **31.** no real number solution   **33.** 82 units

35. $r \geq \sqrt{\dfrac{1}{5}}$ or $\dfrac{\sqrt{5}}{5}$ **37.** \$45   **39.** $(0, 1), (1, 2)$ **41.** $(0.7035, 0.4949)$ **43.** $(1.7549, 1.3247)$ **45.** $(-0.7071, 0.7071), (0.7071, 0.7071)$

47. $(1, 5)$ **49.** $(-1, 1), (1, -1)$ **51.** $(1, -2), (-1, 2)$

Prepare for Section 6.4, page 537

54. $(x^2 + 7)^2$ **55.** $\dfrac{6x + 9}{(x - 1)(x + 2)}$ **56.** $\dfrac{x^2 + 2x + 7}{x(x - 1)^2}$ **57.** $(-1, 2)$ **58.** $(2, -2, -1)$ **59.** $x + 3 + \dfrac{2x - 35}{x^2 - 7x}$

Exercise Set 6.4, page 544

1. $A = -3, B = 4$ **3.** $A = -\dfrac{2}{5}, B = \dfrac{1}{5}$ **5.** $A = 1, B = -1, C = 4$ **7.** $A = 1, B = 3, C = 2$ **9.** $A = 1, B = 0, C = 1, D = 0$

11. $\dfrac{3}{x} + \dfrac{5}{x + 4}$ **13.** $\dfrac{7}{x - 9} + \dfrac{-4}{x + 2}$ **15.** $\dfrac{5}{2x + 3} + \dfrac{3}{2x + 5}$ **17.** $\dfrac{20}{11(3x + 5)} + \dfrac{-3}{11(x - 2)}$ **19.** $x + 3 + \dfrac{1}{x - 2} + \dfrac{-1}{x + 2}$

21. $\dfrac{1}{x} + \dfrac{2}{x + 7} + \dfrac{-28}{(x + 7)^2}$ **23.** $\dfrac{2}{x} + \dfrac{3x - 1}{x^2 - 3x + 1}$ **25.** $\dfrac{2}{x + 3} + \dfrac{-1}{(x + 3)^2} + \dfrac{4}{x^2 + 1}$ **27.** $\dfrac{3}{x - 4} + \dfrac{5}{(x - 4)^2}$ **29.** $\dfrac{3x - 1}{x^2 + 10} + \dfrac{4x}{(x^2 + 10)^2}$

31. $\dfrac{1}{2k(k - x)} + \dfrac{1}{2k(k + x)}$ **33.** $x + \dfrac{1}{x} + \dfrac{-2}{x - 1}$ **35.** $2x - 2 + \dfrac{3}{x^2 - x - 1}$ **37.** $\dfrac{1}{5(x + 2)} + \dfrac{4}{5(x - 3)}$ **39.** $\dfrac{1}{x} + \dfrac{2}{x^2} + \dfrac{3}{x^4} + \dfrac{-2}{x - 2}$

41. $\dfrac{4}{3(x - 1)} + \dfrac{2x + 7}{3(x^2 + x + 1)}$

Prepare for Section 6.5, page 545

45.   **46.**   **47.**   **48.**   **49.**

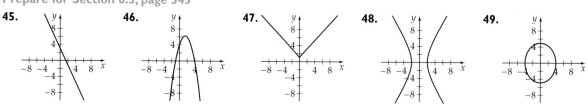

50.

Exercise Set 6.5, page 551

1.   **3.**   **5.**   **7.** 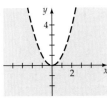 **9.**

11.   **13.**   **15.**   **17.**   **19.**

21.   **23.** 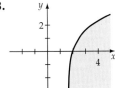 **25.**   **27.**   **29.** no solution

31. 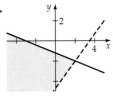 **33.**   **35.** 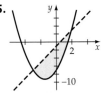 **37.**   **39.**

41. 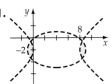 **43.** 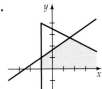 **45.**   **47.** 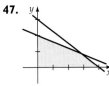 **49.**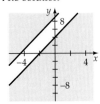

51. 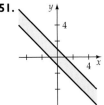 **53.** 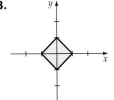 **55.**

57.

$xy > 1$ $y > \dfrac{1}{x}$

If x is a negative number, then the inequality is reversed when both sides of the inequality are divided by a negative number.

Prepare for Section 6.6, page 552

59.

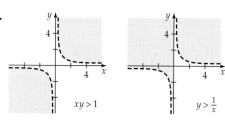

60.

61.

62.

63. $(1, 3)$ **64.** $(1, 6)$

Exercise Set 6.6, page 559

1. minimum at $(0, 8)$: 16   **3.** maximum at $(6, 5)$: 71   **5.** minimum at $\left(0, \dfrac{10}{3}\right)$: 20   **7.** maximum at $(0, 12)$: 72

9. minimum at $(0, 32)$: 32   **11.** maximum at $(0, 8)$: 56   **13.** minimum at $(2, 6)$: 18   **15.** maximum at $(3, 4)$: 25

17. minimum at $(2, 3)$: 12   **19.** maximum at $(100, 400)$: 3400   **21.** 20 acres of wheat and 40 acres of barley

23. 0 starter sets and 18 pro sets   **25.** 24 ounces of group B and 0 ounces of group A yields a minimum cost of \$2.40.

27. Two 4-cylinder engines and seven 6-cylinder engines yields a maximum profit of \$2050.

Chapter 6 True/False Exercises, page 563

1. False; $\begin{cases} x + y = 1 \\ x + y = 3 \end{cases}$ has no solution.   **2.** True   **3.** False; a homogeneous system is one in which the constant term in each equation is zero.

4. True   **5.** True   **6.** False; $\begin{cases} x + y = 2 \\ x + 2y = 3 \end{cases}$ and $\begin{cases} 2x + 3y = 5 \\ 2x - 2y = 0 \end{cases}$ are two systems with the same solution but without common equations.   **7.** True

8. True   **9.** False; it is inconsistent.   **10.** False; $(-1, 1)$ satisfies the first inequality but not the second, and $(-2, -1)$ satisfies the second but not the first.

Chapter 6 Review Exercises, page 563

1. $\left(-\dfrac{18}{7}, -\dfrac{15}{28}\right)$ [6.1]   **2.** $\left(\dfrac{3}{2}, -3\right)$ [6.1]   **3.** $(-3, -1)$ [6.1]   **4.** $(-4, 7)$ [6.1]   **5.** $(3, 1)$ [6.1]   **6.** $(-1, 1)$ [6.1]   **7.** $\left(\dfrac{1}{2}(5 - 3c), c\right)$ [6.1]

8. no solution [6.1]   **9.** $\left(\dfrac{1}{2}, 3, -1\right)$ [6.2]   **10.** $\left(\dfrac{16}{3}, \dfrac{10}{27}, -\dfrac{29}{45}\right)$ [6.2]   **11.** $\left(\dfrac{1}{11}(7c - 3), \dfrac{1}{11}(16c - 43), c\right)$ [6.2]   **12.** $\left(\dfrac{74}{31}, -\dfrac{1}{31}, \dfrac{3}{31}\right)$ [6.2]

13. $\left(2, \dfrac{1}{2}(3c + 2), c\right)$ [6.2]   **14.** $\left(1, -\dfrac{2}{3}, \dfrac{1}{4}\right)$ [6.2]   **15.** $\left(\dfrac{14}{11}c, -\dfrac{2}{11}c, c\right)$ [6.2]   **16.** $(0, 0, 0)$ [6.2]   **17.** $\left(\dfrac{1}{2}(c + 1), \dfrac{1}{4}(3c - 1), c\right)$ [6.2]

18. $\left(\dfrac{65 - 11c}{16}, \dfrac{19 - c}{8}, c\right)$ [6.2]   **19.** $(2, -3)$ [6.3]   **20.** $\left(-\dfrac{1}{2}, 0\right)$ and $(1, 3)$ [6.3]   **21.** no real solution [6.3]   **22.** $\left(\dfrac{3}{2}, 3\right)$ and $(1, -1)$ [6.3]

23. $\left(\dfrac{1}{5}, \dfrac{18}{5}\right)$, $(1, 2)$ [6.3]   **24.** $(0, -3)$ and $(2, 1)$ [6.3]   **25.** $(2, 0)$, $\left(\dfrac{18}{17}, -\dfrac{64}{17}\right)$ [6.3]   **26.** $(0, 2)$ and $\left(-\dfrac{32}{25}, \dfrac{26}{25}\right)$ [6.3]

27. $(2, 1)$, $(-2, -1)$ [6.3]   **28.** $(1, 3)$, $(-1, -3)$, $\left(\dfrac{\sqrt{6}}{6}, -\dfrac{\sqrt{6}}{3}\right)$, and $\left(-\dfrac{\sqrt{6}}{6}, \dfrac{\sqrt{6}}{3}\right)$ [6.3]   **29.** $(2, -3)$, $(-2, 3)$ [6.3]   **30.** $\left(\dfrac{\sqrt{15}}{15}, \dfrac{\sqrt{15}}{15}\right)$,

$\left(-\dfrac{\sqrt{15}}{15}, -\dfrac{\sqrt{15}}{15}\right)$, $(1, -1)$, $(-1, 1)$ [6.3]   **31.** $\dfrac{3}{x - 2} + \dfrac{4}{x + 1}$ [6.4]   **32.** $\dfrac{1}{x - 1} + \dfrac{2}{(x - 1)^2}$ [6.4]   **33.** $\dfrac{6x - 2}{5(x^2 + 1)} + \dfrac{-6}{5(x + 2)}$ [6.4]

34. $\dfrac{7}{3(x - 2)} + \dfrac{3}{(x - 2)^2} + \dfrac{8}{3(x + 1)}$ [6.4]   **35.** $\dfrac{2}{x} + \dfrac{4}{x - 1} + \dfrac{5}{x + 1}$ [6.4]   **36.** $1 + \dfrac{x + 2}{x^2 + 1}$ [6.4]   **37.**   [6.5]

38. 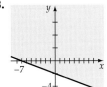 [6.5] **39.** 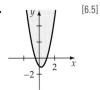 [6.5] **40.** 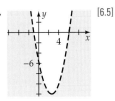 [6.5] **41.** 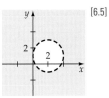 [6.5]

42. 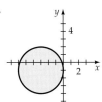 [6.5] **43.** 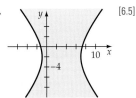 [6.5] **44.** 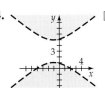 [6.5] **45.** 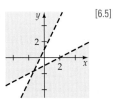 [6.5]

46. 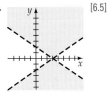 [6.5] **47.** 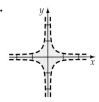 [6.5] **48.** 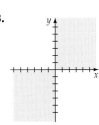 [6.5] **49.** 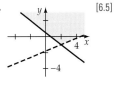 [6.5]

50. 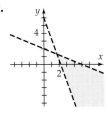 [6.5] **51.** 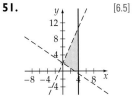 [6.5] **52.** [6.5] **53.** 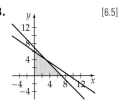 [6.5]

54. 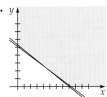 [6.5] **55.** 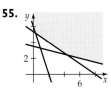 [6.5] **56.** 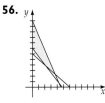 [6.5] **57.** 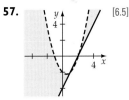 [6.5]

58. 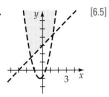 [6.5] **59.** 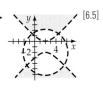 [6.5] **60.** 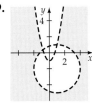 [6.5]

61. The maximum is 18 at (4, 5). [6.6] **62.** The maximum is 44 at (6, 4). [6.6] **63.** The minimum is 8 at (0, 8). [6.6] **64.** The minimum is 20 at (10, 0). [6.6] **65.** The minimum is 27 at (2, 5). [6.6] **66.** The maximum is 43 at (3, 7). [6.6] **67.** $y = \frac{11}{6}x^2 - \frac{5}{2}x + \frac{2}{3}$ [6.2]

68. $x^2 + y^2 - \frac{47}{11}x - \frac{21}{11}y + \frac{10}{11} = 0$ [6.2] **69.** $z = -2x + 3y + 3$ [6.2] **70.** $x = 15$ liters [6.1] **71.** wind: 28 mph, plane: 143 mph [6.1]

72. 4 nickels, 3 dimes, 3 quarters; 1 nickel, 7 dimes, 2 quarters [6.2] **73.** (0, 0, 0), (1, 1, 1), (1, −1, −1), (−1, −1, 1), (−1, 1, −1) [6.2]

Chapter 6 Test, page 565

1. $(-3, 2)$ [6.1] **2.** $\left(\frac{1}{2}(6 + c), c\right)$ [6.1] **3.** $\left(\frac{173}{39}, \frac{29}{39}, -\frac{4}{3}\right)$ [6.2] **4.** $\left(\frac{1}{4}(c + 3), \frac{1}{8}(7c + 1), c\right)$ [6.2] **5.** $\left(\frac{1}{13}(c + 10), \frac{1}{13}(5c + 11), c\right)$ [6.2]

6. $\left(\frac{1}{14}c, -\frac{9}{14}c, c\right)$ [6.2] **7.** $(2, 5), (-2, 1)$ [6.3] **8.** $(-2, 3), (-1, -1)$ [6.3] **9.** 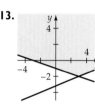 [6.5] **10.** 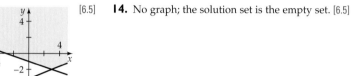 [6.5]

11. 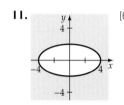 [6.5] **12.** 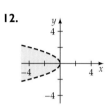 [6.5] **13.** [6.5] **14.** No graph; the solution set is the empty set. [6.5]

15. 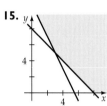 [6.5] **16.** 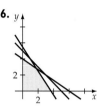 [6.5] **17.** $\dfrac{7}{5(x - 4)} + \dfrac{8}{5(x + 1)}$ [6.4] **18.** $\dfrac{1}{x} + \dfrac{-x + 2}{x^2 + 1}$ [6.4]

19. $\dfrac{680}{7}$ acres of oats and $\dfrac{400}{7}$ acres of barley [6.6] **20.** $x^2 + y^2 - 2y - 24 = 0$ [6.2]

Cumulative Review Exercises, page 566

1. $-\dfrac{14}{27}$ [2.3] **2.** $\{y \mid y \le -3\}$ [2.4] **3.** 91 [P.1] **4.** $\log_6[8x^3(x - 5)]$ [4.4] **5.** $(x - 4)^2 = -25(y - 2)$ [8.1] **6.** $d_0 = \dfrac{Fd_1}{d_1 - F}$ [1.2]

7. $y = -\dfrac{1}{2}x$ [2.2] **8.** even [2.5] **9.** $\dfrac{300}{199}$ [4.5] **10.** $\dfrac{(x - 6)^2}{16} - \dfrac{(y - 2)^2}{20} = 1$ [8.3] **11.** 5 [2.2] **12.** 30 [2.6] **13.** 3 [4.3]

14. $x^2 + 0.4x - 0.8$ [2.7] **15.** $x^3 + 2x^2 + 9x + 18$ [3.4] **16.** $Q^{-1}(r) = \dfrac{r - 2}{2}$ [4.1] **17.** $y = 2x + 1$ [3.5] **18.** 81 [4.2]

19. 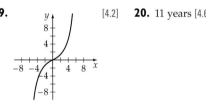 [4.2] **20.** 11 years [4.6]

Exercise Set 7.1, page 578

1. $\begin{bmatrix} 2 & -3 & 1 & 1 \\ 3 & -2 & 3 & 0 \\ 1 & 0 & 5 & 4 \end{bmatrix}, \begin{bmatrix} 2 & -3 & 1 \\ 3 & -2 & 3 \\ 1 & 0 & 5 \end{bmatrix}, \begin{bmatrix} 1 \\ 0 \\ 4 \end{bmatrix}$ **3.** $\begin{bmatrix} 2 & -3 & -4 & 1 & 2 \\ 0 & 2 & 1 & 0 & 2 \\ 1 & -1 & 2 & 0 & 4 \\ 3 & -3 & -2 & 0 & 1 \end{bmatrix}, \begin{bmatrix} 2 & -3 & -4 & 1 \\ 0 & 2 & 1 & 0 \\ 1 & -1 & 2 & 0 \\ 3 & -3 & -2 & 0 \end{bmatrix}, \begin{bmatrix} 2 \\ 2 \\ 4 \\ 1 \end{bmatrix}$ **5.** $\begin{bmatrix} 1 & -1 & 2 & 2 \\ 0 & 1 & -1 & -6 \\ 0 & 0 & 1 & -\frac{27}{2} \end{bmatrix}$

7. $\begin{bmatrix} 1 & -2 & -1 & 3 \\ 0 & 1 & 2 & -\frac{11}{2} \\ 0 & 0 & 1 & -\frac{13}{6} \end{bmatrix}$ **9.** $\begin{bmatrix} 1 & -2 & 3 & -4 \\ 0 & 1 & 2 & -\frac{1}{2} \\ 0 & 0 & 1 & -2 \\ 0 & 0 & 0 & 0 \end{bmatrix}$ **11.** $\begin{bmatrix} 1 & -3 & 4 & 2 & 1 \\ 0 & 1 & -1 & -2 & -1 \\ 0 & 0 & 0 & 1 & 3 \end{bmatrix}$ **13.** $(2, -1, 1)$ **15.** $(1, -2, -1)$

17. $\left(2 - 2c, 2c + \dfrac{1}{2}, c\right)$ **19.** $\left(\dfrac{1}{2}, \dfrac{1}{2}, \dfrac{3}{2}\right)$ **21.** $(16c, 6c, c)$ **23.** $(7c + 6, -11c - 8, c)$ **25.** $(c + 2, c, c)$ **27.** no solution

29. $(2, -2, 3, 4)$ **31.** $\left(\dfrac{21}{10}, -\dfrac{8}{5}, \dfrac{2}{5}, -\dfrac{5}{2}\right)$ **33.** $\left(3, -\dfrac{3}{2}, 1, -1\right)$ **35.** $\left(\dfrac{27}{2}c + 39, \dfrac{5}{2}c + 10, -4c - 10, c\right)$

37. $\left(c_1 - \dfrac{12}{7}c_2 + \dfrac{6}{7}, c_1 - \dfrac{9}{7}c_2 + \dfrac{1}{7}, c_1, c_2\right)$ **39.** $p(x) = 2x - 3$ **41.** $p(x) = x^2 - 2x + 3$ **43.** $p(x) = x^3 - 2x^2 - x + 2$

45. $p(x) = 2x + 5$ **47.** $z = 2x + 3y - 2$ **49.** $x^2 + y^2 + 2x - 4y - 20 = 0$ **51.** $(1, 0, -2, 1, 2)$

53. $\left(\dfrac{77c + 151}{3}, \dfrac{-25c - 50}{3}, \dfrac{14c + 34}{3}, -3c - 7, c\right)$ **55.** all values of a except $a = 1$ and $a = -6$ **57.** $a = -6$

Prepare for Section 7.2, page 581

58. The additive inverse of c is $-c$. The additive inverse of zero is zero.   **59.** 1   **60.** No   **61.** $a = 5, b = -1$ **62.** 3×1

63. $\begin{cases} 3x - 5y = 16 \\ 2x + 7y = -10 \end{cases}$

Exercise Set 7.2, page 595

1. a. $\begin{bmatrix} 1 & 2 \\ 5 & 4 \end{bmatrix}$ **b.** $\begin{bmatrix} 3 & -4 \\ 1 & 2 \end{bmatrix}$ **c.** $\begin{bmatrix} -2 & 6 \\ 4 & 2 \end{bmatrix}$ **d.** $\begin{bmatrix} 7 & -11 \\ 0 & 3 \end{bmatrix}$ **3. a.** $\begin{bmatrix} -3 & 0 & 5 \\ 3 & 5 & -5 \end{bmatrix}$ **b.** $\begin{bmatrix} 3 & -2 & 1 \\ -1 & -5 & 1 \end{bmatrix}$ **c.** $\begin{bmatrix} -6 & 2 & 4 \\ 4 & 10 & -6 \end{bmatrix}$

d. $\begin{bmatrix} 9 & -5 & 0 \\ -4 & -15 & 5 \end{bmatrix}$ **5. a.** $\begin{bmatrix} 1 & 5 \\ 3 & -5 \\ 2 & -4 \end{bmatrix}$ **b.** $\begin{bmatrix} -7 & 3 \\ 1 & -1 \\ -4 & 4 \end{bmatrix}$ **c.** $\begin{bmatrix} 8 & 2 \\ 2 & -4 \\ 6 & -8 \end{bmatrix}$ **d.** $\begin{bmatrix} -18 & 5 \\ 1 & 0 \\ -11 & 12 \end{bmatrix}$ **7. a.** $\begin{bmatrix} -1 & 1 & -1 \\ 2 & 2 & 1 \\ -1 & 2 & 5 \end{bmatrix}$ **b.** $\begin{bmatrix} -3 & 5 & -1 \\ -2 & -4 & 3 \\ -7 & 4 & 1 \end{bmatrix}$

c. $\begin{bmatrix} 2 & -4 & 0 \\ 4 & 6 & -2 \\ 6 & -2 & 4 \end{bmatrix}$ **d.** $\begin{bmatrix} -7 & 12 & -2 \\ -6 & -11 & 7 \\ -17 & 9 & 0 \end{bmatrix}$ **9.** $\begin{bmatrix} -10 & 17 \\ 6 & -8 \end{bmatrix}\begin{bmatrix} 0 & 22 \\ 1 & -18 \end{bmatrix}$ **11.** $\begin{bmatrix} 10 & 6 \\ 14 & -7 \end{bmatrix}\begin{bmatrix} 14 & -1 \\ 0 & -11 \end{bmatrix}$ **13.** $\begin{bmatrix} 0 & -4 & 5 \\ 6 & 0 & 3 \\ -3 & -2 & 1 \end{bmatrix}\begin{bmatrix} 5 & -13 \\ 5 & -4 \end{bmatrix}$

15. $\begin{bmatrix} 9 & -2 & -6 \\ 0 & -1 & 2 \\ 4 & -2 & -4 \end{bmatrix}\begin{bmatrix} 4 & -2 & 6 \\ 2 & -3 & 4 \\ 4 & -4 & 3 \end{bmatrix}$ **17.** $[0, 8]$ **19.** The product is not possible.   **21.** $\begin{bmatrix} 0 & 0 \\ 0 & 0 \end{bmatrix}$ **23.** The product is not possible.

25. $\begin{bmatrix} \frac{1}{3} & -\frac{5}{3} \\ -\frac{1}{3} & \frac{4}{3} \\ \frac{1}{3} & -\frac{4}{3} \end{bmatrix}$ **27.** $\begin{bmatrix} -1 & 1 \\ 3 & 2 \\ 7 & -2 \end{bmatrix}$ **29.** $\begin{bmatrix} 1 & -3 \\ 1 & -2 \end{bmatrix}$ **31.** $\begin{bmatrix} 7 & -1 & 1 \\ 1 & 2 & 0 \\ 5 & -1 & 4 \end{bmatrix}$ **33.** $\begin{cases} 3x - 8y = 11 \\ 4x + 3y = 1 \end{cases}$ **35.** $\begin{cases} x - 3y - 2z = 6 \\ 3x + y = 2 \\ 2x - 4y + 5z = 1 \end{cases}$

37. $\begin{cases} 2x_1 - x_2 + 2x_4 = 5 \\ 4x_1 + x_2 + 2x_3 - 3x_4 = 6 \\ 6x_1 + x_3 - 2x_4 = 10 \\ 5x_1 + 2x_2 - x_3 - 4x_4 = 8 \end{cases}$ **39. a.** 3×4. Three different fish were caught in four different samples.   **b.** Fish A was caught in sample 4.

c. Fish B   **41.** $\begin{bmatrix} 1.96 & 1.37 & 2.94 & 1.37 \\ 0.78 & 1.08 & 1.96 & 0.88 \\ 3.53 & 1.18 & 4.41 & 1.47 \end{bmatrix}$ **43. a.** $\begin{bmatrix} 87 & 74 \\ 85 & 77 \\ 83 & 79 \end{bmatrix}$ **b.** The matrix represents the total number of wins and losses for each team.

c. $\begin{bmatrix} 1 & -2 \\ -1 & 1 \\ 7 & -7 \end{bmatrix}$ **d.** The matrix represents the difference between performance at home and performance away.   **45. a.** $\begin{bmatrix} 0 & 6 & 4 & -2 \\ 4 & 1 & -3 & 0 \end{bmatrix}$

b.   **c.** The new rectangle is shifted 2 units to the right and 1 unit down from the original rectangle.

47. a. $\begin{bmatrix} -5 & -2 & 2 & -1 \\ -2 & 4 & 2 & -4 \end{bmatrix}$ **b.**

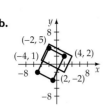

c. The second rectangle is obtained by reflecting the first about $y = x$ and then reflecting the result about $x = 0$.

49. $A - B = \begin{bmatrix} 50 & 150 & 140 \\ 15 & 170 & 370 \\ 85 & 250 & 130 \\ 80 & 115 & 25 \end{bmatrix}$ $A - B$ is the number of each item sold during the week. **51.** $\begin{bmatrix} 65 & 88.5 \\ 54 & 72 \\ 68.5 & 94.5 \end{bmatrix}; T_2$ **53. a.** 45.6% **b.** 46.7%

55. a. 16.1% **b.** 23.5% **57.** 11 months **59.** $\begin{bmatrix} 24 & 21 & -12 & 32 & 0 \\ -7 & -8 & 3 & 21 & 20 \\ 32 & 10 & -32 & 1 & 5 \\ 19 & -15 & -17 & 30 & 20 \\ 29 & 9 & -28 & 13 & -6 \end{bmatrix}$ **61.** $\begin{bmatrix} 46 & -100 & 36 & 273 & 93 \\ 82 & -93 & 19 & 27 & 97 \\ 73 & -10 & -23 & 109 & 83 \\ 212 & -189 & 52 & 37 & 156 \\ 68 & -22 & 54 & 221 & 58 \end{bmatrix}$

63. $\begin{bmatrix} 76 & -8 & -25 & 30 & 6 \\ 14 & 16 & -10 & 14 & 2 \\ 39 & 0 & -45 & 22 & 27 \\ 0 & -4 & 23 & 83 & -16 \\ 56 & -20 & -22 & 7 & 5 \end{bmatrix}$ **65.** $\begin{bmatrix} 6 + 9i & 3 - 6i \\ 3 + 3i & 6 - 3i \end{bmatrix}$ **67.** $\begin{bmatrix} 2 + 2i & -6 + 4i \\ -4 + 6i & 2 + 8i \end{bmatrix}$ **69.** $\begin{bmatrix} 3 + 2i & 3 + i \\ 4 + 3i & 6 - 2i \end{bmatrix}$ **71.** $\begin{bmatrix} 12 - 3i & -3 + 3i \\ 10 + i & 6 - i \end{bmatrix}$

73. $\begin{bmatrix} -2 + 11i & 8 - 6i \\ 2 + 6i & 6 - 5i \end{bmatrix}$

Prepare for Section 7.3, page 600

80. $-\dfrac{3}{2}$ **81.** $\begin{bmatrix} 1 & 0 & 0 \\ 0 & 1 & 0 \\ 0 & 0 & 1 \end{bmatrix}$ **82.** See Section 7.1. **83.** $\begin{bmatrix} 1 & -2 & 3 \\ 0 & 3 & -2 \\ 0 & -4 & 11 \end{bmatrix}$ **84.** $X = A^{-1}B$ **85.** $\begin{cases} 2x + 3y = 9 \\ 4x - 5y = 7 \end{cases}$

Exercise Set 7.3, page 610

1. $\begin{bmatrix} -5 & -3 \\ -2 & -1 \end{bmatrix}$ **3.** $\begin{bmatrix} 5 & -2 \\ -1 & \frac{1}{2} \end{bmatrix}$ **5.** $\begin{bmatrix} -16 & -2 & 7 \\ 7 & 1 & -3 \\ -3 & 0 & 1 \end{bmatrix}$ **7.** $\begin{bmatrix} 15 & -1 & -4 \\ -\frac{11}{2} & \frac{1}{2} & \frac{3}{2} \\ 3 & 0 & -1 \end{bmatrix}$ **9.** $\begin{bmatrix} \frac{7}{2} & -2 & -2 \\ -\frac{5}{2} & 1 & 2 \\ -1 & 0 & 1 \end{bmatrix}$

11. $\begin{bmatrix} \frac{19}{2} & -\frac{1}{2} & -\frac{3}{2} & \frac{3}{2} \\ \frac{7}{4} & \frac{1}{4} & -\frac{1}{4} & \frac{3}{4} \\ -\frac{7}{2} & \frac{1}{2} & \frac{1}{2} & -\frac{1}{2} \\ \frac{1}{4} & -\frac{1}{4} & \frac{1}{4} & \frac{1}{4} \end{bmatrix}$ **13.** $\begin{bmatrix} 2 & \frac{3}{5} & -\frac{7}{5} & \frac{4}{5} \\ 4 & -\frac{7}{5} & \frac{2}{5} & \frac{4}{5} \\ -6 & \frac{14}{5} & \frac{1}{5} & -\frac{3}{5} \\ 3 & -\frac{8}{5} & \frac{2}{5} & \frac{1}{5} \end{bmatrix}$ **15.** $(2, 1)$ **17.** $\left(\dfrac{7}{4}, -\dfrac{25}{8} \right)$ **19.** $(1, -1, 2)$ **21.** $(23, -12, 3)$

23. $(0, 4, -6, -2)$ **25.** $x_1: 49.7°F, x_2: 53.7°F$ **27.** $x_1: 55°F, x_2: 57.5°F, x_3: 52.5°F, x_4: 55°F$ **29.** on Saturday 80 adults, 20 children; on Sunday 95 adults, 25 children **31.** Sample 1: 500 grams of additive 1, 200 grams of additive 2, 300 grams of additive 3; Sample 2: 400 grams of

additive 1, 400 grams of additive 2, 200 grams of additive 3 **33.** $\begin{bmatrix} -5.667 & -3.667 & 5 & 0.333 \\ -27.667 & -18.667 & 24 & 2.333 \\ -19.333 & -13.333 & 17 & 1.667 \\ 15 & 10 & -13 & -1 \end{bmatrix}$ **35.** $\begin{bmatrix} -0.150 & -0.217 & 0.302 \\ 0.248 & -0.024 & 0.013 \\ 0.217 & -0.200 & -0.195 \end{bmatrix}$

37. \$194.67 million worth of manufacturing, \$157.03 million worth of transportation, \$121.82 million worth of services **39.** \$39.69 million

worth of coal, \$14.30 million worth of iron, \$32.30 million worth of steel **47. a.** $\begin{bmatrix} -\frac{5}{2} & \frac{3}{2} \\ -2 & 1 \end{bmatrix}$ **b.** $\begin{bmatrix} 2 & -3 \\ -\frac{3}{2} & \frac{5}{2} \end{bmatrix}$ **c.** $\begin{bmatrix} 1 & \frac{1}{4} \\ -1 & 0 \end{bmatrix}$

Prepare for Section 7.4, page 613

50. 2   **51.** 1   **52.** 4   **53.** 1   **54.** $\begin{bmatrix} -6 & 3 \\ 9 & -15 \end{bmatrix}$ **55.** $\begin{bmatrix} 1 & 3 & -2 \\ 0 & 5 & -3 \\ 0 & -12 & 9 \end{bmatrix}$

Exercise Set 7.4, page 621

1. 13   **3.** -15 **5.** 0   **7.** 0   **9.** 19, 19   **11.** 1, -1 **13.** $-9, -9$ **15.** $-9, -9$ **17.** 10   **19.** 53   **21.** 20   **23.** 46   **25.** 0
27. Row 2 consists of zeros, so the determinant is zero.   **29.** 2 was factored from row 2.
31. Row 1 was multiplied by -2 and added to row 2.   **33.** 2 was factored from column 1.
35. The matrix is in triangular form. The value of the determinant is the product of the terms on the main diagonal.
37. Row 1 and row 3 were interchanged, so the sign of the determinant was changed.   **39.** Each row of the determinant was multiplied by a.

41. 0   **43.** 0   **45.** 6   **47.** -90 **49.** 21   **51.** 3   **53.** -38.933 **55.** $\dfrac{9}{2}$ square units   **57.** $46\dfrac{1}{2}$ square units   **63.** $7x + 5y = -1$

65. 263.5 square units

Prepare for Section 7.5, page 623

66. -11 **67.** 9   **68.** $\begin{bmatrix} 2 & -7 \\ 3 & 5 \end{bmatrix}$ **69.** 10   **70.** $-\dfrac{7}{13}$ **71.** No

Exercise Set 7.5, page 627

1. $x_1 = \dfrac{44}{31}, x_2 = \dfrac{29}{31}$ **3.** $x_1 = \dfrac{1}{3}, x_2 = -\dfrac{2}{3}$ **5.** $x_1 = 2, x_2 = -7$ **7.** $x_1 = 0, x_2 = 0$ **9.** $x_1 = 1.28125, x_2 = 1.875$

11. $x_1 = \dfrac{21}{17}, x_2 = -\dfrac{3}{17}, x_3 = -\dfrac{29}{17}$ **13.** $x_1 = \dfrac{32}{49}, x_2 = \dfrac{13}{49}, x_3 = \dfrac{6}{7}$ **15.** $x_1 = -\dfrac{29}{64}, x_2 = -\dfrac{25}{64}, x_3 = -\dfrac{19}{32}$

17. $x_1 = \dfrac{50}{53}, x_2 = \dfrac{62}{53}, x_3 = \dfrac{4}{53}$ **19.** $x_1 = 0, x_2 = 0, x_3 = 0$ **21.** $x_2 = -\dfrac{35}{19}$ **23.** $x_1 = -\dfrac{121}{131}$ **25.** $x_4 = \dfrac{4}{3}$

27. The determinant of the coefficient matrix is zero, so Cramer's Rule cannot be used. The system of equations has infinitely many solutions.
29. all values of k except $k = 0$ **31.** all values of k except $k = 2$ **33.** $r = 3, s = -3$

Chapter 7 True/False Exercises, page 631

1. False; $A^2 = A \cdot A = \begin{bmatrix} 7 & 18 \\ 6 & 19 \end{bmatrix}$.   **2.** True   **3.** False; a singular matrix does not have a multiplicative inverse.

4. False; as an example, $A = \begin{bmatrix} 2 & -1 \\ -4 & 2 \end{bmatrix}$, $B = \begin{bmatrix} 3 & 4 \\ 1 & 5 \end{bmatrix}$, and $C = \begin{bmatrix} 4 & 7 \\ 3 & 11 \end{bmatrix}$. $AB = AC$ but $B \neq C$.   **5.** True   **6.** False; for example,

if $A = \begin{bmatrix} 1 & 4 \\ -2 & 3 \end{bmatrix}$ and $B = \begin{bmatrix} 2 & 0 \\ -1 & 5 \end{bmatrix}$, then $\det(A) + \det(B) \neq \det(A + B)$.   **7.** False; if the determinant of the coefficient matrix is zero,
Cramer's Rule cannot be used to solve the system of equations.   **8.** False; matrix multiplication is not commutative—that is, $AB \neq BA$,
$AB - BA \neq 0$.   **9.** True   **10.** False; by the Associative Property of Matrix Multiplication, given square matrices A, B, and C of order n,
$(AB)C = A(BC)$.   **11.** False; if the number of equations is less than the number of variables, the Gaussian elimination method can be used to
solve the system of linear equations. If the system of equations has a solution, the solution will be given in terms of one or more of the
variables.   **12.** False; for example, for a 2×2 matrix, $\det(2A) = 2 \cdot 2 \det(A)$, and for a 3×3 matrix, $\det(2A) = 4 \cdot 2 \det(A)$.   **13.** True

14. False; for example, given $A = \begin{bmatrix} -3 & 2 \\ -6 & 4 \end{bmatrix}$ and $B = \begin{bmatrix} 2 & 4 \\ 3 & 6 \end{bmatrix}$, then $AB = \begin{bmatrix} 0 & 0 \\ 0 & 0 \end{bmatrix} = O$, but $A \neq O$ and $B \neq O$.   **15.** True

Chapter 7 Review Exercises, page 631

1. $\begin{bmatrix} 6 & -3 & 9 \\ 9 & 6 & -3 \end{bmatrix}$ [7.2]   **2.** $\begin{bmatrix} 0 & 4 \\ -8 & -4 \\ -2 & 6 \end{bmatrix}$ [7.2]   **3.** $\begin{bmatrix} -5 & 5 & -1 \\ 1 & -4 & 6 \end{bmatrix}$ [7.2]   **4.** $\begin{bmatrix} 13 & -14 & 0 \\ -6 & 10 & -17 \end{bmatrix}$ [7.2]   **5.** $\begin{bmatrix} -1 & -15 \\ 7 & 1 \end{bmatrix}$ [7.2]

6. $\begin{bmatrix} 18 & 8 \\ -3 & -27 \end{bmatrix}$ [7.2]   **7.** $\begin{bmatrix} -6 & -4 & 2 \\ 14 & 0 & 10 \\ -7 & -7 & 6 \end{bmatrix}$ [7.2]   **8.** $\begin{bmatrix} -8 & 4 & -10 \\ -4 & 12 & 18 \\ -15 & 10 & -13 \end{bmatrix}$ [7.2]   **9.** $\begin{bmatrix} 12 & 28 & -5 \\ 2 & 6 & 0 \\ 6 & 16 & -1 \end{bmatrix}$ [7.2]   **10.** $\begin{bmatrix} 42 & 108 & -11 \\ 10 & 24 & -4 \\ 26 & 64 & -9 \end{bmatrix}$ [7.2]

11. $\begin{bmatrix} -12 & -36 & -4 \\ 48 & 124 & 4 \\ -9 & -32 & -6 \end{bmatrix}$ [7.2]   **12.** not possible [7.2]   **13.** not possible [7.2]   **14.** not possible [7.2]   **15.** $\begin{bmatrix} 7 & 24 & 9 \\ -10 & -22 & 1 \end{bmatrix}$ [7.2]

16. $\begin{bmatrix} 7 & 24 & 9 \\ -10 & -22 & 1 \end{bmatrix}$ [7.2]   **17.** $\begin{bmatrix} -1 & -5 & 4 \\ \frac{1}{2} & 2 & -\frac{3}{2} \\ 0 & -2 & 1 \end{bmatrix}$ [7.3]   **18.** -2 [7.4]   **19.** $(2, -1)$ [7.1]   **20.** $(1, -3)$ [7.1]   **21.** $(3, 0)$ [7.1]

22. $\left(\frac{40}{29}, -\frac{42}{29}\right)$ [7.1]   **23.** $(3, 1, 0)$ [7.1]   **24.** $(2, 1, 3)$ [7.1]   **25.** $(1, 0, -2)$ [7.1]   **26.** $(0, 2, 3)$ [7.1]   **27.** $(3, -4, 1)$ [7.1]
28. $(4, -2, -2)$ [7.1]   **29.** $(-c - 2, -c - 3, c)$ [7.1]   **30.** $(5, -2, 0)$ [7.1]   **31.** $(1, -2, 2, 3)$ [7.1]   **32.** $(2, 3, -1, 4)$ [7.1]
33. $(-37c + 2, 16c, -7c + 1, c)$ [7.1]   **34.** $(63c + 2, -14c + 1, 5c, c)$ [7.1]   **35.** $y = x^2 + 3x - 2$ [7.1]   **36.** $y = -x^2 - 2x + 3$ [7.1]

37. $\begin{bmatrix} -1 & 1 \\ -\frac{3}{2} & 1 \end{bmatrix}$ [7.3]   **38.** $\begin{bmatrix} 3 & -4 \\ -2 & 3 \end{bmatrix}$ [7.3]   **39.** $\begin{bmatrix} -\frac{2}{7} & \frac{3}{14} \\ \frac{1}{7} & \frac{1}{7} \end{bmatrix}$ [7.3]   **40.** $\begin{bmatrix} \frac{1}{11} & \frac{2}{11} \\ -\frac{3}{22} & \frac{5}{22} \end{bmatrix}$ [7.3]   **41.** $\begin{bmatrix} 2 & -2 & 1 \\ 0 & \frac{3}{2} & -1 \\ -1 & -1 & 1 \end{bmatrix}$ [7.3]

42. $\begin{bmatrix} 27 & -12 & 5 \\ 4 & -2 & 1 \\ -7 & 3 & -1 \end{bmatrix}$ [7.3]   **43.** $\begin{bmatrix} -10 & 20 & -3 \\ -5 & 9 & -1 \\ 3 & -6 & 1 \end{bmatrix}$ [7.3]   **44.** $\begin{bmatrix} 27 & -39 & 5 \\ -7 & 10 & -1 \\ 4 & -6 & 1 \end{bmatrix}$ [7.3]   **45.** $\begin{bmatrix} -1 & -7 & 4 & 2 \\ -6 & -3 & 2 & 3 \\ 1 & 2 & -1 & -1 \\ -2 & 0 & 0 & 1 \end{bmatrix}$ [7.3]

46. $\begin{bmatrix} \frac{116}{7} & -\frac{50}{7} & \frac{46}{7} & -\frac{51}{7} \\ -\frac{45}{7} & \frac{20}{7} & -\frac{17}{7} & \frac{19}{7} \\ 2 & -1 & 1 & -1 \\ \frac{9}{7} & -\frac{4}{7} & \frac{2}{7} & -\frac{1}{7} \end{bmatrix}$ [7.3]   **47.** The matrix does not have an inverse. [7.3]   **48.** $\begin{bmatrix} 14 & -\frac{33}{2} & -6 & \frac{5}{2} \\ 14 & -\frac{31}{2} & -7 & \frac{5}{2} \\ -9 & \frac{21}{2} & 4 & -\frac{3}{2} \\ 2 & -\frac{5}{2} & -1 & \frac{1}{2} \end{bmatrix}$ [7.3]

49. a. $(18, -13)$ **b.** $(-22, 16)$ [7.3]   **50. a.** $(41, 17)$ **b.** $(-39, -16)$ [7.3]   **51. a.** $\left(-\frac{18}{7}, \frac{23}{7}, -\frac{6}{7}\right)$ **b.** $\left(-\frac{31}{14}, \frac{20}{7}, \frac{3}{7}\right)$ [7.3]

52. a. $\left(-\frac{4}{3}, -1, 2\right)$ **b.** $(-9, -11, 6)$ [7.3]   **53.** -2 [7.4]   **54.** 1 [7.4]   **55.** -1 [7.4]   **56.** -1 [7.4]   **57.** 0 [7.4]   **58.** 3 [7.4]

59. 0 [7.4]   **60.** 0 [7.4]   **61.** $x_1 = \frac{16}{19}, x_2 = -\frac{2}{19}$ [7.5]   **62.** $x_1 = \frac{1}{13}, x_2 = -\frac{21}{26}$ [7.5]   **63.** $x_1 = \frac{13}{44}, x_2 = \frac{1}{4}, x_3 = -\frac{17}{44}$ [7.5]

64. $x_1 = -\frac{17}{22}, x_2 = \frac{19}{22}, x_3 = -\frac{13}{22}$ [7.5]   **65.** $x_1 = \frac{18}{23}, x_2 = -\frac{26}{69}, x_3 = \frac{38}{69}$ [7.5]   **66.** $x_1 = \frac{21}{83}, x_2 = \frac{12}{83}, x_3 = -\frac{40}{83}$ [7.5]

67. $x_3 = \frac{115}{126}$ [7.5]   **68.** $x_2 = -\frac{289}{230}$ [7.5]   **69.** $34.47 million computer division, $14.20 million monitor division, $23.64 million disk drive division [7.3]   **70.** $30.82 million lumber division, $20.86 million paper division, $11.79 million prefabricated walls division [7.3]

Chapter 7 Test, page 633

1. $\begin{bmatrix} 2 & 3 & -3 & 4 \\ 3 & 0 & 2 & -1 \\ 4 & -4 & 2 & 3 \end{bmatrix}$, $\begin{bmatrix} 2 & 3 & -3 \\ 3 & 0 & 2 \\ 4 & -4 & 2 \end{bmatrix}$, $\begin{bmatrix} 4 \\ -1 \\ 3 \end{bmatrix}$ [7.1]   **2.** $\begin{cases} 3x - 2y + 5z - w = 9 \\ 2x + 3y - z + 4w = 8 \\ x + 3z + 2w = -1 \end{cases}$ [7.1]   **3.** $(2, -1, 2)$ [7.1]   **4.** $(3, -1, -1)$ [7.1]

5. $(3c - 5, -7c + 14, 4 - 3c, c)$ [7.1]   **6.** $\begin{bmatrix} 3 & -9 & -6 \\ -3 & -12 & 3 \end{bmatrix}$ [7.2]   **7.** $A + B$ is not defined. [7.2]   **8.** $\begin{bmatrix} 4 & 1 & 3 \\ 8 & 0 & -19 \\ 11 & 0 & 10 \end{bmatrix}$ [7.2]

9. $\begin{bmatrix} 16 & -1 & -2 \\ 15 & -11 & -3 \end{bmatrix}$ [7.2]   **10.** $\begin{bmatrix} 17 & -4 & -4 \\ 14 & -15 & -2 \end{bmatrix}$ [7.2]   **11.** CA is not defined. [7.2]   **12.** $\begin{bmatrix} -6 & -1 & -19 \\ -15 & -25 & -27 \\ 1 & 3 & 31 \end{bmatrix}$ [7.2]

13. A^2 is not defined. [7.2]   **14.** $\begin{bmatrix} 9 & 6 & 13 \\ -3 & -2 & 12 \\ 20 & -3 & 11 \end{bmatrix}$ [7.2]   **15.** $\begin{bmatrix} 18 & -5 & 7 \\ 4 & -1 & 2 \\ -3 & 1 & -1 \end{bmatrix}$ [7.3]   **16.** $M_{21} = -8, C_{21} = 8$ [7.4]   **17.** 49 [7.4]

18. -1 [7.4]   **19.** $-\frac{140}{41}$ [7.5]   **20.** $\left(\begin{bmatrix} 1 & 0 & 0 \\ 0 & 1 & 0 \\ 0 & 0 & 1 \end{bmatrix} - \begin{bmatrix} 0.15 & 0.23 & 0.11 \\ 0.08 & 0.10 & 0.05 \\ 0.16 & 0.11 & 0.07 \end{bmatrix}\right)^{-1} \begin{bmatrix} 50 \\ 32 \\ 8 \end{bmatrix}$ [7.3]

Cumulative Review Exercises, page 634

1. $x^2 + y^2 + 4x - 8y - 5 = 0$ [2.1]   **2.** $2(4x + 3)(3x - 4)$ [P.4]   **3.** $y = -\dfrac{1}{2}x + 3$ [2.3]   **4.** $2x^2 + x - 10$ [3.1]   **5.** 0.3679 [4.2]   **6.** $(1, 1)$ [5.1]

7. $(8, 5)$ [6.1]   **8.** $\dfrac{3}{17} - \dfrac{5}{17}i$ [P.6]   **9.** $\{x \mid -3 \le x \le 3\}$ [2.2]   **10.** yes. [2.5]   **11.** $x = -5, x = 1$ [3.5]   **12.**

[2.5]

13. $(-\infty, -2) \cup (-1, \infty)$ [1.5]   **14.** $\dfrac{(x - 3)^2}{36} + \dfrac{(y + 4)^2}{20} = 1$ [5.2]   **15.** $(-10, 15, 24)$ [6.2]   **16.** $2x - 3 + h$ [2.6]   **17.** $-\dfrac{2}{3}$ [4.5]

18. $\dfrac{4}{7(x - 6)} + \dfrac{3}{7(x + 1)}$ [6.4]   **19.** 0.3828 [4.5]   **20.** 6.4 miles [6.1]

Exercise Set 8.1, page 644

1. $0, 2, 6, a_8 = 56$ **3.** $0, \dfrac{1}{2}, \dfrac{2}{3}, a_8 = \dfrac{7}{8}$ **5.** $1, -\dfrac{1}{4}, \dfrac{1}{9}, a_8 = -\dfrac{1}{64}$ **7.** $-\dfrac{1}{3}, -\dfrac{1}{6}, -\dfrac{1}{9}, a_8 = -\dfrac{1}{24}$ **9.** $\dfrac{2}{3}, \dfrac{4}{9}, \dfrac{8}{27}, a_8 = \dfrac{256}{6561}$

11. $0, 2, 0, a_8 = 2$ **13.** $1.1, 1.21, 1.331, a_8 = 2.14358881$ **15.** $1, -\dfrac{\sqrt{2}}{2}, \dfrac{\sqrt{3}}{3}, a_8 = -\dfrac{\sqrt{2}}{4}$ **17.** $1, 2, 6, a_8 = 40{,}320$

19. $0, 0.3010, 0.4771, a_8 = 0.9031$ **21.** $1, 4, 2, a_8 = 4$ **23.** $3, 3, 3, a_8 = 3$ **25.** $5, 10, 20$ **27.** $2, 4, 12$ **29.** $2, 4, 16$ **31.** $2, 8, 48$

33. $3, \sqrt{3}, \sqrt[6]{3}$ **35.** $2, \dfrac{5}{2}, \dfrac{9}{4}$ **37.** 4320 **39.** 72 **41.** 56 **43.** 100 **45.** 15 **47.** 40 **49.** $\dfrac{25}{12}$ **51.** 72 **53.** -24 **55.** $3 \log 2$

57. 256 **59.** $\displaystyle\sum_{i=1}^{6} \dfrac{1}{i^2}$ **61.** $\displaystyle\sum_{i=1}^{7} 2^i(-1)^{i+1}$ **63.** $\displaystyle\sum_{i=0}^{4} (7 + 3i)$ **65.** $\displaystyle\sum_{i=1}^{4} \dfrac{1}{2^i}$ **67.** 2.6457520 **69.** $a_{20} \approx 1.0000037, a_{100} \approx 1$

71. $\dfrac{1}{2}\left(-1 + i\sqrt{3}\right), \dfrac{1}{2}\left(-1 - i\sqrt{3}\right), 1, \dfrac{1}{2}\left(-1 + i\sqrt{3}\right), \dfrac{1}{2}\left(-1 - i\sqrt{3}\right), 1, a_{99} = 1$

Prepare for Section 8.2, page 645

74. -2 **75.** $\dfrac{5}{2}$ **76.** $\dfrac{6525}{4}$ **77.** 21 **78.** -5 **79.** Yes

Exercise Set 8.2, page 651

1. $a_9 = 38, a_{24} = 98, a_n = 4n + 2$ **3.** $a_9 = -10, a_{24} = -40, a_n = 8 - 2n$ **5.** $a_9 = 16, a_{24} = 61, a_n = 3n - 11$ **7.** $a_9 = 25, a_{24} = 70, a_n = 3n - 2$
9. $a_9 = a + 16, a_{24} = a + 46, a_n = a + 2n - 2$ **11.** $a_9 = \log 7 + 8 \log 2, a_{24} = \log 7 + 23 \log 2, a_n = \log 7 + (n - 1) \log 2$
13. $a_9 = 9 \log a, a_{24} = 24 \log a, a_n = n \log a$ **15.** 45 **17.** -79 **19.** 185 **21.** -555 **23.** 468 **25.** 525 **27.** -465 **29.** $78 + 12x$

31. $210x$ **33.** $3, 7, 11, 15, 19$ **35.** $\dfrac{5}{2}, 2, \dfrac{3}{2}, 1$ **39.** 20 in sixth row, 135 in the six rows   **41.** $\$1500, \$48{,}750$ **43.** 784 feet

47. $a_n = 7 - 3n$ **49.** $a_{50} = 197$

Prepare for Section 8.3, page 652

50. 2 **51.** $\dfrac{15}{8}$ **52.** 33 **53.** $S = a(1 + r)$ **54.** $-\dfrac{3}{2}, \dfrac{3}{4}, -\dfrac{3}{8}$ **55.** $2, 6, 14$

Exercise Set 8.3, page 659

1. geometric; $r = 4$ **3.** not geometric   **5.** geometric; $r = 2^x$ **7.** geometric; $r = 2$ **9.** geometric; $r = x^2$ **11.** not geometric   **13.** 2^{2n-1}

15. $-4(-3)^{n-1}$ **17.** $6\left(\dfrac{2}{3}\right)^{n-1}$ **19.** $-6\left(-\dfrac{5}{6}\right)^{n-1}$ **21.** $\left(-\dfrac{1}{3}\right)^{n-3}$ **23.** $(-x)^{n-1}$ **25.** c^{3n-1} **27.** $3\left(\dfrac{1}{100}\right)^n$ **29.** $5(0.1)^n$ **31.** $45(0.01)^n$

33. 18 **35.** -2 **37.** 363 **39.** $\dfrac{1330}{729}$ **41.** $\dfrac{279{,}091}{390{,}625}$ **43.** -341 **45.** $147{,}620$ **47.** $\dfrac{1}{2}$ **49.** $-\dfrac{2}{5}$ **51.** $\dfrac{9}{91}$ **53.** $\dfrac{1}{9}$ **55.** $\dfrac{5}{7}$

57. $\dfrac{1}{3}$ **59.** $\dfrac{5}{11}$ **61.** $\dfrac{41}{333}$ **63.** $\dfrac{422}{999}$ **65.** $\dfrac{229}{900}$ **67.** $\dfrac{997}{825}$ **69.** $\$2271.93$

71. Because $\log r$ is a constant, the sequence $\log a_n$ is an arithmetic sequence.   **73.** Yes. The common ratio is x.   **75.** $a^n r^{[(n-1)n]/2}$ **77.** 45 feet
79. 2044

Prepare for Section 8.4, page 661

81. $(k + 1)(k + 2)(2k + 3)$ **82.** $\dfrac{k + 1}{k + 2}$ **83.** 3   **84.** $\dfrac{(n + 1)(n + 2)}{2}$

Exercise Set 8.4, page 668

No answers are provided because each exercise is a verification.

Prepare for Section 8.5, page 669

36. $a^3 + 3a^2b + 3ab^2 + b^3$ **37.** 120   **38.** 1   **39.** 15   **40.** 35   **41.** 1

Exercise Set 8.5, page 674

1. 35   **3.** 36   **5.** 220   **7.** 1   **9.** $x^6 - 6x^5y + 15x^4y^2 - 20x^3y^3 + 15x^2y^4 - 6xy^5 + y^6$ **11.** $x^5 + 15x^4 + 90x^3 + 270x^2 + 405x + 243$
13. $128x^7 - 448x^6 + 672x^5 - 560x^4 + 280x^3 - 84x^2 + 14x - 1$ **15.** $x^6 + 18x^5y + 135x^4y^2 + 540x^3y^3 + 1215x^2y^4 + 1458xy^5 + 729y^6$

17. $16x^4 - 160x^3y + 600x^2y^2 - 1000xy^3 + 625y^4$ **19.** $x^6 + 6x^4 + 15x^2 + 20 + \dfrac{15}{x^2} + \dfrac{6}{x^4} + \dfrac{1}{x^6}$

21. $x^{14} - 28x^{12} + 336x^{10} - 2240x^8 + 8960x^6 - 21{,}540x^4 + 28{,}672x^2 - 16{,}384$ **23.** $32x^{10} + 80x^8y^3 + 80x^6y^6 + 40x^4y^9 + 10x^2y^{12} + y^{15}$

25. $\dfrac{16}{x^4} - \dfrac{16}{x^2} + 6 - x^2 + \dfrac{x^4}{16}$ **27.** $s^{-12} + 6s^{-8} + 15s^{-4} + 20 + 15s^4 + 6s^8 + s^{12}$ **29.** $-3240x^3y^7$ **31.** $1056x^{10}y^2$ **33.** $126x^2y^2\sqrt{x}$

35. $\dfrac{165b^5}{a^5}$ **37.** $180a^2b^8$ **39.** $60x^2y^8$ **41.** $-61{,}236a^5b^5$ **43.** $126s^{-1}, 126s$ **45.** $-7 - 24i$ **47.** $41 - 38i$ **49.** 1

51. $nx^{n-1} + \dfrac{n(n-1)x^{n-2}h}{2} + \dfrac{n(n-1)(n-2)x^{n-3}h^2}{6} + \cdots + h^{n-1}$ **57.** 1.1712   **59.** 756   **61.** 56

Prepare for Section 8.6, page 675

62. 5040   **63.** 1   **64.** 7   **65.** 56   **66.** 90   **67.** 720

Exercise Set 8.6, page 681

1. 30   **3.** 70   **5.** 1   **7.** 1   **9.** 210   **11.** 12   **13.** 16   **15.** 720   **17.** 125   **19.** 53,130   **21.** There are 676 ways to arrange 26 letters taken 2 at a time. Now, if there are more than 676 employees, then at least 2 employees will have the same first and last initials.   **23.** 1120
25. 1024   **27.** 3,838,380   **29. a.** 21   **b.** 105   **c.** 21   **31.** 1.8×10^9 **33.** 112   **35.** 120   **37.** 21   **39.** 112   **41.** 184,756
43. 62,355,150   **45.** 5456   **47.** 19!   **49. a.** 3,991,680   **b.** 31,840,128   **51.** 120   **53.** 252

Prepare for Section 8.7, page 683

55. 12   **56.** 42   **57.** 21   **58.** $\dfrac{189}{8192}$ **59.** 16

Exercise Set 8.7, page 692

1. $\{S_1R_1, S_1R_2, S_1R_3, S_2R_1, S_2R_2, S_2R_3, R_1R_2, R_1R_3, R_2R_3, S_1S_2\}$ **3.** $\{H1, H2, H3, H4, T1, T2, T3, T4\}$ **5.** Let the three cans be represented by A, B, and C and let (x, y) represent the cans that balls 1 and 2 are placed in; e.g., (A, B) means ball 1 in can A and ball 2 in can B. $S = \{(A, A), (A, B),$ $(A, C), (B, B), (B, C), (B, A), (C, C), (C, A), (C, B)\}$ **7.** $\{HSC, HSD, HCD, SCD\}$ **9.** $\{ae, ai, ao, au, ei, eo, eu, io, iu, ou\}$ **11.** $\{HHHH\}$
13. $\{TTTT, HTTT, THTT, TTHT, TTTH, TTHH, THTH, HTHT, THHT, HTTH, HHTT\}$ **15.** $\varnothing$ **17.** $\{(1, 1), (2, 2), (3, 3), (4, 4), (5, 5), (6, 6)\}$

19. $\{(1, 4), (2, 4), (3, 4), (4, 4), (5, 4), (6, 4)\}$ **21. a.** $\dfrac{1}{13}$ **b.** $\dfrac{1}{4}$ **23.** 0.97   **25.** $\dfrac{3}{5}$ **27.** 0.59   **29.** 0.25   **31.** 0.1   **33.** 0.1   **35.** 0.025

37. 0.9999   **39.** $\dfrac{1}{16}$ **41.** 0.2262   **43.** 0.2137   **45.** $\left(\dfrac{7}{8}\right)^2$ **47.** $\dfrac{56}{729}$

Chapter 8 True/False Exercises, page 697

1. False; $0! \cdot 4! = 1 \cdot 4 \cdot 3 \cdot 2 \cdot 1 = 24$.   **2.** False; $\left(\sum\limits_{i=1}^{3} i\right)\left(\sum\limits_{i=1}^{3} i\right) \neq \sum\limits_{i=1}^{3} i^2$.   **3.** True   **4.** False; the constant sequence has all terms equal.

5. False; $\dfrac{(k+1)^3}{k^3} = \left(1 + \dfrac{1}{k}\right)^3$ is not a constant.   **6.** True   **7.** True   **8.** False; $\sum\limits_{i=1}^{\infty} \dfrac{1}{2^i} = 1$.   **9.** False; see Project 1, Section 8.4.

10. False; the exponent is 4.   **11.** False; there are $m \cdot n$ ways.   **12.** False; $P(n, r) = \dfrac{n!}{(n - r)!}$.   **13.** True   **14.** False; $P(A \cap B) = P(\varnothing) = 0.$

15. True

Chapter 8 Review Exercises, page 697

1. $a_3 = 9, a_7 = 49$ [8.1]   **2.** $a_3 = 6, a_7 = 5040$ [8.1]   **3.** $a_3 = 11, a_7 = 23$ [8.1]   **4.** $a_3 = -5, a_7 = -13$ [8.1]   **5.** $a_3 = \frac{1}{8}, a_7 = \frac{1}{128}$ [8.1]

6. $a_3 = 27, a_7 = 2187$ [8.1]   **7.** $a_3 = \frac{1}{6}, a_7 = \frac{1}{5040}$ [8.1]   **8.** $a_3 = \frac{1}{3}, a_7 = \frac{1}{7}$ [8.1]   **9.** $a_3 = \frac{8}{27}, a_7 = \frac{128}{2187}$ [8.1]

10. $a_3 = -\frac{64}{27}, a_7 = -\frac{16,384}{2187}$ [8.1]   **11.** $a_3 = 18, a_7 = 1458$ [8.1]   **12.** $a_3 = -4, a_7 = -64$ [8.1]   **13.** $a_3 = 6, a_7 = 5040$ [8.1]

14. $a_3 = 72, a_7 = 50,803,200$ [8.1]   **15.** $a_3 = 8, a_7 = 16$ [8.1]   **16.** $a_3 = -3, a_7 = -15$ [8.1]   **17.** $a_3 = 2, a_7 = 256$ [8.1]   **18.** $a_3 = 2, a_7 = 1$ [8.1]
19. $a_3 = -54, a_7 = -3,674,160$ [8.1]   **20.** $a_3 = 48, a_7 = 645,120$ [8.1]   **21.** neither [8.1]   **22.** neither [8.1]   **23.** arithmetic [8.2]
24. arithmetic [8.2]   **25.** geometric [8.3]   **26.** geometric [8.3]   **27.** neither [8.1]   **28.** neither [8.1]   **29.** geometric [8.3]
30. geometric [8.3]   **31.** geometric [8.3]   **32.** geometric [8.3]   **33.** neither [8.1]   **34.** neither [8.1]   **35.** arithmetic [8.2]
36. arithmetic [8.2]   **37.** neither [8.1]   **38.** neither [8.1]   **39.** neither [8.1]   **40.** neither [8.1]   **41.** 63 [8.2]   **42.** -187 [8.2]   **43.** 152 [8.2]

44. 415 [8.1]   **45.** 378 [8.3]   **46.** 682 [8.3]   **47.** $-14,763$ [8.3]   **48.** -170 [8.3]   **49.** $\frac{116,050}{59,049} \approx 1.9653$ [8.3]   **50.** $\frac{525,297}{2048} \approx 256.4927$ [8.3]

51. 0.8280 [8.1]   **52.** $0.6\overline{3}$ [8.1]   **53.** $\frac{1}{3}$ [8.3]   **54.** $-\frac{5}{11}$ [8.3]   **55.** $-\frac{4}{9}$ [8.3]   **56.** $\frac{5}{4}$ [8.3]
65. $1024a^5 - 1280a^4b + 640a^3b^2 - 160a^2b^3 + 20ab^4 - b^5$ [8.5]   **66.** $x^6 + 18x^5y + 135x^4y^2 + 540x^3y^3 + 1215x^2y^4 + 1458xy^5 + 729y^6$ [8.5]
67. $a^4 + 16a^{7/2}b^{1/2} + 112a^3b + 448a^{5/2}b^{3/2} + 1120a^2b^2 + 1792a^{3/2}b^{5/2} + 1792ab^3 + 1024a^{1/2}b^{7/2} + 256b^4$ [8.5]

68. $128x^7 - 224x^5 + 168x^3 - 70x + \frac{35}{2x} - \frac{21}{8x^3} + \frac{7}{32x^5} - \frac{1}{128x^7}$ [8.5]   **69.** $241,920x^3y^4$ [8.5]   **70.** $-78,732x^7$ [8.5]   **71.** 26^8 [8.6]

72. $10^6 \cdot 26$ [8.6]   **73.** 2730 [8.6]   **74.** 880 [8.6]   **75.** 672 [8.6]   **76.** $\frac{8}{15}$ [8.7]   **77.** $\frac{1}{8}, \frac{3}{8}$ [8.4]   **78.** $\frac{10}{21}$ [8.7]   **79.** 0.285 [8.7]

80. $\frac{2}{5}$ [8.7]   **81.** drawing an ace and a ten-card from one deck [8.7]   **82.** $\frac{1}{2}$ [8.7]   **83.** $\frac{1}{4}$ [8.7]

Chapter 8 Test, page 699

1. $a_3 = \frac{4}{3}, a_5 = \frac{4}{15}$ [8.1]   **2.** $a_3 = \frac{1}{6}, a_5 = \frac{1}{10}$ [8.1]   **3.** $a_3 = 12, a_5 = 48$ [8.1]   **4.** arithmetic [8.3]   **5.** neither [8.1]   **6.** geometric [8.3]

7. $\frac{49}{20}$ [8.1]   **8.** $\frac{1023}{1024}$ [8.3]   **9.** 590 [8.2]   **10.** 58 [8.2]   **11.** $\frac{3}{5}$ [8.3]   **12.** $\frac{5}{33}$ [8.3]   **15.** $x^5 - 10x^4y + 40x^3y^2 - 80x^2y^3 + 80xy^4 - 32y^5$ [8.5]

16. $x^6 + 6x^4 + 15x^2 + 20 + \frac{15}{x^2} + \frac{6}{x^4} + \frac{1}{x^6}$ [8.5]   **17.** $48,384x^3y^5$ [8.5]   **18.** 132,600 [8.6]   **19.** 568,339,200 [8.6]   **20.** $\frac{5}{17}$ [8.7]

Cumulative Review Exercises, page 700

1. $\left[-\frac{1}{5}, \frac{7}{5}\right]$ [1.5]   **2.** $y = 1.7x + 3.6$ [2.7]   **3.**   [2.1]   **4.** -24 [2.3]   **5.** $x^2 - x + 1 + \frac{-2}{x+1}$ [3.1]   **6.** $\frac{3 \pm \sqrt{41}}{4}$ [1.3]

7. $\log_b x + 2\log_b y - 3\log_b z$ [4.4]   **8.** $\frac{3}{5}$ [5.2]   **9.** $x = 1, y = -2$ [6.1]   **10.** $\begin{bmatrix} -17 & 12 \\ 3 & -1 \\ -2 & 13 \end{bmatrix}$ [7.2]   **11.** $5\sqrt[4]{5}$ [P.2]   **12.** No [2.2]

13. $\left(\frac{5}{4}, \frac{9}{8}\right)$ [2.4]   **14.** $-\frac{5}{16}$ [2.6]   **15.** $y = 0$ [3.5]   **16.** -6 [4.3]   **17.** -2.1 [4.5]

18. $\left(\frac{1 + \sqrt{13}}{2}, \frac{-1 + \sqrt{13}}{2}\right), \left(\frac{1 - \sqrt{13}}{2}, \frac{-1 - \sqrt{13}}{2}\right)$ [6.3]   **19.** $\begin{bmatrix} 2 & 9 & 11 & -3 \\ -6 & -6 & 2 & -5 \\ 10 & 3 & -15 & 13 \end{bmatrix}$ [7.3]   **20.** 105 mph [4.5]

APPENDIX
INSTRUCTOR ANSWER ART

Exercise Set P.1, page 15

1. Integers: 0, −44, $\sqrt{81}$, 53; Rational numbers: $-\dfrac{1}{5}$, 0, −44, 3.14, $\sqrt{81}$, 53; Irrational numbers: π, 5.05005000500005...; Prime number: 53;

Real numbers: All the numbers are real numbers.   **2.** Integers: 31, 51; Rational numbers: $\dfrac{5}{7}$, 31, $-2\dfrac{1}{2}$, 4.235653907493, 51, 0.888...;

Irrational numbers: $\dfrac{5}{\sqrt{7}}$; Prime number: 31; Real numbers: All the numbers are real numbers.

19. $\{x \mid -2 < x < 3\}$,

20. $\{x \mid 1 \le x \le 5\}$,

21. $\{x \mid -5 \le x \le -1\}$,

22. $\{x \mid -3 < x < 3\}$,

23. $\{x \mid x \ge 2\}$,

24. $\{x \mid x < 4\}$,

25. $(3, 5)$,

26. $(-\infty, -1)$,

27. $[-2, \infty)$,

28. $[-1, 5)$,

29. $[0, 1]$,

30. $(-4, 5]$,

51.

52.

53.

54.

55.

56.

57.

58.

59.

60.

61.

62.

63.

64.

65.

66.

Exercise Set P.6, page 71
Project, page 73
Exercises 1–8.

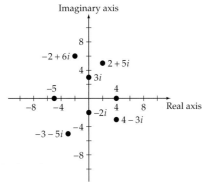

Chapter P Review Exercises, page 76

15. $(-4, 2]$ [P.1]   **16.** $(-\infty, -1] \cup (3, \infty)$ [P.1]

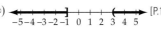

17. $-3 \leq x < 2$![number line] [P.1]   **18.** $x > -1$![number line] [P.1]

Exercise Set 1.5, page 140

1. $\{x \mid x < 4\}$, ![number line -3 to 7]   **2.** $\{x \mid x > 7\}$, ![number line 2 to 12]   **3.** $\{x \mid x < -6\}$, ![number line -11 to -1]

4. $\left\{x \mid x < -\dfrac{5}{3}\right\}$, ![number line] $-\frac{5}{3}$ **5.** $\left\{x \mid x \geq -\dfrac{13}{8}\right\}$, ![number line] $-\frac{13}{8}$

6. $\left\{x \mid x \leq \dfrac{5}{6}\right\}$, ![number line] $\frac{5}{6}$ **7.** $\{x \mid x < 2\}$, ![number line]   **8.** $\left\{x \mid x \geq \dfrac{61}{7}\right\}$, ![number line] $\frac{61}{7}$

9. $\left\{x \mid -\dfrac{3}{4} < x \leq 4\right\}$, ![number line] $-\frac{3}{4}$ **10.** $\left\{x \mid -\dfrac{21}{2} < x < 2\right\}$, ![number line] $-\frac{21}{2}$

11. $\left\{x \mid \dfrac{1}{3} \leq x \leq \dfrac{11}{3}\right\}$, ![number line] $\frac{1}{3}$ $\frac{11}{3}$ **12.** $\{x \mid -3 \leq x \leq 24\}$, ![number line -6 to 24]

13. $\{x \mid x < -3 \text{ or } x \geq -1\}$, 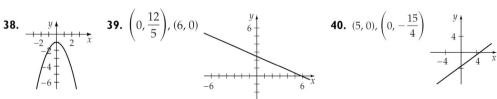   **14.** $\{x \mid x \leq 1 \text{ or } x > 3\}$,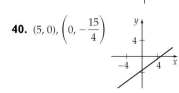

15. $\{x \mid x < 1\}$, 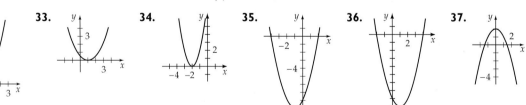   **16.** $\{x \mid x \leq 11\}$, ![number line 4 to 14]

Exercise Set 2.1, page 174

1. 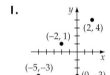   **2.** ![graph with points (-4,3), (-2,0), (0,2), (-3,-5)]   **3. a.** 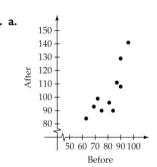   **25.** 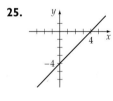   **26.**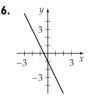

points: (2, 4), (-2, 1), (-5,-3), (0, -3)

Before (x-axis), After (y-axis), 50 60 70 80 90 100

27. ![parabola graph]   **28.** ![parabola graph]   **29.** ![graph]   **30.** ![V graph]   **31.** ![parabola graph]

32. ![parabola graph]   **33.** ![parabola graph]   **34.** ![parabola graph]   **35.** ![parabola graph]   **36.** ![parabola graph]   **37.** ![parabola graph]

38. 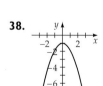   **39.** $\left(0, \dfrac{12}{5}\right)$, $(6, 0)$ 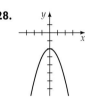 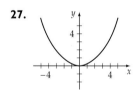 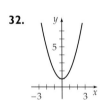 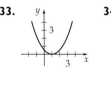   **40.** $(5, 0)$, $\left(0, -\dfrac{15}{4}\right)$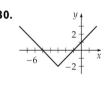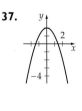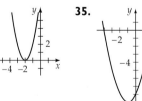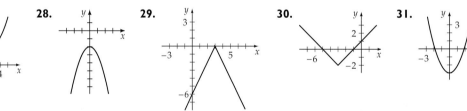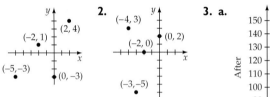

41. $(5, 0); \left(0, \sqrt{5}\right), \left(0, -\sqrt{5}\right)$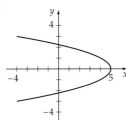

42. $(-6, 0); \left(0, \sqrt{6}\right), \left(0, -\sqrt{6}\right)$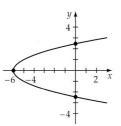

43. $(-4, 0); (0, 4), (0, -4)$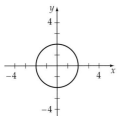

44. $(-2, 0), \left(0, \sqrt[3]{2}\right)$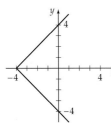

45. $(\pm 2, 0), (0, \pm 2)$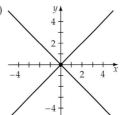

46. $(0, 0)$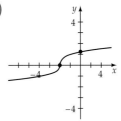

47. $(\pm 4, 0), (0, \pm 4)$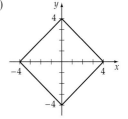

48. $(\pm 8, 0), (0, \pm 2)$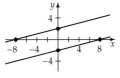

77.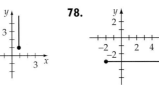

78.

79.

80.

81.

82.

83.

84.

85.

86.

Exercise Set 2.2, page 190

39.

40.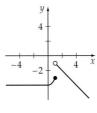

41.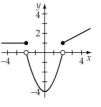

42.

43.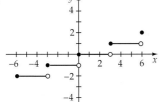

44.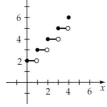

45.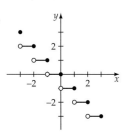

46.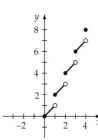

47. b.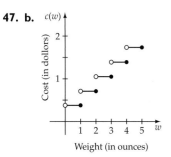

85.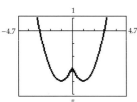

86.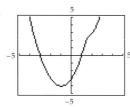

87.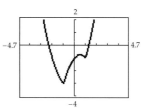

88.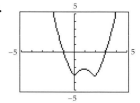

89.

90.

101.

102.

Exercise Set 2.3, page 207

15. $m = 2$, y-intercept: $(0, -4)$

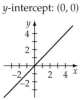

16. $m = -1$, y-intercept: $(0, 1)$

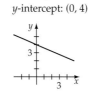

17. $m = -\dfrac{1}{3}$, y-intercept: $(0, 4)$

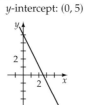

18. $m = \dfrac{2}{3}$, y-intercept: $(0, -2)$

19. $m = 0$, y-intercept: $(0, 3)$

20. $m = 1$, y-intercept: $(0, 0)$

21. $m = 2$, y-intercept: $(0, 0)$

22. $m = -3$, y-intercept: $(0, 0)$

23. $m = -2$, y-intercept: $(0, 5)$

24. $m = 1$, y-intercept: $(0, -4)$

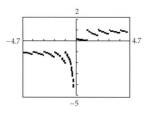

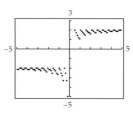

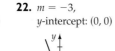

25. $m = -\dfrac{3}{4}$,

    y-intercept: $(0, 4)$

26. $m = -\dfrac{2}{3}$,

    y-intercept: $(0, -2)$

Exercise Set 2.4, page 222

9. $f(x) = (x + 2)^2 - 3$
vertex: $(-2, -3)$
axis of symmetry: $x = -2$

10. $f(x) = (x + 3)^2 - 10$
vertex: $(-3, -10)$
axis of symmetry: $x = -3$

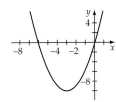

11. $f(x) = (x - 4)^2 - 11$
vertex: $(4, -11)$
axis of symmetry: $x = 4$

12. $f(x) = (x - 5)^2 - 22$
vertex: $(5, -22)$
axis of symmetry: $x = 5$

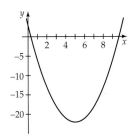

13. $f(x) = \left(x + \dfrac{3}{2}\right)^2 - \dfrac{5}{4}$

    vertex: $\left(-\dfrac{3}{2}, -\dfrac{5}{4}\right)$

    axis of symmetry: $x = -\dfrac{3}{2}$

14. $f(x) = \left(x + \dfrac{7}{2}\right)^2 - \dfrac{41}{4}$

    vertex: $\left(-\dfrac{7}{2}, -\dfrac{41}{4}\right)$

    axis of symmetry: $x = -\dfrac{7}{2}$

15. $f(x) = -(x - 2)^2 + 6$
vertex: $(2, 6)$
axis of symmetry: $x = 2$

16. $f(x) = -(x + 1)^2 + 6$
vertex: $(-1, 6)$
axis of symmetry: $x = -1$

17. $f(x) = -3\left(x - \dfrac{1}{2}\right)^2 + \dfrac{31}{4}$

    vertex: $\left(\dfrac{1}{2}, \dfrac{31}{4}\right)$

    axis of symmetry: $x = \dfrac{1}{2}$

18. $f(x) = -2(x + 1)^2 + 7$
vertex: $(-1, 7)$
axis of symmetry: $x = -1$

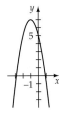

25. vertex: $\left(\dfrac{3}{4}, \dfrac{47}{8}\right)$, $f(x) = 2\left(x - \dfrac{3}{4}\right)^2 + \dfrac{47}{8}$

26. vertex: $\left(\dfrac{5}{3}, -\dfrac{19}{3}\right)$, $f(x) = 3\left(x - \dfrac{5}{3}\right)^2 - \dfrac{19}{3}$ **27.** vertex: $\left(\dfrac{1}{8}, \dfrac{17}{16}\right)$, $f(x) = -4\left(x - \dfrac{1}{8}\right)^2 + \dfrac{17}{16}$

28. vertex: $\left(-\dfrac{3}{5}, \dfrac{24}{5}\right)$, $f(x) = -5\left(x + \dfrac{3}{5}\right)^2 + \dfrac{24}{5}$

Exercise Set 2.5, page 238

1.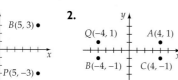
C(−5, 3)   B(5, 3)
A(−5, −3)   P(5, −3)

2.
Q(−4, 1)   A(4, 1)
B(−4, −1)   C(4, −1)

3.
R(−2, 3)   A(2, 3)
B(−2, −3)   C(2, −3)

4.
S(−5, 3)   A(5, 3)
B(−5, −3)   C(5, −3)

5.
B(−4, 5)   C(4, 5)
T(−4, −5)   A(4, −5)

6.
A(−5, 1)   U(5, 1)
C(−5, −1)   B(5, −1)

7.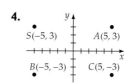

8.

9.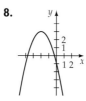

10.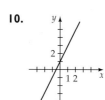

11.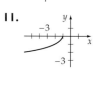

12.

31.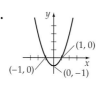

32.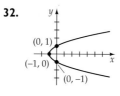

33.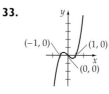

34.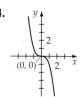

35.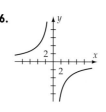

36.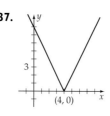

37.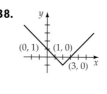

38.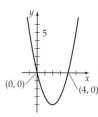

39.

40.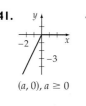

41.

42.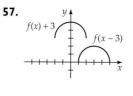

57.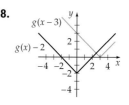

58.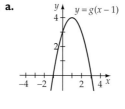

59. a. 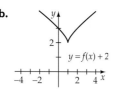   **b.**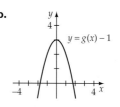

60. a. **b.**

63. a. 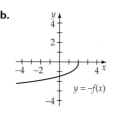   **b.**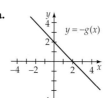

64. a. **b.**

67.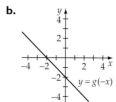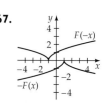

68.

69.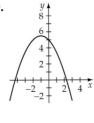

70.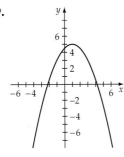

71. a.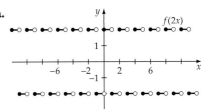

b.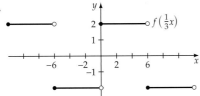

72. a.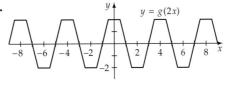

b.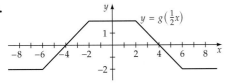

73. a.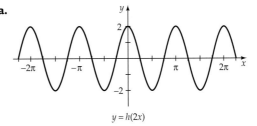

b.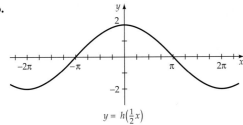

74. a.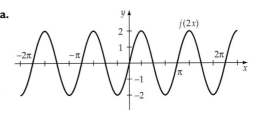

b.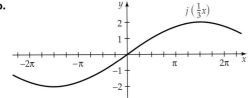

75.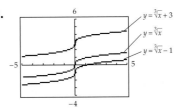

76.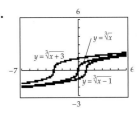

77.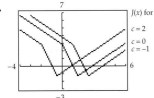

78.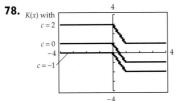

79.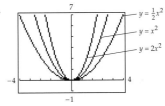

80.

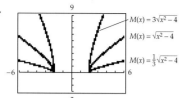

$M(x) = 3\sqrt{x^2 - 4}$

$M(x) = \sqrt{x^2 - 4}$

$M(x) = \frac{1}{3}\sqrt{x^2 - 4}$

81.

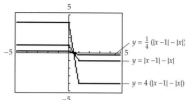

$y = \frac{1}{4}(|x-1| - |x|)$

$y = |x-1| - |x|$

$y = 4(|x-1| - |x|)$

82.

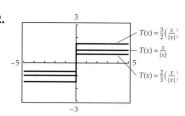

$T(x) = \frac{3}{2}\left(\frac{x}{|x|}\right)$

$T(x) = \frac{x}{|x|}$

$T(x) = \frac{2}{3}\left(\frac{x}{|x|}\right)$

83. a.

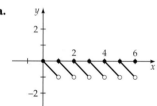

b.

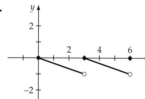

c.

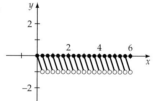

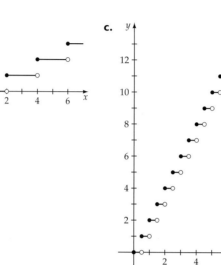

84. a.

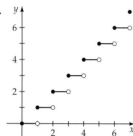

b.

c.

Exercise Set 2.6, page 251

1. $f(x) + g(x) = x^2 - x - 12$,   Domain is the set of all real numbers.
$f(x) - g(x) = x^2 - 3x - 18$,   Domain is the set of all real numbers.
$f(x) \cdot g(x) = x^3 + x^2 - 21x - 45$,   Domain is the set of all real numbers.
$\dfrac{f(x)}{g(x)} = x - 5$,   Domain $\{x \,|\, x \neq -3\}$

2. $f(x) + g(x) = x^2 + x - 30$,   Domain is the set of all real numbers.
$f(x) - g(x) = x^2 - x - 20$,   Domain is the set of all real numbers.
$f(x)g(x) = x^3 - 5x^2 - 25x + 125$,   Domain is the set of all real numbers.
$\dfrac{f(x)}{g(x)} = x + 5$,   Domain $\{x \,|\, x \neq 5\}$

3. $f(x) + g(x) = 3x + 12$,   Domain is the set of all real numbers.
$f(x) - g(x) = x + 4$,   Domain is the set of all real numbers.
$f(x) \cdot g(x) = 2x^2 + 16x + 32$,   Domain is the set of all real numbers.
$\dfrac{f(x)}{g(x)} = 2$,   Domain $\{x \,|\, x \neq -4\}$

4. $f(x) + g(x) = 6x - 18$,   Domain is the set of all real numbers.
$f(x) - g(x) = 4x - 12$,   Domain is the set of all real numbers.
$f(x)g(x) = 5x^2 - 30x + 45$,   Domain is the set of all real numbers.
$\dfrac{f(x)}{g(x)} = 5$,   Domain $\{x \,|\, x \neq 3\}$

5. $f(x) + g(x) = x^3 - 2x^2 + 8x$,   Domain is the set of all real numbers.
$f(x) - g(x) = x^3 - 2x^2 + 6x$,   Domain is the set of all real numbers.
$f(x) \cdot g(x) = x^4 - 2x^3 + 7x^2$,   Domain is the set of all real numbers.
$\dfrac{f(x)}{g(x)} = x^2 - 2x + 7$,   Domain $\{x \,|\, x \neq 0\}$

6. $f(x) + g(x) = x^2 - 6x - 8$,   Domain is the set of all real numbers.
$f(x) - g(x) = x^2 - 4x - 8$,   Domain is the set of all real numbers.
$f(x)g(x) = -x^3 + 5x^2 + 8x$,   Domain is the set of all real numbers.
$\dfrac{f(x)}{g(x)} = -x + 5 + \dfrac{8}{x}$,   Domain $\{x \,|\, x \neq 0\}$

7. $f(x) + g(x) = 4x^2 + 7x - 12$,   Domain is the set of all real numbers.
$f(x) - g(x) = x - 2$,   Domain is the set of all real numbers.
$f(x) \cdot g(x) = 4x^4 + 14x^3 - 12x^2 - 41x + 35$,   Domain is the set of all real numbers.
$\dfrac{f(x)}{g(x)} = 1 + \dfrac{x - 2}{2x^2 + 3x - 5}$,   Domain $\left\{ x \,\middle|\, x \neq 1, x \neq -\dfrac{5}{2} \right\}$

8. $f(x) + g(x) = 9x^2 + x$,   Domain is the set of all real numbers.
$f(x) - g(x) = 3x^2 - x + 20$,   Domain is the set of all real numbers.
$f(x)g(x) = 18x^4 + 6x^3 - 30x^2 + 10x - 100$,   Domain is the set of all real numbers.
$\dfrac{f(x)}{g(x)} = 2 + \dfrac{-2x + 30}{3x^2 + x - 10}$,   Domain $\left\{ x \,\middle|\, x \neq -2, x \neq \dfrac{5}{3} \right\}$

9. $f(x) + g(x) = \sqrt{x - 3} + x$,   Domain $\{x \,|\, x \geq 3\}$
$f(x) - g(x) = \sqrt{x - 3} - x$,   Domain $\{x \,|\, x \geq 3\}$
$f(x) \cdot g(x) = x\sqrt{x - 3}$,   Domain $\{x \,|\, x \geq 3\}$
$\dfrac{f(x)}{g(x)} = \dfrac{\sqrt{x - 3}}{x}$,   Domain $\{x \,|\, x \geq 3\}$

10. $f(x) + g(x) = \sqrt{x - 4} - x$,   Domain $\{x \,|\, x \geq 4\}$
$f(x) - g(x) = \sqrt{x - 4} + x$,   Domain $\{x \,|\, x \geq 4\}$
$f(x)g(x) = -x\sqrt{x - 4}$,   Domain $\{x \,|\, x \geq 4\}$
$\dfrac{f(x)}{g(x)} = -\dfrac{\sqrt{x - 4}}{x}$,   Domain $\{x \,|\, x \geq 4\}$

11. $f(x) + g(x) = \sqrt{4 - x^2} + 2 + x$,   Domain $\{x \,|\, -2 \leq x \leq 2\}$
$f(x) - g(x) = \sqrt{4 - x^2} - 2 - x$,   Domain $\{x \,|\, -2 \leq x \leq 2\}$
$f(x) \cdot g(x) = \left(\sqrt{4 - x^2}\right)(2 + x)$,   Domain $\{x \,|\, -2 \leq x \leq 2\}$
$\dfrac{f(x)}{g(x)} = \dfrac{\sqrt{4 - x^2}}{2 + x}$,   Domain $\{x \,|\, -2 < x \leq 2\}$

12. $f(x) + g(x) = \sqrt{x^2 - 9} + x - 3$,   Domain $\{x \,|\, x \leq -3 \text{ or } x \geq 3\}$
$f(x) - g(x) = \sqrt{x^2 - 9} - x + 3$,   Domain $\{x \,|\, x \leq -3 \text{ or } x \geq 3\}$
$f(x)g(x) = \left(\sqrt{x^2 - 9}\right)(x - 3)$,   Domain $\{x \,|\, x \leq -3 \text{ or } x \geq 3\}$
$f(x)/g(x) = \dfrac{\sqrt{x^2 - 9}}{x - 3}$,   Domain $\{x \,|\, x \leq -3 \text{ or } x > 3\}$

68.

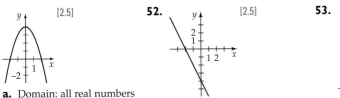

Chapter 2 Review Exercises, page 272

15. [2.2]

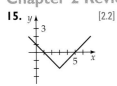

increasing on $[3, \infty)$
decreasing on $(-\infty, 3]$

16. [2.2]

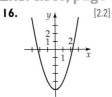

increasing on $[0, \infty)$
decreasing on $(-\infty, 0]$

17. [2.2]

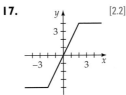

increasing on $[-2, 2]$
constant on $(-\infty, -2] \cup [2, \infty)$

18. [2.2]

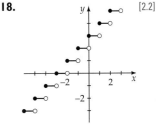

constant on$\ldots$, $[-6, -5)$, $[-5, -4)$,
$[-4, -3)$, $[-3, -2)$, $[-2, -1)$,
$[-1, 0)$, $[0, 1)$, $\ldots$

19. [2.2]

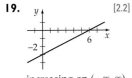

increasing on $(-\infty, \infty)$

20. [2.2]

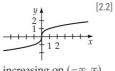

increasing on $(-\infty, \infty)$

41. [2.5]

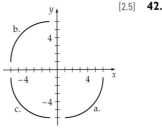

42. [2.5]

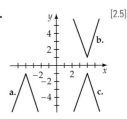

51. [2.5]

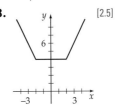

a. Domain: all real numbers
Range: $\{y \,|\, y \leq 4\}$
b. even

52. [2.5]

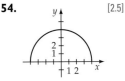

a. Domain: all real numbers
Range: all real numbers
b. g is neither even nor odd

53. [2.5]

a. Domain: all real numbers
Range: $\{y \,|\, y \geq 4\}$
b. even

54. [2.5]

a. Domain: $\{x \,|\, -4 \leq x \leq 4\}$
Range: $\{y \,|\, 0 \leq y \leq 4\}$
b. even

55. [2.5]

    a. Domain: all real numbers
       Range: all real numbers
    b. odd

56. [2.5]

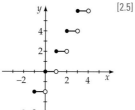

    a. Domain: $\{x \mid x \text{ is a real number}\}$
       Range: $\{y \mid y \text{ is an even integer}\}$
    b. g is neither even nor odd

57. $F(x) = (x + 2)^2 - 11$ [2.5]

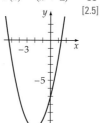

58. $A(x) = (x - 3)^2 - 14$ [2.5]

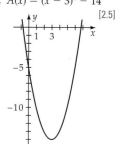

59. $P(x) = 3(x - 0)^2 - 4$ [2.5]

60. $G(x) = 2(x - 2)^2 - 5$ [2.5]

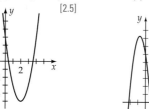

61. $W(x) = -4\left(x + \dfrac{3}{4}\right)^2 + \dfrac{33}{4}$ [2.5]

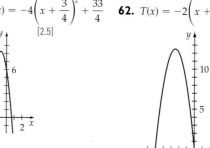

62. $T(x) = -2\left(x + \dfrac{5}{2}\right)^2 + \dfrac{25}{2}$ [2.5]

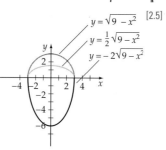

63. [2.5]

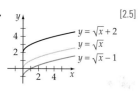

$y = \sqrt{x} + 2$
$y = \sqrt{x}$
$y = \sqrt{x} - 1$

64. [2.5]

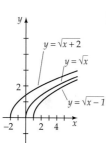

$y = \sqrt{x + 2}$
$y = \sqrt{x}$
$y = \sqrt{x - 1}$

65. [2.5]

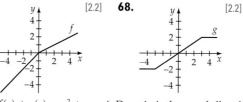

$y = \sqrt{9 - x^2}$
$y = \dfrac{1}{2}\sqrt{9 - x^2}$
$y = -2\sqrt{9 - x^2}$

66. [2.2]

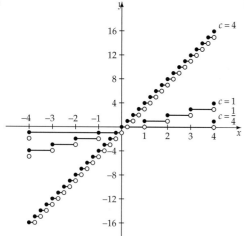

67. [2.2]

(graph labeled f)

68. [2.2]

(graph labeled g)

69. $f(x) + g(x) = x^2 + x - 6$, Domain is the set of all real numbers.
    $f(x) - g(x) = x^2 - x - 12$, Domain is the set of all real numbers.
    $f(x) \cdot g(x) = x^3 + 3x^2 - 9x - 27$, Domain is the set of all real numbers.
    $\dfrac{f(x)}{g(x)} = x - 3$, Domain $\{x \mid x \neq -3\}$ [2.6]

70. $(f + g)(x) = x^3 + x^2 - 2x + 12$, Domain is the set of all real numbers.
    $(f - g)(x) = x^3 - x^2 + 2x + 4$, Domain is the set of all real numbers.
    $(fg)(x) = x^5 - 2x^4 + 4x^3 + 8x^2 - 16x + 32$, Domain is the set of all real numbers.
    $\left(\dfrac{f}{g}\right)(x) = x + 2$, Domain is the set of all real numbers. [2.6]

Chapter 2 Test, page 274

2. $(-4, 0); (0, \sqrt{2}), (0, -\sqrt{2})$ [2.1]

3. 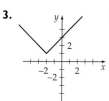   [2.1]

6. 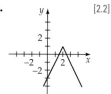   [2.2]

a. increasing on $(-\infty, 2]$
b. not consistent on any interval
c. decreasing on $[2, \infty)$

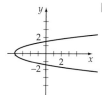

8. 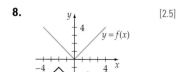   [2.5]

$y = f(x)$

$y = -f(x + 2) - 1$

Exercise Set 3.2, page 301

15.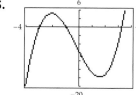

16.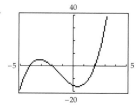

17.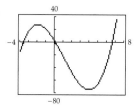

18.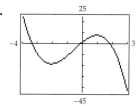

19.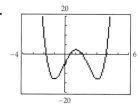

20.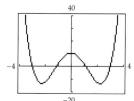

41.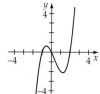

42.

43.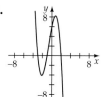

44.

45.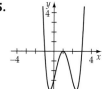

46.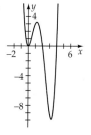

Exercise Set 3.4, page 327

7. $-3, -\dfrac{1}{2}, 2 + i, 2 - i; P(x) = (x + 3)\left(x + \dfrac{1}{2}\right)(x - 2 - i)(x - 2 + i)$

8. $-4, -\dfrac{1}{3}, 5 + 2i, 5 - 2i; P(x) = (x + 4)\left(x + \dfrac{1}{3}\right)(x - 5 - 2i)(x - 5 + 2i)$

9. $4, 2, \dfrac{1}{2} + \dfrac{3}{2}i, \dfrac{1}{2} - \dfrac{3}{2}i; P(x) = (x - 4)(x - 2)\left(x - \dfrac{1}{2} - \dfrac{3}{2}i\right)\left(x - \dfrac{1}{2} + \dfrac{3}{2}i\right)$

Exercise Set 3.5, page 341

9. 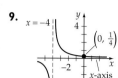 $x = -4$, $(0, \frac{1}{4})$, x-axis, -2

10. 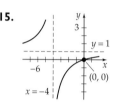 $(0, -\frac{1}{2})$, x-axis, $x = 2$

11. 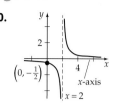 $(0, \frac{4}{3})$, $x = 3$, x-axis

12. 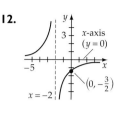 x-axis $(y = 0)$, -5, $(0, -\frac{3}{2})$, $x = -2$

13. 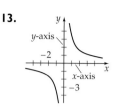 y-axis, -2, x-axis, -3

14. 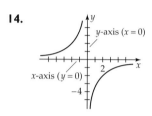 y-axis $(x = 0)$, x-axis $(y = 0)$

15. 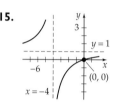 $y = 1$, -6, $(0, 0)$, $x = -4$

16. 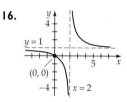 $y = 1$, $(0, 0)$, 5, $x = 2$

17. 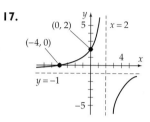 $(0, 2)$, $x = 2$, $(-4, 0)$, 4, $y = -1$, -5

18. 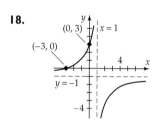 $(0, 3)$, $x = 1$, $(-3, 0)$, 4, $y = -1$

19. 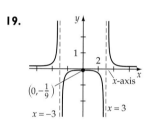 $(0, -\frac{1}{9})$, x-axis, $x = -3$, $x = 3$

20. 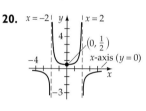 $x = -2$, $x = 2$, $(0, \frac{1}{2})$, -4, x-axis $(y = 0)$

21. 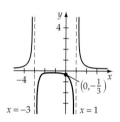 -4, $(0, -\frac{1}{3})$, $x = -3$, $x = 1$

22. 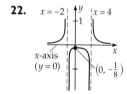 $x = -2$, $x = 4$, x-axis $(y = 0)$, $(0, -\frac{1}{8})$

23. 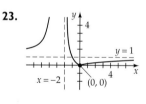 $y = 1$, $x = -2$, $(0, 0)$

24. 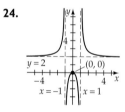 $y = 2$, $(0, 0)$, -4, $x = -1$, $x = 1$

25. 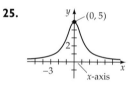 $(0, 5)$, -3, x-axis

26. 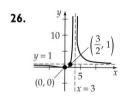 10, $(\frac{3}{2}, 1)$, $y = 1$, $(0, 0)$, $x = 3$

27. 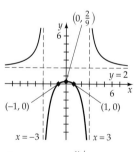 $(0, \frac{2}{9})$, $y = 2$, $(-1, 0)$, $(1, 0)$, $x = -3$, $x = 3$

28. 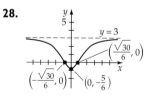 $y = 3$, $(\frac{\sqrt{30}}{6}, 0)$, $(-\frac{\sqrt{30}}{6}, 0)$, $(0, -\frac{5}{6})$

29. 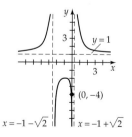 $y = 1$, 3, $(0, -4)$, $x = -1 - \sqrt{2}$, $x = -1 + \sqrt{2}$

30. 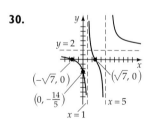 $y = 2$, $(-\sqrt{7}, 0)$, $(\sqrt{7}, 0)$, $(0, -\frac{14}{5})$, $x = 5$, $x = 1$

35. 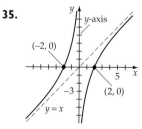 y-axis, $(-2, 0)$, $(2, 0)$, -3, 5, $y = x$

36. 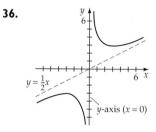 $y = \frac{1}{2}x$, 6, y-axis $(x = 0)$

37. 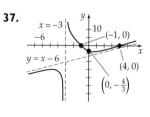 $x = -3$, -6, $(-1, 0)$, $y = x - 6$, $(4, 0)$, $(0, -\frac{4}{3})$

38.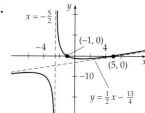

$x = -\frac{5}{2}$

$(-1, 0)$

$(5, 0)$

$y = \frac{1}{2}x - \frac{13}{4}$

39.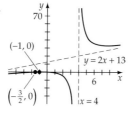

$(-1, 0)$

$y = 2x + 13$

$\left(-\frac{3}{2}, 0\right)$

$x = 4$

40.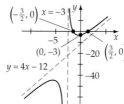

$\left(-\frac{3}{2}, 0\right)$ $x = -3$

$(0, -3)$ $\left(\frac{3}{2}, 0\right)$

$y = 4x - 12$

41.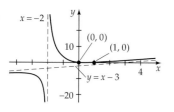

$x = -2$

$(0, 0)$

$(1, 0)$

$y = x - 3$

42.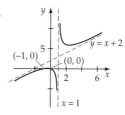

$y = x + 2$

$(-1, 0)$ $(0, 0)$

$x = 1$

43.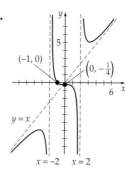

$(-1, 0)$ $\left(0, -\frac{1}{4}\right)$

$y = x$

$x = -2$ $x = 2$

44.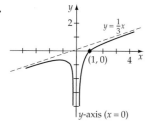

$y = \frac{1}{3}x$

$(1, 0)$

y-axis ($x = 0$)

45.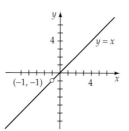

$y = x$

$(-1, -1)$

46.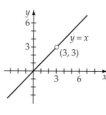

$y = x$

$(3, 3)$

47.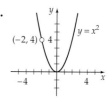

$y = x^2$

$(-2, 4)$

48.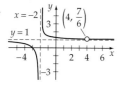

$x = -2$ $\left(4, \frac{7}{6}\right)$

$y = 1$

49.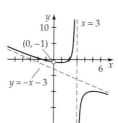

$x = 3$

$(0, -1)$

$y = -x - 3$

50.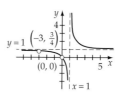

$y = 1$ $\left(-3, \frac{3}{4}\right)$

$(0, 0)$

$x = 1$

51.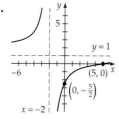

$y = 1$

-6 $(5, 0)$

$\left(0, -\frac{5}{2}\right)$

$x = -2$

52.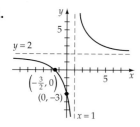

$y = 2$

$\left(-\frac{3}{2}, 0\right)$

$(0, -3)$

$x = 1$

55. c.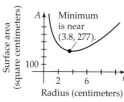

$x = 100$

61. a.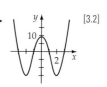

Minimum is near $(3.8, 277)$.

Surface area (square centimeters)

Radius (centimeters)

Chapter 3 Review Exercises, page 348

15.   [3.2]

16.   [3.2]

17.   [3.2]

18. 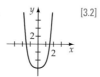 [3.2]

19. 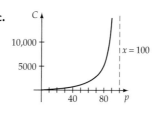 [3.2]

20. [3.2]   **23.** $\pm 1, \pm 2, \pm 3, \pm 4, \pm 6, \pm 12, \pm\frac{1}{3}, \pm\frac{2}{3}, \pm\frac{4}{3}, \pm\frac{1}{5}, \pm\frac{2}{5}, \pm\frac{3}{5}, \pm\frac{4}{5}, \pm\frac{6}{5}, \pm\frac{12}{5}, \pm\frac{1}{15}, \pm\frac{2}{15}, \pm\frac{4}{15}$ [3.3]

47. [3.5]   **48.** [3.5]   **49.** [3.5]   **50.** [3.5]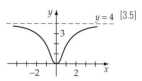

51. [3.5] 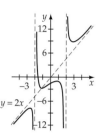   **52.** [3.5] 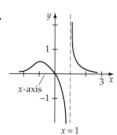   **53.** [3.5] 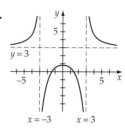   **54.** [3.5]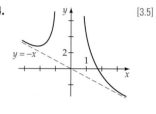

Chapter 3 Test, page 349

17. [3.5] 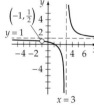   **18.** [3.5]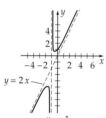

Exercise Set 4.1, page 364

9. 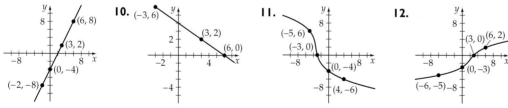   **10.**   **11.**   **12.**

13. 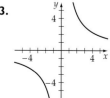   **14.** 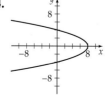   **15.** 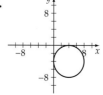   **16.**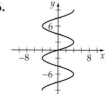

Exercise Set 4.2, page 376

17.

18.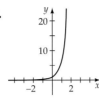

19.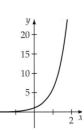

20.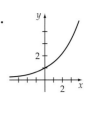

21.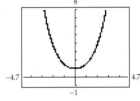

22.

23.

24.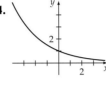

35.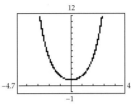

no horizontal asymptote

36.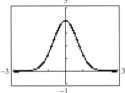

horizontal asymptote $y = 0$

37.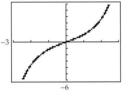

no horizontal asymptote

38.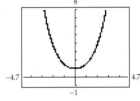

no horizontal asymptote

39.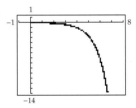

horizontal asymptote $y = 0$

40.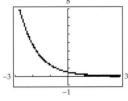

horizontal asymptote $y = 0$

41.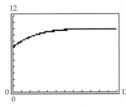

horizontal asymptote $y = 10$

42.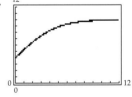

horizontal asymptote $y = 10$

62.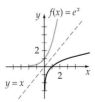

63.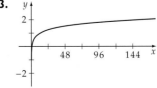

Exercise Set 4.3, page 391

31.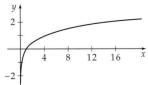

32.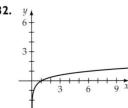

33.

34.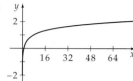

35.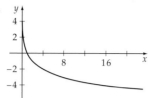

36.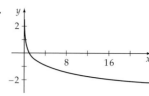

37.

38.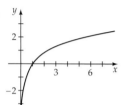

49.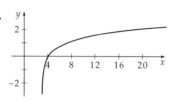

50.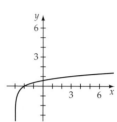

51.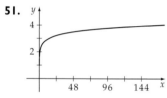

52.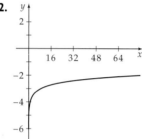

53.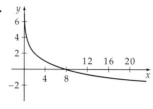

54.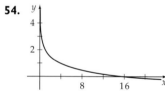

55.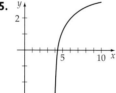

56.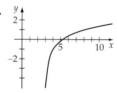

59.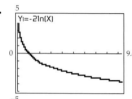

60.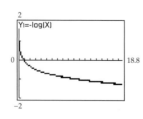

61.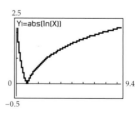

62.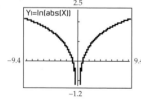

63.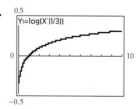

64.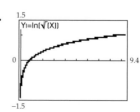

65.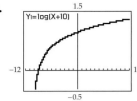

66.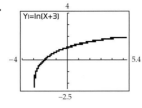

67.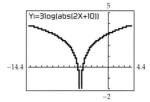

68.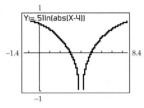

Exercise Set 4.4, page 403

23.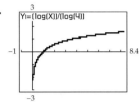

24.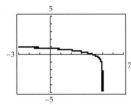

25.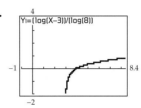

26.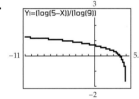

27.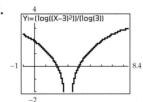

28.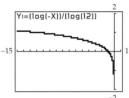

29.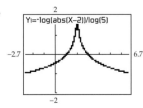

30.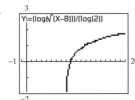

Exercise Set 4.5, page 415

61. a.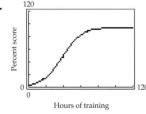

62. a.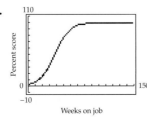

63. a.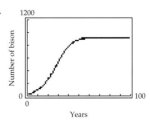

64. a.

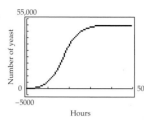

65. a.

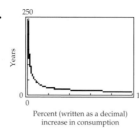

66. a.

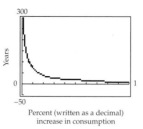

71. a.

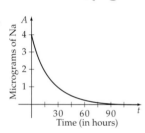

72. a.

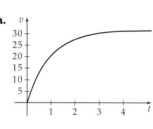

Exercise Set 4.6, page 430

19. a.

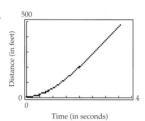

31. a.

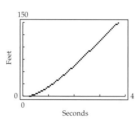

32. a.

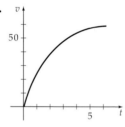

33. a.

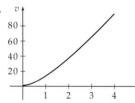

34. a.

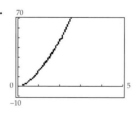

Exercise Set 4.7, page 444

1.

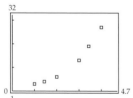

increasing exponential function

2.

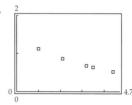

decreasing exponential function; decreasing logarithmic function

3.

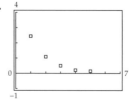

decreasing exponential function; decreasing logarithmic function

4.

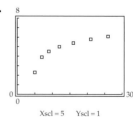

increasing logarithmic function

5.

decreasing logarithmic
function

6.

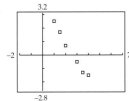

increasing logarithmic
function

35. a. Logistic: distance in ft $\approx \dfrac{71.84158}{1 + 13.77825e^{-0.07915t}}$;

logarithmic: distance in ft $\approx -22.58293 + 20.91655 \ln t$

40. b. Use a horizontal translation. For instance, add 1 to each of the
x-coordinates. Find the logarithmic regression function for this
new data set. Remember that each x-value in the regression function represents $x - 1$ in the original data.

Chapter 4 Review Exercises, page 454

5. [4.1]

6. [4.1]

7. [4.1]

8. [4.1]

both k
and k^{-1}

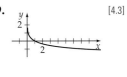

21. [4.2]

22. [4.2]

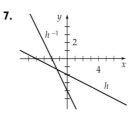

23. [4.2]

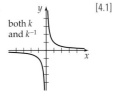

24. [4.2]

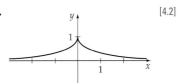

25. [4.2]

26. [4.2]

27. [4.3]

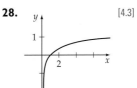

28. [4.3]

29. [4.3]

30. [4.3]

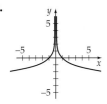

31. [4.2]

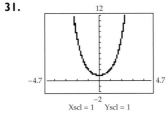

Xscl = 1   Yscl = 1

32. [4.2]

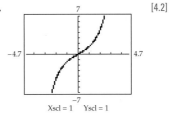

Xscl = 1   Yscl = 1

Chapter 4 Test, page 456

1. [4.1]

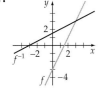

7. [4.2]

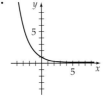

8. [4.3]

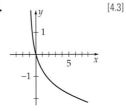

Exercise Set 5.1, page 468

1. vertex: $(0, 0)$

focus: $(0, -1)$

directrix: $y = 1$

2. vertex: $(0, 0)$

focus: $\left(\dfrac{1}{8}, 0\right)$

directrix: $x = -\dfrac{1}{8}$

3. vertex: $(0, 0)$

focus: $\left(\dfrac{1}{12}, 0\right)$

directrix: $x = -\dfrac{1}{12}$

4. vertex: $(0, 0)$

focus: $\left(0, -\dfrac{1}{16}\right)$

directrix: $y = \dfrac{1}{16}$

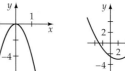

5. vertex: $(2, -3)$

focus: $(2, -1)$

directrix: $y = -5$

6. vertex: $(1, -1)$

focus: $\left(\dfrac{5}{2}, -1\right)$

directrix: $x = -\dfrac{1}{2}$

7. vertex: $(2, -4)$

focus: $(1, -4)$

directrix: $x = 3$

8. vertex: $(3, -2)$

focus: $\left(3, -\dfrac{9}{4}\right)$

directrix: $y = -\dfrac{7}{4}$

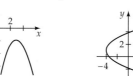

9. vertex: $(-4, 1)$

focus: $\left(-\dfrac{7}{2}, 1\right)$

directrix: $x = -\dfrac{9}{2}$

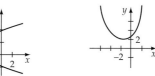

10. vertex: $(-2, 2)$

focus: $\left(-2, \dfrac{11}{4}\right)$

directrix: $y = \dfrac{5}{4}$

11. vertex: $(2, 2)$

focus: $\left(2, \dfrac{5}{2}\right)$

directrix: $y = \dfrac{3}{2}$

12. vertex: $(-2, 2)$

focus: $\left(-2, \dfrac{5}{2}\right)$

directrix: $y = \dfrac{3}{2}$

13. vertex: $(-4, -10)$

focus: $\left(-4, -\dfrac{39}{4}\right)$

directrix: $y = -\dfrac{41}{4}$

14. vertex: $(3, -1)$

focus: $\left(3, -\dfrac{5}{4}\right)$

directrix: $y = -\dfrac{3}{4}$

15. vertex: $\left(-\dfrac{7}{4}, \dfrac{3}{2}\right)$

focus: $\left(-2, \dfrac{3}{2}\right)$

directrix: $x = -\dfrac{3}{2}$

16. vertex: $(-13, -2)$

focus: $\left(-\dfrac{51}{4}, -2\right)$

directrix: $x = -\dfrac{53}{4}$

17. vertex: $(-5, -3)$

focus: $\left(-\dfrac{9}{2}, -3\right)$

directrix: $x = -\dfrac{11}{2}$

18. vertex: $(4, -4)$

focus: $\left(\dfrac{13}{4}, -4\right)$

directrix: $x = \dfrac{19}{4}$

19. vertex: $\left(-\dfrac{3}{2}, \dfrac{13}{12}\right)$

focus: $\left(-\dfrac{3}{2}, \dfrac{1}{3}\right)$

directrix: $y = \dfrac{11}{6}$

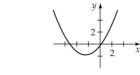

20. vertex: $\left(-\dfrac{5}{2}, -\dfrac{29}{16}\right)$

focus: $\left(-\dfrac{5}{2}, -\dfrac{13}{16}\right)$

directrix: $y = -\dfrac{45}{16}$

21. vertex: $\left(2, -\dfrac{5}{4}\right)$

focus: $\left(2, -\dfrac{3}{4}\right)$

directrix: $y = -\dfrac{7}{4}$

22. vertex: $\left(-\dfrac{8}{3}, -2\right)$

focus: $\left(-\dfrac{13}{6}, -2\right)$

directrix: $x = -\dfrac{19}{6}$

23. vertex: $\left(\dfrac{9}{2}, -1\right)$

focus: $\left(\dfrac{35}{8}, -1\right)$

directrix: $x = \dfrac{37}{8}$

24. vertex: $\left(\dfrac{3}{2}, \dfrac{1}{6}\right)$

focus: $\left(\dfrac{3}{2}, -\dfrac{7}{12}\right)$

directrix: $y = \dfrac{11}{12}$

25. vertex: $\left(1, \dfrac{1}{9}\right)$

focus: $\left(1, \dfrac{31}{36}\right)$

directrix: $y = -\dfrac{23}{36}$

26. vertex: $\left(-\dfrac{47}{8}, \dfrac{3}{2}\right)$

focus: $\left(-\dfrac{137}{24}, \dfrac{3}{2}\right)$

directrix: $x = -\dfrac{145}{24}$

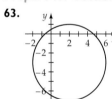

52.

$F\left(3, -\dfrac{1}{2}\right)$

$\left(4, -\dfrac{1}{2}\right)$

$\left(2, -\dfrac{1}{2}\right)$

53.

55.

Prepare for Section 5.2, page 470

63.

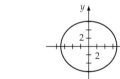

Exercise Set 5.2, page 480

1. center: $(0, 0)$
vertices: $(0, 5), (0, -5)$
foci: $(0, 3), (0, -3)$

2. center: $(0, 0)$
vertices: $(\pm 7, 0)$
foci: $\left(\pm\sqrt{13}, 0\right)$

3. center: $(0, 0)$
vertices: $(3, 0), (-3, 0)$
foci: $\left(\sqrt{5}, 0\right), \left(-\sqrt{5}, 0\right)$

4. center: $(0, 0)$
vertices: $(\pm 8, 0)$
foci: $\left(\pm\sqrt{39}, 0\right)$

5. center: $(0, 0)$
vertices: $(0, 3), (0, -3)$
foci: $\left(0, \sqrt{2}\right), \left(0, -\sqrt{2}\right)$

6. center: $(0, 0)$
vertices: $\left(\pm\sqrt{5}, 0\right)$
foci: $(\pm 1, 0)$

7. center: $(0, 0)$
vertices: $(0, 4), (0, -4)$
foci: $\left(0, \dfrac{\sqrt{55}}{2}\right), \left(0, -\dfrac{\sqrt{55}}{2}\right)$

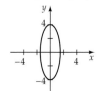

8. center: $(0, 0)$
vertices: $(\pm 3, 0)$
foci: $\left(\pm\dfrac{\sqrt{65}}{3}, 0\right)$

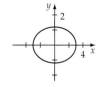

9. center: $(3, -2)$
vertices: $(8, -2), (-2, -2)$
foci: $(6, -2), (0, -2)$

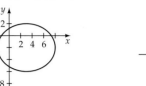

10. center: $(-3, -1)$
vertices: $(-3, 3), (-3, -5)$
foci: $\left(-3, -1 \pm \sqrt{7}\right)$

11. center: $(-2, 0)$
vertices: $(-2, 5), (-2, -5)$
foci: $(-2, 4), (-2, -4)$

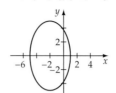

12. center: $(0, 2)$
vertices: $(0, 11), (0, -7)$
foci: $\left(0, 2 \pm 2\sqrt{14}\right)$

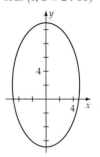

13. center: $(1, 3)$
vertices: $\left(1 + \sqrt{21}, 3\right), \left(1 - \sqrt{21}, 3\right)$
foci: $\left(1 + \sqrt{17}, 3\right), \left(1 - \sqrt{17}, 3\right)$

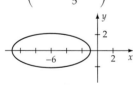

14. center: $(-5, 3)$
vertices: $(-2, 3), (-8, 3)$
foci: $\left(-5 \pm \sqrt{2}, 3\right)$

15. center: $(1, -1)$
vertices: $(1, 2), (1, -4)$
foci: $\left(1, -1 + \dfrac{\sqrt{65}}{3}\right), \left(1, -1 - \dfrac{\sqrt{65}}{3}\right)$

16. center: $(-6, 0)$
vertices: $(-1, 0), (-11, 0)$
foci: $\left(-6 \pm \dfrac{\sqrt{481}}{5}, 0\right)$

17. center: $(0, 0)$
vertices: $(2, 0), (-2, 0)$
foci: $(1, 0), (-1, 0)$

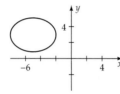

18. center: $(0, 0)$
vertices: $\left(0, \pm\sqrt{5}\right)$
foci: $(0, \pm 1)$

19. center: $(0, 0)$
vertices: $(0, 5), (0, -5)$
foci: $(0, 3), (0, -3)$

20. center: $(0, 0)$
vertices: $(0, \pm 5)$
foci: $\left(0, \pm\sqrt{13}\right)$

21. center: $(0, 0)$
vertices: $(0, 4), (0, -4)$
foci: $\left(0, \dfrac{\sqrt{39}}{2}\right), \left(0, -\dfrac{\sqrt{39}}{2}\right)$

22. center: $(0, 0)$
vertices: $(\pm 4, 0)$
foci: $\left(\pm\dfrac{\sqrt{55}}{2}, 0\right)$

23. center: $(3, 4)$
vertices: $(3, 6), (3, 2)$
foci: $\left(3, 4 + \sqrt{3}\right), \left(3, 4 - \sqrt{3}\right)$

24. center: $(-3, 2)$

vertices: $(0, 2), (-6, 2)$

foci: $\left(-3 \pm 2\sqrt{2}, 2\right)$

25. center: $(2, -3)$

vertices: $(-1, -3), (5, -3)$

foci: $(0, -3), (4, -3)$

26. center: $\left(-2, \dfrac{1}{2}\right)$

vertices: $\left(2, \dfrac{1}{2}\right), \left(-6, \dfrac{1}{2}\right)$

foci: $\left(-2 \pm \sqrt{7}, \dfrac{1}{2}\right)$

27. center: $(2, 0)$

vertices: $(2, 4), (2, -4)$

foci: $\left(2, \sqrt{7}\right), \left(2, -\sqrt{7}\right)$

28. center: $(0, -2)$

vertices: $(0, -6), (0, 2)$

foci: $\left(0, -2 \pm \sqrt{7}\right)$

29. center: $(-1, 1)$

vertices: $(-1, 6), (-1, -4)$

foci: $(-1, 4), (-1, -2)$

30. center: $(2, 3)$

vertices: $(2, -1), (2, 7)$

foci: $\left(2, 3 \pm \sqrt{7}\right)$

31. center: $(3, -1)$

vertices: $\left(\dfrac{11}{2}, -1\right), \left(\dfrac{1}{2}, -1\right)$

foci: $\left(3 + \dfrac{\sqrt{17}}{2}, -1\right), \left(3 - \dfrac{\sqrt{17}}{2}, -1\right)$

32. center: $(-3, -1)$

vertices: $\left(-\dfrac{5}{2}, -1\right), \left(-\dfrac{7}{2}, -1\right)$

foci: $\left(-3 \pm \dfrac{\sqrt{5}}{6}, -1\right)$

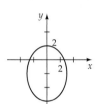

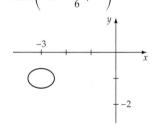

64. $y = \pm \dfrac{4}{3} \sqrt{-x^2 + 4x + 5}$

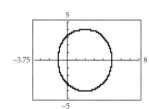

65. $y = \dfrac{-36 \pm \sqrt{1296 - 36(16x^2 - 108)}}{18}$

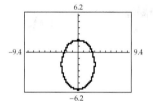

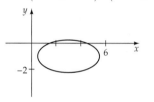

66. $y = \dfrac{32 \pm \sqrt{1024 - 64(25x^2 + 50x - 359)}}{32}$

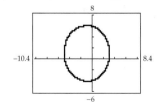

67. $y = \dfrac{54 \pm \sqrt{2916 - 36(16x^2 - 64x + 1)}}{18}$

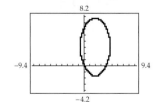

68. $y = \dfrac{-50 \pm \sqrt{2500 - 100(8x^2 - 48x + 47)}}{50}$

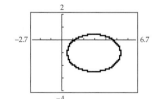

69. $y = \dfrac{-18 \pm \sqrt{324 - 36(4x^2 + 24x + 44)}}{18}$

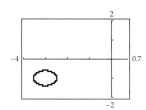

70. This is not the equation of an ellipse because there is no y^2 term. It is a quadratic equation in x.

Prepare for Section 5.3, page 484

88.

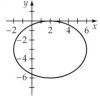

Exercise Set 5.3, page 495

1. center: $(0, 0)$
vertices: $(\pm 4, 0)$
foci: $(\pm\sqrt{41}, 0)$
asymptotes: $y = \pm\dfrac{5}{4}x$

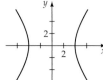

2. center: $(0, 0)$
vertices: $(\pm 4, 0)$
foci: $(\pm 5, 0)$
asymptotes: $y = \pm\dfrac{3}{4}x$

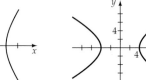

3. center: $(0, 0)$
vertices: $(0, \pm 2)$
foci: $(0, \pm\sqrt{29})$
asymptotes: $y = \pm\dfrac{2}{5}x$

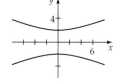

4. center: $(0, 0)$
vertices: $(0, \pm 5)$
foci: $(0, \pm\sqrt{61})$
asymptotes: $y = \pm\dfrac{5}{6}x$

5. center: $(0, 0)$
vertices: $(\pm\sqrt{7}, 0)$
foci: $(\pm 4, 0)$
asymptotes: $y = \pm\dfrac{3\sqrt{7}}{7}x$

6. center: $(0, 0)$
vertices: $(\pm\sqrt{5}, 0)$
foci: $(\pm 3, 0)$
asymptotes: $y = \pm\dfrac{2\sqrt{5}}{5}x$

7. center: $(0, 0)$
vertices: $\left(\pm\dfrac{3}{2}, 0\right)$
foci: $\left(\pm\dfrac{\sqrt{73}}{2}, 0\right)$
asymptotes: $y = \pm\dfrac{8}{3}x$

8. center: $(0, 0)$
vertices: $(\pm 3, 0)$
foci: $\left(\pm\dfrac{\sqrt{97}}{3}, 0\right)$
asymptotes: $y = \pm\dfrac{4}{9}x$

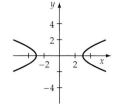

9. center: $(3, -4)$
vertices: $(7, -4), (-1, -4)$
foci: $(8, -4), (-2, -4)$
asymptotes: $y + 4 = \pm\dfrac{3}{4}(x - 3)$

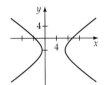

10. center: $(-3, 0)$
vertices: $(-3 \pm 5, 0) = (2, 0), (-8, 0)$
foci: $\left(-3 \pm \sqrt{29}, 0\right)$
asymptotes: $y = \pm\dfrac{2}{5}(x + 3)$

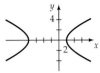

11. center: $(1, -2)$
vertices: $(1, 0), (1, -4)$
foci: $\left(1, -2 \pm 2\sqrt{5}\right)$
asymptotes: $y + 2 = \pm\dfrac{1}{2}(x - 1)$

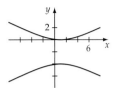

12. center: $(-1, 2)$
vertices: $(-1, 8), (-1, -4)$
foci: $\left(-1, 2 \pm \sqrt{85}\right)$
asymptotes: $y - 2 = \pm\dfrac{6}{7}(x + 1)$

13. center: $(-2, 0)$
vertices: $(1, 0), (-5, 0)$
foci: $\left(-2 \pm \sqrt{34}, 0\right)$
asymptotes: $y = \pm\dfrac{5}{3}(x + 2)$

14. center: $(0, 2)$
vertices: $(5, 2), (-5, 2)$
foci: $\left(\pm\sqrt{106}, 2\right)$
asymptotes: $(y - 2) = \pm\dfrac{9}{5}x$

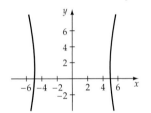

15. center: $(1, -1)$
vertices: $\left(\dfrac{7}{3}, -1\right), \left(-\dfrac{1}{3}, -1\right)$
foci: $\left(1 \pm \dfrac{\sqrt{97}}{3}, -1\right)$
asymptotes: $y + 1 = \pm\dfrac{9}{4}(x - 1)$

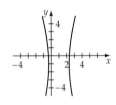

16. center: $(-6, 0)$
vertices: $(-1, 0), (-11, 0)$
foci: $\left(-6 \pm \dfrac{\sqrt{769}}{5}, 0\right)$
asymptotes: $y = \pm\dfrac{12}{25}(x + 6)$

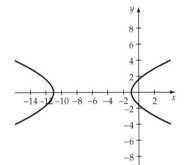

17. center: $(0, 0)$
vertices: $(\pm 3, 0)$
foci: $\left(\pm 3\sqrt{2}, 0\right)$
asymptotes: $y = \pm x$

18. center: $(0, 0)$
vertices: $(\pm 2, 0)$
foci: $\left(\pm 2\sqrt{5}, 0\right)$
asymptotes: $y = \pm 2x$

19. center: $(0, 0)$

vertices: $(0, \pm 3)$

foci: $(0, \pm 5)$

asymptotes: $y = \pm \dfrac{3}{4} x$

20. center: $(0, 0)$

vertices: $(0, \pm 5)$

foci: $\left(0, \pm \sqrt{34}\right)$

asymptotes: $y = \pm \dfrac{5}{3} x$

21. center: $(0, 0)$

vertices: $\left(0, \pm \dfrac{2}{3}\right)$

foci: $\left(0, \pm \dfrac{\sqrt{5}}{3}\right)$

asymptotes: $y = \pm 2x$

22. center: $(0, 0)$

vertices: $\left(\pm \dfrac{3}{4}, 0\right)$

foci: $\left(\pm \dfrac{3\sqrt{41}}{20}, 0\right)$

asymptotes: $y = \pm \dfrac{4}{5} x$

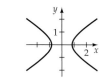

23. center: $(3, 4)$
vertices: $(3, 6), (3, 2)$
foci: $\left(3, 4 \pm 2\sqrt{2}\right)$

asymptotes: $y - 4 = \pm (x - 3)$

24. center: $(-2, 1)$
vertices: $(-7, 1), (3, 1)$
foci: $\left(-2 + \sqrt{29}, 1\right), \left(-2 - \sqrt{29}, 1\right)$

asymptotes: $y - 1 = \pm \dfrac{2}{5}(x + 2)$

25. center: $(-2, -1)$
vertices: $(-2, 2), (-2, -4)$
foci: $\left(-2, -1 \pm \sqrt{13}\right)$

asymptotes: $y + 1 = \pm \dfrac{3}{2}(x + 2)$

26. center: $(1, -3)$

vertices: $(1, 1), (1, -7)$
foci: $(1, 2), (1, -8)$

asymptotes: $(y + 3) = \pm \dfrac{4}{3}(x - 1)$

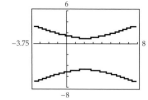

27. $y = \dfrac{-6 \pm \sqrt{36 + 4(4x^2 + 32x + 39)}}{-2}$

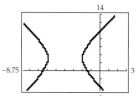

28. $y = \dfrac{64 \pm \sqrt{4096 + 64(x^2 + 8x + 16)}}{-32}$

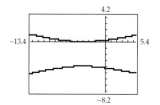

29. $y = \dfrac{64 \pm \sqrt{4096 + 64(9x^2 - 36x + 116)}}{-32}$

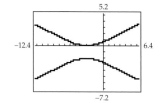

30. $y = \dfrac{18 \pm \sqrt{324 + 36(2x^2 + 12x + 18)}}{-18}$

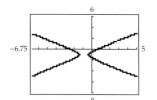

31. $y = \dfrac{18 \pm \sqrt{324 + 36(4x^2 + 8x - 6)}}{-18}$

32. $y = \dfrac{-36 \pm \sqrt{1296 + 36(2x^2 - 8x - 46)}}{-18}$

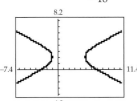

57. ellipse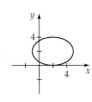

58. parabola

59. parabola

60. hyperbola

61. parabola

62. ellipse

63. ellipse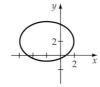

64. parabola

73.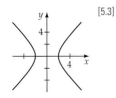

74.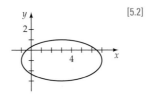

Chapter 5 Review Exercises, page 500

1. center: $(0, 0)$; vertices: $(\pm 2, 0)$; foci: $(\pm 2\sqrt{2}, 0)$; asymptotes: $y = \pm x$ [5.3]

2. vertex: $(0, 0)$; directrix: $x = -4$; focus: $(4, 0)$ [5.1]

3. center: $(3, -1)$; vertices: $(-1, -1), (7, -1)$; foci: $(3 \pm 2\sqrt{3}, -1)$ [5.2]

4. center: $(-2, -3)$; vertices: $(0, -3), (-4, -3)$; foci: $(-2 \pm \sqrt{7}, -3)$; asymptotes: $(y + 3) = \pm \dfrac{\sqrt{3}}{2}(x + 2)$ [5.3]

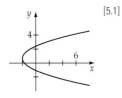 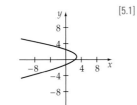 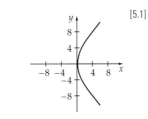 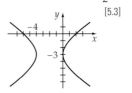

5. vertex: $(-2, 1)$; directrix: $x = -\dfrac{35}{16}$; focus: $\left(-\dfrac{29}{16}, 1\right)$ [5.1]

6. vertex: $(3, 1)$; directrix: $x = \dfrac{27}{8}$; focus: $\left(\dfrac{21}{8}, 1\right)$ [5.1]

7. center: $(-2, 1)$; vertices: $(-2, -2), (-2, 4)$; foci: $(-2, 1 \pm \sqrt{5})$ [5.2]

8. center: $(2, -1)$; vertices: $(7, -1), (-3, -1)$; foci: $(8, -1), (-4, -1)$; asymptotes: $y + 1 = \pm \dfrac{\sqrt{11}}{5}(x - 2)$ [5.3]

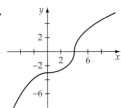 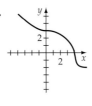 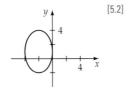 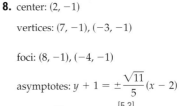

9. center: $\left(1, \frac{2}{3}\right)$

vertices: $\left(-5, \frac{2}{3}\right), \left(7, \frac{2}{3}\right)$

foci: $\left(1 \pm 2\sqrt{13}, \frac{2}{3}\right)$

asymptotes: $y - \frac{2}{3} = \pm\frac{2}{3}(x - 1)$

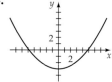 [5.3]

10. center: $\left(-2, \frac{1}{2}\right)$

vertices: $\left(2, \frac{1}{2}\right), \left(-6, \frac{1}{2}\right)$

foci: $\left(-2 \pm \sqrt{7}, \frac{1}{2}\right)$

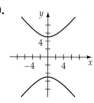 [5.2]

11. vertex: $\left(-\frac{7}{2}, -1\right)$

directrix: $y = 1$

focus: $\left(-\frac{7}{2}, -3\right)$

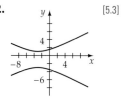 [5.1]

12. vertex: $(3, 2)$

directrix: $y = -\frac{3}{4}$

focus: $\left(3, \frac{17}{4}\right)$

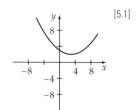 [5.1]

Chapter 5 Test, page 501

4. 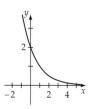 [5.1] **6.** 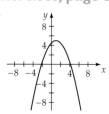 [5.2] **10.**   [5.3] **12.** 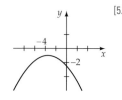 [5.3]

Cumulative Review Exercises, page 502

9. 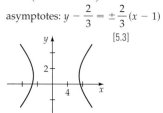 [4.2] **11.** 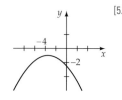 [2.5]

Exercise Set 6.4, page 544

37. $\dfrac{1}{5(x+2)} + \dfrac{4}{5(x-3)}$ **38.** $\dfrac{-1}{4x} + \dfrac{5}{4(x-4)}$ **39.** $\dfrac{1}{x} + \dfrac{2}{x^2} + \dfrac{3}{x^4} + \dfrac{-2}{x-2}$ **40.** $\dfrac{1}{x-1} - \dfrac{1}{x+1} + \dfrac{1}{(x+1)^2}$ **41.** $\dfrac{4}{3(x-1)} + \dfrac{2x+7}{3(x^2+x+1)}$

42. $\dfrac{-1}{x-1} + \dfrac{1}{x+1} + \dfrac{x}{x^2-x+1}$ **44. a.** $\dfrac{1}{-3(x^2+4)} + \dfrac{1}{3(x^2+1)}$ **b.** $\dfrac{1}{8(x^2+1)} + \dfrac{1}{-8(x^2+9)}$ **c.** $\dfrac{1}{x^2+x+1} - \dfrac{1}{x^2+x+2}$

d. $\dfrac{1}{5(x^2+2x+4)} - \dfrac{1}{5(x^2+2x+9)}$

Prepare for Section 6.5, page 545

45.   **46.**   **47.**   **48.** 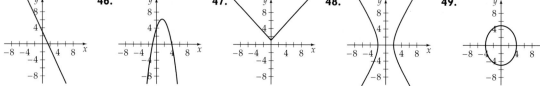 **49.**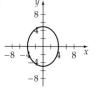

50.

Exercise Set 6.5, page 551

1.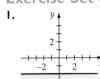

2.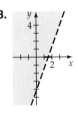

3.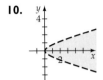

4.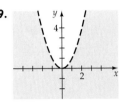

5.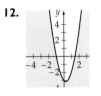

6.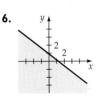

7.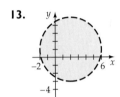

8.

9.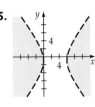

10.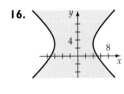

11.

12.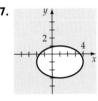

13.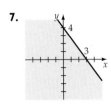

14.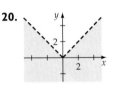

15.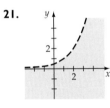

16.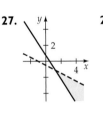

17.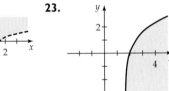

18.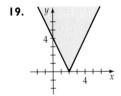

19.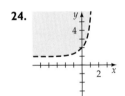

20.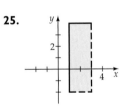

21.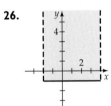

22.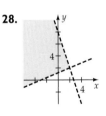

23.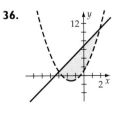

24.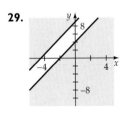

25.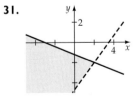

26.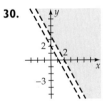

27.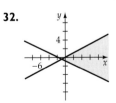

28.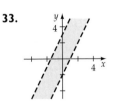

29.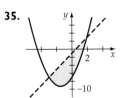

30.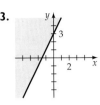

31.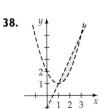

32.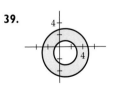

33.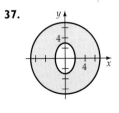

35.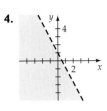

36.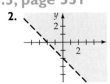

37.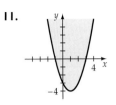

38.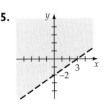

39.

41.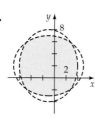

42.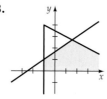

43.

44.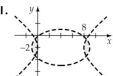

45.

46.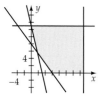

47.

48.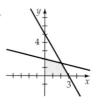

49.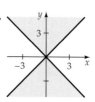

50.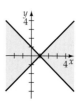

51.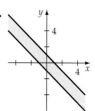

52.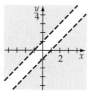

53.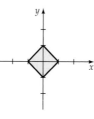

54.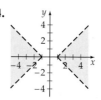

55.

56.

57. If x is a negative number, then the inequality is reversed when dividing both sides of the inequality by a negative number.

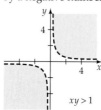

$xy > 1$ $y > \dfrac{1}{x}$

58. If y is a negative number, then the inequality is reversed when multiplying both sides of the inequality by a negative number.

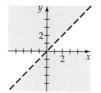

Prepare for Section 6.6, page 552

59.

60.

61.

62.

Chapter 6 Review Exercises, page 563

37.   [6.5]

38. 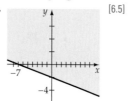 [6.5]

39. 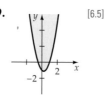 [6.5]

40. 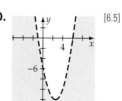 [6.5]

41. [6.5]
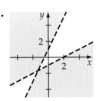

42. [6.5]
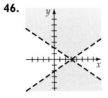

43. [6.5]
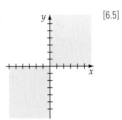

44. [6.5]
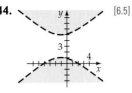

45. [6.5]

46. [6.5]
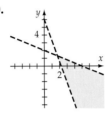

47. [6.5]
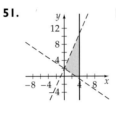

48. [6.5]
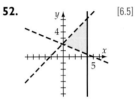

49. [6.5]

50. [6.5]
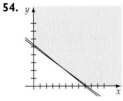

51. [6.5]
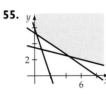

52. [6.5]
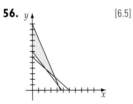

53. [6.5]
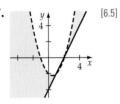

54. [6.5]

55. [6.5]
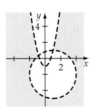

56. [6.5]
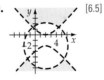

57. [6.5]

58. [6.5]

59. [6.5]
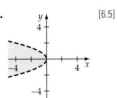

60. [6.5]

Chapter 6 Test, page 565

9. [6.5]
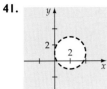

10. [6.5]
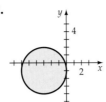

11. [6.5]
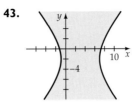

12. [6.5]
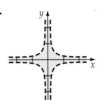

13. [6.5]

15. [6.5]
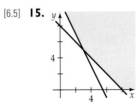

16. [6.5]
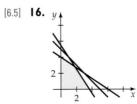

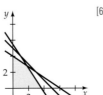

Cumulative Review Exercises, page 566

19. 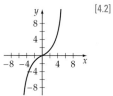 [4.2]

Exercise Set 7.1, page 578

1. $\begin{bmatrix} 2 & -3 & 1 & | & 1 \\ 3 & -2 & 3 & | & 0 \\ 1 & 0 & 5 & | & 4 \end{bmatrix}, \begin{bmatrix} 2 & -3 & 1 & | & 1 \\ 3 & -2 & 3 & | & 0 \\ 1 & 0 & 5 & | & 4 \end{bmatrix}$
2. $\begin{bmatrix} 0 & -3 & 2 & | & 3 \\ 2 & -1 & 0 & | & -1 \\ 3 & -2 & 3 & | & 4 \end{bmatrix}, \begin{bmatrix} 0 & -3 & 2 & | & 3 \\ 2 & -1 & 0 & | & -1 \\ 3 & -2 & 3 & | & 4 \end{bmatrix}$
3. $\begin{bmatrix} 2 & -3 & -4 & 1 & | & 2 \\ 0 & 2 & 1 & 0 & | & 2 \\ 1 & -1 & 2 & 0 & | & 4 \\ 3 & -3 & -2 & 0 & | & 1 \end{bmatrix}, \begin{bmatrix} 2 & -3 & -4 & 1 & | & 2 \\ 0 & 2 & 1 & 0 & | & 2 \\ 1 & -1 & 2 & 0 & | & 4 \\ 3 & -3 & -2 & 0 & | & 1 \end{bmatrix}$

4. $\begin{bmatrix} 1 & -1 & 2 & 3 & | & -2 \\ 2 & 0 & 1 & -2 & | & 1 \\ 3 & 0 & 0 & -2 & | & 3 \\ -1 & 3 & -1 & 0 & | & 3 \end{bmatrix}, \begin{bmatrix} 1 & -1 & 2 & 3 & | & -2 \\ 2 & 0 & 1 & -2 & | & 1 \\ 3 & 0 & 0 & -2 & | & 3 \\ -1 & 3 & -1 & 0 & | & 3 \end{bmatrix}$
5. $\begin{bmatrix} 1 & -1 & 2 & | & 2 \\ 0 & 1 & -1 & | & -6 \\ 0 & 0 & 1 & | & -\frac{27}{2} \end{bmatrix}$
6. $\begin{bmatrix} 1 & 2 & 4 & | & 1 \\ 0 & 1 & \frac{1}{2} & | & -\frac{1}{2} \\ 0 & 0 & 1 & | & 1 \end{bmatrix}$
7. $\begin{bmatrix} 1 & -2 & -1 & | & 3 \\ 0 & 1 & 2 & | & -\frac{11}{2} \\ 0 & 0 & 1 & | & -\frac{13}{6} \end{bmatrix}$

8. $\begin{bmatrix} 1 & 1 & 2 & | & 3 \\ 0 & 1 & 1 & | & 3 \\ 0 & 0 & 1 & | & \frac{1}{5} \end{bmatrix}$
9. $\begin{bmatrix} 1 & -2 & 3 & -4 \\ 0 & 1 & 2 & -\frac{1}{2} \\ 0 & 0 & 1 & -2 \\ 0 & 0 & 0 & 0 \end{bmatrix}$
10. $\begin{bmatrix} 1 & 2 & -1 & 3 \\ 0 & 1 & -1 & \frac{4}{5} \\ 0 & 0 & 0 & 1 \\ 0 & 0 & 0 & 0 \end{bmatrix}$
11. $\begin{bmatrix} 1 & -3 & 4 & 2 & | & 1 \\ 0 & 1 & -1 & -2 & | & -1 \\ 0 & 0 & 0 & 1 & | & 3 \end{bmatrix}$
12. $\begin{bmatrix} 1 & -2 & 2 & 1 & | & -1 \\ 0 & 1 & -7 & -5 & | & 6 \\ 0 & 0 & 1 & \frac{3}{4} & | & -\frac{7}{10} \end{bmatrix}$

Exercise Set 7.2, page 595

1. a. $\begin{bmatrix} 1 & 2 \\ 5 & 4 \end{bmatrix}$ **b.** $\begin{bmatrix} 3 & -4 \\ 1 & 2 \end{bmatrix}$ **c.** $\begin{bmatrix} -2 & 6 \\ 4 & 2 \end{bmatrix}$ **d.** $\begin{bmatrix} 7 & -11 \\ 0 & 3 \end{bmatrix}$ **2. a.** $\begin{bmatrix} 5 & -3 \\ 5 & 3 \end{bmatrix}$ **b.** $\begin{bmatrix} -5 & -1 \\ -1 & 3 \end{bmatrix}$ **c.** $\begin{bmatrix} 10 & -2 \\ 6 & 0 \end{bmatrix}$ **d.** $\begin{bmatrix} -15 & -1 \\ -5 & 6 \end{bmatrix}$

3. a. $\begin{bmatrix} -3 & 0 & 5 \\ 3 & 5 & -5 \end{bmatrix}$ **b.** $\begin{bmatrix} 3 & -2 & 1 \\ -1 & -5 & 1 \end{bmatrix}$ **c.** $\begin{bmatrix} -6 & 2 & 4 \\ 4 & 10 & -6 \end{bmatrix}$ **d.** $\begin{bmatrix} 9 & -5 & 0 \\ -4 & -15 & 5 \end{bmatrix}$ **4. a.** $\begin{bmatrix} 3 & -7 & 10 \\ 4 & -5 & -7 \end{bmatrix}$ **b.** $\begin{bmatrix} 1 & 3 & -2 \\ -4 & -1 & -1 \end{bmatrix}$

c. $\begin{bmatrix} 2 & -10 & 12 \\ 8 & -4 & -6 \end{bmatrix}$ **d.** $\begin{bmatrix} 1 & 11 & -10 \\ -12 & 0 & 1 \end{bmatrix}$ **5. a.** $\begin{bmatrix} 1 & 5 \\ 3 & -5 \\ 2 & -4 \end{bmatrix}$ **b.** $\begin{bmatrix} -7 & 3 \\ 1 & -1 \\ -4 & 4 \end{bmatrix}$ **c.** $\begin{bmatrix} 8 & 2 \\ 2 & -4 \\ 6 & -8 \end{bmatrix}$ **d.** $\begin{bmatrix} -18 & 5 \\ 1 & 0 \\ -11 & 12 \end{bmatrix}$

6. a. $\begin{bmatrix} 1 & 6 \\ 5 & 2 \\ -3 & 3 \end{bmatrix}$ **b.** $\begin{bmatrix} 3 & -10 \\ 1 & 6 \\ 5 & -3 \end{bmatrix}$ **c.** $\begin{bmatrix} -2 & 16 \\ 4 & -4 \\ -8 & 6 \end{bmatrix}$ **d.** $\begin{bmatrix} 7 & -28 \\ 0 & 14 \\ 14 & -9 \end{bmatrix}$ **7. a.** $\begin{bmatrix} -1 & 1 & -1 \\ 2 & 2 & 1 \\ -1 & 2 & 5 \end{bmatrix}$ **b.** $\begin{bmatrix} -3 & 5 & -1 \\ -2 & -4 & 3 \\ -7 & 4 & 1 \end{bmatrix}$ **c.** $\begin{bmatrix} 2 & -4 & 0 \\ 4 & 6 & -2 \\ 6 & -2 & 4 \end{bmatrix}$

d. $\begin{bmatrix} -7 & 12 & -2 \\ -6 & -11 & 7 \\ -17 & 9 & 0 \end{bmatrix}$ **8. a.** $\begin{bmatrix} -1 & 4 & 4 \\ 4 & 0 & 1 \\ 1 & 8 & 1 \end{bmatrix}$ **b.** $\begin{bmatrix} 1 & 0 & -4 \\ -2 & -6 & 5 \\ 9 & 0 & -5 \end{bmatrix}$ **c.** $\begin{bmatrix} -2 & 4 & 8 \\ 6 & 6 & -4 \\ -8 & 8 & 6 \end{bmatrix}$ **d.** $\begin{bmatrix} 3 & -2 & -12 \\ -7 & -15 & 12 \\ 22 & -4 & -13 \end{bmatrix}$ **9.** $\begin{bmatrix} -10 & 17 \\ 6 & -8 \end{bmatrix}, \begin{bmatrix} 0 & 22 \\ 1 & -18 \end{bmatrix}$

10. $\begin{bmatrix} -3 & -11 \\ -4 & 0 \end{bmatrix}, \begin{bmatrix} -7 & 1 \\ 16 & 4 \end{bmatrix}$ **11.** $\begin{bmatrix} 10 & 6 \\ 14 & -7 \end{bmatrix}, \begin{bmatrix} 14 & -1 \\ 0 & -11 \end{bmatrix}$ **12.** $\begin{bmatrix} -4 & 2 \\ 4 & -4 \end{bmatrix}, \begin{bmatrix} 4 & -4 \\ 14 & -12 \end{bmatrix}$ **13.** $\begin{bmatrix} 0 & -4 & 5 \\ 6 & 0 & 3 \\ -3 & -2 & 1 \end{bmatrix}, \begin{bmatrix} 5 & -13 \\ 5 & -4 \end{bmatrix}$

14. $\begin{bmatrix} 3 & 7 & -14 \\ 1 & 0 & 0 \\ -2 & -1 & 2 \end{bmatrix}, \begin{bmatrix} -8 & -5 \\ 15 & 13 \end{bmatrix}$ **15.** $\begin{bmatrix} 9 & -2 & -6 \\ 0 & -1 & 2 \\ 4 & -2 & -4 \end{bmatrix}, \begin{bmatrix} 4 & -2 & 6 \\ 2 & -3 & 4 \\ 4 & -4 & 3 \end{bmatrix}$ **16.** $\begin{bmatrix} 0 & 11 & -2 \\ 3 & -8 & 4 \\ -2 & 13 & -5 \end{bmatrix}, \begin{bmatrix} -4 & 5 & -1 \\ 11 & -5 & 6 \\ -8 & 7 & -4 \end{bmatrix}$ **24.** $\begin{bmatrix} 8 & 2 & -8 & 12 \\ 1 & 2 & -3 & -2 \\ 7 & -3 & -5 & 4 \end{bmatrix}$

25. $\begin{bmatrix} \frac{1}{3} & -\frac{5}{3} \\ -\frac{1}{3} & \frac{4}{3} \\ \frac{1}{3} & -\frac{4}{3} \end{bmatrix}$ **26.** $\begin{bmatrix} -\frac{2}{3} & \frac{16}{3} \\ -\frac{1}{3} & -\frac{17}{3} \\ -\frac{14}{3} & \frac{17}{3} \end{bmatrix}$ **27.** $\begin{bmatrix} -1 & 1 \\ 3 & 2 \\ 7 & -2 \end{bmatrix}$ **28.** $\begin{bmatrix} 1 & -1 \\ -3 & -2 \\ -7 & 2 \end{bmatrix}$ **29.** $\begin{bmatrix} 1 & -3 \\ 1 & -2 \end{bmatrix}$ **30.** $\begin{bmatrix} -1 & 0 \\ 0 & -1 \end{bmatrix}$ **31.** $\begin{bmatrix} 7 & -1 & 1 \\ 1 & 2 & 0 \\ 5 & -1 & 4 \end{bmatrix}$

32. $\begin{bmatrix} 20 & -5 & 3 \\ 7 & -5 & -2 \\ 17 & -3 & 9 \end{bmatrix}$ **41.** $\begin{bmatrix} 1.96 & 1.37 & 2.94 & 1.37 \\ 0.78 & 1.08 & 1.96 & 0.88 \\ 3.53 & 1.18 & 4.41 & 1.47 \end{bmatrix}$ **42.** $\begin{bmatrix} 19.1 & 20.0 & 21.2 & 22.8 \\ 20.1 & 21.5 & 23.9 & 26.0 \\ 21.2 & 22.7 & 25.4 & 28.6 \end{bmatrix}$ **45. b.**

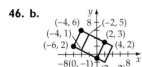

46. b.

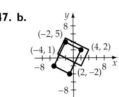

47. b.   **48. b.**

49. $A - B = \begin{bmatrix} 50 & 150 & 140 \\ 15 & 170 & 370 \\ 85 & 250 & 130 \\ 80 & 115 & 25 \end{bmatrix}$; $A - B$ is the number of each item sold during the week.

50. $\begin{bmatrix} 515 & 375 & 765 \\ 435 & 265 & 480 \\ 380 & 245 & 425 \end{bmatrix}$; $A + B$ gives the number of employees in each area for both branches of the company.

59. $\begin{bmatrix} 24 & 21 & -12 & 32 & 0 \\ -7 & -8 & 3 & 21 & 20 \\ 32 & 10 & -32 & 1 & 5 \\ 19 & -15 & -17 & 30 & 20 \\ 29 & 9 & -28 & 13 & -6 \end{bmatrix}$ **60.** $\begin{bmatrix} 30 & -27 & 3 & 13 & 28 \\ 7 & -13 & -3 & -5 & 21 \\ 17 & -7 & -3 & 12 & 33 \\ 34 & -8 & 23 & 2 & -17 \\ 12 & 14 & -7 & 14 & -8 \end{bmatrix}$ **61.** $\begin{bmatrix} 46 & -100 & 36 & 273 & 93 \\ 82 & -93 & 19 & 27 & 97 \\ 73 & -10 & -23 & 109 & 83 \\ 212 & -189 & 52 & 37 & 156 \\ 68 & -22 & 54 & 221 & 58 \end{bmatrix}$ **62.** $\begin{bmatrix} 55 & -65 & 65 & 291 & -154 \\ -60 & -72 & 69 & 87 & -26 \\ 98 & -94 & -33 & 128 & -124 \\ 149 & 213 & -49 & 114 & -93 \\ 44 & -57 & 55 & 63 & -121 \end{bmatrix}$

63. $\begin{bmatrix} 76 & -8 & -25 & 30 & 6 \\ 14 & 16 & -10 & 14 & 2 \\ 39 & 0 & -45 & 22 & 27 \\ 0 & -4 & 23 & 83 & -16 \\ 56 & -20 & -22 & 7 & 5 \end{bmatrix}$ **64.** $\begin{bmatrix} -6 & 48 & -15 & 19 & -28 \\ -14 & 5 & 6 & 26 & -1 \\ 15 & 17 & -29 & -11 & -28 \\ -15 & -7 & -40 & 28 & 37 \\ 17 & -5 & -21 & -1 & 2 \end{bmatrix}$ **65.** $\begin{bmatrix} 6 + 9i & 3 - 6i \\ 3 + 3i & 6 - 3i \end{bmatrix}$ **66.** $\begin{bmatrix} -2 + 2i & -4 - 6i \\ -6 - 4i & -8 + 2i \end{bmatrix}$

67. $\begin{bmatrix} 2 + 2i & -6 + 4i \\ -4 + 6i & 2 + 8i \end{bmatrix}$ **68.** $\begin{bmatrix} -9 + 6i & 6 + 3i \\ -3 + 3i & 3 + 6i \end{bmatrix}$ **69.** $\begin{bmatrix} 3 + 2i & 3 + i \\ 4 + 3i & 6 - 2i \end{bmatrix}$ **70.** $\begin{bmatrix} 1 + 4i & -1 - 5i \\ -2 - i & -2 \end{bmatrix}$ **71.** $\begin{bmatrix} 12 - 3i & -3 + 3i \\ 10 + i & 6 - i \end{bmatrix}$

72. $\begin{bmatrix} 4 + 6i & 6 + i \\ 5 + 16i & 14 - 10i \end{bmatrix}$ **73.** $\begin{bmatrix} -2 + 11i & 8 - 6i \\ 2 + 6i & 6 - 5i \end{bmatrix}$ **74.** $\begin{bmatrix} +11i & 16 + 11i \\ 19 + 4i & 15 + 5i \end{bmatrix}$

Exercise Set 7.3, page 610

5. $\begin{bmatrix} -16 & -2 & 7 \\ 7 & 1 & -3 \\ -3 & 0 & 1 \end{bmatrix}$ **6.** $\begin{bmatrix} \frac{21}{2} & \frac{3}{2} & -4 \\ -\frac{9}{2} & -\frac{1}{2} & 2 \end{bmatrix}$ **7.** $\begin{bmatrix} 15 & -1 & -4 \\ -\frac{11}{2} & \frac{1}{2} & \frac{3}{2} \\ 3 & 0 & -1 \end{bmatrix}$ **8.** $\begin{bmatrix} 5 & -\frac{1}{2} & -\frac{3}{2} \\ -7 & 1 & 2 \\ 2 & 0 & -1 \end{bmatrix}$ **9.** $\begin{bmatrix} \frac{7}{2} & -2 & -2 \\ -\frac{5}{2} & 1 & 2 \\ -1 & 0 & 1 \end{bmatrix}$ **11.** $\begin{bmatrix} \frac{19}{2} & -\frac{1}{2} & -\frac{3}{2} & \frac{3}{2} \\ \frac{7}{2} & 1 & -\frac{1}{2} & \frac{3}{2} \\ \frac{7}{4} & \frac{1}{4} & \frac{1}{4} & -\frac{1}{4} \\ -\frac{7}{2} & \frac{1}{2} & \frac{1}{2} & \frac{1}{2} \\ \frac{1}{4} & -\frac{1}{4} & \frac{1}{4} & \frac{1}{4} \end{bmatrix}$

12. $\begin{bmatrix} 0 & 1 & -1 & 0 \\ -13 & -1 & 2 & 3 \\ -6 & 0 & 1 & 1 \\ 4 & 0 & 0 & -1 \end{bmatrix}$ **13.** $\begin{bmatrix} 2 & \frac{3}{5} & -\frac{7}{5} & \frac{4}{5} \\ 4 & -\frac{7}{5} & -\frac{2}{5} & \frac{4}{5} \\ -6 & \frac{14}{5} & -\frac{1}{5} & -\frac{3}{5} \\ 3 & -\frac{8}{5} & \frac{2}{5} & \frac{1}{5} \end{bmatrix}$ **33.** $\begin{bmatrix} -5.667 & -3.667 & 5 & 0.333 \\ -27.667 & -18.667 & 24 & 2.333 \\ -19.333 & -13.333 & 17 & 1.667 \\ 15 & 10 & -13 & -1 \end{bmatrix}$ **34.** $\begin{bmatrix} 0.1 & 0.143 & -0.057 & 0.071 \\ -0.5 & 0.071 & 0.071 & 0.286 \\ -0.4 & 0.286 & 0.086 & 0.143 \\ 0.2 & -0.357 & 0.243 & 0.071 \end{bmatrix}$

35. $\begin{bmatrix} -0.150 & -0.217 & 0.302 \\ 0.248 & -0.024 & 0.013 \\ 0.217 & -0.200 & -0.195 \end{bmatrix}$ **36.** $\begin{bmatrix} 0.097 & -0.073 & 0.064 \\ 0.143 & 0.159 & -0.075 \\ 0.053 & 0.106 & 0.258 \end{bmatrix}$ **47. a.** $\begin{bmatrix} -\frac{5}{2} & \frac{3}{2} \\ -2 & 1 \end{bmatrix}$ **b.** $\begin{bmatrix} 2 & -3 \\ -\frac{3}{2} & \frac{5}{2} \end{bmatrix}$ **c.** $\begin{bmatrix} 1 & \frac{1}{4} \\ -1 & 0 \end{bmatrix}$

Exercise Set 7.5, page 627

11. $x_1 = \dfrac{21}{17}, x_2 = -\dfrac{3}{17}, x_3 = -\dfrac{29}{17}$ **12.** $x_1 = -\dfrac{1}{4}, x_2 = -\dfrac{39}{4}, x_3 = -\dfrac{27}{4}$ **13.** $x_1 = \dfrac{32}{49}, x_2 = \dfrac{13}{49}, x_3 = \dfrac{6}{7}$ **14.** $x_1 = \dfrac{47}{18}, x_2 = -\dfrac{7}{3}, x_3 = -\dfrac{61}{18}$

15. $x_1 = -\dfrac{29}{64}, x_2 = -\dfrac{25}{64}, x_3 = -\dfrac{19}{32}$ **16.** $x_1 = \dfrac{43}{46}, x_2 = -\dfrac{4}{23}, x_3 = \dfrac{45}{46}$ **17.** $x_1 = \dfrac{50}{53}, x_2 = \dfrac{62}{53}, x_3 = \dfrac{4}{53}$ **18.** $x_1 = \dfrac{8}{9}, x_2 = -\dfrac{89}{27}, x_3 = -\dfrac{26}{27}$

19. $x_1 = 0, x_2 = 0, x_3 = 0$ **20.** $x_1 = \dfrac{4}{25}, x_2 = -\dfrac{18}{25}, x_3 = -\dfrac{37}{25}$

Chapter 7 True/False Exercises, page 631

4. False; as an example, $A = \begin{bmatrix} 2 & -1 \\ -4 & 2 \end{bmatrix}$, $B = \begin{bmatrix} 3 & 4 \\ 1 & 5 \end{bmatrix}$, and $C = \begin{bmatrix} 4 & 7 \\ 3 & 11 \end{bmatrix}$. $AB = AC$ but $B \neq C$.   **6.** False; for example, if $A = \begin{bmatrix} 1 & 4 \\ -2 & 3 \end{bmatrix}$ and $B = \begin{bmatrix} 2 & 0 \\ -1 & 5 \end{bmatrix}$, then $\det(A) + \det(B) \neq \det(A + B)$.   **11.** False; if the number of equations is less than the number of variables, the Gaussian elimination method can be used to solve the system of linear equations. If the system of equations has a solution, the solution will be given in terms of one or more of the variables.   **12.** False; for example, for a 2×2 matrix, $\det(2A) = 2 \cdot 2 \det(A)$, and for a 3×3 matrix, $\det(2A) = 4 \cdot 2 \det(A)$.   **14.** False; for example, given $A = \begin{bmatrix} -3 & 2 \\ -6 & 4 \end{bmatrix}$ and $B = \begin{bmatrix} 2 & 4 \\ 3 & 6 \end{bmatrix}$, then $AB = \begin{bmatrix} 0 & 0 \\ 0 & 0 \end{bmatrix} = O$, but $A \neq O$ and $B \neq O$.

Chapter 7 Review Exercises, page 631

1. $\begin{bmatrix} 6 & -3 & 9 \\ 9 & 6 & -3 \end{bmatrix}$ [7.2]   **2.** $\begin{bmatrix} 0 & 4 \\ -8 & -4 \\ -2 & 6 \end{bmatrix}$ [7.2]   **3.** $\begin{bmatrix} -5 & 5 & -1 \\ 1 & -4 & 6 \end{bmatrix}$ [7.2]   **4.** $\begin{bmatrix} 13 & -14 & 0 \\ -6 & 10 & -17 \end{bmatrix}$ [7.2]   **5.** $\begin{bmatrix} -1 & -15 \\ 7 & 1 \end{bmatrix}$ [7.2]

6. $\begin{bmatrix} 18 & 8 \\ -3 & -27 \end{bmatrix}$ [7.2]   **7.** $\begin{bmatrix} -6 & -4 & 2 \\ 14 & 0 & 10 \\ -7 & -7 & 6 \end{bmatrix}$ [7.2]   **8.** $\begin{bmatrix} -8 & 4 & -10 \\ -4 & 12 & 18 \\ -15 & 10 & -13 \end{bmatrix}$ [7.2]   **9.** $\begin{bmatrix} 12 & 28 & -5 \\ 2 & 6 & 0 \\ 6 & 16 & -1 \end{bmatrix}$ [7.2]   **10.** $\begin{bmatrix} 42 & 108 & -11 \\ 10 & 24 & -4 \\ 26 & 64 & -9 \end{bmatrix}$ [7.2]

11. $\begin{bmatrix} -12 & -36 & -4 \\ 48 & 124 & 4 \\ -9 & -32 & -6 \end{bmatrix}$ [7.2]   **12.** not possible [7.2]   **13.** not possible [7.2]   **14.** not possible [7.2]   **15.** $\begin{bmatrix} 7 & 24 & 9 \\ -10 & -22 & 1 \end{bmatrix}$ [7.2]

16. $\begin{bmatrix} 7 & 24 & 9 \\ -10 & -22 & 1 \end{bmatrix}$ [7.2]   **17.** $\begin{bmatrix} -1 & -5 & 4 \\ \frac{1}{2} & 2 & -\frac{3}{2} \\ 0 & -2 & 1 \end{bmatrix}$ [7.3]   **18.** -2 [7.4]   **37.** $\begin{bmatrix} -1 & 1 \\ -\frac{3}{2} & 1 \end{bmatrix}$ [7.3]   **38.** $\begin{bmatrix} 3 & -4 \\ -2 & 3 \end{bmatrix}$ [7.3]   **39.** $\begin{bmatrix} -\frac{2}{7} & \frac{3}{14} \\ \frac{1}{7} & \frac{1}{7} \end{bmatrix}$ [7.3]

40. $\begin{bmatrix} \frac{1}{11} & \frac{2}{11} \\ -\frac{3}{22} & \frac{5}{22} \end{bmatrix}$ [7.3]   **41.** $\begin{bmatrix} 2 & -2 & 1 \\ 0 & \frac{3}{2} & -1 \\ -1 & -1 & 1 \end{bmatrix}$ [7.3]   **42.** $\begin{bmatrix} 27 & -12 & 5 \\ 4 & -2 & 1 \\ -7 & 3 & -1 \end{bmatrix}$ [7.3]   **43.** $\begin{bmatrix} -10 & 20 & -3 \\ -5 & 9 & -1 \\ 3 & -6 & 1 \end{bmatrix}$ [7.3]   **44.** $\begin{bmatrix} 27 & -39 & 5 \\ -7 & 10 & -1 \\ 4 & -6 & 1 \end{bmatrix}$ [7.3]

45. $\begin{bmatrix} -1 & -7 & 4 & 2 \\ -6 & -3 & 2 & 3 \\ 1 & 2 & -1 & -1 \\ -2 & 0 & 0 & 1 \end{bmatrix}$ [7.3]   **46.** $\begin{bmatrix} \frac{116}{7} & -\frac{50}{7} & \frac{46}{7} & -\frac{51}{7} \\ -\frac{45}{7} & \frac{20}{7} & -\frac{17}{7} & \frac{19}{7} \\ \frac{2}{7} & -1 & 1 & -1 \\ \frac{9}{7} & -\frac{4}{7} & \frac{2}{7} & -\frac{1}{7} \end{bmatrix}$ [7.3]   **48.** $\begin{bmatrix} 14 & -\frac{33}{2} & -6 & \frac{5}{2} \\ 14 & -\frac{31}{2} & -7 & \frac{5}{2} \\ -9 & \frac{21}{2} & 4 & -\frac{3}{2} \\ 2 & -\frac{5}{2} & -1 & \frac{1}{2} \end{bmatrix}$ [7.3]   **61.** $x_1 = \dfrac{16}{19}, x_2 = -\dfrac{2}{19}$ [7.5]

62. $x_1 = \dfrac{1}{13}, x_2 = -\dfrac{21}{26}$ [7.5]   **63.** $x_1 = \dfrac{13}{44}, x_2 = \dfrac{1}{4}, x_3 = -\dfrac{17}{44}$ [7.5]   **64.** $x_1 = -\dfrac{17}{22}, x_2 = \dfrac{19}{22}, x_3 = -\dfrac{13}{22}$ [7.5]

65. $x_1 = \dfrac{18}{23}, x_2 = -\dfrac{26}{69}, x_3 = \dfrac{38}{69}$ [7.5]   **66.** $x_1 = \dfrac{21}{83}, x_2 = \dfrac{12}{83}, x_3 = -\dfrac{40}{83}$ [7.5]

Chapter 7 Test, page 633

1. $\begin{bmatrix} 2 & 3 & -3 & 4 \\ 3 & 0 & 2 & -1 \\ 4 & -4 & 2 & 3 \end{bmatrix}, \begin{bmatrix} 2 & 3 & -3 \\ 3 & 0 & 2 \\ 4 & -4 & 2 \end{bmatrix} \begin{bmatrix} 4 \\ -1 \\ 3 \end{bmatrix}$ [7.1]   **2.** $\begin{cases} 3x - 2y + 5z - w = 9 \\ 2x + 3y - z + 4w = 8 \\ x + 3z + 2w = -1 \end{cases}$ [7.1]   **6.** $\begin{bmatrix} 3 & -9 & -6 \\ -3 & -12 & 3 \end{bmatrix}$ [7.2]

7. $A + B$ is not defined. [7.2]   **8.** $\begin{bmatrix} 4 & 1 & 3 \\ 8 & 0 & -19 \\ 11 & 0 & 10 \end{bmatrix}$ [7.2]   **9.** $\begin{bmatrix} 16 & -1 & -2 \\ 15 & -11 & -3 \end{bmatrix}$ [7.2]   **10.** $\begin{bmatrix} 17 & -4 & -4 \\ 14 & -15 & -2 \end{bmatrix}$ [7.2]   **11.** CA is not defined. [7.2]

12. $\begin{bmatrix} -6 & -1 & -19 \\ -15 & -25 & -27 \\ 1 & 3 & 31 \end{bmatrix}$ [7.2]   **13.** A^2 is not defined. [7.2]   **14.** $\begin{bmatrix} 9 & 6 & 13 \\ -3 & -2 & 12 \\ 20 & -3 & 11 \end{bmatrix}$ [7.2]   **15.** $\begin{bmatrix} 18 & -5 & 7 \\ 4 & -1 & 2 \\ -3 & 1 & -1 \end{bmatrix}$ [7.3]

20. $\left(\begin{bmatrix} 1 & 0 & 0 \\ 0 & 1 & 0 \\ 0 & 0 & 1 \end{bmatrix} - \begin{bmatrix} 0.15 & 0.23 & 0.11 \\ 0.08 & 0.10 & 0.05 \\ 0.16 & 0.11 & 0.07 \end{bmatrix} \right)^{-1} \begin{bmatrix} 50 \\ 32 \\ 8 \end{bmatrix}$ [7.3]

Cumulative Review Exercises, page 634

12.   [2.5]

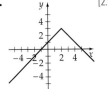

Exercise Set 8.5, page 674

9. $x^6 - 6x^5y + 15x^4y^2 - 20x^3y^3 + 15x^2y^4 - 6xy^5 + y^6$ **10.** $a^5 - 5a^4b + 10a^3b^2 - 10a^2b^3 + 5ab^4 - b^5$
11. $x^5 + 15x^4 + 90x^3 + 270x^2 + 405x + 243$ **12.** $x^4 - 20x^3 + 150x^2 - 500x + 625$
13. $128x^7 - 448x^6 + 672x^5 - 560x^4 + 280x^3 - 84x^2 + 14x - 1$ **14.** $64x^6 + 192x^5y + 240x^4y^2 + 160x^3y^3 + 60x^2y^4 + 12xy^5 + y^6$
15. $x^6 + 18x^5y + 135x^4y^2 + 540x^3y^3 + 1215x^2y^4 + 1458xy^5 + 729y^6$ **16.** $x^5 - 20x^4y + 160x^3y^2 - 640x^2y^3 + 1280xy^4 - 1024y^5$

17. $16x^4 - 160x^3y + 600x^2y^2 - 1000xy^3 + 625y^4$ **18.** $81x^4 + 216x^3y + 216x^2y^2 + 96xy^3 + 16y^4$ **19.** $x^6 + 6x^4 + 15x^2 + 20 + \dfrac{15}{x^2} + \dfrac{6}{x^4} + \dfrac{1}{x^6}$

20. $128x^7 - 448x^6\sqrt{y} + 672x^5y - 560x^4y\sqrt{y} + 280x^3y^2 - 84x^2y^2\sqrt{y} + 14xy^3 - y^3\sqrt{y}$
21. $x^{14} - 28x^{12} + 336x^{10} - 2240x^8 + 8960x^6 - 21,504x^4 + 28,672x^2 - 16,384$ **22.** $x^6 - 6x^5y^3 + 15x^4y^6 - 20x^3y^9 + 15x^2y^{12} - 6xy^{15} + y^{18}$
23. $32x^{10} + 80x^8y^3 + 80x^6y^6 + 40x^4y^9 + 10x^2y^{12} + y^{15}$ **24.** $64x^6 - 192x^5y^3 + 240x^4y^6 - 160x^3y^9 + 60x^2y^{12} - 12xy^{15} + y^{18}$

25. $\dfrac{16}{x^4} - \dfrac{16}{x^2} + 6 - x^2 + \dfrac{x^4}{16}$ **26.** $\dfrac{a^3}{b^3} + \dfrac{3a}{b} + \dfrac{3b}{a} + \dfrac{b^3}{a^3}$ **27.** $s^{-12} + 6s^{-8} + 15s^{-4} + 20 + 15s^4 + 6s^8 + s^{12}$
28. $32r^{-5} + 80r^{-4}s^{-1} + 80r^{-3}s^{-2} + 40r^{-2}s^{-3} + 10r^{-1}s^{-4} + s^{-5}$

Exercise Set 8.7, page 692

5. Let the three cans be represented by A, B, and C and let (x, y) represent the cans that balls 1 and 2 are placed in; e.g., (A, B) means ball 1 in can A and ball 2 in can B. $S = \{(A, A), (A, B), (A, C),(B, B), (B, C), (B, A), (C, C), (C, A), (C, B)\}$
20. $\{(1, 1), (1, 2), (1, 3), (1, 4), (1, 5), (1, 6),(2, 1), (2, 2), (2, 3), (2, 4), (2, 5), (2, 6),(3, 1), (3, 2), (3, 3), (3, 4), (3, 5), (3, 6),(4, 1), (4, 2), (4, 3), (4, 4), (4, 5), (4, 6),$
$(5, 1), (5, 2), (5, 3), (5, 4), (5, 5), (5, 6),(6, 1), (6, 2), (6, 3), (6, 4), (6, 5), (6, 6)\}$

Chapter 8 Review Exercises, page 697

21. neither [8.1]   **22.** neither [8.1]   **23.** arithmetic [8.2]   **24.** arithmetic [8.2]   **25.** geometric [8.3]   **26.** geometric [8.3]   **27.** neither [8.1]
28. neither [8.1]   **29.** geometric [8.3]   **30.** geometric [8.3]   **31.** geometric [8.3]   **32.** geometric [8.3]   **33.** neither [8.1]   **34.** neither [8.1]
35. arithmetic [8.2]   **36.** arithmetic [8.2]   **37.** neither [8.1]   **38.** neither [8.1]   **39.** neither [8.1]   **40.** neither [8.1]
65. $1024a^5 - 1280a^4b + 640a^3b^2 - 160a^2b^3 + 20ab^4 - b^5$ [8.5]   **66.** $x^5 + 18x^5y + 135x^4y^2 + 540x^3y^3 + 1215x^2y^4 + 1458xy^5 + 729y^6$ [8.5]
67. $a^4 + 16a^{7/2}b^{1/2} + 112a^3b + 448a^{5/2}b^{3/2} + 1120a^2b^2 + 1792a^{3/2}b^{5/2} + 1792ab^3 + 1024a^{1/2}b^{7/2} + 256b^4$ [8.5]

68. $128x^7 - 224x^5 + 168x^3 - 70x + \dfrac{35}{2x} - \dfrac{21}{8x^3} + \dfrac{7}{32x^5} - \dfrac{1}{128x^7}$ [8.5]

Cumulative Review Exercises, page 700

3.   [2.1]

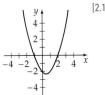

INDEX

A Library of Functions

Identity function

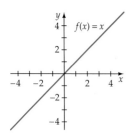

$f(x) = x$

Linear function

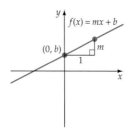

$f(x) = mx + b$

$(0, b)$

m

1

Constant function

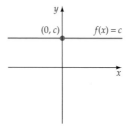

$(0, c)$

$f(x) = c$

Absolute value function

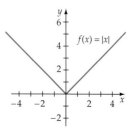

$f(x) = |x|$

Squaring function

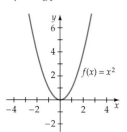

$f(x) = x^2$

Cubing function

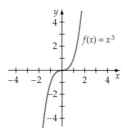

$f(x) = x^3$

Square root function

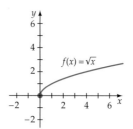

$f(x) = \sqrt{x}$

Cube root function

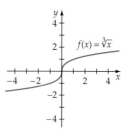

$f(x) = \sqrt[3]{x}$

Exponential function

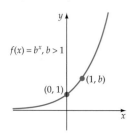

$f(x) = b^x, b > 1$

$(1, b)$

$(0, 1)$

Exponential function

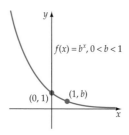

$f(x) = b^x, 0 < b < 1$

$(0, 1)$

$(1, b)$

Logarithmic function

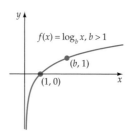

$f(x) = \log_b x, b > 1$

$(b, 1)$

$(1, 0)$

Logarithmic function

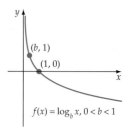

$(b, 1)$

$(1, 0)$

$f(x) = \log_b x, 0 < b < 1$

Logistic function

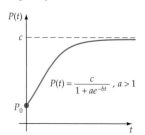

c

$P(t) = \dfrac{c}{1 + ae^{-bt}}, a > 1$

P_0

Logistic function

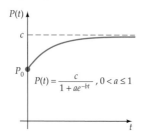

c

P_0

$P(t) = \dfrac{c}{1 + ae^{-bt}}, 0 < a \le 1$

Reciprocal function

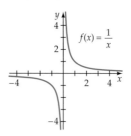

$f(x) = \dfrac{1}{x}$

A rational function

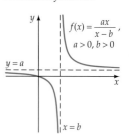

$f(x) = \dfrac{ax}{x - b}$,

$a > 0, b > 0$

$y = a$

$x = b$

Properties of Exponents

$$a^m a^n = a^{m+n} \qquad \frac{a^m}{a^n} = a^{m-n} \qquad (a^m)^n = a^{mn}$$

$$(a^m b^n)^p = a^{mp} b^{np} \qquad \left(\frac{a^m}{b^n}\right)^p = \frac{a^{mp}}{b^{np}} \qquad b^{-p} = \frac{1}{b^p}$$

Properties of Logarithms

$y = \log_b x$ if and only if $b^y = x$

$$\log_b b = 1 \qquad \log_b 1 = 0 \qquad \log_b (b)^p = p$$

$$b^{\log_b p} = p \qquad \log x = \log_{10} x \qquad \ln x = \log_e x$$

$$\log_b (MN) = \log_b M + \log_b N$$

$$\log_b (M/N) = \log_b M - \log_b N$$

$$\log_b M^p = p \log_b M$$

Properties of Radicals

$$(\sqrt[n]{b})^m = \sqrt[n]{b^m} = b^{m/n} \qquad \frac{\sqrt[n]{a}}{\sqrt[n]{b}} = \sqrt[n]{\frac{a}{b}}$$

$$\sqrt[n]{a}\,\sqrt[n]{b} = \sqrt[n]{ab} \qquad \sqrt[m]{\sqrt[n]{b}} = \sqrt[mn]{b}$$

Properties of Absolute Value Inequalities

$|x| < c \ (c \geq 0)$ if and only if $-c < x < c$.

$|x| > c \ (c \geq 0)$ if and only if either $x > c$ or $x < -c$.

Important Theorems

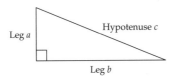
Leg a Hypotenuse c Leg b

Pythagorean Theorem
$$c^2 = a^2 + b^2$$

Remainder Theorem
If a polynomial $P(x)$ is divided by $x - c$, then the remainder is $P(c)$.

Factor Theorem
A polynomial $P(x)$ has a factor $(x - c)$ if and only if $P(c) = 0$.

Fundamental Theorem of Algebra
If P is a polynomial of degree $n \geq 1$ with complex coefficients, then P has at least one complex zero.

Binomial Theorem
$$(a + b)^n = a^n + \binom{n}{1}a^{n-1}b + \binom{n}{2}a^{n-2}b^2$$
$$+ \cdots + \binom{n}{k}a^{n-k}b^k + \cdots + b^n$$

Important Formulas

The *distance* between $P_1(x_1, y_1)$ and $P_2(x_2, y_2)$ is
$$d(P_1, P_2) = \sqrt{(x_1 - x_2)^2 + (y_1 - y_2)^2}$$

The *slope m* of a line through $P_1(x_1, y_1)$ and $P_2(x_2, y_2)$ is
$$m = \frac{y_2 - y_1}{x_2 - x_1}, \quad x_1 \neq x_2$$

The *slope-intercept form* of a line with slope m and y-intercept b is $y = mx + b$

The *point-slope formula* for a line with slope m passing through $P_1(x_1, y_1)$ is
$$y - y_1 = m(x - x_1)$$

Quadratic Formula
If $a \neq 0$, the solutions of $ax^2 + bx + c = 0$ are
$$x = \frac{-b \pm \sqrt{b^2 - 4ac}}{2a}$$

Properties of Functions

A *function* is a set of ordered pairs in which no two ordered pairs that have the same first coordinate have different second coordinates.

If a and b are elements of an interval I that is a subset of the domain of a function f, then

- f is an *increasing* function on I if $f(a) < f(b)$ whenever $a < b$.
- f is a *decreasing* function on I if $f(a) > f(b)$ whenever $a < b$.
- f is a *constant* function on I if $f(a) = f(b)$ for all a and b.

A *one-to-one* function satisfies the additional condition that given any y, there is one and only one x that can be paired with that given y.

Graphing Concepts

Odd Functions
A function f is an odd function if $f(-x) = -f(x)$ for all x in the domain of f. The graph of an odd function is symmetric with respect to the origin.

Even Functions
A function is an even function if $f(-x) = f(x)$ for all x in the domain of f. The graph of an even function is symmetric with respect to the y-axis.

Vertical and Horizontal Translations

If f is a function and c is a positive constant, then the graph of

- $y = f(x) + c$ is the graph of $y = f(x)$ shifted up vertically c units.
- $y = f(x) - c$ is the graph of $y = f(x)$ shifted down vertically c units.
- $y = f(x + c)$ is the graph of $y = f(x)$ shifted left horizontally c units.
- $y = f(x - c)$ is the graph of $y = f(x)$ shifted right horizontally c units.

Reflections

If f is a function then the graph of

- $y = -f(x)$ is the graph of $y = f(x)$ reflected across the x-axis.
- $y = f(-x)$ is the graph of $y = f(x)$ reflected across the y-axis.

Vertical Shrinking and Stretching

- If $c > 0$ and the graph of $y = f(x)$ contains the point (x, y), then the graph of $y = c \cdot f(x)$ contains the point (x, cy).
- If $c > 1$, the graph of $y = c \cdot f(x)$ is obtained by stretching the graph of $y = f(x)$ away from the x-axis by a factor of c.
- If $0 < c < 1$, the graph of $y = c \cdot f(x)$ is obtained by shrinking the graph of $y = f(x)$ toward the x-axis by a factor of c.

Horizontal Shrinking and Stretching

- If $a > 0$ and the graph of $y = f(x)$ contains the point (x, y), then the graph of $y = f(ax)$ contains the point $\left(\dfrac{1}{a}x, y\right)$.
- If $a > 1$, the graph of $y = f(ax)$ is a *horizontal shrinking* of the graph of $y = f(x)$.
- If $0 < a < 1$, the graph of $y = f(ax)$ is a *horizontal stretching* of the graph of $y = f(x)$.

Formulas for the Conic Sections

Parabola: $x^2 = 4py$

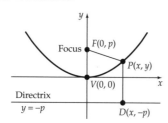

Hyperbola: $\dfrac{x^2}{a^2} - \dfrac{y^2}{b^2} = 1$

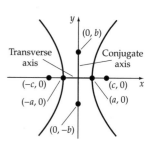

Ellipse: $\dfrac{x^2}{a^2} + \dfrac{y^2}{b^2} = 1, a > b$

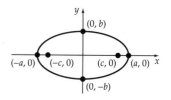

Formulas for Area A, Circumference C, Surface Area S, and Volume V

Triangle

$A = \dfrac{1}{2}bh$

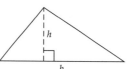

Parallelogram

$A = bh$

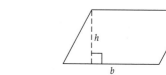

Circle

$A = \pi r^2$

$C = 2\pi r$

Sphere

$V = \dfrac{4}{3}\pi r^3$

$S = 4\pi r^2$

Right Circular Cylinder

$V = \pi r^2 h$

$S = 2\pi rh + 2\pi r^2$

Right Circular Cone

$V = \dfrac{1}{3}\pi r^2 h$